THE PHYSIOPATHOLOGY OF CANCER

THE PHYSIOPATHOLOGY OF CANCER

A treatise for investigators, physicians, and students

EDITED BY FREDDY HOMBURGER, M.D.

RESEARCH PROFESSOR OF MEDICINE
TUFTS COLLEGE MEDICAL SCHOOL

AND WILLIAM H. FISHMAN, Ph.D.

RESEARCH PROFESSOR OF BIOCHEMISTRY
TUFTS COLLEGE MEDICAL SCHOOL

WITH 28 CONTRIBUTORS

FOREWORD BY C. C. LITTLE

HIH

A HOEBER—HARPER BOOK

THE PHYSIOPATHOLOGY OF CANCER

I-C

Printed in the United States of America

Library of Congress catalog card number: 52-5721

THIS BOOK IS DEDICATED TO

DOBIE*

* Konrad Dobriner, 1902 to 1952. A dear friend of ours and of a great many investigators in cancer research, who stimulated the important developments in the steroid endocrinology of cancer.

Contents

Contributors

AUSTIN M. BRUES, M.D.
Professor of Medicine, University of Chicago, and Director, Division of Biological and Medical Research, Argonne National Laboratory, Chicago, Illinois.

I. N. DUBIN, M.D.
Chief, Hepatic Pathology Section, Armed Forces Institute of Pathology, Washington, D.C.

THELMA B. DUNN, M.D.
Medical Officer (Pathology), National Cancer Institute, National Institutes of Health, Public Health Service, Bethesda, Maryland.

FRANCISCO DURAN-REYNALS, M.D.
Research Associate and Lecturer, Department of Bacteriology, Yale University School of Medicine, New Haven, Connecticut.

LEWIS L. ENGEL, Ph.D.
Assistant Professor of Biological Chemistry, Harvard Medical School at the Massachusetts General Hospital, Boston, Massachusetts.

HARLAN I. FIRMINGER, M.D.
Assistant Professor of Pathology and Oncology, University of Kansas Medical Center, Kansas City, Kansas.

WILLIAM H. FISHMAN, Ph.D.
Research Professor of Biochemistry and Nutrition, Tufts College Medical School, Boston, Massachusetts.

L. HENRY GARLAND, M.D.
Clinical Professor of Radiology, Stanford University Medical School, San Francisco, California.

WILLIAM U. GARDNER, Ph.D.
Professor of Anatomy, Yale University School of Medicine, New Haven, Connecticut.

ALFRED GELLHORN, M.D.
Associate Professor, Department of Medicine, College of Physicians and Surgeons, Columbia University, New York.

GEORGE GOMORI, M.D.
Associate Professor of Medicine, University of Chicago, Chicago, Illinois.

ALEXANDER HADDOW, M.D.
Director, the Chester Beatty Research Institute, The Royal Cancer Hospital, London, England.

FREDDY HOMBURGER, M.D.
Research Professor of Medicine, Tufts College Medical School, Boston, Massachusetts.

WILHELM C. HUEPER, M.D.
Chief, Environmental Cancer Section, National Cancer Institute, National Institutes of Health, Public Health Service, Bethesda, Maryland.

DAVID A. KARNOFSKY, M.D.
Associate Professor of Medicine, Sloan-Kettering Division, Cornell University Medical College, New York.

S. CHARLES KASDON, M.D.
Clinical Investigator, Cancer Research and Cancer Control Unit; and Instructor, Department of Surgery, Tufts College Medical School, Boston, Massachusetts.

HERBERT L. LOMBARD, M.D.
Director, Division of Cancer and Other Chronic Diseases, Department of Public Health, Commonwealth of Massachusetts, Boston, Massachusetts.

LEONIDAS D. MARINELLI, Ph.D.
Associate Director, Division of Biological and Medical Research, Argonne National Laboratory, Chicago, Illinois.

CARROLL A. PFEIFFER, Ph.D.
Professor of Anatomy, University of Puerto Rico, San Juan, Puerto Rico.

GERHARD SCHMIDT, M.D.
Research Professor of Biochemistry and Nutrition, Tufts College Medical School, Boston, Massachusetts.

BERTRAM SELVERSTONE, M.D.
Professor of Neurosurgery, Tufts College Medical School, Boston Massachusetts.

GEORGE D. SNELL, Sc.D.
Roscoe B. Jackson Memorial Laboratory, Bar Harbor, Maine.

HAROLD L. STEWART, M.D.
Chief, Pathology Section, National Cancer Institute, National Institutes of Health, Public Health Service, Bethesda, Maryland.

ALBERT TANNENBAUM, M.D.
Director, Department of Cancer Research, Medical Research Institute, Michael Reese Hospital, Chicago, Illinois.

JOHN J. TRENTIN, Ph.D.
Assistant Professor of Anatomy, Yale University School of Medicine, New Haven, Connecticut.

RICHARD J. WINZLER, Ph.D.
Professor and Head of Department of Biological Chemistry, University of Illinois College of Medicine, Chicago, Illinois.

J. T. WOLSTENHOLME, M.D.
United States Public Health Service Fellow in Cancer, Yale University School of Medicine, New Haven, Connecticut.

GEORGE W. WOOLLEY, Ph.D.
Professor of Biology, Sloan-Kettering Division, Cornell University Medical College, New York.

Foreword

The problem of the origin, nature, and development of cancer is everywhere recognized today as one which requires for its solution a vast extent and penetration of scientific information.

No one individual can hope to span or to contain all the specialized knowledge necessary for leadership and direction in the multitude of techniques which are utilized and which will be developed in the laboratory and clinic.

No one discipline in experimental research, or in preventive or therapeutic practice will prove to be the sole and sufficient solution to more than a part of the total question that is posed by the various manifestations of neoplastic growth.

In the face of this situation, the natural tendency is for the investigator or clinician to push the development of his training and skills as far as he can along the particular line of attack for which he feels best adapted.

This procedure is entirely reasonable and it has led to more progress in our knowledge during the past thirty years than in the three hundred that preceded them. There is encouraging evidence on all sides that, for at least twenty years to come, a continuation of the same policy will pay rich dividends in decreasing suffering and in saving lives.

But while this procedure is sound as a *major emphasis* it is not the whole story.

There must be a deliberate and intelligent program of comparison and coordination of discoveries and of information in the various fields. A definite attitude of sympathetic understanding of all the major lines of attack is essential for two vital reasons.

First, direction and leadership of research or clinical groups, departments, or institutions must be conceived and executed on broad, comprehensive, tolerant, and imaginative lines. This is only possible when those in control develop and maintain contact with all the possible recognized channels to progress.

Second, those entering or recently engaged in the attack on cancer need, from the earliest possible moment, to establish the habit of maintaining at least a speaking acquaintance with the objectives, obstacles, and advances in phases of the problem other than their own. Only by such an effort can they expect to contribute to laying the foundation for the correlation and synthetic interpretation of the complex life processes which cause, maintain, and influence neoplasia.

The editors of the present volume are excellent individual examples of the successful application of these general basic principles which are the prerequisites of accelerated and intensified progress.

They have assembled a series of treatises by experts, each of whom has attained distinction in his chosen field or fields, and have presented this material in extremely logical and utilizable form.

This is a very real and timely service enabling the student, physician, or investigator to obtain an adequate general summary of our present knowledge under any and all of the included topics. From these summaries, programs of further and more detailed coverage of one or more selected subjects can be launched with a minimum of waste effort or time.

The service which *The Physiopathology of Cancer* is certain to perform will be a very real and important one.

C. C. LITTLE, SC.D.

Preface

The purpose of this book is to bring together in one volume the present-day knowledge in all the active fields of cancer research. Emphasis has been placed on those areas of investigation that have found clinical application.

The need for such a comprehensive survey of current information on cancer became evident when the editors conducted for the first time a "vertical" cancer course at Tufts College Medical School under a cancer teaching grant of the U. S. Public Health Service. Although the diagnosis and therapy of cancer are well covered in the conventional curriculum and while excellent practical texts are available, students and instructors lacked convenient access to any presentation of the broad perspective of the dynamic activities of cancer research and of its contributions to present-day medical practice.

The book has been divided into four sections: Biology, Chemistry and Physics, Clinical Investigation, and Practical Applications. It is expected that medical students should familiarize themselves with all of this material. The investigator will have primary interest in the first two sections, and the practicing physician will find helpful material in the sections on Clinical Investigation and Practical Applications.

An effort has been made to render each chapter sufficiently complete so that newcomers to each field can rapidly orient themselves and find easy reference to the relevant literature.

The first part of this text deals with a functional and morphologic study of tumors induced by carcinogens in mice and other experimental animals, with the genetics of neoplastic disease, the importance of hormones and viruses in the causation of experimental cancer, and with the nutritional factors that affect the biological behavior of tumors.

The next section covers the mechanisms of carcinogenesis, the chemical and enzymatic properties of tumors, the cytochemical approaches to these problems, and experimental studies on the effects of chemotherapeutic agents and radiation.

The following sections cover the problems encountered in clinical investigation of cancer, such as studies of steroid metabolism in patients with cancer, the problems of occupational cancer, and the fundamentals of biometrics applied to such studies.

The final section is devoted to those phases of cancer research that have found practical uses, such as the evaluation of diagnostic tests, the principles of clinical chemotherapy, exfoliative cytology, and the use of radiation and isotopes in the treatment and the diagnosis of cancer.

It is hoped that this book will aid in attracting the interest of specialists in one field to problems in related fields and may thus serve as a catalyst for interdisciplinary exchange of ideas.

Some phases of cancer research have had a longer productive life than others, which explains the more extensive treatment that some chapters have received. Other fields, no less important and deserving of attention, are yet in their early formative stages and have, therefore, been included to stimulate interest.

Each contributor has attempted to be critical in the evaluation of information in his field so that the book is not merely a catalogue of findings, but a sound analysis of progress.

The editors wish to thank the contributors for their cooperation, and the American Cancer Society, the U.S. Public Health Service, and the Charles Pfizer Company of Brooklyn, New York, for their generous financial support. Contributions from Smith, Kline & French Laboratories and from the Burroughs Wellcome Company are also gratefully acknowledged.

F. H.

Boston, Massachusetts W. H. F.

PART I

Biology

CHAPTER 1

Experimental Cancer of the Alimentary Tract

Harold L. Stewart

EXPERIMENTAL CARCINOMA OF ORAL MUCOSA AND ESOPHAGUS

It is possible to induce squamous carcinoma and sarcoma of the tongue of mice by direct injection of 20-methylcholanthrene (Stewart, unpublished data). Levy[58]* obtained only sarcoma in hamsters receiving an injection of 5,9-dimethyl 1,2-benzanthracene under the gingiva. When methylcholanthrene mixed with the diet is fed, papillomas and a few squamous carcinomas of the mouth and the skin of the face develop in some animals.[126] Tumors of these tissues are attributable to direct and more or less prolonged contact with the methylcholanthrene during feeding periods, the food particles tending to adhere to the skin about the mouth, or to the mucosa of the oral cavity.

When aqueous oil emulsions containing 1,2,5,6-dibenzanthracene and 20-methylcholanthrene are administered orally to mice, a few early carcinomas and precancerous lesions of the esophagus occur (Fig. 1).[111] The paucity of these lesions in mice drinking the carcinogen-containing emulsions may be attributed to the brevity of exposure. Although the mice drink frequently, they also eat often, and therefore any carcinogen remaining in the mouth or esophagus rapidly passes into the stomach with the food and saliva. There is probably little contact between the carcinogen and the tissues of the oral mucosa and esophagus since the carcinogenic component of the emulsion is contained in the oil droplets which are surrounded by a soap film. A third factor is that carcinoma of the forestomach or of the small intestine develops relatively rapidly in susceptible mice ingesting carcinogens, and death results from these neoplasms. If these tumors could be prevented, then it is probable that more neoplastic lesions of the esophagus and oral mucosa would develop in feeding experiments, since the early changes of carcinoma have been observed in these areas.

* Superior numbers refer to the lists of references, to be found at the end of each chapter.

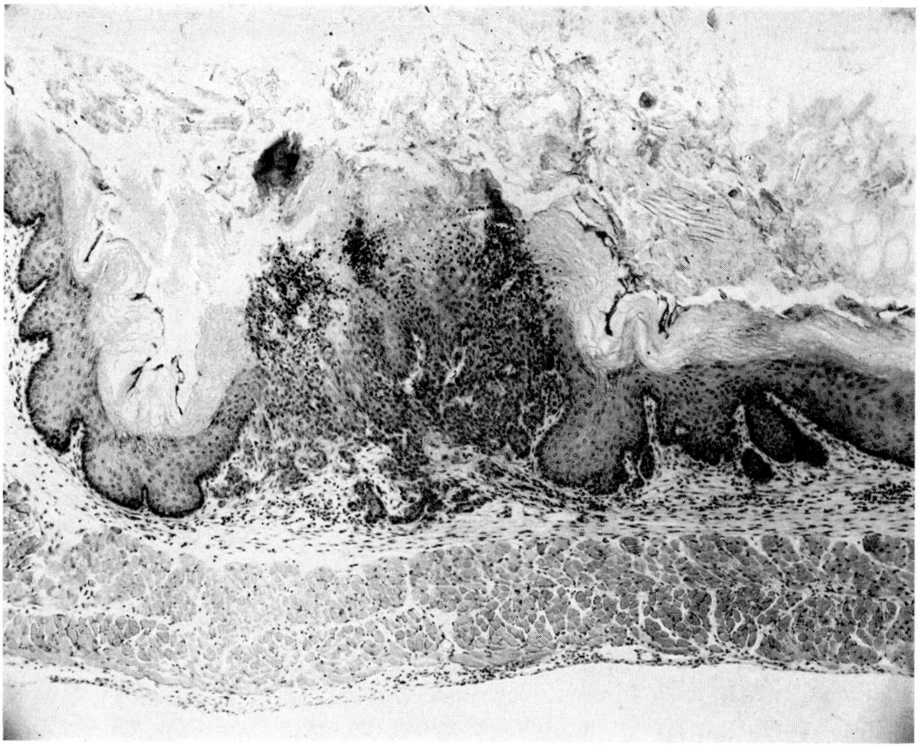

FIG. 1. Esophagus of mouse, with focus of nearocarcinoma with limited infiltration. × 70.

EXPERIMENTAL CARCINOMA OF THE STOMACH

SPONTANEOUS TUMORS

Gastric carcinoma is one of the commonest malignant growths in man, and is one of the rarest in animals. Even in species in which other types of tumors are frequent, carcinoma of the stomach seldom occurs. Feldman[32] estimates that 8 to 10 per cent of old dogs have neoplasms of which 40 to 50 per cent are malignant, and many other animals similarly develop tumors in old age, yet the occurrence of spontaneous gastric cancer is exceedingly rare in domestic, laboratory, and wild animals, fish, reptiles, and insects.[17, 23, 52, 78, 86, 95, 98, 125] In a series of 33,000 postmortem examinations of rats,[16] 9 sarcomas of the stomach were found but only one adenocarcinoma. In over 142,000 mice of the now famous Slye stock dying of natural causes, Wells, Slye, and Holmes[125] reported 12 gastric cancers, of which 8 were squamous cell carcinoma, 3 adenocarcinoma, and 1 sarcoma. In addition there were 2 adenomas which may have been early carcinomas. This represents all the gastric carcinomas in the Slye stock of mice in over twenty years of careful observation. There is therefore no species of animal in which gastric cancer appears regularly or indeed with sufficient frequency to warrant an attempt to develop a high gastric-cancer strain.

Anatomy of Stomach

The animals almost universally used in experimental investigations of carcinoma of the stomach are the mouse and rat. Each has a stomach consisting of two chambers: (1) the forestomach, comprising about two-thirds of the entire viscus and lined by squamous epithelium continuous with that of the esophagus; and (2) the glandular stomach, separated from the forestomach by a slight elevation, the limiting ridge. It follows, therefore, that two independent histologic types of carcinoma may develop: (1) squamous cell carcinoma of the forestomach, and (2) adenocarcinoma of the glandular stomach. Adenoacanthoma may occur as a mixture of Types 1 and 2 or may develop from the glandular mucosa associated with squamous metaplasia.

Criteria of Carcinoma

The term *carcinoma* is applied by the author to an epithelial neoplasm that extends through all muscle layers of the stomach into the serosa. The term *precancer* is used in a broad sense to include neoplastic lesions of lesser extent. These precancerous lesions range from foci of atypical appearing neoplastic cells limited to the mucosa, to those more advanced growths in which the neoplastic cells are variously present in the stroma or muscularis, but have not penetrated the serosa or metastasized. If one thinks only in terms of human medicine, these criteria seem unduly rigid. Clinical pathologists do not insist on peritoneal extension before making a diagnosis of gastric cancer. It is evident, however, from the experimental literature of the past that the criteria for the diagnosis of induced gastric carcinoma have been so flexible that on close scrutiny the reports of many positive claims either are not convincing or do not permit objective evaluation of the malignant nature of the changes reported. To appreciate this and the practical difficulties involved in the problem, one has only to read the reviews of the field[10, 13, 55, 56, 116] and to study a number of neoplastic and non-neoplastic gastric lesions in mice and rats where the line of distinction between cancer and non-cancer is by no means as sharply drawn as in man but overlaps to a surprising extent. The point of view of the experimentalist, therefore, is different from that of the clinical pathologist. The interpretation of disputable lesions by the latter is influenced by clinical considerations. The patient is properly given the benefit of any doubt that the pathologist may entertain regarding the malignant nature of a given lesion. On the other hand, the experimentalist, unencumbered by this bias, can afford and indeed strives to be purely objective in arriving at a correct diagnosis of malignancy. He is in a position to insist on the fulfillment of all the rigid criteria necessary to support unequivocally a diagnosis of carcinoma. After more studies of the experimental problem have been made, it is probable that these criteria will be relaxed.

Methods of Induction

The methods used to induce gastric carcinoma generally fall into one or another of the following categories: (1) parasites; (2) dietetic irritants; (3) nutritional deficiencies; and (4) carcinogens.

1. Parasites. The use of parasites is of historical interest, because the earliest attempts at experimental production of cancer to attract worldwide attention were those of Fibiger.[34, 35, 36] In 1913 Fibiger published the first of a series of beautifully illustrated reports on the production of squamous-cell carcinoma in the forestomach of rats following infestation by a nematode, *Gongylonema neoplasticum*.[34] This infestation developed after laboratory rats were fed cockroaches containing the parasite. The animals were maintained on a diet of white bread and water. Although Fibiger was awarded the Nobel Prize for this work, it has subsequently been adversely criticized and remains unconfirmed.[19, 79, 131] It is generally supposed that the forestomach lesions developing in Fibiger's rats were non-neoplastic and in large part due to the inadequate diet on which the animals subsisted. Now, almost forty years later, it is obvious that Fibiger's criteria and interpretation of the forestomach lesion as carcinoma lacked objectivity. His work, however, antedated the discovery of the carcinogenic potency of tar by Yamagiwa and Ichikawa[130] and represents one of the earliest and most laborious attempts to induce cancer, and so Fibiger deserves the grateful remembrance of all scientists in this field.

2. Dietary Irritants. Foremost among the dietary irritants which have been tested in attempts to induce carcinoma are fats, particularly heated fats, which are suspected of playing a role in the etiology of gastric cancer in man. Roffo[88, 89, 90, 91] published a long series of papers purporting to show that heated fats are carcinogenic for the rat stomach. Similar results have been claimed following feeding of a mixture of tar, hydrous wool fat, aniline oil, and tolylenediamine to rats,[123] and cholesterol oleate,[124] and a diet of rice and 20 per cent olive oil to mice.[24] Roffo's claims that he induced carcinoma of the stomach have not been accepted by most pathologists because his descriptions and illustrations are not convincing. There is no doubt, however, that he obtained severe inflammatory and degenerative lesions of the glandular stomach and, to a lesser extent, of the forestomach, and that some of his animals developed genuine sarcomas. It has been recently confirmed[57] that gastric sarcoma may be induced by ingesting fat, browned by heating. Peacock and Beck[80] reported the induction of glandular carcinomas of the stomach of mice fed previously-heated cottonseed oil. The areas suggesting adenocarcinoma in these specimens may actually be formations of squamous-cell carcinoma in which the cornified centers have liquefied or dropped out, leaving empty spaces. This is a not uncommon occurrence in experimental squamous carcinoma of the forestomach[111] and the resulting spaces are readily mistaken for gland lumina. Whether squamous or glandular, it is nevertheless significant that a carcinogenic effect has been demonstrated by this technic.

3. Nutritional Deficiencies. No experimental diets deficient in various components have been found to evoke gastric cancer, although numerous attempts have been made.[56]

4. Carcinogens. From the literature published up to the year 1940, Klein and Palmer[56] were able to cite examples in which some success had attended efforts to induce squamous-cell carcinoma of the forestomach in mice and rats by the carcinogenic hydrocarbons. They expressed the opinion, however, that the positive results fell considerably short of the claims in the literature. No reliable method for inducing adenocarcinoma of the glandular chamber in animals was found, and indeed the reviewers doubted that any well-authenticated example of this lesion had been produced experimentally. Since 1940 the progress in experimental gastric cancer has been reviewed by several authors[10, 13, 55, 82, 116] who agree that methods are now available by which both adenocarcinoma of the glandular stomach and squamous cell carcinoma of the forestomach can be induced by carcinogenic hydrocarbons.

SQUAMOUS CELL CARCINOMA OF FORESTOMACH

Reports have been made on the induction of squamous cell carcinoma in the forestomach of mice by intramural injection of 20-methylcholanthrene[37, 102] and by oral administration of 1,2,5,6-dibenzanthracene,[66, 111] 20-methylcholanthrene[66, 81, 111, 126] 3,4-benzpyrene,[13, 18, 81, 124] 9,10-dimethyl-1,2-benzanthracene,[93] and 3,4,5,6-dibenzcarbazole;[5] in the rat by oral administration of *p*-dimethylaminobenzene-1-azo-1-naphthalene,[75] and in the crop of fowls injected with 2-acetylaminofluorene.[121]

Incidence in Mice

The pathologic anatomy of carcinoma of the forestomach in mice has been described by workers at the National Cancer Institute. One of these studies was based upon experiments in which mice of six inbred strains and of one hybrid group were given orally 20-methylcholanthrene and 1,2,5,6-dibenzanthracene dissolved in aqueous mineral oil or olive oil emulsions which were administered in lieu of drinking water.[64, 67, 68, 111] The incidence of carcinoma of the forestomach was related to the strain of mouse, the carcinogen used, the total amount of the latter ingested, and the length of time of treatment. Of 425 mice tested, 71 developed forestomach carcinoma. In another study[37] mice were given an injection of 20-methylcholanthrene in an aqueous methocel suspension into the wall of the forestomach, following which the animals were killed at the rate of at least two per week. Those surviving for more than one year were killed at irregular intervals. Squamous cell carcinoma occurred at the site of injection in more than 70 per cent of the animals living three months or longer following injection.

Pathologic Features

Carcinoma induced by the technic of injecting a carcinogen into the submucosa of the forestomach arises in the vicinity of the injection site. In the feeding experiments, on the other hand, all of the forestomach mucosa is exposed to the carcinogen, and so, although some of the carcinomas are localized (Fig. 2), even these may be multiple, and many others are massive and diffusely involve the entire mucosa (Fig. 3). Discrete tumors measuring 3 mm. to 20 mm. in diameter present a mucosal surface that is papillary and elevated or broad and sessile. The cut surface consists of firm, gray tissue with areas of hemorrhage and necrosis. The remainder of a forestomach containing a solitary tumor is often distorted by the neoplasm and may show acanthosis, hyperkeratosis, and papillomas. Massive carcinoma of the forestomach is characterized by neoplastic involvement of virtually the entire mucosal surface, with extension through the wall onto the serosa in multiple areas. The stomach is converted into a large, solid, firm object measuring as much as 30×25×20 mm., in over-all dimensions. It is mottled gray, white, red, yellow, and brown, due to a combination of hemorrhage, necrosis, and inflammatory change. The inner aspect of the chamber presents a granular or cheesy, necrotic, and hemorrhagic lining, filling and obstructing the lumen.

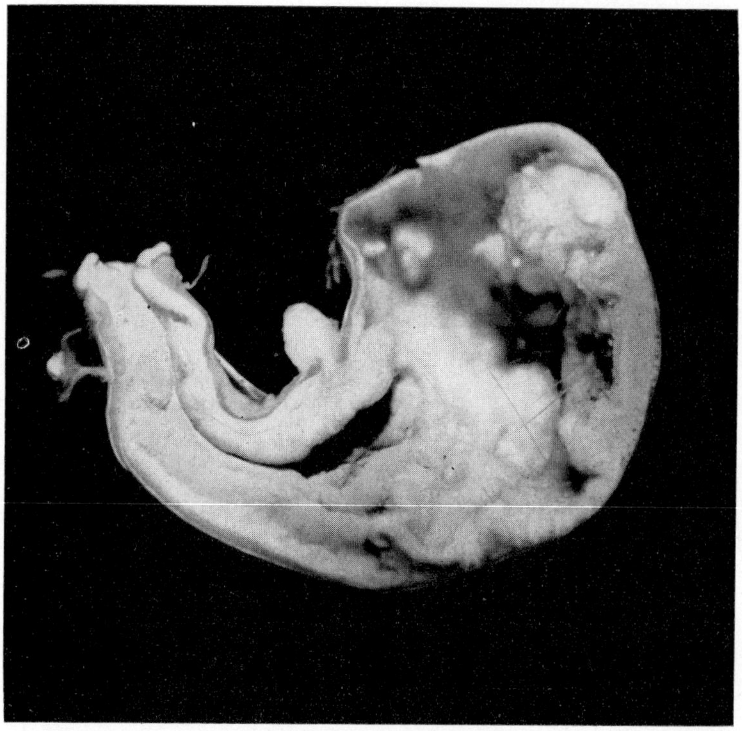

FIG. 2. Forestomach of mouse, with localized carcinoma and multiple papillomas. × 4.

Histologically the induced carcinomas of the forestomach are of the squamous cell type (Fig. 4). They vary considerably in pattern, in the proportion of cells to stroma, in papillary formation, in the number of pearls and extent of keratinization, and in the amount of hemorrhage, necrosis, and inflammatory reaction. The stroma, generally minimal in amount, is composed of mature connective tissue containing reticulum and collagen. The blood vessels are of capillary structure. The invading massive carcinomas are often partially surrounded by a thick peripheral wall of compressed inflammatory connective tissue which, however, is ineffectual in pre-

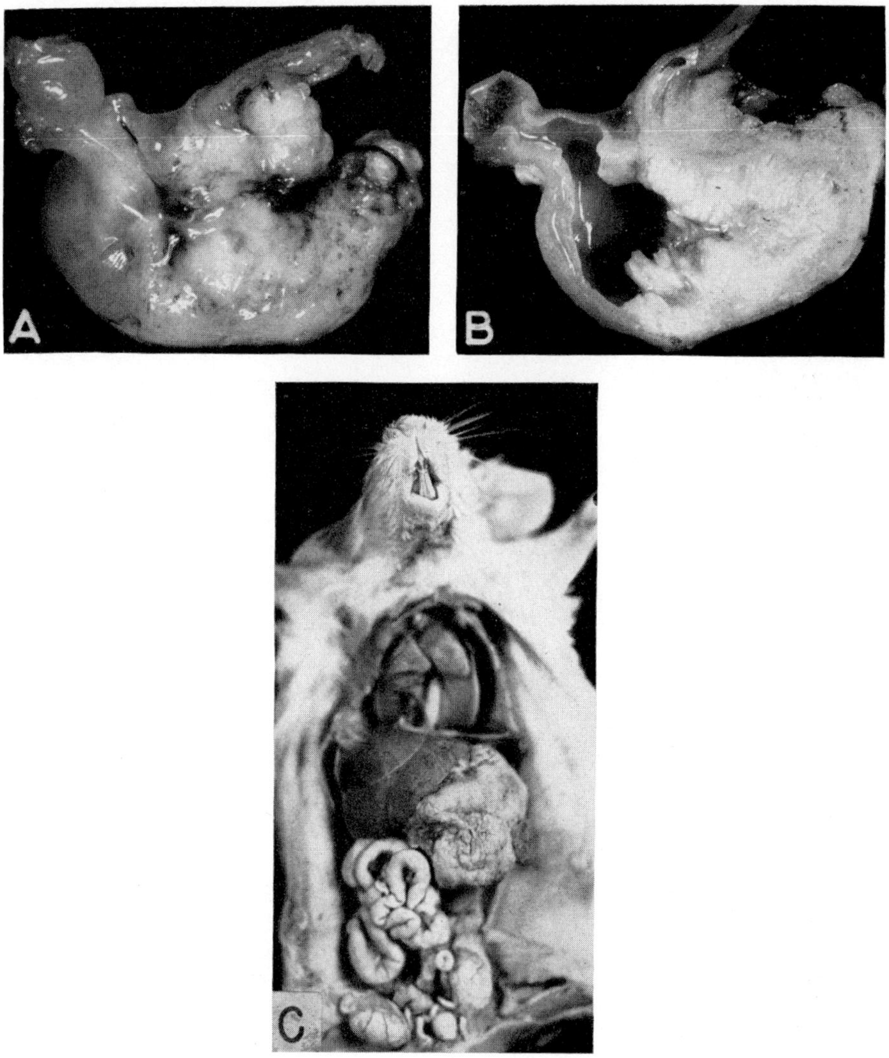

FIG. 3. Forestomach of mouse. A and B, with massive carcinoma; C, with squamous carcinoma.

venting infiltration and metastases. The tumor is usually transplantable, and infiltration of adjacent organs and tissues, peritoneal implantation, and metastases chiefly to liver and lymph nodes have been observed in as many as 50 per cent of animals with carcinoma of the forestomach.

HISTOGENESIS

Studies of the histogenesis of carcinoma of the forestomach have been made on material from mice treated with the carcinogens either by the injection method (local effect) or by feeding (diffuse effect).

Acanthosis. The epithelium immediately overlying the focus of injected methylcholanthrene in the submucosa rapidly develops into a plaque due to acanthosis and hyperkeratosis. Umbilicate lesions and papillomas (see below) appear and exhibit the various complicated and evolutionary changes of early carcinoma. Before the advent of these lesions, however, a disorder of keratinization appears in this thickened epithelium, characterized superficially by single-cell keratinization, parakeratosis, and *corps ronds*, whereas in the lower spinous and basal cells keratohyaline- or pre-eleidin-like granules appear. After the first week, small cellular buds project downward, imparting a scalloped appear-

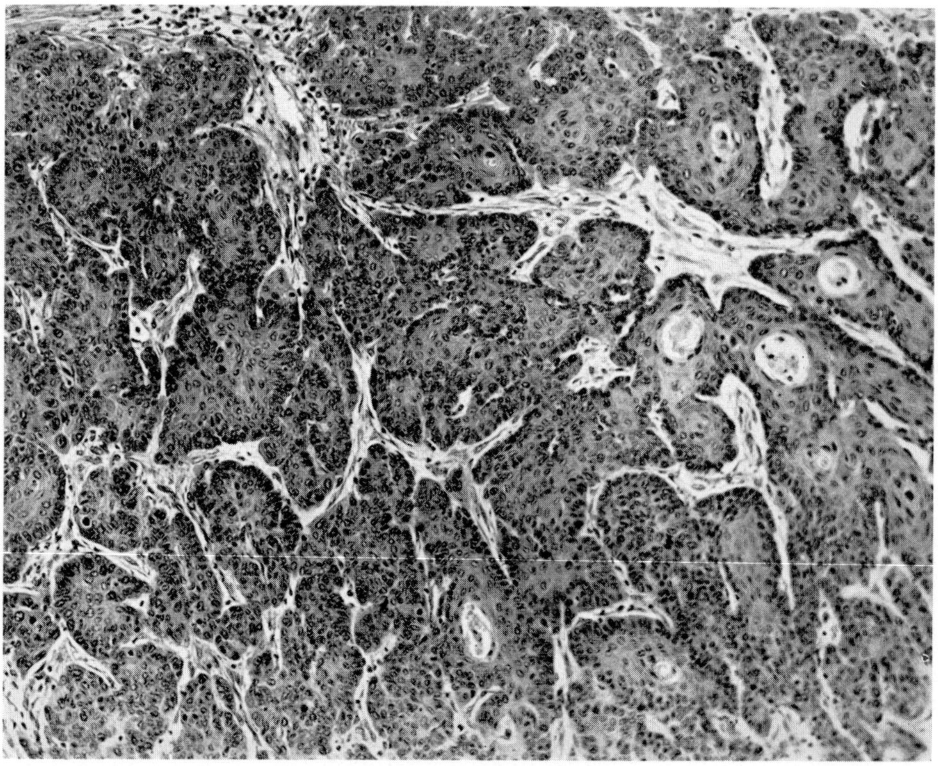

FIG. 4. Forestomach of mouse, with squamous carcinoma. × 130.

ance to the rete and impinging upon and infiltrating the muscularis mucosa. As these buds enlarge, the growing tip sometimes shows an inversion of keratinization, characterized by disappearance of the basal cells and replacement by keratinizing squamous cells which are then in direct contact with the mesenchymal tissues. The significance of this inversion of the epithelium at the infiltrating tip of the epithelial bud is not clearly evident.

Mice fed the carcinogenic hydrocarbons frequently show diffuse acanthosis and hyperkeratosis of the forestomach mucosa due to exposure of the entire surface of the forestomach (Fig. 5). In the development of this lesion retia form and become increased numerically, elongated and broadened, sometimes interlaced and anastomosed, giving the appearance of sessile papillary formations with marked hyperkeratosis. The relationship of this early diffuse lesion to the subsequent development of carcinoma is more difficult to assess in comparison with some of the other precancerous lesions that appear to be of more immediate significance. The diffuse lesion is not necessarily precancerous. It may occur spontaneously,[103] or be induced by a dietary deficiency,[5] or follow the oral administration of noncarcinogenic agents such as Aerosol OT (dioctyl ester of sulfosuccinic acid). The frequency and intensity of its development in relation to Aerosol OT in different vehicles is interesting. Aerosol OT dissolved in water and administered orally induces the diffuse lesion in mild form. It is more pronounced if the Aerosol OT is incorporated in an aqueous olive oil emulsion and

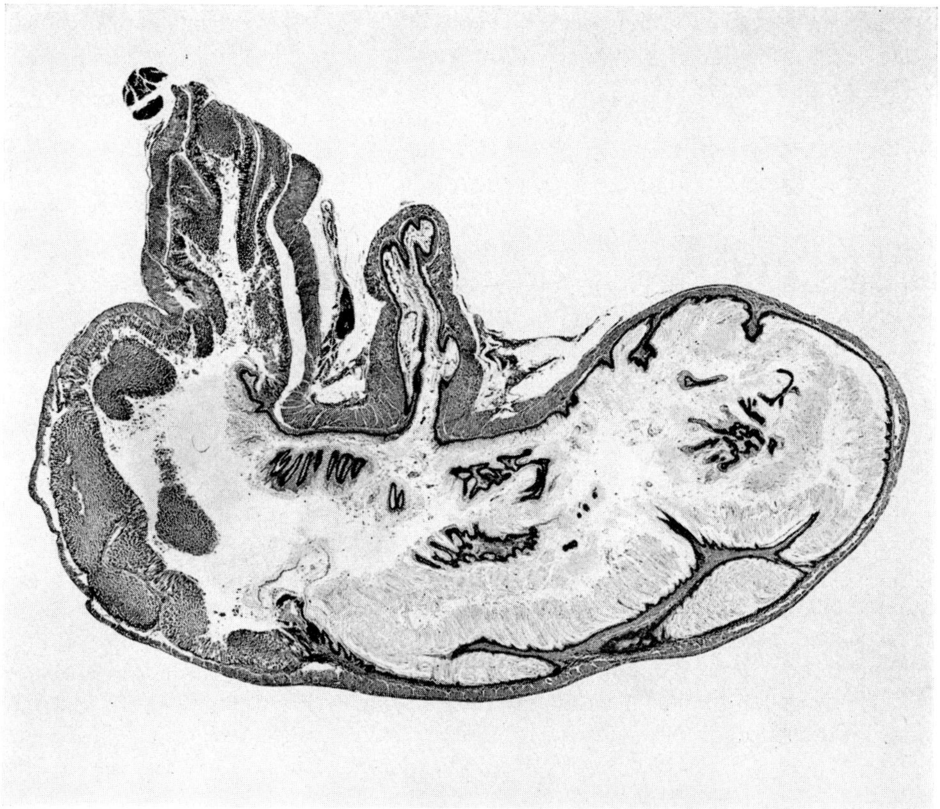

FIG. 5. Forestomach of mouse, with acanthosis, hyperkeratosis, and papillomas. × 10.

still more pronounced if an aqueous mineral oil emulsion is used as the vehicle. These, then, are examples of the induction of this diffuse lesion, in order of increasing intensity, by methods which in themselves do not evoke cancer. When, however, a carcinogen such as methylcholanthrene is added to these aqueous oil emulsions containing Aerosol OT, the diffuse lesion develops rapidly and to a severe degree.[111] Also under these circumstances carcinoma develops much more rapidly and in higher incidence than in similar feeding experiments in which acanthosis is of lesser extent. It would appear, therefore, that the mucosal thickening of the forestomach, although not necessarily a precancerous change in itself, accelerates the neoplastic process. Possibly the thicker the layer of keratin, the larger the amount of the carcinogen absorbed, and so the underlying epithelium is exposed more continuously to a heavier concentration of the hydrocarbon than would be the case in mice without this marked hyperkeratosis.

Papilloma and Umbilicate Lesion. In a large percentage of mice fed carcinogens, single, multiple, branching, or sessile papillomas, arising from any and all parts of the chamber of the forestomach, often fill the lumen and may overhang the limiting ridge. Early neoplastic changes in a papilloma are similar to those in other parts of the mucosa and usually take the form of umbilicate foci. However, rapidly developing carcinoma may be unheralded by the appearance of the more specific precancerous lesions that are so frequently recognized, in which case single or multiple elongated retia composed of atypical cells extend directly into the muscularis propria below the papilloma.

The umbilicate lesion is of more immediate importance in the evolution of the neoplastic process than is the diffuse lesion (Figs. 6 and 7). It is possible to trace many developing carcinomas to this lesion. The umbilicate lesion consists of a localized, shallow depression bordered on either side by hypertrophied retia. The deeper layers of stratified squamous epithelium which line the saucer-like portion of the lesion become thickened and give rise to infiltrating buds of atypical cells, beneath which the reticular basement membrane disintegrates. The granular layer of the mucosa containing parakeratotic cells and *corps ronds* may be hypertrophied, atrophied, distorted, or absent. A vertical defect regularly develops in the thick layer of keratin covering the surface in association with an infiltration of inflammatory cells in the underlying epithelium and stroma. As this defect becomes wider it probably facilitates more direct contact between the ingested carcinogen within the lumen of the forestomach and the epithelium at its base, and this is reflected in the progressive development of malignancy in this umbilicate lesion. The umbilicate lesion appears both in the surface mucosa and in papillomas, in association with the changes of malignant dyskeratosis or so-called "nearocarcinoma." The idea that a papilloma is necessarily transformed into carcinoma any more frequently than the surface mucosa is incorrect and misleading. This idea is equally fallacious in clinical medicine. In man, carcinoma of the skin, lip, tongue, and oral mucosa is rarely preceded by papilloma except for the verrucal type of leukoplakia and of senile keratosis. In the forestomach of the mouse, foci of early carcinoma may involve a portion of a papilloma at its base or on its sides or may occur in either acanthotic or atrophic surface epithelium in areas from which papilloma is absent.

Multicentric Carcinoma. Neoplastic foci may arise singly or simultaneously in several areas both in close proximity to and at varying intervals from each other, frequently becoming confluent to form a diffuse superficial carcinoma (Fig. 8). This latter lesion is characterized by the rather sudden development of an extensive, exaggerated, composite picture of the various features of early localized carcinoma, that is widely distributed, often involving the forestomach mucosa in its entirety. The atypical proliferating retia impinge upon and infiltrate the muscularis mucosae, submucosa, muscularis propria, serosa, and adjacent vessels.

Diverticulum. A diverticulum-like lesion frequently occurs in the intramural injection experiments. This may develop early and extend rapidly through the wall

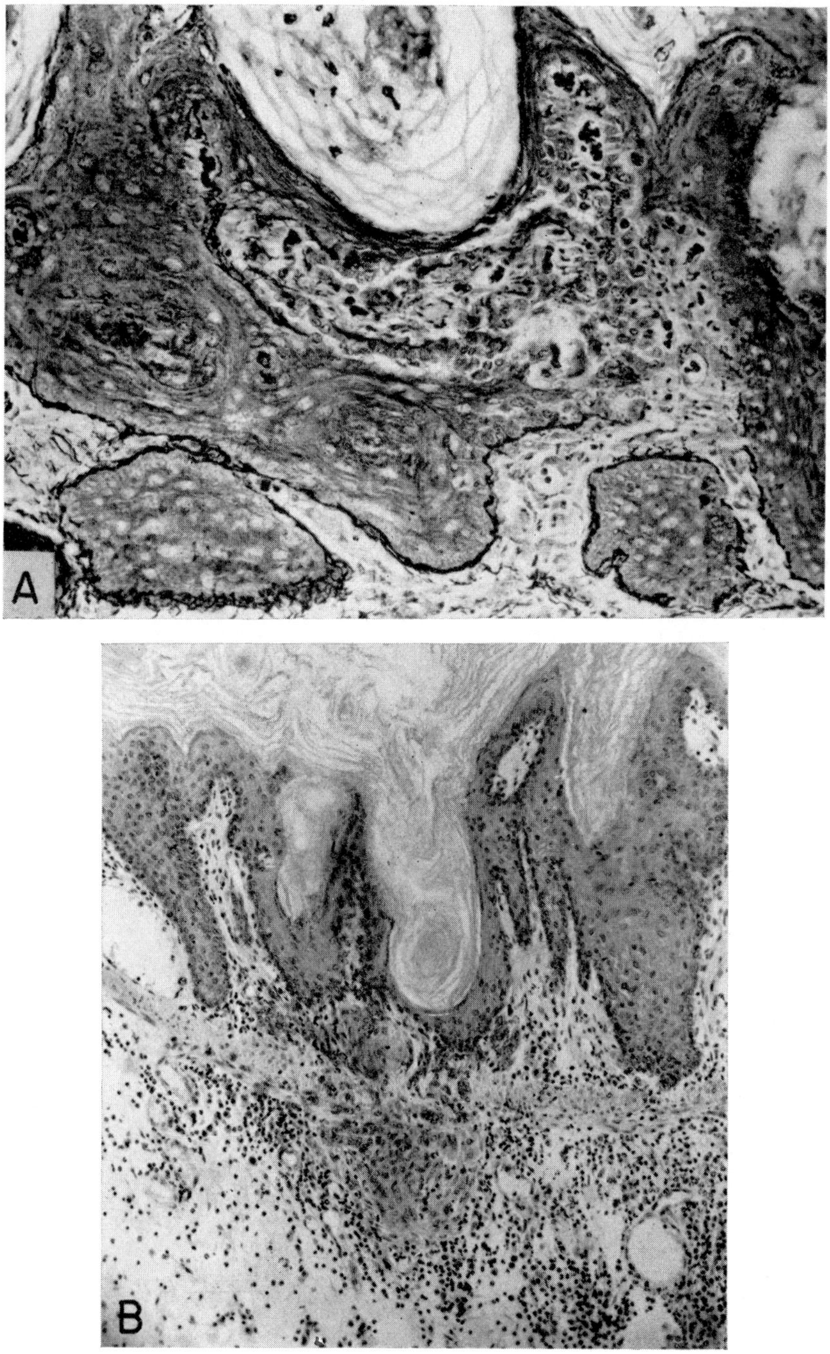

FIG. 6. Forestomach of mouse. A, with an umbilicate lesion with fragmentation of reticular basement membrane (× 216); B, with an umbilicate lesion showing early infiltration (× 108).

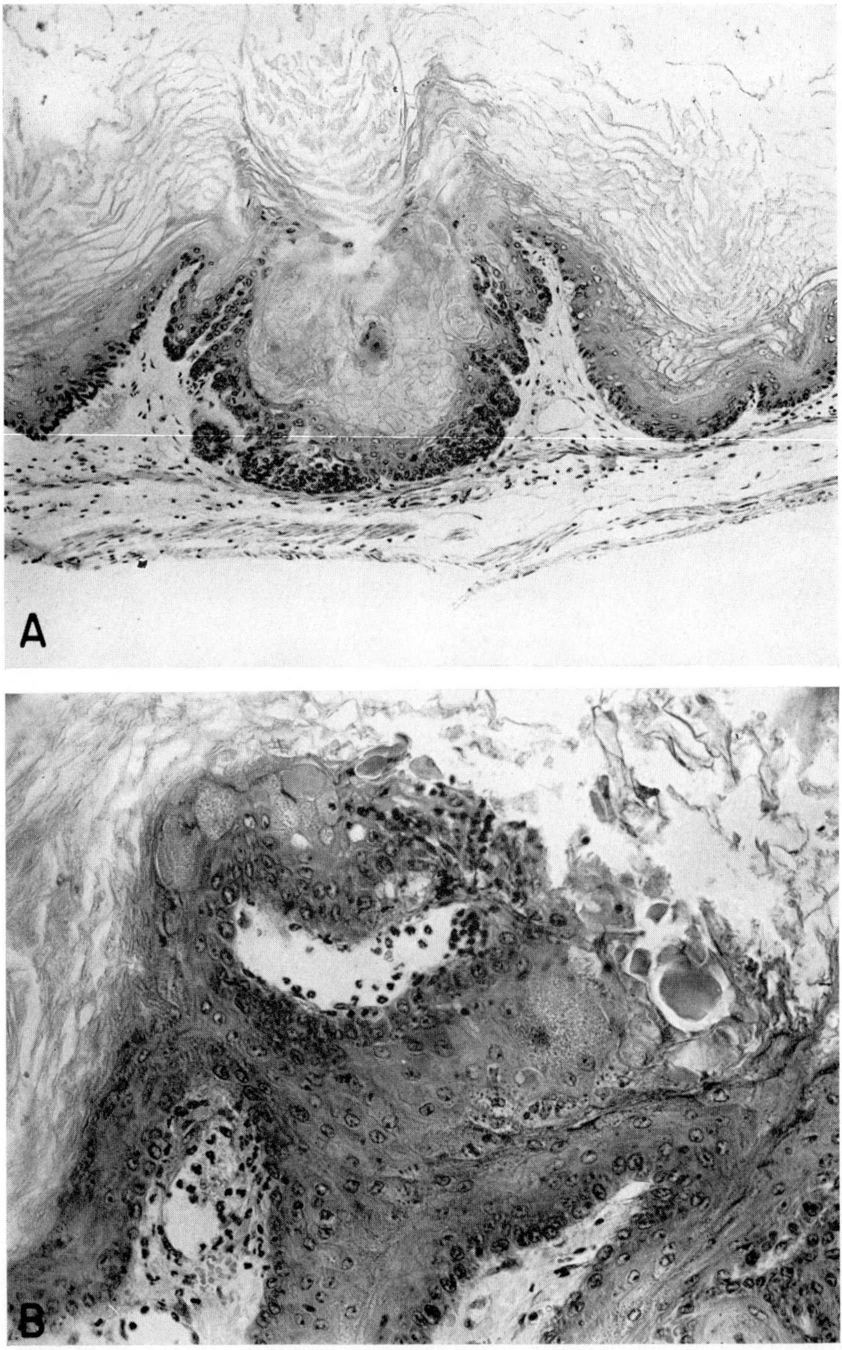

FIG. 7. Forestomach of mouse. A, with an umbilicate lesion (× 108); B, with dyskeratosis (× 214).

of the forestomach. This diverticular lesion appears to be in part an exaggeration of the umbilicate lesion, and in part it is due to the traumatic, toxic, and inflammatory destruction of the supporting stroma and muscularis resulting from the procedure of injection and from the degenerative and inflammatory changes associated with methylcholanthrene. At the growing tip of the diverticulum there is frequent replacement of basal cells by atypical keratinizing cells which probably accelerate the deep extension of this lesion. After penetrating the wall of the forestomach the di-

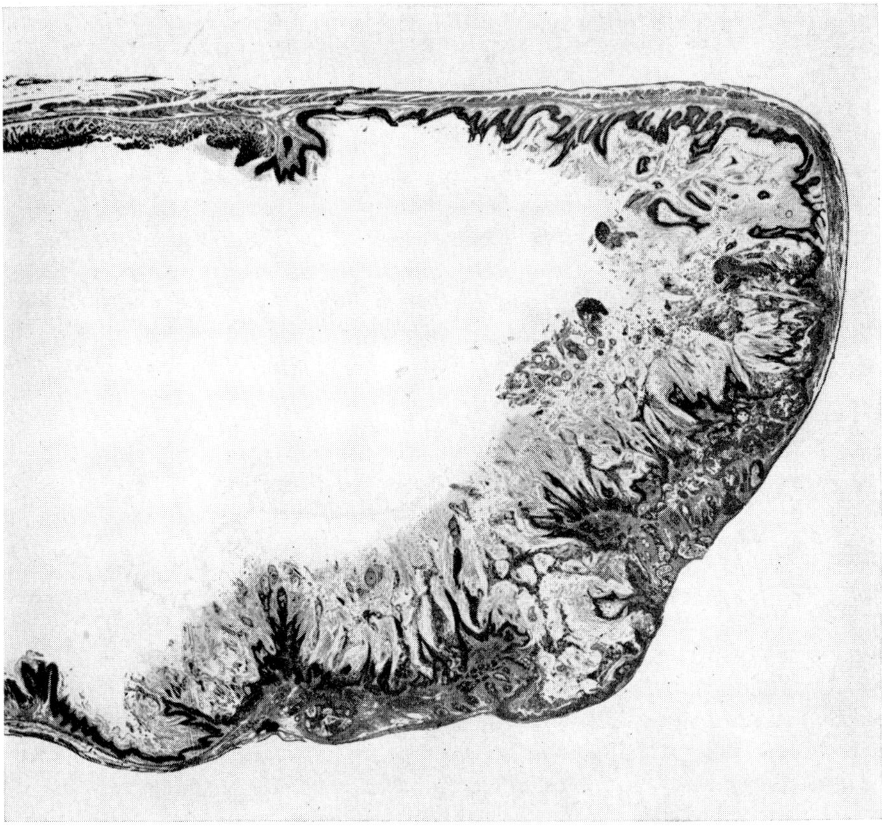

FIG. 8. Forestomach of mouse, with multicentric carcinoma. × 44.

verticulum may form a bulbous extension on the peritoneal surface and become adherent to adjacent organs and structures. Apparently it may then remain quiescent for a relatively long period of time. Foci of malignant dyskeratosis ultimately appear in the epithelium, sometimes in the neck portion of the lesion near the injected carcinogen or in the epithelial lining of small cysts that develop beneath the junction of the diverticulum and the lining mucosa of the forestomach. It is from these foci that carcinoma subsequently develops.

Stromal Change. In the feeding experiments the muscularis mucosae and muscularis propria are retracted at the base of a papilloma. They show thickening and changes in cell orientation coincident with the inception of neoplasia in the mucosa above. All coats of the viscus are subjected to a more or less intense inflammatory cell infiltration which may form a complete, continuous ring encircling the entire forestomach or which occurs focally in the vicinity of the papillomas and umbilicate lesions. New fibroblasts appear which are large, with vesicular, pale nuclei. Coincident with the onset of neoplasia in the mucosa, the underlying collagen often exhibits fibrinoid degeneration. The reticular basement membrane disintegrates, leaving the infiltrating neoplastic cells at first unsupported by reticulum. However, with time and with continued infiltration, a new reticulum develops in relation to the neoplastic epithelial cells and persists in the fully formed tumor.

In the injection experiments stromal changes are similar except for the reaction to the crystalline methylcholanthrene in the tissues. An acute inflammatory reaction develops about the deposit of methylcholanthrene in the submucosa, forming a well-circumscribed focus within the first few hours. This focus goes through an evolutionary process characterized by degeneration and necrosis in the center, and infiltration of macrophages from without which phagocytose the crystalline material, while around the periphery fibrinoid degeneration occurs in muscle, collagen and blood vessels. After one week these changes are followed by lymphangiectasis, telangiectasis, and fibrosis, all of which progressively increase. There is an infiltration of lymphocytes and plasma cells, and later on foreign-body giant cells develop. Although the macrophages persist for some time, the crystal clefts within them generally disappear after several weeks.

Forestomach Carcinoma in Rats

The azo dyes have long been known as powerful hepatocarcinogenic agents. Less well known is their ability to induce papillomas of the forestomach.[5, 56] Mulay and Firminger[75] reported the induction of squamous cell carcinoma and an interesting type of precancerous lesion of the forestomach in Osborne-Mendel rats fed *p*-dimethylaminobenzene-1-azo-1-naphthalene for a long period of time. This precancerous lesion consists of a marked thickening of the mucosa due to neoplastic proliferation of the basal cells. The deep surface of the mucosa is characterized by an irregular, scalloped lower border which later forms small budlike projections. In some animals this lesion eventually progresses to infiltrating carcinoma, attesting to its malignant nature from the beginning. Its early stage is clearly distinguishable from the non-neoplastic hyperplasia and acanthosis of the forestomach induced by methods, such as starvation, which do not lead to cancer.[73] This precancerous lesion promises to be of value as an experimental test object for the study of carcinoma *in situ*.

Comparison Between Cancer of the Forestomach and Cutaneous Carcinoma

It is interesting and profitable to compare and to contrast early cutaneous and forestomach carcinoma in the mouse induced respectively by painting and feeding carcinogenic hydrocarbons. The mucosa of the forestomach is composed of basal, spinous, granular, and cornified cells with granules in the stratum granulosum. This layering of cells does not occur in the skin of the mouse except on the foot pad, ear, and some areas of the abdominal wall which are rarely subjected to painting. The mucous membrane of the forestomach is well protected, always moist, and unlike the skin is not subjected to biting, scratching, rubbing, and other trauma. The histogenesis of forestomach carcinoma is uncomplicated by the presence of hair follicles and sebaceous glands, which are assumed to play a prominent role in the development of cutaneous cancer. The exposure of the forestomach to ingested carcinogen is virtually continuous in contrast to the intermittent exposure of the skin two or three times weekly. However, this factor of exposure is somewhat equalized due to the absorption and retention of the carcinogen by the sebaceous glands, which in the skin tend to keep the painted area more or less constantly under the influence of the agent employed.

Skin painted with a carcinogen is described as showing, initially, dilatation and incipient growth of hair follicles which go on to form epithelial cysts, which in turn give rise to papillomas. Carcinoma is alleged to develop both from hyperplastic hair follicles and from the keratinized cysts believed to be remnants of hair follicles. Indeed, the role attributed to the hair follicles and sebaceous glands in the neoplastic process is so important that Suntzeff, Carruthers, and Cowdry[117] attributed their failure to induce epidermal tumors in painted newborn mice to the rudimentary condition of these structures. From the knowledge of the histogenesis of forestomach carcinoma, one wonders if the role of the cutaneous appendages, and of the cystic structures derived from them, has not been overemphasized in the histogenesis of cutaneous cancer. In the forestomach, the umbilicate lesion, from which carcinoma develops so frequently, originates from the surface epithelium. So closely do many of these umbilicate lesions resemble the so-called hair follicle cysts that consideration should be given to the possibility that these keratinized cysts from which cutaneous cancer originates may similarly arise from the surface epidermis instead of from the hair follicles. Perhaps also the cutaneous papilloma has been overemphasized as a precancerous lesion because, in the forestomach, carcinoma is more likely to arise from the surface mucosa than from papillomas.

Sarcoma does not develop in the forestomach of mice fed the carcinogenic hydrocarbons.* This is in contrast to its occasional development in skin painting experiments during which it is assumed sufficient carcinogen penetrates to the subepidermal tissues, possibly aided by cutaneous ulceration, to induce sarcoma. Susceptibility of the forestomach to sarcoma is indicated by the development of this lesion following intramural injection of the carcinogen. Stromal degeneration in the feeding experiments has been attributed to the effects of the ingested carcinogen, presumed to have penetrated the wall of the stomach from the lumen. If this is true, the amount of hydrocarbon in contact with the mesodermal tissues is too small to induce sarcoma.

* Recently, Hitchcock has reported the induction of gastric fibrosarcoma in 4 mice fed 20-methylcholanthrene. (HITCHCOCK, C. R. Failure of bile as abetting agent for 20-methylcholanthrene in induction of gastric tumors in mice, *J. Nat. Cancer Inst. 12:* 369-397, 1951.)

ADENOCARCINOMA OF THE GLANDULAR STOMACH

Since 1940 several studies have dealt with the successful induction of adenocarcinoma of the glandular stomach of mice by the intramural injection of the carcinogenic hydrocarbons.[10, 13, 55, 116] However, all attempts to induce this lesion by feeding methods have failed. These negative results are probably attributable to: (1) the more resistant nature of the glandular epithelium as compared to the squamous epithelium of the stomach; (2) the rapidity with which ingested carcinogen passes from the forestomach through the pyloric chamber into the duodenum; and (3) to the mucous barrier. Due to the flow of mucous, the glandular mucous membrane is constantly bathed, and so the ingested carcinogens are washed away before there is time for the prolonged contact necessary to induce adenocarcinoma. Physiologically, ingested materials are stored for some time in the forestomach and pass rapidly through the glandular stomach; hence, exposure to the carcinogen is much shorter in the glandular than in the forestomach.

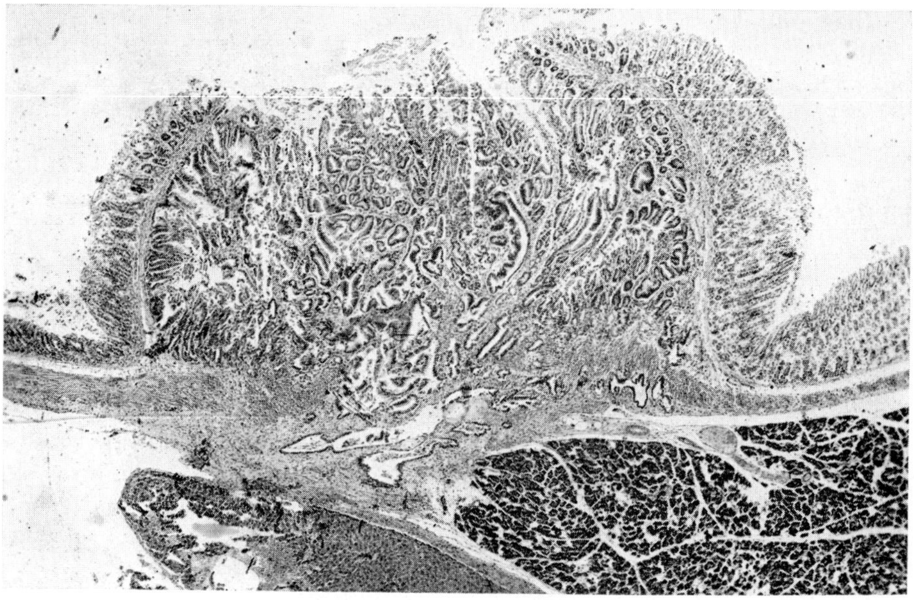

FIG. 9. Glandular stomach of mouse, with adenocarcinoma. × 30.

Experiments have been reported[108, 109] in which 20-methylcholanthrene, 1,2,5,6-dibenzanthracene or 3,4-benzpyrene dissolved in lard or in mineral oil, suspended in horse serum or impregnated on a cotton thread, were introduced into the wall of the glandular stomach. Of 296 mice so treated, the following lesions of the glandular stomach were found: precancerous lesions, 44; adenocarcinoma, 11 (Fig. 9); adenoacanthoma, 8; combined neoplastic epithelial lesions and sarcoma, 20; and sarcoma, 30. All the carcinomas developed in mice receiving 20-methylcholanthrene.

Transplants of an induced carcinoma of the glandular stomach of a mouse studied for enzymatic activity possessed little if any pepsin and alkaline phosphatase activity whereas the thymonucleodepolymerase activity was the same as in normal gastric glandular mucosa of the mouse.[40]

To test the significance of strain, a single dose of 20-methylcholanthrene was injected intramurally into the glandular stomach of 250 mice of five strains.[106] Of these, 90 had precancerous lesions; 9, adenocarcinoma; 2, adenoacanthoma; 37, mixed neoplastic epithelial lesions and sarcoma; and 24, sarcoma. The malignant tumors occurred between two and eleven months, but the precancerous lesions were fairly evenly distributed throughout a period of one to eighteen months following operation. Although mice of strain DBA spontaneously develop an adenomatous hyperplastic gastritis of the glandular stomach, they are resistant to the induction of carcinoma by this technic. The mice of four other Strains, C, C57BL, C3H, and C3Hb, are approximately equally susceptible to the induction of epithelial neoplasms and there is no sex difference. There is, however, a difference in the incidence of sarcoma. Since the development of sarcoma is an undesirable complication in experiments of this type, designed as they are to study the problem of gastric carcinoma, mice of the C57BL Strain may prove to be one of the best experimental test objects for such studies because, while susceptible to the induction of epithelial tumors, the C57BL mice are relatively resistant to induction of sarcoma of the stomach.

Hyperplastic Gastritis of the Glandular Stomach

The spontaneous development of a type of hyperplastic adenomatous gastritis in mice of several inbred strains, notably strain I and strain DBA mice, has been reported.[1, 2, 4, 42, 103] In rats and monkeys, somewhat similar changes have been induced by shale oil.[70] In mice, the spontaneous lesion is characterized by an adenomatous hypertrophic and hyperplastic overgrowth of the rugae of the glandular chamber of the stomach, with associated inflammatory changes and occasionally ulceration. The hyperplastic gastric lesion of strain I mice appears earlier and develops more rapidly in the male than in the female, although by six months of age it becomes obvious in virtually all mice of both sexes. Efforts to demonstrate an infectious etiologic agent have been unsuccessful. Although histologic studies reveal some features somewhat suggestive of malignant growth, metastases are not observed. Within the wall of the stomach, displaced foci of atypical mucosa and dilated glands are found frequently in the submucosa, occasionally in the muscularis propria, rarely in the subserosa, and still more rarely within thin-walled vessels in the submucosa. The deep extensions of glandular tissue are always supported by lamina propria and appear to be in continuity with the surface mucosa even when occupying an intravascular location. This altered gastric mucosa from Strain I mice, when finely macerated and injected intravenously into mice of homologous strains, displays a greater capacity for survival and growth in the lungs of the host animals than glandular mucosa similarly treated from mice of other strains.[3] This transplanted tissue, while able to survive and perhaps to proliferate to a limited extent in its new habitat, still does not exhibit the outright characteristics of a malignant neoplasm. The entire significance of this phenomenon is not immediately clear, but it would appear to indicate more aggressive growth potential on the part of the altered gastric mucosa of Strain I mice as compared with that of mice of other strains.

The reports of Strong and his associates[7, 99, 113, 114, 115] of a strain of mice alleged to develop spontaneous carcinoma of the glandular stomach would constitute a contribution of the first order if verified. However, not all workers who have examined the lesion agree that it is primary adenocarcinoma of the glandular stomach. McPeak and Warren[71] and Kaplan[53] studied this lesion and concluded that it is hyperplastic gastritis, not unlike the lesion which occurs in Strain I mice. They were unwilling to diagnose any of the cases available to them for study as adenocarcinoma of the glandular stomach. Therefore, proof of the truly neoplastic nature of this lesion awaits confirmation.

Carcinoma of the Glandular Stomach in the Rat

The rat, like the mouse, has been successfully used as an experimental animal for the induction of adenocarcinoma of the glandular stomach following the intramural injection of a carcinogenic hydrocarbon. However, this technic has not been attended by as much success as the claims in the literature would appear to indicate.[10, 56] Rusch and co-workers[92] claimed to have induced a low-grade adenocarcinoma without metastasis in 1 of 5 rats receiving an intramural injection of 3,4-benzpyrene into the glandular stomach. This report is rejected by Klein and Palmer[56] on the basis of lack of objective pathologic description and of illustrations. Barrett,[10] on the other hand, accepts it as the first example of this experimental lesion. From our more recent knowledge it is probable that the lesion described by Rusch *et al.*[92] should be classified as the precancerous adenomatous diverticulum similar to those described on page 12. In dealing with experimentally induced lesions of the glandular stomach, caution in diagnosing carcinoma is just as essential in the rat as in the mouse (see p. 5).

In the experiment of Howes and de Oliveira[50] a silk thread impregnated with 20-methylcholanthrene was inserted into the wall of the stomach between the serosa and the mucosa under the central or acid glandular portion. Approximately 150 rats were killed at varying intervals over a period of 590 days. These experiments were designed primarily to study the evolutionary changes leading up to the development of carcinoma of the stomach (see p. 24). It is difficult to be certain how many of the gastric lesions were diagnosed as definite carcinoma and what criteria were used in arriving at this diagnosis. The authors state that in 2 animals large tumors grew outside the stomach and that there were local peritoneal implantations, but no metastases were found in the liver or lungs. Presumably these 2 lesions were considered to be carcinomas. There were also 7 sarcomas, 2 of which were combined with epithelial growths.

In another experiment[104, 105] 0.6 mg. of 20-methylcholanthrene was injected intramurally into each of two sites, one in the antrum near the pyloric ring and the other in the acid glandular portion of the stomach about 5 mm. from the limiting ridge. Postmortem examinations were done on 265 animals, all within three years of the time of injection. The most frequently occurring lesion was the adenomatous diverticulum which is regarded as precancerous (see p. 12). Malignant tumors were present in 25 animals as follows: 4 adenocarcinomas (Fig. 10), 4 adenoacanthomas, 3 mixed carcinomas and sarcomas, 13 sarcomas, and 1 unclassified. Paralleling the experience in man, in whom the antral region is a frequent site for gastric carcinoma, most of the malignant epithelial tumors in the rat also arose in this location. Of the 13 cases of sarcoma, 4 occurred at the antral

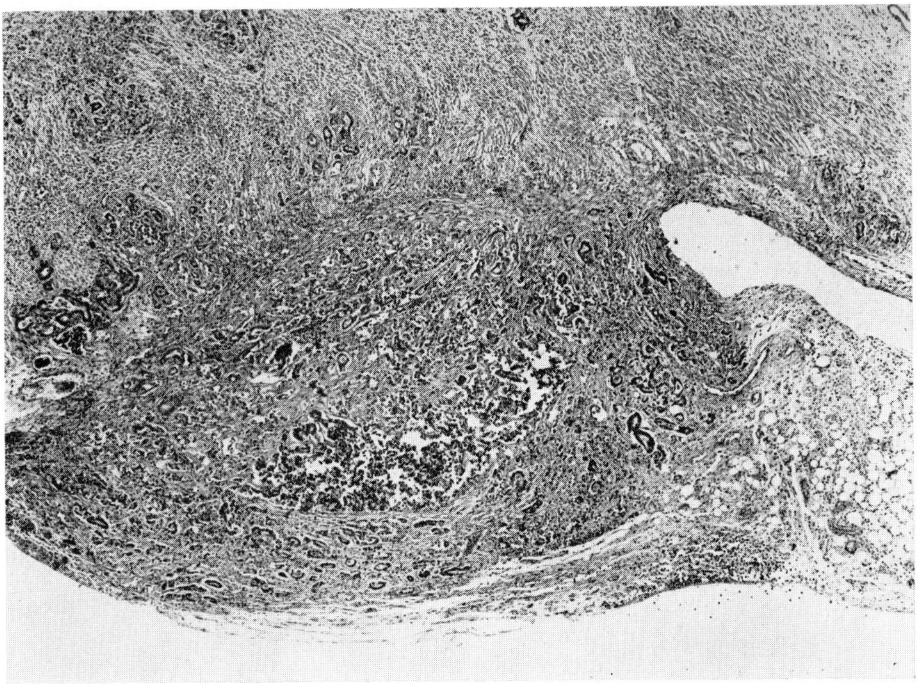

FIG. 10. Glandular stomach of rat, with carcinoma. × 40.

site, 7 at the acid-secreting site, and 2 embraced both sides. The mesenchymal growths therefore exhibited a predilection for the acid-secreting portion of the glandular stomach.

ADENOMATOUS DIVERTICULUM

The most frequent lesion observed in the rats in the experiment cited[104, 105] was an adenomatous diverticulum (273 lesions occurred in 265 rats), (Figs. 11, 12, 13). This lesion has no counterpart in human pathology. In the rat it is considered to be precancerous. Characteristically it consists of a diverticulum-like mass in continuity with the lumen of the stomach, which it often equals or exceeds in size. Externally there is chronic peritonitis with fibrous adhesions to surrounding structures which may be mistaken for infiltrating carcinoma. Although the development of the lesion is accompanied by thinning of the wall of the stomach, the integrity of the serosa and in part of the muscularis propria is maintained. The most deeply placed glands are

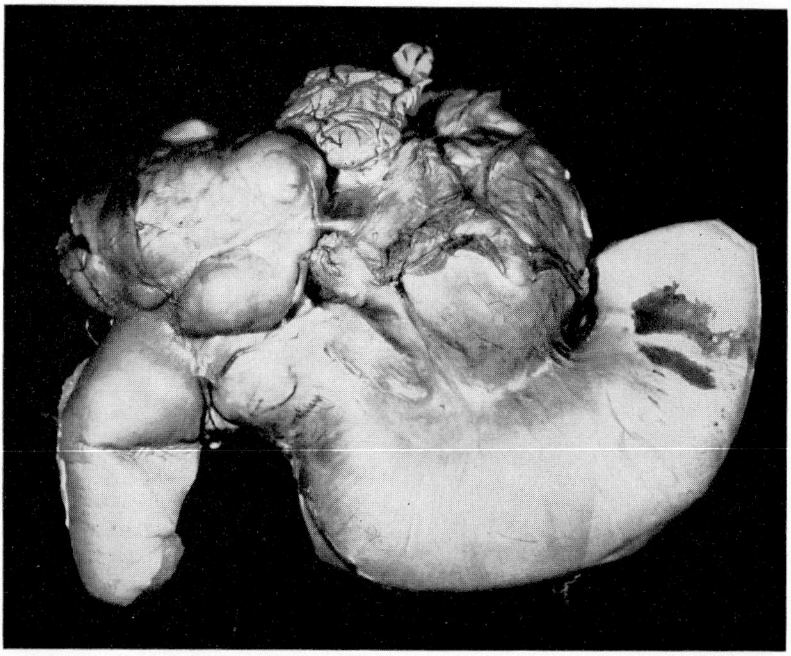

FIG. 11. Glandular stomach of rat, with adenomatous diverticulum. × 1.

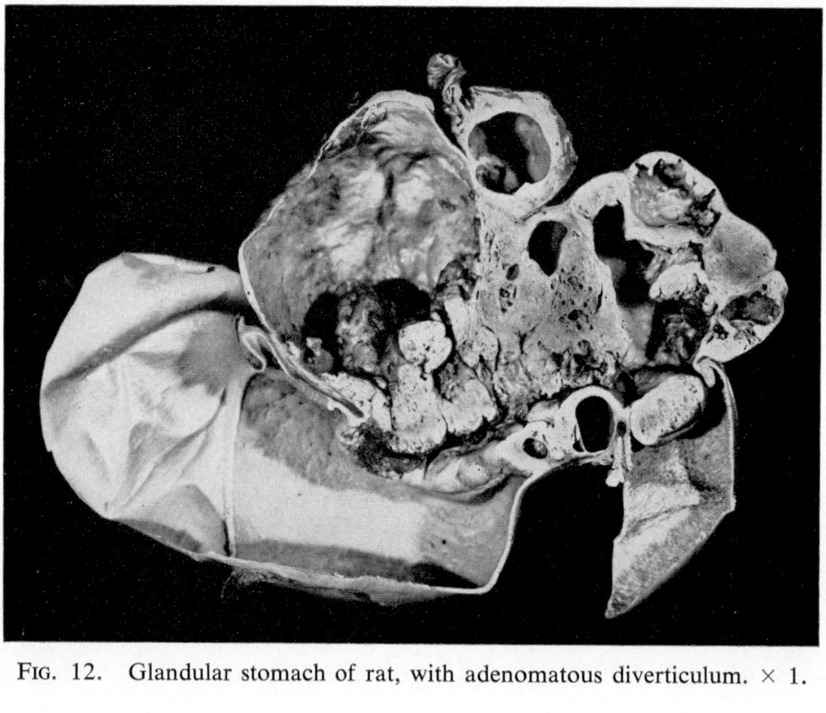

FIG. 12. Glandular stomach of rat, with adenomatous diverticulum. × 1.

separated from the surrounding viscera by a thick barrier consisting of peritoneum and fibrous inflammatory tissue, in which there are remnants of the muscularis. Areas of the fibrous tissue and many of the arteries show fibrinoid degeneration, and often the latter are partially or completely occluded and show chronic arteritis. The adenomatous diverticulum presents a honey-combed appearance, being riddled with microcysts and macrocysts, the largest being as large as or larger than the lumen of the stomach. These cysts are lined by altered gastric mucosa and many of them contain pultaceous necrotic material consisting of mucus and inflammatory exudate which is also present in the glands and stroma. Polypoid adenomatous nodules extend into the cysts and into the lumen of the stomach, and are composed of cells which are chiefly of the mucous variety. Although hyperchromatic and hyperplastic in appearance, these cells do not in most instances show the convincing cytologic variations characteristic

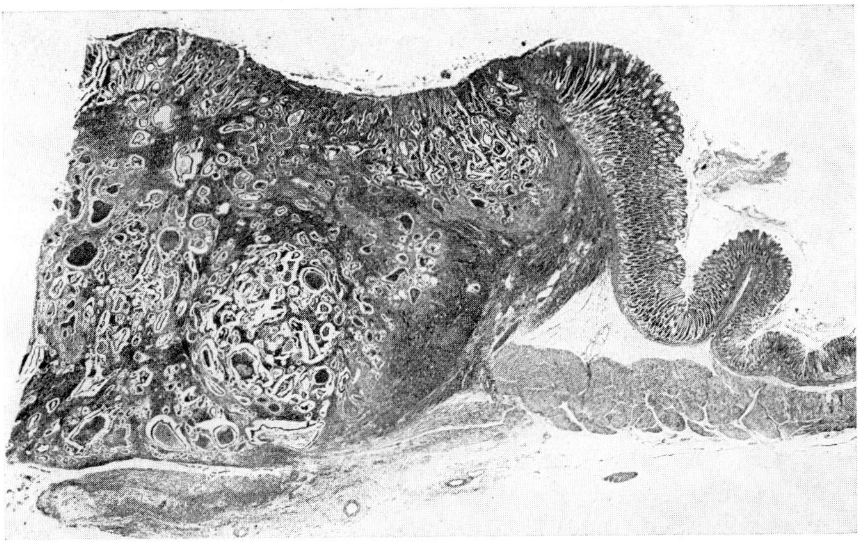

FIG. 13. Glandular stomach of rat, with adenomatous diverticulum. × 15.

of a truly malignant neoplastic process. In about 7 per cent of the cases there is squamous metaplasia even though the lesion may have no physical connection with the fore-stomach.

Exactly the same amount of methylcholanthrene was injected intramurally at each of two sites, one in the antral region, the other in the acid-secreting region. The vast majority of the adenomatous diverticuli occur in the antrum. If, as suspected, this is a precancerous lesion, its more frequent occurrence in the antrum is significant in view of the more frequent development of gastric carcinoma in man at this site. That it is indeed precancerous is suggested by the occasional occurrence of carcinoma in association with it. Attempts at transplantation failed in 25 cases. However, in view of the failure of the carcinomas to grow on transplantation, this criterion of malignancy so valuable in mice may not be valid in rats. These studies indicate the need for caution in distinguishing between carcinoma and other lesions which are composed of atypical epithelial elements and which may be confused with cancer.

Histogenesis

Howes and de Oliveira[50] found that shortly after implantation of methylcholanthrene-impregnated threads between the serosa and the acid-secreting mucosa, a round-cell infiltration and edema appeared, followed by ulceration. The acid and pepsin cells were destroyed and did not regenerate. The mucous cells that survived relined the cleft rapidly and proliferated backward along the thread to form a sinus lined by epithelium. This process took approximately two weeks. The cells became arranged as acini and shortly thereafter those that were able to continue their existence beneath the muscularis mucosae began to proliferate.[48, 49, 50] Adenomas formed in the clefts and grew outward toward the lumen of the stomach, pushing open the mouth of the cleft, and sometimes filling the lumen of the stomach. This type of growth did not disturb the reticulum boundary that had been formed beyond the new mucosa lining the cleft. In the sinus, on the other hand, atypical cells suggesting an adenocarcinomatous pattern grew within the wall of the stomach coincident with which process the reticulum barrier already formed about the sinus was destroyed. Whether these cells were in actuality early carcinomas is not clear from the report,[50] for it is uncertain how many, if any, of the later lesions were truly carcinoma and how many were simply the adenomatous diverticulum.

Carcinogens in the lumen of the stomach make contact, if at all, only with the surface mucous cells, which under normal conditions are more or less continually desquamating. The mucous barrier tends to prevent the prolonged contact between the carcinogen and the mucosa necessary to induce cancer. By contrast the carcinogen injected intramurally evokes carcinoma. Within the wall of the stomach the mucous cells are in direct contact with the carcinogen in a new environment where perhaps their protective secretion may be lost and where damage can be done by the carcinogen to the surrounding reticulum barrier and blood vessels. The mucous cells must be added to the list of cells able to survive destruction caused by the carcinogens. Like the fibroblasts and the epithelial cells of the forestomach and skin, they possess a high rate of proliferation in response to injury by a carcinogen, and so may be converted into a neoplasm.

COCKROACH TUMORS

No review of the problem of experimental gastric cancer is complete without reference to the induction of tumors in *Leucophaea*.[95] This is a large cockroach. After section of the recurrent nerve, tumors develop in organs which are innervated by this nerve in a large percentage of the adults and nymphs subjected to this operation. The organs affected are the anterior portion of the alimentary canal (the foregut and anterior midgut) and the salivary organs (the salivary reservoir and salivary glands). Histologically the neoplasm of the alimentary canal has been described as consisting of layers of cells which in the course of development become progressively abnormal and many of them finally necrotic. The tumor is sarcoma-like, invades surrounding tissues, and occasionally perforates the chitinous body wall. Definite proof that this lesion is genuinely neoplastic is lacking.

PRECANCEROUS LESIONS OF THE STOMACH OF MAN

Preinvasive carcinoma of the stomach of man occurs in the form of a polyp which develops malignant cytologic alterations[15] and as a nonpolypoid form, very prone to ulceration, which occurs in the prepyloric region.[30, 31, 41] A third type of lesion,[74, 112] designated by Mallory[72] carcinoma *in situ*, is characterized by changes in the mucosa histologically suggestive of a malignant neoplasm with numerous and atypical mitotic figures widely distributed in the area of involvement. The atypical epithelial change involves the entire thickness of the mucous membrane but tends to remain within these limits, so that the base of the mucosa is involved least, and only one of Mallory's cases showed limited infiltration. There is either no ulceration or else the deep type of peptic ulceration. Although definitely malignant, there is no proof that this entity is related to the more frequently seen types of infiltrating gastric carcinoma.

The question of the possible importance of the non-neoplastic lesions of chronic gastritis and of peptic ulcer in the etiology of gastric cancer in man has attracted wide attention. There is a great difference of opinion about this matter. Some observers, pointing out that the incidence of chronic gastritis increases with age, believe its association with gastric cancer is purely incidental. Others, admittedly without much evidence, assume it is closely related etiologically to gastric cancer. The relationship of peptic ulcer to carcinoma of the stomach is likewise uncertain, having been variously reported as from 1 per cent[15] to 71 per cent.[128] Such divergent opinions are not convincing proof that chronic gastritis and peptic ulceration are precancerous lesions in man. With respect to pernicious anemia, there is substantial evidence to indicate that gastric carcinoma occurs more frequently in patients with this condition than in persons without it.

The multicentric development of gastric carcinoma in man versus the unicentric or unicellular theory of origin has been ably discussed by Willis.[127] Early tumors of the human stomach, particularly multiple papillomas, showing neoplastic transformation still in progress have been traced to the intact mucosal epithelium in several areas. Hauser[43, 44] and Versé[122] describe early carcinomas which originated from many or all of the glands in considerable areas of the mucous membrane with the marginal extension of the cancerous change still in progress. Both Hauser[43, 44] and Kaufmann[54] state that multicentric development of carcinoma is frequent and occasionally may be widespread over virtually the entire gastric mucosa. Tsunoda[120] described a case of early gastric carcinoma with three separate areas showing transition from normal to cancerous epithelium. Gall,[39] in a personal survey of large sections of 114 gastric cancers, detected foci of carcinoma *in situ* at variable distances from the grossly visible tumor in more than 30 per cent of the specimens. Recognizing that gastric carcinoma often arises progressively over a field of prepared mucous membrane, Willis[127] conceives of extensive diffuse carcinoma ("leather-bottle" carcinoma) not as the product of spread from a solitary original focus but as arising simultaneously or successively over a large area or from several areas of the mucous membrane. He believes that even in the lesion of carcinoma *in situ* (see Mallory[72]) the replacement of normal by malignant cells occurs over a wide area and not from a single focus. This opinion is shared by the author of this chapter as a result of his studies on experimental carcinoma which, although arising in a small area, shows neoplastic changes so universal in that area that even the earliest stages observable could not possibly have arisen from a single cell or from a single-cell focus. Hence the idea that gastric carcinoma is frequently multicentric in its development is supported by material from both man and experimental animals.

The study of the histogenesis of early cancer of the stomach in man leaves a gap between hyperplastic overgrowth and definite carcinoma. This gap appears to be bridged, if at all, by a rather acute morphologic change which becomes established rapidly. Uncertainty has often existed as to whether the lesions described as early cancer would inevitably progress into cancer. The data supporting this progression are rather meager. The experimental field is free from this difficulty. Suitable test animals have been developed for the induction of gastric carcinoma, and these can be sacrificed at any stage during the development and progression of the lesion. The experimentalist is not forced to wait for a lucky chance to find a few early cancers hidden in a large volume of autopsy or surgical material that may have required years to accumulate.

EXPERIMENTAL CARCINOMA OF SMALL INTESTINE OF MICE

Spontaneous carcinoma of the small intestine is not frequently found in man,[59, 60, 77, 84, 107] and it is exceedingly rare in laboratory animals. No case of this lesion was found at autopsy in 142,000 mice[125] or in 33,000 rats.[20] That it may occur, however, is attested by the occasional mention, illustration, or description of it in mice[11, 12, 46, 76, 119, 129] and once in a grouse.[129] In the mice maintained at the National Cancer Institute, mucinous carcinoma occasionally occurs at the ileocecal junction. Dogs, cats, cattle, and horses appear virtually immune to this lesion.

The reports on the experimental induction of adenocarcinoma of the small intestine in mice describe the development of such tumors following the oral administration of 20-methylcholanthrene and 1,2,5,6-dibenzanthracene.[28, 65, 67, 68, 110, 126] Dunn and Kessel[28] describe a carcinoma of the small intestine in a rat fed N-acetylaminofluorene. Judging from Bielschowsky's[14] illustrations, at least 1 of 5 intestinal carcinomas, occurring among 104 rats receiving acetylaminofluorene by mouth, arose in the small intestine.

In one experiment[126] mice were maintained on a dietary mixture to which 20-methylcholanthrene was added, and each animal ingested approximately 1 to 1.5 mg. of the hydrocarbon daily. The animals that survived on the experimental diet for six months were then placed on the basal diet to which no methylcholanthrene had been added. Carcinoma of the small intestine occurred in 12, and precancerous lesions in 24, of 50 Strain C3H mice. Of 32 Strain C mice, 4 developed carcinoma and 5 precancerous lesions.

In other experiments[64, 65, 66, 68, 110] aqueous oil emulsions containing 1,2,5,6-dibenzanthracene or 20-methylcholanthrene instead of drinking water were administered to mice of 6 inbred strains and 1 hybrid group. Two types of olive oil emulsion were prepared—a standard (less stable) and a stable (more stable) emulsion. The *standard* aqueous olive oil emulsion was made alkaline by the addition of sodium hydroxide to prevent cracking. The *stable* olive oil emulsion differed from the standard olive oil emulsion in that it contained Aerosol OT in addition to the ingredients of the standard emulsion. Carcinoma of the small intestine occurred in 75 of 287 mice, or in 26 per cent of the animals ingesting the carcinogen-containing olive oil emulsions. This lesion was observed in mice of all strains except Strain I. Single or multiple precancerous lesions of the small intestine occurred in most of the 75 mice with carcinoma and in 46 additional animals. It appeared that more males than females developed tumors. The time at which the first tumor was observed varied considerably in mice of different strains, owing partly to variation in the daily dose of the carcinogen. The amount of methylcholanthrene ingested, up to the time the first carcinoma was observed, ranged from 75 to 121 mg. in mice of strains C57BR, C57BL, C3H, and A. Similarly, the amount of dibenzanthracene ingested by strains C3H, DBA, and A mice until the first tumor was observed ranged from 106 to 160 mg. The hybrid A backcross mice showed a considerably longer latent period. The first precancerous lesion was observed after 66 days in a strain C57BR female mouse, while the first carcinoma was found after 92 days.

RECIPROCAL EFFECTS OF DIFFERENT EMULSIONS

Mineral oil emulsions containing 20-methylcholanthrene or 1,2,5,6-dibenzantracene, administered orally to mice instead of drinking water, induce tumors in the forestomach—but very few in the small intestine. A mouse may ingest from 0.3 to 1.2 mg. of the hydrocarbon daily, or a total amount of 275 mg., and may survive on the regimen for as long as thirteen months. The administration of these carcinogenic hydrocarbons in either mineral oil or olive oil aqueous emulsions induces tumors in two principal sites in the gastrointestinal tract, the forestomach and the small intestine. The forestomach tumor arises from the squamous epithelial lining, and the small intestinal tumor from the glandular mucosa. Methylcholanthrene is more potent than dibenzanthracene in inducing tumors in either of the foregoing locations. This is in accordance with reports of the comparative carcinogenic potency of these compounds when tested upon other tissues such as skin or subcutaneous connective tissue. There is also a variation in the number of tumors induced, depending upon the strain of mouse employed. Carcinomas of the glandular stomach or of the colon have not been induced by these carcinogens administered by the oral route.

A notable difference in response is observed between the forestomach and the small intestine when the physical characteristics of the olive oil emulsion are altered. When the *standard* olive oil emulsion is employed as a vehicle, the carcinogenic effect of the hydrocarbons is manifested in the small intestine, and very few forestomach tumors are induced. When, however, the olive oil emulsion is *stabilized* by the addition of Aerosol OT, squamous-cell carcinoma of the forestomach is induced in high incidence. This striking difference between the forestomach and intestinal mucosa in their respective response to the carcinogenic effect of the same hydrocarbon in these two olive oil emulsions has been explained on the assumption that the standard nonstabilized emulsion will break at the *p*H of the forestomach with formation of large oil globules, thus preventing intimate contact of the carcinogen with the squamous mucosa. The stabilized emulsion, on the other hand, probably coats the mucosa of the forestomach, providing a more or less constant exposure to the carcinogen. It is necessary in experimental tumor induction for the carcinogenic hydrocarbon to be in contact with the tissue in which carcinoma arises for a certain minimum period of time in order to induce the neoplasm, and intermittent exposure increases the induction time.

Like the stabilized olive oil emulsion, the mineral oil emulsion induces carcinoma of the forestomach in a large percentage of mice, probably owing to its ability to coat the mucosa of the forestomach. However, when the mineral oil emulsion enters the small intestine, only the organic constituents of the emulsion are digested to any extent and of these only the cetyl alcohol and the glycerol monostearate carry along with them small amounts of carcinogen. Thus, the bulk of the carcinogen remains dissolved in the mineral oil and passes through the intestinal canal without being absorbed. The high incidence of intestinal tumors with the standard olive oil emulsion may be accounted for by the fact that during and after digestion of the olive oil the hydrocarbon is precipitated and thus comes into intimate contact with the mucosa of the small intestine, by which it is absorbed. This assumption is favored by the fact that multiple pulmonary tumors occur in susceptible mice, and sarcoma and hemangioendothelioma develop in the mesentery and retroperitoneal tissues along the probable route of absorption of the carcinogen after it leaves the intestine. Moreover, there is also evidence of systemic effects due to absorption of the carcinogen, such as atrophy of the genital organs, the spleen, the lymph nodes, and the hematopoietic tissue. The mineral oil emulsion, on the other hand, does not undergo digestion to any great extent, and so its content of hydrocarbon is not released for carcinogenic action upon, or for absorption by, the small intestine. Therefore the incidence of carcinoma of the small intestine and of other tissues outside the gastrointestinal tract, as well as the toxic effects of the hydrocarbons, are notably diminished in mice ingesting the mineral oil emulsion.

MORBID ANATOMY

A given cytologically atypical neoplastic lesion of the mucosa of the small intestine, although in the process of infiltrating, is by definition considered to be in a precancerous stage until after infiltration of all coats of the wall of the viscus is accomplished and a tumor nodule appears on the peritoneum. Only neoplasms fulfilling these rigid criteria are classified as carcinomas. Those of lesser extent are considered precancerous. The induced carcinomas may occur anywhere in the small intestine, excepting the duodenum, and are most frequent in a segment of gut 7.5 to 17.5 cm. from the pylorus. Grossly they are firm, gray nodules constricting and more or less encircling the intestine (Fig. 14). They are composed of atypical epithelial cells showing moderate variation in size, shape and staining, and arranged in acini, nests, and solid masses (Fig. 15). Mitotic figures are usually frequent. Most tumors show varying numbers of mucous cells which occasionally comprise the bulk of the neoplasm. Inflammatory changes regularly occur and may be severe, but hemorrhage and necrosis are not particularly prominent. However, some mice die from intestinal hemorrhage. The tumors may be successfully transplanted to other mice, although some transplants succumb to infection. Transplants of an induced carcinoma of the small intestine of a mouse studied biochemically for enzymatic activity revealed little if any alkaline phosphatase activity, whereas thymonucleodepolymerase activity was the same as in the intestinal mucosa, the tissue of origin.[40] Metastases

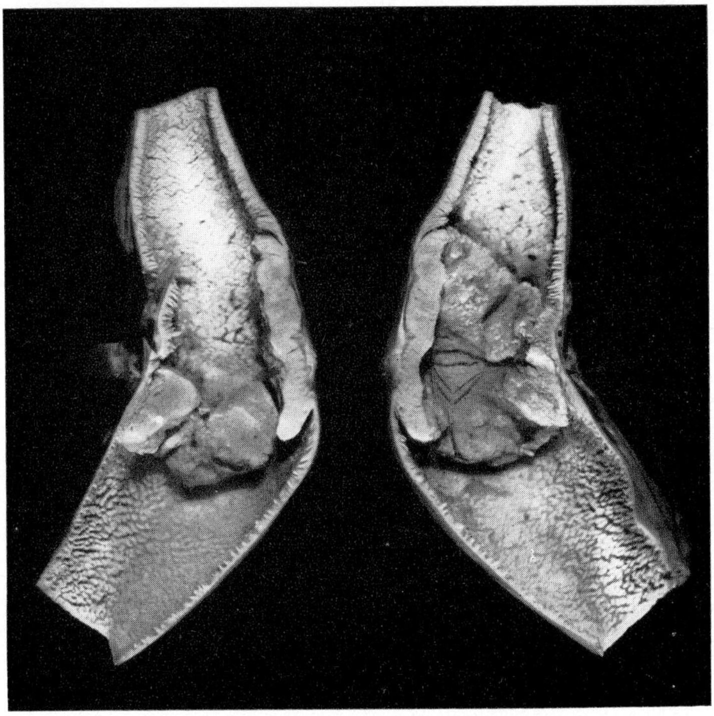

FIG. 14. Small intestine of mouse, with carcinoma. × 8.

occur in the mesenteric lymph nodes, pancreas, liver, and lung. The incidence of metastases is low, because in a narrow tube like the small intestine of the mouse, intestinal obstruction is an early result of carcinoma and death ensues before there is opportunity for widespread dissemination.

EXPERIMENTAL PRECANCEROUS LESIONS

The small intestine, particularly the jejunum, of mice receiving the emulsions containing the carcinogenic hydrocarbons, is usually relaxed, pale, edematous, and smooth, and the loops are more rounded than normally. These changes disappear if water is substituted for the emulsions a week or more preceding autopsy. The distribution of the precancerous lesions is like that of the carcinomas. The smallest, and probably earliest, grossly detectable precancerous lesions are sharply circumscribed, 1 to 4 mm.

in diameter, with a central umbilicate depression surrounded by a slightly elevated, circular border which because of its smooth and firm nature stands out in sharp relief against the velvety background of the surrounding mucosa. Occasionally tumors develop in the region of the lymphoid follicles. In a given mouse there may be only one precancerous lesion, or several scattered widely throughout the length of the small intestine. Occasionally the multiple lesions may be localized within a segment of intestine 3 to 9 cm. long which, owing to the multicentric nature of the lesion, is thickened and rigid and resembles in miniature the so-called "garden hose" lesion of man. It is not always

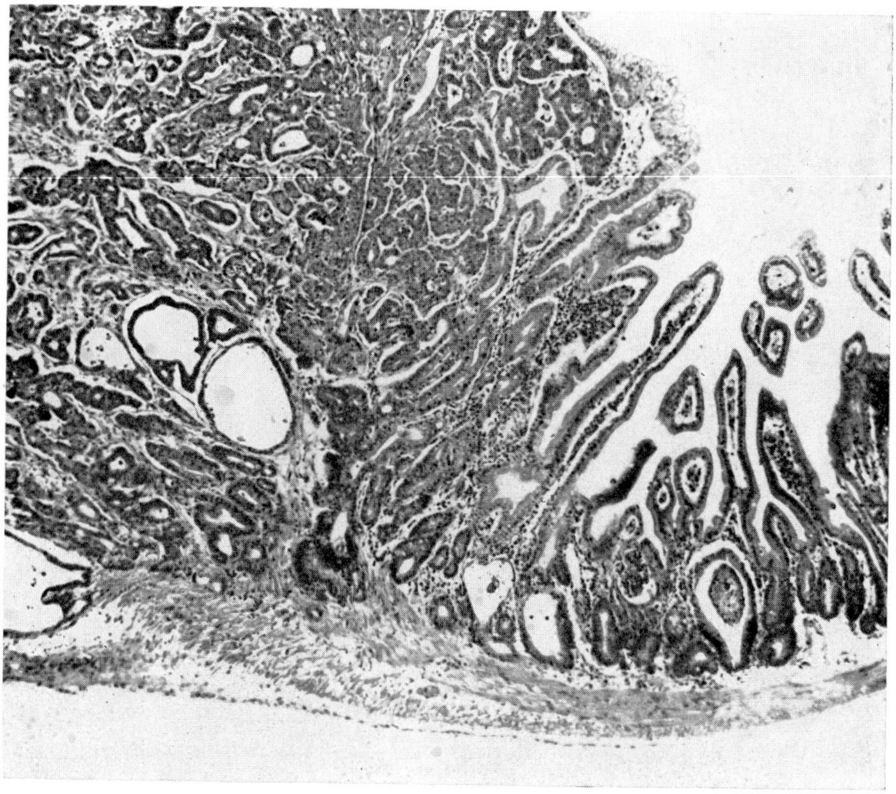

FIG. 15. Small intestine of mouse, with carcinoma. × 56.

possible to distinguish between the precancerous lesion and frank carcinoma at autopsy because the former merges imperceptibly into the latter. Most localized precancerous lesions are less than 4 mm. in diameter. Carcinoma, on the other hand, is likely to be larger and more elevated on the mucous surface, although almost never polypoid. Instead of being umbilicated, carcinoma is more plaquelike or ulcerated, with a variable degree of annular constriction. A palpable nodule on the peritoneum is always suggestive of cancer but may be due to organizing granulation tissue opposite a precancerous lesion.

Microscopically, the studies of the histogenesis of early carcinoma of the stomach and, to a lesser extent, of the colon in man leave a gap between atypical hyperplasia and definite carcinoma. This gap appears to be bridged, if at all, by a rather sharp morphologic change which becomes established rapidly. Thus, there has always been uncertainty and doubt regarding the histogenesis of "early cancer" of the internal viscera in man and the possibility that the lesions described would inevitably progress into infiltrating and metastasizing cancer. The intermediate stages have been imperfectly elucidated. It is virtually impossible to compare precancerous lesions of the small intestine of mice with those of man because of the low incidence of carcinoma of the small intestine in human beings.[59, 60, 77, 84, 107] With respect to experimental intestinal carcinoma in mice, it is possible to examine animals at autopsy at different intervals after they have ingested the carcinogenic hydrocarbons administered so as to yield a high incidence of intestinal carcinoma, and then to compare the early changes observed in them with those of controls and with those having fully developed carcinoma with metastases. Observations based upon such experimental material are therefore free from the criticism so frequently directed against the studies of precancerous lesions in man.

ORIGIN OF INDUCED CARCINOMA OF THE SMALL INTESTINE

MUCOSAL CHANGES IN PRECANCEROUS LESIONS

During the evolution of an induced precancerous lesion of the small intestine of mice, the earliest departure from normal structure may involve a few or several intestinal glands (Fig. 16). These foci, located in the mid- and basal mucosa, enlarge and are followed by new foci that develop independently within the area of involvement. The resulting hyperplastic mucosa becomes crowded with glands, some with a single layer and others with several layers of epithelium. There are many more mitotic figures than in normal epithelium, and the nuclei are hyperchromatic. The newly formed glands are not only dilated and longer and wider than normal glands, but also are often tortuous and labyrinthine owing to intricate branching and irregularly formed papillations. The buds which branch off the acini are at first solid and later lumenize, and while still in continuity, the parent gland and the buds have a common basement membrane that is pushed ahead by the growing bud. As these buds enlarge and secondary ones develop, they become branched and complicated and come to be supported by a new reticulum. Parts of the gland atrophy, or may be destroyed by infection and inflammation. However, new buds form, while the old buds continue to enlarge, or they in turn may degenerate until finally an entirely new generation of prolific acini develops with great potentialities for infiltration. The original glands of the superficial mucosa, overlying the precancerous focus, become inflamed and show evidence of cellular exfoliation and ulceration. These glands finally wither and disappear. Then, *the structural continuity between the original glands of the superficial mucosa and those of the neoplastic growth in the deeper mucosa is ultimately severed.* This is apparently the first real neoplastic phenomenon. The newly proliferated neoplastic glands replacing those of the lost mucosa open into the lumen of the intestine.

From this it may be inferred that the proliferative force of the newly forming glandular cells overcomes the retaining power of the surrounding normal, non-proliferative tissues (which may indeed be weakened by degeneration)—and the glands then penetrate the wall of the intestine. This phenomenon is somewhat reminiscent of the normal embryologic development of intestinal tissues. This same process of proliferation and resorption with subsequent replacement occurs during the longitudinal growth of the expanding embryonic intestine. In some precancerous lesions, the neoplastic glands infiltrate the stroma and muscular

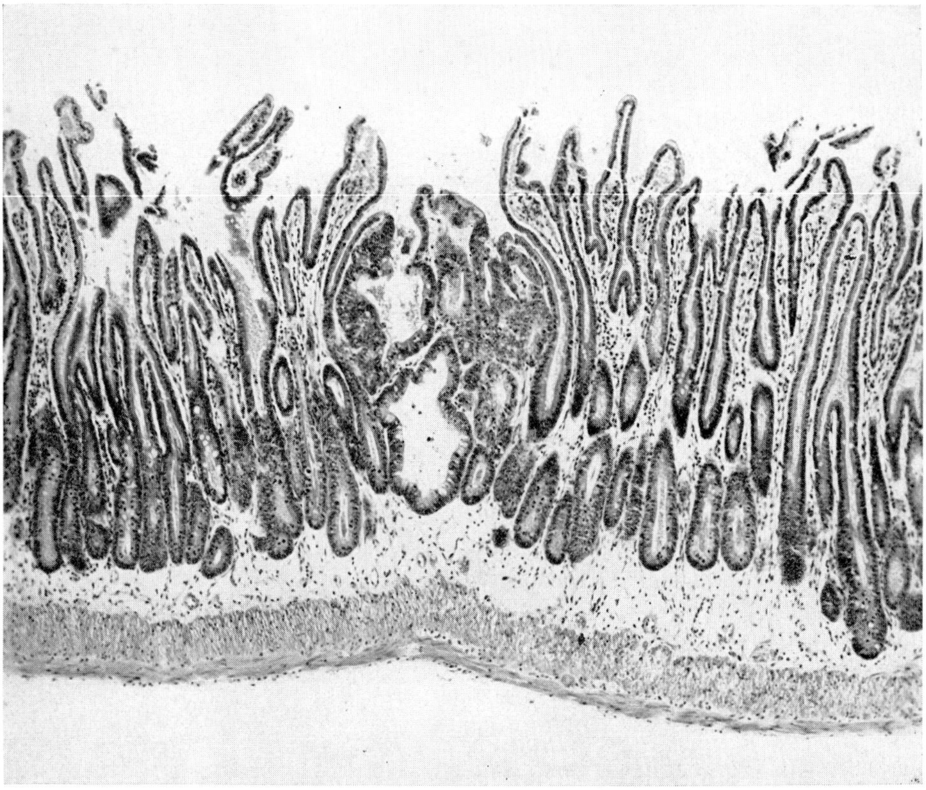

FIG. 16. Small intestine of mouse, with focal precancerous lesion in the mid-mucosa and hyperplasia of basal glands. × 75.

coats apparently very rapidly. In others, the circular layer of muscle acts as a temporary but ineffectual barrier to the infiltrating neoplasm. Under such circumstances, *the acini flatten out, grow laterally in either direction, and later penetrate the intestinal wall by way of a natural interruption in the muscularis propria at the entrance of a blood vessel with its perivascular connective tissue, finally reaching the serosa.* This is the second important phenomenon of neoplasia.

All types of cells of the intestinal mucosa may be involved at one time or another in the transformation of hyperplastic tissue to neoplastic tissue, and often highly variable numbers of different types of cells may participate in the formation of particular precancerous lesions. It is particularly noteworthy that most of the neoplastic lesions are composed of undifferentiated glandular cells (probably derived from the principal cells of the mucosa). In other cases, however, goblet cells and Paneth cells are numerous in precancerous lesions, and some of the fully developed local tumors and their metastases may be composed almost exclusively of either of these two types of cell.[28] No one has yet reported the experimental induction of an argentaffinoma of the small intestine. Nonetheless, the argentaffin cells are often numerically increased in the developing tumor induced by oil emulsions of carcinogens. While the methods of fixation and staining employed have been adequate for identification of argentaffin cells, they were not especially designed for detailed study of these cells. The exact role of the argentaffin cells in the neoplastic process, particularly in relation to goblet cells, awaits study by special methods such as those devised by Popoff.[83]

UMBILICATED FOCI

The umbilicated precancerous lesion is depressed below the surface and consists of hyperplastic basal glands and atypical midmucosal gland tissue. The marginal tissue on all sides of the lesion is edematous and elevated by elongated, atypically dilated glands with overhanging hyperplastic villi. This hyperplastic gland tissue blends laterally into the more normal mucosa. The primordial neoplastic area, as exemplified by the umbilicate lesion, expands by deep infiltration, lateral spread, and confluence of adjacent foci of atypical gland tissue. The deeply eroded and ulcerated surface epithelium is usually covered with mucus and cellular detritus, often showing evidence of infection. Individual umbilicated neoplastic foci may be so juxtapositional as to nearly obliterate the narrow intervening septal wedges of relatively normal mucosa that may be revealed by histologic examination. Apparently, at a later date during treatment with the carcinogen, the early neoplastic foci (Fig. 17) expand to encompass greater areas and finally coalesce. It is by this mechanism that the so-called "garden hose" type of lesion is formed.

From the foregoing it is clear that the two points of predilection for initial development of intestinal tumors are the midportion of the mucosa and the base of the crypts of Lieberkühn. This neoplastic change occurs in the deep mucosa, despite the fact that the superficial mucosa is earlier and more conspicuously exposed to the action of the ingested carcinogen than the deeper portions. Many years ago Schaper and Cohen[94] stated that the neoplastic process in early cancer of the stomach and intestine of man begins in the midmucosa and in the crypts of Lieberkühn, which act as centers of growth or regeneration for the cellular replacement of the mucosa, in a manner similar to the role of the basal-cell layer in replacement of the epidermal cells of the skin.

ORIGIN FROM MULTIPLE FOCI

Two theories have been widely discussed: (1) one contends that a malignant tumor may originate from a single circumscribed focus, possibly constituted by one cell, and then, by enlargement and expansive growth of the solitary center of the focus, form a tumor; (2) another theory contends that the neoplastic process may be initiated in several foci concomitantly over wide areas, or successively so that in addition to enlarging by expansion from a central focus the tumor may enlarge through confluence and apposition. In experimental intestinal carcinoma, none of the early cancers has been traced to a single cell of origin. The earliest detectable departure from the normal state involves many cells in what appear to be distinctly separate foci, even though usually confined to a relatively small area. The histologic distribution of such an early neoplastic change encompasses too extensive an area to account for the malignant process on the basis of spread from a single-cell focus of neoplasia, and the change also involves too many

FIG. 17. Small intestine of mouse, with multicentric carcinoma. × 35.

otherwise intact crypts. Hence, the evidence so far available from studies of experimental intestinal carcinoma in mice indicates a multicentric origin.

There have always been conflicting theories regarding the marginal spread of malignant tumors, particularly those involving the stomach and intestine of man.[15] Many observers account for the progressive enlargement of a neoplasm on the basis of either (1) a more or less continuous malignant conversion of the marginal tissue, or (2) the recurrent infiltration of the borders by neoplastic cells migrating radially to increase the diameter of the tumor. Experimental observations on mice seem to indicate that both of these mechanisms play a role in the formation of the tumor. Histologic study of an early umbilicated lesion, which undoubtedly would eventuate in cancer, suggests that the neoplastic change involves a wider area than that estimated by gross examination. The neoplastic changes at the margin continue to progress during further development of the precancerous lesion and seem to account, in part at least, for enlargement of the peripheral limits of the growth. At the same time, the lesion expands by central proliferation and the tumor cells infiltrate the mucosa radially to mushroom onto the mucosal surface of the intestine—thus forming a plaquelike lesion. The size of the tumor is evidently limited by arrest of the neoplastic change at the periphery of the growth, so that it is fairly well limited to the precancerous or small-cancer stage. What the limiting factors of size of a tumor are, is not well understood.

CHANGES IN MUSCLE STROMA AND VESSELS

Induced intestinal cancer in mice represents the ultimate phase of a series of changes, some of which, as described, are neoplastic from onset, while others contribute to the neoplastic process, and still others, while non-neoplastic, apparently play some as yet unknown role in the evolutionary process of cancer. Examples of the latter are such changes as tenting and proliferation of the muscularis mucosae and the inner circular layer of the muscularis propria. The latter becomes thickened immediately below the area of the developing tumor, and there is actually new proliferation of smooth-muscle cells, which extend upward in the direction of the downward-growing glands. It is probable that this change is in part secondary to the stress and strain in the region of a developing tumor. No doubt the contracting stroma supporting the precancerous lesion exerts a pull on the bowel wall, and this results at first in tenting of the muscularis mucosae and later in proliferation and invagination of the muscularis propria. This process, once commenced, continues, and is increased by peristalsis and further accelerated by the continued contraction of the stroma as the latter becomes more abundant to support the growing tumor. The belief that this is a reactive but a non-neoplastic process, rather than that these smooth-muscle changes are in direct response to the carcinogenic agent, is strengthened by the fact that intestinal neoplasms of smooth-muscle-cell origin (leiomyosarcomas) are not induced in the feeding experiments.

During the entire course of development of a carcinogen-induced tumor, a wholly new generation of stromal fibroblasts develops in the mucosa and submucosa of the intestine. They are more rounded and less fibrillar than normal fibroblasts. The lymph vessels are distended and the blood vascular capillaries become hyperemic. The lesion becomes infiltrated diffusely as well as focally with inflammatory cells of various types. Thrombi are occasionally noted in the vessels although they are not definitely correlated with focal areas of necrosis. The collagenic and reticular fibers of the lamina propria and of the submucosa (including the basement membrane of the original mucosal glands) show degenerative changes following administration of the carcinogen. Between and below the crypts of Lieberkühn there appear areas of fibrinoid degeneration. As soon as the glands begin to proliferate, however, they immediately develop a well-stained, healthy reticulum for a basement membrane which is present throughout all subsequent stages of tumor development and is carried over finally to the fully formed carcinoma. The significance of these connective tissue changes during the evolution of experimental intestinal cancer is probably comparable to those noted in connection with developing cutaneous and forestomach carcinoma.

The spread of the neoplastic glands through the intestinal wall appears to be chiefly by direct infiltration, and not by way of lymphatic vessels. The lymphatic vessels of the intestine are found to be dilated shortly after the mouse begins the hydrocarbon-emulsion drinking water regimen, and this dilatation persists until the vessels become constricted and subsequently obliterated by the progressively increasing bulk of new stromal elements. Thus, during the early developmental stages of a precancerous lesion, ample physical circumstances obtain for the invasion of dilated lymphatic vessels by the actively proliferating glandular tissue while it is yet in close proximity to the vessels of the lamina propria and submucosa. By this route, then, the glands might be expected to penetrate the wall of the intestine. This usually does not occur, however. Instead, the lymphatic vessels in the mucosal and submucosal stroma become obliterated and disappear, and rarely play a role in accelerating the down growth of the glands. However, once the growth has extended through the muscularis propria and onto the peritoneum, invasion of lymphatic vessels is readily accomplished, and tumor deposits are transported by this route to secondary locations.

PRECANCEROUS LESIONS OF THE COLON IN MAN

POLYPS

Carcinoma of the small intestine occurs so infrequently in man that there has been virtually no opportunity to examine early developing stages of this lesion. Therefore some of the results of the observations on precancerous lesions of the large intestine are presented for comparison with experimental precancerous changes in the small intestine. Due allowance should be made for the structural differences in the two sites. The early studies of human carcinoma of the colon were based largely on necropsy findings.[44, 45, 122] Since, however, many of the bowel carcinomas arise in the rectum, rectosigmoid, and lower sigmoid, and these areas are available for direct inspection by proctoscopic examination, lesions are observed from time to time which are suspected of being early carcinoma.[6, 21, 22, 25, 26, 27, 62, 63] Schmieden and Westhues[96] described histologic transitional stages, from apparently harmless adenomatous hypertrophy of the mucosa, through polyps with partially undifferentiated cells, to fully developed adenocarcinoma. The lesions were classified into three groups: The third group, which was still considered to be precancerous, was characterized by invasion of the pedicle and perforation of the muscular layer. In view of the beginning invasion, and since the atypical epithelial cells could not be distinguished morphologically from those seen in outright cancer, there arises the question whether this third stage with definite signs of malignancy should not be considered carcinoma.

Feyrter[33] examined 1110 autopsy specimens of the colon from subjects over 20 years of age and found adenomatous proliferations in about one-third of them. The total number of polyps found was about 1000, but only 6 of these were carcinomatous, and 4 were suspicious for malignancy. The incidence of malignancy in multiple polyposis is generally accepted as being from 40 to 50 per cent, although it may not be possible from histologic and clinical examination to predict whether or not a given polyp will become malignant.[8, 9, 38, 85] Of interest in this connection is a case[51] of multiple polyposis of the colon, in which the first biopsy did not show any histologic evidence of malignancy. Two years later an adenocarcinoma of the rectosigmoid junction was biopsied. Apart from this carcinoma, with no suggestion of its having arisen from a polyp, the autopsy showed no carcinomatous changes in any of the polyps that extended from the ileocecal valve to the rectum. Observations of this kind led Stahr[101] to the conclusion that rectal polyps, like other atypical epithelial proliferations, are not necessarily true precancerous stages but can be regarded only as indicators of some kind of epithelial change that is capable eventually of producing cancer under circumstances not yet well understood.

"SCHULTZE PICTURE"

The mucosa of segments of the large intestine surgically excised for carcinoma has been subjected to careful gross and microscopic study which might be expected to reveal precancerous lesions. Bargen, Cromar, and Dixon[8, 9] examined areas of the intestine in the neighborhood of cancers of the colon in such specimens and described interesting changes involving lymphoid aggregations, in the submucosa, with resultant damage to the muscularis mucosae. The lymphoid aggregations were variable in size and number, were situated immediately below the epithelial layer, and seemed to arise as perivascular infiltrations. When large, the lymphoid aggregation became encapsulated, developed a well-marked germinal center, and seemed to disrupt the continuity of the muscularis mucosae. This was followed by secondary changes in the overlying epithelium consisting of glandular proliferation, with the production of atypical glands and cyst formation. The subsequent events seemed to be more or less mechanical in origin. In some instances the follicles ruptured into the lumen and the epithelium prolapsed into their substance, with the escape of the atypical glandular structures, composed of primitive epithelial cells, into the loose connective tissue. This change is often referred to as the "Schultze picture."[97] Ulceration followed the rupture of other lymphoid follicles, and in the course of healing, epithelial cells, less differentiated and more primitive than usual, were trapped in the deeper tissues. Occasionally, a small patch of epithelium became isolated from the rest of its stratum by a circle of follicles, which enlarged progressively, coincident with destruction of the muscularis mucosae, and the epithelium became pegged down to the underlying submucosa. The surrounding muscularis then contracted, elevating the enclosed tissue, thus forming the first stage of an adenomatous polyp. The lymphoid tissue at the base was slowly replaced by fibrous tissue which formed the core of the polyp. Bargen, Cromar, and Dixon[9] found that in other cases there was no evidence of polyps, and they believed that cancer in these cases arose from atypical cells buried in the submucosa as a result of either ulceration or rupture of the lymphoid follicle. The structure of the small cancer reported by Raven[87] suggests this mode of origin.

The evidence would therefore indicate that many carcinomas of the bowel in man are traceable to polyps as the source of origin.[38, 85, 118] In any event, it is now generally agreed that rectal polyps constitute the most dangerous as well as perhaps the most common predisposing factor in the development of rectal cancer. The intestinal adenomas, which are often numerous and separated from one another by normal mucosa,[47] may remain stationary for many years or may abruptly assume invasive properties recognized clinically and histologically as cancer. Since the region of the sigmoid colon and that below it are available for direct inspection by proctoscopic examinations, it is to be hoped that many observations of the precancerous lesions of this region will be forthcoming and that in addition to studying the epithelial changes, observations will be made on the stromal reactions which play so important a role in experimental intestinal carcinoma.

EXPERIMENTAL CARCINOMA OF THE COLON

Three successful methods for the induction of carcinoma of the colon in the rat have been reported, one by feeding radioactive yttrium, a second by the subcutaneous injection of benzidine, and a third by oral administration of acetylaminofluorene and related compounds.

Lisco, Brues, Finkel and Grundhauser[61] fed rats radioactive yttrium, which emits pure beta rays with an energy of 1.5 mev. and which has a half-life of 57 days. It is essentially not absorbed and remains longest in the colon. Of 33 animals receiving a single feeding by stomach tube of from 1.0 to 6.0 mc. of Y^{91}, 4 died with adenocarcinoma of the colon. The earliest tumor was seen at 135 days and the latest at 506 days. Six of 8 animals given 78 feedings of 0.46 or 0.20 mc. of Y^{91} per feeding over a period of three months died with carcinoma of the colon, 304 to 548 days after the first feeding.

Spitz and associates[100] reported 7 instances of adenocarcinoma of the rectum among 385 rats injected subcutaneously with benzidine; all of these occurred in males 200 or more days after injections were begun. These carcinomas arose at the junction of the rectum and colon, generally encircled and involved 1 to 2 cm. of the length of the gut, and extended through the wall into the surrounding tissues; no metastases were noted. Histologically these carcinomas were described as presenting a glandular pattern of cells containing mucus similar to human intestinal cancer, and all showed large gelatinous areas that were grossly visible.

Carcinoma of the colon induced by oral administration of acetylaminofluorene has been reported by Cox[18a] and Bielschowsky.[14] Few other attempts to induce carcinoma of the large intestine have been made. Stewart (unpublished data) administered by enema to mice carcinogenic hydrocarbons dissolved in mineral oil and obtained a carcinoma of the colon. Duque[29] injected methylcholanthrene into the wall of the colon of mice and obtained a few lesions having the characteristics of early carcinoma.

On the negative side, carcinoma of the colon has not been induced in mice ingesting the carcinogenic hydrocarbons. It was shown by absorption spectrum analysis of feces that in the experiments in which dibenzanthracene olive oil emulsion was administered orally[65] the carcinogen was converted into a new, apparently noncarcinogenic compound in the colon, owing possibly to the action of the intestinal flora. This was thought to be the reason for the failure to induce carcinoma of the large intestine when the hydrocarbon dissolved in olive oil was fed. When mineral oil emulsions are administered orally, the carcinogenic hydrocarbons probably remain dissolved in the mineral oil as it passes through the intestinal canal and so are excreted without establishing sufficient contact with the mucosal cells of the colon to induce carcinoma.

BIBLIOGRAPHY

1. ANDERVONT, H. B. Development and genetic characteristics of adenomatous stomach lesion in Strain I mice. *Pub. Health Rep. 54:* 1851-1855, 1939.
2. ANDERVONT, H. B. Studies on some possible causative factors of spontaneous adenomatous lesion of stomach in mice of Strain I. *Pub. Health Rep. 54:* 2085-2093, 1939.
3. ANDERVONT, H. B., and SHIMKIN, M. B. Intrapulmonary transplantation of the adenomatous gastric lesion of Strain I mice. *J. Nat. Cancer Inst. 2:* 151-155, 1941.
4. ANDERVONT, H. B., and STEWART, H. L. Adenomatous lesion in stomach of Strain I mice. *Science 68:* 566-567, 1937.
5. ARMSTRONG, E. C., and BONSER, G. M. Squamous carcinoma of the forestomach and other lesions in mice following oral administration of 3,4,5,6-dibenzcarbazole. *Brit. J. Cancer 4:* 203-211, 1950.
6. BACON, H. E. *Anus-Rectum-Sigmoid Colon: Diagnosis and Treatment.* Philadelphia, J. B. Lippincott Co., 1938.
7. BAGSHAW, M. A., and STRONG, L. C. The occurrence of tumors of the forestomach in mice after parenteral administration of methylcholanthrene: a histopathologic and genetic analysis. *J. Nat. Cancer Inst. 10:* 141-176, 1950.
8. BARGEN, J. A. Important newer concepts concerning cancer of the intestines and their bearing on management. *West Virginia M. J. 37:* 433-442, 1941.
9. BARGEN, J. A., CROMAR, C. D. L., and DIXON, C. F. Early carcinoma of the colon. II. Relation between subclinical inflammatory processes and carcinoma. *Arch. Surg. 43:* 192-208, 1941.
10. BARRETT, M. K. Avenues of approach to the gastric-cancer problem. *J. Nat. Cancer Inst. 7:* 127-157, 1946.
11. BASHFORD, E. F. Illustrations of propagated cancer. *Brit. M. J. 1:* 1211-1214 (Fig. 4), 1906.
12. BASHFORD, E. F., MURRAY, J. A., and CRAMER, W. Parallel between propagated and sporadic malignant new growths. Imperial Cancer Research Fund (Great Britain), *Second Scientific Report*, pp. 47-48, 1905.
13. BECK, S. The effect of feeding carcinogenic hydrocarbons dissolved in aqueous soap solution on the stomach of CBA mice. *Brit. J. Exper. Path. 27:* 155-157, 1946.
14. BIELSCHOWSKY, F. Distant tumours produced by 2-amino- and 2-acetylaminofluorene. *Brit. J. Exper. Path. 25:* 1-4, 1944.
15. BORRMANN, R. "Geschwülste des Magens und Duodenums." In HENKE, F., and LUBARSCH, O. *Handbuch der speziellen pathologischen Anatomie and Histologie.* vol. 4, pt. 1, pp. 838-855, 920-936. Berlin, J. Springer, 1926.
16. BULLOCK, F. D., and CURTIS, M. R. Spontaneous tumors of the rat. *J. Cancer Research 14:* 1-115, 1930.

17. Chapter on "Neoplastic diseases." In *Diseases of Poultry* (Biester, H. E. and DeVries, L., eds.) Ames, Iowa, Iowa State Coll. Press, 1945, p. 571.
18. Collins, V. J., Gardner, W. U., and Strong, L. C. Experimental gastric tumors in mice. *Cancer Research 3:* 29-35, 1943.
18a. Cox, A. J. Carcinogenic activity of 2-acetylaminofluorene: Characteristics of lesions in albino rats. *Cancer Research 7:* 647-657, 1947.
19. Cramer, W. Papillomatosis in forestomach of rat and its bearing on work of Fibiger. *Am. J. Cancer 31:* 537-555, 1937.
20. Curtis, M. R., Bullock, F. D., and Dunning, W. F. A statistical study of the occurrence of spontaneous tumors in a large colony of rats. *Am. J. Cancer 15:* 67-121, 1931.
21. Daniels, E. A. Early diagnosis in rectal cancer and prognosis on basis of Dukes' classification. *Canad. M. A. J. 31:* 612-616, 1934.
22. Daniels, E. A. Precancerous lesion of the rectum and sigmoid. *Internat. Clin. 2:* 140-151, 1939.
23. Davis, C. L., and Naylor, J. R. Carcinoma of the stomach of a dog. *J. Am. Vet. M. A. 102:* 286-288, 1943.
24. Domagk, G. Weitere experimentelle Untersuchungen über die Ursachen des Krebses. *Ztschr. f. Krebsforsch. 48:* 283-297, 1939.
25. Dukes, C. E. Simple tumours of the large intestine and their relation to cancer. *Brit. J. Surg. 13:* 720-733, 1926.
26. Dukes, C. E. Discussion on the early diagnosis of carcinoma of the rectum and colon. *Proc. Roy. Soc. Med. 21:* 1549-1551, 1928.
27. Dukes, C. E. Classification of cancer of rectum. *J. Path. & Bact. 35:* 323-332, 1932.
28. Dunn, T. B., and Kessel, A. M. Paneth cells in carcinomas of the small intestine in a mouse and in a rat. *J. Nat. Cancer Inst. 6:* 113-118, 1945.
29. Duque, O., (personal communication).
30. Ewing, J. The beginnings of gastric cancer. *Am. J. Surg. 31:* 204-205, 1936.
31. Ewing, J. *Neoplastic Diseases; A Treatise on Tumors* (ed. 4). Philadelphia, W. B. Saunders Co., 1942.
32. Feldman, W. H. *Neoplasms of Domesticated Animals.* Philadelphia, W. B. Saunders Co., 1932.
33. Feyrter, F. Zur Geschwulstlehre (nach Untersuchungen am menschlichen Darm; Polypen und Krebs). *Beitr. z. path. Anat. u. z. allg. Path. 86:* 663-760, 1931.
34. Fibiger, J. Untersuchung über eine Nematode (Spiroptera sp. n.) und deren Fähigkeit, papillomatöse und carcinomatöse Geschwulstbildungen im Magen der Ratte hervorzurufen. *Ztschr. f. Krebsforsch. 13:* 217-280, 1913.
35. Fibiger, J. Weitere Untersuchungen über das Spiropteracarcinom der Ratte. *Ztschr. f. Krebsforsch. 14:* 295-326, 1914.
36. Fibiger, J. Spiroptera carcinomata and their relation to true malignant tumors. *J. Cancer Research 4:* 367, 1919.
37. Firminger, H. I., and Stewart, H. L. Histogenesis of squamous cell carcinoma in the forestomach of mice induced by intramural injection of 20-methylcholanthrene (abstract). *Am. J. Path. 25:* 815, 1949; and *J. Nat. Cancer Inst. 12:* 491-531, 1951.
38. Fitzgibbon, G., and Rankin, F. W. Polyps of the large intestine. *Surg., Gynec. & Obst. 52:* 1136-1150, 1931.

39. GALL, E. A. "Problem of early cancer." In *1949 Year Book of Pathology and Clinical Pathology* (Karsner, H. T., and Sanford, A. H., eds.). Chicago, The Year Book Publishers Inc., 1950, p. 74.
40. GREENSTEIN, J. P., and STEWART, H. L. Note on the enzymatic activity of a transplanted adenocarcinoma of the glandular stomach of a mouse. *J. Nat. Cancer Inst. 2:* 631-633, 1942.
41. GUTMANN, R. A., SENEQUE, J., BERTRAND, I., and BEAUGEARD, G. Un cas de cancer ulcériforme de l'estomac au début. *Bull. et mém. Soc. méd. d. hôp. de Paris 53:* 649-656, 1937.
42. HARE, W. V., and STEWART, H. L. Spontaneous adenomatous gastritis of mice of Strain dba (abstract). *Federation Proc. 8:* 357, 1949.
43. HAUSER, G. Das chronische Magengeschwür, sein Vernarbungsprozess und dessen Beziehungen zur Entwicklung des Magencarcinoms. Leipzig, 1883. Rev. of *Bibl. f. Laeger*, Kjobenh, *14:* 195-259, 1884.
44. HAUSER, G. *Das Cylinderepithel-Carcinom des Magens und des Dickdarms.* Jena, G. Fischer, 1890.
45. HAUSER, G. Über Polyposis intestinalis adenomatosa und deren Beziehungen zur Krebsentwicklung. *Deutsches Arch. f. klin. Med.* 1 v., Festschr. F. A. von Zenker, etc., Leipzig. pp. 429-448, 1895.
46. HEIDENHAIN, L. Eine seltene Geschwulst des Blinddarms bei einer Impfmaus: Ein weiterer Beitrag zur Morphogenese. *Virchow's Arch. f. path. Anat. 273:* 541-552, 1929.
47. HELLWIG, C. A. The scientific basis of biopsy in tumors. *Arch. Path. 14:* 517-554, 1932.
48. HOWES, E. L. Carcinogens and the regeneration patterns after injury. *Cancer Research 6:* 298-310, 1946.
49. HOWES, E. L. The role of mucous cells in the production of gastric neoplasms. *J. Nat. Cancer Inst. 10:* 377-397, 1949.
50. HOWES, E. L., and DE OLIVEIRA, J. R. Early changes in the experimentally produced adenomas and adenocarcinomas of the stomach. *Cancer Research 8:* 419-428, 1948.
51. HULLSIEK, H. E. Adenomatous polyps of colon and rectum. *Minnesota Med. 13:* 229-234, 1930.
52. JACKSON, C. The incidence and pathology of tumours of domesticated animals in South Africa: A study of the Onderstepoort collection of neoplasms with special reference to their histopathology. *Onderstepoort J. Vet. Sc. and An. Ind. 6:* 3-460, 1936.
53. KAPLAN, H. S. Lesions of the gastric mucosa in Strong Strain NHO mice. *J. Nat. Cancer Inst. 10:* 407-422, 1949.
54. KAUFMANN, E. *Pathology for Students and Practitioners; Authorized Translation of the Lehrbuch der Pathologischen Anatomie* (Translated by S. P. Reimann). Philadelphia, P. Blakiston Sons & Co., 1929.
55. KIRBY, A. H. M. Attempts to induce stomach tumors. I. The effect of cholesterol heated to 300° C. *Cancer Research 3:* 519-525, 1943.
56. KLEIN, A. J., and PALMER, W. L. Experimental gastric carcinoma: A critical review with comments on the criteria of induced malignancy. *Arch. Path. 29:* 814-844, 1940. Also with additions in *J. Nat. Cancer Inst. 1:* 559-584, 1941.
57. LANE, A., BLICKENSTAFF, D., and IVY, A. C. The carcinogenicity of fat "browned" by heating. *Cancer 3:* 1044-1051, 1950.

58. LEVY, B., and RING, J. R. The experimental production of jaw tumors in hamsters. *Oral Surg., Oral Med., & Oral Path. 3:* 262-271, 1950.
59. LIEBER, M. M., STEWART, H. L., and LUND, H. Carcinoma of the infrapapillary portion of the duodenum. *Arch. Surg. 35:* 268-289, 1937.
60. LIEBER, M. M., STEWART, H. L., and LUND, H. Carcinoma of the peripapillary portion of the duodenum. *Ann. Surg. 109:* 219-245, 383-429, 1939.
61. LISCO, H., BRUES, A. M., FINKEL, M. P., and GRUNDHAUSER, W. Carcinoma of the colon in rats following the feeding of radioactive yttrium (abstract). *Cancer Research 7:* 721, 1947.
62. LOCKHART-MUMMERY, J. P., and DUKES, C. Precancerous changes in rectum and colon. *Surg., Gynec. & Obst. 46:* 591-596, 1928.
63. LOCKHART-MUMMERY, J. P. *Diseases of the Rectum and Colon and Their Surgical Treatment* (ed. 2). Baltimore, Wm. Wood and Co., 1934.
64. LORENZ, E. Preparation of emulsions and suspensions containing carcinogenic hydrocarbons. *J. Nat. Cancer Inst. 10:* 355-358, 1949.
65. LORENZ, E., and STEWART, H. L. Intestinal carcinoma and other lesions in mice following oral administration of 1,2,5,6-dibenzanthracene and 20-methylcholanthrene. *J. Nat. Cancer Inst. 1:* 17-40, 1940.
66. LORENZ, E., and STEWART, H. L. Squamous cell carcinoma and other lesions of the forestomach in mice, following oral administration of 20-methylcholanthrene and 1,2,5,6-dibenzanthracene (preliminary report). *J. Nat. Cancer Inst. 1:* 273-276, 1940.
67. LORENZ, E., and STEWART, H. L. Tumors of the alimentary tract induced in mice by feeding olive-oil emulsions containing carcinogenic hydrocarbons. *J. Nat. Cancer Inst. 7:* 227-238, 1947.
68. LORENZ, E., and STEWART, H. L. Tumors of alimentary tract in mice fed carcinogenic hydrocarbons in mineral-oil emulsions. *J. Nat. Cancer Inst. 9:* 173-180, 1948.
69. LORENZ, E., and STEWART, H. L. Tumors of the alimentary tract in mice fed carcinogenic hydrocarbons in mineral oil emulsions. *J. Nat. Cancer Inst. 9:* 173-180, 1949.
70. LUSHBAUGH, C. C. Experimental hyperplastic gastritis and gastric polyposis in monkeys. *J. Nat. Cancer Inst. 7:* 313-320, 1947.
71. MCPEAK, E., and WARREN, S. The pathology of gastric carcinoma in mice. *J. Nat. Cancer Inst. 7:* 309-312, 1947.
72. MALLORY, T. B. Carcinoma *in situ* of the stomach and its bearing on the histogenesis of malignant ulcers. *Arch. Path. 30:* 348-362, 1940.
73. MORRIS, H. P., and LIPPINCOTT, S. W. Production of gastric lesions in rats by fasting, partial inanition, and deficiency of certain dietary constituents. *J. Nat. Cancer Inst. 2:* 459-477, 1942.
74. MOSZKOWICZ, L. Über einen Fall von jungem "Ulcuscarcinom" des Magens. *Virchows Arch. path. Anat. 253*: 511-533, 1924.
75. MULAY, A. S., and FIRMINGER, H. I. Precancerous and cancerous lesions of the forestomach and dermal-subcutaneous tumors in rats fed *p*-dimethylaminobenzene-1-azo,1-naphthalene. *J. Nat. Cancer Inst. 13:* 57-72, 1952.
76. MURRAY, J. A. Spontaneous tumour in the mouse; histology, metastasis, transplantability and the relations of malignant new growths to spontaneously affected animals. Imperial Cancer Research Fund (Great Britain), *Third Scientific Report,* pp. 69-114, 1908.

77. NICKERSON, D. A., and WILLIAMS, R. H. Malignant tumors of the small intestine. *Am. J. Path. 13:* 53-64, 1937.
78. NIGRELLI, R. F. Spontaneous neoplasms in fishes. II. Fibrocarcinoma-like growth in the stomach of *Borophryne apogon* Regan, a deep-sea ceratioid fish. *Zoologica 31:* 183-184, 1947.
79. PASSEZ, R. D., LESSE, A., and KNOX, J. C. Spiroptera cancer and diet deficiency (abstract). *J. Path. & Bact. 40:* 198-199, 1935.
80. PEACOCK, P. R., and BECK, S. Induced adenocarcinoma of the stomach in mice. *Nature*, London: *162:* 252-523, 1948.
81. PEACOCK, P. R., and KIRBY, A. H. M. Attempts to induce stomach tumors: II. The action of carcinogenic hydrocarbons on stock mice. *Cancer Research 4:* 88-93, 1944.
82. PFEIFFER, C. A., and ALLEN, E. Attempts to produce cancer in rhesus monkeys with carcinogenic hydrocarbons and estrogens. *Cancer Research 8:* 97-127, 1948.
83. POPOFF, N. W. Epithelial functional rejuvenation observed in the mucous cells of the gastro-intestinal tract and the parietal cells of the stomach. *Arch. Path. 27:* 841-887, 1939.
84. RAIFORD, T. S. Tumors of the small intestine. *Arch. Surg. 25:* 122-177, 1932.
85. RANKIN, F. W. Surgical lesions of the large bowel. *J. Michigan M. Soc. 31:* 1-9, 1932.
86. RATCLIFFE, H. L. Incidence and nature of tumors in captive wild mammals and birds. *Am. J. Cancer 17:* 116-135, 1933.
87. RAVEN, R. W. Early carcinoma of the rectum. *Proc. Roy. Soc. Med. 32:* 907-908, 1939.
88. ROFFO, A. H. Acción cancerígena de los derivados fenantrénicos del colesterol. *Bol. Inst. de med. exper. para el estud. y trat. d. cancer 15:* 837-843, 1938.
89. ROFFO, A. H. Tumeurs malignes développées dans l'appareil digestif par l'ingestion de graisses oxydées par chauffage. *Bull. Assoc. franç. p. l'étude du cancer 28:* 556-588, 1939.
90. ROFFO, A. H. Krebserzeugende Wirkung des aus dem Cholesterin gewonnenen Phenanthrenderivates. *Ztschr. f. Krebsforsch. 49:* 341-347, 1939.
91. ROFFO, A. H. Pirólisis del colesterol; alquitrán cancerígeno del colesterol. *Bol. Inst. de med. exper. para el estud. y trat. d. cáncer 18:* 929-948, 1941.
92. RUSCH, H. P., BAUMANN, C. A., and MAISON, G. L. Production of internal tumors with chemical carcinogens. *Arch. Path. 29:* 8-19, 1940.
93. SAXÉN, E., EKWALL, P., and SETÄLÄ, K. Squamous cell carcinoma of the forestomach in mice, following oral administration (cannula feeding) of 9,10-dimethyl-1, 2-benzanthracene solubilized in an aqueous solution of an associated colloid. *Acta path. et microbiol. scandinav. 27:* 270-275, 1950.
94. SCHAPER, A., and COHEN, C. Beiträge zur Analyse des thierischen Wachstums. II. Teil. Über zellproliferatorische Wachstumszentren und deren Beziehungen zur Regeneration und Geschwulstbildung. *Arch. f. Entwcklngsmechn. d. Organ. 19:* 348-445, 1905.
95. SCHARRER, B., and LOCHHEAD, M. S. Tumors in the invertebrates: A review. *Cancer Research 10:* 403-419, 1950.
96. SCHMIEDEN, V., and WESTHUES, H. Zur Klinik und Pathologie der Dickdarmpolypen und deren klinische und pathologisch-anatomischen Beziehungen zum Dickdarmkarzinom. *Deutsche Ztschr. f. Chir. 202:* 1-124, 1927.

97. SCHULTZE, W. Über Beziehungen der Lieberkühnschen Krypten zu den Lymphknötchen des Dickdarmes. *Centralbl. f. allg. Path. u. path. Anat. 16:* 99-103, 1905.

98. SLYE, M., HOLMES, H. F., and WELLS, H. G. Comparative pathology of cancer of the stomach with particular reference to the primary spontaneous malignant tumors of the alimentary canal in mice. Studies on the incidence and inheritability of spontaneous tumors in mice, eleventh communication. *J. Cancer Research 2:* 401-425, 1917.

99. SMITH, F. W., and STRONG, L. C. Studies on gastric neoplasia in mice. The histogenesis and influence of some endocrine factors. *J. Nat. Cancer Inst. 10:* 423-428, 1949.

100. SPITZ, S., MAGUIGAN, W. H., and DOBRINER, K. The carcinogenic action of benzidine. *Cancer 3:* 789-804, 1950.

101. STAHR, H. Zur Frage des Praecancer. *Ztschr. f. Krebsforsch. 31:* 67-71, 1930.

102. STEWART, H. L. Induction of gastric tumors in strain A mice by methylcholanthrene. *Arch. Path. 29:* 153-162, 1940.

103. STEWART, H. L., and ANDERVONT, H. B. Pathologic observations on the adenomatous lesion of the stomach in mice of Strain I. *Arch. Path. 26:* 1009-1022, 1938.

104. STEWART, H. L., and HARE, W. V. The lesions induced by intramural injection of 20-methylcholanthrene at two sites in the glandular stomach of the rat (abstract). *Proc., V[e] Congres International du Cancer,* Paris, pp. 41-42 (Hermann and Cie), 1950; *Unio Internationalis Contra Cancrum—Acta 7:* 176-177, 1950; and *J. Nat. Cancer Inst. 12:* 1019-1055, 1952.

105. STEWART, H. L., HARE, W. V., LORENZ, E., and BENNETT, J. G. The induction of adenocarcinoma and other lesions of glandular stomach in rats by intramural injection of 20-methylcholanthrene (abstract). *Cancer Research 9:* 618-619, 1949.

106. STEWART, H. L., HARE, W.V., LORENZ, E., and BENNETT, J. G. Adenocarcinoma and other lesions of the glandular stomach of mice following intramural injection of 20-methylcholanthrene. *J. Nat. Cancer Inst. 10:* 359-360, 1949.

107. STEWART, H. L., and LIEBER, M. M. Carcinoma of the suprapapillary portion of the duodenum. *Arch. Surg. 35:* 99-129, 1937.

108. STEWART, H. L., and LORENZ, E. Induction of adenocarcinoma of the pyloric stomach in mice by methylcholanthrene. *J. Nat. Cancer Inst. 2:* 193-196, 1941.

109. STEWART, H. L., and LORENZ, E. Adenocarcinoma of the pyloric stomach and other gastric neoplasms in mice induced with carcinogenic hydrocarbons. *J. Nat. Cancer Inst. 3:* 175-189, 1942.

110. STEWART, H. L., and LORENZ, E. Histopathology of induced precancerous lesions of the small intestine of mice. *J. Nat. Cancer Inst. 7:* 239-268, 1947.

111. STEWART, H. L., and LORENZ, E. Morbid anatomy, histopathology and histopathogenesis of forestomach carcinoma in mice fed carcinogenic hydrocarbons in oil emulsions. *J. Nat. Cancer Inst. 10:* 147-166, 1949.

112. STROMEYER, F. Die Pathogenese des Ulcus ventriculi, zugleich ein Beitrag zur Frage nach den Beziehungen zwischen Ulcus und Carcinom. *Beitr. z. path. Anat. u. z. allg. Path. 54:* 1-67, Jena, 1912.

113. STRONG, L. C. Genetic analysis of induction of tumors by methylcholanthrene: IX. Induced and spontaneous adenocarcinomas of the stomach in mice. *J. Nat. Cancer Inst. 5:* 339-362, 1945.

114. STRONG, L. C. Further observations on the genetic nature of gastric cancer in mice. *J. Nat. Cancer Inst. 7:* 305-308, 1947.
115. STRONG, L. C., COLLINS, V. J., and DURAND, E. A. Genetic analysis of induction of tumors by methylcholanthrene. IV. Probable remote induction of various types of gastric lesions. *Cancer Research 3:* 21-28, 1943.
116. SUGIURA, K. The relation of diet to the development of gastric lesions in the rat. *Cancer Research 2:* 770-775, 1942.
117. SUNTZEFF, V., CARRUTHERS, C., and COWDRY, E. V. The role of sebaceous glands and hair follicles in epidermal carcinogenesis in mice. *Cancer Research 7:* 439-443, 1947.
118. SWINTON, N. W., and WARREN, S. Polyps of the colon and rectum and their relation to malignancy. *J.A.M.A. 113:* 1927-1933, 1939.
119. TRONT, cited by Murray.[76]
120. TSUNODA, T. Über die Histogenese des multiplen beginnenden Magenkrebses. *Ztschr. f. Krebsforsch. 9:* 436-444, 1910.
121. Twenty-sixth Annual Report covering the year 1948 of the British Empire Cancer Campaign (Report of The Research Department of the Glasgow Royal Cancer Hospital), p. 195.
122. VERSÉ, M. Über die Entstehung, den Bau, u. das Wachstum der Polypen, Adenome u. Carcinome des Magen-Darmkanals. *Arb. Path. Inst. Leipsig* Bd. 1, Heft 5, 1908.
123. VORONOFF, S., and ALEXANDRESCU, G. Tumeurs abdominales multiples chez le rat blanc expérimentales produits par l'ingestion longtemps répetée d'un mélange à base de goudron. *Néoplasmes 8:* 129-181, 1929.
124. WATERMAN, N. Experimental production of carcinoma in the stomach of mice. *Acta cancrol. 2:* 375-388, 1936.
125. WELLS, H. G., SLYE, M., and HOLMES, H. F. Comparative pathology of cancer of the alimentary canal, with report of cases in mice; studies in incidence and inheritability of spontaneous tumors in mice: 34th report. *Am. J. Cancer 33:* 223-238, 1938.
126. WHITE, J., and STEWART, H. L. Intestinal adenocarcinoma and intra-abdominal hemangio-endothelioma in mice ingesting methylcholanthrene. *J. Nat. Cancer Inst. 3:* 331-347, 1942.
127. WILLIS, R. A. *Pathology of Tumours.* St. Louis, Mo., C. V. Mosby Co., 1948, pp. 106-125.
128. WILSON, L. B., and MACCARTY, W. C. The pathological relationships of gastric ulcer and gastric carcinoma. *Tr. A. Am. Physicians 24:* 593-602, 1909.
129. WOGLOM, W. H. "The study of experimental cancer. A review." In *Studies in Cancer and Allied Subjects.* New York, Columbia University Press, 1913, Vol. I, pp. 183-184.
130. YAMAGIWA, K., and ICHIKAWA, K. Über die atypische Epithelwucherung. *Verhandl. Jap. Path. Ges. 4:* 136, 1914.
131. HITCHCOCK, C. R., and BELL, E. T. Studies on the Nematode parasite, *Gonglyomena neoplasticum* (*Spiroptera neoplasticum*), and avitaminosis A in the forestomach of rats; Comparison with Fibiger's results. *J. Nat. Cancer Inst. 12:* 1345-1387, 1952.

CHAPTER 2

Tumors Induced by Subcutaneously Injected Carcinogens

Harold L. Stewart

The study of experimental tumors induced in the subcutaneous tissue was greatly facilitated by the discovery of the highly potent carcinogenic hydrocarbons. The subcutaneous injection of these agents, however, is complicated by the fact that a variety of different types of cells may be directly exposed to their carcinogenic action. If, for example, the axilla is chosen as the injection site, then (depending in part upon the depth of the injection) the various tissues lying between and including the skin and the costal cage and perhaps the pleura also may be variably exposed to the effect of the carcinogen. These tissues include not only epidermis and skin appendages, but also fibrous tissue, smooth and skeletal muscle, melanoblasts, lymphoid tissue, mammary gland tissue, nerves, endothelium, bone cartilage, periosteum, synovial tissue and fat. It is not surprising, therefore, that tumors induced by this technic may originate from different types of cells and therefore be of mixed histologic pattern, and consequently are difficult to classify precisely as to cell or cells of reference.

The evocation of tumors by the subcutaneous injection of carcinogens is further modified by a number of additional factors. Thus, by this technic differences have been demonstrated between species, between strains within species, and between the sexes. The dose and potency of different carcinogens and the solvent employed modify the reaction. Moreover, in the case of at least one carcinogen (*ortho*-aminoazotoluene) there is a difference in the site of origin and the histologic type of the primary tumor depending upon which of two locations, whether the axilla or the base of the tail, is selected for the subcutaneous injection, and whether the crystalline compound or an olive oil solution of it is employed. A complete account of the different carcinogens tested in different species, and the different doses employed, is given in Hartwell's monograph.[21] Shear[35, 36, 38] showed that among the most potent of the carcinogenic hydrocarbons were 20-methylcholanthrene, cholanthrene, and the 10-methyl, the 5,10-dimethyl, and the 5,9-

dimethyl derivatives of 1,2-benzanthracene. He induced a transplantable subcutaneous sarcoma with as little as 0.0004 mg. of 1,2,5,6-dibenzanthracene in a cholesterol pellet.

Contrary to the findings of many previous investigators, Steiner and Falk[39a] showed that 1,2-benzanthracene and chrysene are carcinogenic upon subcutaneous injection. Moreover, these two carcinogens injected together show summation of carcinogenic effects if not actually a potentiating synergistic action. In other words, when the two are dissolved in the same solvent and injected, the tumor yield is greater than the sum of their individual tumor yields despite the halving of the dose of each compound. By contrast the carcinogenic effects of 1,2-benzanthracene and 1,2,5,6-dibenzanthracene injected together are not those of summation but apparently of inhibition or deficient summation. The carcinogenic effects of 1,2,5,6-dibenzanthracene and 20-methylcholanthrene injected together are additive, although imperfectly so. The summation or additive effects of carcinogenic agents have received a great deal of attention in efforts made to understand the action of the carcinogens on the skin and the events that occur in cutaneous carcinogenesis, but relatively few such studies have been made using the subcutaneous injection route. The pure chemical substances which are known to inhibit the action of a chemical carcinogen seem to interfere with the sulfur metabolism of the target cell. Some of the inhibiting compounds of the aromatic series are closely related to actual carcinogens, suggesting that the mode of action is a competition for available –SH groups.

Of several strains of mice tested for their reaction to the development of subcutaneous sarcoma following the injection of 20-methylcholanthrene and 1,2,5,6-dibenzanthracene, Strains C3H, A, and C showed a high susceptibility and Strains Yblack and I low susceptibility;[1, 2, 3] the most susceptible proved to be Strain C3H mice. Tumors appear earlier in male than in female mice of Strain C3H and this is also true of male and female castrates, although castration appears to delay slightly the development of tumors in both sexes.[41] In Strain A mice the incidence of induced subcutaneous tumors is about 50 per cent higher in the male than in the female.[25] In a study of 5000 Strain A mice, each of which received a subcutaneous injection of from 0.05 to 0.2 mg. of 3,4-benzpyrene in various lipid solvents, Leiter and Shear[25] found that lard was unsatisfactory as a vehicle because of the variations in results. These variations were apparently a consequence of the different proportions of retarding and promoting substances in various specimens of lard filtrate employed. Of a number of other solvents tested, tricaprylin was found to be the most suitable vehicle for quantitative experiments.

The induction of tumors of mesenchymal tissues by those neoplastic agents which evoke tumors in epithelial tissues is of great theoretical interest as regards the nature of the neoplastic process. It suggests, as pointed out by Willis,[45] that in spite of the great diversity in the origin, structure, and behavior of tumors, the neoplastic change is probably fundamentally similar in all tissues and that gains in our knowledge of the nature of this change in any one tissue will probably shed light on the entire cancer problem.

PATHOLOGY

Since the discovery of the potent carcinogens by Kennaway and his associates[24] and the first successful testing[13] of one of these (1,2,5,6-dibenzanthracene) in the subcutaneous tissue of mice and rats, a number of other species have been tested,[30, 39] but most of the studies have been carried out in mice.[12, 19, 23, 32] One of the earliest attempts at classifying histologically a group of induced subcutaneous sarcomas of mice was the study by Haagensen and Krehbiel.[19] Of 49 tumors induced by 1,2,5,6-dibenzanthracene, 11 were classified as fibrosarcoma, 6 as leiomyosarcoma, 10 as rhabdomyosarcoma, while 22 of the growths remained unclassified. This reflects the difficulty of distinguishing among the different tumors that may be induced in the subcutaneous region. They also reported the induction of a liposarcoma by benzpyrene. Bonser and Orr[12] studied 160 tumors induced in mice by the subcutaneous administration of one of several carcinogenic hydrocarbons. These tumors were described as spindle-cell and pleomorphic-cell sarcomas showing considerable variation in pattern. The appearance of many of them suggested leiomyosarcoma; others, chiefly owing to the high degree of vascularity, resembled angiosarcoma. The giant cell tumors, similar to those classified by Haagensen and Krehbiel[19] as rhabdomyosarcoma, were considered by Bonser and Orr[12] to have arisen from structures other than skeletal muscle. In all justice it should be pointed out that Haagensen and Krehbiel,[19] although classifying this particular type of growth as rhabdomyosarcoma, were the first to admit this designation as uncertain because no cross-striations were demonstrated in the tumor giant cells in their neoplasms.

The three most frequent tumors developing in the subcutaneous tissue into which one of the carcinogenic hydrocarbons is injected are fibrosarcoma, leiomyosarcoma, and rhabdomyosarcoma. Grossly these are fairly similar. They are gray or pink, firm, rather sharply circumscribed, nonencapsulated, nodular, spherical tumors which may show areas of necrosis and hemorrhage. Microscopically their peripheral extensions are always well beyond their palpable limits and they may actively invade and destroy bone, muscle, and perivascular tissues. They are often fixed to the skin and deeper tissues and may or may not be ulcerated. The incidence of metastases varies a good deal in the different tumors and depends in part on the rapidity of growth and how long the animal survives after the tumor develops. When metastases occur they are usually found in the lungs and rarely in regional lymph nodes.

FIBROSARCOMA

Fibrosarcoma is usually composed of plump bundles of elongated spindle-shaped cells which form interweaving patterns. The spindle-shaped tumor cells are usually large, with elongated, darkly staining nuclei, and may vary considerably in size, shape, and staining. Mitotic figures are variable in number and often exceedingly numerous. The cytoplasm of the cells is frequently drawn out into thin, unipolar or bipolar processes which fuse with those of adjacent cells at their extremities. Collagenic and reticulum fibers are always present, and, when abundant, the growth is relatively less cellular. The reticulum fibers form an extremely intimate meshwork, embracing cells singly and in small groups and being closely applied to the sides of the cells. It is frequently possible to demonstrate fibroglia by appropriate staining methods. The blood vessels of the fibrosarcoma are usually numerous, and simple or immature in structure, thin-walled and irregular in outline. They are lined by endothelial cells, but the lining may be incomplete, in which case the tumor cells seem to border directly upon the vascular channel or to be growing into it.

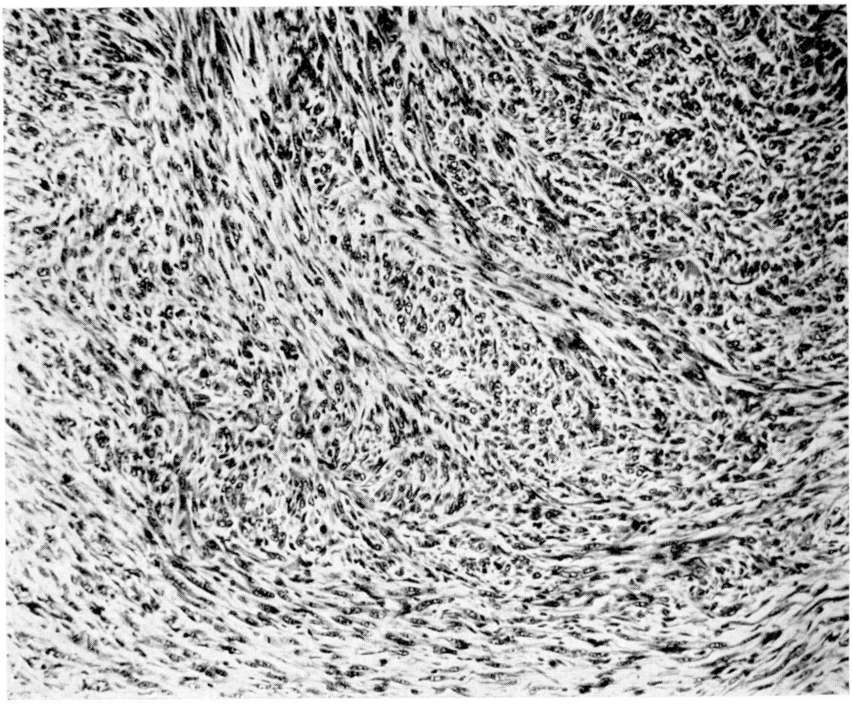

FIG. 18. Fibrosarcoma. × 140.

LEIOMYOSARCOMA

These tumors histologically resemble the fibrosarcomas in being composed of interlacing bundles of rather large, darkly staining, spindle-shaped cells which, since they are cut in various planes, appear round or oval (Fig. 18). Giant cells may occur with one to several large nuclei. Mitotic figures are usually numerous. In comparison with fibrosarcoma, the cells of the leiomyosarcoma are more fleshy and possess an abundant and acidophilic cytoplasm. Reticulum occurs throughout all parts of the tumor, surrounding cells singly and in small groups. Collagen is usually minimal in amount compared to that of the fibrosarcoma. With the phosphotungstic acid–hematoxylin stain, myofibrils are demonstrated in variable numbers in different parts of the tumor and are of real diagnostic significance. If myofibrils are absent the diagnosis of leiomyosarcoma can only be regarded as tentative. The blood vessels are similar to those of the fibrosarcoma.

Rhabdomyosarcoma

These tumors are composed of interlacing bundles or sheets of cells which vary a great deal in size and shape (Fig. 19). Many of the cells are spindle shaped and resemble those of the fibrosarcomas. Other cells are straplike, rounded or polygonal and are bulky and fleshy, possessing a large amount of acidophilic cytoplasm and

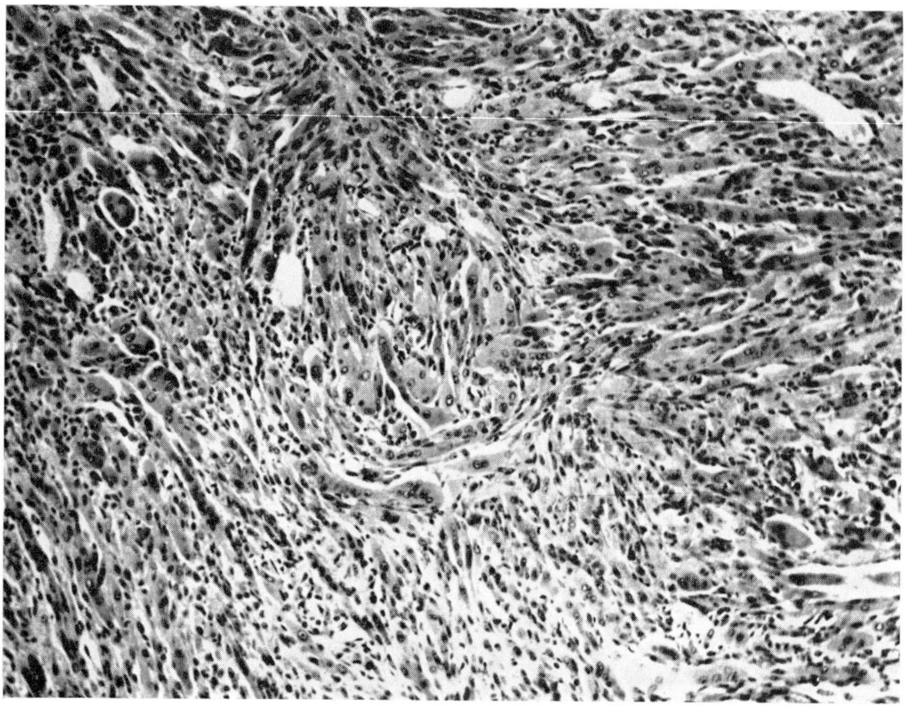

Fig. 19. Rhabdomyosarcoma.

having one or several nuclei which vary considerably in size, shape and staining. There may be one or several large nucleoli. Mitotic figures are numerous. The growth is everywhere permeated by reticulum. Collagen is usually scanty. The blood vessels are immature, like those of the other sarcomas, and may or may not be numerous. Cross-striations are usually not demonstrated in the tumor cells. Regenerating skeletal muscle fibers with cross striations are frequently seen following the subcutaneous injection of the carcinogenic hydrocarbons, and of non-carcinogenic irritants such as turpentine. They may be seen in close relationship to induced tumors other than rhabdomyosarcoma. Hence caution is necessary in interpreting cross striation in straplike cells in the neighborhood of any induced subcutaneous sarcoma. Under these circumstances it is necessary to rule out the possible presence of pre-existing muscle fibers. In rhabdomyosarcoma the bulk of the tumor may be composed of greatly elongated, straplike, giant cells, with rows and clusters of atypical nuclei and with an abundance of acidophilic cytoplasm containing longitudinal myofibrils. In these it is rarely possible to demonstrate cross-striations although the cell pattern of the growth is strongly suggestive of rhabdomyosarcoma.

Any trained pathologist who has examined large numbers of these experimental giant-cell sarcomas is convinced that many of them arise from skeletal muscle and should be classified as rhabdomyosarcoma. When these tumors are propagated in tissue culture or transplanted by serial subcutaneous inoculation into animals, the straplike cells usually diminish in number and ultimately disappear from successive transplants, so that with time the final transplant growth may assume the histologic appearance of fibrosarcoma. The disappearance of the modified muscle elements suggests, according to Lewis,[26] that they either differentiate into spindle cells which are malignant and indistinguishable from those of connective tissue origin, or are lost or die out. Not all induced subcutaneous tumors with numerous giant cells are rhabdomyosarcomas. Many histologic types of soft tissue sarcoma in man possess giant cells. Rhabdomyosarcoma enters prominently into the differential diagnosis of many of these. Aside from the skill and the experience of the observer and the demonstration of cross striations in rhabdomyosarcoma, histopathologic methods are at present far from satisfactory in establishing conclusively a differential diagnosis between many of the tumors of this confusing group that occurs in man. In view of the uncertainty in the field of human neoplasms—which have been the subject of intensive study for many years—it is not surprising that the precise classification of experimental subcutaneous sarcomas of mice is less than satisfactory at present. Moreover, in dealing with soft tissue sarcomas of man it is generally assumed that each individual tumor arose from a single cell type. No such assumption can be made in the case of experimental tumors, since the carcinogen in the subcutaneous tissue is in contact with so many diverse tissues, from one or many of which neoplasms may be evoked, and in all probability, frequently are. Indeed, one is surprised not that more of the experimental sarcomas have not been accurately classified (Fig. 20) but that more mixed types of tumor have not been reported. In our own work we have found the use of the phosphotungstic acid hematoxylin stain of inestimable value in demonstrating fibroglia, myoglia, and cross striations whereby experimental tumors or at least areas of such tumors can be distinguished as fibrosarcoma, leiomyosarcoma, or rhabdomyosarcoma respectively.

Liposarcoma

These tumors are usually soft, yellowish, often fluctuant and sharply demarcated peripherally owing to compression of the surrounding tissues. On section the tumor tissue is more or less greasy, depending upon the proportional amount of fat and fibrous tissue stroma, which is usually minimal. The tumor cells tend to be rounded or polygonal, more or less sheetlike in arrangement, but may be spindle shaped and form interlacing bundles (Fig. 21). The cytoplasm is pale and extensively vacuolated. The vacuoles may be single and large, giving the cell a signet ring appearance, or they may be multiple and small. Virtually every cell stains positively for fat. Mitotic figures are numerous, and many of the tumor cells are multinucleated. The reticulum is found between the cells. The collagen is usually minimal in amount.

Liposarcoma rarely develops in mice following subcutaneous injection of the carcinogenic hydrocarbons. Haagensen and Krehbiel,[19, 20] for example, mentioned only one liposarcoma in their series of induced subcutaneous tumors in mice. The only

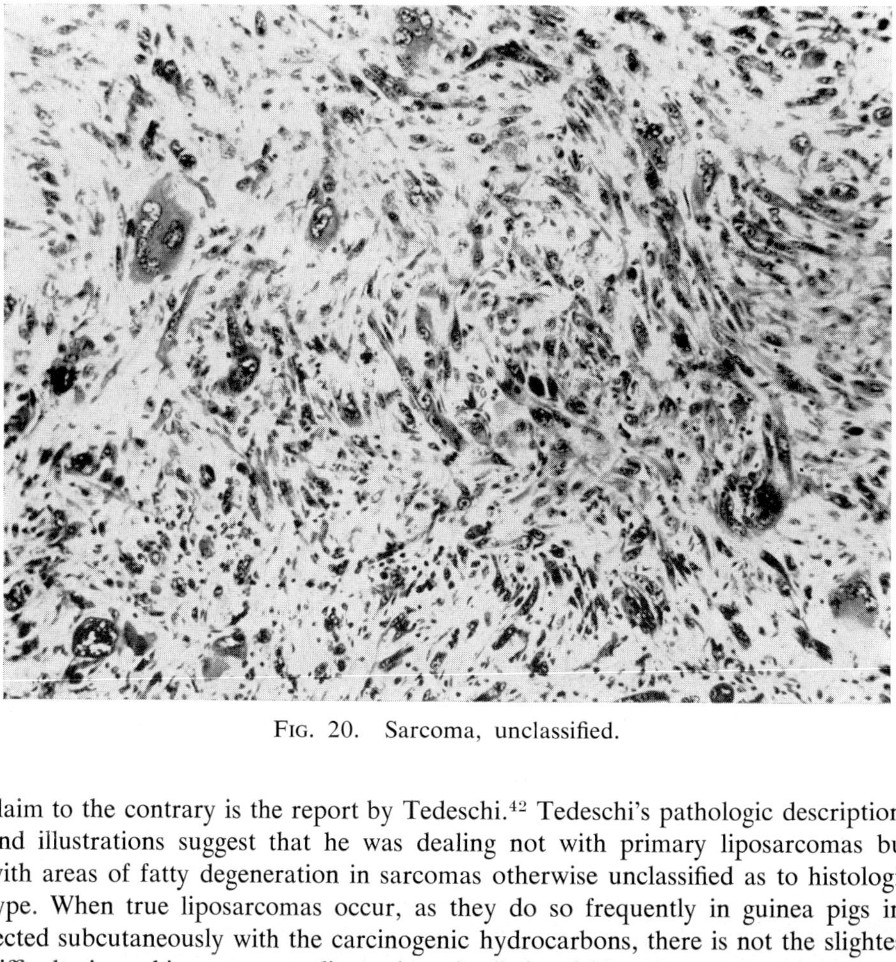

FIG. 20. Sarcoma, unclassified.

claim to the contrary is the report by Tedeschi.[42] Tedeschi's pathologic descriptions and illustrations suggest that he was dealing not with primary liposarcomas but with areas of fatty degeneration in sarcomas otherwise unclassified as to histologic type. When true liposarcomas occur, as they do so frequently in guinea pigs injected subcutaneously with the carcinogenic hydrocarbons, there is not the slightest difficulty in making a correct diagnosis or in distinguishing these tumors from other types of subcutaneous sarcoma. The liposarcomas are grossly greasy and loaded with fat in frozen sections of the primary and transplanted growths. Haagensen and Krehbiel[19, 20] reported the induction of liposarcoma in guinea pigs, and this type of growth constituted 20 per cent of the tumors obtained by Shimkin and Mider[39] following injection of large doses (20–40 mg.) of methylcholanthrene subcutaneously into guinea pigs. Indeed, this observation represents one of the striking species differences in the response of different tissues simultaneously exposed to a carcinogen. The reasons why liposarcoma is so frequently induced in guinea pigs by the subcutaneously injected carcinogens and so rarely in mice, constitute an experimental problem of the first order of importance that has not as yet been seriously studied.

FIG. 21. Liposarcoma. (I am indebted to Doctors G. B. Mider and N. J. Shimkin for the use of this illustration.) × 300.

MAMMARY GLAND TUMORS

Tumors arising from mammary gland tissue in mice near the site of a subcutaneously injected carcinogenic hydrocarbon have been noted by Bonser and Orr,[12] Stewart,[40] and others and have been comprehensively described by Andervont and Dunn.[6] These carcinomas more or less reproduce the glandular pattern regarded as characteristic of mammary carcinoma occurring in mice with the milk factor, but exhibit a pronounced tendency to undergo squamous metaplasia. For this reason Andervont and Dunn[6] believe many of these methylcholanthrene-induced tumors arise from the mammary ducts rather than from the mammary gland acini which probably give rise to the tumors associated with the milk factor. Several other types of breast tumor in mice treated with methylcholanthrene were described by Andervont and Dunn,[6] including the highly organoid, so-called molluscoid or Haaland tumor, undifferentiated carcinoma, carcinosarcoma, and sarcoma. Many tumors of the latter two types were believed to have arisen from the specialized connective tissue supporting the ducts and acini of the mammary gland. Some of the squamous cell carcinomas may have arisen from the cutaneous epidermis or from skin appendages.

Hemangioendothelioma

This tumor can be induced in the subcutaneous tissue of mice of various inbred strains by a variety of agents such as the carcinogenic hydrocarbons,[22, 37] colloidal thorium dioxide,[9, 34] and *ortho*-aminoazotoluene,[4] and by exposing the skin to ultraviolet irradiation.[18] Andervont[4] has reviewed the literature on the spontaneous occurrence and the experimental induction of this neoplasm in the soft tissue and viscera of mice.[9, 10, 15, 16, 17, 27, 44]

Grossly, hemangioendotheliomas are usually distinguishable from other types of tumors by their red color, which is due to the presence of innumerable blood spaces.[5, 7, 18, 44] In general, the tumor masses are firm, sometimes cystic, irregularly nodular, red-brown or dark. As in many other tumors of the mouse, the peripheral limits may be sharply circumscribed. Microscopically hemangioendotheliomas are composed of atypical blood vessel endothelium which forms both vascular channels and solid cellular masses (Fig. 22). The degree of cellularity varies considerably, as does also the size, shape, number and appearance of the vascular channels. Some parts of the tumor are composed almost exclusively of closely packed, thin-walled vascular channels of capillary or large cavernous size. Other areas are chiefly cellular, with and without blood spaces. The nuclei of the tumor cells may be single or multiple, irregular in shape and size, often excessively lobated, with large masses of chromatin. The mitotic figures, which are usually numerous, are frequently bizarre. A striking feature of these tumors is the intravascular endothelial cell proliferation, which varies from a single to a many-layered blood vessel lining, partially or completely occluding the lumen. The blood vessels which do possess a lumen usually contain blood. Some, however, are empty, others are thrombosed, and a fair number contain leukocytes. Throughout the tumor there are areas of necrosis, inflammatory foci, hemorrhage, and blood pigment. Peripherally there is active invasion of the surrounding tissue. In the vascular areas of the tumor the reticulum fibers occupy a basement membrane-like position with respect to the vessel wall, very much like that of normal vessels. In those areas containing cellular nonvascular nodules, the reticulum is sparse and surrounds relatively large cellular aggregations which are only slightly permeated by this fibrillar material.

Although hemangioendotheliomas may be induced in mice by a variety of carcinogenic agents, the azo dye, *o*-aminoazotoluene, is unique in this regard. Andervont's[4] studies of this compound injected subcutaneously show that under different circumstances it is capable of evoking both hemangioendothelioma and sarcoma in mice of Strains C, A, C3H, and C57black. The hemangioendotheliomas arise at a variety of sites distant from the site of application, whereas the sarcomas always appear locally at the site of subcutaneous administration. Olive oil solutions of the dye induce both hemangioendothelioma and sarcoma, but the crystalline compounds induce the former growth only. When the crystalline material is injected subcutaneously into the axillary region, most of the induced hemangioendotheliomas arise in the interscapular fat, but when it is injected subcutaneously at the base of the tail or mid-dorsally, or when administered orally, the majority of the neoplasms which are hemangioendotheliomas occur in the lungs. Andervont's studies not only

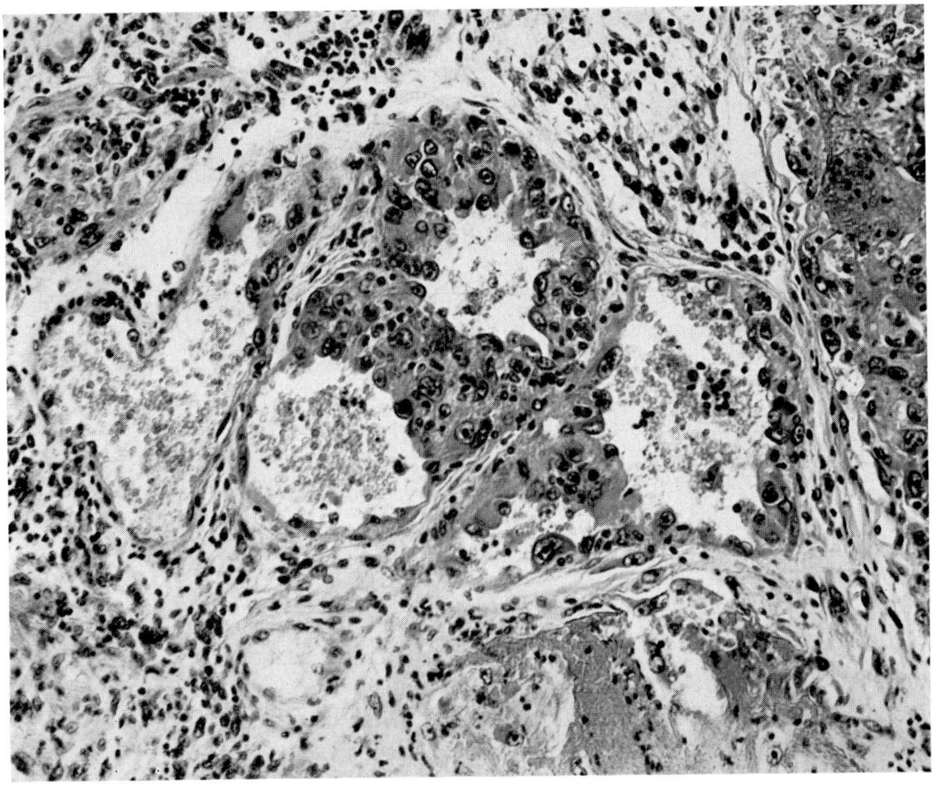

FIG. 22. Hemangioendothelioma. × 235.

establish *o*-aminoazotoluene as an effective carcinogen for eliciting hemangio-endothelioma in mice, but emphasize the point that a single carcinogen administered under different conditions produces either of two different histologic types of neoplastic response. The crystalline compound induces sarcoma, whereas the olive oil solution induces hemangioendothelioma; the latter tumor is induced in the lung if the injection is made at the base of the tail, whereas hemangiomatous tumors arise in the interscapular fat when the injection is made into the axillary region. Female Strain C mice are more susceptible than males to the induction of hemangio-endotheliomas, and the incidence is increased significantly in castrate males. The same analogy is found in human beings, the incidence of angioma in the female being twice that in the male.[43]

HISTOGENESIS AND LATENT PERIOD OF SUBCUTANEOUS TUMORS

Several studies having a bearing upon the histogenesis and upon the latent period of subcutaneous tumor induction have been reported. In one of these studies[8] methylcholanthrene pellets introduced into the subcutaneous tissue were removed from mice in successive groups every week up to the twelfth week after implantation. Removal of the pellet was accomplished through a short incision in the shaved skin over one end of the pellet. In this study Andervont and Shear[8] set out to ascertain if tumors could be induced if the carcinogen-containing pellets were kept in contact with the subcutaneous tissues for short periods of time and, if so, what would be the shortest period of time necessary for the induction of tumors in most animals. Their experiments showed that exposure to the pellets for two weeks induced tumors in 23 per cent of the animals; exposure for four weeks gave tumors in 56 per cent; and for six weeks in 88 per cent of the mice. This work therefore emphasizes the importance of the continual contact of the carcinogen with the susceptible tissues during the latent period of tumor induction.

Another study[40] compared the results of histologic examination and of transplantation to other mice of the tissue adjacent to a carcinogenic agent in the form of a 5 per cent methylcholanthrene cholesterol pellet (Fig. 23). The tissue for study was obtained from mice autopsied at the rate of 3 per week during the latent period of tumor development. Tissue from each donor mouse was transplanted into each of 3 recipient mice. A fragment of tissue excised from the neighborhood of the pellet in a mouse killed at 42 days grew progressively as a sarcoma after transplantation into a recipient mouse. The next similar, positive transplant was obtained from a pellet bearing mouse at 49 days. After the forty-ninth day there was a lapse of 4 weeks during which time the transplants, made weekly, failed to grow in recipient mice. However, positive results were again obtained at 77, 91, and 98 days respectively. After excising the small bit of tissue at autopsy for transplantation, the pellet and the remaining tissue around it were imbedded in paraffin and sectioned for histologic examination. A study of the tissues surrounding the 42-day pellets revealed the presence of atypical cells consistent with neoplastic cells, although lacking the organizational arrangement of a fully developed tumor. The observation that such tissue from one mouse grew upon transplantation indicates that a malignant change may be induced in cells exposed to the carcinogenic action of methylcholanthrene before all the criteria usually required for the histopathologic recognition of malignancy become fully established. More difficult to explain, however, was the failure of similar atypical cells around the pellets at 49, 56, 63, and 70 days to yield tumors on transplantation to recipient mice. At 77 days and thereafter, the histopathologic changes became progressively more atypical and characteristic of neoplasm.

Other pertinent observations made in this study[40] have a bearing on the latent time period required for tumors to develop in the recipient mice following transplantation of the tissue taken from the vicinity of a pellet. In general, the longer the tissue to be transplanted remains in contact with the carcinogen, the more likely it is to grow successfully as a tumor in the recipient animal, the less time is required for it to show the first sign of progressive growth in the new host, and the more rapid its growth—all characteristic of the malignant state. These studies of tumor development suggest that the property of autonomous growth which cells assume during the evolution of malignancy may be retarded or inhibited when they are separated too early from the carcinogenic agent which initiates this property. Whether this is due

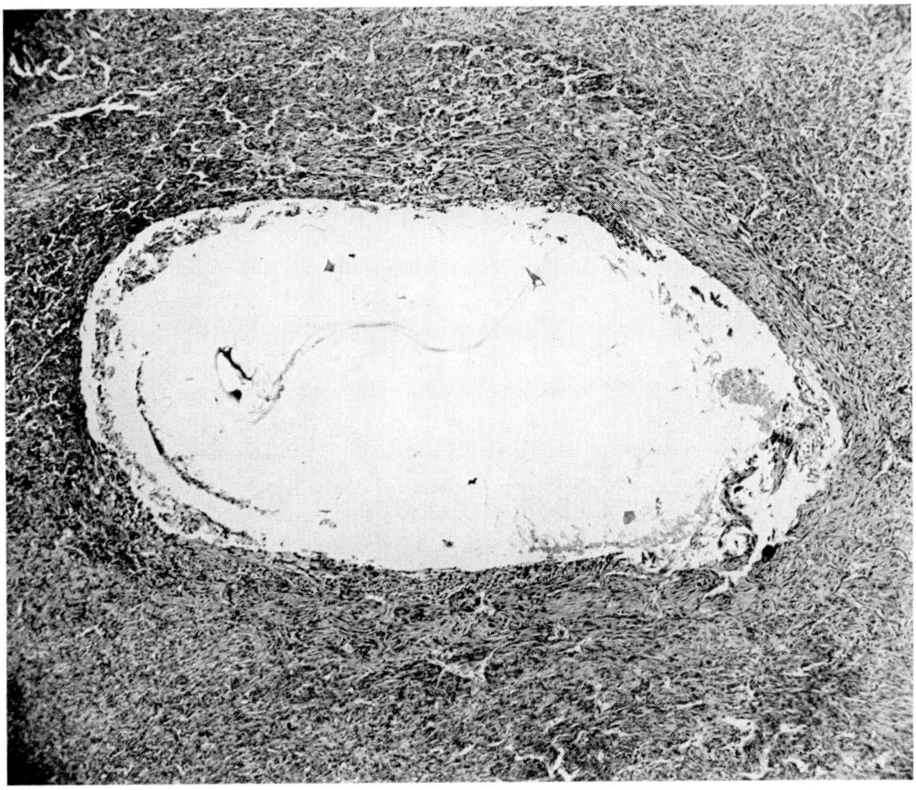

FIG. 23. Sarcoma developing around a methylcholanthrene pellet. × 63.

to the number of cells affected or to the degree of effect on individual cells has not been determined.

Studies have also been made of the uninterrupted sequence of the histologic changes leading to experimental sarcoma in the subcutaneous tissue of mice. Peacock and Beck[31] found that sarcoma does not develop in immediate contiguity with the carcinogen but in the tissues a few millimeters distant. An acute inflammatory process has no apparent influence on the neoplastic reaction under these circumstances.[11] Orr[29] compared the tissue reaction around control pellets of paraffin with that around experimental pellets containing paraffin and several of the carcinogenic hydrocarbons, including 3,4-benzpyrene, 1,2,5,6-dibenzanthracene, and 20-methylcholanthrene. Paraffin pellets induce a mild foreign-body reaction leading to encapsulation of the object by firm collagen in less than two months. In contrast, pellets containing the carcinogenic agents prevent the occurrence of an adequate fibrous reaction, the collagen being small in amount or loose in texture, with fibrinoid material on the inside. Orr[29] attributed the development of sarcoma under these circumstances to the frustrated capsulation of the foreign body containing the carcinogenic agents. At a later stage, foci of secondary cellular proliferation—from which sarcoma develops—appear further out in the primary collagen and at a distance from the pellet. The mechanism of carcinogenesis was explained by Orr on the basis that the presence of carcinogens prevents the foreign-body reaction from reaching an effective endpoint, possibly as a result of their injurious action on the cells and tissue fibers, and that sarcomas may be the inevitable result of such persistently incomplete reactions.

APPLICATIONS OF TISSUE CULTURE TO PROBLEM OF SUBCUTANEOUS SARCOMAS

The use of tissue culture technics in the study of the problem of induced subcutaneous sarcomas has several applications. One of these is its use in the diagnosis and identification of the cells of a tumor. Murray and Stout[28] grew a variety of primary tumors of man for short periods of time in tissue cultures, and in certain cases in which the diagnosis was obscure in the histologic sections, the morphology of the tissue culture explant gave the clue that led to the correct diagnosis. For example, this technic proved to be an important diagnostic aid in some cases of sympathicoblastoma which were otherwise indistinguishable from a malignant lymphoma. In the tissue culture preparations of this type of neoplasm the correct diagnosis was established by the outgrowth of neurites. It was also possible to identify the epithelioid cells of a glomus tumor as pericytes when grown in tissue culture. The use of the tissue culture technic as a diagnostic aid has not as yet been fully explored, but would seem to hold promise as a supplementary procedure in the difficult problem involved in the accurate diagnosis of experimental subcutaneous sarcomas.

Earle and co-workers[14, 14a] have demonstrated that cells of a bit of tissue excised from the subcutaneous connective tissue of a mouse and grown in tissue culture may undergo a malignant neoplastic change. This neoplastic conversion is manifested by changes in the growth characteristics of the cells while still in tissue culture. When these neoplastic cells are transplanted to the subcutaneous tissue of mice, a malignant tumor rapidly arises at the site of inoculation and may metastasize. The histologic sections of these sarcomas reveal considerable differences in the appearance of their cells, some of the tumors being exceedingly anaplastic. Others appear as well differentiated fibrosarcomas. It has been presumed that Earle's neoplasms arose from fibroblasts. However, since a fragment of subcutaneous tissue from which the original culture was started may contain, in addition to fibroblasts, primitive cells with unknown potentialities for differentiation, or other cells as, for example, endothelial cells, histiocytes, myocytes, or Schwann's cells, the exact cell of reference for each of Earle's neoplasms is by no means established. Indeed, some of the resulting tumors from the different tissue culture lines are so anaplastic and undifferentiated as to cast doubt on the belief that they all arose from one cell type. The more recent work of Earle and his associates[33] has demonstrated that tissue cultures may be successfully obtained from the isolation of a single cell, a hitherto impossible feat. It is difficult to refrain from overemphasizing the tremendous possibilities inherent in this technic. Theoretically, by systematically isolating identified cells from different tissues, growing them in tissue culture and, if possible, converting them to neoplastic cells, our knowledge of the histopathologic types of tumors that might arise from a single tissue cell would be unbelievably enhanced and expanded.

BIBLIOGRAPHY

1. ANDERVONT, H. B. The production of dibenzanthracene tumors in pure strain mice. *Pub. Health Rep. 49:* 620-624, 1934.
2. ANDERVONT, H. B. The incidence of induced subcutaneous and pulmonary tumors and spontaneous mammary tumors in hybrid mice. *Pub. Health Rep. 53:* 1665-1671, 1938.
3. ANDERVONT, H. B. Susceptibility of mice to spontaneous, induced and transplantable tumors; comparative study of 8 strains. *Pub. Health Rep. 53:* 1647-1665, 1938.
4. ANDERVONT, H. B. Induction of hemangio-endotheliomas and sarcomas in mice with *o*-aminoazotoluene. *J. Nat. Cancer Inst. 10:* 927-941, 1950.
5. ANDERVONT, H. B., and DUNN, T. B. Effect of castration and sex hormones on the induction of tumors in mice with *o*-aminoazotoluene. *J. Nat. Cancer Inst. 7:* 455-461, 1947.
6. ANDERVONT, H. B., and DUNN, T. B. Response of mammary-tumor-agent-free strain dba female mice to percutaneous application of methylcholanthrene. *J. Nat. Cancer Inst. 10:* 895-925, 1950.
7. ANDERVONT, H. B., GRADY, H. G., and EDWARDS, J. E. Induction of hepatic lesions, hepatomas, pulmonary tumors and hemangioendotheliomas in mice with *o*-aminoazotoluene. *J. Nat. Cancer Inst. 3:* 131-153, 1942.
8. ANDERVONT, H. B., and SHEAR, M. J. Production of tumors in mice following the removal of methylcholanthrene cholesterol pellets. *J. Nat. Cancer Inst. 2:* 333-334, 1942.
9. ANDERVONT, H. B., and SHIMKIN, M. B. Tumors in mice injected with colloidal thorium dioxide. *J. Nat. Cancer Inst. 1:* 349-353, 1940.
10. ANDERVONT, H. B., WHITE, J., and EDWARDS, J. E. Effect of two azo compounds when added to the diet of mice. *J. Nat. Cancer Inst. 4:* 583-586, 1940.
11. BECK, S. On the failure of acute and subacute inflammation to influence carcinogenesis with 3:4-benzpyrene. *Brit. J. Exper. Path. 19:* 319-323, 1938.
12. BONSER, G. M., and ORR, J. W. The morphology of 160 tumors induced by carcinogenic hydrocarbons in the subcutaneous tissues of mice. *J. Path. & Bact. 49:* 171-183, 1939.
13. BURROWS, H., HIEGER, I., and KENNAWAY, E. L. The experimental production of tumours of connective tissue. *Am. J. Cancer 16:* 57-67, 1932.
14. EARLE, W. R., SCHILLING, E. L., STARK, T. H., STRAUS, N. P., BROWN, M. F., and SHELTON, E. Production of malignancy in vitro. IV. The mouse fibroblast cultures and changes seen in the living cells. *J. Nat. Cancer Inst. 4:* 165-212, 1943.

14a. Sanford, K. K., Earle, W. R., Shelton, E., Schilling, E. L., Duchesne, E. M., Likely, G. D., and Becker, M. M. Production of malignancy in vitro. XII. Further transformations of mouse fibroblasts to sarcomatous cells. *J. Nat. Cancer Inst. 11:* 351-375, 1950.
15. Edwards, J. E., Andervont, H. B., and Dalton, A. J. A transplantable malignant hemangioendothelioma of the liver in the mouse. *J. Nat. Cancer Inst. 2:* 479-490, 1942.
16. Foulds, L. Angioendothelioma in the mouse. Imperial Cancer Research Fund (Great Britain), *Ninth Scientific Report,* pp. 89-91, 1930.
17. Furth, J., and Furth, O. B. Monocytic leukemia and other neoplastic diseases occurring in mice following intrasplenic injection of 1:2-benzpyrene. *Am. J. Cancer 34:* 169-183, 1938.
18. Grady, H. G., Blum, H. F., and Kirby-Smith, J. S. Types of tumor induced by ultraviolet radiation and factors influencing their relative incidence. *J. Nat. Cancer Inst. 3:* 371-378, 1943.
19. Haagensen, C. D., and Krehbiel, O. F. The morphology of the sarcomas produced by 1,2,5,6-dibenzanthracene. *Am. J. Cancer 26:* 368-377, 1936.
20. Haagensen, C. D., and Krehbiel, O. F. Liposarcoma produced by 1,2-benzpyrene. *Am. J. Cancer 27:* 474-484, 1936.
21. Hartwell, J. L. *Survey of Compounds which have been Tested for Carcinogenic Activity* (ed. 2). U. S. Public Health Service Publication No. 149. Washington, D.C., U. S. Government Printing Office, 1951.
22. Hartwell, J. L., and Stewart, H. L. Action of 5,9,10-trimethyl-1,2-benzanthracene on the skin of the mouse. *J. Nat. Cancer Inst. 3:* 277-285, 1942.
23. Hval, E. *Om 1:2:5:6-Dibenzantracensarkomenes Utvikling.* Skrifter utgitt av Klaus Hanssens Fond, 1937, Nr. 14.
24. Kennaway, E. L. Further experiments on cancer-producing substances. *Biochem. J. 24:* 497-504, 1930.
25. Leiter, J., and Shear, M. J. Quantitative experiments on the production of subcutaneous tumors in strain A mice with marginal doses of 3,4-benzpyrene. *J. Nat. Cancer Inst. 3:* 455-477, 1943.
26. Lewis, W. H. Dibenzanthracene mouse sarcomas; histology. *Am. J. Cancer 37:* 521-530, 1939.
27. Lorenz, E., and Stewart, H. L. Tumors of the alimentary tract induced in mice by feeding olive oil emulsions containing carcinogenic hydrocarbons. *J. Nat. Cancer Inst. 7:* 227-238, 1947.
28. Murray, M. R., and Stout, A. P. Distinctive characteristics of the sympathicoblastoma cultivated in vitro. *Am. J. Path. 23:* 429-441, 1947.
29. Orr, J. W. An investigation of the histological changes in the subcutaneous tissues of mice during the induction of sarcoma by carcinogenic hydrocarbons. *J. Path. & Bact. 49:* 157-170, 1939.
30. Peacock, P. R. The production of tumours in fowl by carcinogenic agents: tar; 1:2:5:6-dibenzanthracene-lard. *J. Path. & Bact. 36:* 141-152, 1933.
31. Peacock, P. R., and Beck, S. Rate of absorption of carcinogens and local tissue reaction as factors influencing carcinogenesis. *Brit. J. Exper. Path. 19:* 315-319, 1938.
32. Rondoni, P. Vergleichende histologische Beobachtungen über die Bindegewebsreaktionen einigen cancerogenen und nichtcancerogenen Stoffen gegenüber. *Ztschr. f. Krebsforsch. 47:* 59-83, 1937.

33. Sanford, K. K., Earle, W. R., and Likely, G. D. The growth *in vitro* of single isolated tissue cells. *J. Nat. Cancer Inst. 9:* 229-246, 1948.
34. Selbie, F. R. Tumours in rats and mice following injection of thorotrast. *Brit. J. Exper. Path. 19:* 100-107, 1938.
35. Shear, M. J. Studies in carcinogenesis. I. The production of tumors in mice with hydrocarbons. *Am. J. Cancer 26:* 322-332, 1936.
36. Shear, M. J. Studies in carcinogenesis. V. Methyl derivatives of 1,2-benzanthracene. *Am. J. Cancer 33:* 499-537, 1938.
37. Shear, M. J., and Ilfeld, F. W. Studies in carcinogenesis. IX. Hydrocarbon-cholesterol pellets in strain D mice. *Am. J. Path. 16:* 287-293, 1940.
38. Shear, M. J., and Perrault, A. Studies in carcinogenesis. VII. Compounds related to 3,4-benzpyrene. *Am. J. Cancer 36:* 211-228, 1939.
39. Shimkin, M. B., and Mider, G. B. Induction of tumors in guinea pigs with subcutaneously injected methylcholanthrene. *J. Nat. Cancer Inst. 1:* 707-725, 1941.
39a. Steiner, P. E., and Falk, H. L. Summation and inhibition effects of weak and strong carcinogenic hydrocarbons: 1,2-benzanthracene, chrysene, 1,2,5,6-dibenzanthracene and 20-methylcholanthrene. *Cancer Research 11:* 56-63, 1951.
40. Stewart, H. L. Study of the histological changes and transplantation of tissues surrounding methylcholanthrene pellets during the latent period of tumor development in female C3H mice. *Am. J. Path. 15:* 707-722, 1939.
41. Stewart, H. L. Influence of castration on the induction of subcutaneous tumors in mice of the C3H strain by 1,2,5,6-dibenzanthracene. *Pub. Health Rep. 54:* 1026-1031, 1939.
42. Tedeschi, C. G. Experimental liposarcoma: characteristics of growth under low and under high caloric intake. *Arch. Path. 47:* 160-174, 1949.
43. Watson, W. L., and McCarthy, W. D. Blood and lymph vessel tumors; report of 1,056 cases. *Surg., Gynec. & Obst. 71:* 569-588, 1940.
44. White, J., and Stewart, H. L. Intestinal adenocarcinoma and intra-abdominal hemangio-endothelioma in mice ingesting methylcholanthrene. *J. Nat. Cancer Inst. 3:* 331-347, 1942.
45. Willis, R. A. *Pathology of Tumors.* St. Louis, Mo., C. V. Mosby Co., 1948, p. 35.

CHAPTER 3

Experimental Cutaneous Carcinoma

Harold L. Stewart

The forerunner of modern studies of carcinogenesis was the important finding of Percival Pott published in *Chirurgical Observations* in 1775 that a particular form of carcinoma of the skin, cancer scroti, occurs in chimney sweeps. He traced this lesion to a specific cause, exposure to soot. Following Pott, a number of English, Scottish, and German physicians published reports which indicated that not only soot but also tar and lubricating oil could cause cutaneous cancer in man. An experimental approach to the problem was not undertaken until 1889, when Hanau attempted to induce malignant skin tumors by tar painting, but he chose the rat as his experimental animal and was unsuccessful. Had he chosen the mouse he might have anticipated the first successful experiment of this type by some twenty-five years. Cazin in 1894 was no more successful because he also chose a resistant animal, the dog. In 1912 Bayon selected a satisfactory animal, the rabbit, but his persistence fell short of the mark and, because the period of observation was too short, he produced only epithelial hyperplasia by tar painting and not carcinoma. However, two years later, in 1914, Yamagiwa and Ichikawa,[44] again using tar as the carcinogen and the rabbit as the experimental animal, induced for the first time cutaneous papillomas and carcinomas after painting for a sufficient period of time. Thus, despite the fact that Percival Pott called attention to the long latent period of scrotal cancer in chimney sweeps, this very obvious clue to the experimental production of cancer was overlooked, and 140 years were allowed to pass before the cause of this lesion, learned from clinical and social observations, was successfully tested experimentally.

INDUCTION OF CARCINOMA

Since 1914, many attempts have been made to obtain an insight into the manner by which cutaneous carcinoma develops. Experimental studies have been carried out in various animals, particularly the mouse and rabbit, using chiefly tar and the more recently discovered carcinogenic polycyclic hydrocarbons. Experimental conditions have varied, depending upon the species or strain of animal used, the carcinogen, the solvent, the concentration of the carcinogen, the frequency and length of the period of application, the size of the skin area exposed, and the method of delivering the agent to the skin.[20]

Perhaps the most frequently employed technic has been the repeated application of a powerful carcinogenic hydrocarbon to the skin of mice. An example of this is the experiment of Cramer and Stowell[10, 11] in which the skin of Swiss mice was painted with 20-methylcholanthrene dissolved in benzene in a concentration of 0.6 per cent applied three times a week by the stroke of a camel's hair brush. At each painting approximately 0.1 mg. of methylcholanthrene was delivered to an area of skin extending from the nape of the neck to the rump. The first tumors began to appear at fourteen weeks, at which time the application was discontinued. Between fourteen and eighteen weeks, the majority, and after twenty-four weeks, all the surviving mice, had malignant neoplasms.

Clinically, the first visible effects of methylcholanthrene applied in this manner are epilation, usually persistent, and hyperemia. Areas of ulceration next appear. Many of these ulcers persist for some time, while others heal. Next in order of appearance is the tumor-like swelling, due chiefly to edema of the dermis. This tumor-like swelling may completely disappear or regress in size to form an isolated small semiglobular warty swelling. This secondary non-neoplastic warty swelling is also due to edema of the dermis, but the overlying epithelium is more hyperplastic than that of its precursor. Papillomas may develop from the non-neoplastic swellings or elsewhere in the painted area, and sometimes regress if painting is discontinued. Carcinomas may appear anywhere in the painted skin in isolated, sharply circumscribed areas, frequently but not necessarily being derived from the base of a pre-existing papilloma (Fig. 24). Two or more carcinomas may be present at the same time sometimes in widely separated parts of the skin. Sarcomas develop only very occasionally.

HISTOGENESIS OF CARCINOMA AFTER A SINGLE PAINTING

The histogenesis of cutaneous cancer may be advantageously studied by applying a single dose of the carcinogen. By this technic, Mider and Morton[36] and Cramer and Stowell[10, 11] have induced squamous cell carcinoma of the skin with 20-methylcholanthrene. The normal epidermis of the mouse consists of two layers of small undifferentiated epithelial cells. The first change effected by the carcinogen is an alteration of the epidermis, which begins to resemble the stratified squamous epidermis of man and shows differentiation into basal cells, spinous cells, and cells of the stratum granulosum and stratum corneum. Glücksmann[16] attributed this epidermal transformation to increased mitotic activity of resting epidermal cells combined with a delay in the onset of differentiation. This reaction of the epidermis is not specific since it may be induced by toxic agents that are noncarcinogenic. By the third or fourth day following a single painting with methylcholanthrene the cells in the center of the painted area are necrotic, leaving a single layer of thin elongated epithelial cells covered by a massive layer of keratin. At the margins of the painted area the epithelium is hyperplastic. The hair follicles in the central and peripheral areas undergo changes corresponding to those observed in the epidermis. In the central area the hair follicles show extensive and severe degeneration while in the periphery they are only partially and temporarily damaged.

By the end of the first week after a single painting with methylcholanthrene, regeneration of the epithelium in the center of the painted area begins from remaining cells of the old epidermis as well as from the cells of hair follicles at the margin of the lesion. The repair of the epithelial defect results in a multilayered well-differentiated keratinized epithelium. At this stage, the small blood vessels and lymphatics of the dermis become dilated, and inflammatory cells including macrophages appear. The damaged sebaceous glands regenerate very slowly. The

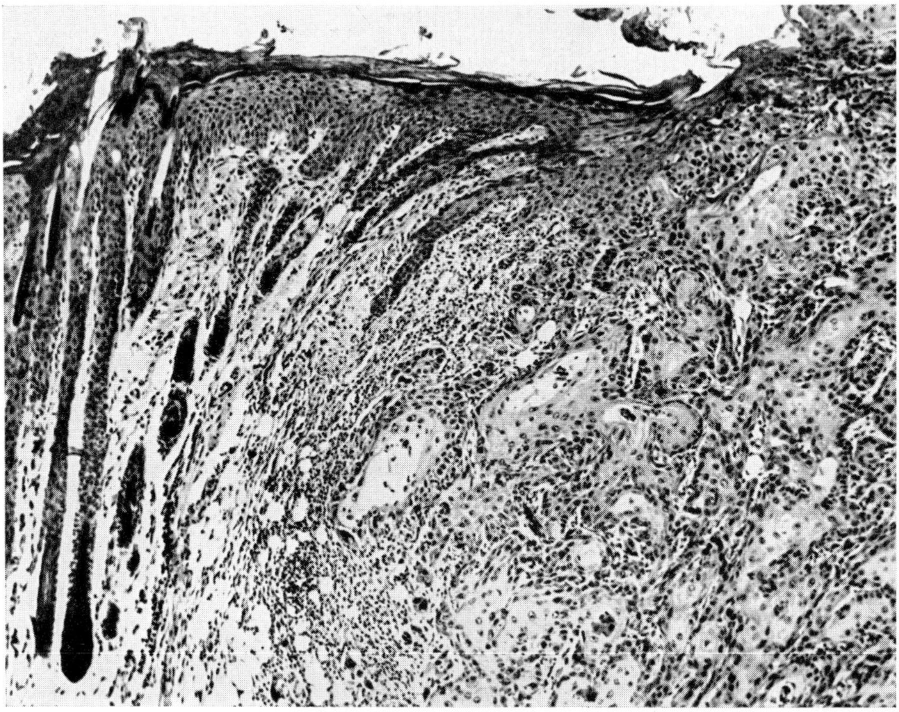

FIG. 24. Squamous carcinoma of skin.

carcinogen, which is apparently retained by the fatty material of the skin appendages, disappears in about four days[1] after the original application.

Regeneration of the epithelium in the central areas is usually completed during the second week. This is accompanied by pronounced mitotic activity in the cells of the bulbs of the hair follicles flanking the central area. Many of these hair follicles, which have increased in length and thickness, resume their normal functional activity of hair formation. In some mice, the reaction stops at this stage and the changes remain more or less stationary. Sections of the skin show a differentiated epidermal epithelium with complete or partial atrophy of the hair follicles in the central area. At the other extreme some animals show progressive changes leading to the development of carcinoma.

The progressive changes leading to carcinoma consist of increased rate of mitotic division, primarily in the epithelial stumps of the transformed hair follicles, and thickening of the epidermis with dislocation and variation in size and shape of the spinous and other types of cells. Broad masses of epithelium may be observed in the dermis, either lying free or attached to the epidermis. Cysts form in the modified hair follicles. A keratin-filled cyst may be open on the surface or be sealed in the dermis. During the third and fourth weeks after a single painting this hyperplastic condition proceeds to: (1) irregularity in the already formed epithelial masses lying in the dermis; and (2) thickening of the epithelial lining of the keratinized cysts—both structures having been derived from the hair follicles. Hyperkeratosis becomes progressively more marked and is roughly proportional to the degree of the epithelial hyperplasia. Swellings, probably not neoplastic in nature, appear in this area and are often covered by hyperplastic epithelium.

Cramer and Stowell[9] hold the view that mitotic activity is not directly stimulated by the carcinogenic hydrocarbons but, on the contrary, that these agents exert a transient toxic effect on the epithelium, inhibiting or suppressing mitotic activity. They believe that the later epithelial proliferation which eventually leads to cancer is due to the formation in the skin of a substance that stimulates epithelial cells to rapid division over a prolonged period of time. They do not postulate the chemical or physical nature of this agent.

Comparison of the effects on the skin of a carcinogenic and a noncarcinogenic injurious agent reveals that the former induces a more irregular arrangement and appearance of the regenerated epithelium. The complex chemical trauma inflicted by a carcinogen requires several days for development, as compared with the changes induced by the noncarcinogenic agent. Epithelial repair following application of a carcinogen depends chiefly upon hyperplasia of the epithelium of the hair follicles, and the regenerative process may result in carcinoma during the long period of repair—while repair of injury due to a noncarcinogenic agent is complete and final. Many authors have emphasized the striking resemblance between the carcinogenic effects of the polycyclic hydrocarbons and those of such physical agents as roentgen and ultraviolet irradiation which actually retard tissue growth, and also induce cancer. These chemical agents, far from being stimulants to tissue growth, actually retard growth for a time during the latent period of carcinogenesis.[15, 18, 19, 27, 28, 39, 42, 43]

HISTOGENESIS OF CARCINOMA FOLLOWING REPEATED PAINTINGS

Mice painted repeatedly with methylcholanthrene show, at first, skin reactions similar to those found after a single application of the carcinogen. During the first week, the epithelium of the epidermis and of the hair follicles in the center of the painted area undergoes degeneration. In the flanking areas the epidermal epithelium becomes thick and more differentiated, and early regeneration is initiated mainly in the hair follicles. Subsequently the changes in some of these mice progress rapidly toward the development of carcinoma. In other mice the skin changes stop in a particular stage during the second week after the process of regeneration is evidently completed. However, if the dose of carcinogen is large enough and is repeated sufficiently often, skin carcinoma develops in all of the animals treated.

Contrary to what might be expected, the changes that occur in the skin after the first painting are not reduplicated and intensified after each subsequent painting. Instead, the regeneration of epithelium in the central area, although delayed, is not prevented. Ulceration does not usually occur. The hyperplasia of the hair follicles in the marginal area proceeds as usual, with the exceptions that they become elongated and broadened to a greater extent and there is more cellular variation and irregularity. Epithelial hyperplasia is more pronounced, more persistent and occurs earlier; there is a greater degree of hyperkeratosis; and the nontumorous swellings are intensified. These are the additive effects of repeated paintings as contrasted with the more simple changes that follow a single painting.

Evidence is often found suggesting retardation of the early epithelial hyperplasia, apparently due to the toxic effects of repeated doses of the carcinogen. After two or three weeks, however, the epithelium appears to develop greater resistance and reacts to subsequent applications with more active epithelial proliferation and with increased mitosis. The early change in the reaction of the epidermal epithelium to a toxic carcinogenic chemical substance is a biologic phenomenon for which an analogy can be found in the work of MacNider,[32, 33, 34, 35] who observed similar changes in the epithelium of the kidney and liver after the administration of uranium salts. However, the subsequent excessive proliferation of the regenerated epithelium without any further intervention is a biologic phenomenon, peculiar to carcinogenesis, for which there is no known analogy in other pathologic processes.[12]

The length of the various phases preceding carcinogenesis varies considerably, depending upon the presence of such lesions as papillomas, keratinized cysts, and ulcers—as well as upon such factors as the individual genetic constitution of the experimental animals. With continued exposure to repeated doses of the carcinogen, foci of neoplastic cells may be recognized in different parts of the painted area. The epithelial lining of the keratinized cysts proliferates further, leading to the development of broad based, heavily keratinized papillomas. The first recognizable malignant transformation of the epithelium begins as a rule in a circumscribed area of the hyperplastic epithelium and not necessarily throughout the whole papilloma. Hence the common statement that a papilloma is necessarily transformed into a carcinoma seems to be misleading. The papillomas with thin stalks are the least likely to give rise to carcinomas and may even regress. A carcinoma may develop anywhere from the hyperplastic epidermis. In some cases such a carcinoma may develop in the immediate neighborhood of a papilloma. The neoplastic foci in mouse skin may appear simultaneously or at short intervals within the treated area and frequently coalesce to form a single large composite tumor. Most carcinomas develop without relation to previous ulceration, which varies considerably throughout the entire period of painting. Some ulcers are apparently due to trauma from scratching, biting, or other factors. Ulceration, of course, frequently accompanies a fully developed carcinoma.

Glücksmann[16] found, in a study of the foci from which skin cancer may arise after repeated application of a carcinogen, that the malignant change occurs in the basal layer among the resting cells, while the more differentiated layers remain at first unaltered. The induction of malignancy is a gradual process, since no clear line of demarcation between malignant cells and their nonmalignant neighbors has been found. Even fairly small foci of malignant dyskeratosis in skin painted with a carcinogen are not usually very sharply outlined. Glücksmann[16] summed up the characteristics of the transformation to a malignant state as consisting of: (1) cellular changes such as increase in volume of cytoplasm, nucleus, and nucleolus; (2) qualitatively and quantitatively abnormal differentiation; and (3) invasive properties. The invasive properties of cells of young malignant foci are considered to be due in part to their high mitotic rate combined with a histolytic capacity and ability to evoke a localized inflammatory reaction. These proliferating cells have the ability to dissolve the basement membrane at the growing tip of the infiltrating focus.

DERMAL CHANGES DURING DEVELOPMENT OF CARCINOMA

Following the repeated application of the carcinogenic hydrocarbon to the skin, the dermal connective tissue and its contained structures exhibit changes in the neighborhood of developing carcinomas, concomitant with the changes in the epidermis and hair follicles. There is hyperemia and progressively increasing telangiectasis of the blood vessels. An inflammatory reaction is regularly present and in part accomplishes removal of detritus from the degenerated epithelial cells. Mast cells appear in larger numbers as the epidermis becomes more hyperplastic. Just prior to the development of cancer, dermal mast cells reach their highest number and thereafter rapidly decline in number. The significance of the mast cells is not clear.

The dermis of the mouse shows no differentiation into two layers of fine and heavily woven bands as occurs in some species of animal. Instead, the entire dermis consists of heavily interwoven coarse bands of highly refractile collagenic fibers. Orr[38] reported that after three weekly applications of methylcholanthrene the superficial parts of the dermis are altered in texture. The coarse collagenic fibers become fine strands and lose their refractility. In some instances only a narrow subepithelial zone of the dermis is affected while in other animals the change extends quite deeply. Orr could not determine whether the phenomenon represents an alteration in the fibrillar texture of pre-existing collagenic fibers, or whether the fine fibrils should be regarded as newly formed. He favored the former hypothesis. Later on, after further treatment with the carcinogen, new collagenic fibers form, which may become abundant and which extend in some places to the subcutaneous tissue, thus resembling scar tissue.

The dermal elastic tissue during the process of epidermal carcinogenesis has been studied by Ma[30] during repeated applications of methylcholanthrene. He found that the number of elastic fibers was increased ten days after the first application of the carcinogen. This increase is progressive until it reaches a maximum at thirty days. After ten days, individual elastic fibers are thickened. Some become rather irregular in girth at about forty days, but in general they retain this diameter to approximately sixty days. From thirty days onward the number of fibers decreases, and at sixty days the elastic tissue is enclosed only within fibrous islands in the dermis, that is otherwise free of elastic fibers.

Foci of melanin-containing cells may develop in the subcutaneous tissue of mice painted repeatedly with tar[29] or with the chemical carcinogen 5,9,10-trimethyl-1,2-benzanthracene (Fig. 25*A*).[5] These foci consist of macrophages acting as melanophores and storing melanotic pigment which is probably formed by the dermal melanoblasts (Fig. 25*B*, *top*). In some inbred and hybrid mice dermal melanoblasts become very hyperplastic after painting with these substances (Fig. 25*B, bottom*). Burgoyne *et al.* also described a malignant melanoma in one of their mice. Berenblum[3] reported induction in a guinea pig of such a tumor, which metastasized to an axillary lymph node following cutaneous application of 9,10-dimethyl-1,2-benzanthracene.

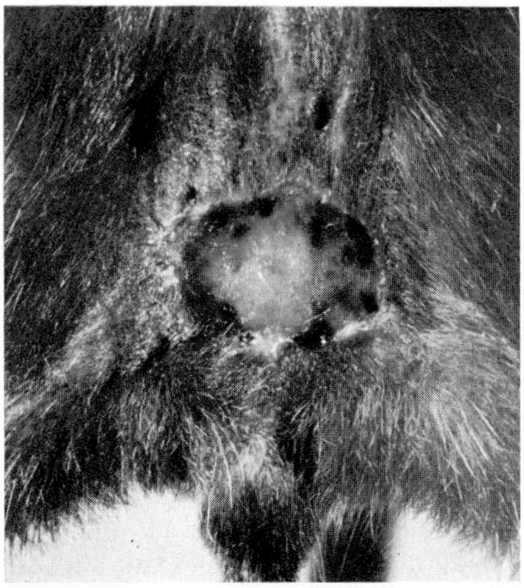

FIG. 25A. Pigment deposits at margin of ulcer in area of skin painted with 5,9,10-trimethyl-1,2-benzanthracene. × 3.

CYTOLOGIC AND CHEMICAL CHANGES ASSOCIATED WITH CARCINOGENESIS

1. CYTOLOGY

Marked cytologic changes occur in the epidermal cells following administration of single or repeated doses of 20-methylcholanthrene by painting. Cowdry[7] separated the epidermis from the dermis of normal mice and of mice during different stages of the development of induced squamous cell carcinoma. He employed a variety of special cytologic methods for studying this tissue composed entirely of epithelial cells. Mitotic figures show no significant numerical alteration at six and twelve hours, but are increased at two days, continue to increase up to sixteen days, and then remain fairly constant at a high level until fifty-one days. The chromosomes are enlarged during the first forty-eight hours and are further increased in size three days after application of the carcinogen. The enlarged chromosomes remain fairly

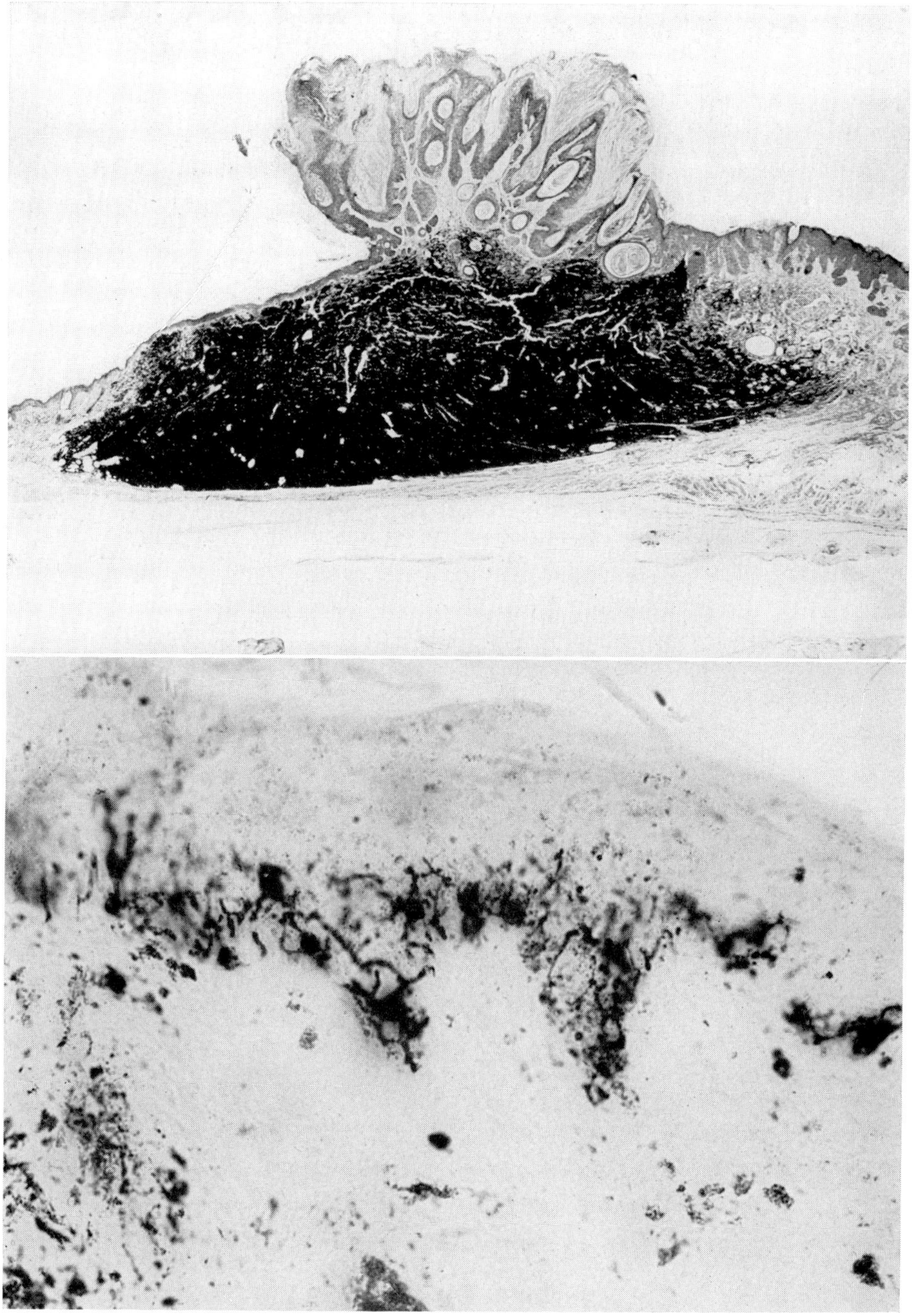

FIG. 25B. *Top,* Papilloma and pigment deposit in skin painted with 5,9,10-trimethyl-1,2-benzanthracene. × 20. *Bottom,* Hyperplastic melanoblasts of skin following repeated applications of 5,9,10-trimethyl-1,2-benzanthracene. × 385.

constant thereafter until the fifty-seventh day, when there is a concomitant pronounced increase in the mitotic index typical of carcinomas.

Thymonucleic acid,[7] measured by the intensity of the color of the Feulgen reaction in sections with an electrophotometer, is decreased in skin at twelve days and twenty-three days after treatment with methylcholanthrene, but is variable in cancerous tissue at later periods. A marked increase in cytoplasmic ribonucleic acid is observed at twelve hours, the maximum being reached from the third to the tenth day, after which the amount of this amino acid drops to an intermediate value by the fifty-seventh day, only to rise again in a fully developed cancer. The alkaline phosphatase activity of the nuclei of basal cells and in the reticular layer of dermis increases considerably on the second and third days. It then decreases as epidermal hyperplasia progresses and hair follicles are destroyed. Finally, it increases greatly to about the same degree in papillomas and in carcinomas.

2. CHEMISTRY

Studies of the chemical alterations during the transformation of mouse epidermis to squamous cell carcinoma have been carried out by Cowdry and associates. The studies, as summarized by Carruthers,[6] have been made on normal epidermis, on epidermis during the process of carcinogenesis, and on the tissue of a transplantable squamous cell carcinoma.

Of the minerals studied, the levels of calcium, iron, copper, and zinc are significantly reduced in the hyperplastic epidermis and in carcinoma. Comparison of these results with those obtained in studies of epidermis rendered hyperplastic by noncarcinogenic agents indicates that the drop in calcium, and perhaps other constituents, may be associated with altered cell types rather than with a change specific for premalignant epidermis. Investigations with radiocalcium suggest an alteration in the calcium-binding complex at the cell surface of the transplantable squamous cell carcinoma. Other studies indicate that the decreased adhesiveness of squamous carcinoma cells, which have a low calcium content, may play a role in metastasis.

The role of the sebaceous glands appears to be important in the response of mice to methylcholanthrene, since the skin of newborn mice in which these structures are rudimentary do not respond to this carcinogen. Furthermore, adult skin treated with this carcinogen loses its sebaceous glands concomitantly with a drop in the content of phospholipid, total lipid, and cholesterol. Repeated application of the carcinogen leaves the epidermal cells without secretions from these glands and in a new chemical environment. In the lipids extractable by alcohol and ether from epidermis undergoing carcinogenesis there is a lipid-like substance which undergoes alteration at the onset of malignancy.

During carcinogenesis the content of pyridoxine, choline, inositol, and *para*-aminobenzoic acid in the epidermis is increased, while the biotin and ascorbic acid levels are not appreciably changed from that in normal epidermis. The rise in the level of choline and inositol may be associated with the increased amount of phospholipid in the tumor.

Mouse epidermis is characterized by a low activity of succinic dehydrogenase, cytochrome oxidase, and apyrase. Of the many constituents studied in late hyperplastic epidermis, cytochrome oxidase is the only enzymatic component that has changed significantly prior to cancer. In the carcinoma, the activity of apyrase, succinic dehydrogenase, and arginase are markedly increased, while the levels of cytochrome oxidase and cytochrome are decreased.

The distribution of twelve amino acids in the epidermis undergoing carcinogenesis is quite similar to that of the hyperplastic epidermis, but the sum of the amino acids in these two stages of carcinogenesis is significantly increased over that of normal epidermis. Hyperplastic epidermis contains larger amounts of free amino acids than normal epidermis, while the carcinoma shows an over-all decrease in these compounds, below the amount in normal epidermis.

In hyperplastic epidermis it has been found that (with but one exception, cytochrome oxidase in late hyperplasia) all the components change abruptly from the normal to the precancerous epidermis and abruptly from the latter to the carcinoma. Since all chemical analysis of hyperplastic epidermis represents pooled samples of large areas of treated epidermis, chemical alterations arising in the few actual premalignant areas are diluted with cells of the former. Until methods become available for localizing the precancerous foci in epidermis or in any other tissue, a study of the chemistry of the intermediate stages in carcinogenesis is virtually impossible. So even in a tissue such as epidermis, in which the experimental conditions for carcinogenesis can be rigidly controlled, assessment of chemical changes due to alterations in cell types from those characteristic of real premalignancy is most difficult. Such conditions must certainly exist to an even greater degree in other organs or tissues where criteria for the premalignant state are even more difficult to establish and to assess.

PATHOGENESIS OF EXPERIMENTAL CARCINOMA

The dermal connective tissue and its structures as well as the epithelium of the epidermis and of the hair follicles exhibit histological changes in the neighborhood of developing carcinomas induced by the carcinogenic hydrocarbons and other cancer-provoking agents such as tar, roentgen rays and ultraviolet irradiation applied to the skin.[2, 13, 14, 16, 17, 21, 23, 24, 25, 26, 38, 40] The relative importance and the interpretation of these various changes are highly speculative.

It has been supposed that the hyperemia due to telangiectatic blood vessels, with their inevitable thrombosis and sporadic occlusion, plays a dominant role in experimental carcinogenesis. The mechanism is considered somewhat comparable to the situation late in life, when the blood vessels show senile degenerative changes at which period, of course, the incidence of cancer is higher than at earlier ages. Moreover, cutaneous cancer in x-ray workers usually arises in an atrophic scar showing telangiectatic vessels. This blood vessel theory, however, is somewhat weakened by the rarity of cancer at sites of hemangioma, keratoangioma, and telangiectatic foci in erythremia. In patients suffering from such disorders, a high incidence of neoplasms should be expected were the vascular change the chief inciting factor. Furthermore, no statistical correlation has been shown to exist between senile vascular changes and the occurrence of spontaneous cancer at different sites in man and animals.

Others emphasize the degenerative changes in the connective tissue stroma and their correlation with degeneration of collagenic fibers in the skin. Such changes virtually always precede the development of epitheliomas in sailors and ranchers exposed excessively to intense sunlight. Experimental skin carcinoma, induced by methylcholanthrene, also is frequently associated with fibrinoid degeneration of collagen. Fibrinoid degeneration of collagen is found in a number of diseases of man of the visceral angiitides type, such as disseminated lupus erythematosus, rheumatic fever, and periarteritis. No relationship has been established between these diseases and cancer, except for the lesion of discoid lupus in the skin which may give rise to epithelioma. From this it would appear either that fibrinoid degeneration is not the sole important factor in carcinogenesis or that its potentialities vary in different disease conditions.

Still other observers postulate a constitutional factor as important in experimental and spontaneous carcinogenesis. This they consider to be possibly hormonal. They cite as examples the influence of sex on the incidence of different tumors, the stimulating influence of testosterone on prostatic carcinoma, and the etiologic effect of diethylstilbestrol on experimental breast cancer and interstitial cell tumors of the testis of the mouse.

Perhaps the most widely held theory is that the mechanism of cutaneous carcinogenesis resides in the epithelium and that the neoplastic change is an irreversible phenomenon, possibly a mutation, involving a single cell and attributable to a direct effect of the carcinogen. In the case of experimentally induced cancer of the skin, the areas painted with a carcinogen, in which carcinoma is arising, exhibit concomitant changes involving the epithelium and the stroma of the connective tissue with its fibroblasts, collagenic fibers, reticulum, elastic fibers, blood vessels, and nerves. Moreover, the three-dimensional expanse of epidermis involved even in the earliest and smallest focus of early carcinoma is of such magnitude and shows such varied cell changes as to throw doubt on the hypothesis that the mechanism of carcinogenesis resides in a single epithelial cell. Orr's[38] findings, while not denying the importance of the proliferative changes in the epithelium, point to the possible influence of vascular and other changes in the subepithelial tissue. In his experiments invasive carcinoma appeared to develop most often in relation to areas of damaged elastic tissue and dermal scars. In summary, it may be said that the large body of morphologic observations in the field of experimental carcinoma of the skin emphasizes the complexity and the evolutionary nature of the process of experimental neoplasia and makes it difficult to assess the value of each change in itself or in its relation to other morphologic changes.

CUTANEOUS PRECANCEROUS LESIONS IN MAN

In clinical medicine, the term precancer or precancerous dermatosis has been used to designate a group of cutaneous conditions which are early cancers or cancers with limited infiltration or which are followed more or less consistently by cancer. A partial list of these conditions includes: (1) farmer's or sailor's skin; (2) keratoses (arsenical, senile, occupational—due to tar, pitch, oil, etc.); (3) xeroderma pigmentosum; (4) Bowen's disease; (5) radiodermatitis; (6) erythroplasia; (7) kraurosis vulvae; (8) lupus erythematosus; (9) lupus vulgaris; (10) cornu cutaneum; (11) cicatrix; (12) sebaceous cyst; (13) syphilitic scars; (14) long-standing ulcers. The pathologic, cytologic, and cytochemical features of the precancerous dermatoses and carcinoma *in situ* in man are described in the publications of Bloch,[4] Montgomery,[37] Mackee and Cipollaro,[31] Willis,[41] Hueper,[22] and Cowdry and Andrew.[8]

Some of these conditions, as for example erythroplasia and the rare disease xeroderma pigmentosum, are almost always followed by cancer sooner or later. Others, such as senile keratoses, radiation injuries, and burns, frequently give rise to cancer. In still other conditions carcinoma occurs only occasionally, as for example, in the areas of dermatitis associated with varicose ulcers and in draining sinuses in osteomyelitis. Whether cutaneous cancer can ever develop in normal tissue or whether every malignant tumor is preceded by some abnormality has not been definitely established. However, the fact remains that in man carcinoma is regularly preceded by a lesion which, while it cannot be called cancer or even always precancer, from the standpoint of pathology, yet provides a favorable soil for neoplastic development.

During the last three decades our knowledge of the development of the early stages of cutaneous cancer in man has advanced rapidly. This has been due particularly to pathologic studies of surgically excised suspicious lesions of the skin and to studies of occupational skin cancer. The long prevalent view that each tumor has a simple unicentric origin, arising at a single point of time, from a small focus of cells, and that it enlarges only by multiplication of these cells and their descendants, has been attacked by Willis.[41] This unicentric view is based on Cohnheim's hypothesis of embryonic rests, which precludes the possibility of precancerous changes in neighboring adult tissues. Although Cohnheim's hypothesis of the origin of tumors from superfluous embryonic cells has been abandoned by most modern pathologists, his concept of restricted unicentric origin and purely intrinsic growth has largely persisted. As stated in the foregoing, most of the experimental studies of carcinoma induced in animals by painting with tar and the carcinogenic hydrocarbons have tended to indicate the multicentric origin of cancer under these conditions. In man, more and more studies are appearing in the literature which substantiate this view: namely, that the unicentric origin of cancer is incorrect and that instead, tumors arise from small or large fields of tissue and increase not only by cellular proliferation but also by progressive neoplastic conversion of tissue within those fields.

In many cases the extent of the potentially neoplastic field is much greater than the small size of the initially appearing tumor would appear to indicate. This is evidenced not only by finding multiple precancerous foci in surgically excised specimens of the skin but also in the new development of cancer adjacent to areas where cancer has been surgically excised under conditions where the incision has been too limited to include all the potentially malignant area. Indeed the multicentric foci of early cancer in a field in which cancer is developing contributes to the enlargement of the growth both by coalescence of adjacent neoplastic foci and by the continuous development of new neoplastic foci at the margin of the cancer. Willis[41] states that in cases of multiple squamous cell carcinoma of the face and neck in fair-skinned people with numerous keratoses due to long exposure to sunlight, all the epidermis of exposed areas is potentially cancerous and the multiple tumors which actually develop merely denote the foci of maximal cancer potential in these areas. The extreme example of this is seen in the disease entity xeroderma pigmentosum in which numerous carcinomas develop in areas of the skin exposed to light. Less striking but equally pertinent are the many skin cancers arising in association with scars or chronic ulcers or draining sinuses where the origin is not unifocal but multiple over wide areas. Multiple foci of early cancer are also seen in areas of Bowen's disease, in vulval leukoplakia, and in erythroplasia. In the spreading type of rodent ulcer, the main tumor mass is continuously reinforced by the coalescence of exactly similar but smaller early foci in the neighborhood of the main bulk of the tumor.

BIBLIOGRAPHY

1. Beck, S., and Peacock, P. R. The latent carcinogenic action of 3,4-benzpyrene; results of intermittent applications to the skin of mice. *Brit. J. Exper. Path. 21:* 227-230, 1940.
2. Berenblum, I. The mechanism of carcinogenesis. Irritation and carcinogenesis. *Arch. Path. 38:* 233-244, 1944.
3. Berenblum, I. The carcinogenic action of 9,10-dimethyl-1,2-benzanthracene on the skin and subcutaneous tissues of the mouse, rabbit, rat, and guinea pig. *J. Nat. Cancer Inst. 10:* 167-174, 1949.
4. Bloch, B. Cancers and precancerous affections from the dermatological viewpoint. *Cancer Rev. 7:* 65-98, 1932.
5. Burgoyne, F. H., Heston, W. E., Hartwell, J. L., and Stewart, H. L. Cutaneous melanin production in mice following application of the carcinogen 5,9,10-trimethyl-1,2-benzanthracene. *J. Nat. Cancer Inst. 10:* 665-688, 1949.
6. Carruthers, C. Chemical studies on the transformation of mouse epidermis to squamous-cell carcinoma: A review. *Cancer Research 10:* 255-265, 1950.
7. Cowdry, E. V. Properties of squamous cell cancer compared with those of normal epidermis. *Pontificiae Academiae Scientiarum Scripta Varia 7:* 173-191, 1949; Semaine d'Etude sur le Problème Biologique du Cancer.
8. Cowdry, E. V., and Andrew, W. Some cytochemical and cytologic features of senile keratosis. *J. Gerontol. 5:* 97-111, 1950.
9. Cramer, W., and Stowell, R. E. Carcinogenesis in the mouse's skin by the infrequent application at long intervals of methylcholanthrene. *Cancer Research 1:* 849-852, 1941.
10. Cramer, W., and Stowell, R. E. The early stages of carcinogenesis by 20-methylcholanthrene in the skin of the mouse: I. Experimental technique and macroscopic changes. *J. Nat. Cancer Inst. 2:* 369-378, 1942.
11. Cramer, W., and Stowell, R. E. The early stages of carcinogenesis by 20-methylcholanthrene in the skin of the mouse: II. Microscopic tissue changes. *J. Nat. Cancer Inst. 2:* 379-402, 1942.
12. Cramer, W., and Stowell, R. E. Skin carcinogenesis by a single application of 20-methylcholanthrene. *Cancer Research 3:* 36-42, 1943.
13. Deelman, H. T. Das Präcarcinom. *Ztschr. f. Krebsforsch. 29:* 307-319, 1929.
14. Doderlein, G. Der Teerkrebs der weissen Maus. (Tar cancer of white mouse; experimental study.) *Ztschr. f. Krebsforsch. 23:* 241-339, 1926.

15. EARLE, W. R., and VOEGTLIN, C. A further study of the mode of action of methylcholanthrene on normal tissue cultures. *Pub. Health Rep. 55:* 303-322, 1940.

16. GLÜCKSMANN, A. The histogenesis of benzpyrene-induced epidermal tumors in the mouse. *Cancer Research 5:* 385-400, 1945.

17. GULDBERG, G. Experimental researches on precancerous changes in the skin and skin cancer; investigation of local action of tar on skin and its different elements. *Acta path. et microbiol. Scandinav.* (supp. 8) pp. 1-223, 1931.

18. HADDOW, A., and ROBINSON, A. M. The influence of various polycyclic hydrocarbons on the growth rate of transplantable tumours. *Proc. Roy. Soc., London,* s. B, *122:* 442-476, 1937.

19. HADDOW, A., and ROBINSON, A. M. The association of carcinogenicity and growth-inhibitory power in the polycyclic hydrocarbons and other substances. *Proc. Roy. Soc., London,* s. B, *127:* 277-287, 1939.

20. HARTWELL, J. L. *Survey of Compounds which have been Tested for Carcinogenic Activity.* U. S. Public Health Service Publication No. 149. Washington, D.C., U. S. Government Printing Office, 1951.

21. HOWES, E. L. Carcinogens and regeneration patterns after injury. *Cancer Research 6:* 298-310, 1946.

22. HUEPER, W. C. *Occupational Tumors.* Springfield, Ill., C. C Thomas, 1942, pp. 31-307.

23. KREYBERG, L. On local alterations of the blood-vessels of tar-painted white mice. *Norsk. mag. f. lægevidensk 88:* 1101-1107, 1927; *Brit. J. Exper. Path. 8:* 465-470, 1927.

24. KREYBERG, L. Lakale karforandringer fremkaldt ved tjaerepensling av huden hos hvite mus. *Norsk mag. f. lægevidensk. 11-12:* 956-1010, 1927. Abstr. in *Index analyt. cancerol. 2:* 23, 1928.

25. KREYBERG, L. Die Rolle der Blutgefässe in der Genese der Teertumoren. *Ztschr. f. Krebsforsch. 26:* 191-193, 1928.

26. KREYBERG, L. Über präcanceröse Gefässveränderungen. *Virchows Arch. f. path. Anat. 273:* 367-440, 1929.

27. LEES, J. C. The inhibition of growth by 1,2,5,6-dibenzanthracene and other agents. *Quart. J. Exper. Physiol. 27:* 161-170, 1937.

28. LEES, J. C., and ROBSON, J. M. The action of 1,2,5,6-dibenzanthracene on the metabolism of rats. *Quart. J. Exper. Physiol. 27:* 171-180, 1937.

29. LIPSCHÜTZ, B. Untersuchungen über experimentelle Pigmenterzeugung durch Teerpinselung von Mäusen. (Pigment production in mouse tar cancer.) *Arch. f. Dermat. u. Syph. 147:* 161-176, 1924.

30. MA, C. K. Morphological and chemical investigation of dermal elastic and collagenic tissue during epidermal carcinogenesis. *Cancer Research 9:* 481-487, 1949.

31. MACKEE, G. M., and CIPOLLARO, A. C. *Cutaneous Cancer and Precancer. A Practical Monograph.* New York, Am. J. Cancer, 1937.

32. MACNIDER, W. DE B. A study of the acquired resistance of fixed tissue cells morphologically altered through processes of repair. Liver injury induced by uranium nitrate. Consideration of type of epithelial repair which imparts to liver resistance against subsequent uranium intoxications. *J. Pharmacol. & Exper. Therap. 56:* 359-372, 1936.

33. MacNider, W. de B. A study of the acquired resistance of fixed tissue cells morphologically altered through processes of repair. Resistance of liver epithelium altered morphologically as a result of injury from uranium, followed by repair, to hepatoxic action of chloroform. *J. Pharmacol. & Exper. Therap. 56:* 373-381, 1936.

34. MacNider, W. de B. A study of the acquired resistance of fixed tissue cells morphologically altered through processes of repair. Resistance to chloroform of naturally acquired atypical type of liver epithelium occurring in senile animals. *J. Pharmacol. & Exper. Therap. 56:* 383-387, 1936.

35. MacNider, W. de B. A study of the acquired resistance of fixed tissue cells morphologically altered through processes of repair. Concerning the persistence of acquired type of atypical liver cell with observations on the resistance of such cells to the toxic action of chloroform. *J. Pharmacol. & Exper. Therap. 59:* 393-400, 1937.

36. Mider, G. B., and Morton, J. J. Skin tumors following a single application of methylcholanthrene in C57 Brown mice. *Am. J. Path. 15:* 299-302, 1939.

37. Montgomery, H. Precancerous dermatosis and epithelioma in situ. *Arch. Dermat. & Syph. 39:* 387-408, 1939.

38. Orr, J. W. The changes antecedent to tumour formation during the treatment of mouse skin with carcinogenic hydrocarbons. *J. Path. & Bact. 46:* 495-515, 1938.

39. Pullinger, B. D. The first effects on mouse skin of some polycyclic hydrocarbons. *J. Path. & Bact. 50:* 463-471, 1940.

40. Stewart, H. L., and Lorenz, E. Histopathology of induced precancerous lesions of the small intestine of mice. *J. Nat. Cancer Inst. 7:* 239-268, 1947.

41. Willis, R. A. *The Pathology of Tumors.* St. Louis, Mo., C. V. Mosby Co., 1948, pp. 106-125.

42. Wolbach, S. B. The latent period in experimental carcinogenesis. *Arch. Path. 22:* 279, 1936.

43. Wolbach, S. B. Responses to carcinogenic chemicals antecedent to tumor formation. *Am. J. Path. 13:* 662-663, 1937.

44. Yamagiwa, K., and Ichikawa, K. Über die atypische Epithelwucherung. *Verhandl. Jap. Path. Ges. 4:* 136, 1914.

CHAPTER 4

Experimental Tumors of Bone

Harold L. Stewart

SPONTANEOUS TUMORS

Spontaneous osteogenic sarcoma in mice of different strains is relatively rare[3, 4, 7, 20, 22, 25], with one exception. Pybus and Miller[25] reported a high incidence of this neoplasm in a strain of mouse derived principally from Simpson stock. During five years of observation, more than 300 osteogenic sarcomas were found in these mice. In recent years, however, bone tumors have failed to appear in the mice of this stock in England and the animals reimported into this country never did exhibit any bone tumors. With respect to sarcomas of bone that sporadically arise in mice, their bone-producing characteristics are usually lost on transplantation. A bone sarcoma which arose in a C3H mouse, and which was carried through eighteen transplant generations,[20] showed malignant osteoblasts, osteoid tissue, and bone formation and a high alkaline phosphatase activity in the primary growth, in the early subcutaneous transplants, and in the pulmonary metastases therefrom. Later generations (sixth or seventh) exhibited an increased growth rate, early metastases to the regional lymph nodes and lungs, but an inhibition or loss of alkaline phosphatase activity and of the capacity for forming osteoid tissue. A similar tumor arising in the same strain of mouse has been carried through eighteen transplant generations by Eyestone.[11] This tumor has followed essentially the same course as that reported by Barrett *et al.*[3] The Wagnar osteogenic sarcoma[17] which had bony areas scattered through the primary tumor has now lost this characteristic but has, however, retained its high alkaline phosphatase activity. Attempts have failed to reconvert these spindle-cell tumor transplants to their original histologic pattern.

ROENTGEN-RAY RADIATION, RADIUM, AND RADIOACTIVE ELEMENTS

The earliest reports of the deliberate induction of osteogenic sarcoma in irradiated bones are from animal experiments done about 1910. Inadvertent induction of this tumor in human beings resulted from clinical and industrial accidents[15, 21, 24,] such as happened: (1) to radium dial workers ingesting radium; (2) to patients receiving therapeutic injections of radium into tuberculous joints; and (3) to patients with neoplastic diseases other than bone tumors treated with roentgen irradiation, in whom parts of the skeletal system were included within the irradiated field. The literature on the experimental induction of tumors in animals treated with radium salts was reviewed by Uehlinger[28] and Uehlinger and Schürch.[29] They reported their own experience with mesothorium incorporated in Vaseline pellets and injected in a dose of 0.005 mg. into the marrow cavity of the femur of rabbits. Of 21 animals so treated, 15 developed sarcoma of the femur after a latent period of eighteen months. The tumors were classified as osteogenic sarcoma, periosteal fibrosarcoma, and in one case Ewing's tumor. The tumors metastasized to the lung, bone, and other organs.

The induction of experimental bone tumors in animals has not been accomplished with such low concentration of radium as has resulted in osteogenic sarcoma in man, probably because the life span of the animal is shorter. However, tumors can be induced rapidly with the more recently available radioactive elements. The animals most widely used for such experiments are rats, mice, rabbits, and dogs. A large number of isotopes tend to localize in bone, namely, phosphorus, calcium, strontium, barium, some of the rare earths, and some of the heavier rare earths such as plutonium.[24] Animals of different species react similarly to radioelements. The localization of the resultant tumors depends upon the distribution of the agent. The majority of the tumors arising after treatment with strontium occurs in the extremities, and after plutonium in the axial skeleton. The latent period between the dose of radioelement and the appearance of tumor may be as short as three months. With strontium, for example, the latent period decreases as the dose is increased, and conversely the latent period is prolonged with lower doses. However, this is not a linear function. At the highest dose, all of the animals develop tumors, but with decreasing doses fewer tumors appear. Both alpha and beta emitters have been noted to act qualitatively the same in mice. The types of tumor produced in order of frequency are osteogenic sarcoma, fibrosarcoma, hemangioendothelioma, and rarely liposarcoma. Brues[24] induced chondrosarcoma and reticulum-cell sarcoma in animals. Multiple bone tumors appear in animals that have a high probability of tumor development. Continued repetition of the dose of the radioelement yields increasing numbers of tumors.

CARCINOGENIC HYDROCARBONS

The experimental induction of malignant bone tumors has been reported following the injection of the carcinogenic hydrocarbons into the bone marrow of the mouse and the rat. However, the yield of tumors induced by these agents is not large and the field has not been extensively explored.[5, 6, 12] Fibrosarcoma and occasionally osteogenic sarcoma have been described. Levy and Ring[19] induced sarcoma of the jaw of the hamster by 9,10-dimethyl-1,2-benzanthracene. The carcinogen in the form of crystals or pellets was implanted into the mandible or in the subgingival tissue in contact with the mandible. Tumors obtained in 16 of 20 animals were all fibrosarcomas with one exception, which was classified as a rhabdomyosarcoma.

BERYLLIUM

The important discovery in 1946 that certain beryllium-containing powders administered to the rabbit lead to the development of osteogenic sarcoma was reported by Gardner and Heslington.[13] This has been confirmed by several workers.[8, 10, 23, 2, 14] Both rats and guinea pigs have been tested, but to date the rabbit is apparently the only species susceptible to the carcinogenic action of beryllium.* Moreover, only the insoluble salts of beryllium have produced tumors. In the study by Barnes *et al.*,[2] 7 of 21 rabbits that survived the injection of beryllium silicate for thirty weeks or more developed sarcoma, the earliest tumor appearing at thirty-two weeks. Hoagland *et al.*[14] injected a finely ground powder consisting of insoluble beryllium compounds, beryllium oxide, beryllium phosphate, and a zinc-beryllium-silicate mixture, intravenously into 24 rabbits so as to administer a total dose of approximately 1 Gm. of the powder per animal. Seven animals developed osteogenic sarcoma in from eleven to twenty-four months.

The first sign of disease is a precipitous drop in body weight accompanied by marked crippling and trophic changes in the skin of the affected extremity. The tumors are highly malignant, grow rapidly, and metastasize. Dutra and Largent[10] succeeded in transplanting one growth into the eye of a guinea pig. Coincident with the development and enlargement of the local bone tumor, the serum alkaline phosphatase activity rises rapidly and roughly parallels the spread of the tumor throughout the body. It is of great theoretical interest that an extremely malignant sarcoma can be produced by a simple metal oxide. This is especially significant because of the known effects of beryllium on certain enzyme systems. In this connection several points deserve emphasis: (1) the abnormality in endochondral calcification in experimentally produced so-called "beryllium rickets," [16] which cannot be prevented or cured in rats ingesting beryllium phosphate even though the serum organic phosphate is maintained at normal levels by administration of vitamin D;[30] (2) imperfect *in vitro* calcification of cartilage of rats fed beryllium, when incubated in solutions containing adequate concentrations of calcium and inorganic phosphate;[27] (3) inhibition of alkaline phosphatase by beryllium in low concentration which is more selective in this respect than any other chemical or physical agent yet employed including cyanide and formaldehyde.[18] For a more complete discussion of this important problem, the reader is referred to the original publications.

PATHOLOGY

The malignant bone tumors induced by beryllium are of particular interest because of their similarity to the sarcomas that develop spontaneously in man. Among the experimental tumors, some show extensive sclerosis and bone formation, others cartilaginous differentiation, while a few consist of extremely anaplastic growths which possess osteolytic propensities. Indeed, just as in their human counterparts, the experimental tumors not unusually exhibit all these different

* Vorwald has recently reported the induction of pulmonary neoplasms in rats treated with beryllium salts. (Vorwald, A. J. "Pulmonary cancer in experimental exposures to beryllium." In *Seventh Saranac Symposium.* The Saranac Laboratory, Saranac Lake, N. Y., Sept. 22-26, 1952.)

structural patterns within a single lesion. On gross examination the tumor often cuts with difficulty, imparting a gritty sensation, whereas others, devoid of bone, cut with ease. Areas of hemorrhage and necrosis are frequent. The tumors are highly invasive, so that the shaft of the bone is sometimes completely destroyed. Locally, the tumors not only distend the marrow cavity and destroy the overlying bone but appear beneath the periosteum, forming an expanding lesion that invades the surrounding muscle. Very little cellular or fibrous reaction to the tumor occurs in the surrounding tissues. The cellular picture is that of osteogenic sarcoma varying from extreme anaplasia to a well-differentiated bone-forming tumor but almost always with some evidence of bone matrix formation. The cells, and particularly their nuclei, vary in size, shape, and staining with numerous multinucleated tumor giant cells and with many mitotic figures. The tumor tissue is rich in alkaline phosphatase. The blood vessels are invaded early and the tumor may metastasize widely. In general, the metastatic deposits are less differentiated than the primary tumor. The secondary pulmonary deposits are likely to be confined within blood vessels. In addition to metastasizing via the blood stream, local lymph-node deposits are found in approximately 50 per cent of animals with primary tumors. Not only are the lungs and regional lymph nodes involved, but secondary deposits may also be found in the liver, peritoneum and pleura.

HISTOGENESIS

Barnes, Denz and Sissons[2] studied the tissue reaction to the deposits of particulate material following the intravenous injection of zinc beryllium silicate (Zn_2SiO_4 and Be_2SiO_4) into rabbits.

The particles of zinc silicate seen in the tissues differ in appearance from those of beryllium silicate in being rounded, less angular, less refractile, and tending to form aggregates. The beryllium silicate particles are at first scattered but later become aggregated within macrophages and giant cells. In the lung there is generally an increase in fibrous tissue leading to thickening of the alveolar septa within three months. The fibrosis is diffuse and not directly associated with the deposits containing silicate. In the red pulp of the spleen the beryllium silicate particles are phagocytosed by macrophages which form foreign-body giant cells consisting of large syncytial objects loaded with particulate matter and containing up to 100 nuclei in a single section. Coincident with this, there is cellular depletion of the organ, atrophy, and fibrosis. In the liver the Kupffer cells ingest the particles and by three or four months increase in size and number to form cellular foci, which although filling and distending the sinusoids cause little or no fibrosis.

The earliest changes in the bone marrow resemble those in the liver and spleen. On gross inspection of the sectioned bone, numerous nodules are scattered throughout the marrow of all parts of the skeletal system. Histologically the nodules consist of aggregates of macrophages containing engulfed granules of the injected material. This is soon followed by replacement of the marrow elements by fibrous tissue in which there is an extensive development of bone trabeculae. In some of the lesions stages of transition between fibrous tissue, developing bone trabeculae, and malignant bone-forming tumor tissue may be present in the same lesion, indicating a continuing process in the development of frankly malignant tissue. Intermediate cellular forms can be traced between the osteoblastic cells lining the trabecular bone of the marrow cavity and the spindle-shaped cells which form the bulk of the fibrous tissue surrounding the deposits of beryllium. Various intermediate stages are also noted between fibroblasts that appear normal and those that are actively proliferating and have assumed malignant cytologic characteristics. The varying histologic pattern in the marrow is reflected in the radiographic appearance of the lesion clinically and at autopsy. Areas of neoplastic bone formation and of calcification in cartilage can both be seen. The tumors may occur in one or more of the long bones or in flat bones as in vertebrae, scapula and pelvis. While the fully developed tumors present a very different appearance from the medullary bone formation that occurs early, various stages of transition between the two can be traced. The neoplastic process secondarily works its way from the medullary cavity through the bone into the surrounding soft tissues.

MECHANISM OF CARCINOGENESIS

Barnes *et al.*[2] compared the tissue reactions produced by zinc silicate, a non-carcinogen, and beryllium silicate, a carcinogen. The early lesions produced by these respective substances were indistinguishable by the usual histologic methods. However, the presence of the beryllium within the marrow nodule is in some way responsible for the progressive changes that result in malignancy. Although beryllium silicates are considered to be insoluble even in strong acids, the observations following intradermal injection into the rabbit indicate that beryllium is liberated from the particles and diffuses into the surrounding tissues where it can be identified histochemically.[9] Experience with the behavior of both soluble and insoluble beryllium compounds leads to the conclusion that its toxic action is exerted locally at the site of inoculation or deposition.[1] It is furthermore probable that the beryllium, which is assumed to be directly responsible for the tumors, is liberated locally in the marrow rather than from more distant deposits in spleen, lung, and liver. The fact that beryllium is the responsible agent has been shown by Barnes[1] following injection of a suspension of beryllium metal particles into two rabbits which developed characteristic sarcomas. The possibility that the silicate may play some part in the development of the tumors is excluded by the fact that Gardner and Heslington[13] produced tumors with beryllium oxide. It is apparent that in the development of the neoplastic process the marrow tissue itself must contribute a factor. Similar nodules of the metal in the liver and lungs excite very little fibrous tissue reaction as compared with bone marrow, while in the spleen fibrosis and atrophy may go to extreme degrees without showing evidence of malignant change.

OTHER METALS

The positive results obtained in the production of bone tumors by beryllium suggest the testing of other metals for carcinogenic properties in bone tissue. This is particularly important in view of the work of Schinz and Uehlinger[26] who obtained bone sarcomas in rabbits with chromium and cobalt following a latent period of almost six years. Although it is doubtful that in young people bone tumors are due to such substances, in elderly individuals, where there has been time for long exposure and a long latent period, metals may indeed play an etiologic role.

BIBLIOGRAPHY

1. Barnes, J. M. Experimental production of malignant tumours by beryllium. *Lancet 1:* 463, 1950.
2. Barnes, J. M., Denz, F. A., and Sissons, H. A. Beryllium bone sarcomata in rabbits. *Brit. J. Cancer 4:* 212-222, 1950.
3. Barrett, M. K., Dalton, A. J., Edwards, J. E., Greenstein, J. P., and Briggs, J. C. A transplantable osteogenic sarcoma originating in a C3H mouse. *J. Nat. Cancer Inst. 4:* 389-402, 1944.
4. Bashford, E. F. The behavior of tumor cells during propagation. Imperial Cancer Research Fund, *Fourth Scientific Report* (Great Britain), pp. 131-214, 1911.
5. Brunschwig, A. Production of primary bone tumors (fibrosarcoma of bone) by intramedullary injection of methylcholanthrene. *Am. J. Cancer 34:* 540-542, 1938.
6. Brunschwig, A., and Bissell, A. D. Production of osteosarcoma in a mouse by the intramedullary injection of 1,2-benzpyrene. *Arch. Surg. 36:* 53-60, 1938.
7. Brunschwig, A., and Harmon, P. H. Studies in bone sarcoma. I. Malignant osteoblastomata as evidence for the existence of true osteoblasts. *Surg., Gynec. & Obst. 57:* 711-718, 1933.
8. Cloudman, A. M., Vining, D., Barkulis, S., and Nickson, J. J. Bone changes observed following intravenous injections of beryllium (abstract). *Am. J. Path. 25:* 810-811, 1949.
9. Denz, F. A. The histochemical detection of beryllium. *Quart. J. Microscop. Sci. 90:* 317-322, 1949.
10. Dutra, F. R., and Largent, E. J. Osteosarcoma induced by beryllium oxide. *Am. J. Path. 26:* 197-209, 1950.
11. Eyestone, W. H. (Personal communication)
12. Franseen, C. C., Aub, J. C., and Simpson, C. L. The experimental production of fibrosarcomas of bone. *Cancer Research 1:* 393-396, 1941.
13. Gardner, L. U., and Heslington, H. F. Osteosarcoma from intravenous beryllium compounds in rabbits. *Federation Proc. 5:* 221, 1946.
14. Hoagland, M. B., Grier, R. S., and Hood, M. B. Beryllium and growth: I. Beryllium-induced osteogenic sarcomata. *Cancer Research 10:* 629-635, 1950.
15. Hueper, W. C. Occupational Tumors and Allied Diseases. Springfield, Ill., C. C Thomas, 1942, chap. 7.
16. Jacobson, S. A. Bone lesions in rats produced by the substitution of beryllium for calcium in the diet. *Arch. Path. 15:* 18-26, 1933.
17. Karnofsky, D. A., Parisette, L. M., Patterson, P. A., and Jacquez, J. A. The behavior and growth of homologous and heterologous normal and neoplastic tissues in the chick embryo: and the influence of various agents on tumor growth. *Unio Internationalis Contra Cancrum, Acta 6:* 641-651, 1949, Fig. 4.
18. Klemperer, F. W., Miller, J. M., and Hill, C. J. Inhibition of alkaline phosphatase by beryllium. *J. Biol. Chem. 180:* 281-288, 1949.

19. LEVY, B., and RING, J. R. The experimental production of jaw tumors in hamsters. *Oral Surg., Oral Med., & Oral Path. 3:* 262-271, 1950.
20. LIPPINCOTT, S. W., EDWARDS, J. E., GRADY, H. G., STEWART, H. L. A review of some spontaneous neoplasms in mice. *J. Nat. Cancer Inst. 3:* 199-210, 1942.
21. MARTLAND, H. S. The occurrence of malignancy in radioactive persons; general review of data gathered in study of radium dial painters, with special reference to the occurrence of osteogenic sarcoma and interrelationship of certain blood diseases. *Am. J. Cancer 15:* 2435-2516, 1931.
22. MURRAY, J. A. Spontaneous cancer in the mouse; histology, metastasis, transplantability and the relations of malignant new growth to spontaneous affected animals. Imperial Cancer Research Fund (Great Britain), *Third Scientific Report,* pp. 69-114, 1908.
23. NASH, P. Experimental production of malignant tumours by beryllium. *Lancet 1:* 519, 1950.
24. *Panel on Bone Tumors.* Proceedings of the First National Cancer Conference, 1949; Published by the American Cancer Society, New York, pp. 217-227.
25. PYBUS, F. C., and MILLER, E. W. The gross pathology of spontaneous bone tumors in mice. *Am. J. Cancer 40:* 47-53, 1940.
26. SCHINZ, H. R., and UEHLINGER, E. Der Metallkrebs: Ein neues Prinzip der Krebserzeugung. *Ztschr. f. Krebsforsch. 52:* 425-437, 1942.
27. SOBEL, A. E. The local factor in calcification. *Trans. Second Conference on Metabolic Interrelations,* 1950; Published by Josiah Macy, Jr. Foundation, New York, pp. 113-143.
28. UEHLINGER, E. Experimentelle Geschwulsterzeugung mit radioaktiven Substanzen. *Schweiz. Ztschr. f. allg. Path. u. Bakt. 1:* 444-462, 1938.
29. UEHLINGER, E., and SCHÜRCH, O. Uber experimentelle Erzeugung von Sarkomen mit Radium und Mesothorium. *Deutsche Ztschr. f. Chir. 251:* 12-33, 1938.
30. YÜ, T. F., and GUTMAN, ALEXANDER B. Effect of beryllium on *in vitro* calcification of cartilage. *Proc. Soc. Exper. Biol. & Med. 75:* 481-484, 1950.

CHAPTER 5

Experimental Brain Tumors

Harold L. Stewart

The experimental induction of gliomas of the brain provides a research tool of the greatest importance for the study of neoplasia of the central nervous system.

The first successful induction of brain tumors in animals was reported in 1939 by Seligman and Shear.[6] These workers implanted fused pellets of 100 per cent 20-methylcholanthrene directly into one of the cerebral hemispheres through a trephine opening in the skull following incision of the scalp and reflection of the galea. Of 20 mice so treated, 11 developed gliomas, while 2 had fibrosarcomas that were thought to be of meningeal origin.[1] This observation was confirmed in mice by Peers[3, 4] and Zimmerman *et al.*,[2, 9, 10, 11, 12] and in rats by Russell.[5] In both species the incidence and types of tumor induced are, in general, comparable. Peers[5] pointed out the advantage of using the carcinogen in a 10 per cent concentration in cholesterol to avoid nonspecific necrosis.

Two other methods for the experimental induction of brain tumors have been developed more recently. Vasquez-Lopez[8] found a glioma of the brain in a rat following oral administration of 2-acetylaminofluorine. This has also been confirmed by others[2a] and in one instance by workers at the National Cancer Institute. Under present conditions, the yield of these tumors by this agent is so small that they are not as yet a useful experimental tool. Uehlinger[7] has induced brain tumors in rabbits by the intracerebral implantation of radioactive thorium, but he has not yet published a description of the neoplasms.

RESULTS

The least potent of the three carcinogenic hydrocarbons tested for their ability to induce gliomas in mice is 1,2,5,6-dibenzanthracene. With pellets containing 5 per cent of this carcinogen no gliomas were obtained in 53 mice[3] and with 100 per cent pellets only 2 gliomas in 21 mice.[2] Using 20-methylcholanthrene in pellets composed of 10 per cent of the hydrocarbon fused with cholesterol, Peers[4] induced 32 tumors in 99 mice. Of these, 17 were of mesodermal and 15 of neuroectodermal origin. Pellets of 100 per cent purified 20-methylcholanthrene implanted in the cerebral meninges, the right cerebral hemisphere, or the cerebellum of 103 C3H male mice by Zimmerman and Arnold[10] induced, in all, 48 tumors: 25 gliomas, 13 sarcomas, 7 mixed gliomas and sarcomas, and 3 unclassified tumors. A comparison of the carcinogenic potency of benzpyrene and methylcholanthrene, based upon the number of tumors induced in the cerebral hemispheres, indicates that they are quantitatively equal. Qualitatively, however, methylcholanthrene proved to be much more potent in the induction of gliomas than benzpyrene.[11] Sex appears to have no influence on tumor incidence with benzpyrene. In some experiments there is but little difference in the time required for development of glioma as compared with that of sarcoma whereas, in others, sarcoma appeared to develop more rapidly. Although the tumors in mice and rats are comparable, it is noteworthy that 2 of the neurogenic tumors induced in the rat were classified as nerve cell tumor. No such nerve cell tumors were found in mice.

CLINICAL MANIFESTATIONS

Mice tolerate the operation for implantation of the carcinogenic pellet very well, and after recovering from the effects of the anesthetic they get along well under laboratory conditions. With the development of an intracranial tumor, the sutures of the skull separate, the head becomes enlarged, and the neoplasm may extend through the cranial defect and beneath or into the galea. It is surprising that many mice with large brain tumors show no apparent motor abnormality. Zimmerman,[9] however, has recorded early neurologic signs of brain tumors characterized by motor weakness and ataxia manifested one hundred days or more following intracerebral implantation of pellets of methylcholanthrene.

PATHOLOGY

The following histopathologic types of tumor have been identified one or more times in the various experiments reported to date: glioblastoma multiforme, medulloblastoma, medulloepithelioma, astrocytoma, oligodendroglioma, spongioblastoma polare, malignant nerve cell tumor (rat), ependymoma, pinealoma, meningeal sarcoma, fibrosarcoma, leiomyosarcoma, rhabdomyosarcoma, and squamous cell carcinoma. Pinealoma was distinguished but once, and no tumors of the posterior lobe of the pituitary gland or of the optic nerve have been reported. In almost all of the experiments, a few of the gliomatous tumors could not be classified precisely as to pattern. More than one type of glioma, or glioma and mesodermal tumor, may arise more or less simultaneously in the same animal, and these may eventually coalesce. Experimentally induced gliomas are generally of the more highly malignant varieties. This is in harmony with the now established general rule that the carcinogenic hydrocarbons induce almost exclusively tumors that are histologically undifferentiated and rapidly growing. Within the cranial cavity, sarcomas may arise from the meninges and from other mesodermal tissues. If the pellet extrudes extracranially through the cranial defect, or if the wound is contaminated by the carcinogen during operation, sarcoma and squamous-cell carcinoma may develop from the galea and scalp. The growth behavior of the gliomas is distinct from that of the sarcomas. Whereas the gliomas infiltrate and fade imperceptibly into the brain tissue, the sarcomas are circumscribed and sharply demarcated from the parenchyma. Experimental gliomas are quite similar to human gliomas both in cellular structure and cellular arrangement. The gliogenous tumors may be of pure type but rather frequently display histologic features which vary in different areas just as do the human gliomas. The following pathologic descriptions are taken to a large extent unchanged from the original publications.

GLIOBLASTOMA MULTIFORME

These tumors are less homogeneous in histologic structure than any others of the group. They are densely cellular, with medium-sized spindle cells predominating, mingled with a few polygonal cells and a variable number of large tumor giant cells. Occasional mitoses are seen. The chromatin structure of the pleomorphic nuclei is dense. Many of the predominant cells show bizarre cytoplasmic processes while others show polar orientation of the cytoplasm. The cytoplasm of the smaller cells is poorly defined, and between them the background consists of frayed cell processes and a few glial fibrils. Small foci of necrosis occur, with prominent palisading of cells about the margins. Vessels are small and few in number, and usually show no proliferation of endothelial cells. Reticulum is absent except in the walls of blood vessels and in the meninges.

MEDULLOBLASTOMA

The histologic structure of this group of tumors is quite uniform. They are composed of closely packed, small, round, oval, heavily chromatic nuclei embedded in a scanty and delicate fibrillary matrix that is not specifically stainable. Mitoses are very numerous. A narrow, ill-defined rim of cytoplasm is visible about the nuclei. Occasionally, this is drawn out to one side, forming a small carrot-shaped cell body. The cells grow chiefly in diffuse sheets, but in some fields they are arranged in tiny spherules and rosettes, the centers of which are filled with a fibrillar matrix. No tumor giant cells are seen, but occasional large astrocytic cells are present. A few minute patches of necrosis appear in the larger tumors. No glial fibrils are produced by the tumor cells, and the reticulum is limited to a few delicate strands from the walls of blood vessels and meninges. The tumors blend without demarcation into the adjacent brain tissue and spread along and beneath the dura and meninges. Small implants may be seen on the wall of the ventricle. Such behavior is similar to that of human medulloblastomas, which may also form widespread implants in the cerebrospinal pathway.

OLIGODENDROGLIOMA

This tumor is densely cellular, having scarcely any stroma that is visible with ordinary stains, and rather extensive areas of necrosis. The cells are small, with scanty acidophilic cytoplasm and small, dark, round nuclei. Frequently the nucleus seems to lie in a naked, clear, unstained halo, but occasionally it may be surrounded by narrow rings of stainable cytoplasm within the halo. The nuclei are usually uniform in size and shape, most of them being round and showing a rather loose chromatin structure. Mitotic figures vary in number and may be numerous. Those tumors with numerous mitoses might also be medulloblastomas, since the classical oligodendroglioma is a slowly growing tumor. With appropriate stains, scanty cell bodies with fine threadlike processes resemble oligodendrocytes and oligodendroblasts. There is no reticulum. Parts of the same tumor may show varying amounts of astrocytic stroma.

ASTROCYTOMA

The cells form no definite pattern, being arranged in random fashion. Each contains a small, deeply stained, round nucleus, often possessing one or more nucleoli, in a thin rim of cytoplasm which shows multipolar processes. The vast majority of the cells are readily identified as astrocytes. In some of the tumors the majority of the cells may be fibrillary astrocytes. Frequently the cells are arranged around spaces containing homogeneous colloid-like material. Dividing cells are rather numerous, and bizarre mitotic figures are sometimes seen. This reported presence of cellular anaplasia and rapid growth raises the question whether some of these tumors may not be glioblastoma multiforme.

MEDULLOEPITHELIOMA

The tumor is composed of rather uniform epithelial-like cells of medium size, showing in certain areas a characteristic arrangement in the form of tubes, rosettes, and epithelial strands. In some fields, the cells are closely packed in cords and alveolar masses. Their cytoplasm is basophilic, finely granular or slightly foamy, and the nuclei are large and round, with heavy membranes and two to six large clumps of chromatin in each. Only a few cells are multinucleated. Mitoses are numerous. Among the epithelial-like cells constituting the bulk of the tumor, there are occasionally small, darkly stained cells considered to be neuroblasts. The tumor cells produce no glial fibrils. The vessels are numerous, thin-walled, and often contain thrombi. Small areas of necrosis may be present.

EPENDYMOMA

This tumor is rather cellular, the cells are often carrot-shaped and occasionally multinucleated, and there are generally one or two cellular processes. The cells radiate from the blood vessels, and form rosettes that contain an acellular acidophilic fibrillar material. The tumor cells accumulate in dense garland-shaped annular rows about the central part of the rosette and the tubular space, while they are less densely distributed throughout the intervening solid parts of the tumor. The nuclei are densely chromatic, and either ovoid, round or elongated. In some of the tumor cells lining the tubes and rosettes, the cytoplasm has been described on one occasion as showing blepharoplast granules, which are usually close to the nucleus. Mitotic figures are numerous. Small calcareous deposits may occur.

SPONGIOBLASTOMA POLARE

This neoplasm is composed of large zones of spindle-shaped cells arranged in parallel rows, bands, or whorls. The cells contain elongated nuclei and their cytoplasm shows single or bipolar processes. The nuclei are uniform in size and shape, varying from ovoid to elongated elements having a dense chromatin structure. Parts of the tumor may be composed of closely packed, bizarre-shaped giant cells, some multinucleated, with an abundance of cytoplasm which forms prominent processes. There is no reticulum. Foci of necrosis, hemorrhage and calcareous deposits may be present. Here again the cellular anaplasia and rapid growth raise the question whether such tumors belong to the glioblastoma group.

PINEALOMA

This tumor was described in one single instance. It was composed of two distinct cell types, aggregated partially in separate groups, or partly admixed. There were large epithelioid cells with vesicular nuclei of loose chromatin structure as well as small round cells with a rather dense chromatin structure. A few giant cells were present. The tumor involved the brain stem, including parts of the right thalamus, epithalamus and metathalamus, Ammon's horn, and the central white matter of the right hemisphere. Hence this tumor may be a pinealoma as suggested by its location and its histologic similarity to the pinealoma of man.

MENINGEAL SARCOMA

These tumors are structurally continuous with meningeal tissue. They consist of spindle-shaped cells arranged in strands, whorls, or interlacing bundles. The spindle cells are bipolar and possess long processes. The nuclei are oval or elongated and contain many large chromatin granules. There are many mitotic figures. A delicate reticulum network permeates the neoplasm including the whorls, but there are few or no collagenic fibers. This tumor is distinguished with difficulty from fibrosarcoma.

NERVE CELL TUMOR

This remarkable type of tumor occurred in 2 rats. The predominant cell in these 2 tumors was large and stellate, with pale eosinophilic cytoplasm that usually possessed 2 to 4 short-pointed processes. The nucleus was round or slightly oval, and rarely double, with scanty chromatin most heavily concentrated at the nuclear membrane and with a prominent round nucleolus. Intermingled with and surrounding the large collections of stellate cells were smaller cells, varying from a size nearly equal to that of the predominant cell to that of a small lymphocyte. The smaller cells were round, with a small amount of pale, eosinophilic cytoplasm, and in contrast to the stellate elements rarely showed any processes. Mitotic figures occasionally occurred in both types of cell. The cytoplasm of the stellate cells contained peripherally distributed basophilic material in masses somewhat larger than ordinary Nissl bodies. Neurofibrils were demonstrated in many of the stellate cells and they often extended into the cytoplasmic processes. The stellate cells of these tumors were identified as nerve cells since their cytoplasm contained a chromophilic substance and argyrophilic fibrils. They also possessed nuclei characteristic of nerve cells. The presence in these tumors of less well differentiated cells, with no resemblance to nerve cells, together with transition forms to the stellate cells, suggested that the latter were indeed differentiated from the former type of cell.

HISTOGENESIS

Although in man tumors of nerve cells occur as ganglioneuroma and sympathicoblastoma and the latter may metastasize, neoplasia of nerve cells in experimental animals has been observed only in the rat and in only two instances. It is generally accepted that the fully mature and differentiated nerve cell represents in all probability the most specialized and highly differentiated cell in the animal body. It possesses no power to proliferate, only a limited capacity to regenerate its peripheral processes, and is highly sensitive to anoxemia and toxic agents in concentrations so low that other somatic cells are not affected. For these reasons, neoplasia induced by a carcinogenic agent acting directly on the mature nerve cell appears to be highly improbable. According to Russell[5] a more plausible explanation of the histogenesis of these 2 tumors is that the carcinogen elicited neoplasia in some primitive cell in the brain that possesses the potentialities of differentiating into nerve cells. Presumably the tumor cells that resembled nerve cells represented a further differentiation of such postulated immature cells which were not recognizable as nerve cells.

Peers[4] examined early gliomas by killing a number of mice at a time when the neoplasms were beginning to appear, although the carcinogenic pellets had not yet been displaced, and the tissue relations had not been distorted by massive tumor growth. In several instances, it was possible to demonstrate the origin of special varieties of gliomas from specific types of brain tissue in contact with the pellet. These specimens clearly demonstrated, for example, that the gliomas classified as medulloblastomas were formed in the zone of contact between the pellet and the gray matter, commonly the cerebral cortex, less often the hippocampus or thalamus. The cellular origin of the medulloblastoma was not clear. Important, however, was the observation that an adequate stimulus can evoke this variety of glioma from cortical gray matter remote from the natural site of predilection in human beings, the cerebellum. Tumors classified as glioblastoma multiforme appeared to arise subcortically in the cerebrum at points where the pellets lay in contact with the corona radiata or the fornix. This observation seems to establish the fact that the glioblastoma multiforme may be formed by anaplasia of the astrocytes of the white matter. In view of Peers' observation that the site of origin of a brain tumor might influence its histologic type, Zimmerman and Arnold[10] implanted pellets in 3 different locations: (1) in contact with the meninges; (2) in the cerebrum; and (3) in the cerebellum. Of 9 tumors which developed in location 1, 7 were sarcomas, as expected, and 2 were gliomas which arose where the pellet came in contact with the nervous parenchyma. In location 2 the converse of this also occurred; namely, the development of sarcoma due probably to extrusion of pellets through the cranial defect. Of the several gliomas arising in the cerebrum, 1 was a medulloblastoma, an unusual site for this tumor. In the cerebellum (location 3), the glioblastomas that were found could not have been anticipated, but the 3 medulloblastomas were entirely in keeping with clinical experience. According to Zimmerman and Arnold[10] the appearance of ependymomas around pellets implanted in the ventricular system particularly lends support to the concept that the type of glioma is a function of the site of development. This behavior of the ependyma is in contrast to the earlier experience of Peers,[4] who found this tissue element completely unresponsive to the carcinogen.

With certain definite reservations, therefore, the site of origin influenced the type of neoplasm. This, however, is not to be interpreted as implying that any considerable light has been shed on the more immediate histogenesis of the gliomas. That problem still remains unsolved. It was at first hoped that a study of the beginnings of a glioma in a young tumor would explain its histogenesis. The brain would seem to be a particularly favorable organ in which to study the early stages of chemical carcinogenesis. In reality, however, the malignant cells in early stages are unidentifiable with respect to the subsequent type of tumor that develops, and remain so until they proliferate sufficiently to produce a recognizable architectural pattern. In Zimmerman's[9] experience the subcutaneous transplants aided almost as much in the study of the histogenesis as of the growth behavior of these tumors, but it is still not possible to state what the factors are which determine whether a given glial cell will form an astrocytoma, an oligodendroglioma, or any other type of glioma.

Peers[3] observed a rather constant non-neoplastic reaction in the brain, consisting of a coarse spongy state in the white matter external to the mild gliosis surrounding the pellet. Whether this was due to trauma or to irritative effects of the carcinogen was not determined, but it was observed that this change was not accompanied by gliosis and bore no apparent relation to the development of tumors. Indeed, the absence of recognizable intermediate stages between nonreacting and tumor-bearing animals in Peers' experience was noteworthy. Once started, the neoplastic process apparently developed with great rapidity and obliterated transitional stages, if any, in even the earliest tumors examined.

TRANSPLANTATION

The proof that experimentally induced gliomas could be transplanted subcutaneously to other mice of the same inbred strain as the animal in which the primary neoplasm arose was first demonstrated by Seligman and Shear.[6] Since then these tumors have been grown intraperitoneally, intrathoracically, and in the anterior chamber of the eye. Difficulties have been encountered in growing human glioma material in the anterior chamber of the eye of animals, and Zimmerman[9] confirmed the low percentage of takes in the case of experimental gliomas. He found that, in general, the slower-growing neoplasms of mice usually grow less well in the guinea pig's eye than the more malignant varieties. Zimmerman[9] studied the subcutaneous transplants of the usual varieties of gliogenous tumor induced in several inbred strains of mice. When serially transplanted, the tumors may at first exhibit accelerated growth, but successive transplants become stabilized at about the twelfth generation. A primary neoplasm is rather frequently of mixed type, displaying histologic features which vary in different areas. By serial subcutaneous transplantation it is possible to separate into pure lines the component parts of these mixed neoplasms, the individual entities growing out as pure types, somewhat in the manner of bacterial subcultures. According to Zimmerman,[9] continued transplantation of the established lines has yielded samples of astrocytoma, ependymoma, oligodendroglioma, and polar spongioblastoma. The constancy of behavior is paralleled by the microscopic appearance. In the case of a glioblastoma multiforme, which is a heterogeneous neoplasm composed of many different cell types, it has proved possible to derive an ependymoma, an astrocytoma and an oligodendroglioma from a single tumor. This method not only permits the separation of so-called "mixed" tumors into their component parts, but unclassifiable primary gliomas frequently develop characteristic structural patterns in the transplants which make identification possible. It is of some interest to note that the glioma transplants grow with great facility in their new mesodermal environment. This is perhaps all the more surprising, as emphasized by Zimmerman and Maier,[12] since the human tumors of this variety are never found as extracranial metastases. However even human gliomas, though not establishing distant metastases, are not restricted by cellular function alone to growth within the nervous tissue, since occasionally fungating growth of malignant gliomas into the scalp tissue may follow craniotomy. According to Zimmerman and Maier[12] there is no local tissue resistance against the ectodermal gliomas, but rather an absence of an available pathway for metastasis. Even the most malignant of the gliomas fail to invade blood vessels.

BIBLIOGRAPHY

1. ALEXANDER, L. A note on the differential diagnosis of experimentally produced brain tumors and their relation to brain tumors in man. *Am. J. Cancer 37:* 395-399, 1939.
2. ARNOLD, H., and ZIMMERMAN, H. M. Experimental brain tumors: III. Tumors produced with dibenzanthracene. *Cancer Research 3:* 682-685, 1943.

2a. HOCH-LIGETI, C., and RUSSELL, D. S. Primary tumours of the brain and meninges in rats fed 2-acetylaminofluorene. *Unio Internationalis Contra Cancrum—Acta 7:* 126-129, 1950.

3. PEERS, J. H. The response of the central nervous system to the application of carcinogenic hydrocarbons: I. Dibenzanthracene. *Am. J. Path. 15:* 261-272, 1939.
4. PEERS, J. H. The response of the central nervous system to the application of carcinogenic hydrocarbons: II. Methylcholanthrene. *Am. J. Path. 16:* 799-816, 1940.
5. RUSSELL, W. O. The response of the central nervous system of the rat to methylcholanthrene: I. The induction of tumors derived from nervous tissue. *Cancer Research 5:* 140-151, 1945.
6. SELIGMAN, A. M., and SHEAR, M. J. Studies in carcinogenesis: VIII. Experimental production of brain tumors in mice with methylcholanthrene. *Am. J. Cancer 37:* 364-394, 1939.
7. UEHLINGER, E. (Personal communication).
8. VASQUEZ-LOPEZ, E. Glioma in a rat fed with 2-acetylaminofluorene. *Nature 156:* 296-297, 1945.
9. ZIMMERMAN, H. M. *Proceedings of the First National Cancer Conference.* New York, The American Cancer Society, 1949, p. 243.

10. ZIMMERMAN, H. M., and ARNOLD, H. Experimental brain tumors: I. Tumors produced with methylcholanthrene. *Cancer Research 1:* 919-938, 1941.
11. ZIMMERMAN, H. M., and ARNOLD, H. Experimental brain tumors: II. Tumors produced with benzpyrene. *Am. J. Path. 19:* 939-955, 1943.
12. ZIMMERMAN, H. M., and MAIER, N. The transplantation of experimentally induced brain tumors (abstract). *Am. J. Path. 25:* 801-802, 1949.

CHAPTER 6

Pulmonary Tumors in Mice

Harold L. Stewart

Livingood,[27] during the course of experiments on bacterial infections in 1896, discovered 5 spontaneous tumors in mice, 1 of which was a spontaneous pulmonary tumor, apparently the first to be reported in the literature. This tumor was found in an albino mouse in which no other growths were noted, and Livingood believed it to be an adenocarcinoma arising within a bronchus. During the period from 1905 to 1914 a large number of cases were reported and described in detail by Haaland,[11, 12] Tyzzer,[49] Murray,[38] Jobling,[23] and Slye, Holmes, and Wells.[44] All of these pulmonary tumors were believed to be spontaneous in origin and primary in the lung, although a number of them occurred in mice bearing tumors in other locations, particularly in the breast. They were variously diagnosed as adenoma, papillary cystadenoma, or adenocarcinoma. Tyzzer,[49] and Wells, Slye, and Holmes[44] observed growths which were thought to be epidermoid carcinomas. With the exception of this latter type, a reading of the descriptions and reference to the available illustrations strongly suggest the essential histologic similarity of most of them. As to their point of origin, there was no absolute agreement among the various authors, although a great many of these tumors were thought to arise from alveolar epithelium. Tyzzer[49] remarked on the resemblance of the tumor cells to bronchial epithelium but, on the other hand, noted in one instance that the tumor was small and completely independent of the bronchi. By the use of serial sections Jobling[23] traced the origin of one growth to papillary outgrowths from the wall of a bronchiole.

The largest series in the early literature was studied by Slye, Holmes, and Wells.[44] They concluded that the tumors might arise either from the alveolar or from the bronchial epithelium, although they admitted that it was extremely difficult to decide this point on the character of the tumor cells. However, they believed that the papillary type of tumor arose more frequently from the alveolar epithelium. Interest in these tumors apparently waned until 1925 when Murphy and Sturm[37] induced pulmonary tumors in mice by the repeated cutaneous application of a coal-tar distillate. They gave no detailed account of the histologic character of the tumors but illustrated a growth which was apparently identical with the type described by the earlier workers. Their work was soon repeated by a number of investigators, most of whom simply referred to the induced tumors as pulmonary adenomas or adenocarcinomas. With the establishment of the highly inbred Strain A albino mice by Strong[47] in 1921, a suitable test animal for the study of primary tumors of the lung became available. Bittner[6] reported on the spontaneous incidence of pulmonary tumors in this strain of mouse, and Andervont[1] showed that practically all young mice of this strain will develop multiple tumors of the lung within two months following subcutaneous injection of suitable quantities of 1,2,5,6-dibenzanthracene. The origin of the tumor from the pulmonary alveoli was demonstrated by Grady and Stewart.[10] Although displaying an adenomatous pattern in its primary location within the lung, the metastases[50] and transplants[4] of the pulmonary tumor may exhibit a spindle-cell pattern which Stewart, Grady, and Andervont[46] demonstrated to be compatible with fibrosarcoma.

With the exception of man and the mouse, spontaneous lung tumors are rare in all other species studied, such as the horse, ox, sheep, cat, rat, kangaroo, and fowl. The author of this chapter has observed only a single spontaneous pulmonary tumor in a rat, although they have been induced in multiple form in this species by urethane.[34]

CARCINOGENIC AGENTS AND METHODS OF INDUCTION

There are now a number of technics for the successful induction of pulmonary tumors in mice. In addition to tar and the carcinogenic hydrocarbons, such diverse agents as nitrogen mustard,[18] sulfur mustard,[19] gamma radiation,[28] and urethane[30] have all been shown to be carcinogenic. One of the most potent of all carcinogens for lung tissue of mice is urethane administered parenterally or in the drinking water. Larsen[24] studied a number of related substances, such as a series of homologous esters and a series of N-alkylated derivatives of urethane and found none as active as ethyl carbamate. Numerous other sedatives including ethyl alcohol, the barbiturates, chloral hydrate, and paraldehyde have been tested and found to be ineffective. Although pulmonary tumors almost never develop spontaneously in the rat, they have been induced by urethane[34] and by radioactive cerium.[26]

The carcinogenic hydrocarbons and related chemicals have been successfully employed to induce pulmonary tumors in mice by various routes including cutaneous painting, feeding, and injection subcutaneously, intravenously, intraperitoneally, intrapleurally, and directly into pulmonary tissue. The following compounds are carcinogenic for the lung of Strain A mice following intravenous or subcutaneous injection: 20-methylcholanthrene; 1,2,5,6-dibenzanthracene; 3,4,5,6-dibenzcarbazole; 3,4-benzpyrene; 15,16-benzdehydrocholanthrene; 1,2,5,6-dibenzacridine; 1,2,7,8-dibenzacridine; 2-methyl-3,4-benzphenanthrene; 4-methyl-3,4-benzpyrene; and 2-amino-5-azotoluene. In contrast, the following compounds similarly tested have been shown not to be carcinogenic: 1,2-benzanthracene; 3-methoxy-10-propyl-1,2-benzanthracene; and colloidal thorium dioxide.[5] A given hydrocarbon which is a potent carcinogen for the pulmonary tissue of mice may not show the same quantitative or qualitative carcinogenic activity when tested on other tissues, as, for example, the subcutaneous or cutaneous tissue. Indeed, the potency of any given carcinogen to induce pulmonary tumors differs in mice of different strains. The method of intravenous injection is one of the best ways to test exogenous pulmonary carcinogens. Here the particle size is important, for the larger the particles the more apt they are to be entrapped within the pulmonary capillaries and consequently the greater is the observed carcinogenic effect. No difference has been noted in the excretion rate of a carcinogen by resistant, as compared with susceptible animals. It is generally admitted that in Strain A mice the pulmonary carcinogens act directly upon the pulmonary tissue in which there resides a potential neoplastic process as evidenced by the spontaneous incidence of these tumors. It is believed that the carcinogens act by accelerating this inherent neoplastic tendency and that such acceleration is rapid and continuous following the single application of an agent. With present methods of quantitative absorption spectrum analysis it is usually impossible to detect the presence of the carcinogenic hydrocarbons in pulmonary tissue later than one week following its administration.[29]

The pulmonary tissue of mice of strains susceptible to spontaneous lung tumors is therefore a sensitive test object for suspected carcinogens. With this in mind, Lorenz *et al.*[30] exposed Strain A mice to the inhalation of tobacco smoke four hours a day for twelve months. At the end of the experiment no increase in the occurrence of lung tumors was noted. It is probable that, in the presence of oxygen, polycyclic hydrocarbons of known carcinogenic activity are not formed upon combustion of tobacco. Recent reports, including that of Mills and Porter,[33] suggest that the high incidence of pulmonary cancer in man is associated with excessive smoking of tobacco. If true, it has not been determined whether this is due to the smoke *per se* (hardly likely in view of the experiments of Lorenz and Stewart),[30] or to the material which the smoker swallows with the saliva during smoking, or to other as yet unknown factors and mechanisms.*†

SUSCEPTIBILITY OF STRAINS OF MICE

Among the various strains of inbred mice currently used in cancer research there is a pronounced difference in the incidence of spontaneous and induced pulmonary tumors. Strain A mice have generally proved to have the highest incidence of spontaneously developed pulmonary tumors, the figure being from 80 to 90 per cent in animals living eighteen months or longer, whereas Strain L mice rarely develop this neoplasm. Shimkin[43] tested seven strains of mice for their susceptibility to induction of primary pulmonary tumors by the intravenous injection of 20-methylcholanthrene. Strain A was the most susceptible; Strain C was next in susceptibility; Strains Y, I, and C3H were of medium susceptibility; while Strains C57BL

* For an excellent discussion of the use of the pulmonary tumor of the mouse for testing suspected carcinogens in human cancer, the reader is referred to the article by SMITH, W. E. Lung cancer with special reference to experimental aspects. *A.M.A. Arch. Indust. Hyg. 5:* 209-217, 1952.

† It has been shown recently, that exposure of Strain A mice to cigarette smoke for longer periods of time seems to increase the incidence of pulmonary cancer in the exposed animals (91.3%) over that observed in control animals (59.4%). ESSENBERG, J. M. Cigarette smoking and the incidence of primary neoplasms of the lung in the albino mouse. *Science, 116:* 561-562, 1952.

and L were relatively resistant. The relative susceptibility to induction of primary pulmonary tumors was parallel to the susceptibility to spontaneous development of pulmonary tumors; that is, strains of mice having the highest incidence of spontaneous pulmonary tumors also showed the highest incidence of induced pulmonary tumors. The pulmonary tumors induced in mice were adenomatous and almost always identical in appearance. There was no morphologic difference (1) between spontaneous and induced tumors; (2) between tumors induced in the seven strains of mice; (3) between tumors produced by methylcholanthrene and those produced by 1,2,5,6-dibenzanthracene; (4) between tumors induced by different routes of injection (subcutaneous, intravenous, intratracheal); or (5) between tumors induced by the carcinogen in different states (in lard, in horse serum, as a cholesterol pellet, or adsorbed on charcoal). Cowen[7] found that, like pulmonary tumors induced by the carcinogenic hydrocarbons, the incidence of the urethane induced tumors depends upon the spontaneous incidence of these tumors in different strains of mice.

GENETICS OF PULMONARY TUMORS

The study of the genetics of pulmonary tumors has been greatly enhanced by the fact that the incidence of spontaneous pulmonary tumors in mice differs in different inbred strains.[13, 14, 25, 32, 43] Furthermore, inbred mice having a high incidence of spontaneous pulmonary tumors are also more susceptible to the induction of these neoplasms by carcinogenic hydrocarbons. Thus there is available experimental biologic material of the utmost value for studies of the genetics of pulmonary tumors. Lynch[32] was the first to show that heredity as well as environment influenced susceptibility to the development of pulmonary tumors. In an analysis of the susceptibility to induced pulmonary tumors, Heston[15, 16] used two strains of mice, Strain A, which is a high pulmonary tumor strain, and Strain L, which is a low pulmonary tumor strain. By studying the F_1, F_2 and backcross hybrid generations of mice receiving at sixty-five days of age an intravenous injection of 0.5 mg. of 1,2,5,6-dibenzanthracene, he found that genetic factors as well as environmental factors are involved in the susceptibility to induced lung tumors. The genetic factors influencing susceptibility are multiple in number and not due to one larger factor with modifying factors. The minimum number of susceptibility factors by which Strain A and Strain L differ in this respect is four pairs, and in all probability more. In the F_2 generation in this experiment, Heston estimated that 86 per cent of the susceptibility to pulmonary tumors depended upon genetic factors, and 14 per cent upon nongenetic factors. Susceptibility to induced pulmonary tumors has been shown to be associated with the chromosome carrying the genes (1) Shaker-2 and Waved-2; (2) Flexed-tail; (3) Lethal Yellow; and (4) Hairless. Susceptibility to spontaneous pulmonary tumors is inherited in the same manner as susceptibility to induced tumors, and the two genes tested, namely, the Lethal Yellow and the Hairless genes, affect both in the same manner.[17, 18, 20, 21]

In order to determine whether genic action controlling the development of pulmonary tumors in mice is localized in the lung tissue or is manifested through some general systemic mechanism, lung tissue from mice of Strain A (highly susceptible to pulmonary tumors) and from Strain L (highly resistant to pulmonary tumors) was transplanted subcutaneously into a common host, the F_1 hybrid of the two strains, which was then injected intravenously with dibenzanthracene.[21a] Pulmonary tumors developed in 39.1 per cent of the transplants from Strain A donors and in 3.6 per cent of the transplants from Strain L donors. Thus, in large part, the difference in genetic susceptibility to pulmonary tumors of the donor strains of mice was retained in the transplanted tissue. This suggests that the action of at least most of the susceptibility genes by which these two strains differ is

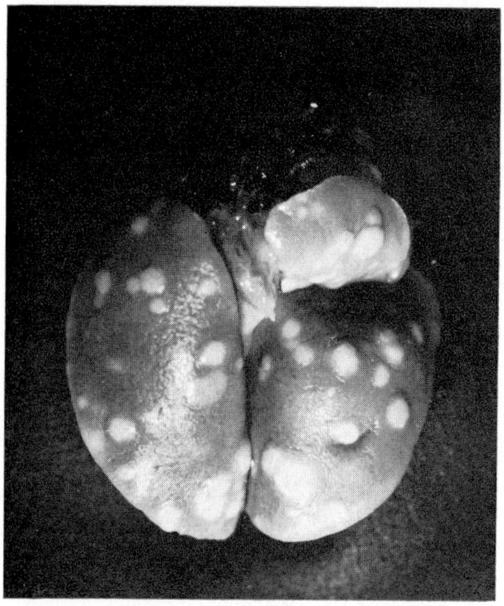

FIG. 26. Multiple induced tumors of lung. × 38.

localized in the lung tissue. Proliferation of the bronchial epithelium occurred in the transplanted lung fragments but was readily distinguishable from the neoplastic change.

GROSS AND MICROSCOPIC APPEARANCE AND METASTASES

The common pulmonary tumor (alveologenic carcinoma) of the mouse may be single or multiple, and occurs in either lung and in any lobe. It is often situated close to the pleura so that it may be seen upon inspection of the surface (Fig. 26). The spontaneous tumors are frequently solitary but, if multiple, usually do not exceed 2 to 4 per animal. The induced tumors are almost invariably multiple, and both lungs may be extensively riddled with these growths. Larsen (personal communication) has frequently counted 100, and occasionally as many as 150, tumors per mouse treated with urethane. Despite the fact that much of the lung tissue may be occupied by these multiple tumors, osteoarthropathy has not been observed. Both spontaneous and induced tumors are similar in appearance. The tumors appear to grow expansively, being surrounded by compressed pulmonary tissue, but are not encapsulated. They are therefore usually sharply circumscribed, pearly-white nodules often projecting slightly above the pleural surface of the lung. Fresh or fixed material examined under the low power of a dissecting microscope gives a reasonably accurate index of the total number of tumors throughout the lung, and inferentially of the potency of the carcinogen being tested. In estimating the number of lung tumors by the surface counting method, it should be remembered that these lesions grow by expansion and that several closely adjacent tumors, each of which is at first solitary, eventually become confluent. Thus, instead of being counted as

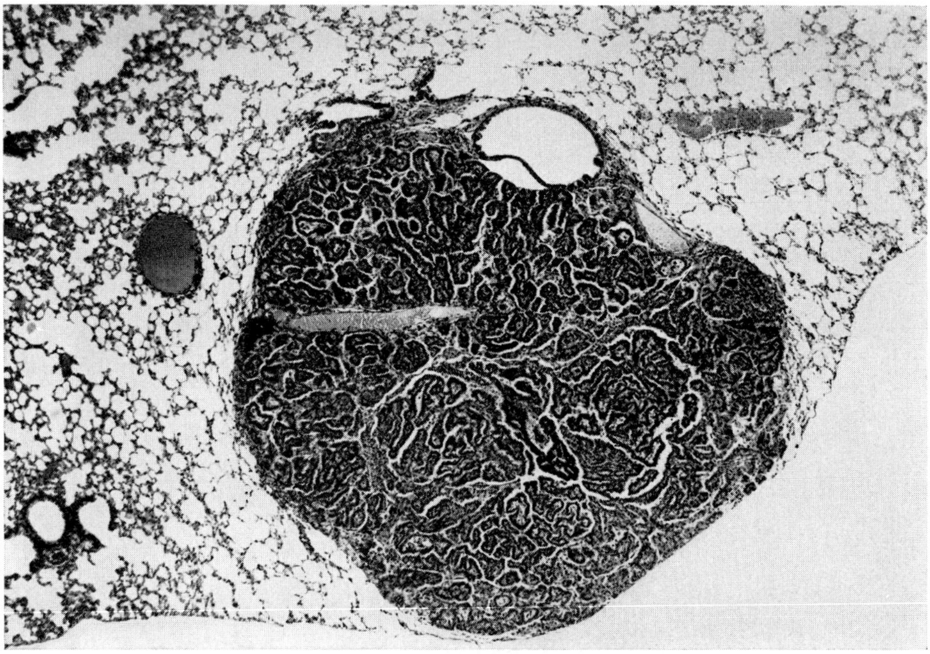

FIG. 27. Alveologenic carcinoma. × 60.

several, they may easily be counted as one after they have fused. This error is inherent in a technic in which a potent carcinogen in large dosage is employed in young mice whose life span is not interrupted. Although this permits the fullest effect of the carcinogen to operate on the pulmonary tissue, at the same time many adjacent tumors coalesce. Surface counts therefore may be numerically lower after coalescence of tumors than if made earlier or if smaller doses or a less potent carcinogen are used.

Microscopically, spontaneous and induced tumors are similar, most of them presenting a uniform picture of closely packed columns of cuboidal or columnar cells (Fig. 27). The cellular elements are supported by a sparse stroma of mature fibrous tissue containing small amounts of reticulum and collagenic fibrils. Few blood vessels are present. The cells of the tumor are arranged in acini, showing papillary formation, and the stromal pattern is similar to that of an epithelial growth. The cytoplasm of the tumor cells is generally smooth, slightly acidophilic, and the free borders of the cells are devoid of cilia. The nuclei are single, round or oval, and vary from lightly stained vesicular to deeply stained types. Acidophilic nuclear inclusions are occasionally observed. Mitotic figures are usually not numerous. Apparently, two or more adjacent growths may coalesce, as manifested by partial separation of the tumors and by minor differences of architectural pattern.

That the pulmonary tumor of the mouse is a malignant neoplasm is evident from its lack of encapsulation, its local invasiveness, transplantability, and ability to metastasize. Although both lungs are often studded with multiple tumor growths, it is the experience of the author of this chapter that metastasis is infrequent. When metastasis does occur, the secondary deposits are apt to show sarcomatous characteristics. Wells, Slye, and Holmes[50] reported that of 147,132 mice coming to autopsy in Slye's laboratory, where every mouse was permitted to live its full life span, 2865 mice (2 per cent) had spontaneous pulmonary tumors. Of these cases, 104 (3.6 per cent) showed metastasis outside the lungs. All showed metastasis in the mediastinal lymph nodes; many also showed growths along the chest wall and on the diaphragm. Only 10 animals showed metastasis to other sites: 5 to the kidney, 3 to the heart, 1 to the seminal vesicle, and 1 to the skull. Of the 104 cases with metastasis, 33 of the metastatic growths showed more or less the structure of a sarcoma. This was true even when no sarcomatous elements were identified in the primary growth. Although in a number of primary lung tumors this sarcomatous structure was apparent, no primary sarcomas of the lung without epithelial elements were observed in these mice.

OTHER TYPES OF PULMONARY TUMOR

In addition to alveologenic carcinoma, which is the common pulmonary tumor of the mouse, two other histologic types of tumor have been induced in this species. Primary hemangioendothelioma of the lung has been induced by the subcutaneous injection of *o*-aminoazotoluene.[4] A squamous cell carcinoma has been induced by inserting directly into the lung[2] a piece of silk thread impregnated with 1,2,5,6-dibenzanthracene, around which the neoplasm develops, which may be bronchial in origin.

Lisco and Finkel[27] reported in a short abstract the occurrence of metaplastic changes in the bronchial epithelium and the development of malignant tumors therefrom in rats receiving radioactive cerium (Ce^{144}) administered as an aerosol into the lungs. Vorwald has reported the induction of metastasizing carcinoma of the lung in rats treated with beryllium.*

INDUCTION OF PULMONARY TUMORS IN EMBRYONIC MICE

It is noteworthy that the carcinogen urethane can pass through the placental membrane. Larsen reported a high incidence of pulmonary tumors in the offspring of mice injected intravenously with urethane during pregnancy. In the embryos of the

* VORWALD, A. J. "Pulmonary cancer in experimental exposures to beryllium." In *Seventh Saranac Symposium.* The Saranac Laboratory, Saranac Lake, N. Y., Sept. 22-26, 1952.

pregnant mice treated with urethane, Smith and Rous[45] found cellular accumulations in the lung which were interpreted as the early stage of pulmonary cancer. This is one of the few examples of the establishment of the carcinogenic process in tissues during embryonic life. Larsen[24] observed that the stage of pregnancy modifies the degree of the carcinogenic process in the fetal lung. He injected urethane into mice at different stages of pregnancy. The offspring of mothers injected during the final twenty-four hours of gestation exhibited fully five times as many pulmonary tumors as did mice whose mothers received the injection two to five days *ante partum*. Much speculation has been stimulated regarding the significance of this phenomenon, but there are as yet no experimental data explaining its mechanism.

HISTOGENESIS

The early reports dealing with alveologenic carcinoma of the mouse variously classified this growth as adenoma, papillary cystadenoma, or adenocarcinoma. There was no absolute agreement among the various authors as to its exact point of origin, although in a great many instances it was thought to arise from cells of the alveoli. Others concluded that the tumor might arise either from alveolar cells or from the bronchial epithelium but that it was extremely difficult to decide this point on the character of the tumor cells. Judging from the observations of early workers, some tumors involved alveoli only, and their origin from alveolar cells was indubitable; other tumors involved both alveoli and bronchi, and hence the origin of these was not clear. No tumors were described which involved bronchi alone, and this constant involvement of the alveoli made it seem improbable that these growths ever originated from bronchi. The chief hindrances to the use of spontaneous pulmonary tumors in a study of histogenesis are their paucity and their slow development and evolution. These obstacles are overcome by employing modern methods for the rapid induction of these neoplasms in large numbers in susceptible inbred mice by potent chemical carcinogens.

Using such methods, the histogenesis of these tumors was studied by Grady and Stewart[10] using inbred Strain A mice that are highly susceptible to induced lung tumors. The animals were injected subcutaneously with 1,2,5,6-dibenzanthracene and 20-methylcholanthrene which induce multiple pulmonary tumors within three months. Animals were killed daily or at the rate of several per week beginning immediately following injection and terminating in the eleventh week. Complete serial sections of one lobe of the lung were cut and stained routinely. Thus, consecutive morphologic changes could be studied prior to and during the development of the pulmonary tumor due to the carcinogen. Mostofi and Larsen[35, 36] repeated this same type of experiment, using urethane, administered orally, to produce pulmonary tumors. The results of these two studies are quite comparable. They revealed that the common pulmonary tumor arises from a preliminary proliferation of alveolar cells that occurs usually throughout the lung tissue but is frequently prominent in the peripheral alveoli remote from bronchi or bronchioles —hence the designation "alveologenic" carcinoma. In the majority of instances in both experiments, none of the usual evidence of inflammation was present in the lungs of these animals in which pulmonary tumors were developing. Some animals of the urethane experiment had pneumonia in one or more lobes of the lung as revealed at autopsy. In these animals tumors were sometimes observed in the pneumonic areas as well as in other lobes free of pneumonic consolidation, so that there appeared to be no causal relationship between inflammatory changes and the development of pulmonary tumors. Horning[22] also found no evidence to indicate that inflammatory changes are associated with the development of pulmonary tumors induced by carcinogens in homologous grafts of adult lung tissue. This point is emphasized because Orr[42] reported that pulmonary tumors arose from bronchi within areas of inflammation and atelectasis. Orr's conclusions were evidently reached from a study of large, relatively mature tumors since many of them had already extended into bronchi. The studies of Grady and Stewart[10] and of Mostofi and Larsen[35] have shown that involvement of bronchi by such pulmonary tumors is a relatively late manifestation—probably an extension of the tumor originally formed in the alveoli.

The importance of technic cannot be emphasized too strongly in the study of this perplexing problem of the histogenetic origin of pulmonary tumors. Sample animals should be secured at daily intervals following administration of the carcinogen, and one pulmonary lobe should be studied by complete serial sections to ascertain in three-dimensional view the topographic relationship of the bronchus and the alveolus to the site of the earliest formation of the tumor. By such serial sections, it has been shown[10, 35] that many pulmonary tumors originate in an area completely removed from any possible contact with bronchi or bronchioles. This seems to prove conclusively that induced pulmonary tumors in mice certainly arise from alveolar cells. Only in the later stages of the experiment do some tumors which originated in close proximity to bronchi secondarily invade the lumen of the bronchus. No tumor was found confined within the lumen of a bronchus without involvement of its adjacent alveoli. The epithelium of the bronchial tree at no time during the experiment exhibited hyperplasia or proliferation or an increase in the number of mitotic figures, suggestive of a preneoplastic change. Even in cases revealing tumor tissue present within the lumen of a bronchus, the junction area between neoplastic cells and bronchial epithelium failed to disclose any evidence of a hyperplastic transition zone that would be expected had the tumor originated from the bronchus. All the evidence from these studies supports the view that the common pulmonary tumor of the mouse arises from alveolar cells.

During the first and second weeks of their experiment, Grady and Stewart[10] found a diffuse, though slight, cellular increase involving the alveolar walls, particularly in areas close to the pleura. The cells in question were approximately 15 to 20 μ in diameter, mostly round or oval, possessed a round, palely stained, centrally located nucleus, with one or two small, prominent nucleoli. The cytoplasm was faintly acidophilic and very finely granular. It was extremely difficult to determine the exact location of these cells with respect to the alveolar septum. None were noted free in the alveolar lumen. Some cells partly projected into the lumen of the alveolus from the septal wall, particularly in the angles formed by adjacent alveoli. In many instances, these peculiar cells appeared to be within the alveolar walls although not within the capillary lumen, and none were observed inside the lumen of an arteriole or venule. The cells rather seemed to represent swollen cells of the alveolar walls.

During the third and fourth weeks following administration of the carcinogen these localized collections of cells were present in most parts of the lungs, chiefly in the angles between adjacent alveoli and often close to or immediately beneath the pleura. A few cells could be seen lying free in the alveolar lumen. The alveolar cells giving rise to the tumors exhibited more mitotic figures after treatment with urethane[35] than after that with hydrocarbons.

During the fifth and sixth weeks, 5 of the test animals developed minute tumors. Complete serial sections showed the nodules to be confined to a subpleural location considerably removed from even the smallest bronchioles. However, at this time the cuboidal tumor cells distinctly resembled the lining cells of the bronchi. The alveoli bordering the developing tumors showed cuboidal cells budding off the septal walls, indicating that enlargement of the tumor occurs as a result of continuing neoplastic change at its periphery.

By the seventh and eighth weeks, 9 animals had developed pulmonary tumors of which 7 were multiple. The larger growths in general conformed to two types. One, the more commonly encountered, consisted of solid, closely packed, curving and sometimes sinuous columns of cuboidal cells, whose intercellular boundaries were frequently prominent and gave the impression that the cells were forcibly pressed together. Some of the tumor cells were rather large and hyperchromatic, and mitoses were present. The epithelial cells were supported by thin connective tissue stroma. A second type of tumor revealed recognizable alveoli that were in various stages of collapse and completely invested by single or sometimes multiple layers of cuboidal cells similar in every respect to those of the more solid type of tumor.

During the ninth, tenth, and eleventh weeks after treatment with the carcinogen, 11 test animals developed tumors in the right lower lobe, while a single tumor nodule was found in an untreated control animal. Only 1 tumor in the series was noted in intimate contact with a bronchiole, and this was considered to represent simply partial envelopment of the bronchiole by a tumor that had originated from the surrounding alveoli. In this regard it is exceedingly important to emphasize the use of complete serial sections since the fully developed tumor cells may closely resemble bronchial epithelium, particularly when the latter becomes pressed into cuboid shape by the intratracheal injection of fixing solutions.

One of the most difficult points of interpretation in this study is, of course, the nature of the cell giving rise to the tumor. That the tumor is virtually always derived from cells of the alveolus is certain, but the identification of these cells is not absolute. In mice, as in many mammals including man, the presence of living cells in the pulmonary alveolus has been the subject of many controversies.[8] Embryologic studies suggest that the epithelial lining of the terminal alveolar vesicles begins to disappear during fetal life. The epithelium of the respiratory tract in the adult appears to terminate more or less abruptly at the beginning of the alveolar ducts. With respect to the alveoli, three views exist at present: (1) the alveoli in the adult have a continuous epithelial lining; (2) the alveoli have a discontinuous lining in the form of isolated cells or nests in the niches between the capillaries; and (3) no true lining exists, but the capillaries are contained in a ground substance with occasional so-called "alveolar" or "septal" cells, probably of mesenchymal origin. It is agreed, however, that under certain pathologic conditions the alveoli have a definite lining. On the basis of important contributions to the study of the specificity of the germ layers, Oppenheimer[41] concludes that the doctrine of the absolute specificity of the germ layers must be abandoned. The germ layers are probably capable under certain conditions of undergoing variations.

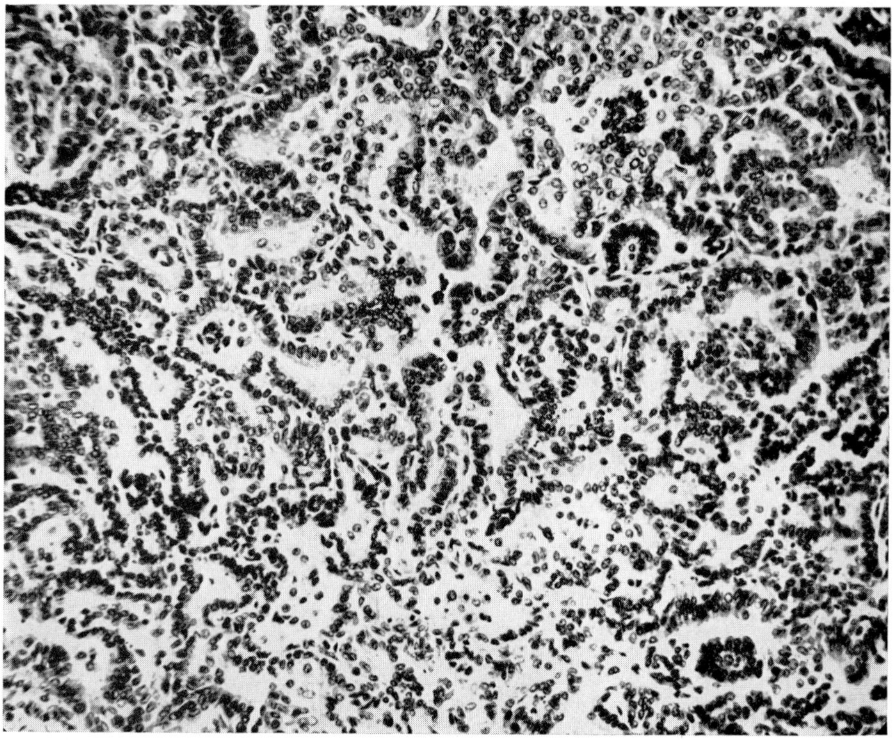

FIG. 28. Primary pulmonary tumor showing glandular pattern. × 200.

Neubuerger[40] concludes that the possibility of mesenchymal cells giving rise to a tumor with epithelial-like cellular elements cannot at present be rejected. Whatever the final solution of this problem, it is at present definite that tumors of alveolar origin can be induced in mice by appropriate experimental methods and that these tumors have the characteristic histologic pattern of papillary adenocarcinoma.

TRANSPLANTATION STUDIES

Alveologenic carcinoma, the common primary pulmonary tumor of the mouse, which arises as a papillary adenomatous growth, often exhibits a sarcomatous pattern in its metastases (Figs. 28, 29, 30).[50] The same change in histologic structure occurs when these tumors are transplanted serially to the subcutaneous tissue of mice of the same strain as the animal in which the primary tumor arose.[3] This change from a glandular to a spindle-cell pattern on serial transplantation has been reported for other tumors, notably the mammary tumor of the mouse. As might be expected, the report of this observation near the turn of the century occasioned considerable controversy among workers in the field of experimental oncology. Many doubted the accuracy of the histologic diagnosis and there was and still is no satisfactory explanation for the mechanism of such change. The observations that such a profound alteration in structure can occur was still accepted with

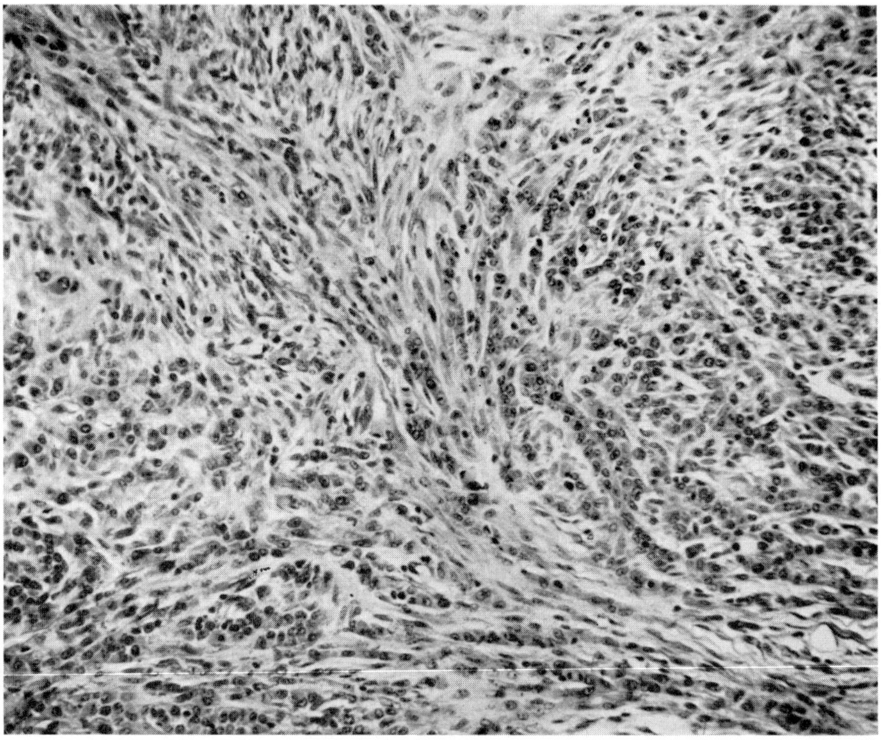

FIG. 29. Transplanted pulmonary tumor showing mixed carcinomatous and sarcomatous pattern. × 200.

reluctance and reservation as late as a few years ago. Many workers, although not denying the possibility, still believed that the so-called "sarcomatous change" represents merely the occurrence of spindle-shaped epithelial cells in a carcinomatous growth. That the final change in pattern truly represents a sarcoma was supported by the observations of Ludford and Barlow,[31] who grew the transplant in tissue culture and reported the growth characteristics of sarcoma *in vitro* which had developed after transplanting a mammary carcinoma of a mouse. This point was finally confirmed by Stewart, Grady, and Andervont[46] who showed that on the basis of histopathologic criteria accepted as proving the diagnosis of fibrosarcoma, the final spindle-cell pattern of the serially transplanted pulmonary tumor was indeed fibrosarcoma.

The structural features of the transplanted tumors are on the whole uniform after they have become sarcomatous. These growths are composed of plump bundles of elongated spindle cells which form interweaving and interlacing patterns. The spindle-shaped tumor cells are usually large, with elongated darkly staining nuclei; mitotic figures are numerous. The cytoplasm is frequently drawn out into thin, unipolar or bipolar processes, which suggestively fuse with those of adjacent cells at their extremities. The van Gieson and silver preparations reveal a pronounced increase in the amount of collagenic fibers and reticulum, as well as a pro-

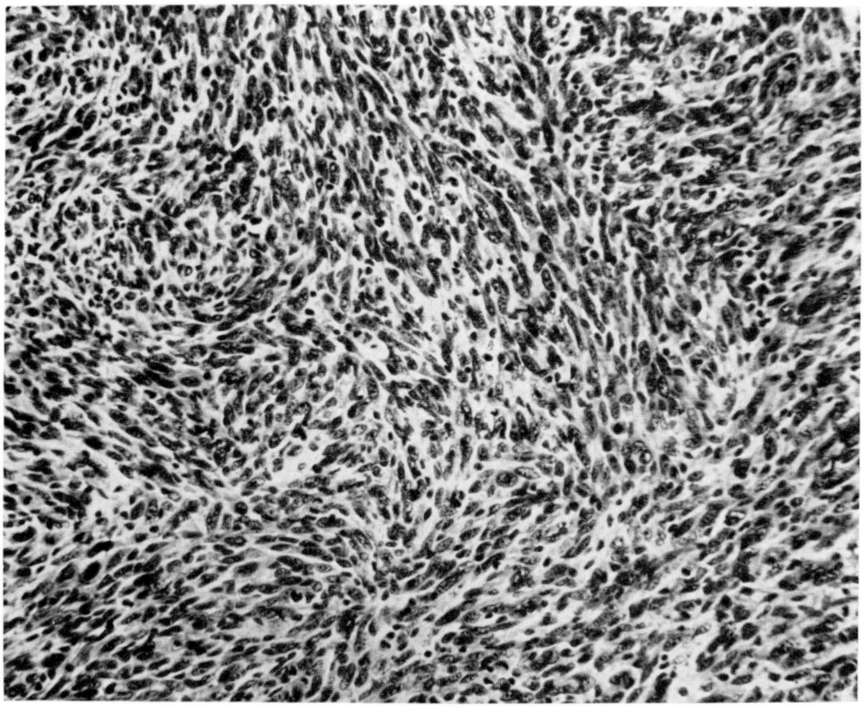

FIG. 30. Transplanted pulmonary tumor showing sarcomatous pattern. Compare with Fig. 27. × 200.

found change in the distribution of these intercellular fibers, when compared with the epithelial growths. The reticulum fibers form an extremely close meshwork enclosing cells singly and in small groups and are intimately applied to the sides of the cells. In the phosphotungstic acid-hematoxylin preparations, numerous fine fibroglial fibrils are associated with the tumor cells. Blood vessels are usually numerous, immature, thin-walled, and irregular in outline. They are lined partially or completely with endothelial cells, although in some areas the tumor cells seem to border directly upon the vascular channel or to be growing into it. In dealing with tumors with this morphologic pattern, it is difficult to consider them as being anything other than fibrosarcoma.

The serial transplants of pulmonary tumors that underwent sarcomatous change, in the studies of Stewart, Grady and Andervont,[46] included 1 spontaneous tumor and 21 neoplasms induced by 1,2,5,6-dibenzanthracene arising in Strains A, C, and C3H mice. Hence, this sarcomatous change develops in transplants of both spontaneous and induced tumors and in different inbred strains of mice. At the time of transplantation, each tumor was divided into two parts; one part was saved for histologic study and the other was used for subcutaneous inoculation. Several collateral lines were established. At first, the tumors were transplanted every two to three months, but as the sarcomatous change developed the growth rate increased so that successive transplantations were made at three- to four-week intervals. More than one-half of the tumor series was carried for six generation transplants, and several others for more. In the different specimens studied, all the various combinations of a papillary glandular carcinoma, solid carcinoma, and sarcoma were observed, either intermingled with each other or with one or more predominating types in different areas. A study of the final histologic status of the 22 original tumors and their collateral lines revealed that in 5 lines the tumor transplant had become wholly sarcomatous in type, in 13 lines the tumor was composed of a combination of sarcomatous and carcinomatous structures, in 8 lines only the glandular carcinoma type was found, in 3 lines the solid carcinoma type, and in the remaining 8 lines combinations of glandular and solid carcinoma. The tendency was for the glandular type of carcinoma to be replaced by the solid carcinoma type, and this in turn to be replaced by sarcoma. The sarcomatous pattern often made its first appearance early in the course of transplantation.

The mechanism and underlying causes of the development of a sarcoma following serial transplantation of the primary pulmonary tumor of the mouse cannot be explained satisfactorily at present. There are certain immediately obvious theoretical explanations which have been examined, but no definite conclusion has been reached. The primary pulmonary tumors possess a stroma that is sparse and delicate. It is conceivable that this stroma assumes neoplastic properties following transplantation and overgrows the epithelial tumor. However, nothing has been observed to indicate that this is the correct explanation.

A second possibility is that the stroma of the host undergoes malignant transformation. If this is actually the mechanism of sarcoma development, it is not to be explained on the basis of transfer of a known carcinogenic chemical, for this phenomenon has followed the transplantation of a spontaneous pulmonary tumor, and, furthermore, spectroscopic studies[29] have shown that the carcinogenic hydrocarbons disappear from the lungs of mice within seven days following a single intravenous injection. Histologic studies, while giving evidence of an active stromal reaction about the periphery of many of the transplanted tumors, have not yielded satisfactory indications that this stromal reaction on the part of the host becomes neoplastic.

A third possibility is that the primary tumor cells undergo such fundamental alterations in their character as to become transformed into fibrosarcoma cells. This possibility has been examined by Stewart, Grady, and Andervont[46] in their transplantation experiments and, while the columnar and cuboidal cells of the tumor and the elongated and spindle-shaped epithelial cells were sometimes intermingled with definitely sarcomatous areas, the observers could not definitely agree as to the significance of this relationship in material studied. However, this association may indeed be more than incidental.

A fourth possibility that requires further exploration is that the primary pulmonary tumors are potentially mixed tumors to begin with. The cell from which they arise may possess the potentialities of a synovial cell which, after undergoing a malignant change, can grow as carcinoma or as sarcoma. The pulmonary tumor may possibly arise from two or more cell types. There is much to recommend this line of speculation although at present the absence of direct proof precludes any positive deductions. The so-called endothelial tumors in man, as exemplified by the malignant synovioma, duplicate histologically the carcinosarcomatous features of the transplanted pulmonary tumors. In different fields of synovioma, some areas resemble adenocarcinoma, other areas fibrosarcoma, and in still other areas the epithelial component of the growth shows a glandular or cordlike arrangement, and yet the supporting stroma is obviously malignant and has the appearance of fibrosarcoma. Since the tumors employed in transplantation studies have generally been selected from the periphery of the lung and almost certainly contained serosal cells from the pleura (an additional complicating factor), it would be interesting to repeat this work using only deeply situated pulmonary tumors not in contact with the pleura.

HISTOGENESIS OF HUMAN PULMONARY CARCINOMA

Primary Pulmonary Carcinoma

Primary pulmonary carcinoma in man is generally considered to be bronchiogenic in origin and may be distinguished histologically as: (1) squamous cell carcinoma; (2) adenocarcinoma; and (3) undifferentiated carcinoma. That such tumors may arise from alveolar cells or from the mucous glands of the bronchi is highly disputed. The epithelial lining of the bronchus, the admitted source of carcinoma in man, is composed of three types of cells: ciliated cells, goblet cells, and basal cells. The basal cells are small oval-shaped elements having a thin cytoplasm and a large, deeply stained nucleus. Any defect caused by injury to the bronchial lining is repaired by these basal cells which, after their preliminary proliferation, give rise to transitional cells which subsequently become stratified to form the newly regenerated lining of the bronchus. The transitional cells of this new bronchial lining may then differentiate normally, or in the event of persistent injury may undergo metaplasia to form squamous cells. The squamous type of epithelium does not therefore represent a transformation of the adult columnar lining cells, but instead develops from the undifferentiated basal cells by way of the transitional type of cell. The basal cells of the bronchi, acting as progenitors for the repair and regeneration of the bronchial epithelium, are in this respect analogous to the cells in the regenerative centers of the crypts of Lieberkühn of the intestine and also to the cells of the basal layer of the cutaneous epidermis. Furthermore, bronchiogenic carcinoma is believed to originate from these basal cells of the bronchial epithelium. Just as carcinoma of the skin is frequently preceded by a precancerous lesion, so is carcinoma of the lung believed to be preceded by a lesion of carcinoma *in situ*.[9, 42a, 51] Bronchiogenic carcinoma arises usually in a principal stem of the main bronchus near the hilus of the lung, and rarely in a small bronchus or bronchiole close to the periphery of the lung, or from several bronchi simultaneously. The distinction between the lesion of carcinoma *in situ* of the bronchus, on the one hand, and benign hyperplasia, on the other, is clearly revealed in photomicrographs of histologic sections of these respective lesions.

Pulmonary Adenomatosis

Pulmonary adenomatosis in man[48] and animals is of interest in this connection because the histologic pattern of its lesion may resemble in some respects that of the alveolar-cell carcinoma of the mouse. Although regarded by some as neoplastic in nature, most observers regard pulmonary adenomatosis as a reactive process in which the alveoli of the lung come to be lined by large epithelial cells. The lesion in man is almost an exact replica of that of an epizoötic disease in sheep designated *Jagziekte* or Montana progressive pneumonia. In the epizoötic disease of sheep, an etiologic agent has not been demonstrated although its infectious nature is suspected. The shepherds who tend the flocks of diseased animals have not been known to contract pulmonary adenomatosis as a result of their exposure to the sheep. Pulmonary lesions somewhat similar to those of sheep have been described in horses, mules, guinea pigs, and cats. Serial roentgenologic examinations of patients with pulmonary adenomatosis reveal widespread areas of consolidation or multiple mottling of the entire lung, or of parts of it only. Following excision of a given lobe to which the disease may be confined in its early stages, the process may spread to other lobes of the same and of the opposite lung. Grossly, the consolidated areas resemble the gray stage of lobar pneumonia, or they may appear as multiple nodules of varying size, widely scattered throughout both lungs. Such abnormal tissue does not metastasize to extrapulmonary organs. When metastasis occurs, the lesion is considered to have been carcinomatous from the beginning rather than adenomatous in nature. Microscopically, the involved areas reveal pulmonary alveoli lined with a single layer of columnar or cuboidal epithelial cells containing mucus. These cells do not show the variation in size, shape and staining capacity characteristic of malignant neoplastic cells. The origin of the epithelial cells lining the pulmonary alveoli of human beings affected by adenomatosis is a disputed question. Such cells in adenomatosis may possibly be derived by proliferation of cells of the terminal bronchi, or they may have grown from a pre-existing alveolar-lining epithelium.

A recent paper[52] placed on record 2 cases of pulmonary adenomatosis in untreated mice, one a virgin wild mouse and the other a male C3Hb mouse. This paper referred to a previous one[53] reporting the occurrence of this pulmonary lesion in 9 mice of the DBA strain (some males, some females) ingesting olive oil emulsions containing 1,2,5,6-dibenzanthracene and 20-methylcholanthrene. These lesions of pulmonary adenomatosis in the mouse were strikingly similar to those in man, in having present a single layer of columnar cells lining the pulmonary alveoli. The cytoplasm of each lining cell contained a large globule of mucus and papillary tufts of proliferating adenomatosis cells projected into the alveolar spaces in many places.

By contrast, the neoplastic cells of the common lung tumor of the mouse, alveologenic carcinoma, are all virtually devoid of mucoid material. The opinion was expressed that the lesion of pulmonary adenomatosis in mice does not represent a malignant neoplastic process and certainly it is readily distinguishable from alveologenic carcinoma in this species.

COMPARISON OF PULMONARY TUMORS OF MOUSE AND MAN

There are many differences between the pathologic characteristics of alveologenic carcinoma of the mouse and of bronchiogenic carcinoma of man. In the mouse, the spontaneous tumor is often multiple, and apparently arises from alveolar cells rather than from the bronchial epithelium, as in man. It exhibits an adenomatous pattern, whereas the majority of pulmonary tumors in man are squamous cell or undifferentiated carcinoma. The tumors of mice show a predilection for the peripheral zones of the lung, are of low-grade malignancy and are rarely fatal. In man, on the other hand, pulmonary cancer arises in the region of the hilus and is invariably so highly malignant that it is always fatal unless successfully treated. The metastases of untreated pulmonary cancer in man are usually widespread and exhibit a selective affinity for certain organs (e.g., brain and adrenal gland) in contrast to the tumor of the mouse which rarely metastasizes and, if so, then not selectively to any site.

The squamous type of pulmonary carcinoma of the mouse produced by inserting a dibenzanthracene-impregnated thread into the lung[2] differs from the ordinary spontaneous pulmonary tumor of the mouse and may prove to be more comparable to bronchial carcinoma of man. What relation, if any, exists between the common pulmonary tumor of the mouse and pulmonary adenomatosis of man and animals awaits clarification of the neoplastic or non-neoplastic nature and of the histogenesis of the latter process.[8] There is as yet no detailed report in the literature of the tumors induced in the lung of rats by radioactive cerium (Ce^{144}) administered as an aerosol into the lungs. The abstract[26] reporting this observation indicates the occurrence of metaplastic changes in the bronchial epithelium and the development of malignant tumors therefrom. If this neoplasm develops in the bronchus as stated, it may prove to be sufficiently similar to bronchiogenic carcinoma in man to be used as a suitable experimental test object.

BIBLIOGRAPHY

1. Andervont, H. B. Pulmonary tumors in mice: I. The susceptibility of the lungs of albino mice to the carcinogenic action of 1,2,5,6-dibenzanthracene. *Pub. Health Rep. 52:* 212-221, 1937.
2. Andervont, H. B. Pulmonary tumors in mice: IV. Lung tumors induced by subcutaneous injection of 1,2,5,6-dibenzanthracene in different media and by its direct contact with lung tissues. *Pub. Health Rep. 52:* 1584-1589, 1937.
3. Andervont, H. B. Pulmonary tumors in mice: III. The serial transmission of lung tumors occurring in inbred mice. *Pub. Health Rep. 54:* 1519-1524, 1939.
4. Andervont, H. B. Induction of hemangio-endotheliomas and sarcomas in mice with *o*-aminoazotoluene. *J. Nat. Cancer Inst. 10:* 927-941, 1950.

5. ANDERVONT, H. B., and SHIMKIN, M. B. Biologic testing of carcinogens: II. Pulmonary-tumor-induction technique. *J. Nat. Cancer Inst. 1:* 225-239, 1940.
6. BITTNER, J. J. Breast and lung carcinoma in "A" stock mice. *Pub. Health Rep. 54:* 380-392, 1939.
7. COWEN, P. N. Strain differences in mice to the carcinogenic action of urethane and its non carcinogenicity in chicks and guinea pigs. *Brit. J. Cancer 4:* 245-253, 1950.
8. EDITORIAL. Alveolar cell tumor of the lung. *J.A.M.A. 144:* 1567-1568, 1950.
9. FRIED, B. M. *Bronchiogenic Carcinoma and Adenoma.* Baltimore, Md., Williams and Wilkins Company, 1948.
10. GRADY, H. G., and STEWART, H. L. Histogenesis of induced pulmonary tumors in Strain A mice. *Am. J. Path. 16:* 417-432, 1940.
11. HAALAND, M. Contributions to the study of the development of sarcoma under experimental conditions. Imperial Cancer Research Fund (Great Britain), *Third Scientific Report*, 1908, pp. 175-261.
12. HAALAND, M. Spontaneous tumors in mice. Imperial Cancer Research Fund (Great Britain), *Fourth Scientific Report*, 1911, pp. 1-113.
13. HESTON, W. E. Lung tumors and heredity: I. The susceptibility of four inbred strains of mice and their hybrids to pulmonary tumors induced by subcutaneous injection. *J. Nat. Cancer Inst. 1:* 105-111, 1940.
14. HESTON, W. E. Relationship between susceptibility to induced pulmonary tumors and certain known genes in mice. *J. Nat. Cancer Inst. 2:* 127-132, 1941.
15. HESTON, W. E. Genetic analysis of susceptibility to induced pulmonary tumors in mice. *J. Nat. Cancer Inst. 3:* 69-78, 1942.
16. HESTON, W. E. Inheritance of susceptibility to spontaneous pulmonary tumors in mice. *J. Nat. Cancer Inst. 3:* 79-82, 1942.
17. HESTON, W. E. Relationship between the lethal yellow (A^y) gene of the mouse and susceptibility to induced pulmonary tumors. *J. Nat. Cancer Inst. 3:* 303-308, 1942.
18. HESTON, W. E. Induction of pulmonary tumors in Strain A mice with methyl-bis (β-chloroethyl) amine hydrochloride. *J. Nat. Cancer Inst. 10:* 125-130, 1949.
19. HESTON, W. E. Carcinogenic action of the mustards (abstract). *Cancer Research 10:* 224, 1950.
20. HESTON, W. E., and DERINGER, MARGARET K. Relationship between the lethal yellow (A^y) gene of the mouse and susceptibility to spontaneous pulmonary tumors. *J. Nat. Cancer Inst. 7:* 463-465, 1947.
21. HESTON, W. E., and DERINGER, M. K. Relationship between the hairless gene and susceptibility to induced pulmonary tumors in mice. *J. Nat. Cancer Inst. 10:* 119-124, 1949.
21a. HESTON, W. E., and DUNN, T. B. Tumor development in susceptible strain A and resistant strain L lung transplants in LAF_1 hosts. *J. Nat. Cancer Inst. 11:* 1057-1071, 1951.
22. HORNING, E. S. Studies on the induction of lung cancer in mice. *Brit. J. Cancer 4:* 235-244, 1950.
23. JOBLING, J. W. Spontaneous tumors of the mouse. *Monographs, Rockefeller Inst. M. Research 1:* 81-119, 1910.
24. LARSEN, C. D. Pulmonary tumor induction with alkylated urethanes. *J. Nat. Cancer Inst. 9:* 35-37, 1948.
25. LAW, L. W. Mouse Genetic News #2. *J. Hered. 39:* 300-308, 1948.

26. LISCO, H., and FINKEL, M. P. Observations on lung pathology following the inhalation of radioactive cerium (abstract). *Federation Proc. 8:* 360, 1949.
27. LIVINGOOD, L. E. Tumors in the mouse. *Bull. Johns Hopkins Hosp. 7:* 177-178, 1896.
28. LORENZ, E., HESTON, W. E., DERINGER, M. K., and ESCHENBRENNER, A. B. Increase in incidence of lung tumors in Strain A mice following long-continued irradiation with gamma rays. *J. Nat. Cancer Inst. 6:* 349-353, 1946.
29. LORENZ, E., and SHIMKIN, M. B. Disappearance of intravenously injected methylcholanthrene in mice of different susceptibility to pulmonary tumors. *J. Nat. Cancer Inst. 2:* 491-498, 1942.
30. LORENZ, E., STEWART, H. L., DANIEL, J. H., and NELSON, C. V. The effects of breathing tobacco smoke on Strain A mice (abstract). *Cancer Research 3:* 123, 1943.
31. LUDFORD, R. J., and BARLOW, H. Sarcomatous transformation of the stroma of mammary carcinomas that stimulated fibroblastic growth in vitro. *Cancer Research 5:* 257-264, 1945.
32. LYNCH, C. J. Studies on the relation between tumor susceptibility and heredity: III. Spontaneous tumors of the lung in mice. *J. Exper. Med. 43:* 339-355, 1926.
33. MILLS, C. A., and PORTER, M. M. Tobacco smoking habits and cancer of the mouth and respiratory system. *Cancer Research 10:* 539-542, 1950.
34. MOSTOFI, F. K., and LARSEN, C. D. Pulmonary lesions induced in Wistar rats by urethane. *Am. J. Path. 25:* 807-808, 1949.
35. MOSTOFI, F. K., and LARSEN, C. D. Cytogenesis of pulmonary tumors induced by urethane (abstract). *Cancer Research 9:* 544, 1949.
36. MOSTOFI, F. K., and LARSEN, C. D. The histopathogenesis of pulmonary tumors induced in Strain A mice by urethane. *J. Nat. Cancer Inst. 11:* 1187-1221, 1951.
37. MURPHY, J. B., and STURM, E. Primary lung tumors in mice following the cutaneous application of coal tar. *J. Exper. Med. 42:* 693-700, 1925.
38. MURRAY, J. A. Spontaneous cancer in the mouse; histology, metastasis, transplantability, and the relations of malignant new growths to spontaneously affected animals. Imperial Cancer Research Fund (Great Britain), *Third Scientific Report,* 1908, pp. 69-114.
39. NETTLESHIP, A., and HENSHAW, P. S. The induction of pulmonary tumors in mice with ethyl carbamate (urethane). *J. Nat. Cancer Inst. 4:* 309-319, 1943.
40. NEUBUERGER, K. T., and GEEVER, E. F. Alveolar cell tumor of the human lung. *Arch. Path. 33:* 551-569, 1942.
41. OPPENHEIMER, J. M. The non-specificity of the germ-layers. *Quart. Rev. Biol. 15:* 1-27, 1940.
42. ORR, J. W. The induction of pulmonary adenomata in mice by urethane. *Brit. J. Cancer 1:* 311-316, 1947.
42a. PAPANICOLAU, G. N., and KOPROWSKA, I. Carcinoma in situ of the right lower bronchus. A case report. *Cancer 4:* 141-146, 1951.
43. SHIMKIN, M. B. Induced pulmonary tumors in mice. I. Susceptibility of seven strains of mice to the action of intravenously injected methylcholanthrene. *Arch. Path. 29:* 229-238, 1940.
44. SLYE, M., HOLMES, H. F., and WELLS, H. G. The primary spontaneous tumors of the lungs in mice. Studies on the incidence and inheritability of spontaneous tumors in mice. *J. M. Research 33:* 417-442, 1914.

45. SMITH, W. E., and ROUS, P. The neoplastic potentialities of transplanted embryo tissue: the gastric and pulmonary tumors induced with methylcholanthrene. *J. Exper. Med. 88:* 529-553, 1948.
46. STEWART, H. L., GRADY, H. G., and ANDERVONT, H. B. Development of sarcoma at site of serial transplantation of pulmonary tumors in inbred mice. *J. Nat. Cancer Inst. 7:* 207-225, 1947.
47. STRONG, L. C. The establishment of the "A" strain of inbred mice. *J. Hered. 27:* 21-24, 1936.
48. SWAN, L. L. Pulmonary adenomatosis of man: A review of the literature and a report of nine cases. *Arch. Path. 47:* 517-544, 1949.
49. TYZZER, E. E. A series of spontaneous tumors in mice with observations on the influence of heredity on the frequency of their occurrence. *J. M. Research 21:* 479-518, 1909.
50. WELLS, H. G., SLYE, M., and HOLMES, H. F. The occurrence and pathology of spontaneous carcinoma of the lung in mice. *Cancer Research 1:* 259-261, 1941.
51. WILLIS, R. A. *The Pathology of Tumors.* St. Louis, Mo., C. V. Mosby Company, 1948.
52. HORN, H. A., CONGDON, C. C., ESCHENBRENNER, A. B., ANDERVONT, H. B., and STEWART, H. L. Pulmonary adenomatosis in mice. *J. Nat. Cancer Inst. 12:* 1297-1316, 1952.
53. LORENZ, E., and STEWART, H. L. Tumors of the alimentary tract induced in mice by feeding olive oil emulsions containing carcinogenic hydrocarbons. *J. Nat. Cancer Inst. 7:* 227-238, 1947.

CHAPTER 7

Comparative Pathology of Early Cancer of the Thyroid Gland

I. N. Dubin

In recent years the genesis of tumors of the thyroid gland has been studied in experimental animals. Hyperplastic and neoplastic lesions of the thyroid gland have been produced in rats and mice by the administration of thiourea compounds, either alone or in combination with known carcinogens or with radioactive iodine.

HISTOGENESIS OF TUMORS

RATS

The thyroid gland responds to thiourea compounds in the following ways: [2, 3, 18, 20, 21, 22, 27] The first stage is the development of a diffuse hyperplasia of the thyroid gland. The epithelium becomes hyperplastic, and the intrafollicular colloid deposits disappear (Fig. 31). Papillary extrusions into follicles develop. Hyperplastic (Fig. 32) and neoplastic nodules appear and become especially prominent usually about one year after treatment, at which time the phase of degeneration begins.

The degenerative changes involve the hyperplastic tissue to a much greater extent than the adenomatous tissue. Hall and Bielschowsky[18] describe pyknosis of nuclei, vacuolization and loss of staining capacity of the cytoplasm, desquamation of degenerated cells and loss of alveolar structure. Money and Rawson[22] also describe atrophy of epithelium in late stages of the process. This atrophy is accompanied by the appearance of large sinus-like structures filled with blood. Areas of undifferentiated cells also develop both in the hyperplastic and adenomatous regions. These areas may appear as solid masses of undifferentiated cells, or as tubular proliferations and cordlike projections of acinar cells resembling fetal thyroid gland. Money and Rawson noted that these cordlike projections later formed tiny follicles and suggested that this tissue may probably differentiate later into thyroid glandular tissue that may appear to be normal.*

The localized adenomas appear to arise from single follicles.[22] They may present hemorrhage, fibrosis, and colloid lakes. The adenomas do not regress when stimulation ceases[2] and have been found as long as nine months after stopping the administration of thiourea.[21]

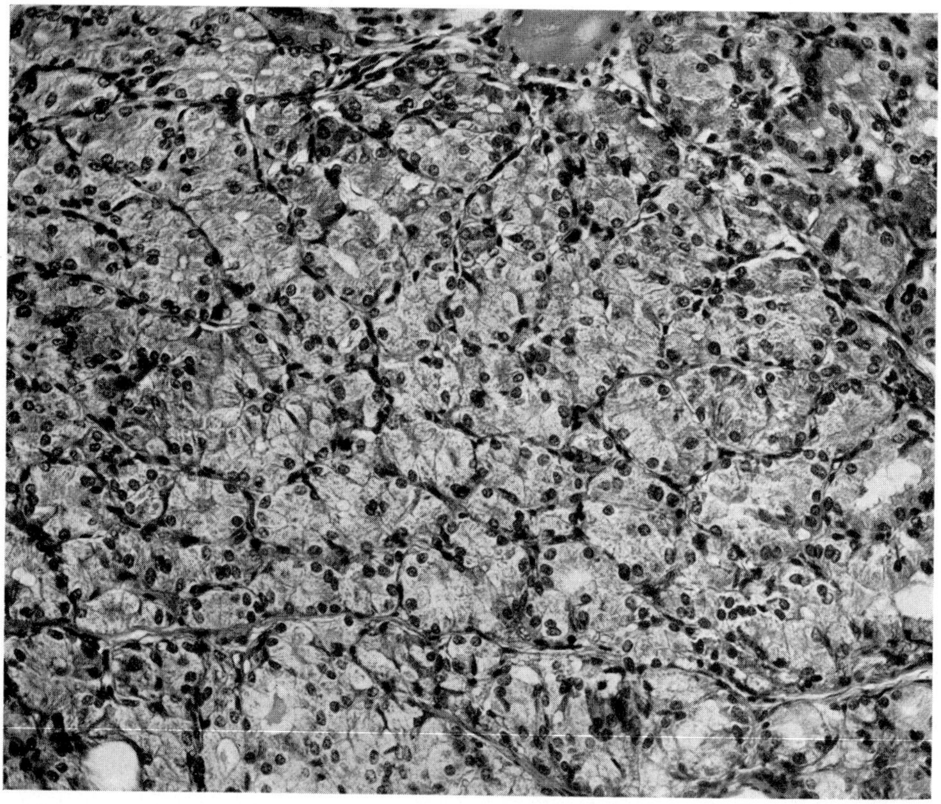

FIG. 31. Diffuse hyperplasia of thyroid gland of a female rat after 266 days of 0.1 per cent thiouracil in the diet. This thyroid gland weighed 150 mg., compared to a normal weight of 10-20 mg. Hematoxylin and eosin. × 220. (Figures 31 and 32 are reproduced through the courtesy of Dr. G. Laqueur.)

The incidence of malignant tumors in the lesions produced by thiourea compounds has varied from worker to worker. In Laqueur's experiments,[20] which lasted one year, no malignant tumors were observed. Money and Rawson[22]

* Analogies have been drawn between this kind of tissue in experimental animals[27] and so-called "fetal adenoma" in man. The association of "fetal adenoma" with carcinoma of the thyroid in man has led some pathologists to the view that "fetal adenoma" may give rise to carcinoma. Insofar as experimental animals are concerned, tissue resembling fetal thyroid gland can develop as a result of a reparative process of proliferation, having no significance in the subsequent development of malignancy.

believe that most of the tumors produced by thiouracil are benign. In the experience of Purves and Griesbach,[27] most of the rats showed adenomatous growths in the second year of thiourea administration and after twenty months of treatment approximately half of these tumors (7 out of 13) revealed histologic evidence of malignancy.

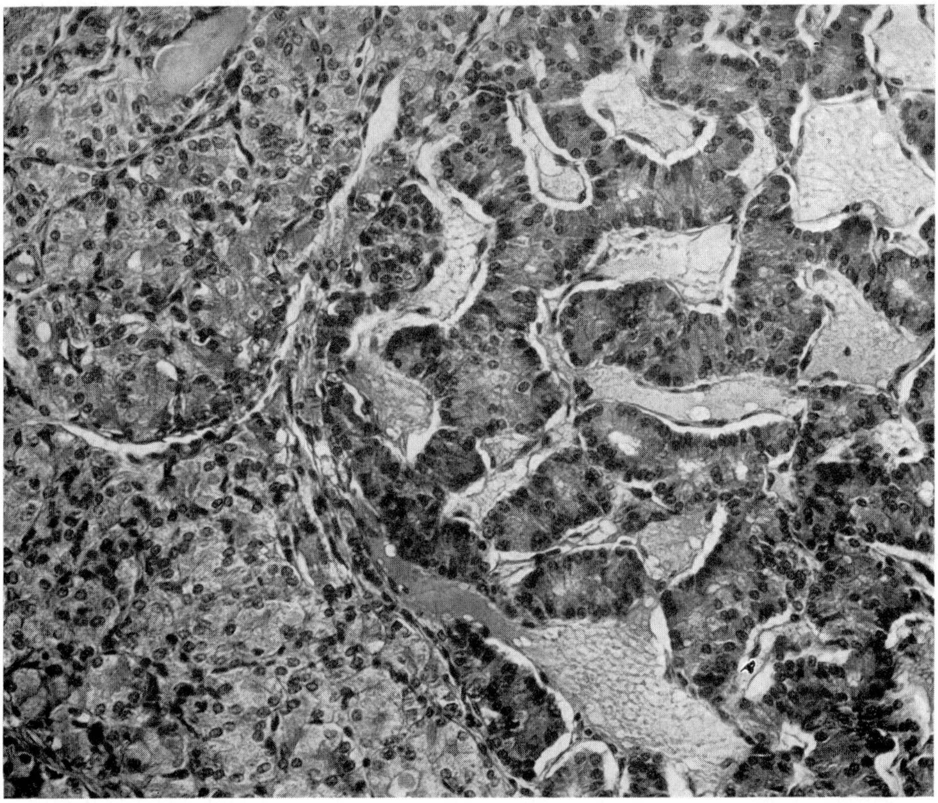

FIG. 32. Same animal as in Fig. 31. An area of nodular hyperplasia of thyroid glandular tissue. Note prominent vascular channels within the nodule. Hematoxylin and eosin. × 112.

MICE

The changes produced by goitrogens in the thyroid gland of the mouse differ in some respects from those observed in the rat. In addition, Dalton, Morris and Dubnik[8, 9] found that the thyroid gland of C3H mice reacted differently from that of Strain C mice.

In C3H mice,[8] there was an early development of extreme and diffuse hyperplasia of the thyroid gland (Fig. 33). After one year of treatment with thiouracil the thyroid gland reached a weight of 50 mg. as compared to the normal weight of about 4 mg. In 2 mice thyroid tissue was found outside the limits of the capsule. Pulmonary metastases (Fig. 34) were found in approximately half the animals.

The thyroid glands of Strain C mice reacted somewhat differently to the goitrogens.[9] Here too there was an early phase of diffuse hyperplasia with disappearance of colloid. But in later stages some of the hyperplastic tissue underwent necrosis, and this was accompanied by the formation of lakes of blood and by nodular proliferations of thyroid glandular tissue (Fig. 35). In contradistinction to the high incidence of pulmonary metastases in the C3H mice, metastases in Strain C mice were found in only 1 of 30 animals.

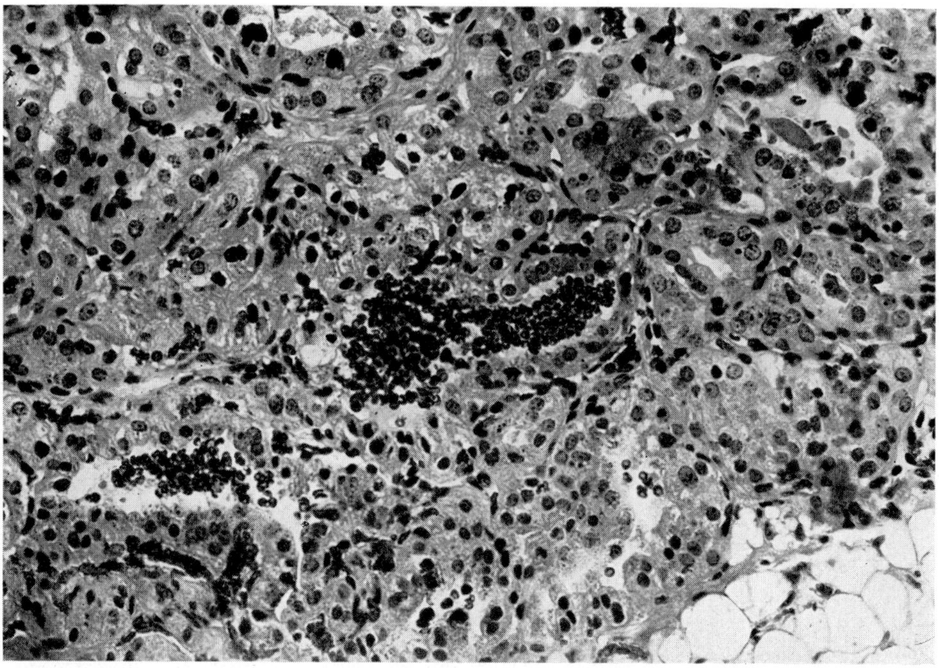

FIG. 33. Thyroid gland showing characteristic diffuse hyperplasia from a strain C3H mouse which had been treated with thiouracil for 119 days. Hematoxylin and eosin. (Figures 33–35 are reproduced through the courtesy of Dr. A. J. Dalton.)

Gorbman[12] treated various strains of mice with thiourea compounds. The thyroid gland reacted by a prolonged period of diffuse epithelial hyperplasia, without nodule formation. After 150 days of treatment, large cysts developed which were gradually filled with papillary ingrowths. Later, solid masses of cells were observed, forming solid cords or tiny follicles. In 2 cases, thyroid tissue was found in the small extrathyroidal veins. Serial sections of the lungs of 22 mice revealed pulmonary nodules in 7, which were similar to thyroid glandular tissue. Return of the animals to a normal diet after 300 to 450 days of treatment with thiourea compounds produced in about two weeks' time a prompt involution of the anaplastic-appearing epithelium in the thyroid gland and reappearance of intrafollicular colloid deposits.

MECHANISM OF ACTION OF THIOUREA COMPOUNDS

The thiourea compounds prevent the formation of diiodotyrosine and thyroxin, presumably by inhibiting the oxidase activity during the conversion of inorganic iodide to iodine and possibly by reacting with iodine itself by reducing it.[32] The pituitary gland responds to the resultant thyroxin deficiency by increased secretion of thyrotropin which in turn stimulates the thyroid gland to become hyperplastic. This hyperplasia is coincident with a state of hypothyroidism.[1] It can be abolished by the administration of thyroid gland powder.[1]

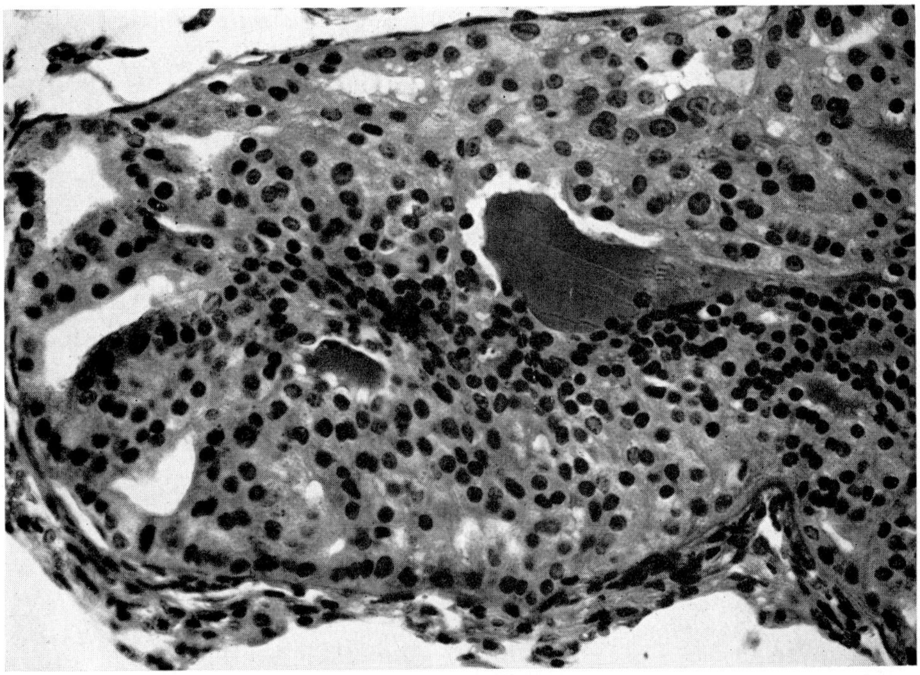

FIG. 34. Pulmonary metastasis of thyroid tissue in a strain C3H mouse which had been treated with thiouracil for 464 days. The metastasis was remarkably similar to the thyroid gland itself. Hematoxylin and eosin. × 355.

Adenomas of the thyroid gland can be produced in rats not only by thiouracil, but also by certain diets deficient in iodine,[19, 30] by partial thyroidectomy,[4] or by radioactive iodine.[10]

Hyperplasia of the thyroid gland produced by thiouracil compounds can be abolished by hypophysectomy.[1] Furthermore, the pituitary gland of rats fed thiourea compounds regularly contains "thyroidectomy cells," [8, 16, 20] indicating response of the pituitary gland to thyroxin deficiency. Unfortunately, studies on the concentration of thyrotropin in the blood serum of rats treated with thiourea compounds have been limited and have produced conflicting results.[13, 15,]

Griesbach, Kennedy, and Purves[14] tested the hypothesis that thyroid gland neoplasms may result from a repeated cycle of hyperplasia and involution and concluded that in the rat the stimulation of the thyroid gland had to be continuous in order for adenomas to be produced.

RELATION OF CARCINOGENS TO THIOUREA COMPOUNDS

It is clear that the thiourea compounds by themselves are capable of producing hyperplasia, adenoma, and even adenocarcinoma of the thyroid gland, but the role of carcinogens (such as acetylaminofluorene) when given in conjunction with these goitrogens is still not settled.

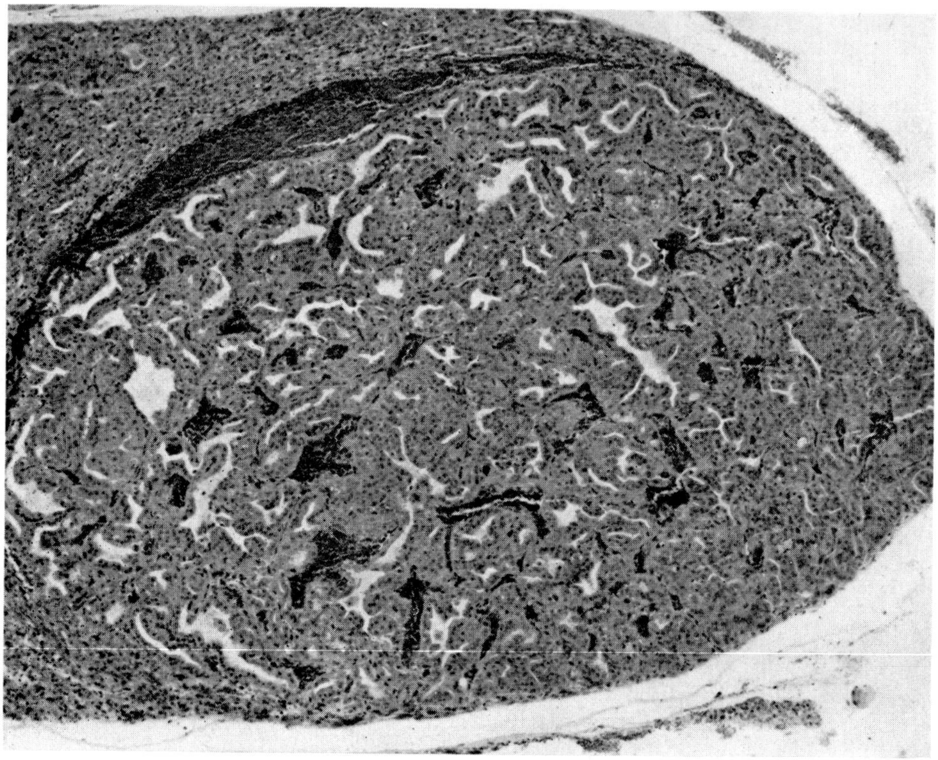

FIG. 35. Hyperplastic nodule of thyroid glandular tissue in a strain C male mouse which had been treated with thiouracil for 681 days. The nodule presents greater cell size than the adjacent tissue. Note the hemorrhage and pressure atrophy immediately surrounding the nodule. Hematoxylin and eosin. × 85.

Acetylaminofluorene alone produces few[6] or no[2] neoplasms of the thyroid gland. Tumors of the thyroid gland have been produced by radioactive iodine itself,[10] but it is not clear whether this substance produced this effect by merely destroying thyroid glandular tissue or by acting directly as a carcinogen.

Dibenzanthracene[22] and 3,4-benzpyrene[12] produced no obvious augmenting effect when given with thiourea compounds. While Gorbman[12] found no enhancing effect of acetylaminofluorene, other workers[10, 18, 24] have noted that this carcinogen hastened the development and increased the incidence of thyroid adenomas and even carcinomas.[24]

AUTONOMY OF INDUCED TUMORS

As in the case of human tumors of the thyroid gland, questions have been raised concerning the degree of autonomy exhibited by the induced neoplasms. Information has been derived from transplantation experiments, from studies on the reaction of the neoplastic tissues to hormonal influences, and from histopathologic examinations.

CRITERIA FOR DETERMINING MALIGNANT STATE

Authors disagree upon the factors to be used in establishing the diagnosis of malignancy for the induced neoplasms described above. Bielschowsky and co-workers[5] based the diagnosis of malignancy of the rat tumors on: (1) invasive growth and ability to metastasize; and (2) the close histologic resemblance to malignant neoplasms of the human thyroid gland. They considered that like many tumors of the human thyroid gland, the experimental tumors in rats showed only a low grade of malignancy.

Money and Rawson[22] found no pulmonary metastases in their material; furthermore, only one of their transplants was successful. They were, therefore, not satisfied with histologic criteria alone and desired additional biologic proof such as the transplantability of tumors. Purves and Griesbach[26] and Paschkis and co-workers[24] felt that criteria for malignancy were satisfied by invasion of muscle and blood vessels and by pulmonary metastases.

TRANSPLANTATION EXPERIMENTS

Morris, Dalton and Green,[23] in transplantation studies on induced neoplasms of the thyroid gland of mice, found that subcutaneous transplants would at first grow only when the host was given thiouracil, indicating dependence of the transplant on thyrotropin. In subsequent generations, however, some of these transplants began to grow in the absence of thiouracil, still maintaining a histologic structure typical of thyroid gland. This independence of thyrotropin indicates the development of a considerable degree of autonomy.

Bielschowsky and co-workers[5] noted that the experimental thyroid gland tumors of rats could only be transplanted into animals in which a thyroxin deficiency was present. In other words, continued growth of such transplants was dependent upon the presence of pituitary thyrotropin. Money and Rawson[22] also transplanted induced thyroid tumors into rats. In only one case did a transplant show signs of growth in the recipient.

The results of transplantation experiments indicate a low degree of autonomy on the part of induced tumors of the thyroid gland. Nevertheless, malignant behavior is not necessarily ruled out by a low degree of autonomy and by dependence of tumor tissue on a hormone. Metastases from breast and prostatic carcinoma in man react to hormonal influences and nevertheless behave like malignant tissue. For a more complete discussion of the problem of dependency of tumors on hormones see pages 160, 225, and following.

REACTION OF TUMORS OF THE THYROID GLAND TO HORMONAL INFLUENCES

The limited autonomy of these neoplasms is further indicated by their ability to react to hormonal influences. Doniach[10] found that an induced adenoma took up radioactive iodine although less actively than the surrounding follicles. Others[14] have observed that induced adenomas, while able to react to thyroxin by colloid involution, would still persist as localized neoplasms. Reaction to treatment with thyroid has also been observed in some of the induced carcinomas of the thyroid gland, although to a lesser degree than that exhibited by the benign tumors.[26, 27]

The experience with the induced tumors is paralleled by the results of recent investigations on neoplasms in man. Rawson and co-workers[28] found that benign tumors of the thyroid gland in man have an avidity for iodine, but usually to a lesser degree than that possessed by normal thyroid glandular tissue. The degree of avidity of benign tumors for iodine increased with the degree of histologic differentiation. Conversely, most malignant tumors of the thyroid gland demonstrated little or no avidity for iodine. The avidity of metastases from thyroid gland cancers for iodine was increased in certain selected cases by removing or destroying the normal thyroid gland, suggesting that possibly the metastases might not have completely lost the ability to respond to thyrotropin and had taken over the function of the thyroid gland.

RELATIONSHIP BETWEEN HYPERPLASIA AND NEOPLASM OF THE THYROID GLAND

Wegelin,[30, 31] basing his conclusions on animal experiments and on experience derived from spontaneous tumors of the thyroid gland in man and animals, believed that neoplasia of the thyroid gland is preceded by hyperplasia. Bielschowsky[2] stated that there exists general agreement that adenomatous goiter is a main factor in the origin of cancer of the thyroid gland in man and he believed that his experiments confirmed this opinion. Money and Rawson[21] stated that their experimental data gave additional support to the theory that hyperplasia of the thyroid gland is a precursor of neoplasia.

ANALOGIES BETWEEN LESIONS OF THE THYROID GLAND IN MAN AND EXPERIMENTAL ANIMALS

In experimental animals, the stimulus which causes hyperplasia and neoplasia of the thyroid gland is prolonged stimulation by thyrotropin which follows a deficiency of thyroxin. In man, this mechanism has yet to be proved.

The histologic changes in the hyperplastic and neoplastic thyroid glands of rats are quite similar to some of those in the human thyroid gland. The difficulty of distinguishing between hyperplastic and neoplastic foci holds for lesions in both human and animal thyroid gland. Experiments on animals and recent experience with human material[7, 11, 25, 29] indicate, however, that the criteria of malignancy hitherto accepted (such as invasion of blood vessels, penetration beyond the limits of the capsule, and metastasis) represent sound criteria for diagnosis of malignancy in neoplasms of the thyroid gland.

The induced neoplasms proceed through a definite course of development: (1) hyperplasia; (2) local areas of proliferation of altered cells; (3) formation of adenomas; and finally (4) development of carcinomas. In man, there is less certainty concerning the relationship between diffuse and nodular hyperplasia of the thyroid gland and subsequent development of neoplasia in this gland.

In the field of human cancer one of the striking examples of malignant tumors of limited autonomy is a certain group of thyroid gland carcinomas. An interesting parallel is seen in the fact that virtually all the induced thyroid gland cancers in animals similarly exhibit a limited degree of autonomy.

BIBLIOGRAPHY

1. Astwood, E. B., Sullivan, J., Bissell, A., and Tyslowitz, R. Action of certain sulfonamides and of thiourea upon the function of the thyroid gland of the rat. *Endocrinology 32:* 210-225, 1943.
2. Bielschowsky, F. Tumours of the thyroid produced by 2-acetylaminofluorene and allyl-thiourea. *Brit. J. Exper. Path. 25:* 90-95, 1944.
3. Bielschowsky, F. Experimental nodular goitre. *Brit. J. Exper. Path. 26:* 270-275, 1945.
4. Bielschowsky, F. The role of thyroxine deficiency in the formation of experimental tumours of the thyroid. *Brit. J. Cancer 3:* 547-549, 1949.
5. Bielschowsky, F., Griesbach, W. E. Hall, W. H., Kennedy, T. H., and Purves, H. D. Studies on experimental goitre: The transplantability of experimental thyroid tumours of the rat. *Brit. J. Cancer 3:* 541-546, 1949.
6. Cox, A. J., Wilson, R. H., and De Eds, F. The carcinogenic activity of 2-acetylaminofluorene: Characteristics of the lesions in albino rats. *Cancer Research 7:* 647-657, 1947.
7. Crile, G., Jr. Cancer of the thyroid. *J. Clin. Endocrinol. 10:* 1152-1170, 1950.
8. Dalton, A. J., Morris, H. P., and Dubnik, C. S. Morphologic changes in the organs of female C3H mice after long-term ingestion of thiourea and thiouracil. *J. Nat. Cancer Inst. 9:* 201-223, 1948.
9. Dalton, A. J. Morris, H. P., Striebich, M. J., and Dubnik, C. S. Histologic changes in strain C mice following long-term ingestion of thiouracil. *J. Nat. Cancer Inst. 11:* 397-413, 1950.
10. Doniach, I. The effect of radioactive iodine alone and in combination with methyl thiouracil and acetylaminofluorene upon tumour production in the rat's thyroid gland. *Brit. J. Cancer 4:* 223-234, 1950.
11. Frazell, E. L., and Foote, F. W., Jr. The natural history of thyroid cancer: Review of 301 cases. *J. Clin. Endocrinol. 9:* 1023-1030, 1949.
12. Gorbman, A. Thyroidal and vascular changes in mice following chronic treatment with goitrogens and carcinogens. *Cancer Research 7:* 746-758, 1947.
13. Gordon, A. S., Goldsmith, E. D., and Charipper, H. A. Thyrotrophic hormone content of the blood sera and pituitary glands of thiourea-, sulfadiazine-treated and thyroidectomized rats. *Endocrinology 36:* 53-61, 1945.

14. Griesbach, W. E., Kennedy, T. H., and Purves, H. D. Studies on experimental goitre: VI. Thyroid adenomata in rats on Brassica seed diet. *Brit. J. Exper. Path. 26:* 18-24, 1945.
15. Griesbach, W. E., and Purves, H. D. Studies on experimental goitre: V. Pituitary function in relation to goitrogenesis and thyroidectomy. *Brit. J. Exper. Path. 24:* 174-184, 1943.
16. Griesbach, W. E., and Purves, H. D. The significance of the basophil changes in the pituitary accompanying various forms of thyroxine deficiency. *Brit. J. Exper. Path. 26:* 13-17, 1945.
17. Hall, W. H. The role of initiating and promoting factors in the pathogenesis of tumours of the thyroid. *Brit. J. Cancer 2:* 273-280, 1948.
18. Hall, W. H., Bielschowsky, F. The development of malignancy in experimentally induced adenomata of the thyroid. *Brit. J. Cancer 3:* 534-541, 1949.
19. Hellwig, C. A. Thyroid adenoma in experimental animals. *Am. J. Cancer 23:* 550-555, 1935.
20. Laqueur, G. L. Nodular hyperplasia of thyroid glands induced by thiouracil. *Cancer Research 9:* 247-255, 1949.
21. Money, W. L., and Rawson, R. W. The experimental production of thyroid tumors in the male rat. *Tr. Am. A. Study Goiter.* 171-178, 1947.
22. Money, W. L., and Rawson, R. W. The experimental production of thyroid tumors in the rat exposed to prolonged treatment with thiouracil. *Cancer 3:* 321-335, 1950.
23. Morris, H. P., Dalton, A. J., and Green, C. D. Malignant thyroid tumors occurring in the mouse after prolonged hormonal imbalance during the ingestion of thiouracil. *J. Clin. Endocrinol. 11:* 1281-1295, 1951.
24. Paschkis, K. E., Cantarow, A., and Stasney, J. Influence of thiouracil on carcinoma induced by 2-acetoaminofluorene. *Cancer Research 8:* 257-263, 1948.
25. *Panel on Head-and-Neck Tumors: Cancer of the Thyroid.* Proceedings of the First National Cancer Conference, American Cancer Society, New York, 1949.
26. Purves, H. D., and Griesbach, W. E. Studies on experimental goitre: VII. Thyroid carcinomata in rats treated with thiourea. *Brit. J. Exper. Path. 27:* 294-297, 1946.
27. Purves, H. D., and Griesbach, W. E. Studies on experimental goitre: VIII. Thyroid tumours in rats treated with thiourea. *Brit. J. Exper. Path. 28:* 46-53, 1947.
28. Rawson, R. W., Skanse, B. N., Marinelli, L. D., and Fluharty, R. G. Radioactive iodine; its use in studying certain functions of normal and neoplastic thyroid tissues. *Cancer 2:* 279-292, 1949.
29. Warren, S., and Feldman, J. D. The nature of lateral "aberrant" thyroid tumors. *Surg., Gyn. & Obst. 88:* 31-49, 1949.
30. Wegelin, C. Zur experimentellen Kropfforschung. *Schweiz. med. Wchnschr. 57:* 848-850, 1927.
31. Wegelin, C. Malignant disease of the thyroid gland and its relation to goitre in man and animals. *Cancer Review 3:* 297-313, 1928.
32. Williams, R. H. *Textbook of Endocrinology.* Philadelphia, W. B. Saunders, 1950.

CHAPTER 8

Morphology of Mammary Tumors in Mice

Thelma B. Dunn

VALUE OF MAMMARY TUMORS IN CANCER RESEARCH

A most significant event in experimental cancer research, which marked its real beginning, was the publication of Jensen's work in 1903.[26] He performed the first successful serial transplantation of a mammary tumor in the mouse, and understood the importance of this accomplishment in relation to the biology of cancer. (Previously a transplantation had been done by Morau, but he supposed that he was transplanting an infectious agent.) Since this beginning the mammary tumor of the mouse has probably been the most completely studied of all tumors. Jensen's original tumor was distributed to other laboratories in Europe and America and this stimulated cancer research at many different centers. These tumors were easily observed, they were frequent, and they were transplantable even in the period before inbred strains were available. These facts made them easily accessible to many scientists. Working with these tumors, they quickly recognized that tumor transplantation depended upon a transfer of living cells and not upon the propagation of some extracellular organism. This separated cancer from the group of bacterial diseases which were so vigorously and profitably studied at that time, and directed research into the complex and baffling problems of cell morphology and physiology.

It would be impossible in a brief survey to recount all the important advances in our knowledge of neoplastic growth which have been aided by the use of the mammary tumor of the mouse.[35] For instance, the study of its morphology disclosed many general principles concerned with the histogenesis of cancer and the correlation of histologic structure with biologic behavior. This tumor has proved an invaluable tool in investigations along the lines of genetics, endocrinology, nutrition, chemotherapy, and virology. It was observed that in certain colonies of mice many females had mammary cancer. Geneticists took advantage of this clue and patient endeavor finally led to the development of inbred strains of mice having a high and fairly predictable incidence of mammary tumors. As a further development, strains were bred which had a high or extremely low incidence of different forms of tumor. By the use of these diverse strains many variations in environment and extrinsic stimuli have been tested, and reductions or increases in the expected incidence of tumors have been produced. The cancer biologist, therefore, has a quantitative measure of the effect of many procedures.

Another advantage of the mammary tumor in experimental work is its accessibility to palpation, so that the size and growth rate can be estimated with reasonable accuracy. When tumors develop internally, or become generalized as in leukemia, the scientist is usually unable to determine the time of the initiation or the extent of the process before the death of the host. The nutritionist has found that the incidence and growth rate of spontaneous mammary tumors have responded delicately to variations in diet, and the endocrinologist has noted a similar delicate response to the hormonal status, so that the effects of caloric and other dietary restriction or hormonal variation have been accurately reflected by the number and size of developing tumors. In the course of these studies it was learned that a nonfunctioning or abnormally functioning ovary greatly affected the incidence of these hormonally controlled tumors, so that the condition of the ovaries should be ascertained by morphologic examination in all experiments using mammary tumors.[30]

In attempts to find a chemotherapeutic substance the mammary tumor of the mouse has been a favorite test object because of its availability and high degree of standardization. Natural regression in spontaneous or induced mammary tumors has seldom been observed;[47] and for this reason experiments with these tumors have disclosed the ineffectiveness of most of the chemotherapeutic agents tested in the past. When transplanted tumors have been used, however, unless highly inbred strains of animals were employed and the experimental animals and procedures rigidly controlled, some misleading data have been reported.

Finally, the recognition of the milk agent has greatly stimulated research on mammary tumors in mice and the virologists have taken part in many recent investigations. This extrachromosomal factor is transmitted by the milk of a high mammary strain female to its young and in some way so modifies the responsiveness of the mammary gland tissue or the stimuli acting upon it that with the proper hormonal stimulation, mammary tumors develop at a comparatively early age and in high incidence. This agent can be transferred to young mice of low mammary tumor strains by foster nursing, or it may be removed from the high tumor strain if milk from a low tumor strain female only is received. A prodigious amount of work has been carried out on this agent in the past ten years but scientists are not yet assured as to its nature. Geneticists know that the effect of this agent varies considerably in different strains of mice. Each strain must be individually tested, and no general rule or prediction as to the response to the agent can be applied.[21] Even the size of the dose appears to have an influence on the reaction of the agent; it is not a simple all-or-none response.[7] The milk factor is such an important modifying element that in all present-day research using the mammary tumor, it must be kept in mind. For this reason it is desirable to discuss separately the work done on the morphology of the mammary tumor in the "pre-milk-agent" period and that done later in the "post-milk-agent" period.

In this later period scientists have used inbred mice, and have been fully aware of the presence or absence of the agent. These conditions have altered some of our older conceptions as to the significance of morphology in relation to mammary tumors.

EARLY WORK

The early work on the morphology of mammary tumors was practically complete by 1913, at which time Woglom[48] published a review on experimental cancer research and summarized what had been done by previous pathologists. Apolant[3] in 1906 made the first detailed histologic study of mammary tumors. He had 76 tumors available and from these he devised a classification which was standard for many years. Apolant emphasized the same features which we recognize as characteristic today: a basic acinar structure, or "mother terrain," on which were developed innumerable variations resulting from such secondary modifications as cyst formation, papillary ingrowth into the cysts, solid cellular growths without lumen formation, cordlike structures of one to several layers of cells, and various other architectural arrangements of a glandular tumor. He tried to separate these varying forms into strict categories, but at the conclusion of this work he reported that it might be of no practical value since it appeared, first, that mammary tumors in the mouse formed a structural entity, and second, that different types were not sharply defined, but blended gradually into each other so that systematic divisions were more or less illusory. Apolant attempted to distinguish between benign and malignant forms, and remarked that while a malignant change in mammary gland adenomas was rare in human pathology, it was an everyday occurrence in the mouse: when a tumor in the mouse had grown to the size of a cherry, a malignant change could nearly always be found. He attempted to identify the histologic features of this malignant change, using the criteria relied upon in human pathology. Later experience has proved that such criteria are unreliable, and that, in mice, a high degree of histologic differentiation may accompany a rapid growth rate and early metastasis.

Following the report of Apolant, the most important papers on the morphology of mammary tumors came from pathologists working at the laboratories of the Imperial Cancer Research Fund in England. They agreed with Apolant on one essential point, that in all these tumors the basic type was more or less the same and reproduced mammary acini, although all gradations of structure were to be found, from this "adenomatous" form to a solid carcinoma.[37] A suggestion was made by Haaland[20] that while in most tumors derivation from the mammary acini was evident, in others where cordlike and tubular formations were frequent, an origin from ducts must be considered. He did not insist, however, that any sharp distinction could be drawn, since the two forms blended. Like many other pathologists who have attempted to classify mammary tumors; he provided categories for each tumor and then admitted that the tumors did not fit them snugly.

A great service of the English group was a study made of mammary tumors during serial transplantations and a description of morphologic changes.[5, 19]

Variations in the degree of keratinization were observed, and extreme keratinization was correlated with a slow growth rate. The transformation of pure epithelial tumors to morphologic types indistinguishable from fibrosarcoma during transplantation was also reported. In Haaland's experiments[19] an increased growth energy was noted to accompany this change. (Two of our most frequently employed transplantable tumors, sarcoma 37 and sarcoma 180, which grow in many different strains of mice, are said to have been derived from mammary tumors by this process.) A number of other epithelial tumors, among them pulmonary tumors[44] and squamous cell carcinomas, have later been reported to undergo such a change, and it usually occurs in early transplant generations. On the other hand, apparently identical epithelial tumors have been carried in transplants for many years without any change in morphology. A satisfactory explanation for this behavior has been sought by many pathologists. If cancer tissue can infect or by some means alter other tissue contiguous to it, new concepts as to its nature must be entertained. An interesting experiment pertinent to this problem was the growing of mammary tumor cells and normal fibroblasts together in tissue culture. A malignant change developed in the fibroblasts. Some objections have been raised as to the identification of the cells in tissue culture and the technic employed, so further efforts are required to solve this puzzle.[32]

These early workers described several special forms of mammary tumor which are usually found in any large collection. These will be discussed in a later section of this chapter. The early investigators also noted that mammary tumors were usually multicentric in origin, and this stimulated histologic investigations of the mammary glands of old mice, in an attempt to identify precancerous lesions. Studies of this same type have been repeated in recent years on inbred strains of mice with a predictable tumor incidence, and known presence or absence of the milk agent. This early work is, therefore, postponed for later discussion when the morphology of the precancerous lesion is considered.

Other important facts regarding morphology were established in this "pre-milk-agent" period. When inbred mice became available, it was noted that the mammary tumors still followed the same well-recognized pattern, and no strain differences were detected.[43] When estrogen-induced tumors from male mice were examined, they were histologically similar in all aspects to those arising spontaneously in the female of the same strain.[29]

Metastatic growth of mammary tumors was of interest from the first days of experimental cancer research. It was an important point in establishing the truly malignant nature of this tumor, and in proving its reliability as a tool for the investigations of the neoplastic process. Jensen failed to observe metastases in his tumors, but Borrel[11] early described metastases to the lungs which were of two general types: (1) an embolus within the larger blood vessels, sometimes covered by proliferating endothelium; and (2) a type in which the cancer cells reached the smaller pulmonary vessels and infiltrated the tissue. We see the same forms of pulmonary metastases today. Metastases to lymph nodes are extremely rare. Ashburn in 1937 investigated metastases of mammary tumors.[4] With the possible exception of an almost solidly cellular histologic form in which the number of metastases was rather high, there was no correlation between morphology and malignancy as represented by metastatic growth. On the other hand, such factors as the multiplicity, the duration, the size, and the rapidity of growth of the tumors were correlated with metastases in the lungs.

LATER WORK

With the development of inbred strains of mice, and our present ability to add or subtract the milk agent in many of these strains, there has been a renewed interest in the morphology of mammary tumors, and the changes in the mammary gland which may lead to the development of neoplasms. Close comparison of the morphology of tumors from different sources is now warranted, since such other factors as genetic constitution, hormonal effects, and the presence of the milk agent can be controlled. Knowledge from these new investigations is still accumulating, and it will be some time before all the reports can be properly evaluated. Some of them now appear to be contradictory, but this may be due to differences in the strains of mice.

PRECANCEROUS CHANGES

Many efforts have been concentrated on the recognition and identification of the earliest neoplastic change to be found in a tissue or cell. Animal experiments are indispensable for this, since tumors in man are usually of considerable bulk before they can be removed and examined histologically. The mammary glands from strains of mice with a high incidence of tumors have been much utilized for such studies.

Haaland[20] described a chronic inflammation of the interstitial tissue, and a dilatation of the ducts with consequent cyst formation in the mammary glands of old female mice bearing tumors. Occasionally these cysts were lined by squamous epithelial cells, but Haaland considered them of less consequence than another lesion which he called "nodular hypertrophy." This lesion resulted from an initial increase in the number of apparently normal acini which proceeded to the formation of large accumulations of acinar-like structures no longer connected with the mammary ducts. These nodules were regarded as probable precancerous foci which passed imperceptibly to cancer. Our present knowledge supports this suggestion, although Haaland's observations were made on non-inbred mice and nematodes were found in the subcutaneous tissue of many of his animals. In addition to the present advantage of high-mammary-tumor strains of mice which provide a tissue in which many precancerous foci are expected, morphologists now employ a technic for making whole mounts of the mammary glands which affords a means for an over-all survey of the mammary tissue. Suspicious areas can be selected from such whole mounts and prepared for histologic study. A recent report[25] employing these methods has described a "hyperplastic nodule" composed of budding acinar tissue; this was generally considered to be the most significant precancerous lesion. This formation probably bears a relation to the presence of the milk agent, since it was found in highest number only in mice of the proper genetic background with adequate hormonal stimulation, and with the agent. Areas composed of an overgrowth of fine ducts were also reported as frequent in the breast tissue of mice of a high cancer strain but such lesions are less common than the acinar proliferations. On the other hand, inflammatory foci were not shown to be associated with an increased incidence of mammary tumors. Chemical carcinogens have also been employed to induce mammary tumors, and the earliest precancerous foci under such conditions have been studied.[28] Mice of the same genetic background with and without the agent were used, and a precancerous lesion different from the "hyperplastic nodule" was found. It was described as a "proliferative squamous epithelial response," and the fully developed tumor consisted of a "mixed squamous and alveolar structure." These results were interpreted as indications that the carcinogenic hydrocarbon has its own independent mode or focus of action, since it did not merely accelerate the usual preneoplastic process of acinar proliferation which develops spontaneously or from the activity of the milk agent.

Still another recent report has described the spontaneous development of squamous differentiation in the mammary glands from a strain of mouse freed from the milk agent.[41] Similar lesions were also induced by methylcholanthrene, and some of these lesions eventually developed into "purely squamous mammary carcinomas." Another approach to the problem of identifying the precancerous lesion has been to treat male mice of different strains with estrogenic hormones.[9] In the susceptible strain with the milk agent, growth of ducts and localized proliferation of acini occurred, and cancer developed in a few cases. In the nonsusceptible males without the milk agent, widespread proliferation of acini, and cystic dilatation of the ducts resulted but no cancer developed.*

Despite the confusion on certain points, the following facts seem to be established: (1) The "hyperplastic nodule" consisting of a large cluster of budding acini is probably the most significant precancerous lesion in mice of a susceptible strain which have an adequate hormonal stimulation and the milk agent. (2) Squamous cell hyperplasia or metaplasia of the ducts is a significant precancerous lesion, especially in carcinogenesis induced by methylcholanthrene in mice without the agent. (3) "Inflammatory lesions" are relatively unimportant. It is obvious that the results of studies on the precancerous lesion are difficult to standardize and interpret and that only mice of known ancestry carefully tested as to the presence of the milk agent should be used. The age of the animals also affects the incidence of precancerous changes and must be considered.[27] The identification of these precancerous lesions in the mouse is of great importance in considering the histogenesis of the fully developed tumor.

* Several recent reports have appeared which give important data regarding the hyperplastic nodule:

(a) PULLINGER, B. D. Spontaneous mammary adenoma and carcinoma in R III b mice deprived of milk agent. *Brit. J. Cancer 6:* 69-77, 1952.

(b) PULLINGER, B. D. A gland of predilection for mammary nodules in a strain of mice deprived of the milk agent. *Brit. J. Cancer 6:* 78-79, 1952.

(c) MÜHLBOCK, O., TONGBERGER, W. VAN E., and VAN RIJSSEL, T. G. Studies on the development of mammary tumors in dilute brown DBAb mice without the agent. *J. Nat. Cancer Inst. 13:* 505-531, 1952.

THE FULLY DEVELOPED MAMMARY TUMOR

All the early work on mammary tumors in the mouse indicated that morphologically they showed a restricted range of modification from an easily recognized basic acinar structure. Variation from one area of a tumor to another was usual and different tumors from the same mouse showed different histologic structures. The gradual merging of one form into another, depending upon the degree of cyst formation, keratinization, and the proportion of areas reproducing acini, was recognized by all who examined large tumor collections. No correlation between biologic behavior and tumor morphology had been discovered. For these reasons most pathologists were agreed that no rigid scheme of classification could be devised for the mammary tumor, and that there would be no practical value in such an attempt. However, with the present use of inbred strains, the control of the milk agent, and the ability of such external agents as carcinogens and irradiation to elicit breast tumors, we have found it desirable to devise a "sorting scheme" by which these tumors can be grouped. The one in current use at the National Cancer Institute will be presented,[2, 23] along with a discussion of the representative tumor types. This scheme may need to be altered to accommodate new types which may be developed as a result of the many different conditions under which mammary tumors are now arising spontaneously or being induced. When large groups of tumors in mice of known ancestry, in which certain carcinogenic agents have been used, are analyzed by this scheme, significant morphologic variations are seen in the proportionate number of the different types of mammary tumors. If only single tumors are considered, no histologic features can be selected which reveal the strain of the mouse, the presence or absence of the milk agent, or the effect of carcinogenic agents such as methylcholanthrene or x-ray. Tumors of each of the types described below have been seen in nearly every large group from whatever source, but the proportion of certain types in distinctive groups of mice has been found to vary greatly.

MAMMARY TUMORS CLASSIFIED BY HISTOLOGIC CHARACTERISTICS

Adenocarcinoma, Type A

Synonyms. Typical mammary tumor, mammary adenoma, mammary tumor of basic acinar structure, alveolar carcinoma (Fig. 36).

A fine uniform acinar structure occupies over one-half of the section. All other tumor tissue in the section is of glandular epithelial origin, except for insignificant areas of squamous epithelium which may appear in many of these tumors. The acinar origin of this tumor is indicated by groups of rather small cuboidal epithelial cells arranged in single rows surrounding small to medium-sized gland spaces. Histologically it appears well differentiated and the orderly arrangement of cells, the small and uniform size, and the paucity of mitotic figures led some of the early pathologists to the conclusion that this represented a benign adenoma. Tumors of this type, however, metastasize readily, often reproducing the same

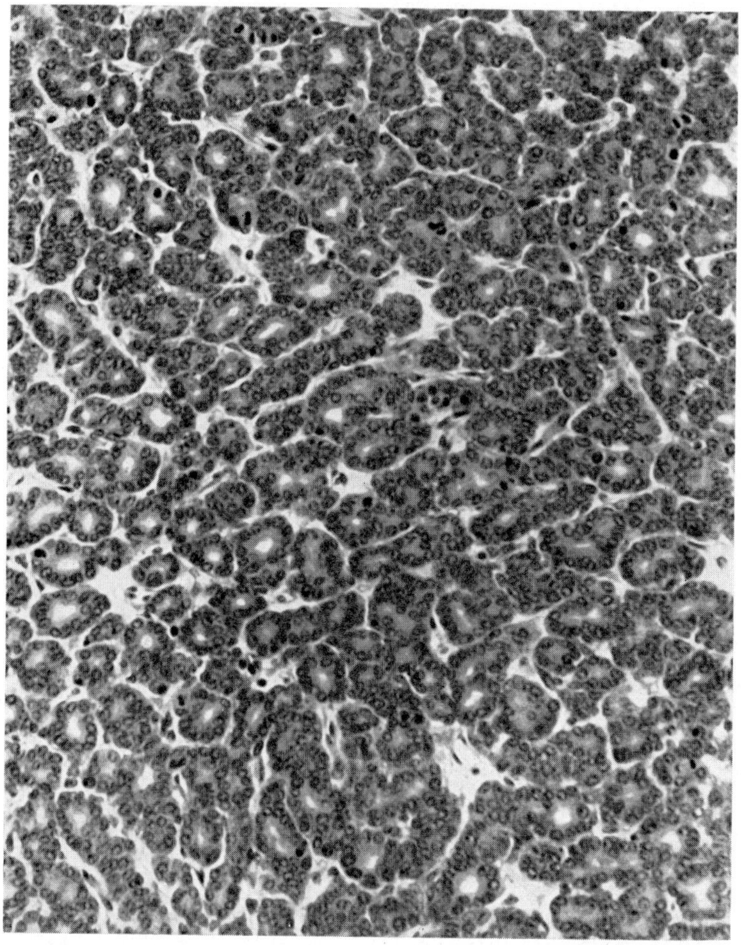

FIG. 36. Adenocarcinoma, type A, showing characteristic acinar structure. Hematoxylin and eosin. × 265.

structure, are easily transplanted, and may continue this same pattern indefinitely. Vacuoles may appear in the cell cytoplasm, and the luminal spaces may be distended with fluid (Fig. 39).

ADENOCARCINOMA, TYPE B

Synonyms. Papillary cyst adenocarcinoma, intracanalicular adenocarcinoma, carcinoma simplex (Figs. 37 and 38).

The value of separating this tumor type from type A is questionable, and the two groups are frequently combined. This type may reproduce mammary acini in only a small area of the section, but all the tissue is clearly of glandular epithelial origin. Cysts filled with blood or clear fluid, intracystic papillary projections, cords, and tubes of cells such as were described by Apolant and separately

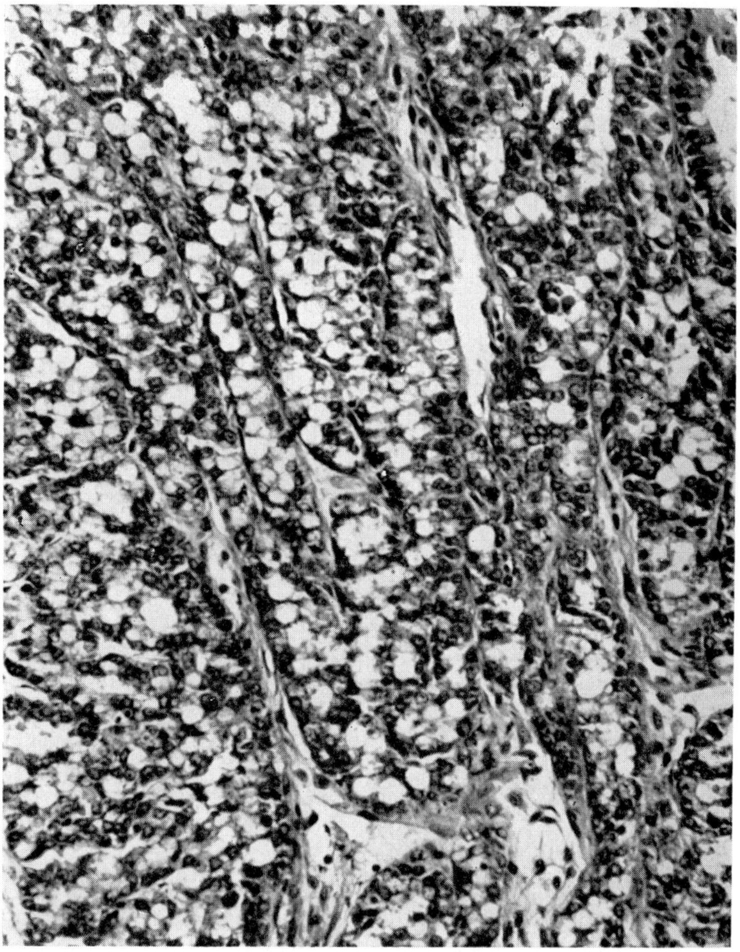

FIG. 37. Adenocarcinoma, type B, showing cyst formation and papillary in growth. Small glandular structures are developing in the more cellular areas. Hematoxylin and eosin. × 265.

classified by him will be found in this tumor form. Occasionally the cells may be arranged in solid sheets or nests, with no appearance of gland formation, and this solid form has been considered especially malignant. When such solid tumors were prepared to demonstrate Golgi material, the arrangement of the Golgi apparatus revealed a polarization characteristic of the acinar structure, supporting the idea that there was a close relation to Type A tumors.[15] Along with Type A these Type B forms represent the "typical" mammary tumors, but they have been separated off in some groups of tumors because the acinar structure is less predominant in Type B. The transition from Type A to Type B in a series of tumors may be very gradual. Many of these tumors suggest the participation or reproduction of mammary ducts along with the acinar proliferation. Such forms appear to be more frequent in Strain C than in Strain C3H females.

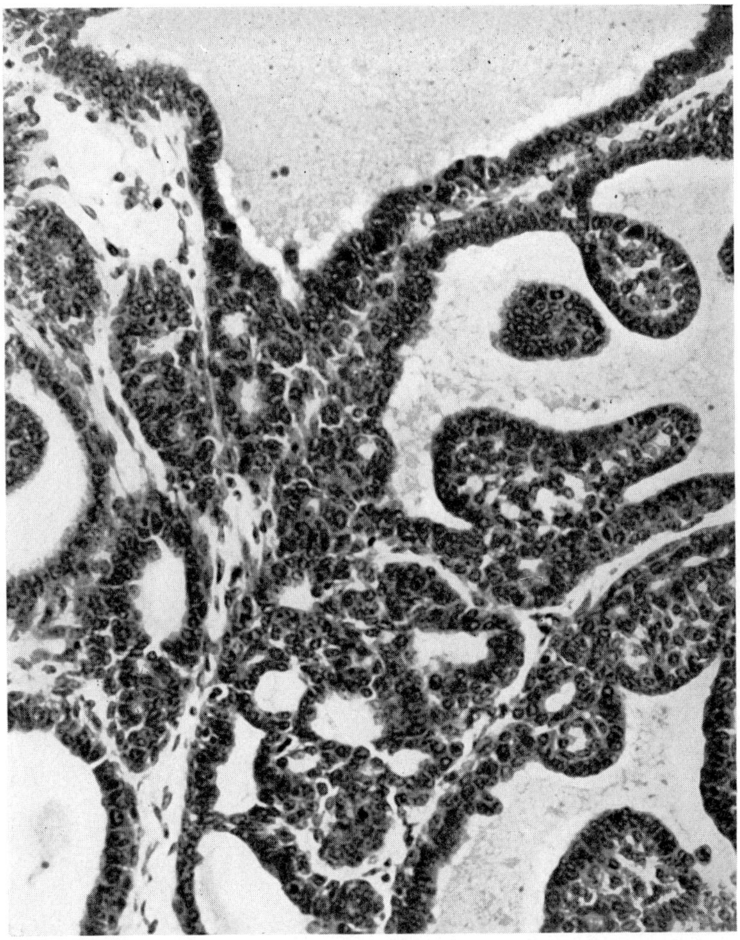

FIG. 38. Adenocarcinoma, type B, showing solid cellular formation, with no apparent glandular structure. Hematoxylin and eosin. × 265.

ADENOCARCINOMA, TYPE C

Synonyms. Fibroadenoma, adenofibroma (Figs. 40 and 41).

Microscopically this tumor is composed of multiple cysts, some extremely small in size, lined by a single layer of cuboidal epithelial cells. These cuboidal cells are closely invested by a layer of spindle cells with eosinophilic cytoplasm, which sometimes appear to fray out into the connective tissue intervening between the cysts. These spindle cells take a yellow color rather than the red of collagen with the van Gieson stain, and this stain is most useful in differentiating this tumor type. The connective tissue of this tumor is often distinctive, for it generally appears edematous, with few cells and few collagen fibers, and it may be basophilic in its staining reaction when hematoxylin and eosin are used. This is a distinctive type of tumor readily separated from other adenocarcinomas. Small areas are

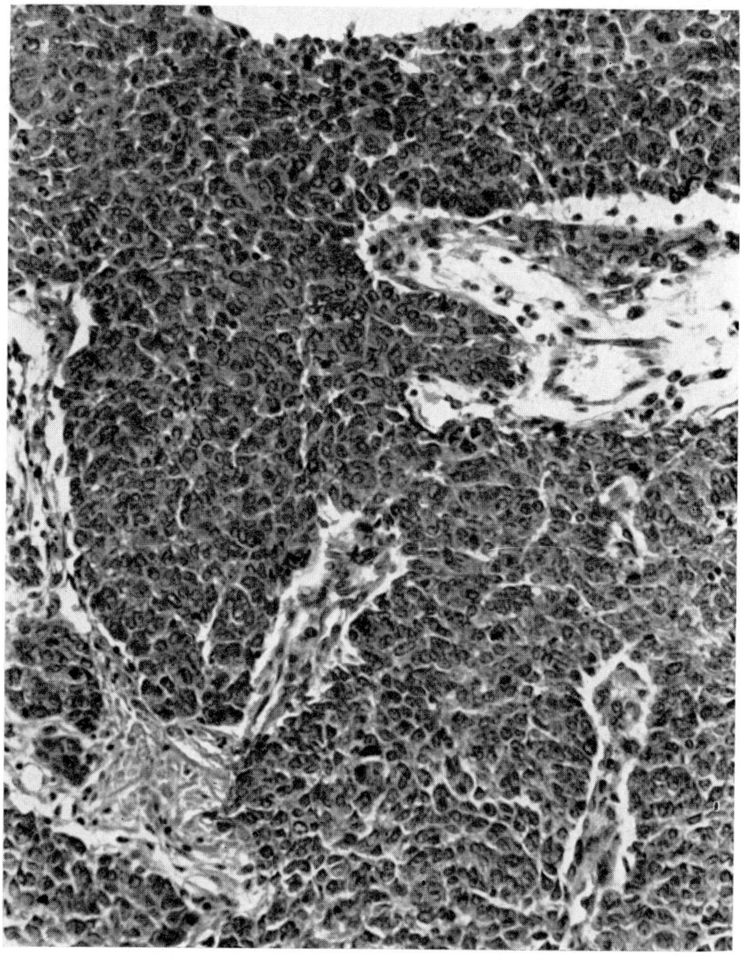

FIG. 39. Adenocarcinoma, type A, showing secretory activity, or lactation effect, in cells of one area. Hematoxylin and eosin. × 265.

occasionally seen in other types of mammary tumor in which this formation appears, but the characteristic Type C tumor is of uniform structure throughout. Its unique structure may reflect a unique origin since it has nearly always been found in very old mice. Many of these were hybrids—often with one Strain C parent—but it has also been seen in old C3H females without the milk agent. When it was first encountered,[1] it was thought to be similar to the "precancerous cystic lesion" described by Haaland in the mammary tissue of old female mice. Further opportunities to observe it, however, leave no doubt that it is a fairly distinct tumor entity. Only one in our experience has been successfully transplanted and the resulting tumor had the structure of an adenocarcinoma, Type B. Cloudman[14] has photographed and described a mammary tumor which appears to be identical with adenocarcinoma Type C. He called it a fibro-adenoma, and

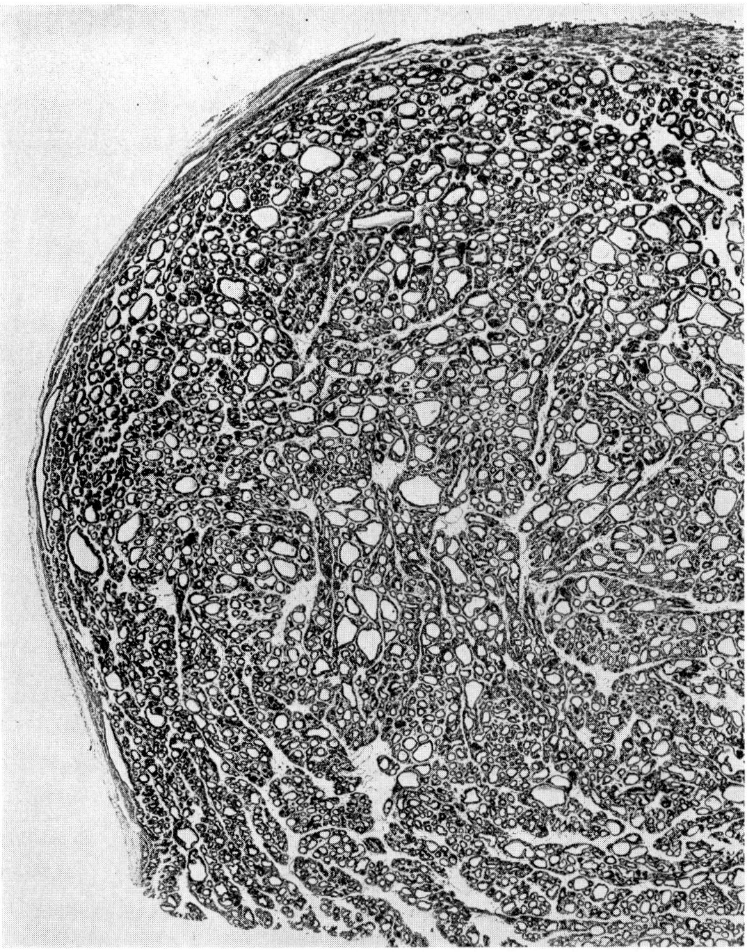

FIG. 40. Adenocarcinoma, type C, showing uniform structure of entire tumor, which is composed of small cysts lined by cuboidal epithelium. Hematoxylin and eosin. × 20.

he described the peculiar spindle cells which distinguish this tumor from other mammary tumors, but considered them to be fibroblastic.

ADENOACANTHOMA

Synonyms. Keratinized mammary tumor, adenosquamous carcinoma, adenocancroid, mammary tumor with squamous metaplasia (Fig. 42.)

These are tumors in which a considerable area of the section, usually estimated at one-fourth or more, shows an epidermoid structure. Although the squamous element is often referred to as metaplasia the epidermoid formation appears to be an integral part of the tumor development, and in structure it resembles the adenoacanthoma described in human beings. The recent descriptions of "precancerous"

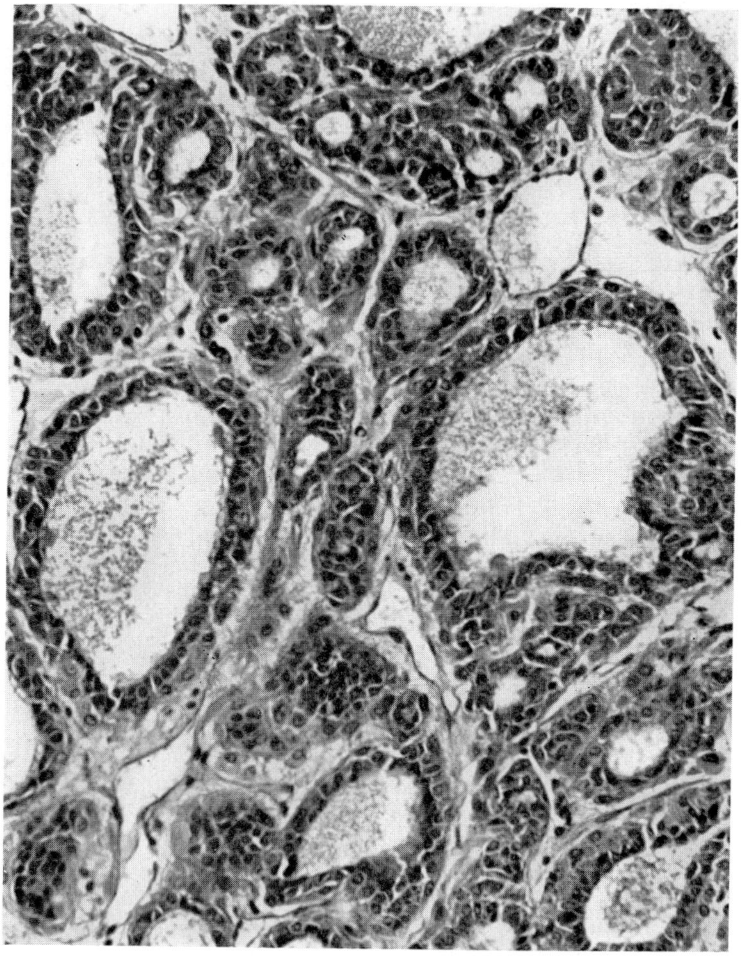

FIG. 41. Adenocarcinoma, type C, showing epithelial cells lining cysts invested by spindle cells. These spindle cells take a yellow color with the van Gieson stain, and are characteristic of this tumor type. Hematoxylin and eosin. × 235.

lesions in which squamous cell elements are prominent give more assurance to the impression that this does not represent a secondary metaplasia. Indications of malignancy such as an increased number of mitoses and anaplasia can be seen in the squamous epithelium, and metastases and transplantation usually reproduce these elements at least for a few generations.[37]

Since the glandular element of this tumor is similar to the structure of adenocarcinoma Types A and B, which may have varying amounts of an epidermoid element, it is not always possible to separate these merging forms exactly. In examining large groups of tumors, however, those in which the squamous element is significantly increased can be separated from other tumors. One variant of the adenoacanthoma is a form which Haaland[20] designated as molluscoid

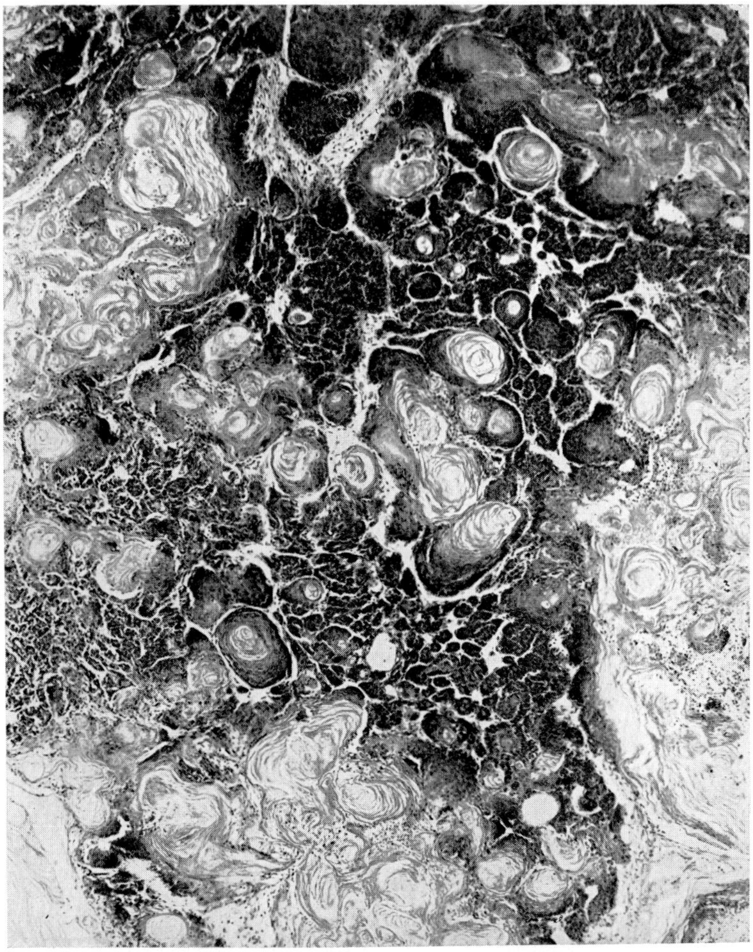

FIG. 42. Adenoacanthoma, showing intimate mixture of glandular tumor tissue and epidermoid tissue. Hematoxylin and eosin. × 65.

(Fig. 43) because of a supposed resemblance to molluscum contagiosum. He described the tumor as composed of lobes radiating like the spokes of a wheel from a central core of squamous epidermoid tissue. Varying amounts of epidermoid tissue are found in the center of this tumor and the radiating spokes suggest a reproduction of mammary ducts. The distal end of these ductlike structures may be surrounded by, and apparently connected with, a neoplastic tissue which reproduces mammary acini. While perfect examples of these formations are rare, imperfect formations of this type, which may involve only a small area of a larger tumor, often without the central epidermoid core, are not infrequent. This tumor is of peculiar interest, for it may furnish a clue to the understanding of many other mammary tumors. It suggests that all epithelial elements of the mammary gland are participating in the neoplastic process, and that we have

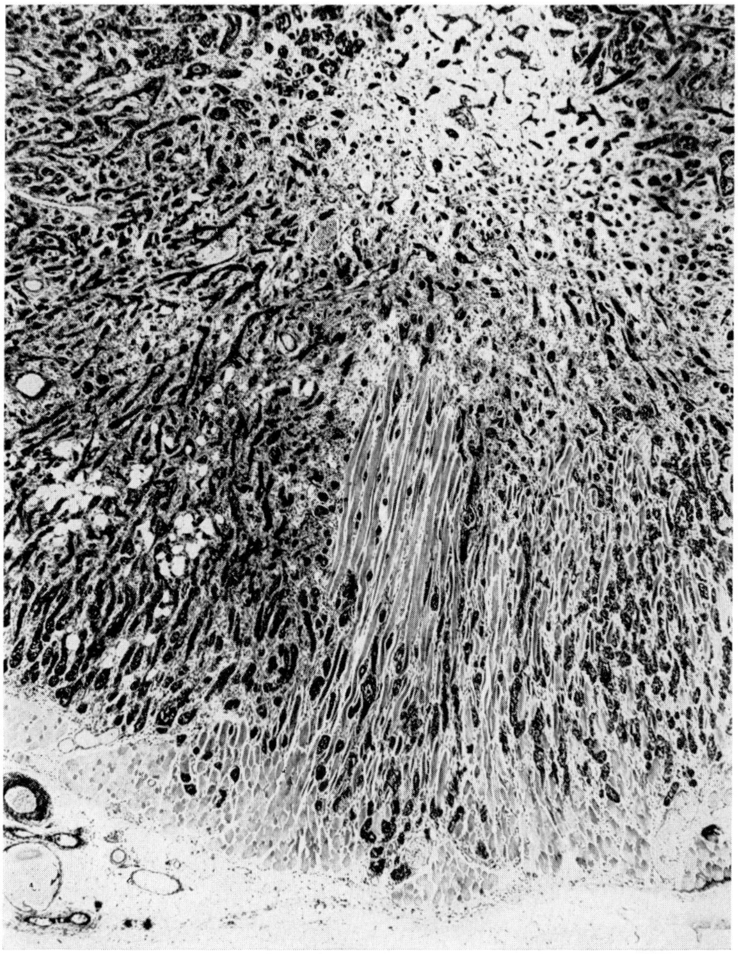

FIG. 43. Adenoacanthoma, molluscoid form. Central portion of this tumor type shows epidermoid formation, with rows of epithelial cells radiating outward. The periphery shows a more glandular structure. Note organoid architecture of this tumor, and how it infiltrates muscle while maintaining its general form. Hematoxylin and eosin. × 40.

a malignant transformation in a complex organ, and not a change in a single cell or small group of identical cells. The diversity of structure in other mammary tumors often suggests an abortive attempt at reproducing acini, ducts, and even the epidermoid structure of the nipple. Attempts at classification, therefore, may do no more than name the predominant element.

A "purely squamous mammary carcinoma" has recently been described.[41] We have either not seen this in mice at the National Cancer Institute, or have failed to recognize it. Provision should be made for this form, however, in a comprehensive scheme for tabulating mammary tumors.

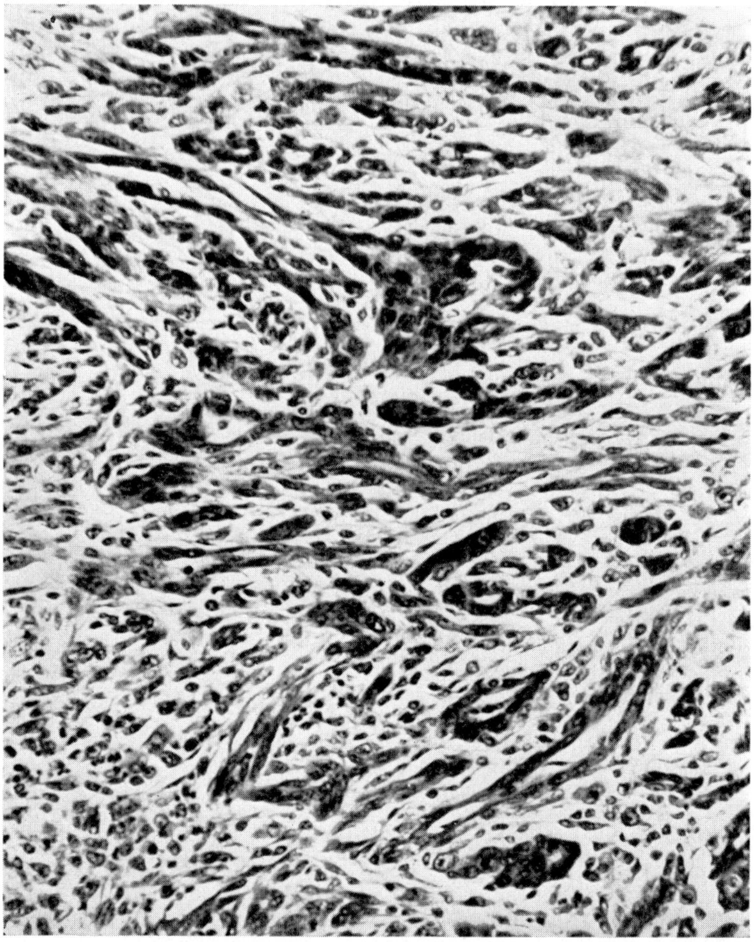

FIG. 44. Carcinosarcoma, showing a blending of neoplastic epithelial cells, and neoplastic spindle cells. Hematoxylin and eosin. × 265.

CARCINOSARCOMA

Synonym. Carcinoma with spindle cell formation, anaplastic carcinoma, mixed tumor (Fig. 44).

Primary tumors of this type, which were recognized by the early pathologists, are a not infrequent development on transplantation of purely glandular tumors, which may pass through a carcinosarcoma stage before becoming pure sarcomas. This tumor form exhibits a blending of cuboidal or round epithelial cells and elongate spindle cells resembling fibroblasts. Both elements may show numerous mitotic figures, and both may appear malignant. In some areas the epithelial cells appear to be assuming a spindle form. Whether this represents anaplasia in carcinoma cells, or whether a malignant change occurs in the stromal cells, either independently or under the influence of the growing carcinoma, has been the subject of much speculation and study.

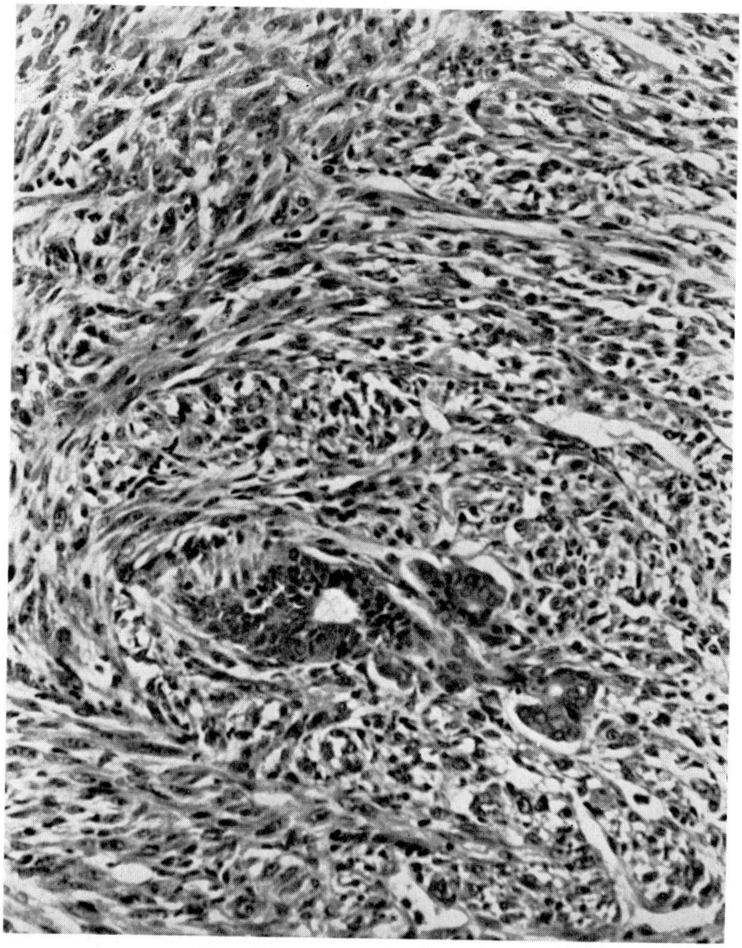

FIG. 45. Sarcoma of mammary gland area, showing typical fibrosarcoma surrounding mammary ducts. Hematoxylin and eosin. × 265.

SARCOMA OF THE MAMMARY GLAND AREA

Synonym. Mammary sarcoma (Fig. 45).

These tumors are composed of interlacing bundles of spindle cells and are similar to sarcomas originating at other sites, except that the spindle cells envelop the mammary ducts. Tumor giant cells are not infrequent. They have been listed because they occur with remarkable frequency in some groups of subcutaneous tumors removed for histologic confirmation and they appear to be increased in number after some experimental procedures which also affect the incidence of other mammary tumors.

MISCELLANEOUS

Unfortunately, very few classifications can avoid a "miscellaneous" category. It is reserved for tumors that do not fit any of the foregoing groups, yet do not form a

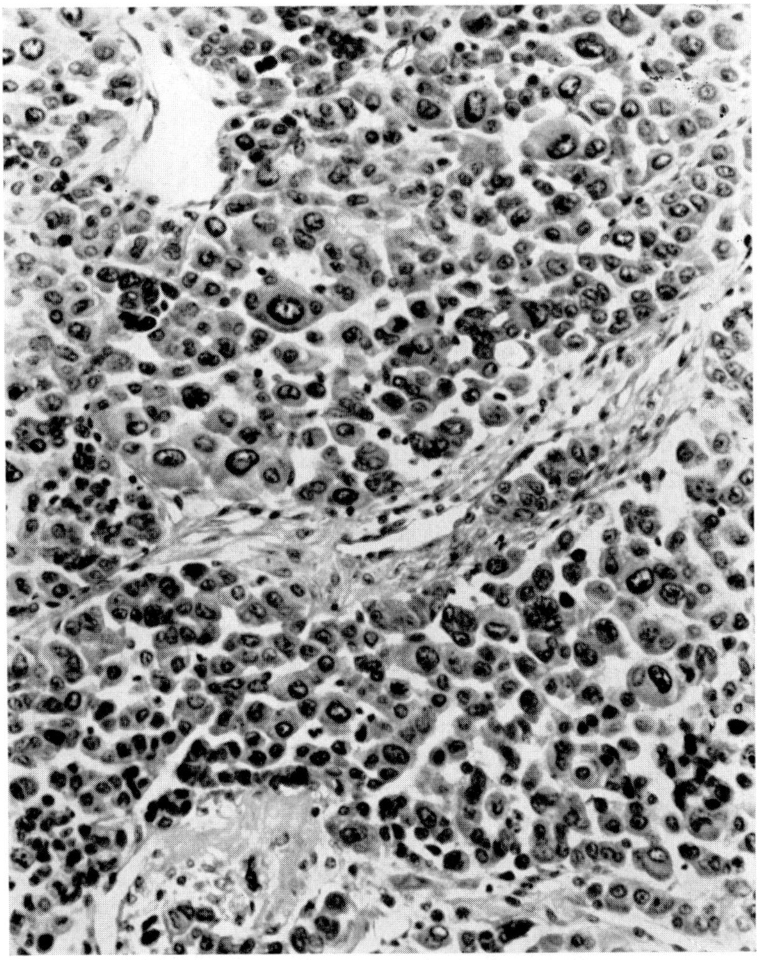

FIG. 46. "Miscellaneous" tumor of a bizarre type, showing detached cells of varying size. Hematoxylin and eosin. × 235.

uniform type among themselves. In all large groups of mammary tumors, particularly in mice freed of the tumor agent, some very bizarre tumors may appear. Tumors composed of extraordinarily large cells, sometimes rounded off and dissociated from the stroma and from other tumor cells, have been seen (Fig. 46). Other tumors have been found with an abundant connective tissue stroma far beyond what is usual for "typical" mammary tumors and resembling "scirrhous" carcinoma in the human breast. Still others show a more lightly stained epithelioid element, which may be myoepithelial in origin. A number of other variations are also found (Fig. 47). All tumors placed in this miscellaneous group should be individually described and separately catalogued.

The pathologist should also be cognizant of other subcutaneous tumors in the mouse which may be mistaken for mammary tumors. Myoepitheliomas originating

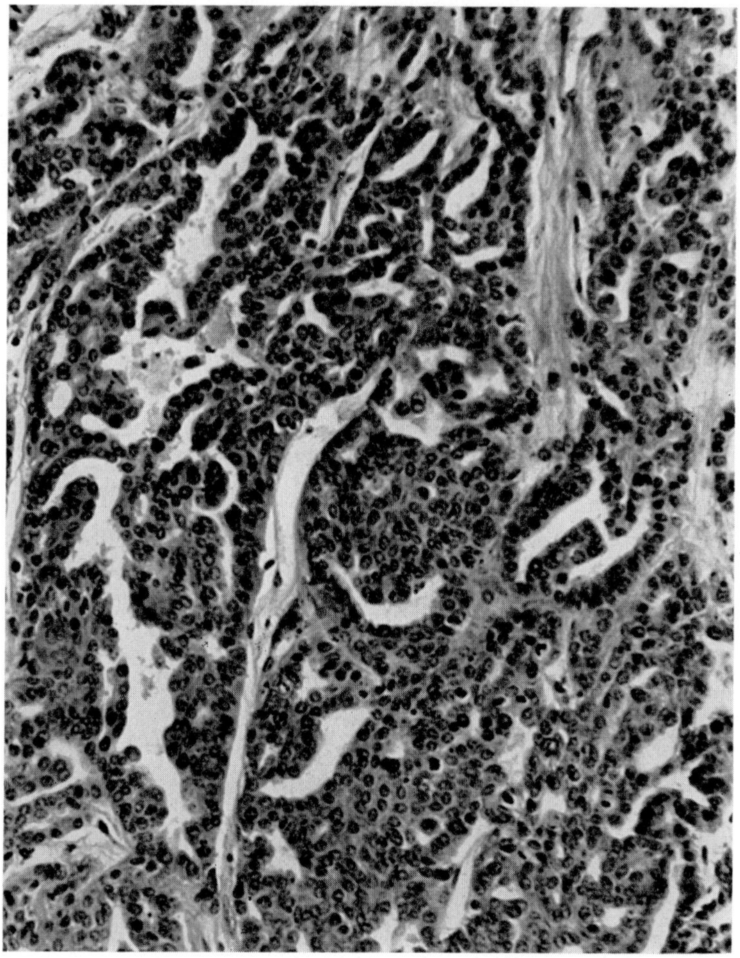

FIG. 47. "Miscellaneous" tumor of an unclassified type, showing epithelial cells with no evidence of an acinar arrangement. Hematoxylin and eosin. × 250.

in the salivary gland, or rarely in the mammary gland, may be confused with mammary cancer. Rhabdomyosarcomas and mast cell tumors have been seen at the site of the mammary gland, though very rarely. Squamous cell carcinomas from the skin, or skin appendage tumors have also been encountered. Lymphosarcomas are readily distinguished by their location in lymph nodes and by their characteristic histology.

In addition to this sorting process, when large groups of mammary tumors are examined it may be worth while to note certain histologic features. Evidence of secretory activity (or lactation) may be revealed by vacuolation of the cell cytoplasm, and filling of the lumen with secretion. Correlation of this apparent functional activity with experimental procedures has not been determined in tumors examined in this laboratory but reports from other laboratories have indicated that it may be significant.[42] By appropriate staining procedures, the number of mast cells in the section or the presence of iron in the surrounding mammary tissue may be determined. Such observations may be of value in some studies.

Using this scheme as a guide, tumors from various groups of mice recently available at the National Cancer Institute have been sorted and tabulated (Table 1).

TABLE 1. MORPHOLOGY OF MAMMARY TUMORS IN MICE WITH AND WITHOUT THE MILK AGENT

			Morphologic type					
Strain	*Milk agent*	*Number of tumors*	*Adeno-carcinoma A and B*	*Adeno-carcinoma C*	*Adeno-acanthoma*	*Car-cinosarcoma*	*Sar-coma*	*Mis-cella-neous*
C	+	94	92		1			1
C3H	+	123	122		1			
C3H	–	82	60		17	1		4
(C × C3H)F_1	?	190	172	17	8			1
Hybrids*	?	17	5	12				
DBA	+	40	40					
DBA	+ (+ MCA)†	29	25	2				2
DBA	– (+ MCA)	86	30		30	20	4	2

* F_1 hybrids derived from Strains C57 black, I,C,C3H, and DBA.[1]

† Treated with methylcholanthrene.

Notable features in this table are the high incidence of adenocarcinomas, Types A and B, in Strain C3H, Strain C, and Strain DBA mice with the mammary tumor agent; the relatively high incidence of adenoacanthomas in Strain C3H mice without the agent; the number of adenocarcinomas Type C in old hybrid mice, and the number of carcinosarcomas in DBA mice without the milk agent but treated with methylcholanthrene. The same group of mice in which carcinosarcomas were most frequent had the largest number of sarcomas. These findings indicate that the mammary tumor agent may exert an especial stimulus on the acini, so that tumors with a predominantly acinar structure develop at a relatively early age and cause death. More unusual forms of tumors will emerge when the agent is absent and the mouse survives to an older age group. It is impossible to determine the effect of age alone on the morphology of mammary tumors in mice, since tumors ordinarily do not appear at an early age unless the milk agent is present. The latter causes death at a relatively early age of all susceptible mice, so that old mice with mammary tumors are seldom found in strains with the agent.

The indication from this table that the acinar tumor is particularly related to the milk agent is supported by reports from other laboratories. In one study[9] castrated male mice from strains with and without the milk agent were treated with estrogens. The mice without the milk agent developed a high degree of "acinous hyperplasia," but this seldom led to cancer whereas in males with the milk agent an acinar type of cancer was frequent. The conclusion was reached that the effect of the milk agent was mainly upon the acini and the resulting tumor was of acinar structure. In discussing these results the author pointed out that in human beings, on the contrary, cancer usually begins in the ducts, and the question was raised as to whether a milk factor exists in the human subject, and if so whether it must not be of a different kind acting primarily upon the ducts.[10] This whole problem is considerably complicated by the variations in the morphology of tumors which may develop in different strains. It is probable that with the removal of the milk agent, strain differences in the histologic structure of mammary tumors may be revealed, and a final understanding of these differences cannot be expected until many different strains have been tested.

Since the milk agent can be removed, it has become possible to study the effects of other carcinogenic agents on susceptible mammary tissue. Methylcholanthrene has produced a greatly increased number of adenoacanthomas in certain strains of mice.[28] Irradiation resulted in an increased number of both adenocarcinomas and sarcomas of the mammary glands in Strain C3H mice without the milk agent.[31] These same mice had a greatly increased incidence of granulosa cell tumors of the ovary or mixed tumors of the ovary containing granulosa cell elements with which the mammary tumors were always associated. Tests on the mammary tumors which developed following irradiation failed to show the presence of the tumor agent.*

COMPARISON OF MAMMARY TUMORS IN MICE TO BREAST CANCER IN WOMEN

PRECANCEROUS STAGES

Attempts have been made to correlate the histologic appearances in the mammary tissue of old female mice of high cancer strains, with supposedly precancerous conditions in women.[13, 18, 45] Such attempts have been much hampered by the fact that there has been no clear agreement as to what constitutes a precancerous condition in either species. It is an attempt to check one unknown against another unknown. An analogy has been made between cystic and inflammatory lesions described in old female mice and chronic cystic mastitis of the human female. In more recent work, however, inflammatory foci in the mammary tissue of the mouse have not been identified as precancerous, and proliferations of mammary acini, or areas of squamous cell metaplasia are given greater importance. Doubt has been expressed that a condition simulating chronic cystic mastitis occurs in the mouse, although the dilatation and secretory activity following estrogenic administration is said to have some of the features of the human disease. Confusion is added by the varying conceptions which pathologists have of "chronic cystic mastitis" in the human breast. Foci of acinar proliferation, or "hyperplastic nodules," which are definitely precancerous in the mouse are very infrequent in women, in whom the most significant precancerous lesions are now considered

* Recently a report on the histologic types of mammary tumors in strain DBA mice without the agent has appeared: Mühlbock, O. G., Tongberger, W. van E., and van Rijssel, J. Studies on the development of mammary tumors in dilute brown DBAb mice without the agent. *J. Nat. Cancer Inst. 13:* 505-531, 1952.

to be proliferations of duct epithelium. The differences in the histologic pattern of the developed tumors in the two species are consistent with the differences in the preneoplastic lesions.

DEVELOPED TUMORS

Breast cancer in the human female is nearly always derived from the ducts; alveolar cancer is rare. In the mouse, on the other hand, acinar or alveolar cancer is the most frequent type, especially in the presence of the milk agent. Statements by Willis[46] regarding interpretations of the structure of mammary carcinoma in human beings apply equally well to histologic examinations of mammary tumors of the mouse. He wrote that different parts of one tumor commonly show different structural variants, and terms such as "comedo," "scirrhous," "medullary," "adeno," and "simplex" when applied to cancer in women have only locally descriptive, not classificatory, value. Further, while individual tumors often show predominance of one or another type of structure, the structure of a breast tumor is rarely uniform throughout. He considered that histologic subdivisions of mammary carcinoma are arbitrary and when they are based on single or few sections of each tumor, they are often misleading. The same lack of uniformity exists in mammary tumors in the mouse. In the absence of the milk agent, when mice reach an advanced age many of the mammary tumors which develop show an adenoacanthomatous structure, which is, like the acinar formation, very rare in human tumors. Some workers have predicted, however, that as more tumors from mice without the milk agent are accumulated, more will be found resembling human breast cancer in structure and a duct origin will more often be simulated. An origin in the ducts is suggested by some of the tumors placed in the adenocarcinomas Type B, and some tumors in the miscellaneous group have an extreme degree of fibrosis resembling scirrhous carcinoma. The opinion is now widely held that breast cancer in women is often multicentric, which has long been recognized as the usual condition in mammary tumors in the mouse.

THE MILK AGENT

The possibility that a tumor agent may exist in human milk by which mammary cancer is transmitted from the mother to female offspring has been seriously considered.[6] No convincing evidence for this has yet been presented; and it seems highly inadvisable to advocate any radical changes in infant feeding on this possibility. All the facts gathered from animal experiments make it appear more and more improbable that such an agent exists in any other species except the mouse. No agent of this type has been demonstrated in any other animal, although the incidence of mammary tumors is high in one strain of rats.[12] A similar agent transmissible through the milk has not been found for any other form of tumor. The histologic type of mammary tumor most closely associated with the milk agent, the acinar (or alveolar), is of rare occurrence in women. Moreover, removal of the tumor agent in mice has not prevented the development of all mammary tumors. Data now being gathered on the incidence of breast cancer in the relatives of cancer patients,[33] and the records of a number of women with breast cancer who never received human milk,[24] do not support the opinion that a milk agent exists in human beings. Many scientists who have been most concerned with investigations of this agent in the mouse decry the impetuosity with which these findings have been applied to the human being.

PRESENT LINES OF RESEARCH

The mammary tumor of the mouse is still important in experimental cancer research. At the present time, many notable studies are concerned with mammary tumors and in these investigations the morphology of the tumors requires consideration.

Evidence is increasing that the mammary tumor agent may be transmitted by the male.[36] Mammary tumors have developed at an early age in hybrid mice presumably free of the agent, since the mothers were agent free, though the fathers carried the agent.[1] Some of these tumors of a "typical" acinar structure were found in young mice in which the agent was demonstrated. A number of "atypical" tumors or tumors of varied structure developed at a later age and were lacking the milk agent. In old mice without the agent, however, typical acinar tumors could still be found, so this morphologic type can develop in the absence of the agent.

An especially interesting group of tumors has been described which show progressive growth during periods of pregnancy and hormonal stimulation, with evidence of regression or quiescence between these periods. Eventually many of these tumors seem to be freed of their dependence and grow progressively irrespective of the hormonal state of the host. During the period when these tumors are partially hormone dependent, they grow on transplantation more readily in female than in male hosts. No microscopic descriptions of these tumors have yet been published, but they are described as exuding a milky fluid when cut or put into the fixative.[17]

Supported by the facts that mammary tumors require estrogenic stimulation of the mammary gland for their initiation, that many of them appear to be secreting as if capable of a functional response, and that they usually become independent of any external hormonal stimulus, the suggestion has been made that they may create their own intracellular hormone, and that this stimulus perpetuates them. Such a suggestion is thought provoking, since it postulates a chemical change as well as a morphologic change in the cancer cell, and proposes that the stimulus for continued growth is manufactured directly in the abnormal cell. Much more concrete evidence is required to establish this hypothesis but the mammary tumor seems to be the best available means of testing it.[42]

The testing of a mammary tumor for the milk agent is an exacting and tedious procedure, requiring a year or more for a positive, and even longer for a negative, answer. In spite of this obstacle, positive evidence is accumulating that many mammary tumors of the mouse have no demonstrable tumor agent.[16] This is conclusive proof that even in the mouse, elimination of the tumor agent will not eliminate all mammary tumors.

The claim that a filterable agent has been isolated from mammary tumors which survives freezing and drying of the cells,[34] and which elicits tumors in a period of days or weeks after injection, has been disproved.[8, 39] The results reporting the presence of a transmissible virus emphasize on the other hand the remarkable power of the mammary tumor cell to withstand harsh treatment, and to remain viable and grow when transplanted to a new host.

Further attempts have been made to visualize the mammary tumor agent by means of the electron microscope. Particulate bodies have been seen in epithelial cells from mammary tumors of a high tumor strain grown in tissue culture.[40] Such bodies have also been found in tissues and fluids known to carry the agent, and similar bodies were said to be absent in fluids extracted from normal tissues.[38] If an exact localization of such bodies in the cancer cell can be determined, this will be a great addition to our present understanding of tumor morphology. The mammary tumor is an excellent object for such a search.

Unpublished data from the National Cancer Institute indicate that when the mammary tumor agent is removed from female mice of certain high tumor strains and they survive to an old age, not only do unusual tumor types appear in the mammary glands, but other reproductive and endocrine organs develop neoplasms never before observed in these strains.[22] Thus elimination of one histologic type of tumor characteristic of an early age period allows another histologic type to develop at a later age. A similar variation in human cancer incidence may be anticipated if effective prevention and treatment is developed for certain types of cancer, or if any other factor is introduced to increase the survival of human beings.

BIBLIOGRAPHY

1. Andervont, H. B., and Dunn, T. B. Mammary tumors in mice presumably free of the mammary-tumor agent. *J. Nat. Cancer Inst. 8:* 227-233, 1948.
2. Andervont, H. B., and Dunn, T. B. Response of mammary-tumor-agent-free strain DBA mice to percutaneous application of methylcholanthrene. *J. Nat. Cancer Inst. 10:* 895-925, 1950.
3. Apolant, H. Die Epithelialen Geschwülste der Maus. *Arb. a. d. Koniglchn. Inst. f. Expt. Ther. 1:* 7-62, 1906.
4. Ashburn, L. L. Spontaneous mammary tumors in mice: Factors influencing the incidence of metastases. *Pub. Health Rpt. 52:* 915-929, 1937.
5. Bashford, E. F. The behaviour of tumour cells during propagation. Imperial Cancer Research Fund (Great Britain), *Fourth Scientific Report,* p. 131-214, 1911.
6. Berner, J. The milk factor in the transmission of mammary carcinoma. *New England J. Med. 243:* 375-383, 1950.
7. Bittner, J. J. Activity of the mammary tumor milk agent as influenced by age and hormonal stimulation in serial dilution studies. Presented before the 37th Annual Meeting of the American Association for Cancer Research, March, 1946. *Cancer Research 6:* 493, 1946 (abstract).
8. Bittner, J. J., and Imagawa, D. T. Assay of frozen mouse mammary carcinoma for the mammary tumor milk agent. *Cancer Research 10:* 739-750, 1950.
9. Bonser, G. M. The effect of oestrone administration on the mammary glands of male mice of two strains differing greatly in their susceptibility to spontaneous mammary carcinoma. *J. Path. & Bact. 42:* 169-181, 1936.

10. BONSER, G. M. A microscopical study of the evolution of mouse mammary cancer: the effect of the milk factor and a comparison with the human disease. *J. Path. & Bact. 57:* 413-422, 1945.

11. BORREL, A. Épithélioses infectieuses et épithéliomas. *Ann Inst. Pasteur 17:* 81-118, 1903.

12. BRYAN, W. R., KLINCK, G. H., JR., and WOLFE, J. M. The unusual occurrence of high incidence of spontaneous mammary tumors in the Albany strain of rats. *Am. J. Cancer 33:* 370-388, 1938.

13. CHEATLE, G. L. Schimmelbusch's disease of the breast and Dr. A. Lacassagne's experiments on mice. *Brit. J. Surgery 22:* 710-715, 1934-1935.

14. CLOUDMAN, A. M. "Spontaneous neoplasms in mice." In STAFF OF THE ROSCOE B. JACKSON MEMORIAL LABORATORY: *Biology of the Laboratory Mouse.* Philadelphia, Blakiston, 1941, chap. 4.

15. DALTON, A. J. "Cytology of mammary tumors of the mouse." In MOULTON, F. R. (ed.): *Symposium on Mammary Tumors in Mice.* American Association for the Advancement of Science (No. 22), 1945.

16. DMOCHOWSKI, L. Spontaneous tumours in some low-breast-cancer strain mice and the mammary tumour agent (abstract). *Fifth International Cancer Congress* p. 59, 1950.

17. FOULDS, L. Mammary tumors in hybrid mice: Growth and progression of spontaneous tumours. *Brit. J. Cancer 3:* 345-375, 1949.

18. GOORMAGHTIGH, N., and AMERLINCK, A. Réalisation expérimentale de la maladie de Reclus de la mamelle chez la souris. *Bul. Assoc. franç. p. étude du cancer 19:* 527-529, 1930.

19. HAALAND, M. Contributions to the study of the development of sarcoma under experimental conditions. Imperial Cancer Research Fund (Great Britain), *Third Scientific Report,* pp. 175-261, 1908.

20. HAALAND, M. Spontaneous tumours in mice. Imperial Cancer Research Fund (Great Britain), *Fourth Scientific Report,* pp. 1-113, 1911.

21. HESTON, W. E. "Genetics of cancer." In DEMEREC, M. (ed.): *Advances in Genetics*, Vol. II, Edited by M. Demerec, New York, Academic Press Inc., vol. II, pp. 99-125, 1948.

22. HESTON, W. E. Unpublished data.

23. HESTON, W. E., DERINGER, M. K., DUNN, T. B., and LEVILLIAN, W. D. Factors in the development of spontaneous mammary gland tumors in agent-free strain C3Hb mice. *J. Nat. Cancer Inst. 10:* 1139-1155, 1950.

24. HORNE, H. W., JR. The "milk factor" in carcinoma of the human breast. *New England J. Med. 243:* 373-375, 1950.

25. HUSEBY, R. A., and BITTNER, J. J. A comparative morphological study of the mammary glands with reference to the known factors influencing the development of mammary carcinoma in mice. *Cancer Research 6:* 240-255, 1946.

26. JENSEN, C. O. Experimentelle Untersuchungen über Krebs bei Maüsen. Centbl. f. Bakt. *34:* 28, i. Abot, Jena 122, 4 pl., 1903.

27. JONES, E. E. A comparative study of hyperplastic nodules in mammary glands of mice with and without the mammary tumor inciter (abstract). *Fifth International Cancer Congress,* p. 59, 1950.

28. KIRSCHBAUM, A., WILLIAMS, W. L., and BITTNER, J. J. Induction of mammary cancer with methylcholanthrene: 1. Histogenesis of the induced neoplasm. *Cancer Research 6:* 354-362, 1946.

29. LACASSAGNE, A. Hormonal pathogenesis of adenocarcinoma of the breast. *Am. J. Cancer 27:* 217-228, 1936.
30. LATHROP, A. E. C., and LOEB, L. Further investigations on the origin of tumors in mice. On the part played by internal secretion in the spontaneous development of tumors. *J. Cancer Res. 1:* 1-20, 1916.
31. LORENZ, E., ESCHENBRENNER, A. B., HESTON, W. E., and UPHOFF, D. Mammary tumor incidence in female C3Hb mice following long continued gamma irradiation. *J. Nat. Cancer Inst. 11:* 947-965, 1951.
32. LUDFORD, R. J., and BARLOW, H. Sarcomatous transformation of the stroma of mammary carcinomas that stimulated fibroblastic growth in vitro. *Cancer Research 5:* 257-264, 1945.
33. MACKLIN, M. T. (Personal communication).
34. MANN, I., and DUNN, W. J. Propagation of mouse carcinoma by dried tumor tissue. *Brit. M. J. 2:* 255-257, 1949.
35. MOULTON, F. R. (ed.). *A Symposium on Mammary Tumors in Mice.* American Association for the Advancement of Science (No. 22), 1945.
36. MÜHLBOCK, O. Mammary tumor-agent in the sperm of high-cancer-strain male mice. *J. Nat. Cancer Inst. 10:* 861-864, 1950.
37. MURRAY, J. A. Spontaneous cancer in the mouse; histology, metastasis, transplantability, and the relations of malignant new growth to spontaneously affected animals. Imperial Cancer Research Fund (Great Britain), *Third Scientific Report* pp. 69-114, 1908.
38. PASSEY, R. D., DMOCHOWSKI, L., ASTBURY, W. T., REED, R., and JOHNSON, P. Electron microscope studies of normal and malignant tissues of high- and low-breast-cancer strains of mice. *Nature* London, *165:* 4186, 1950.
39. PASSEY, R. D., DMOCHOWSKI, L., and GLUCKSMANN, I. Discussion in "Freeze drying of mouse mammary tissues" (abstract). *Fifth International Cancer Congress,* p. 64, 1950.
40. PORTER, K. R., and THOMPSON, H. P. A particulate body associated with epithelial cells cultured from mammary carcinomas of mice of a milk-factor strain. *J. Exper. Med. 88:* 15-24, 1948.
41. PULLINGER, B. D. Squamous differentiation in mouse mammae: Spontaneous and induced. *Brit. J. Cancer 3:* 494-501, 1949.
42. PULLINGER, B. D. The significance of functional differentiation in mammary tumours. *Lancet 2:* p. 823-828, 1949.
43. PYBUS, F. C., and MILLER, E. W. Hereditary mammary carcinoma of mice: A description of 100 consecutive tumours. *Newcastle M. J. 14:* 151-169, 1934.
44. STEWART, H. L., GRADY, H. G., and ANDERVONT, H. B. Development of sarcoma at site of serial transplantation of pulmonary tumors in inbred mice. *J. Nat. Cancer Inst. 7:* 207-225, 1947.
45. TAYLOR, H. C., JR., and WALTMAN, C. A. Hyperplasia of the mammary gland in the human being and in the mouse. *Arch. Surg. 40:* 733-820, 1940.
46. WILLIS, R. A. *Pathology of Tumors.* St. Louis, Mo., C. V. Mosby Co., 1948.
47. WOGLOM, W. H. The regression of spontaneous mammary carcinoma in the mouse. *J. Cancer Research 7:* 379-394, 1922.
48. WOGLOM, W. H. The Study of Experimental Cancer Research: A Review. (George Crocker Spec. Res. Fund, No. 1). New York, Columbia Univ. Press, 1913.

CHAPTER 9

Testicular Tumors

Harlan I. Firminger

COMPONENTS OF THE TESTIS

The testis is a complex organ composed fundamentally of two components, germinal and endocrine. Each of these components is in itself complex and both are interrelated functionally as well as structurally. The germinal (sexual) component consists of spermatogenic cells in various stages of differentiation, developing within the seminiferous tubules. The endocrine component is made up of two types of cells: (1) the interstitial (Leydig) cells which are the main source of androgen and occupy the interstitial tissue of the testis; (2) the Sertoli cells which partially line the seminiferous tubules serve to nourish the spermatogenic cells, and at least in some species appear to secrete estrogen.

The anatomic relationhip between the germinal cells and the endocrine cells is more evident though no more intimate than their functional interrelationship, which also involves other more remote endocrine organs such as the pituitary and adrenal glands.

PROBLEMS OF TESTICULAR TUMORS IN MAN AND ANIMALS

As a result of this complex structural and functional interrelationship of the normal components of the testis, testicular tumors pose especially interesting problems for the investigator in cancer research. Few other tumors offer so many unique aspects for study. As with many tumors of endocrine glands there are the various complex hormonal problems. With respect to tumors of the testis, these fall into two general categories which are not always easily distinguished from each other; one arises as the result of the castrating effect of the tumor, the other, as the result of intrinsic hormonal activity of the tumor itself. Even more intriguing is the fact that teratoid tumors arising in the testis can morphologically resemble almost any tissue in the body, including placenta. In their differentiated form these teratoid growths dramatically illustrate the extreme complexity possible in a single tumor. Their organoid development indicates the action of organizers, probably intrinsic, on the tumor, but more interesting for further study is the evident susceptibility of the tumor cells to such action. The occasional complete atrophy and disappearance of the primary testicular tumor despite previous dissemination and continued growth of metastases is apparently unique among tumors.

SPONTANEOUS TUMORS

IN MAN

The fact that occasionally the primary growth of a tumor of the testis in man can regress completely following previous dissemination raises the question whether tumors ordinarily originating from the specialized germinal cells of the testis (such as seminoma, embryonal carcinoma, teratoma, and choriocarcinoma) ever arise de novo outside the testis. Well-documented teratomas have been reported as originating outside the testis but these do not show choriocarcinomatous areas. It is doubtful whether extragenital choriocarcinomas or teratomas showing choriocarcinomatous areas ever originate outside the genital system and alleged examples in males require especially thorough examination of the testes for the possible presence in such cases of a minute primary focus representing a regressed or healed primary tumor.[57] This distinction of two different types of teratomas was recognized by MacCallum[39] when he ascribed one to a primitive sex cell origin and the other to congenital inclusion of a somatic blastomere.

Primary seminoma-like tumors occur in the pineal region but there is a doubt as to their identity to testicular seminomas. Generally recognized, however, is the occurrence of seminomas (dysgerminomas) in the ovaries of women. Many of these women show anomalous sexual underdevelopment and even pseudohermaphroditism[47] suggesting that a focus of primordial testicular tissue may be the source of such tumors. This hypothesis seems especially attractive when one remembers that seminomas are many times more common in cryptorchid than in normal descended testes.[8, 25]

The chief obstacle to meeting the challenge to research provided by the whole group of testicular tumors is their comparative rarity. One fruitful approach to overcoming the predicament posed by the rarity of occurrence of testicular tumors in any one geographical area, is to establish a central collecting point for such cases. During the Second World War the pathologic material from about 1000 cases of testicular tumor was collected at the Armed Forces Institute of Pathology. This material is almost entirely from men of Army age and does not include many of the unusual testicular tumors arising in infants and children. Furthermore, study of this material is limited to review of clinical histories, examination of preserved pathologic specimens or microscopic sections, and collection of follow-up information.

Despite these limitations, valuable contributions have been made by the study of these cases by Friedman and Moore[19] and Dixon and Moore.[12] These investigators divided the tumors into two main groups, tumors of germinal and nongerminal origin. The first group includes seminoma, embryonal carcinoma, and teratomatous and choriocarcinomatous tumors which together constitute 96.3

per cent of the tumors. The remaining 3.7 per cent Dixon and Moore classify as nongerminal tumors. This group of nongerminal tumors includes (in addition to miscellaneous and unclassified tumors) in descending order of frequency the following types: capsular fibromas, interstitial cell tumors, androblastomas of Teilum (probably Sertoli cell tumors), adrenal cortical rests, and adenomatoid tumors.

From an analysis of the histologic material of the germinal group of tumors and taking into account the morphologic cell types, histologic patterns, transition forms, and the existence of coincident but different tumor types together, Dixon and Moore conclude that the teratomatous and choriocarcinomatous tumors represent differentiations of the more primitive embryonal carcinomas. Seminomas also appear related to this group of tumors but much less frequently and less intimately. The clinical data indicate that seminoma tends to appear in older patients more frequently than embryonal carcinoma and the teratomatous group of tumors. Indeed, no acceptable case of seminoma has been reported before puberty.[42] This finding, together with the increased incidence of seminoma in cryptorchids and in testes of older men, where maturation of seminal cells is limited, would suggest that this tumor may be derived from spermatocytes. Evidence for this hypothesis might be obtained by microspectroscopic measurements of the nucleic acid content of nuclei or chromosomal counts of mitotic figures in seminoma in an attempt to detect significant numbers of cells with only the haploid number of chromosomes.

Follow-up data reported by Dixon and Moore[12] on cases with germinal testicular tumors also tend to separate seminomas from other germinal tumors. These authors found that with essentially the same treatment as that applied to other germinal tumors (89 per cent treated by orchiectomy and x-ray) patients with pure seminoma have the best prognosis, with only 11.3 per cent dead five years from the time of diagnosis. The prognosis is particularly favorable in patients whose tumors show an infiltration by eosinophils, a lymphoid stroma, or focal granulomas. In contrast, those patients bearing seminomas with fibrous stromal proliferation have a somewhat poorer prognosis. Also a positive correlation of poor prognosis with histologic vascular invasion is demonstrated in these studies. Hence the very poor prognosis of the small number of patients with choriocarcinoma may be the result of the tendency for this tumor to invade blood vessels unlike seminoma, embryonal carcinoma, and teratomatous tumors which usually spread via the lymphatics. Next to patients with choriocarcinoma, patients with embryonal carcinoma have the poorest prognosis, 70 to 75 per cent dead in five years. Those cases of embryonal carcinoma showing areas of differentiation to immature teratoma show a distinctly better prognosis, 51.8 per cent dead in five years. When there are teratomatous areas associated with embryonal carcinoma, Dixon and Moore find that the degree of differentiation, whether immature or mature, makes no difference in the prognosis; however, when only adult teratoma is found in the sections examined, the patients have a better prognosis, 40.7 per cent in five years. As evidence of the rapidly fatal progression of tumors of germinal origin, follow-up figures reveal that of all patients dead within five years after diagnosis, 90 per cent die within the first two years. In this study the tumors of nongerminal origin were usually benign. However, they are so rare that even this large collection has provided very little new information.

The results of hormone studies on patients with testicular tumors are quite variable and somewhat confusing.[61] The most valuable study to date has been that of Hamburger[28] who stressed the need for distinguishing between chorionic gonadotrophin and pituitary gonadotrophin in the urine of some of these patients. One important contribution that has evolved from these studies is the fact that patients who excrete chorionic gonadotrophin have a poor prognosis, irrespective of the pathologic diagnosis on the tumor, these tumors often being radioresistant. Changes in the levels of androgen and estrogen excretion with identification of the types excreted, the amount of pituitary gonadotrophin excreted, and extraction and identification of hormones in the tumor tissue, all need further study.

IN ANIMALS

These clinical, hormonal, and morphologic analyses are of great practical value but the experimental approach to the problems of testicular tumors is still largely unexplored. The few attempts which have been made to provide a continuous source of material for experimental study by growing human testicular tumors in the anterior chamber of the eye of guinea pigs have so far been unsuccessful.[26] Analogous tumors of the testis in animals are even more unavailable to the experimentalist than the human testicular tumors. The only mammal in which the occurrence of testicular teratomas is well known is the horse. Willis and Rudduck[66] found teratomas in 29 testes obtained from 27 of 250 horses during gelding; the authors stated about half of the testes were carefully examined. This incidence is considerably higher than that previously reported by Kimura,[35] who found 49 testicular teratomas among 142 tumors of various sites in 77,000 slaughtered horses. Testicular teratomas occur spontaneously in cocks and, like those in horses, are organoid and apparently benign; a few contain undifferentiated and immature embryonal tumorous areas similar to the analogous human tumors.

Teratomas in mice are unknown. The very rare ones which have been found have arisen only in females, apparently from ovarian tissue.[16, 34, 55] Three such ovarian teratomas were found recently in this laboratory but as far as can be determined these are the first ever encountered at this Institute.

Dogs develop at least two types of testicular tumors which are morphologically similar to human tumors: the seminoma and interstitial cell tumor. The occurrence of Sertoli cell tumors, although well known in dogs, is questionable in men and if they do occur they are certainly very rare. Tumors reported in men by Teilum[58, 59] and by Ostergaard[48] resemble most closely this type of tumor in dogs because of their feminizing character and elevated estrogen excretion. Even in dogs they are often benign and are sometimes designated as tubular adenomas.[27, 31, 32, 33, 43, 51] These are not to be confused with the foci of immature tubules found in cryptorchid testes in man which are sometimes inappropriately called tubular adenomas. These foci in the testes in men are not tumors but merely undeveloped seminiferous tubules.

INDUCED TUMORS

ATTEMPTS TO INDUCE TESTICULAR TUMORS IN ANIMALS

Testicular teratomas have been induced in cocks, first by Michalowsky,[41] and later by his associates in Russia[1, 15] and by Bagg[2] in this country. The method of induction consisted of direct intratesticular injection of any one of various inorganic zinc or copper salts. Of interest was the fact that despite repeated attempts at induction at various times tumors developed only in cocks injected during the months of January, February, and March, except for one instance[2] in August following anterior pituitary hormone injections designed to reproduce the state of activity normally present in the testis during late winter and early spring. These induced teratomas were entirely similar morphologically to those occurring spontaneously in this species.[3] No reports have appeared of the successful employment of this method in mammals.

Biskind and Biskind[4] and others[62] have reported the induction of tumors, apparently interstitial (Leydig) cell in type, by the transplantation of testis of the new-born rat into the spleen of the adult of the same strain. The finding in one case of other elements such as well-differentiated straited muscle, smooth muscle, and adult fat by Twombly *et al.*[62] would be adequately explained on the basis of inclusion of peritesticular tissue in the original transplants. This explanation seems reasonable since these authors in many of their cases described cysts developing from epididymis included with the testis in the transplant. The growth of these testicular transplants appears generally limited and their truly neoplastic nature still remains a question. There are no reports of metastases and only a single subtransplant has "grown successfully" and that one in the spleen of a castrated rat. The interpretation of this result is further clouded by the fact that although the original growth was composed "almost exclusively of interstitial cells with only an occasional gland-like space," the growth of the subtransplant was "almost exclusively teratomatous with only a microscopic group of interstitial cells." Unfortunately, as is always the case, one cannot examine microscopic sections of exactly the same tissue that is transplanted.

In mice, intrasplenic transplants of testes into adult castrates have not yielded growths comparable to those in rats, but have rather simulated cryptorchid testis.[20, 38] By contrast interstitial cell tumors can be induced in mice by the administration of estrogen. These tumors were first induced in Strong A mice by administration of triphenylethylene;[6] subsequently, other estrogenic substances have been effective and mice of several but not all strains have been proved susceptible.[5, 23, 30, 53]

Attempts to induce testicular tumors in rats by the administration of estrogen have been unsuccessful.[14, 24, 46] Even AXC rats are resistant although they do develop hyperplasia and tumors of the interstitial cells spontaneously.[29] Following estrogen treatment the testes shrink markedly (75 to 90 per cent) due to early complete loss of spermatogenesis, as in mice, but no interstitial cell hyperplasia develops.[17]

The ease with which interstitial cell tumors can be induced in mice and the unavailability of other testicular tumors for experimental work has resulted in considerable attention being given to these induced tumors. During the process of tumor induction by estrogen a series of changes occur not only in the testes, but also in the adrenal and pituitary glands and secondary sex organs. In Strain C mice with subcutaneously implanted stilbestrol-cholesterol pellets, the lining of the prostatic ducts undergoes metaplasia to stratified squamous epithelium as early as thirty-five days after starting treatment—often with marked hyperkeratosis. Similarly the preputial glands show marked hyperkeratosis and distention with keratin, which sometimes perforates externally through the overlying skin. The keratin production in the prostatic ducts in some mice distends and obstructs the ducts, forming keratin-filled cysts which occasionally obstruct the urethra and cause fatal urinary retention after the first two or three months of treatment.

In the testes and in the adrenal glands after three months of estrogen treatment, yellowish pigmented cells begin to develop which tend to darken after several weeks or months, changing from yellow to brown. In the testes these cells increase in number as the Leydig cells decrease, and finally they occupy the entire interstitium. In the adrenal glands these pigmented cells develop in the innermost portion of the cortex and produce the morphologic picture of so-called "brown degeneration."[7] The cells in both the testes and the adrenal glands are very much like the occasional brown pigmented cells which are found in these organs in old adult mice, though never in the numbers noted in the experimental animals of the C strain.

The yellow-brown cells seem to arise from Leydig cells in the testes and from the cells of the inner zone of the adrenal cortex by the process of degeneration and fusion, and phagocytosis by macrophages. As a result large giant cells are found containing multiple small hyperchromatic, often pyknotic nuclei, usually located peripherally, and abundant cytoplasm filled with yellow-brown lipoid globules of varying sizes. Both in the testes and adrenal glands the cells appear morphologically and histochemically identical (Fig. 48). The lipoid which they contain has all the characteristics of ceroid[18, 60] or waste pigment. This ceroid is

Fig. 48. *1.* Mouse testis 188 days after subcutaneous implantation of a 5-mg. stilbestrol-cholesterol pellet. The interstitium is filled with fusing and fused degenerating Leydig cells with degenerated nuclei and abundant yellow-brown lipoid, ceroid. The seminiferous tubules show marked diminution of spermatogenesis. Hematoxylin and eosin. × 150.

2. Mouse adrenal gland 269 days after subcutaneous implantation of a 5-mg. stilbestrol-cholesterol pellet. The corticomedullary junction is occupied by massive fusing and fused ceroid-filled cells with degenerated nuclei. Hematoxylin and eosin. × 210.

3. Mouse testis 312 days after subcutaneous implantation of a 5-mg. stilbestrol-cholesterol pellet. Note the ceroid-filled cells and inactive seminiferous tubules in the lower half and two nodules of interstitial cells above. On the right are small cells with more deeply basophilic nuclei and clear cytoplasm filled with lipoid (second generation cells of Hooker and Pfeiffer). On the left the cells are large with vesicular nuclei containing prominent nucleoli and with abundant cytoplasm also containing lipoid globules but with more eosinophilic material (third generation cells of Hooker and Pfeiffer). Hematoxylin and eosin. × 210.

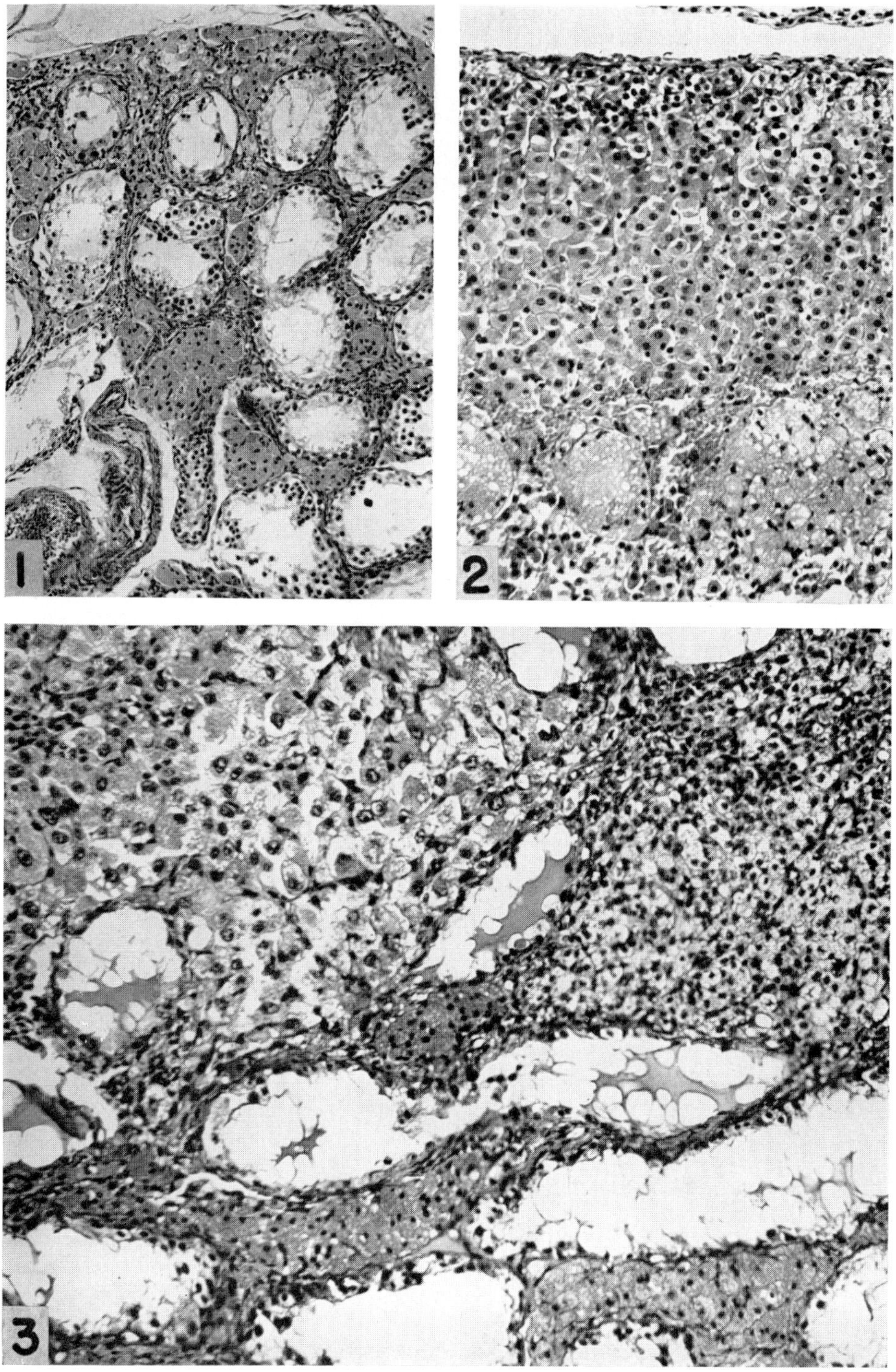
1
2
3

quite different from the lipoid in the normal Leydig and adrenal cortical cells (Table 2) but it does resemble the lipoid in the cytoplasm of a few cells in the same areas, in some apparently untreated aging adult animals.

After about six months of continuous exposure to estrogen the interstitial cells reappear in multiple foci (Hooker's and Pfeiffer's "second generation cells"[30]) often forming small nodules of hyperplastic growth. Eight months or more after implantation of 4 to 6 mg. pellets, containing one-third stilbestrol and two-thirds cholesterol, about half of the animals develop either unilateral or bilateral interstitial cell tumors. Such tumors are at least twice the size of the normal mouse testis and almost completely replace the testicular substance. Where the seminiferous tubules remain they have lost their spermatogenic cells and are shrunken and lined only by a single layer of Sertoli cells.

The pituitary glands of these treated animals during the first few months show a decrease in acidophilic granulated cells and an apparent increase in chromophobe cells. After about eight months of treatment acidophilic cells reappear in normal numbers independent of the appearance of testicular tumors. Other investigators[9] have reported an increase in chromophobe cells with adenomas following estrogen treatment. In castrates, there is a similar but maintained decrease in pituitary acidophiles and Dickie and Woolley[11] noted the development of basophilic adenomas in several strains of mice following gonadectomy. Also, strains of mice susceptible to mammary tumors show a high incidence of mammary tumors in males treated with estrogen.[9]

MECHANISM OF INDUCTION

Hooker and Pfeiffer[30] have given the most plausible explanation of the mode of induction of these estrogen-induced interstitial cell tumors in mice. They feel that the estrogen acts through the pituitary gland by inhibiting the production of follicle-stimulating hormone (FSH) and by increasing the production of interstitial cell stimulating (LH or ICS) hormone. Some evidence for this hypothesis was obtained by Pfeiffer and Hooker[50] when they succeeded in producing hyperplasia of the interstitial cells by the administration of pregnant mare's serum. However, no tumors were obtained. Also of interest is the fact that in contrast to the finding in the estrogen-treated animals, spermatogenesis was maintained. This is well explained by the high FSH content of pregnant mare's serum. This

---

FIG. 48 (*Continued*) ***4.*** Induced interstitial cell tumor in mouse testis 205 days after subcutaneous implantation of a 5-mg. stilbestrol-cholesterol pellet. Hematoxylin and eosin. × 310.

5. Spontaneous interstitial cell tumor of the testis of 12-year-old cocker spaniel with feminization. Hematoxylin and eosin. × 380. (Reproduced by courtesy of Dr. R. M. Mulligan.)

6A. Interstitial cell tumor of the testis of a 32-year-old white man with bilateral gynecomastia which had been present for four years. (Case of Drs. Grabstald, Haines, and Morrow, published in the *Journal of Urology*, in press). Low-power view showing general structure. Hematoxylin and eosin. × 380.

7. Same case. High-power view to show numerous crystalloids of Reinke which were present throughout the tumor. Hematoxylin and eosin. × 1700.

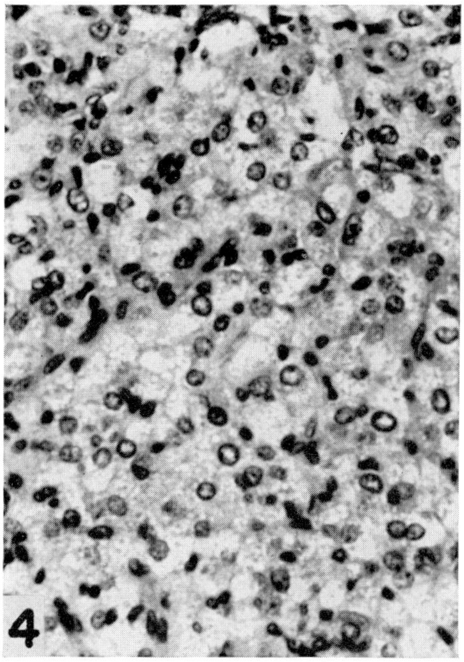
4

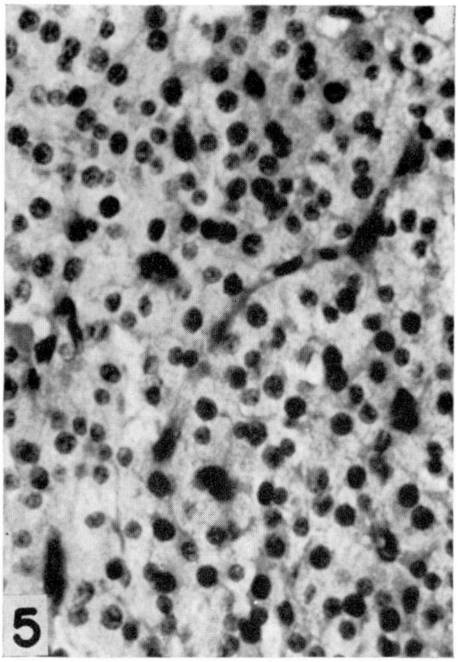
5

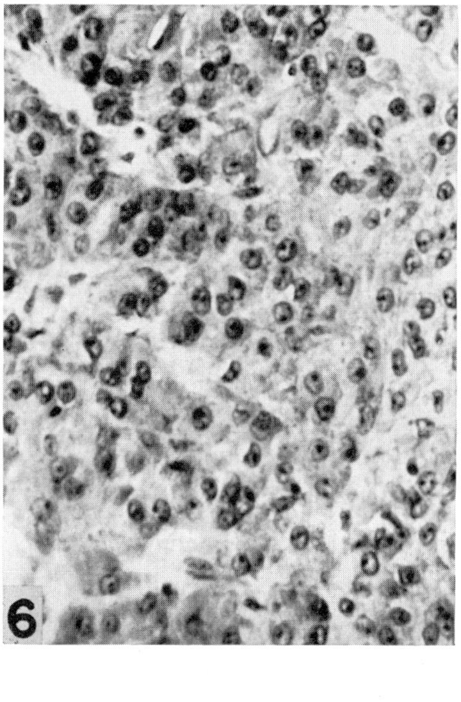
6

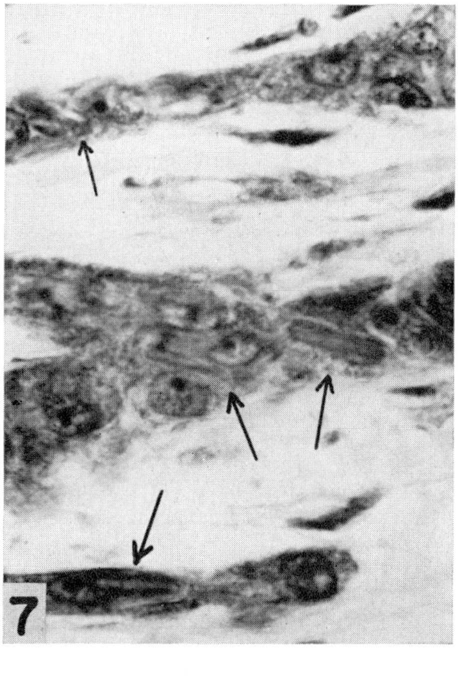
7

TABLE 2. CHARACTERISTICS OF TESTICULAR AND ADRENAL LIPOID IN NORMAL AND ESTROGEN-TREATED MALE MICE

Cell type	*Solubility in fat solvents*	*Birefringent material*	*Fluorescence*	*Sudanophilia*	*Osmic acid*	*Fuchsinophilia*			*Toluidine blue or Giemsa*	*Nile blue sulfate*	*Phenylhydrazine*
						Schiff's	*Plasmal and PAS**	*Acid fast*			
Normal, hyperplastic, and neoplastic Leydig cells	+ + +	+ + +	+ to + +	+ + + +	+ + +	±	+ to + + +	±	–	red	+ + + +
Normal adrenal cortical cells	+ + +	– to +	+ to + +	+ + + +	+ + +	±	+ to + + +	±	–	red	+ + + +
Ceroid-containing cells of testis and adrenal gland	–	– to +	+ + + +	+ + +	+ + + +	±	+ + + +	+ + + +	(green)	purple to blue	+ + + +

* These reactions can be blocked by previous bromination.

experiment has not been repeated with pure ICS. Unfortunately, hypophysectomized mice do not tolerate estrogen administration well enough to attempt induction of interstitial cell tumors by this method.

EVIDENCE OF HORMONE PRODUCTION BY SPONTANEOUS AND INDUCED INTERSTITIAL CELL TUMORS

Most of these induced interstitial cell tumors contain large amounts of lipoid and there is evidence that they have androgenic activity in most cases. The seminal vesicles, prostatic ducts and renal glomeruli which early show morphologic evidence of estrogen predominance, in most instances revert to their original masculine appearance indicating androgen dominance. Hooker and Pfeiffer[30] pointed out that this reversal was not observed in their animals treated in the same manner but failing to develop tumors. Bioassays and chemical extractions of such tumors have not yet been reported.

The functional nature of interstitial cell tumors is not limited to mice. In man, tumors of this type are sometimes associated with endocrine changes. However, care must be taken to differentiate functioning tumors of interstitial cells of the testis from those originating from rests of adrenal cortical tissue in the testis. Morphologically this differentiation is extremely difficult. The finding of crystalloids of Reinke in the tumor cells is the most reliable morphologic evidence of their Leydig cell origin. Hormonal studies also provide a possible means of distinguishing between these two tumors. As Lewis and Stockard[37] point out, true interstitial cell tumors usually are associated with masculinizing changes; however, gynecomastia is not uncommon. Functioning tumors of the adrenal cortex are also usually masculinizing but in rare instances they are associated with feminization.[54] There is one well-authenticated case of a malignant interstitial cell tumor reported by Venning *et al.*[63] in which there was a marked elevation of 17-ketosteroid and androsterone sulfate excretion. This is the expected finding in an androgen-secreting tumor. A recent case reported by Lewis and Stockard[37] showed gynecomastia and large amounts of pregnandiol in the urine. Examination of the histologic sections of the testicular tumor in this case reveals a morphologic picture consistent with an adrenal cortical or interstitial cell tumor. Lewis and Stockard postulated that the pregnandiol excretion indicated a progesterone-producing tumor and termed it a luteoma. However, pregnandiol is also the main urinary excretion product of desoxycorticosterone. It seems more likely that this tumor represents one arising from an adrenal cortical rest in the testis than from ovarian type tissue. Evidence that the hormonal disturbances in these cases are related to the tumor is provided by the regression and disappearance of gynecomastia and abnormal hormone titers which usually follows removal of the tumor.

In women, striking evidence of the functional nature of these tumors is provided by the rare case of Waugh, Venning, and McEachern[65] and those of Sternberg.[56] These authors reported Leydig cell tumors arising in the ovary which produced masculinizing changes. The fact that these tumors originate from Leydig cells rather than from adrenal cortical rests seems evident by the finding of crystalloids of Reinke identical to those in normal and sometimes neoplastic

Leydig cells of the testis and by the known existence of ovarian hilus cells which appear identical to interstitial cells of the testis.

COMPARATIVE MORPHOLOGY

Morphologically the induced tumors in mice are essentially identical to those seen in man which are usually benign.[45, 52, 64] They are equally similar morphologically to those in dogs, which though usually benign are occasionally malignant.[32, 33, 44] One morphologic difference between interstitial cells in man and those in other species is the common presence of crystalloids in man which have not been seen in Leydig cells of any other species except oppossum,[13] deer,[36] cat,[40] and dog.[49] The latter two are unconfirmed.

MALIGNANCY OF INDUCED INTERSTITIAL CELL TUMORS

Morphologic characteristics alone are not sufficiently diagnostic of malignancy in this group of tumors and one of the problems in mice is the determination of their truly neoplastic nature. Some of these tumors are unquestionably malignant as shown by the presence of metastases. The metastatic origin of a few of the intra-abdominal masses has been questioned because of the possibility of their arising in ectopic testicular tissue.[53] Also, ceroid-filled macrophages are commonly found in the regional lymph nodes in these cases, which, although they resemble those in the tumorous testicles, do not constitute metastases. This finding is comparable to, and perhaps as easily misinterpreted as, melanin-containing macrophages in regional lymph nodes in cases with melanomas. However, unquestionable metastases have been found and are illustrated by Bonser[5] both in regional lymph nodes and in the lungs. In this same paper she has illustrated intravascular invasion and growth.

HORMONAL DEPENDENCE OF INTERSTITIAL CELL TUMORS

The information gained from transplantation of these tumors would tend to indicate incomplete autonomy. Gardner[21, 22] in transplantation studies of three separate induced interstitial cell tumors found it necessary to administer estrogen even to female hosts. Curiously, even after a delay of as long as 204 days after transplantation, estrogen administration to the host was effective in promoting growth of the transplanted tumor but no growth occurred until such supplementary treatment was given.

Gardner[22] stated recently, however, that in subsequent generations two of these previously dependent interstitial cell tumors began to grow in untreated females. Now they are completely independent of estrogen after several years of serial transplantation and grow as well in male as in female hosts.

OTHER MALIGNANT TUMORS RESPONDING TO HORMONES

Closely analogous findings have been described for tumors of other endocrine organs or tissues normally responding to hormones. The section on tumors of the thyroid gland described the initial dependency of transplanted tumors of the thyroid gland in rats on thyrotropic hormone followed later by independent growth in subsequent transplant generations. Deming and Hovenanian[10] describe a human prostatic carcinoma which for a number of transplant generations grew only in the anterior chamber of the eye in male guinea pigs and, in one instance, in a female guinea pig given testosterone. Only by the eighth transplant generation had this tumor become independent to the extent that it grew in female guinea pigs without supplementary androgen. Similar dependency of mammary tumors in mice is described in the section on mammary tumors. In man, the responsiveness of metastatic thyroid carcinoma to thyrotropin following thyroidectomy has been shown by its uptake of radioactive iodine. The effectiveness of sex hormones on cancer of the breast and cancer of the prostate in man are well known. Despite the partially hormone-dependent nature of such tumors and their responsiveness to hormones, it is evident from our knowledge of the course of such incompletely autonomous tumors that they are capable of metastasizing and killing the host.

SUMMARY

The challenge provided by the multifaceted research problems of testicular tumors is still largely unmet, primarily because of the unavailability of suitable material in sufficient quantity for study. Much has been learned from careful study of large collections of clinical and pathologic material, but basic clinical and animal experimental studies have yet to be done. The only testicular tumor analogous to those in man which can be induced in mammals is the interstitial cell tumor of the mouse. In the process of induction with estrogens, the early changes in the interstitial cells of the testis are identical to those in the reticular zone of the adrenal glands. Later, hyperplasia and neoplasia develop in the testes but not in the adrenal glands. The resulting tumors, like certain tumors of other hormone sensitive tissues, show evidence of incomplete autonomy, yet they are capable of metastasizing and killing the host.

BIBLIOGRAPHY

1. ANISSIMOVA, V. Experimental zinc teratomas of the testis and their transplantation. *Am. J. Cancer 36:* 229-232, 1939.
2. BAGG, H. J. Experimental production of teratoma testis in the fowl. *Am. J. Cancer 26:* 69-84, 1936.
3. BIESTER, H. E., and DEVRIES, L. (eds.). *Diseases of Poultry.* Ames, Iowa, The Collegiate Press, Inc., 1945, pp. 585-587.
4. BISKIND, M. S., and BISKIND, G. R. Tumor of rat testis produced by heterotransplantation of infantile testis to spleen of adult castrate. *Proc. Soc. Exper. Biol. & Med. 59:* 4-8, 1945.
5. BONSER, G. M. Mammary and testicular tumours in male mice of various strains following oestrogen treatment. *J. Path. & Bact. 56:* 15-26, 1944.
6. BONSER, G. M., and ROBSON, J. M. The effects of prolonged oestrogen administration upon male mice of various strains: development of testicular tumors in the Strong A strain. *J. Path. & Bact. 51:* 9-22, 1940.
7. BURROWS, H. Changes induced by estrogens in the adrenals of male mice. *J. Path. & Bact. 43:* 121-126, 1936.

8. CHRISTOFFERSEN, W. G., and OWEN, S. E. Neoplasms in cryptorchids. *Am. J. Cancer 26:* 259-268, 1936.
9. CRAMER, W., and HORNING, E. S. Experimental production by oestrin of pituitary tumours with hypopituitrism and of mammary cancer. *Lancet 1:* 247-249, 1936.
10. DEMING, C. L., and HOVENANIAN, M. S. The hormonal factor in heterologous growths of human prostatic cancer. *J. Urol. 59:* 215-219, 1948.
11. DICKIE, M. M., and WOOLLEY, G. W. Spontaneous basophilic tumors of the pituitary glands in gonadectomized mice. *Cancer Research 9:* 372-384, 1949.
12. DIXON, F. J., and MOORE, R. A. In: *Acta Unio Internationalis Contra Cancrum 8:* 310-315, 1952.
13. DUESBERG, J. On the interstitial cells of the testicle in Didelphys. *Biol. Bull. 35:* 175, 1918.
14. DUNNING, W. F., CURTIS, M. R., and SEGALOFF, A. Strain differences in response to diethylstilbestrol and the induction of mammary gland and bladder cancer in the rat. *Cancer Research 7:* 511-521, 1947.
15. FALIN, L. I. Self-differentiation and correlation of the tissues in experimental teratomas of the sex glands. *Byull. eksper. biol. i med. 15:* 63-66, 1943.
16. FAWCETT, D. W. Bilateral ovarian teratomas in a mouse. *Cancer Research 10:* 705-707, 1950.
17. FIRMINGER, H. I. Unpublished data.
18. FRANTZ, M. Ceroid pigment in the testis of mice treated with estrogens (abstract). *Anat. Rec. 97:* 388, 1947.
19. FRIEDMAN, N., and MOORE, R. A. Tumors of the testicle. *Mil. Surgeon 99:* 573-593, 1946.
20. FURTH, J., and SOBEL, H. Neoplastic transformation of granulosa cells in grafts of normal ovaries into spleen of gonadectomized mice. *J. Nat. Cancer Inst. 8:* 7-16, 1947.
21. GARDNER, W. U. Some influences of hormones on the growth and persistence of transplanted testicular tumors. *Cancer Research 5:* 497-505, 1945.
22. GARDNER, W. U. Personal communication.
23. GARDNER, W. U., and BODDAERT, J. Testicular interstitial cell tumors in hybrid mice given tri-p-anisyl chloroethylene. *Arch. Path. 50:* 750-764, 1950.
24. GESCHICKTER, C. F., and BYRNES, E. W. Factors influencing the development and time of appearance of mammary cancer in the rat in response to estrogen. *Arch. Path. 33:* 334-356, 1942.
25. GILBERT, J. B., and HAMILTON, J. B. Studies in malignant testis tumors. III. Incidence and nature of tumors in ectopic testes. *Surg., Gyn. & Obst. 71:* 731-743, 1940.
26. GREENE, H. S. N. Personal communication.
27. GREULICH, W. W., and BURFORD, T. H. Testicular tumors associated with mammary, prostatic and other changes in cryptorchid dogs. *Am. J. Cancer 28:* 496-511, 1936.
28. HAMBURGER, C. On the nature of gonadotrophin in cases of malignant tumors of the testis. *Acta path. et microbiol. Scandinav. 18:* 457-484, 1941.
29. HARE, W. V., and STEWART, H. L. Unpublished data.
30. HOOKER, C. W., and PFEIFFER, C. A. The morphology and development of testicular tumors in mice of the A strain receiving estrogens. *Cancer Research 2:* 759-760, 1942.

31. HUGGINS, C., and MOULDER, P. V. Estrogen production by Sertoli cell tumors of the testis. *Cancer Research 5:* 510-514, 1945.
32. HUGGINS, C., and PAZOR, R. Studies on tumors of the testis: The morphology of testicular tumors of dogs. *Am. J. Path. 21:* 299-306, 1945.
33. INNES, J. R. M. The malignancy of testicular cancer in man and dogs. *Brit. J. Surg. 31:* 157-160, 1943.
34. JACKSON, E. B., and BRUES, A. M. Studies on a transplantable embryoma of the mouse. *Cancer Research 1:* 494-498, 1941.
35. KIMURA. *Gann,* 1917. (Referred to by Innes[33] above.)
36. LENNINGER, W. Das Hodenzwischengewebe der Haussäugetiere. *Ztschr. f. Anat. u Entwicklungsgesch. 68:* 230, 1923.
37. LEWIS, L. G., and STOCKARD, C. G. Feminizing testis tumors. *J. Urol. 64:* 518-523, 1950.
38. LI, MIN HSIN, PFEIFFER, C. A., and GARDNER, W. U. Intrasplenic transplantation of testes in castrated mice. *Proc. Soc. Exper. Biol. & Med. 64:* 319-323, 1947.
39. MACCALLUM, W. G. *Textbook of Pathology* (ed. 6). Philadelphia, W. B. Saunders Co., 1937, p. 1183.
40. MATHIEU, C. "De la cellule interstitielle du testicule et de ses produits de secretion (cristalloides)." Theses de Nancy, 1898. [Referred to by Rasmussen, A. T., in COWDRY, E. V. *Special Cytology* (ed. 2). New York, Paul B. Hoeber, Inc., 1932, p. 1685.]
41. MICHALOWSKY, I. Die experimentelle Erzeugung einer teratoiden Neubildung der Hoden beim Hahn. *Central. f. allg. Path. u. path. Anat. 38:* 585-587, 1926.
42. MOSTOFI, F. K. Testicular tumors in infants (abstract). *Am. J. Path. 28:* 536, 1952.
43. MULLIGAN, R. M. Feminization in male dogs: A syndrome associated with carcinoma of the testis and mimicked by the administration of estrogens. *Am. J. Path. 20:* 865-893, 1944.
44. MULLIGAN, R. M. *Neoplasms of the Dog.* Baltimore, Md., The Williams and Wilkins Company, 1949.
45. NATION, E. F., EDMONDSON, H. A., and HAMMACK, R. W. Interstitial cell tumors of the testis: Report of three new cases. *Arch. Surg. 48:* 415-422, 1944.
46. NELSON, W. O. Induction of mammary carcinoma on the rat. *Yale J. Biol. & Med. 17:* 217-228, 1944.
47. NOVAK, E. *Gynecological and Obstetrical Pathology* (ed. 2). Philadelphia, W. B. Saunders Co., 1947, chap. XXVI.
48. OSTERGAARD, E. Feminizing tumor of the testis, presumably aberrant adrenal cortical tumor. *J. Clin. Endocrinol.* 438-445, 1947.
49. PEYRON, A., POUMEAU-DELILLE, G., and SALOMON, L. Sur la présence des cristalloides de Reinke dans les hyperplasies et tumeurs de la glande interstitielle du testicule. *Compt. rend. Soc. de biol. 128:* 649-651, 1938.
50. PFEIFFER, C. A., and HOOKER, C. W. Testicular changes resembling early stages in the development of interstitial cell tumors in mice of the A strain after long-continued injections of pregnant mare serum. *Cancer Research 3:* 762-765, 1943.
51. SCHOTTHAUER, C. V., MCDONALD, J. R., and BOLLMAN, J. W. Testicular tumors in dogs. *J. Urol. 40:* 539-550, 1938.
52. SCULLY, R. E., and PARHAM, A. R. Testicular tumors. II. Interstitial cell and miscellaneous neoplasms. *Arch. Path. 46:* 229-242, 1948.

53. SHIMKIN, M. B., GRADY, H. G., and ANDERVONT, H. B. Induction of testicular tumors and other effects of stilbestrol-cholesterol pellets in Strain C mice. *J. Nat. Cancer Inst. 2:* 65-80, 1941.
54. SIMPSON, S. L., and JOLL, C. A. Feminization in a male adult with carcinoma of the adrenal cortex. *Endocrinology 22:* 595-604, 1938.
55. SLYE, MAUD, HOLMES, H. F., and WELLS, H. G. Primary spontaneous tumors of the ovary in mice. *J. Cancer Res. 5:* 205-226, 1920.
56. STERNBERG, W. H. The morphology, androgenic function, hyperplasia, and tumors of the human ovarian hilus cells. *Am. J. Path. 25:* 493-522, 1949.
57. SYMEONIDIS, A. Betrachtungen über das Hodenteratoid, seine Metastasierung und das sog. "extragenitale" Chorionepitheliom an Hand eines narbigen stecknadelkopfgrossen rudimentären Hodenteratoids mit dreikeimblätterigen und Chorionepitheliom Metastasen. *Virchow's Arch. f. path. Anat. 311:* 509-518, 1943.
58. TEILUM, G. Arrhenoblastoma—androblastoma. *Acta path. & microbiol. Scandinav. 23:* 252-264, 1946.
59. TEILUM, G. Homologous ovarian and testicular tumors: III. Estrogen-producing Sertoli cell tumors (androblastoma tubular lipoides) of the human testis and ovary. *J. Clin. Endocrinol. 9:* 301-318, 1949.
60. TOBIN, C. E., and BIRNBAUM, J. P. Some factors influencing brown degeneration of the adrenal gland in the Swiss albino mouse. *Arch. Path. 44:* 269-281, 1947.
61. TWOMBLY, G. H. "The relationship of hormones to testicular tumors." In *Endocrinology of Neoplastic Diseases, A Symposium.* New York, Oxford University Press, 1947, chap. X, pp. 228-244.
62. TWOMBLY, G. H., MEISEL, DORIS, and STOUT, H. P. Leydig-cell tumors induced experimentally in the rat. *Cancer 2:* 884-892, 1949.
63. VENNING, E. H., HOFFMAN, M. M., and BROWNE, J. S. L. Isolation of androsterone sulfate. *J. Biol. Chem. 146:* 369-379, 1942.
64. WARREN, S., and OLSHAUSEN, K. W. Interstitial cell growths of the testicle. *Am. J. Path. 19:* 307-331, 1943.
65. WAUGH, D., VENNING, E. H., and MCEACHERN, D. Sympathicotropic (Leydig) cell tumor of the ovary with virilism: Report of a case. *J. Clin. Endocrinol. 9:* 486-496, 1949.
66. WILLIS, R. A., and RUDDUCK, H. B. Testicular teratomas in horses. *J. Path. & Bact. 55:* 165-171, 1943.

CHAPTER 10

Endometrial Carcinoma in the Rabbit

Harold L. Stewart

Endometrial carcinoma is a common spontaneous tumor of the rabbit, accounting for 50 per cent of the neoplasms observed in this species. The first example of this lesion was reported by Lack[7] in 1899, and in 1927 Polson[8] was able to collect 25 cases from the literature to which he added 4 of his own. Of these 29 tumors 16 were considered to be locally malignant; 5 showed metastasis; and 8 were classified as benign adenomas. The most detailed account of this tumor was published by Greene and associates in a series of reports[1, 2, 3, 4, 5, 6] which form the basis of much of the following discussion.

They found 145 tumor-bearing animals in a colony of 849 animals two or more years of age and observed over a nine-year period. The incidence of this lesion varies widely in relation to age and genetic constitution. It occurs in a variety of breeds of rabbit. The age incidence of this tumor varies from 4 per cent at two or three years to 80 per cent at five or six years, the over-all incidence being about 17 per cent in a female population two or more years of age. If a female rabbit survives to the fifth year of life without having a uterine tumor—although rarely the case—the chances are better than three to one that a tumor will develop in the next year or two.

PATHOLOGY

The rabbit's uterus is bicornuate and contains two cervices which are lined by columnar epithelium. The junction with stratified squamous epithelium occurs in the region of the urethral meatus at the upper border of the true vulva and the columnar lining is continuous from the uterine cavity to this point. Although only primary tumors 1 cm. in diameter or larger are detected clinically, postmortem examination frequently reveals the presence of smaller growths 0.2 cm. or more in diameter (Figs. 49 and 50). Even smaller nodular thickenings of the endometrium may be observed when the uterus is subjected to careful histologic examination. The tumors that are 1 cm. in diameter are usually situated on the mucosal folds adjacent to the mesometrial insertion. They are pedunculated,

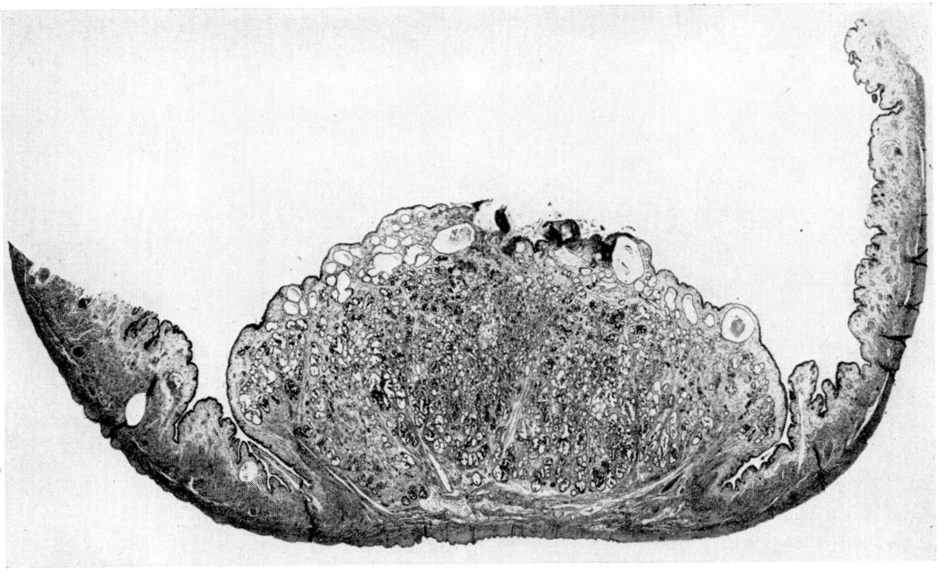

FIG. 49. Carcinoma of the uterus of the rabbit. × 10.

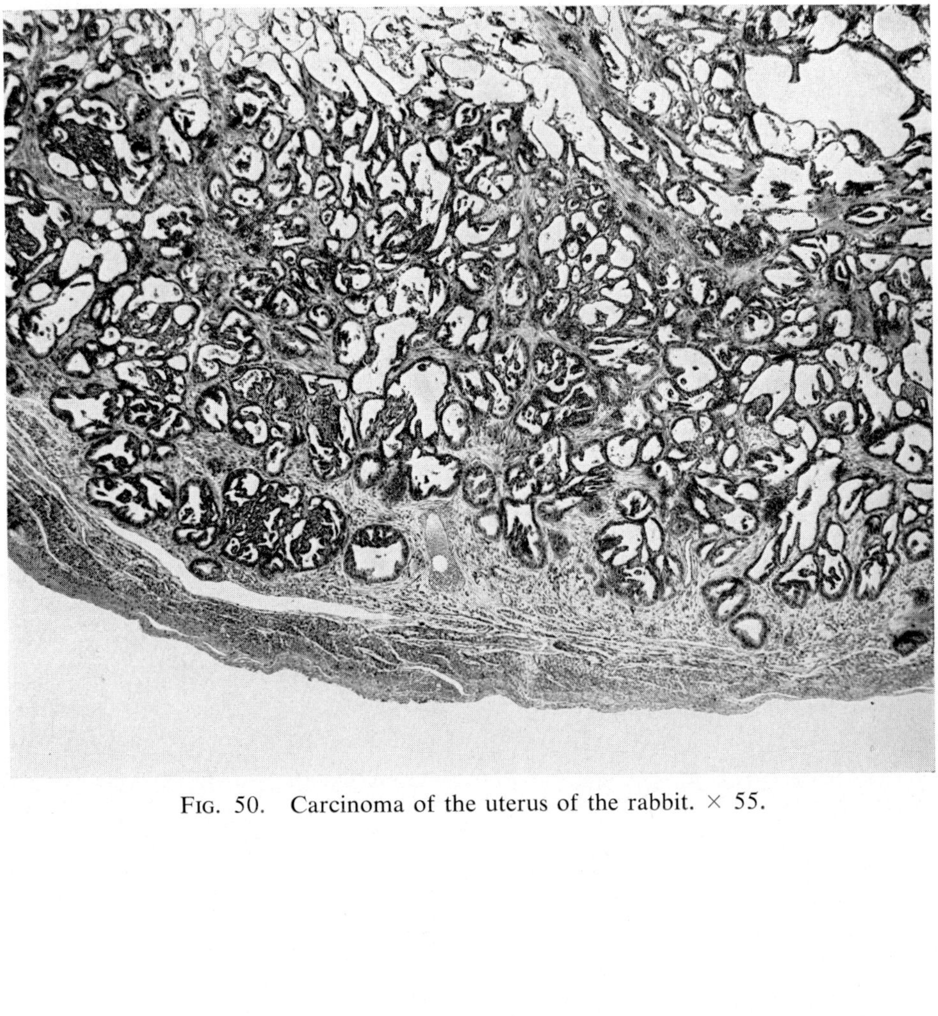

FIG. 50. Carcinoma of the uterus of the rabbit. × 55.

smooth, glistening, frequently multiple tumors that are about the same size and fairly evenly spaced throughout both uterine horns. Solitary tumors may attain a diameter of 4 cm. and may involve any part of the uterus, occurring most frequently in the segment adjacent to the fallopian tube. Larger tumors are usually sessile, consisting of several closely adjacent growths that have coalesced. Occasionally the bulk of the growth may expand to fill the greater part of the lumen of one horn of the uterus, forming an ulcerated and necrotic sausage-shaped mass.

Invasion of blood vessels occurs early although secondary neoplastic deposits are found only late in the course of the disease and generally in association with extensive necrosis in the primary tumor. Direct extension of the tumor occurs into the uterine musculature, mesometrium and surrounding structures, including the rectum, vagina, bladder, pelvic lymph nodes, and fat of the lumbar region. Metastases, generally multiple, have been observed in most of the abdominal and thoracic organs as well as in the thyroid gland, femoral bone marrow, peritoneum, pleura, pericardium, and walls of stomach and intestine. In general, the metastatic growths retain the glandular architecture characteristic of the primary tumor, but in some instances they may exhibit a sarcomatous pattern. The over-all incidence of metastasis is about 15 per cent. Metastasis occurs more frequently from long-standing primary tumors. It is of considerable interest that although invasion of blood vessels occurs early in relation to the local tumor, metastatic spread may be delayed for a year or more. Thus, the opportunity for dissemination of tumor cells is present long before metastasis occurs. This raises a question regarding the factors, other than mechanical, responsible for the spread of such tumors.

Changes also occur in other organs of rabbits bearing endometrial tumors. The thyroid gland in the affected animals frequently develops fetal-type adenomas. The cortex and medulla of the adrenal gland are widely separated by a thickened, homogeneous, pale-staining zona fasciculata which possesses excessive amounts of lipoid material as well as degenerated cells. These adrenal changes resemble the lesion of pregnancy toxemia in the rabbit. The anterior lobe of the pituitary gland shows an increase in the number of nongranular cells with scattered colloid masses. The intermediate lobe is usually wide and contains an abundance of colloid. Corpora lutea may or may not be present in the ovaries depending upon recent mating history.

HISTOGENESIS

Uterine tumors of the rabbit may be associated with placentation, as indicated by their distribution along placental folds in spaced arrangement that simulates the disposition of normal placentas in the gravid uterus. Greene suggested that augmented physiologic activity of the fundic epithelium, with consequent increased liability to altered cellular relations, renders the fundus the most susceptible uterine region to the action of a possible specific endocrinologic factor.

A focus of growth that has been interpreted as the beginning of the neoplastic process consists of small groups of atypical acini lying immediately beneath the surface epithelium in direct continuity with the uninvolved endometrium. The acini of these foci are irregular in size, often branched and lined by epithelial cells that are flattened, pale, and occasionally in mitotic division. Later the acini are seen to be in the form of more or less compact groups lined by pseudostratified columnar epithelial cells and separated by heavy bands of connective tissue. As the neoplastic focus grows older the stroma, at first minimal in amount and infiltrated with lymphocytes, becomes more and more abundant, myxoid, and richly vascular. As the nodular endometrial focus displays more active growth the deepest portion shows coiled branching acini containing papillary proliferations and sometimes solid cellular nests. There is little evidence of infiltration, however, at this stage and the growth is separated from the underlying uterine muscle by a barrier of compressed connective tissue. As the tumor enlarges anaplastic growth becomes more pronounced and finally there is invasion of the myometrium. In such a lesion, well-formed acini are present only as scattered foci particularly toward the center or near the surface, while the greater portion of the tumor, especially that infiltrating other areas, is composed of large irregular columnar or even spindle-shaped cells growing in nests or in solid sheets. Many of the acini present are dilated and irregular with multiple branching processes that show papillary proliferation. These larger tumors are often extensively ulcerated and necrotic. In the majority of animals the neoplastic change occurs in multiple foci of the endometrium, giving rise to multiple primary tumors that progress at about the same rate and show virtually identical histologic changes at different stages of development. Closely adjacent tumors are likely to coalesce by lateral extension. When the tumor invades deeply into the myometrium, the entire uterus may be converted into a thickened tubelike structure showing multicentric carcinoma.

By a study of the morphologic development of the tumor by repeated biopsy, architectural changes may be found to occur in definite sequence that suggests a gradual loss of structural organization from the inception of the tumor to its metastasis.[5] The very early tumors show simple reduplication of well-formed endometrial glands separated by an abundant stroma. Subsequent alteration proceeds in either of two ways. On the one hand the reduplication of small acini continues until the stroma is gradually replaced by epithelial cells and the whole growth comes to resemble histologically a fetal adenoma of the thyroid gland. The second mode of progress is much more common and consists of the development of a papillary architecture. Acini enlarge and become cystic; complicated papillary growths project into their lumina. Further growth is characterized by loss of acinar form and development of diffuse areas of cellular growth that, however, may be still recognizable as epithelial neoplasm. Finally, the tumors may gradually assume an exceedingly disorganized and sarcomatous pattern that lacks resemblance to its ancestral glandular form. Some tumors may be comparatively static throughout their course and may not eventuate in the more anaplastic types of growth. However, even though the architecture of the primary tumor may be glandular, the metastases from it may be histologically sarcomatous in nature. Greene and Newton[5] state that the essential point is that this type of cancer in the rabbit represents not a sudden transformation of normal to neoplastic cells, but rather the final product of the slowly progressive process of carcinogenesis.

TRANSPLANTATION

In many instances the tumor can be propagated by subcutaneous transplantation into the same animal. Areas in these transplants rather frequently show a histologic pattern consistent with that of sarcoma. The tumor has also been transplanted heterologously to the anterior chamber of the eye of guinea pigs, swine, goats and sheep.[4] Greene and Newton[5] compared the transplantability and growth rate of the uterine tumors at different stages of development by biopsying the primary tumor at intervals after clinical detection. Autologous transfer was made at different sites in the primary host and homologous transfers were made to unrelated animals of the same species. The youngest primary tumors studied by this method were 1 cm. in diameter. Well-differentiated tumor tissue removed from lesions smaller than this and transplanted elsewhere in the primary host grows readily but invariably fails to survive homologous transfer. Successful homologous transplantation depends to a large extent upon the development of the highly malignant histopathologic types of tumor.[5]

CLINICAL COURSE

Disturbances in reproductive function are noted regularly four to five months preceding clinical detection of the tumor by palpation of the uterus. Fertility may cease abruptly, or the percentage of sterile matings may be increased. The litters born to affected animals are small and the mother often deserts them. The young are often born dead. Abdominal pregnancy may occur. Abortion or resorption of the products of conception have been noted, or the whole litter may be retained in utero far beyond the normal limits of the gestational period.

Sterility has been observed in cases with the neoplasm limited to one horn of the uterus and is therefore not necessarily due to obstruction. In some animals, no uterine abnormality can be found to account for the reproductive disorders. In others, cystic hyperplasia of the endometrium accompanies tumor formation at an early age.

During the course of development of the neoplasm, unmated animals frequently exhibit signs suggestive of pregnancy. The breasts become engorged; the temperamental changes common to the end of gestation appear and the animals pull fur and build nests. These manifestations are similar to those observed in animals without tumors during pseudopregnancy resulting from sterile mating and indicate an associated endocrine disturbance. When first detected clinically, the tumor nodules are not tender upon palpation, are frequently multiple, may be present in both uterine horns and approximate the size of 10-day pregnancy cysts. Differential diagnosis rests on the firmness, absence of fluctuation, and slow growth of tumor nodules. The tumor may reach the size of a hen's egg within six months or may remain barely palpable for a similar period of time. Occasionally, large tumor masses regress and fragments of necrotic tumor may be discharged from the uterus. On the other hand metastasis may occur without much increase in the size of the primary nodules.

Coincident with the onset of formation of a uterine tumor, approximately 25 per cent of the rabbits develop hyperplastic cystic changes (and, occasionally, adenoma, fibroadenoma, and carcinoma) of the mammary gland. Vaginal bleeding is rare and occurs only in the late stages of the uterine tumor. Cachexia is associated only with disseminated tumors. In those animals dying of metastatic tumors, the average length of life from detection of a palpable uterine tumor to death is twelve months, but may be as long as two years. Some animals die of a disorder clinically and pathologically similar to toxemia of pregnancy. In fact, all of Greene's tumor-bearing animals suffered attacks of toxemia of pregnancy during their early breeding history.[1, 2] The constant occurrence of multiple lesions of endocrine organs in tumor-bearing animals further supports the evidence of an underlying systemic disturbance. The presence of tumors in the uterus is considered by Greene[3] to be merely a local manifestation of a constitutional disorder. The adrenal glands and the thyroid gland show distinctive changes even in the earliest stages of uterine tumor development. The pituitary gland is also altered and the mammary glands frequently show hyperplastic and neoplastic changes. Greene[3] emphasized the similarity of the changes in these organs of animals bearing uterine tumors to the changes induced experimentally in animals by treatment with estrogenic substances. On a theoretical basis, he attributed the subsequent development of uterine carcinoma to liver damage incident to toxemia of pregnancy. Greene believes that the estrogen-inactivating function of the liver is seriously impaired, thus permitting a concentration of estrogen in the blood stream at a carcinogenic level. However, no measurements of the serum estrogen levels of tumor-bearing animals have been made, and there is no report of the induction of this neoplasm in rabbits by estrogen treatment.

BIBLIOGRAPHY

1. Greene, H. S. N. Toxemia of pregnancy in the rabbit: Clinical manifestations and pathology. *J. Exper. Med. 65:* 809-832, 1937.
2. Greene, H. S. N. Toxemia of pregnancy in the rabbit: II. Etiological considerations with especial reference to hereditary factors. *J. Exper. Med. 67:* 369-388, 1938.
3. Greene, H. S. N. Uterine adenomata in the rabbit: III. Susceptibility as a function of constitutional factors. *J. Exper. Med. 73:* 273-292, 1941.
4. Greene, H. S. N. Heterologous transplantation of mammalian tumors: I. The transfer of rabbit tumors to alien species. *J. Exper. Med. 73:* 461-473, 1941.
5. Greene, H. S. N., and Newton, B. L. Evolution of cancer of the uterine fundus in the rabbit. *Cancer 1:* 82-99, 1948.
6. Greene, H. S. N., and Saxton, J. A., Jr. Uterine adenomata in the rabbit: I. Clinical history, pathology and preliminary transplantation experiments. *J. Exper. Med. 67:* 691-708, 1938.
7. Lack, H. L. A preliminary note on the experimental production of cancer. *J. Path. & Bact. 6:* 154-157, 1900.
8. Polson, C. J. Tumours of the rabbit. *J. Path. & Bact. 30:* 603-614, 1927.

CHAPTER 11

Genetics of Neoplastic Diseases

George W. Woolley

This chapter on the genetics of neoplastic diseases makes no pretence of being an exhaustive review of the available literature; the number of papers having some significance to genetics is extremely large. The present material has been developed in an historical manner within broad divisions, or areas, and as a reference review. An effort has been made to reflect the interpretations of the original research workers, so far as possible.

The major part of the review deals with the tumors of the mouse, as does the available literature, and here the classical division indicating the levels at which genetics has been of most significance has been used. This divides the literature into that concerned with (1) transplantation of tumors, (2) induction of tumors, and (3) studies of spontaneous tumors. The first, genetics and transplantation of tumors, an area where the most notable and precise contributions have been made, has been treated in a separate chapter (p. 338). This should be considered first from a historical standpoint. Genetics in relation to tumor induction has been treated in a manner similar to that used by Little (1947), and is based upon the inducing substance, or agent. Genetics in relation to spontaneous tumor occurrence has its major emphasis in the field of mammary tumors, a type of tumor investigated for many years.

The reader is referred to a number of excellent reviews concerned with genetics and experimental cancer: Little (1931, 1934b, 1937, 1941a, 1941b), Little and Gorer (1943), Heston (1945), Little (1947), Heston (1948a, 1948b), and Bittner (1950a). From these it is evident that genetics has been furnishing an important type of experimental approach, or habit of thought, as well as providing valuable research materials. Inbred and hybrid mice of known heredity have yielded our best clues as to the causes of cancer. Strains have been selected which are either resistant or susceptible to cancer. In resistant animals cancer can often be produced by carcinogenic chemicals, but in the absence of exogenous carcinogens the animals never develop cancer. Other strains have been developed in which almost every member will die of cancer; its site and approximate time of appearance can be predicted. Inbred animals, after 20 generations or more of brother-sister mating, behave in a constant manner from generation to generation, permitting the checking and amplification of research progress in various laboratories, with identical biologic material, and over a period of many years.

It is known that most of the hereditary composition of an animal is particulate or atomistic in nature, consisting of discrete and very stable units, the hereditary factors or genes; these genes are carried in the chromosomes in linear beadlike order. Genes are biologic architects. Their task is to use the material from the environment and build the body according to hereditary blueprints. Many genes are usually required in the construction and the work is modified by the material which is made available from the environment during growth and development. It would seem that a useful point of view would be that cancer is a physiopathologic character and as such is chiefly determined by physiologic processes. Genes are precise internal physiologic agents and as such may influence the types of physiopathologic processes which will occur.

Muller (1949), writing on progress and prospects in human genetics brought out the point, worth emphasizing, that no fallacies in genetics are more absurd than the two complementary ones: (1) that because a certain ailment or other characteristic is inherited, we must regard it fatalistically and set it down as something impossible to influence by environmental means; and (2) that because a certain characteristic is found to be the result of the action of environment it is not also subject to hereditary influences.

TUMORS OF MICE

A. INDUCED TUMORS

1. TARS

Tsutsui (1918), a pupil of Yamagiwa, reported on the production of tar cancer in mice. In his experiment 16 cutaneous carcinomas and 1 sarcoma occurred in 67 mice which survived 100 days. Lung metastases were found in 2 of his animals. This report quickly followed the historic work of Yamagiwa and Ichikawa (1918 and earlier), indicating a clear case of direct relationship between chemical treatment and tumor formation. By painting the ears of rabbits these latter investigators produced chronic irritation which was followed by papillomatous, and in some cases malignant neoplasia. Coal-tar had been applied for 30 to 100 days and the tumors occurred about 300 days after treatment had been discontinued.

Fibiger and Bang (1920), Leitch (1922), Russell (1922), and many subsequent workers confirmed and extended the work of Tsutsui on the production and on the nature of coal-tar tumors in mice.

Lynch (1925) studied the effect of coal-tar on two genetically controlled strains of albino mice, one with a high incidence of mammary gland tumors, Strain 1194, from Lathrop stock, and a low-incidence strain obtained from Bagg at Memorial Hospital. When individuals of these two strains were painted between the shoulders with a tar extract, mice of each strain developed tar tumors with almost identical frequency.

Woglom (1926) presented an extensive and excellent review of experimental tar cancer studies. Although there were numerous observations on mice among the 290 studies reviewed, the author found that very little had developed at that time concerning the relation of tar tumors and hereditarily determined susceptibility factors. An excellent early report by Lynch (1927) on tar treatment in relation to the inheritance of induced and spontaneous lung tumors is reviewed under *spontaneous lung tumors*.

Murray (1930) found no clear evidence of resistance to tar-tumor induction in 61 mice with spontaneous mammary cancer or in 2 mice with previous tar cancer. These were random mice of mixed genetic background.

Reinhard and Candee (1932) studied the yield of tar tumors in two groups of mice; one, Strain 3, with an incidence of 93 per cent of spontaneous mammary tumors and the other a hybrid group resulting from the crossing of an albino mouse with a common house mouse. The latter strain was described as having a low or delayed tumor incidence. The yield of tar cancer was approximately the same in the two groups although the hybrid group had a latent period twelve to fourteen weeks longer than the high spontaneous mammary tumor strain.

Twort and Twort (1932) advanced evidence that various color types of mice differed in their susceptibility to tar.

Seelig and Cooper (1933) reviewed the research literature on tar cancer, 1927-1931 inclusive, and included 391 references in the bibliography. The authors stated that unfortunately there had been too little work done on the relation of heredity to cancer. Schabad (1928, 1930; quoted from Seelig and Cooper) observed the incidence of lung tumors during tar painting for a period of four generations of mice. Schabad concluded that an hereditary predisposition was induced by tar painting and that the predisposition was transmitted.

Lynch (1933) was able to report a comparative study involving five genetically different strains of mice. Each strain exhibited characteristic degrees of reaction to tar painting by the formation of skin carcinoma. Evidence had been secured that the strain differences found for tar-induced tumors would segregate out as would be expected if they were dependent upon Mendelian units. Lynch also reported that there was no correlation between the occurrence of tar-induced lung and skin tumors, i.e., that more than one pair of Mendelian factors must be involved.

Kreyberg (1934, 1935) reported on experimental studies in progress since 1929. A study was made of 1200 mice, descendants of a single pair, over a period of fifteen generations. The distribution, or incidence, of tar tumors in different family lines had shown marked segregation. This was especially pronounced in two lines, one characterized by a high incidence of spontaneous breast cancer and another developing no breast cancer at all. The line with no breast cancer (males as well as females), showed an earlier appearance and a higher incidence of tar cancer than the population as a whole. On the other hand the line with a high breast cancer incidence showed a lower incidence of tar tumors than the population as a whole. In this material, evidence was found that genetic influences affected the incidence of tar tumors and that absolute incidence and early reaction were associated. The reactive family was known as "red label" and the less reactive family as "white label." References to these will be found in other studies.

Cramer (1936) found no evidence that strains of mice with a high incidence of spontaneous mammary cancer were especially susceptible to the development of tar tumors; on the contrary when the high spontaneous cancer RIII strain was compared to white mice of a mixed strain having a low incidence of mammary cancer there was evidence of antagonism in the development of carcinoma at the two sites, skin and breast.

Lynch (1937) further studied the possibility of maternal inheritance in lung tumors with reciprocal crosses between strain 1194 with a low incidence, and two strains, Bagg albino and D, with higher incidences. Also three types of backcrosses were made. The incidences of lung tumors in tarred progeny resulting from these crosses and backcrosses gave no evidence of a factor of maternal inheritance.

Bonser and Connal (1939) showed that painting with tar did not affect the incidence of mammary carcinoma in the Kreyberg white-label strain. Presence of mammary carcinoma, on the other hand, definitely delayed the appearance of the tar warts but did not lengthen the interval between their appearance and the onset of malignancy.

Bonser (1938) reported on experiments carried on over an eight-year period. The question was whether individual variation in reaction to a carcinogenic agent is or is not based on a heritable characteristic; and later, what was the difference in reactions between inbred stocks. The tar wart was used. It was observed that a strain termed IF developed tar tumors earlier than: (1) stock mice; (2) two other strains bred in Bonser's laboratory; (3) Kreyberg's white-label (a strain which, as noted above, develops tar warts especially late); (4) Bagg albino mice high in breast cancer incidence; and (5) the CBA strain which had a low incidence of breast cancer. Although the tar warts developed earlier in the IF strain they took longer to become malignant than the warts of the other strains studied. Strong noted a similar relationship in later studies on methylcholanthrene-induced tumors in strain C3H and in a number of other strains.

Brues and Marble (1939) observed a selective strain reaction to tar. In Bagg albino mice the percentage of lymphoblastomas was increased from 2 per cent to 50 per cent with the use of a tar extract. C57 black mice failed to respond with an increase in lymphoblastoma.

Lynch (1940) demonstrated inherited differences in degree of susceptibility to spontaneous and to tar-induced lung tumors in two inbred strains of mice. The criteria for susceptibility included not only the percentage of tumor-bearing animals per group but also the number of tumor nodules per individual.

2. 1:2:5:6-Dibenzanthracene

Andervont (1934) showed that subcutaneous injection of a 1:2:5:6-dibenzanthracene–lard solution induced sarcomas in mice of pure strains and that the tumors were similar to spontaneous tumors in that they grew only in animals of the same strain in which they originated.

Andervont (1935) showed that a single injection of a dibenzanthracene solution containing 0.8 mg. of dibenzanthracene produced tumors in all of the strains employed; A, C3H, CBA, DBA, and stock mice. A, C3H, and CBA were very susceptible to the carcinogenic action of dibenzanthracene. Strain C3H responded to the injections by growing tumors earlier than any of the other strains used in these experiments. It is interesting that in later experiments Strain C3H also responded to methylcholanthrene with early tumor appearance. Practically all of the lung tumors observed, appeared in Strain A or in stock mice. The only common factor in these latter two groups was their white coat color.

Lynch (1935) presented a preliminary report on the susceptibility of seven strains of mice to tumor induction when 1:2:5:6-dibenzanthracene was injected subcutaneously. There was evidence that the strains differed in susceptibility and that susceptibility was organ specific.

Branch (1936) painted 1:2:5:6-dibenzanthracene on the depilated skins of mice of high spontaneous breast cancer Strain A and low spontaneous breast cancer Strain C57 black. Almost twice as many tumors developed in the skins of the Strain A mice as in the skins of Strain C57 black. These results coincide with the results of Kreyberg (1934) with tar.

Andervont (1937a, 1937b) has shown that subcutaneous injection of a 1:2:5:6-dibenzanthracene–lard solution caused more Strain A mice to develop lung tumors and to develop them earlier than other control strains. C57 black mice were resistant to the induction of lung tumors. The first and second hybrid generations after a cross of A and C57 black yielded induced lung tumors in a high percentage of the individuals—90 per cent and 74.7 per cent respectively. A high percentage of first and second generation uninjected control animals were without these lung tumors.

Dobrovolskaia-Zavadskaia and Rouyer (1938) treated mice of Line XXX, a line referred to as refractory to mammary adenocarcinoma, with 1:2:5:6-dibenzanthracene and other external agents. The authors discuss the importance of constitutional (genetic) factors in determining susceptibility to induced tumors.

Andervont (1938a, 1938b, 1938c) reported that Strains I and Y were far more resistant than C3H to the carcinogenic power of 1:2:5:6-dibenzanthracene. Reciprocal breeding tests were carried out between C3H and I and between C3H and Y. The hybrid mice were intermediate in susceptibility when they were compared to the susceptibility of the parent strains. The mice obtained by mating C3H to I were considerably more susceptible to induced pulmonary tumors than those obtained from the mating of C3H and Y. The importance of the genetic constitution of the test was further explored (Andervont, 1938d) by comparing eight inbred strains; C3H, C, C57 black, M "leaden," A, DBA, I, and Y. Wide variations in susceptibility to subcutaneous and pulmonary tumor induction were found.

Heston (1940) studied the susceptibility of four inbred strains of mice, A, L (leaden), N, and W, and their hybrids, to explain more completely the inheritance of susceptibility to induced lung tumors. Dominance of tumor over nontumor had been established. This study: (1) failed to give evidence for single allele Mendelian inheritance; (2) pointed out that nongenetic factors may influence the development of induced lung tumors; and (3) furnished no evidence of linkage between lung tumor susceptibility and the gene for leaden, piebald, dilution, agouti, or brown.

Andervont (1940) further studied mice of the Fi and backcross generations obtained from crosses involving Strains Y, C3H, and I. The tumors were induced with injection of 0.8 mg. of 1:2:5:6-dibenzanthracene in 0.2 cc. of filtered lard. Andervont concluded that the tendency to develop induced subcutaneous, lung, and mammary tumors had a genetic basis under these conditions. The results permitted the conclusion that susceptibility to all three types was inherited in a dominant manner and that multiple genetic factors, or modifying factors, were involved. It was also clear that when inbred strains of mice of known susceptibility were crossed, it was not possible to predict the degree of susceptibility of the resultant hybrids.

Heston (1941) reported on the relationship between susceptibility to 1:2:5:6-dibenzanthracene–induced pulmonary tumors and certain known genes of the mouse. Backcross mice homozygous for the linked genes shaker-2 and waved-2 (sh-2 sh-2, w-2 w-2), were less susceptible than those heterozygous for the normal alleles (Sh-2 sh-2, W-2 w-2). Mice with flexed tails (ff) were less susceptible than those with normal tails (Ff).

Heston (1942a) has shown that susceptibility to 1:2:5:6-dibenzanthracene–induced pulmonary tumors was not a character with alternate (all or none) expression but that susceptibility was expressed in degree. This degree of susceptibility could adequately be measured quantitatively in two ways: (1) by the time required for tumors to develop; and (2) by the number of nodules which were caused to develop. The results obtained by the two methods were strikingly parallel. The results with either method confirmed the conclusion that genetic factors as well as environmental factors were involved. It was also clearly shown by each method that the genetic factors affecting susceptibility were multiple. Of the total variance in susceptibility of the F_2 generation, as measured by the number of tumor nodules, it was estimated that approximately 86 per cent was due to genetic factors and 14 per cent to nongenetic factors.

Heston (1942c) observed that 1:2:5:6-dibenzanthracene induced pulmonary tumor incidence was higher in F_1 hybrid male mice with the gene A^y (yellow) than in their brown litter mates. The evidence indicated that this increase in susceptibility was due to the A^y gene per se. Heston suggested that the physiologic processes which were associated with the A^y gene, and which led to increased body weight of the yellow mice over that of the brown litter mates, may also lead to the increased susceptibility to induced pulmonary tumors in yellow mice.

Lynch (1941, 1943) used the percentage of tumor-bearing mice per group and the number of tumor nodules per individual, as she had done earlier (Lynch, 1940) with tar, to reveal susceptibility among three strains of mice. The mice were observed after intraperitoneal injections of 1:2:5:6-dibenzanthracene into very young animals. Lynch concluded that the degree of susceptibility to induced lung tumor was inherited and that three or more genes must be involved.

Carr (1947) reported that 1:2:5:6-dibenzanthracene produced recessive gene mutations in the mouse.

Lorenz and Stewart (1948) studied the induction of alimentary tract tumors in Strains A, C57 brown, I, DBA, and in A and DBA backcross mice by olive oil emulsions containing 1:2:5:6-dibenzanthracene.

Heston and Deringer (1949a, 1949b) studied the relationship between the hairless gene and susceptibility to induced pulmonary tumors in mice. The tumors were induced by intravenous injection of 0.5 mg. of 1:2:5:6-dibenzanthracene at an early age. In the backcross resulting from mating the F_1 hybrids of the high pulmonary tumor Strain A and a low pulmonary tumor pink eyed hairless strain, the hairless (hr hr) segregants were less susceptible to induced pulmonary tumors than the haired (Hr Hr) segregants. There was no difference in susceptibility between the pink eyed (pp) and the non-pink eyed (Pp) segregants.

Heston and Dunn (1950) extended their studies on induced pulmonary tumors in the following way. Two strains of mice, Strain A, which was highly susceptible to the development of pulmonary tumors and Strain L (C57 leaden) which was highly resistant to the formation of these tumors, were used. To determine if genic action in controlling the development of pulmonary tumors was localized in the lung tissue or was manifested through some general systemic mechanism, lung tissues from the above strains were transplanted subcutaneously into a common host, the F_1 hybrid between these two strains. Following the intravenous injection of 1:2:5:6-dibenzanthracene in the hosts, pulmonary tumors were found in 39.1 per cent of the transplants from Strain A donors and in 3.6 per cent of the transplants from Strain L donors. Thus it was shown that a large part of the difference in genetic susceptibility to pulmonary tumors of the donor strains was retained in the transplant tissue, suggesting that the action of at least most of the susceptibility genes by which these two strains differ was localized in the lung tissue.

3. 20-Methylcholanthrene

Boyland and Warren (1937) compared the effects of injecting one and two doses of methylcholanthrene into normal and castrated mice. The strains compared were CBA and the Simpson albino strain. The CBA mice were less susceptible to the action of methylcholanthrene injected subcutaneously than the Simpson strain. The susceptibility seemed to be the same in both sexes and in normal and castrated mice.

Morton and Mider (1938) demonstrated a specific lymphomatosis response in 10 of 48 Line 212 DBA mice to painting with methylcholanthrene. In addition to the 20 per cent incidence, the time elapsed in the development of the lymphomatosis was one-third of that required for the spontaneous disease to appear. Mider and Morton (1939) were able to report that 48 of 60 Strain DBA mice painted as above developed leukoses.

Strong and Smith (1939) injected female mice of seven distinct strains (NH, HE, CBA, C57, JK, CBAN, and N) subcutaneously with 1 mg. of methylcholanthene dissolved in sesame oil when the animals were two months of age. Of

8 mice developing adenocarcinoma of the mammary gland, 6 were in Strain NH and two in JK. The JK strain is especially resistant to the development of spontaneous mammary gland tumors. Some of the induced tumors had keratinized areas.

Strong (1940) reported a selection experiment based upon the induction of a variety of tumors in hybrid mice. This included the early generations of the NH strain. Strong found divergent substrains and these remained true to type over a period of several generations. Thus the directional path taken by the individual in the induction of a specific tumor type seemed to be the resultant of the genetic constitution of the individual and thus to be determined by heredity.

Lorenz and Stewart (1940) presented a preliminary report on squamous cell carcinoma and lesions of the forestomach which occurred following the oral administration of 20-methylcholanthrene and 1:2:5:6-dibenzanthracene. Strains A, C57 black, C57 brown, C3H, and an A backcross group were used. At the date of the report all of the gastric carcinomas had occurred only in A or A backcross mice. The authors concluded that induction of squamous cell carcinoma in the forestomach of mice depended in part on the strain of mouse used.

Strong (1941), in a further study of the induction of tumors in Strain NH, obtained evidence that the origins of carcinoma of the skin and of spindle cell sarcoma were independent of each other. Strong concluded that these differences were probably brought about by a peculiar biologic constitution of the individual which gave rise to them.

Bonser and Wainman (1941) found no antagonism between the presence of a malignant tumor in one organ and the appearance of a second tumor in another organ. Emphasis was on methylcholanthrene-induced skin cancer in relation to breast cancer.

Kirschbaum *et al.* (1940) painted Strains F and C3H three times weekly, and Strains NH, CHI, CBAN, and C57 black once weekly, with methylcholanthrene. The painting period was three to fourteen months. It is of some interest that of these strains, F showed a high incidence of spontaneous leukemia. After treatment, Strain F mice died with large ulcerating skin tumors. C3H mice had 3 lymphoid tumors out of 94, while none occurred in 280 control mice. No leukemias developed in 90 mice of Strains CHI, NH, C57 black, and CBAN.

Mider and Morton (1940) investigated the importance of local and constitutional effects of methylcholanthrene in the production of skin tumors. A single application of 0.5 per cent solution of methylcholanthrene in benzene to the backs of C57 black mice produced papillomas which disappeared spontaneously. A few carcinomas appeared among the papillomas of C57 brown mice which received the same treatment. These two stocks are distantly related.

Bonser (1940) showed that there was considerable independence of reaction between four strains of mice when methylcholanthrene in lard injected subcutaneously was compared to methylcholanthrene applied to the skin. Mice of the IF strain were most susceptible with skin application and least susceptible of the four when subcutaneous injection was employed. Ulceration of the skin was not a common feature with the doses used, except in the case of the Bagg albino mice. Andervont noticed this latter feature in Strain A mice which were originally derived from the Bagg albino stock.

White and Stewart (1942) fed methylcholanthrene, 55 mg. per 100 Gm. diet, to 50 C3H mice and 32 C mice for a period of six months. Hemangioendotheliomas occurred in 11 Strain C3H and in 21 Strain C mice. Individuals of both strains exhibited intestinal carcinoma. Pulmonary tumors were induced in both strains but with a higher incidence in Strain C mice.

Burdette and Strong (1943) studied the tumors induced by methylcholanthrene (a single injection of 1 mg. in oil of benne) in the following five strains of mice: C3H, CBA, CHI, NH, and JK. Susceptibility as determined by mean induction time was in the above order when arranged from high to low. The survival of mice after developing tumors was in a different order, JK, CBA, C3H, CHI, and NH, when arranged from short to long survival time.

Burdette and Strong (1943b) observed the susceptibility in the progeny of reciprocal crosses between Strains C3H and JK when the mice were injected subcutaneously with 1 mg. of methylcholanthrene in 0.1 cc. of sesame oil. The average time before tumor formation in the F_1 hybrids was intermediate between that of the two parent strains. The survival time of the F_1 mice with tumors was longer than for either parental strain. The predominant type of tumor was that of the JK parents. No evidence of an extrachromosomal influence was found. It was concluded by the authors that there must exist more than one gene for susceptibility to induced tumors, at least one of which was dominant and at least one of which was recessive.

Strong (1943) found that in a relatively hybrid group of mice, generations F_3 to F_8 of NHO mice, the sex of the treated individual was not an important factor in the induction of tumors. Subcutaneous injection of 1 mg. of methylcholanthrene in sesame oil was used.

Orr (1943) observed mammary tumors in a high proportion of IF and CBA mice following intranasal administration of methylcholanthrene. The controls gave no mammary tumors.

Zimmerman and Arnold (1944) tested the validity of the hypothesis that genetic constitution was an important factor in the incidence of primary intracranial neoplasms induced with pure methylcholanthrene implanted intracerebrally. Of six strains of mice tested—C3H, ABC albino, Bagg albino, C57 black, A albino, and DBA—the first four yielded 50 per cent or over of primary intracranial neoplasms, whereas the last two strains were low in incidence of carcinogen-induced brain tumors. The incidence obtained was not correlated with the strain potentialities with regard to spontaneous mammary gland tumors. Hybrids between C3H and DBA of F_1 generation yielded an intracranial tumor incidence of 26 per cent, which was an intermediate value as compared to the parental strains.

Strong (1944) in a further genetic analysis of the induction of tumors by methylcholanthrene, weighted his selection of animals toward resistance to local induction of tumors in NHO mice. This selection led to an increased incidence of hepatoma.

Kirschbaum and Kaplan (1944) found that the susceptibility of Strain F and Strain DBA mice either to spontaneous leukemia or leukemia induced by methylcholanthrene did not imply susceptibility to the induction of leukemia by roentgen-rays. The latter was especially leukemogenic for Strain A mice which were low in incidence of spontaneous leukemia and carcinogen-resistant in relation to the induction of this type of tumor.

Strong (1945a) reported the occurrence of thirteen coat-color mutations in the descendants of mice which had received methylcholanthrene treatment for several generations. Strong interpreted this to mean that methylcholanthrene had affected the germ plasm and had brought out germinal point mutations. It was thought possible that methylcholanthrene may bring about malignancies in tissues by a similar process, that is, by causing somatic mutations to arise within them. Strong (1945c) reported the occurrence of two germinal mutations following the injection of methylcholanthrene which changed the susceptibility to the induction of tumors with this substance.

Strong (1945b) described the occurrence of 231 pathologic lesions of the pyloric part of the stomach in NHO mice following the injection of 1.0 mg. of methylcholanthrene in sesame oil. The carcinogen was used when the mice were 60 days of age. Untreated descendants of the mice developing adenocarcinoma of the stomach continued to develop this tumor spontaneously. Bagshaw and Strong (1949) presented a histopathologic and genetic study of these tumors.

Kirschbaum and Bittner (1945) noted that methylcholanthrene induced mammary gland tumors could be obtained in F_1 C3H × DBA mice with and without the "milk influence."

Strong and Hollander (1947) studied the effect of methylcholanthrene in female mice of several strains when injected intraperitoneally at about the time of conception with 1.0 mg. in sesame oil. High embryonic mortality occurred in Strains C3H and A, but not in JK.

Cowdry *et al.* (1948) observed that epidermoid cancer in mice, induced by methylcholanthrene, appeared more quickly and in a higher percentage of young than of old New Buffalo mice, whereas in old and young CBA mice there was no essential difference in response.

Gottschalk (1948) found that the injection of methylcholanthrene into the embryonic skin of C mice led to the occurrence of epitheliomas as well as to sarcomas. Many carcinomas were also obtained from embryo skin of AKa mice, but less frequently, under the same conditions, in C57 black mice.

Lorenz and Stewart (1948) studied the induction of alimentary tract tumors by olive oil emulsions containing methylcholanthrene and also 1:2:5:6-dibenzanthracene. The results are reported under the latter carcinogen. It may be added here that if the olive oil emulsions were made stable by the addition of a wetting agent, squamous carcinoma of the forestomach developed not only in Strain A and in A backcross mice but with increasing frequency in the other strains studied: C57 brown, I, and DBA.

Pan and Gardner (1948) studied the malignant tumors induced by methylcholanthrene in transplants of young-adult uterine cervical or corneal tissues. Among the 10 inbred, or hybrid, groups studied, more cancers developed in the A strain than in any of the others.

Hollander and Strong (1949) further reported on the effects of methylcholanthrene on the occurrence of mutations. Young female mice of Strains C3H, A, and JK were crossed with males of Strains A, C3H, L, and JK. In observing several thousand offsprings it was found that 0.5 per cent showed abnormalities of development. It was reported that a few possible new mutant types were obtained.

Andervont (1949) further described the spontaneous lesion of the stomach in Strain I mice and pointed out the hereditary relationship between this strain and Strain JK used by Strong in developing NHO mice. Thus there was another possible explanation for the stomach lesions in the latter mice which have been interpreted to "have acquired a new characteristic, cancer of the stomach, following the subcutaneous injection of methylcholanthrene."

Kirschbaum (1949) determined the histologic similarity between methylcholanthrene-induced mammary tumors in Strain DBA with and without the milk factor and those arising spontaneously in NH × DBA F_1, F_2, and F_1 backcrossed to DBA. The maternal influence was always provided by the low-cancer NH strain. The tumors of both groups were different from those arising in Strains DBA and A in C3H × DBA F_1 mice with the milk factor.

Burdette (1948) observed that susceptibility to methylcholanthrene-induced tumors was intermediate to that of the parents in a backcross generation study. C3H × JK F_1 mice were backcrossed to C3H and to JK. The backcross mice had induction times nearer those of the more susceptible parent in both crosses. The mice of the backcross to C3H had a lower average induction time than those in the backcross to JK. The more susceptible hybrids had a significantly longer survival time. Tests for linkage gave no evidence for association between susceptibility and the genes for pink eye, short ear, nonagouti, and brown.

Bonser and Robson (1950) studied the induction of tumors following the direct implantation of methylcholanthrene into the uterus of mice. A higher incidence of both carcinoma and sarcoma occurred in CBA than in white mice. The difference in carcinoma incidence—CBA, 40 per cent and white mice 14.9 per cent—was not statistically significant. The difference in sarcoma incidence—CBA, 53.3 per cent and white mice, 13.4 per cent—was statistically significant. When immature mice were compared—CBA, 40 per cent and white mice, 8.3 per cent—the difference in carcinoma incidence became significant. The average time of carcinoma appearance in CBA, 10.5 months, was earlier than in white mice, 11.5 months. The average induction time for sarcomas was similar in the two groups, 8 months.

Bagshaw and Strong (1950) observed an intimate familial relationship among animals bearing stomach tumors in that one subline of NHO mice had an incidence of 12.7 per cent over a period of five generations while the incidence among all animals studied in this particular line of descent was about 3 per cent. The tumors were induced by a single injection of methylcholanthrene.

Morgan (1950) studied the incidence of pulmonary tumors in 305 inbred Strain Y mice, 105 of which were injected with methylcholanthrene and 200 untreated. The incidence of induced pulmonary tumors was significantly higher in the yellow mice than in their brown litter mates. The increase in susceptibility was found to be correlated with body weight. Fat yellow mice developed more tumors than did lean ones.

Andervont (1950b) studied the induction of mammary gland tumors by methylcholanthrene in DBA mice free of mammary-tumor agent. Andervont reviewed the literature on Strain DBA, showing the importance of controlling sublime variations in experimental work with a long-time inbred strain such as DBA.

Strong (1951) noted a mutation at the pink-eye locus in the descendants of dark-eyed mice injected with methylcholanthrene. Mice showing the recessive mutation and their dark-eyed siblings continued to develop at the same rate and incidence as mice of their dark-eyed ancestry: (1) fibrosarcoma at the site of injection of methylcholanthrene; (2) lung adenomas; and (3) a mucosal lesion just anterior to the pylorus.

4. 3:4-Benzpyrene

Collins *et al.* (1943) administered 3:4-benzpyrene dissolved in sesame oil to 133 mice in five inbred strains, C3H, NH, C57 black, A, and CHI, to determine the effect upon the formation of tumors of the gastrointestinal tract. All tumors involving the stomach apparently arose in the forestomach and were of the squamous cell type. The highest incidence of gastric papillomas and carcinomas occurred in mice of the C3H strain. A high incidence of gastric tumors was observed in mice of C57 and NH strains and a low incidence in CHI and A.

Zimmerman and Arnold (1943) repeated their methylcholanthrene experiments in producing intracranial tumors using in this instance 3:4-benzpyrene. Twenty-eight tumors occurred in 47 Strain C3H mice. Of these 14 were gliomas, 11 were fibrosarcomas, 2 extracranial rhabdomyosarcomas, and 1 a mixed glioma and sarcoma. Males and females were used.

5. 9:10-Dimethyl-1,2-Benzanthracene

Englebreth-Holm and Lefèvre (1941) compared the carcinogenic action of 9:10-dimethyl-1,2-benzanthracene administered to Strains Aka and DBA. Aka was high in incidence of leukemia and low in incidence of mammary gland tumors. Strain DBA was high in incidence of mammary gland tumors and low in incidence of leukemia. Pronounced acceleration of tumors characteristic for the strains, evident in increased incidence, and especially and distinctly earlier appearance of the particular tumor were produced both by subcutaneous injection and painting.

6. 3:4:5:6-Dibenzcarbazole

Andervont and Edwards (1941) tested Strains A, C3H, and C with subcutaneous injection of 0.2 mg. 3:4:5:6-dibenzcarbazole dissolved in filtered lard, sesame oil, or olive oil. The compound induced hepatic changes, as well as subcutaneous sarcoma at the injection site, in all strains. Pulmonary tumors were induced in Strain A. Females were more susceptible to the hepatic changes than the males. Castration of Strain A males increased their susceptibility to induced hepatic tumors when lard was used as the solvent.

Armstrong and Bonser (1950) described an experiment in which an oily solution of 3:4:5:6-dibenzcarbazole was fed mice of the Strong A and CBA strains, with a view to testing this substance as a bladder carcinogen. No epithelial changes were observed in the bladder. Many animals died of liver necrosis unless the dose was reduced to 0.5 mg. per mouse per week. Females were more susceptible than males and Strain CBA more susceptible than Strain A. Papillomatosis and carcinoma of the forestomach were observed in both sexes and in both strains. Pulmonary adenomas were observed in A but not in CBA.

Strong *et al.* (1938) tested the carcinogenic activity of 3:4:5:6-dibenzcarbazole on male mice belonging to Strains A and CBA. The substance produced sarcomas at the site of injection in 100 per cent of both CBA and A, and at the same rate. Eight cases of hepatoma were observed in treated animals of the CBA strain, at an earlier age than spontaneous tumors of this type had been observed, and none in treated animals of the A strain. Spontaneous hepatoma had previously been observed in CBA but not in A.

7. Azo Compounds

Andervont (1939c) studied the carcinogenic properties of 2-amino-5-azotoluene. When this was given by subcutaneous injection to individuals representing five strains the order of susceptibility to liver tumor formation from susceptible to nonsusceptible was C, I, A, C3H, and Y. Since Strain C3H mice were more susceptible to spontaneous hepatoma than Strain A, the results suggested that in these strains the induced tumors were not correlated with susceptibility to spontaneous hepatoma.

Andervont *et al.* (1942) observed the effect of subcutaneous injections of *o*-aminoazotoluene moistened with glycerol. This substance was given mice of Strains A, C3H, C, and C57 black and to hybrids derived from Strains A, C3H, and C. The compound induced hepatomas in all inbred strains and in the hybrids. The females were far more susceptible to induced macroscopic hepatic lesions and hepatomas than were the males. The compound induced pulmonary tumors in Strains A and C and in their F_1 hybrids. The inheritance of susceptibility to the *o*-aminoazotoluene–induced lung tumors was similar to that of spontaneous or hydrocarbon-induced pulmonary growths. Hemangioendotheliomas were induced in all inbred strains and in certain hybrid groups.

Andervont and Edwards (1943) administered olive oil solutions of *p*-dimethylaminoazobenzene and *o*-aminoazotoluene to various strains of mice. *o*-Aminoazotoluene–induced hepatic changes and hepatomas were found in females of Strains C, C57 black, and C3H. Pulmonary tumors were induced in A and C. Hemangioendotheliomas were induced in Strains C and C57 black. Fibrosarcomas were induced at the site of injection in Strains C57 black, and C3H, and C. *p*-Dimethylaminobenzene failed to produce gross or microscopic changes in mice of Strains C, C57 black, or A. In fact, the only tumors produced by the latter substance were fibrosarcomas at the site of injection in two Strain C57 black females.

Kirby (1945a) studied the action of four dyes in mixed and pure strain mice. Hepatoma was induced in C57 black, CBA, and stock mice. Sarcoma at the site of injection was rare in stock and C57 black mice and was never seen in CBA. Hemangioendotheliomas were found in a few stock and C57 black mice.

Kirby (1945b) reviewed the literature concerning strain susceptibility of ten strains which had been used in experiments using azo carcinogenic compounds. The review showed that strain should be considered in experimental work of this type.

8. Urethane

Nettleship and Henshaw (1943) noted that subanesthetizing doses of urethane increased lung-tumor incidence significantly in C3H mice, and shortened the time until occurrence by several months in Strain A mice which normally have a high incidence of lung tumors.

Cowen (1947) noted a difference in the response of various stocks of mice to the carcinogenic action of urethane. RIII mice developed more lung tumors than CBA mice and each developed more than C57 black mice.

Orr (1947) found that urethane would induce lung adenomata in stock mice. It had previously been shown to be effective in C3H and A strains.

Cowen (1950) reported a detailed study of strain differences in response to urethane, using two strains, A and C57 black, which showed a wide divergence with respect to spontaneous incidence of lung tumors. Cowen found that these strains gave different yields of urethane-induced lung tumors, yields correlated positively with spontaneous incidence, and suggested this difference was due to a dominant gene complex. Two criteria which paralleled each other closely were used as an index of response of mice to the carcinogenic action of urethane—the number of tumors per mouse and the size attained by the largest tumor in any of the lungs.

9. Hormones: Direct Chemical Effects and Changes in Endocrine Balance

Bonser (1935a) compared the reactivity of a high mammary-cancer line, Strain A, with a low mammary-cancer line, Strain CBA, to estrone administration by various routes. There was perhaps slightly greater reactivity in CBA. There was no demonstrable difference in age of onset of estrus, duration of cycle, duration of heat, and cessation of estrus.

Bonser (1935b) obtained three mammary gland adenocarcinomas from 19 males of Strain A treated with 300 I. U. oestrone weekly; and none in 34 similarly treated CBA males.

Lacassagne (1936) pointed out the inequality of reactions to the same dose of oestrone in different strains of mice.

Suntzeff *et al.* (1936) compared the mammary-gland tumor incidence in several strains of mice after estrogen treatment. The highest tumor incidence was found in Strain C3H; then followed with decreasing tumor rates, Strains DBA, A, and New Buffalo. In Strains Old Buffalo and C57 black no tumors developed.

Gardner *et al.* (1936) reported the development of a spindle cell sarcoma at the site of injection of ketoestrin benzoate in 86 Strain A mice injected. Six sarcomas appeared in 37 C3H mice, and none in 13 CBA mice treated in a similar manner. Sixteen mammary tumors were obtained in the 86 Strain A mice, 10 in the 37 C3H, and 2 in the 13 CBA mice, after estrogen treatment.

Lacassagne and Nyka (1937) observed adenomas of the anterior lobe of the pituitary in estrogen-treated mice of Lines RIII and 17, but not in Lines 30 and 39.

Robson and Bonser (1938) reported that of 53 RIII males treated with 5 mg. triphenylethylene weekly, later 3 mg. weekly, 9 developed mammary gland tumors between 18 and 29 weeks of age. No mammary gland tumors were observed in 29 CBA males treated in a similar way.

Lacassagne (1938) observed lymphosarcomas after prolonged treatment with estrogen in a line of mice, RIII, selected for low incidence of this tumor. The point of origin of the lymphosarcomas seemed to be the thymus.

Gardner and Allen (1939) observed that estrogen and androgen, in variable amounts, injected into eight different strains of mice produced cervical and vaginal tumorous lesions in Strains CBA, C3H, A, and C121. These did not occur in 39 treated mice of the C57, N, JK, and F strains.

Gardner *et al.* (1940) found that 15.4 per cent of 22 Strain C3H mice developed lymphoid tumors following estrogen treatment. None of 117 untreated mice of this same strain showed lymphoid tumors.

Gardner and Strong (1940) observed that hypophyseal adenomas did not develop in over 700 mice of Strains A, C3H, CBA, C12I, JK, and N following the injection of estrogens for a prolonged period. Fifteen of 106 mice of the C57 black strain, similarly treated, had generalized hypertrophy of the chromophobe cells and distention of the vascular sinuses, or adenomas.

Bonser and Robson (1940) further reported the effect of the synthetic estrogen, triphenylethylene, and of estradiol dipropionate on the occurrence of mammary tumors. There were striking strain differences in that treated male mice of Strain RIII had an incidence of over 60 percent of mammary tumors and Strains A and CBA had none. Previously a few mammary tumors had been obtained in Strain A males when treated with estrone benzoate. Strains RIII and CBA had pituitary tumors while Strain A failed to show these tumors. Interstitial cell tumors occurred in Strain A but none in strains CBA and RIII.

Woolley *et al.* (1940) observed that Strain C57 black, a low breast-tumor strain, responded to early gonadectomy with less adrenal cortical overgrowth and evidence of sex hormone production from the adrenal cortices than Strains DBA and C3H, two high mammary-tumor strains.

Allen and Gardner (1941) observed no influence of the genetic factors involved in the relation of mammary gland cancer to estradiol-induced cancer of the uterine cervix.

Gardner (1941) reported that estradiol produced pituitary tumors in C57 black mice but not in CBA mice. Pituitary tumors occurred in estrogen-treated mice in both reciprocal F_1 hybrid groups produced with the above strains.

Gardner (1941) studied the effect of estrogen administration when a mammary-tumor susceptible strain, CBA, was mated to a mammary-tumor resistant strain, C57 black. Seventy per cent of the females of the CBA strain and none of the latter strain developed mammary adenocarcinoma. Fifty-two mice with CBA mothers and 53 hybrids with C57 mothers received injections of 16.6 or 50 mg. of estradiol benzoate weekly throughout life. Mammary cancers appeared in 59 per cent of the estrogen-treated male and female mice with CBA mothers and in 85 per cent of the breeding females of similar origin. None of the estrogen-treated hybrid mice with C57 mothers developed mammary tumors, although 43 per cent of the breeding females had mammary tumors at death. Only about one-third of the tumors of the latter group were considered malignant. Hypophyseal tumors, which had appeared previously only in estrogen-treated mice of the C57 strain, appeared in the estrogen-treated hybrids of each group. Gardner considered the transmission of the tendency to develop such tumors to be compatible with a genetic interpretation. The incidence of lymphoid tumors was greater in the estrogen-treated hybrids than in the controls.

Bonser (1942) presented a further series of benign and malignant interstitial cell tumors in estrogen-treated Strain A mice. Bonser also reviewed the earlier experiments by Bonser and Robson (1940), Hooker *et al.* (1940), and Shimkin *et al.* (1941-42) in the production of tumors of these types in Strain A and Strain C mice.

Haagensen and Randall (1942) observed differences in mammary growth response and tumor occurrence when estradiol benzoate was given to the limit of tolerance to C57 black and RIII mice. It was interpreted that hereditary factors were dominant over the effects of the administration of estrogen on the incidence of mammary carcinoma.

Miller and Pybus (1942) treated individuals of the Simpson, Edinburgh, and CBA strains with 300 I.U. of ketohydroxyestrin (90 per cent estrone, 5 per cent equilin) in olive oil weekly for five weeks. In occurrence of uterine tumors the strains in order of increasing incidence were: Simpson, Edinburgh, and CBA. In order of increasing incidence of mammary tumors the order was reversed, that is, CBA, Edinburgh, and Simpson.

Shimkin and Andervont (1942) summarized the results of five experiments beginning in 1940. Foster nursing of mice of a strain with a high incidence of mammary cancer, C3H, by mice with a low incidence, C57 black and C, reduced markedly the incidence of mammary tumors in both males and females receiving estrogens. Foster nursing mice of a strain with a low incidence of mammary carcinoma, C, by mice with a high incidence of this neoplasm, C3H, increased the incidence of tumors of the breast in male and female mice treated with estrogen. Foster nursing did not affect the incidence of induction of testicular tumors of the interstitial cell type when the mice were treated with stilbestrol.

Gardner (1943) observed testicular tumors in 3 to 61 untreated Strains A $\times$ C3H and A × C57 black mice. Two of these were of the type produced by estrogens.

Gardner (1943) observed that the estrogen, triphenylethylene, produced testicular tumors in 7 of 13 mice of Strain JK, 7 of 17 mice of Strain A, 1 of 14 mice of Strain C3H, and none in mice of Strains C12I, N, or CBA.

Gardner *et al.* (1944) found that 11 of 822 mice of seven different strains had lymphoid tumors at death (1.34 per cent). Of the mice from these same strains, C3H, CBA, PM, C12I, JK, A, and C57, 11.9 per cent acquired lymphomas when treated with one or more of several steroid or nonsteroid estrogens. Mice of the CBA, C3H, and PM strains showed an incidence of lymphoma of approximately 15 per cent when treated with estrogens. The incidence in mice of the C12I and JK strains was approximately 5 per cent; for the A and C57 strains, approximately 2 per cent.

Bonser (1944) extended her studies on the effect of estrogens on production of testis tumor to other strains. A few small interstitial cell tumors of the testis were produced in Strain IFS, and large tumors in Strains A and RIII. No testis tumors were observed in Strain CBA.

Mühlbock (1945) found that in Strains DBA, A, and C57 black, the sensitivity of the mammary glands to estrin was independent of the mammary tumor agent.

Deringer *et al.* (1945) followed the estrus cycles of inbred A and C3H mice and their reciprocal hybrids for a period of 150 days. It was noted that there was considerable variation in the age at which the vaginas opened in the different groups, the vaginas opening significantly later in Strain A than in Strain C3H and in the two F_1 hybrid groups. Early opening of the vagina was correlated with high incidence of mammary gland tumors in virgin females.

Mühlbock (1947) studied the susceptibility of spayed female mice of Strains C57 black, O2O, and DBA to estrogenic hormones, measured by the vaginal smear reaction. Estrone was administered directly into the vagina. In both C57 black and O2O where the predisposition to mammary carcinoma was lacking, the amount of estrogen required for a positive reaction was 0.001 gamma whereas in the DBA high-cancer strain a "quintuple" quantity was needed.

Furth (1947) noted nodular hyperplasia of the adrenal cortex in gonadectomized AK × Rf F_1 hybrids when ovary transplants to the spleen had failed. Woolley and Little (1946) found that similar nodules could be prevented in gonadectomized Strain CE mice by diethylstilbestrol. Woolley and Chute (1947) extended the prophylactic studies on Strain CE to include a number of effective estrogenic and androgenic compounds.

Korteweg (1948) reported that by the estrus test in spayed females his high-cancer Strain DBA mice produced relatively large amounts of estrone in comparison with low-cancer O2O, and C57 black mice.

Mühlbock (1948) found that the vagina of the high-cancer Strain DBA was much less sensitive to estrone than the low-cancer Strains O2O, and Reit, whereas the mamma was as sensitive as that of the most sensitive of the low-cancer strains.

Smith (1948) studied the relation of the factor modifying hormonal activity in breeding and virgin mice (designated "inherited hormonal influence") in Strain A, Strain C3H and in six hybrid groups between these strains. Adrenal cortical hyperplasia and tumors occurred in those castrate groups with the inherited hormonal factors: C3H high and low-tumor stocks. Mammary tumors were present in castrated mice with the inherited hormonal influence provided an active milk agent was present: C3H high-tumor hybrids.

Frantz and Kirschbaum (1949) observed the type of sex hormone secretion in gonadectomized mice bearing spontaneous adrenal cortical adenomas. NH mice secreted only estrogenic hormones 70 or more days following gonadectomy. Bagg albino mice secreted primarily androgenic hormones. The evidence was that the secretions were both estrogenic and androgenic in CBA and C3H mice.

Vazquez-Lopez (1949) studied the effect of thiourea on RIII and C3H mice and found that the result depended upon strain characteristics. RIII mice, whether of high or low mammary cancer sublines, reacted with intense thyroid hyperplasia and without disturbance of the estrus cycles. The incidence of lymphomas in the low-tumor subline, or of mammary cancer in the original RIII strain was not affected by thiourea. In C3H mice thiourea did not produce a detectable thyroid enlargement but the animals remained anestrous during the period of administration. The incidence of mammary tumors in virgins and in breeding females of the C3H strain was considerably reduced by administration of thiourea during a period of six months, ending before the average tumor age of the control mice.

Dickie and Woolley (1949) observed the occurrence of basophilic tumors of the anterior lobe of the pituitary in gonadectomized F_1 generation mice when the parental strains were CE, DBA, C57 black, A, and C3H. When the hybrid groups were DBA $\times$ CE the incidence of these pituitary tumors was greater than when DBA $\times$ C57 black, CE $\times$ C57 black, or A $\times$ C3H.

Trentin (1950) observed that there was no inverse relationship between vaginal sensitivity to estrogen and mammary tumor incidence. Eleven strains were used in this study. It was also found that the presence or absence of the milk factor did not alter vaginal sensitivity to estrogen.

Li and Gardner (1950) observed ovarian tumors after intrasplenic ovarian grafts in Strains A, C57 black, and CBA.

Gross and Schwartz (1951) studied the relation of thyroxine to mammary tumor incidence. There was a less rapid excretion of I^{131} in C3H animals than in C57 black mice.

Silberberg *et al.* (1951) studied the effects of subcutaneous anterior hypophyseal grafts on intrasplenic ovarian grafts. The intrasplenic tumors tended to appear earlier and with treatment the ratio of granulosa cell to luteoma shifted in favor of the latter. The experiments were done with Strain A where it had previously been ascertained that anterior hypophyseal transplants had increased the incidence of mammary tumors in virgin mice. Males with ovarian and anterior hypophyseal grafts had an increased incidence of mammary cancer when compared with males bearing ovary grafts alone.

Huseby and Bittner (1951) studied the result of transplanting Strain A adrenals into gonadectomized A $\times$ C3H F_1 mice and of Strain CE adrenals into gonadectomized CE $\times$ C3H F_1 mice. The adrenals tended to follow the developmental pattern of the parent of origin and suggested to the authors that the presence or absence of postcastrational adrenal changes, as well as the histologic pattern of such changes is, at least to a large measure, a function of genetically controlled adrenal cortical responsiveness.

Trentin (1951) presented evidence that in male mice of three high-incidence mammary tumor strains, A, C3H, and CBA, castration increased the mammary response to estrogen. Of three low-tumor strains, C57, JK, and N, only JK showed increased mammary response to estrogen following castration. The effect, or lack of effect, of castration upon mammary response to estrogen was not altered by the presence or absence of the milk factor when tested with Strains C3H and C57 black.

10. Physical Agents

Furth (1934) observed an increase of myeloid leukemia in mice after a single dose of roentgen rays (400 r) or smaller doses at monthly intervals. Of 385 irradiated mice, 21 died of myelogenous leukemia. Of 481 control mice, 2 died of myelogenous leukemia.

Rusch and Bauman (1939) exposed young mice of Strains A, C, and C57 black to ultraviolet light. No difference in rate of development, or total incidence of tumors induced by this procedure was observed in the two albino strains A and C. Strain C57 black mice developed a smaller percentage of tumors and the time required was greater.

Kirschbaum and Kaplan (1944) pointed out that: (1) multiple agents could induce leukemia; (2) mice of a given genetic constitution were susceptible to only certain agents; and (3) genetic susceptibility to one agent or to spontaneous disease could not necessarily be correlated with susceptibility to other leukemogenic agents. Strains F, A, DBA 212, and DBA 12 were compared in regard to spontaneous, methylcholanthrene-induced, and roentgen-ray–induced leukemia.

Li *et al.* found that ovarian tumors developed in irradiated intrasplenic ovary grafts in mice of Strains A, C3H, C57 black, and JK as well as in A $\times$ C3H and CBA $\times$ C57 black F_1 hybrid mice.

Kirschbaum and Mixer (1947) further extended the experimental evidence that multiple agents induced leukemia to various degrees in different inbred strains of mice. Tumor incidence after carcinogenic hydrocarbons, roentgen-rays, and estrogens was compared to spontaneous incidence. It was concluded that the effectiveness of each agent depended upon the genetic constitution of the stock involved. Roentgen-rays represented the only agent which might be considered almost universally leukemogenic for mice. However, the degree of responsiveness to this agent varied from strain to strain. Estrogens were probably second in general effectiveness and the carcinogenic hydrocarbons third; although when leukemogenic, the last mentioned represented the most potent leukemogen. Susceptibility to spontaneous and carcinogen-induced leukemia was correlated, although some strains with a very low incidence of spontaneous leukemia developed a high incidence following treatment with a carcinogenic chemical. In this study Strains DBA 212, CBA, B-alb, C3H, A, NH, C57, and F were considered.

Furth and Boon (1947) reported that mice of most, if not all, stocks were susceptible to the induction of ovarian tumors by roentgen rays. Furth and Furth (1936) used Stocks A, R, and S; Furth and Boon (1947) used two hybrid groups between the above strains; and Geist *et al.* (1939) used a still different stock, a homozygous albino strain.

Kaplan (1948) observed that with increasing age both Strain A and Strain C57 black mice showed a pronounced regression of susceptibility to the leukemogenic action of roentgen-rays. Maximal susceptibility occurred at one month of age and was associated with a shorter mean induction time.

Mühlbock (1951) in a study of the effect of roentgen rays on Strains DBA and C57 black, found the nature of the resulting ovarian tumors to be dependent on the strain of mice.

Morton *et al.* (1951) found that the presence or absence of light affected the response of mice of the dilute brown strain (DBA) to percutaneous administration of either 3:4-benzpyrene or 20-methylcholanthrene by altering not only the incidence of skin carcinomas but of leukemias as well.

B. SPONTANEOUS TUMORS

1. Mammary Tumors

Murray (1911) presented the most convincing evidence available at the time, on the inheritance of mammary tumors. Of 340 mice with cancerous ancestry 18.2 per cent developed tumors while 8.6 per cent of 223 mice with noncancerous ancestry developed tumors. In most cases these tumors were mammary carcinomas.

Lathrop and Loeb (1915) investigated the endemic occurrence of tumors in mice. Strain variation was recorded but no accurate data on the percentage of mammary tumors alone were presented.

Loeb (1919) summarized a series of studies where mammary tumors were a predominant type and concluded that in the main three factors were active in the development of cancer: (1) heredity, (2) irritation, and (3) internal secretion. Internal secretions seemed to cause cancer only in cooperation with hereditary factors. On the other hand hereditary factors needed—at least in the case of certain cancers—the cooperation of hormones in a definite quantity, if cancer was to develop. Physical stimulation was also under certain conditions associated with hereditary factors in the origin of cancer. On the other hand, the evidence pointed to the conclusion that if physical stimulation was sufficiently strong, cancer could develop without the cooperation of the hereditary factors. In 1940 Loeb further stated that there was no doubt that different strains of mice differed greatly in their hereditarily transmitted tendency to mammary gland cancer. Loeb reviewed the studies concerning the possibilities: (1) that they were due to inherited differences in the amount of estrogenic hormone produced and given off in the circulation; (2) that they were due to differences in the readiness with which estrogenic hormones were destroyed or eliminated; or (3) that the cause lay in the readiness with which the normal mammary gland tissue reacted to stimulation by estrogenic hormones. Loeb concluded that the hereditary factor consisted of an inherited degree of responsiveness of the mammary gland to stimulation.

Marsh (1929) presented data concerning two lines of albino mice, each descended from one pair, with no outbreeding. One strain yielded spontaneous mammary cancer in about 90 per cent, the other in about 55 per cent of the breeding females. Crosses of these lines with wild mice gave evidence of dominant inheritance of mammary cancer.

Little and McPheters (1932) crossed the dilute brown strain with higher incidence of spontaneous carcinoma of the mammary gland, with a line of yellow mice of lower incidence of mammary cancer. The cancer incidence was determined by the use of 260 virgin F_2 females. Of the yellow mice 38.97 per cent and of the nonyellow mice 59.70 per cent developed mammary gland carcinomas. Thus a clear difference in incidence of mammary cancer was established between yellow and nonyellow mice.

In 1933 the staff of the Jackson Laboratory reported that in crosses between high-tumor strain females and low-tumor strain males the incidence of mammary tumors in F_1 females resembled closely that of the strain from which their high-tumor strain mothers were derived. When the cross was reversed the incidence of mammary tumors resembled that of the low-tumor strain. Since in the two types of crosses the chromosomal constitution of the F_1 generation females was identical, and their amount of mammary tumor development differed widely, it followed that the observed difference, although it had been transmitted, was not primarily dependent upon genes. It appeared to belong to some contribution which was characteristic of the mother.

Little (1933), further called attention to the existence of an extra-chromosomal influence demonstrated by four independent experiments conducted over a three-year period by members of the staff of the Roscoe B. Jackson Memorial Laboratory. The results showed clearly that in the problem of the inheritance of tendencies to form spontaneous mammary tumors in mice, both chromosomal and extrachromosomal factors were operative.

Little (1934a) further reported (see 1932) on F_1 and F_2 generation virgin female mice derived from a strain high in mammary cancer incidence—dilute brown—and one relatively low in incidence of mammary cancer but relatively high in various internal tumors—yellow. In the F_1 and F_2 hybrid generations the yellow animals had a significantly lower incidence of mammary tumors than did the non-yellows. The mammary tumors occurred significantly earlier in the yellow than in the non-yellow mice. The incidence of tumors other than mammary were not significantly different in the yellow and the nonyellow hybrids. This was further evidence that in mice, mammary tumors could not be considered the same biologic phenomenon as other types of tumor.

Strong (1935), reported that he could discover no discernible difference in C3H mice between a mouse that developed cancer of the mammary gland and one that did not, provided they belonged to the same inbred strain.

Murray and Little (1935a, 1935b, 1936) in a study involving 1843 DBA $\times$ C57 black F_1 and F_2 generation mice found that the dB F_1 animals had a significantly higher incidence of mammary tumors than those of the Bd F_1 generation: 39.82 per cent as against 6.06 per cent. This difference persisted in the reciprocal F_2

generation as follows: dB F_2 35.54 per cent; Bd F_2 5.96 per cent. According to the authors, since the chromosomal constitution of the females of the reciprocal F_1 generations was theoretically the same, the above differences in the incidence of mammary tumors must be due to an extrachromosomal influence. Since the difference persisted in the two F_2 generations, whose chromosomal make-up was theoretically the same, its chief basis was obviously transmitted in some manner by influence outside of the chromosomes. The occurrence of some mammary tumors in both F_1 and in both F_2 generations left the possibility of some chromosomal influence in the genesis of mammary gland tumors. The difference in tumor incidence in the reciprocal crosses of both F_1 and F_2 generations lasted throughout all age periods and was strikingly constant. There was no evidence of the linkage of such influence with any of the coat color genes (B-b or D-d) studied. The relative importance of what appeared to be extrachromosomal influence on the incidence of mammary tumors in the mice studied was approximately six times that of the possible chromosomal influence.

Korteweg (1953) in Holland came independently to the same conclusion as the staff of the Jackson Laboratory that an extrachromosomal influence was operative in the inheritance of mammary tumors. Korteweg (1936) further confirmed the existence of a maternal effect. The strains of mice used were C57 black and DBA.

Bittner (1936a) reported further observations on reciprocal crosses between the high-mammary–tumor strain C3H and the I strain which showed internal but no breast tumors. When the maternal parent was from C3H, 33 of 36 F_1 females developed breast tumors at a mean age of 10.4 months. When the maternal parent was from strain I, 7 out of 10 hybrid females were observed with various types of internal tumors, and no breast tumors, at an average age of 21.0 months. Thus further verification was given to the theory that an extrachromosomal influence was operative in the production of mammary tumors in mice.

Bittner and Murray, (1936) compared the tumors occurring in four high-tumor lines of mice; A, DBA, C3H, and a special-diet A strain. The authors found no direct correlation between mammary tumor incidence and breeding behavior as expressed in litter size and weaning percentage according to the age of the female.

Cloudman and Little (1936) attempted to ascertain whether or not the gene T, for brachyury, or its allele t, for normal tail, had any influence on the formation of tumors in mice. In the study evidence was secured that the extrachromosomal influence for mammary tumors was unique and did not apply to non-mammary tumors. The gene T had no apparent influence on either mammary or non-mammary tumors.

Bittner (1936b) in a report which was a turning point for further advances, presented preliminary evidence based on the foster nursing of Strain A mice on Strain CBA mice that the incidence of mammary gland tumors could be affected by nursing.

Bittner and Little (1937) compared the inheritance of mammary gland tumors and lung tumors in an A × C57 black cross, its reciprocal, and an F_2 generation.

The extrachromosomal theory explained the inheritance of mammary tumors but not the lung tumors. A preliminary report included, indicated that when fertilized ova from DBA females were transplanted into the uterus of C57 black mice the descendants failed to have the normally expected mammary tumors.

Bittner (1937a, 1937b) reported in more detail (see Bittner, 1936) the effects of foster nursing on mammary gland tumor incidence; of Strain A on CBA. New data included Strain A mice fostered on C57 black. It was concluded that the incidence of breast tumors could be significantly decreased by fostering females of a high breast tumor stock on low-tumor stock mothers. This offered an explanation for the extrachromosomal influence in the etiology of breast tumors.

Suntzeff *et al.* (1938), in a study involving Strains A, C57 black, DBA, C3H, CBA, New Buffalo and Old Buffalo, observed that the great differences which existed between strains with regard to their readiness to give origin to mammary gland tumors, did not exist as far as their tendency to develop precancerous or early cancerous lesions of the cervix was concerned, when under estrogenic treatment.

Andervont and McEleney (1938) observed that in C3H breeding females there was a high incidence of mammary tumors at an average age of 8 to 9 months and in nonbreeding females at 11.5 months. Strain C3H mice fostered on C57 black had a much lower incidence, 21.5 per cent, at a later average age, 13.5 months. Andervont and McEleney (1939) continued these studies and found that if C3H mice were fostered on C57 black mice within 17 hours after birth the incidence of nearly 100 per cent could be reduced to 25 per cent, when the tested mice were permitted to raise one litter. Foster nursing C57 black on C3H raised the incidence of spontaneous breast tumors from 1 per cent to 9 per cent. The fostered C57 blacks were also permitted to raise one litter.

Bittner (1939a, 1939b) reviewed the available experiments testing the relationship of foster nursing to breast cancer. New data included a preliminary report on the foster nursing of F_1 mice obtained from the reciprocal crossing of A and C57 black. The full report (Bittner, 1940a) clearly showed that susceptibility to milk influence was inherited in a dominant manner.

Murray and Little (1939) presented an extensive analysis of the results of a reciprocal cross between DBA and C57 black and backcrossing for eight generations. The results led to the conclusions that: (1) the extrachromosomal factor was ten times as powerful as any possible chromosomal factor; (2) the extrachromosomal influence became noneffective after eight generations of backcrossing; (3) concentration of the chromatin of the high cancer strain did not return the cancer incidence to that obtained in the first generation hybrid or to the original cancer strain; and (4) the tendency to have mammary cancer was not Mendelian in nature.

Fekete (1940) presented the results of three experiments concerning the so-called functional test. The first involved Strains C57 black and DBA. After frequent pregnancies and limited lactation the percentage of mammary tumors was 87 per cent for DBA and 2 per cent for C57 black. One of the two C57 black tumors was an adenoacanthoma. In the second experiment in which the animals were allowed to become pregnant while nursing, the incidence of mammary tumors was 72 per cent for DBA and zero for C57 black. In the third test where the nursing period was prolonged excessively the percentage for DBA was 56 and for C57 black it was zero. Little and Pearson (1940) found that the Jackson Laboratory strain of C57 black mice did not respond to the so-called functional test with increased breast cancer incidence as had the C57 black mice used by Bagg.

Bittner (1940b) reported that the "breast cancer producing influence" may be transmitted by the inoculation of spleen, thymus, and lactating mammary gland tissue.

Andervont (1941a) reported two experiments using foster nursing. In the first, mice from low-tumor C57 black, I, Y, and C were foster nursed by high-tumor C3H strain and C3H were foster nursed by C57 black, I, Y, and C. In the second, hybrid mice derived by mating C57 black females to Strain I males were foster nursed by C3H females. It was found that C3H tumor incidence was reduced approximately 50 per cent in offspring fostered on C57 black, Y, I, or C. When Y, I, C57 black, and C were fostered on C3H, the first three had an incidence of approximately 15 per cent and the latter 64 per cent. Foster nursing hybrid mice from C57 black female × I male, two low-cancer strains, on C3H high cancer strain gave an incidence of 71 per cent. Before hybridization each produced a low incidence of tumors upon foster nursing.

Andervont (1941b), in a test of the influence of the paternal parent on susceptibility to spontaneous mammary tumors, mated C3H females to males of low-tumor I, or Y strain males. Females of the F_1 generation were also backcrossed to I and Y males. It was found that C3H × I mice were more susceptible than C3H × Y. The incidence of tumors was low in both backcross generations. In a second experiment C3H females were mated to I and to C57 black males and each F_1 mated *inter se*. In both F_1 and F_2 generation mice from the C3H × I mating the mice were more susceptible than similar generation mice from C3H × C57 black. These tests helped establish the importance of chromosomal factors from the male parent in susceptibility to spontaneous breast cancer and to indicate that genetic factors control the degree of susceptibility to this neoplasm.

Bittner (1941a, 1941b, 1941c) reviewed breast cancer as influenced by nursing and pointed out that three influences were active in the etiology of inherited breast cancer in mice: (1) the milk influence, (2) inherited susceptibility, and (3) ovarian hormonal stimulation of the mammary gland. Bittner also reviewed the evidence for variations in tumor incidence in sublines of Strains C3H, A, and DBA, interpreting the variations to mean that the strains had undergone mutation changes. Further evidence was presented that foster nursing did not influence the genetic susceptibility of an individual for development of spontaneous mammary cancer.

Murray (1941) made an analysis of cancer incidence and age attained in DBA × C57 black and DBA × A F_1 reciprocal hybrids and backcrosses of these to the parental strains. The amount of spontaneous cancer in the hybrids of the above three stocks seemed to be dependent upon two factors: (1) the concentration of the extrachromosomal influence transmitted by the mother, and (2) the physiologic resistance of mice of varying constitution to this stimulus.

Fekete and Little (1942) found that when fertilized ova of the C57 black strain were transferred into the uterus of strain DBA and *vice versa*, carcinoma of the mammary gland in the transferred ova of the C57 black mice occurred in 50 per cent, and in none of the transferred ova of the DBA mice. The increase and decrease in incidence was greater than had been obtained by foster nursing. In the first to third generation the C57 black tumor incidence was 73 per cent and in the DBA 11.7 per cent.

Andervont (1943) reported that the F_1 hybrids produced by crossing the high-tumor C3H strain with two low tumor strains, C57 black and I, were far more susceptible to the mammary tumor inciter than either C57 black or I.

Heston *et al.* (1945) found that susceptible-strain backcross females with an average of 75 per cent susceptible-strain chromatin transmitted the milk agent more effectively than did resistant-strain backcross females with an average of 25 per cent susceptible-strain chromatin, although both backcross groups had received identical milk agent and other maternal influences. In the resistant-strain backcross group it was further evident that segregation of genes resulted in a variation in the degree of transmission of the agent, from females which transmitted the agent so effectively that all their test females developed tumors at an earlier age, to those which did not transmit the agent, or transmitted it so ineffectively that none of their test females developed tumors. This suggested the segregation of more than one pair of genes influencing the propagation and transmission of the agent. The results also indicated that there were two sets of genetic factors, apart from those acting through the hormonal mechanism, that influenced mammary tumor development. One set determined the susceptibility of the mammary tissue cell to the hormonal and milk agent stimuli and the other the propagation of the milk agent. The results of a breeding test of the resistant-strain backcross tumorous and nontumorous segregants were such as would have been expected with multiple-factor inheritance.

Heston (1944) made an analysis of the factors causing a difference in tumor incidence in virgin females of Strains A and C3H. Both were high–mammary-tumor strains but differed in that whereas both the breeding and the virgin females of Strain C3H had a high incidence of mammary tumors, only the breeding females of Strain A had a high incidence. Reciprocal crosses between the two strains demonstrated that this difference was due largely to a difference in the genic complex influencing tumor development. In degree of susceptibility to mammary tumors, the F_1 hybrid virgin females were intermediate between the parent strains although more like the parent Strain C3H. Reciprocal foster nursing between the two strains did not give conclusive evidence of a difference in the mammary tumor agent in the milk of the two strains. Heston (1944) reviewed the role of heredity in tumor development, pointing out the importance and the complexity of the problem.

Bittner (1944) presented evidence of linkage between brown coat color and inherited susceptibility to mammary gland tumors. The evidence was obtained in a study of reciprocal hybrids between Strains C57 black and A.

Bittner *et al.* (1944) found that hyperplastic, or precancerous nodules in the mammary glands of mice probably resulted both from the inciting influence of the mammary tumor agent and from the estrogenic hormones. This relationship was independent of the strain used.

Andervont (1945a, 1945b) observed that the Strain C3H milk influence was lost when placed in the environment of Strain C57 black but was retained when placed in Strain C mice; the latter was a strain susceptible to the influence. Apparently the genetic constitution of the host determined not only the susceptibility to the influence but also the ability to transmit and propagate the influence.

Heston (1946) reviewed the evidence for different paths of gene action in mammary tumor development in mice, and pictured how this conditioned the geneticist's view of the problem of breast cancer in man. One path was through the physiology of hormone production, a second through the physiology of propagation and transmission of the milk agent, and a third possible path was through the physiology within the mammary tissue cell and governed its reaction to the hormonal stimulation or to the milk agent. Heston stated that other paths might exist, and it was probable that they were interwoven.

Bittner and Huseby (1946) reported on the genetic make-up of the inherited susceptibility to mammary cancer and the inherited hormonal influence in different strains and their reciprocal hybrids. Observations obtained from breeding females of the cancerous A and C3H strains and their reciprocal F_1 and F_2 generation hybrids were in accord with the theory that the mice of these two strains might have the same inherited susceptibility to mammary cancer. The difference in the incidence of mammary cancer in the virgin females of the A and C3H strains was interpreted as due to gene action in controlling some hormonal mechanism. This inherited hormonal influence was probably due to multiple genes. According to the authors the same genes probably do not produce both the inherited susceptibility and the inherited hormonal influence.

Armstrong (1948) conducted a cross-suckling experiment using mice of Strains RIII and CBA, which have respectively high and low mammary-cancer incidence, with the objective of observing the effect on the estrus cycle. It was concluded that there was some evidence that this feature was genetically determined. Foster nursing appeared to have no effect upon it.

Andervont and Dunn (1948a, 1948c) presented a study involving Strains C and C3H. The former was said to have an incidence of mammary tumors under 1 per cent in breeding females and a pulmonary tumor incidence of 23 per cent. The latter had a high mammary tumor incidence and a low pulmonary tumor incidence. Female F_1 hybrids of Strain C mice with male C3H mice gave a mammary tumor incidence of 60 per cent. The milk and the lactating mammary glands of these F_1 animals were tested for the presence of the mammary tumor agent and none was found. These studies were continued (Andervont and Dunn, 1948b) with three more experiments. Each was started by the mating of Strain C females to C3H, or agent-free C3H males to procure F_1 hybrids. In two experiments, the F_1 hybrids were mated to C3H, or agent-free C3H, to procure backcross mice; in one experiment the F_1 hybrids and successive hybrid generations were mated *inter se*. The results suggested possible routes whereby the agent gained access to the F_1 hybrids.

Heston (1948) discussed the role of the genes in the physiology leading to the development of mammary tumors in mice.

Dmochowski (1948) presented evidence that there were differences in quantity and/or quality of the milk factor derived from two high-cancer Strains RIII and A.

Foulds (1949a) found an incidence in 15 per cent mammary tumors in F_1 breeding females from the cross C57 black female and RIII male and an incidence of 92 per cent in the reciprocal F_1. The milk agent was recovered from a tumor extract originating from an F_1 with a C57 black mother. This and other results led to the interpretation that there might be an erratic transmission of tumor agent by male parents. Foulds (1949b) further observed that hybrids of various genetic constitution derived from the inbred Strains A, C57 black and RIII would respond as far as mammary gland growth was concerned in at least two different ways. The tumors might: (1) be unresponsive and grow steadily throughout pregnancy or the puerperium; or (2) be responsive and grow during pregnancy, regress, and then recur at the next pregnancy.

Andervont (1949a) reported that a single exposure of Strain C mice to the C3H mammary-tumor agent transformed Strain C into a high mammary-tumor strain for at least 23 generations.

Bittner (1950b) reviewed the genetics of spontaneous mammary cancer.

Heston *et al.* (1950) reported the occurrence of a C3H line of mice deprived of the milk factor which produced 38 per cent of mammary gland tumors at an average age of 20.3 months. The authors concluded that in this case, factors such as genotype of the line and intensive inbreeding were strong enough to result in a relatively high incidence of mammary tumors in these C3Hb mice in the absence of the mammary-tumor milk agent.

Mühlbock (1950) found that mice of the dilute brown strain, DBA, and of hybrids between this strain and Strains C57 black and O2O Leeuwenhoek-Huis had no difference in incidence of mammary tumors when kept as virgins or when they were biparous force-bred females. However, the average tumor age of parous females was earlier. Force-bred females with more than three litters had a higher incidence of mammary tumors. This was considered further evidence that the number of litters should be taken into consideration in determining mammary tumor incidence.

Huseby and Bittner (1951b) found that the ovaries of two sublines of Strain A, separated for at least 57 to 71 generations and one an agent-free subline, had the same ability to cause mammary tumor development in male Strain A mice. In each instance the incidence was intermediate between that for virgin and for breeding Strain A females.

Bittner (1951) reported that by crossing females of Strain A—a strain where the virgin females had a low incidence of breast cancer—with other strains the transmission of a hormonal mechanism, termed by Bittner the inherited hormonal influence, may be detected and followed. By such a means it was shown that four strains, C3H, D_2, D_8, and C, transmitted this influence. Bittner emphasized that the inherited hormonal influence may be associated with postcastrational adrenal hyperplasia.

This brief review demonstrates the complexity of the genetic and the milk factors in determining the incidence of mammary cancer in mice of certain strains. There are still other extrachromosomal factors that further complicate the problem.

Jones (1951) observed hyperplastic nodules of the mammary glands in two sublines of Strain C3H, free of the milk agent, yet capable of developing a moderately high incidence of mammary gland tumors.

Gardner *et al.* (1939) found that the mammary glands of adult female mice varied structurally in that the localized nodules of mammary tissue (hyperplastic, resting, or regressing) occurred more frequently in mice of the high-tumor strains than in animals of the low-tumor strains.

Woolley *et al.* (1940) noted that two high-incidence breast cancer strains, DBA and C3H, responded to early gonadectomy with development of nodular hyperplasia of the adrenal cortex and with evidence of estrogenic-like stimulation of uterus, vagina, and mammary glands even to the extent of having mammary gland tumors. The low-tumor C57 black mice when similarly treated failed to show these adrenal cortical and accessory reproductive organ changes.

Johnson and Albert (1949) studied the metabolic activity, in various endocrine glands, in a high–mammary-tumor Strain DBA and a low-incidence Strain C57 black, by the uptake of radioactive phosphorus. Differences were observed and the changes in these recorded for various ages.

Stern (1949) found the reticuloendothelial system of Strain C3H mice tested by various dyes to have a weaker storing alibity than that of Strain C57 black. The author stressed a possible relationship to mammary tumor incidence.

Bagg and Jackson (1937) presented evidence that rapid breeding and nonsuckling increased the incidence of breast tumors in their line of C57 black mice, in F_1 hybrids between females of this low-tumor strain and males of the low-tumor Strain CBA, and F_1 hybrids between the JK low-tumor females and C57 low-tumor males. No increase was observed for Strains JK and CBA.

Fekete and Green (1936) compared the effect of blockage of nipple on breast cancer incidence in dba and C57 black mice. Blockage of nipples, on one side only, increased the incidence of breast cancer on that side in DBA, but did not bring out this type of tumor in C57 black mice.

2. Pulmonary Tumors

Lynch (1926) studied the inheritance of lung tumors in a cross between Strain 1194 (from Lathrop mice) with an incidence of 6.7 per cent and Strain Bagg albino (from Memorial Hospital) with an incidence of 37 per cent. The appearance of tumors in the F_1 and F_2 generations suggested that lung tumor susceptibility was dominant.

Lynch (1927) further reported on the cross of 1194 with Bagg albino. A previous test (Lynch, 1925) showed no difference in the percentage of skin tumors in these two strains after tar painting. Lung tumor incidence was increased in each stock after tar painting—Bagg albino from 37 to 85 per cent and 1194 from 6.7 to 22 per cent. When the two strains were crossed, and the offsprings subjected to tar treatment, the latter gave a high incidence of lung tumors—79 per cent in 28 individuals—about the same as the parental high tumor strain. When F_1 sons were backcrossed to the original stocks, the cross to the high-tumor strain maintained the high-tumor rate, 87 per cent in 37 mice, while in the cross to the low-tumor strain the percentage dropped to 39 per cent in 38 mice. Lynch concluded that the conception that susceptibility to pulmonary tumors is hereditary is upheld by the fact that the two strains of mice described differ conspicuously in respect to spontaneous tumor rates; the strains differ also under experimental conditions described in this report, and when crossed, their offspring by suitable backcrosses again show significant differences.

Lynch (1931) mated a male from the high–lung-tumor incidence Strain D with several females from low–lung-tumor incidence Strain 1194. The first generation offspring were backcrossed to individuals of the original strains. The F_1 incidence was high, 32.2 per cent, or low, 7.3 per cent, according to which parental strain was used. The results of the Lynch (1926) experiments with tar induced lung tumors were thus duplicated with spontaneous lung tumors. The familial influence was evident in both instances. No influence of sex was found.

Bittner (1935) reported observations on inbred Strain A, derived from Bagg albino, a strain used by Lynch in earlier lung tumor studies, which demonstrated lung tumors in 55 per cent of the males living 10 months or longer and in 36 per cent of the breeding females which had mammary gland tumors.

Bittner (1938), in a study involving crosses between Strain A (female lung-tumor incidence 89.2 per cent; male lung-tumor incidence 74.4 per cent) and Strain C57 black (lung-tumor incidence less than 1 per cent), concluded that susceptibility to spontaneous pulmonary tumors was probably transmitted by a single dominant Mendelian factor. The F_1 hybrids had an incidence of 76.5 per cent or close to a theoretical 100 per cent. The F_2 hybrids gave an incidence of 57.4 per cent, which Bittner interpreted as close to that expected for segregation on the basis of a 3:1 ratio.

Bittner (1940c), using the foster nursing technic to lower the incidence of mammary tumors in Strain A, found the incidence of primary lung tumors to be the same for the fostered A mice as for the nonfostered A mice, whether they were: (1) the progeny of lung-cancer fostered mothers or (2) the progeny of non–lung-cancer fostered mothers.

Heston (1942b) presented data in the study of inheritance of susceptibility to spontaneous pulmonary tumors using Strain A as the susceptible and Strain L as the nonsusceptible strain. The results tended to parallel Heston's findings for 1:2:5:6-dibenzanthracene-induced pulmonary tumors, and supported the theory that susceptibility was inherited on a multiple factor basis. Heston also pointed out that multiple factor inheritance offered an explanation for the variation in spontaneous pulmonary tumor incidence seen between the different inbred strains of mice.

Heston and Deringer (1947) reported that the lethal yellow gene was associated with an increased spontaneous pulmonary tumor incidence over the non-yellow litter-mate controls.

3. Leukemia

MacDowell and Richter (1935) reported that the predisposition to leukemia in Strain C58 mice was specifically heritable. In crosses with Strain Sto-Li the incidence was roughly correlated with the proportion of total heredity from Strain

C58. The authors stated that in the incidence of leukemia nonchromosomal variables played a role that grew increasingly important as the proportion of total leukemic heredity was reduced. Among the nonchromosomal factors that were decisive in the incidence of leukemia an important one was transmitted by the mother. MacDowell (1936) further developed the theory of inheritance of spontaneous leukemia, pointing out that there is a mechanism involved so that part of the transmission is through the mother, and not shared by the father.

MacDowell (1937) and MacDowell *et al.* (1940) presented the available facts on the inheritance of leukemia and the theory involved. According to MacDowell intrinsic and extrinsic factors modified the incidence of leukemia; in two hybrid generations the incidence was reduced as the total heredity from the leukemic strain was reduced. In both hybrid generations the incidence was significantly higher when the mother brought in the leukemic heredity. The role of the extrinsic factors was not constant, but varied with the intrinsic factors; thus the identification of the intrinsic factors became exceedingly difficult. In the present experimental animals it was possible to maintain intrinsic uniformity, and, therefore, to proceed with the search for significant extrinsic factors, which from a medical standpoint offer the chief hope for practical application.

Kirschbaum and Strong (1939) presented evidence that Strain F had a moderately high incidence of leukemia of 50 per cent, as compared to 70 per cent for AK and 90 per cent for C58.

Mercier, and Mercier and Goslin (1933-1940) presented a series of six reports concerning the inheritance of lymphosarcoma in lines developed by them in France.

Cole and Furth (1941) published data concerning a cross, AK high-leukemia with Rf low-leukemia. The results indicated that the genic contribution to the inheritance of spontaneous leukemia was due to multiple factors. No evidence was found that nonchromosomal maternal factors were involved in the inheritance.

Kirschbaum and Kaplan (1944) presented data on the spontaneous incidence of leukemia in Strains F, A, DBA 212, and DBA 12. This report is further discussed above with data for roentgen-ray induction of leukemia.

Furth *et al.* (1944) give results obtained in the reciprocal crossing of Strains AK and Rf, and AK and C3H. The incidence was higher when the cross was AK $\times$ C3H than when AK $\times$ Rf. In each case the incidence of spontaneous leukemia was higher when the female parent was from the high-leukemia line.

MacDowell *et al.* (1945a, 1945b) presented data concerning the cross C58 $\times$ B-alb, extended with various family F_1 and backcross generation studies. A strain incidence of 69.3 per cent spontaneous leukemia was given for B-alb, of 15.1 per cent for Sto-Li, and of 90.5 per cent for C58.

MacDowell and Taylor (1948) interpreted the maternal influence responsible for a difference in the incidence of leukemia in reciprocal F_1 hybrids between Strains C58 and Sto-Li to consist of a definite resistance to leukemia contributed by the low-strain mother.

Hogreffe (1948a, 1948b) reported the F_1, F_2, and two backcross incidences of leukemia following a cross of two inbred strains. The parental strains were the high-leukemia AKa (63.0 per cent) and low-leukemia B (0.0 per cent). The F_1 produced 43 per cent deaths due to leukemia, and the F_2, 37 per cent deaths due to leukemia. The backcross to Strain B gave 28 per cent and the backcross to AKa, 49 per cent leukemia. Hogreffe examined his results for the possibility of a maternal influence. In the F_1 of the cross of the B male with the AKa the percentage of leukemia was 46 while in the reciprocal it was 34. The percentage of animals with thymic enlargement in each group was as follows: AKa, 28; B 0.0; F_1, 7.1; F_2, 10.4; $F_1 \times$ AKa, 25; and $F_1 \times$ B, 0.0.

Law and Miller (1950a, 1950b) noted that the thymus played a significant role in the development of spontaneous and induced leukemias in mice. Total thymectomy reduced the incidence of leukemia in Strain RIL from 83.1 to 14.6 per cent, and increased the mean age at death of leukemia from 7.6 to 12.7 months. The incidence of leukemia in Strain C58 was reduced from 90.9 to 34.9 per cent following thymectomy. The mean age at death from lymphoid leukemia was increased from 10.6 to 15.6 months.

4. Liver Tumors

Slye *et al.* (1915-16) showed that liver tumors occurred in certain groups of mice within a large population, and not with equal frequency in other groups.

Strong and Smith (1936), Strong *et al.* (1938), Gorer (1940), and Miller and Pybus (1945) demonstrated that liver tumors developed in Strain CBA with an unusually high incidence for strains of mice as a whole. No liver tumors were found within large numbers of Strain A, and the Simpson strain.

Andervont (1939a), Burns and Schenken (1940, 1943), and Andervont (1950a) observed an incidence of hepatomas in Strain C3H which was as high as that in CBA. Andervont regarded CBA and C3H as the mouse strains most susceptible to hepatoma, and called attention to their common ancestry.

Woolley (1951) crossed Strain C3H and A, hepatoma-susceptible and -resistant strains, and observed a high incidence of hepatomas in F_1 generation males, indicating dominance in inheritance.

5. Stomach Tumors

Andervont and Stewart (1937) described an adenomatous lesion of the stomach which occurred in nearly 100 per cent of Strain I mice 10 months of age, or older. Analogous lesions were not encountered in the stomachs of mice from other strains, except in 3 old Strain C3H mice.

The same authors (1938) presented evidence from records in the literature that spontaneous tumors of the stomach had been rare in mice.

Andervont (1939) found that the stomach lesions of Strain I were recessive in a cross with C57 black and C3H. Backcross data suggests that several genes were involved.

Strong (1945b) found stomach lesions in virtually all mice of Strain I except those dying early in life.

Andervont (1949) again stated that the stomach lesion in Strain I seemed to be recessive in inheritance. Less extensive lesions were reported to be found in older mice of Strains C3H, DBA, and C57 black as well as in commercial mice. In the Strain N the adenomatous hyperplasia was more localized in origin than was the broad widespreading type that developed in I mice spontaneously.

Smith and Strong (1949) described a spontaneous gastric neoplasia in the BrS subline of Strain NHO. At approximately 400 days of age the gastric lesion was present in 100 per cent of the male, and in 60–70 per cent of the female mice. This tumor has been further discussed under methylcholanthrene induction since the ancestral stock had been treated with this carcinogen. (see page 20)

6. Adrenal Cortical Tumors

Slye *et al.* (1921) observed a low incidence of spontaneous tumors of the adrenal cortex in a large population of mice; 4 tumors in 33,000 autopsies.

Kirschbaum *et al.* (1946) and Frantz *et al.* (1947) described the frequent occurrence of spontaneous estrogen-secreting tumors of the adrenal cortex in Strain NH mice. Gonadectomy caused these tumors to occur at an earlier age. Woolley *et al.* (1939), Fekete *et al.* (1941) and Woolley and Little (1945) had observed tumors similar to those occurring spontaneously in Strain NH, in gonadectomized mice of Strains DBA and CE.

7. Lipoid Tumors

Little (1934, 1941b) found 9 lipoid tumors, lipomas and liposarcomas, in hybrids of yellow and nonyellow, and none in the hybrids of nonyellows involving the same strain. The yellow mouse had long been known to be inclined to adiposity.

8. Bone Tumors

Pybus and Miller (1938a) gave a description of the derivation of a group of mice from the Simpson Strain 3 in which the incidence of bone tumors was very high. The sarcoma incidence in the ordinary Simpson strain was about 1 per cent. In the strains derived from sarcoma-bearing mice, the incidence had increased ten times, while in the special inbred strain it had reached a very high percentage. The authors believed, from the evidence at hand, that there could be no doubt that the tendency to develop sarcomas was inherited.

Pybus and Miller (1938b) observed that in the branch of the Simpson strain with a high incidence of bone tumors, the incidence was more than 2.5 times higher in the females than in the males, 77.3 per cent as compared to 29.6 per cent, and the time of occurrence was nearly two and a half months earlier in males.

9. Uterine Tumors

Gardner and Pan (1948) found 13 spontaneous tumors of the uterus and vagina in 56 female mice of the PM strain that survived 200 days or more. Five of the tumors were epidermoid carcinomas, 7 were malignant tumors of undifferentiated cells—probably of epithelial origin—and one was a spindle cell sarcoma. The PM stock traced back to the Simpson strain in which Pybus and Miller (1938) reported a high incidence of bone tumors. Gardner and Pan (1948) also found carcinomas of the uterine cervix and vagina in PM × C3H hybrid mice which had been given estrogen and androgen, but none appeared in the untreated hybrids. Four of 10 estrogen-treated C3H × PM hybrids that tolerated treatment more than 200 days had carcinomas of the uterine cervix or vagina. Five of the 82 control hybrid mice had uterine fibromyomas.

10. Tumors in a Species Cross

Little (1939) found that crossing two species of mice, *Mus musculus* and *Mus bactrianus*, which differed markedly from one another in size, fertility, and growth, greatly increased the incidence of tumors in the first generation hybrids. The increase consisted not only of more tumors but in a greater tendency to form multiple tumors in individual mice.

III. Insect Tumors

A. Drosophila

Hereditary tumors have been described for the insect *Drosophila melanogaster*.

Stark (1918, 1919a, 1919b) using at first a tumor strain discovered by Bridges (1916), was the first to call attention to the significance of *Drosophila* tumors. According to Stark, multiple genetic factors brought about the tumors in strain "Lethal 7." The tumors were sex-linked. Another tumor which was interpreted as benign was found not to be sex-linked (Bridges and Stark, 1926).

Wilson (1924) studied two *Drosophila* tumors which were found to be dependent upon multiple factors.

Gowen (1934) reported on the inheritance of focal melanosis in *Drosophila*.

Ardashnikov (1941), (quoted from Schaarer and Lochhead [1950]), Russell (1942), Harnley and Goldsmith (1949), and Gardner and Woolf (1950) found that environmental factors could influence tumor incidence. In general, crowding and high temperatures tended to decrease the incidence of tumors.

Burdette (1950, 1951a, 1951b) studied the relation of tumor incidence to mutation rate in *Drosophila*.

B. Lepidoptera

Federly (1936) described the occurrence of tumors similar to those of *Drosophila* in the larvae of *Pygaera pigra*. These tumors were inherited in a sex-linked manner.

IV. Tumors of Fish

Gordon and Smith (1938) and Gordon (1941) have shown that spontaneous malignant melanomas are produced in the offspring of the black-spotted platyfish, *Platypoecilus maculatus* and the swordtail, *Xiphophorus hellerii*. It was postulated that the melanomas were evoked genetically in the hybrids by the action of the sex-linked factor for melanophores, Sp of the platyfish with a series of Sp modifiers,

A and B of the swordtail. In natural populations of platyfishes and swordtails, no melanotic tumors were discovered in more than 10,000 specimens. Under laboratory conditions, when a spotted (macromelanophore) member of one natural population was mated to that of another (micromelanophore), melanotic tumors developed in the spotted hybrids. From the above and additional studies, it was thought that the original gene harmful to macromelanophores was accepted by the platyfish through helpful gene-modifying mutations. When crosses were made to the swordtails, the genetic balance was changed and the large pigmented cells were allowed to grow atypically and to produce melanotic tumors.

Lucké (1942) found fish of the snapper family (*Lutianidae*) to be commonly afflicted with tumors which resembled the nerve-sheath tumors of man. Though many fish of other families were examined, no tumors of this variety were found.

Gorbman and Gordon (1951) reported the finding of a high incidence of spontaneous thyroidal tumors in laboratory populations of swordtails (*Xiphophorus montezumae*). In two other species of *Xiphophorus*, four species of *Platypoecilus*, and in *Lebistes reticulatus*, kept under identical conditions, thyroidal tumors were very rare or were never seen.

Gordon (1951) further demonstrated how the dominant, incomplete, sex-linked gene Sd of the platyfish could be changed so that expressivity could vary from no macromelanophore formation to the development of melanomas. When an Sd platyfish × swordtail hybrid was backcrossed to a swordtail, some of the hybrids of the backcross generation developed melanotic tumors of the dorsal fin. The genetic analysis showed that in addition to the Sd-modifying genes which had no other detectable effects of their own, the macromelanophore genes, a series of five dominant multiple alleles, were influenced by color genes such as the albino gene and the golden gene. Gordon concluded that the hereditary control of melanomas in hybrid fishes rests not on one gene but on a constellation of genes. To be effective this assemblage of genes must contain the macromelanophore gene.

V. TUMORS OF FOWL

Amundson and Biely (1932), Hutt *et al.* (1941), Waters and Prickett (1944), Waters (1945, 1946), and Hutt and Cole (1948) presented extensive evidence that breeds of chickens, and families of breeds, had differing and definite susceptibilities to avian lymphomatosis. Evidence indicated that there was organ specificity and that this could be influenced by genetic means.

VI. TUMORS OF MAN

In man a few types of cancer and of potentially cancerous lesions are generally recognized as hereditary. The best examples available seem to come from the association of known hereditary growth abnormalities and cancer, almost, as if these abnormalities of growth were stepping stones of neoplastic disease. The significance of heredity, as a predisposing or susceptibility factor, and the background of its expression in the occurrence of other types of cancer, is more in dispute. When investigating this possibility one or more of several methods of study have been used. One method includes the study of twins. Another is based upon the incidence of cancer of specific sites in family groups, while a third concerns itself with the frequency of postulated genes in a population. Haldane (1933) pointed out that precise analysis of the genetics of human cancer was possible only where, as with retinoblastoma and some sarcomata, its victims were attacked early in life.

A. MULTIPLE FAMILIAL POLYPOSIS

Cripps (1882) (quoted from Dukes [1930]), was one of the first to recognize a familial predisposition to adenomatosis (polyposis).

Lockhart-Mummery (1925) analyzed the records for three family groups and concluded that adenomatosis of the large intestine was a condition which tended to develop in succeeding generations in the same family.

Dukes (1930) presented evidence that the hereditary factor in polyposis intestini, or multiple adenomas, was inherited as a Mendelian dominant. Dukes also reviewed the early evidence of heritability of this trait.

Macklin (1932) cited several cases of rectal polyps associated with carcinoma in family groups.

Wassink (1935) made extensive statistical studies of the families of cancer patients and found that among the relatives of persons affected with cancer of the rectum and stomach, the mortality from cancer is considerably higher than that of the average population.

Lockhart-Mummery and Dukes (1939) pictured the predisposition to polyposis to be the result of inherited instability of the epithelial cells of the large bowel. To these authors the familial character of adenomatosis was obvious, and the inheritance was probably a Mendelian dominant.

Jeghers *et al.* (1949, 1950) described a syndrome of generalized intestinal polyposis and melanin spots of the oral mucosa, lips, and digits, and concluded that the syndrome was inherited as a Mendelian dominant.

Gardner and Stephens (1950) identified 9 cases of cancer of the digestive tract in one family group made up of a total of 45 individuals. The primary site for 8 of the 9 cases was established in the region of the bowel and rectum. A simple dominant inheritance was suggested to explain the inheritance of the predisposing factor (polyposis) for cancer of the digestive tract in this family.

B. XERODERMA PIGMENTOSUM

Siemens and Kohn (1925) and Cockayne (1933) presented evidence that xeroderma pigmentosum had an hereditary predisposition. The latter author came to the conclusion that its inheritance depended upon a recessive Mendelian gene.

Haldane (1936), in an extensive analysis of 82 family histories, came to the conclusion that the gene for xeroderma pigmentosum was located in that particular region of the sex chromosome common to X and Y, and its inheritance as an incomplete sex-linked gene was a high probability.

Koller (1948) presented three new family histories in which one or more in the family were affected with xeroderma. In two families the usual pathologic symptoms were observed, while in a third the condition was manifested in a mild form. Furthermore, it was found that the segregation of xeroderma in this family did not conform to expectations. This behavior suggested that the condition in this particular family might be due to an independent autosomal gene, or to position effect, i.e., the gene had been transferred to a more distal region of the pairing segment of the sex chromosome.

C. MULTIPLE NEUROFIBROMATOSIS

Gates (1946) reviewed the extensive literature concerning the inheritance of multiple neurofibromatosis. In general the character had been interpreted to be due to the inheritance of a Mendelian dominant gene. It appears to occur frequently as a mutation.

D. RETINOBLASTOMA

Bell (1922) presented a summary of the early literature concerning the inheritance of retinoblastoma. Bell also presented the cases of 5 males and 5 females, all of whom had affected eyes removed. Of their offspring, 19 were afflicted with this disease and 14 were normal.

Gates (1946) reviewed the evidence for inheritance of this characteristic and concluded that it was generally thought to be inherited as a dominant, frequently but not always of low penetrance.

Weller (1941) and Falls (1947) failed to find a clear explanation for the method of inheritance but believed the evidence of heritability was strong enough for a retinoblastoma patient, whose life had been saved, to be warned that any offspring he or she might have may possibly develop retinoblastoma.

Neel and Falls (1951) stated that current genetic theory holds that the disease retinoblastoma is due to a dominant gene. The apparently isolated cases are attributable to mutation. The authors found the estimated rate of mutation to be 2.3×10^{-5}.

E. UTERINE CANCER

Brobeck (1949) investigated the incidence of cancer among the relatives of 200 patients with cancer of the cervix and 90 patients with cancer of the fundus of the uterus. Uterine cancer was more frequent among the relatives of probands having cancer of the uterine cervix than among control relatives. This was also true for the relatives of the probands having cancer of the uterine fundus.

Murphy (1952) studied the occurrence of cancer among the relatives of 201 women who were suffering from cancer of the uterine cervix. This was compared to the findings for 215 control probands. The study included 6,445 individuals. The evidence supported the conclusion that hereditary factors affected the frequency with which cancer appeared in the uterus. The quantitative effect of heredity was small.

F. BREAST CANCER

Jacobson (1946) summarized the history of investigations into the genetic aspects of breast cancer in man. Jacobson also made an analysis of the case histories of 200 propositae. The study indicated hereditary predisposition as the chief factor in the development of breast cancer.

Penrose *et al.* (1948) reported the results of the study of a series of 510 cases of mammary cancer in females. Family investigations showed that the same disease occurred with significantly increased frequency in sisters and mothers of these patients. The rate of malignancy of other types of cancer in these relatives was not increased. The authors postulated a specific genetic agent responsible for the disease, which may be inherited mainly through the maternal line.

Smithers (1948) presented a preliminary analysis of 459 family records of patients reporting with carcinoma of the breast. According to the author the analysis suggested that there was a significantly higher death-rate from cancer of the breast in families of patients with that disease, but no higher death-rate from other forms of cancer than would be expected in the general population.

Horn (1950) explored the possibility of vertical transfer through breast feeding of an agent that might be a factor in human mammary cancer. The incidence of absence of breast feeding in the 88 cases of known cancer of the female breast, was compared with that in 86 cases of vaginal plastic surgery. From this study it appeared that a woman might develop cancer of the breast without ever having received any human breast milk.

Passey *et al.* (1949), Gross *et al.* (1950), and Passey *et al.* (1951) presented the results of electron-microscopic examination of human milk comparing, insofar as possible, women having family records of breast cancer, or with breast cancer, with women without immediate relatives with breast cancer. Small spherical particles, of smooth surface and high density to the electron beam, were found to be more numerous in milk of the former than in the milk of the latter. Attention was called to the similarity of these spheroid particles to those observed in mouse milk known to contain the mouse mammary tumor agent.

Macklin (1951), in a study of the genetic aspects of human breast cancer which is still in progress, selected a series from two populations: (1) those related to women with breast cancer, and (2) control cases related to patients without cancer of the same age as the cancer patients. Macklin found that women related to breast cancer patients had breast cancer in significantly higher numbers than had women from the control population. It was concluded that heredity played a leading role in the pathogenesis of human breast cancer.

VII. CONCLUSIONS

(1) Genetics has contributed valuable research materials and research methods to the study of neoplastic disease.

(2) Genetic studies have shown that hereditary factors play a part in the occurrence of several neoplastic diseases in animals and in man.

BIBLIOGRAPHY

Allen, E., and Gardner, W. U. Cancer of the cervix of the uterus in hybrid mice following long continued administration of estrogen. *Cancer Research 1:* 359-366, 1941.

Amundson, V. S., and Biely, J. Inheritance of resistance to fowl paralysis (neurolymphomatosis gallinarum): I. Differences in susceptibility. *J. Cancer Research 6:* 171-176, 1932.

ANDERVONT, H. B. The production of dibenzanthracene tumors in pure strain mice. *Pub. Health Rep. 49:* 620-624, 1934.

ANDERVONT, H. B. Further studies on the production of dibenzanthracene tumors in pure strain and stock mice. *Pub. Health Rep. 50:* 1211-1217, 1935.

ANDERVONT, H. B. Pulmonary tumors in mice: Susceptibility of lungs of albino mice to carcinogenic action of 1:2:5:6-dibenzanthracene. *Pub. Health Rep. 52:* 212-221, 1937a.

ANDERVONT, H. B. Pulmonary tumors in mice: Influence of heredity upon lung tumors induced by subcutaneous injection of lard-dibenzanthracene solution. *Pub. Health Rep. 52:* 304-315, 1937b.

ANDERVONT, H. B. Pulmonary tumors in mice: Further studies on the influence of heredity upon spontaneous and induced lung tumors. *Pub. Health Rep. 53:* 232-237, 1938a.

ANDERVONT, H. B. Incidence of induced subcutaneous and pulmonary tumors and spontaneous mammary tumors in hybrid mice. *Pub. Health Rep. 53:* 1665-1678, 1938b.

ANDERVONT, H. B. Production of tumors in mice of strains C3H and Y by dibenzanthracene and methylcholanthrene. *Pub. Health Rep. 53:* 229-237, 1938c.

ANDERVONT, H. B. Susceptibility of mice to spontaneous, induced and transplantable tumors: Comparative study of 8 strains. *Pub. Health Rep. 53:* 1647-1665, 1938d.

ANDERVONT, H. B. The occurrence of spontaneous and induced pulmonary and liver tumors in strain C3H mice. *Pub. Health Rep. 54:* 1158-1169, 1939a.

ANDERVONT, H. B. Development and genetic characteristics of the adenomatous stomach lesion in strain I mice. *Pub. Health Rep. 54:* 1851-1855, 1939b.

ANDERVONT, H. B. The susceptibility of five inbred strains of mice to liver changes induced by subcutaneous injection of 2-amino-5-azotoluene. *Pub. Health Rep. 54:* 1986-1991, 1939c.

ANDERVONT, H. B. Further studies on the susceptibility of hybrid mice to induced and spontaneous tumors. *J. Nat. Cancer Inst. 1:* 135-145, 1940.

ANDERVONT, H. B. The influence of foster nursing upon the incidence of spontaneous mammary cancer in resistant and susceptible mice. *J. Nat. Cancer Inst. 1:* 147-154, 1941a.

ANDERVONT, H. B. The influence of paternal parent in determining the susceptibility of mice to spontaneous mammary tumors. *J. Nat. Cancer Inst. 2:* 7-11, 1941b.

ANDERVONT, H. B. Influence of hybridization upon the occurrence of mammary tumors in mice. *J. Nat. Cancer Inst. 3:* 359-365, 1943.

ANDERVONT, H. B. Fate of C3H milk influence in mice of strains C and C57 black. *J. Nat. Cancer Inst. 5:* 381-390, 1945a.

ANDERVONT, H. B. Relation of milk influence to mammary tumors of hybrid mice. *J. Nat. Cancer Inst. 5:* 391-395, 1945b.

ANDERVONT, H. B. The incidence of mammary tumors in mice of strain C3H and its descendants of fostered strain C. *J. Nat. Cancer Inst. 10:* 193-200, 1949a.

ANDERVONT, H. B. Spontaneous lesion of stomach in strain I mice. *J. Nat. Cancer Inst. 10:* 405-406, 1949b.

ANDERVONT, H. B. Studies on the occurrence of spontaneous hepatomas in mice of strains C3H and CBA. *J. Nat. Cancer Inst. 11:* 581-592, 1950a.

ANDERVONT, H. B. Response of mammary-tumor-agent free strain DBA female mice to percutaneous application of methylcholanthrene. *J. Nat. Cancer Inst. 10:* 895-926, 1950b.

ANDERVONT, H. B., and DUNN, T. B. Efforts to detect a mammary-tumor-agent in strain C mice. *J. Nat. Cancer Inst. 8:* 235-240, 1948a.

ANDERVONT, H. B., and DUNN, T. B. Mammary tumors in mice presumably free of the mammary tumor agent. *J. Nat. Cancer Inst. 8:* 227-233, 1948b.

ANDERVONT, H. B., and DUNN, T. B. Further studies on the relation of the mammary tumor agent to mammary tumors of hybrid mice. *J. Nat. Cancer Inst. 9:* 89-104, 1948c.

ANDERVONT, H. B., and EDWARDS, J. E. Hepatic changes and subcutaneous and pulmonary tumors induced by 3:4:5:6-dibenzcarbazole. *J. Nat. Cancer Inst. 2:* 139-149, 1941.

ANDERVONT, H. B., and EDWARDS, J. E. Carcinogenic action of 2 azo compounds in mice. *J. Nat. Cancer Inst. 3:* 349-354, 1943.

ANDERVONT, H. B., GRADY, H. G., and EDWARDS, J. E. Induction of hepatic lesions, hepatomas, pulmonary tumors and hemangio-endotheliomas in mice with *o*-aminoazotoluene. *J. Nat. Cancer Inst. 3:* 131-153, 1942.

ANDERVONT, H. B., and MCELENEY, W. J. The influence of non-breeding and foster nursing upon the occurrence of spontaneous breast tumors in strain C3H mice. *Pub. Health Rep. 53:* 777-783, 1938.

ANDERVONT, H. B., and MCELENEY, W. J. The influence of foster nursing upon the incidence of spontaneous breast cancer in strain C3H mice. *Pub. Health Rep. 54:* 1597-1603, 1939.

ANDERVONT, H. B., and STEWART, H. L. Adenomatous lesion in stomach of strain I mice. *Science 86:* 566-567, 1937.

ARDASHNIKOV, S. N. Malignant tumors in *Drosophila melanogaster:* Influence of the left end of the sex chromosome on the development of tumors. *Compt. rend. Acad. d. sc. URSS 30:* 344-346, 1941.

ARMSTRONG, E. C. Observations on the nature of the oestrous cycle and on the effect upon it of the milk factor, in mice of two inbred strains differing in mammary cancer incidence. *Brit. J. Cancer 2:* 59-69, 1948.

ARMSTRONG, E. C., and BONSER, G. M. Squamous carcinoma of the forestomach and other lesions in mice following oral administration of 3:4:5:6-dibenzcarbazole. *Brit. J. Cancer 4:* 203-211, 1950.

BAGG, H. J., and JACKSON, J. The value of a "functional test" in selecting material for a genetic study of mammary tumors in mice and rats. *Am. J. Cancer 30:* 539-548, 1937.

BAGSHAW, M. A., and STRONG, L. C. A histopathologic and genetic study of tumors of the forestomach in mice treated with a single subcutaneous injection of methylcholanthrene. *Cancer Research 9:* 603, 1949.

BAGSHAW, M. A., and STRONG, L. C. The occurrence of tumors of the forestomach in mice after parenteral administration of methylcholanthrene: a histopathologic and genetic analysis. *J. Nat. Cancer Inst. 11:* 141-176, 1950.

BELL, J. Glioma retina. *Treas. Hum. Inher. 2:* 112-123, 1922.

BITTNER, J. J. The breeding behavior and tumor incidence of an albino strain of mice. *Am. J. Cancer 25:* 113-121, 1935.

BITTNER, J. J. Spontaneous tumor incidence in mice, "Z" stock × "I" stock. *J. Hered. 27:* 391-393, 1936a.

BITTNER, J. J. Some possible effects of nursing on mammary gland tumor incidence in mice. *Science 84:* 162, 1936b.

BITTNER, J. J. Mammary tumors in mice in relation to nursing. *Am. J. Cancer 30:* 530-538, 1937a.

BITTNER, J. J. Some possible effects of nursing on mammary gland tumor incidence in mice. *Am. J. Clin. Path. 7:* 430-433, 1937b.

BITTNER, J. J. Spontaneous lung carcinoma in mice. *Pub. Health Rep. 53:* 2197-2202, 1938.

BITTNER, J. J. Relation of nursing to the extra-chromosomal theory of breast cancer in mice. *Am. J. Cancer 35:* 90-97, 1939a.

BITTNER, J. J. "Influences" of breast cancer development in mice. *Pub. Health Rep. 54:* 1590-1597, 1939b.

BITTNER, J. J. Possible method of transmission of susceptibility to breast cancer in mice. *Am. J. Cancer 39:* 104-113, 1940a.

BITTNER, J. J. Further studies on active milk influence in breast cancer production in mice. *Proc. Soc. Exper. Biol. & Med. 45:* 805-810, 1940b.

BITTNER. J. J. Breast cancer in mice as influenced by nursing. *J. Nat. Cancer Inst. 1:* 155-168, 1941a.

BITTNER, J. J. The variability of incidence of mammary carcinoma in inbred strains of mice. *Cancer Research 1:* 115-120, 1941b.

BITTNER, J. J. Foster nursing and lung cancer in "A" stock mice. *Am. J. Cancer 38:* 95-102, 1940c.

BITTNER, J. J. Foster nursing and genetic susceptibility for tumors of the breast in mice. *Cancer Research 1:* 793-794, 1941c.

BITTNER, J. J. The genetics and linkage relationship of inherited susceptibility to mammary cancer in mice. *Cancer Research 4:* 779-784, 1944.

BITTNER, J. J. Genetic aspect of cancer research. *Am. J. Med. 8:* 218-228, 1950a.

BITTNER, J. J. Some enigmas associated with the genesis of mammary cancer in mice. *Cancer Research 8:* 625-639, 1950b.

BITTNER, J. J. Inherited hormonal mechanisms and mammary cancer in virgin female mice. *Cancer Research 11:* 237, 1951.

BITTNER, J. J., HUSEBY, R. A., VISSCHER, M. B., BALL, Z. B., and SMITH, F. Mammary cancer and mammary structure in inbred stocks of mice and their hybrids. *Science 99:* 83-85, 1944.

BITTNER, J. J., and HUSEBY, R. A. Relationship of the inherited susceptibility and the inherited hormonal influence in the development of mammary cancer in mice. *Cancer Research 6:* 235-239, 1946.

BITTNER, J. J., and MURRAY, W. S. Comparative study of four high tumor lines of mice. *Am. Nat. 70:* 443-453, 1936.

BITTNER, J. J., and LITTLE, C. C. The transmission of breast and lung cancer in mice. *J. Hered. 28:* 117-121, 1937.

BONSER, G. M. A comparison of the normal oestrous cycle and the response to the administration of oestrin in two strains of mice differing greatly in incidence of spontaneous mammary cancer. *J. Path. & Bact. 41:* 33-42, 1935a.

BONSER, G. M. Carcinoma of the male breast in mice induced with oestrin: Effect of a vitamin A deficient diet combined with oestrin treatment. *J. Path. & Bact. 41:* 217-218, 1935b.

BONSER, G. M. The hereditary factor in induced skin tumors in mice: The establishment of a strain specially sensitive to carcinogenic agents applied to the skin. *J. Path. & Bact. 46:* 581-602, 1938.

BONSER, G. M. Induction of tumors by injected methylcholanthrene in mice of a strain especially sensitive to carcinogenic agents applied to the skin, and a comparison with some other strains. *Am. J. Cancer 38:* 319-327, 1940.

BONSER, G. M. Malignant tumors of interstitial cells of the testis in Strong A mice treated with triphenylethylene. *J. Path. & Bact. 54:* 149-154, 1942.

BONSER, G. M. Mammary and testicular tumors in male mice of various strains following oestrogen treatment. *J. Path. & Bact. 56:* 15-26, 1944.

BONSER, G. M., and CONNAL, K. I. The effect of the presence of a malignant tumour upon the development of a second malignant tumour. *J. Path. & Bact. 48:* 263-274, 1939.

BONSER, G. M., and ROBSON, J. M. The effects of prolonged oestrogen administration upon male mice of various strains: Development of testicular tumours in Strong A strain. *J. Path. & Bact. 51:* 9-22, 1940.

BONSER, G. M., and ROBSON, J. M. The induction of tumours following the direct implantation of 20-methyl-1-cholanthrene into the uterus of mice. *Brit. J. Cancer 4:* 196-202, 1950.

BONSER, G. M., and WAINMAN, L. M. Further experimental study of antagonism between one malignant tumour and the appearance of another in the same animal. *J. Path. & Bact. 52:* 263-266, 1941.

BOYLAND, E., and WARREN, F. L. Induction of tumours by methylcholanthrene in 2 strains of mice. *J. Path. & Bact. 45:* 171-178, 1937.

BRANCH, C. F. Dibenzanthracene tumors in controlled strains of mice. *Am. J. Cancer 26:* 110-114, 1936.

BRIDGES, C. B. Non-disjunction as proof of the chromosome theory of heredity. *Genetics 1:* 1-52, 107-163, 1916.

BROBECK, O. Heredity in cancer uteri: A genetical and clinical study of 200 patients with cancer of the cervix uteri and 90 patients with cancer of the corpus uteri. Aarhus, Denmark, Universitetsforlaget, 1949.

BRUES, A. M., and MARBLE, B. B. Lymphoblastoma in mice following administration of carcinogenic tar. *Am. J. Cancer 37:* 45-53, 1939.

BURDETTE, W. J. Inheritance of susceptibility to tumors induced in mice: Tumors induced by methylcholanthrene in progeny of C3H and JK mice. *Cancer Research 3:* 318-320, 1943.

BURDETTE, W. J. The inheritance of susceptibility to tumors induced in mice: III. Tumors induced with methylcholanthrene in the backcross of C3H and JK mice. *J. Nat. Cancer Inst. 9:* 105-110, 1948.

BURDETTE, W. J. Tumors and mutation in *Drosophila. Texas Rep. Biol. & Med. 8:* 123-133, 1950.

BURDETTE, W. J. Tumor incidence and lethal mutation rate in Drosophila following treatment with formaldehyde. *Cancer Research 11:* 241, 1951a.

BURDETTE, W. J. Tumor incidence and lethal mutation rate in a tumor strain of Drosophila treated with formaldelhyde. *Cancer Research 11:* 555-558, 1951b.

BURDETTE, W. J., and STRONG, L. C. Inheritance of susceptibility to tumors induced in mice; tumors induced by methylcholanthrene in five inbred strains of mice. *Cancer Research 3:* 13-20, 1943.

BURNS, E. L., and SCHENKEN, J. R. Spontaneous primary hepatomas in mice of strain C3H: A study of incidence, sex distribution and morbid anatomy. *Am. J. Cancer 39 (1):* 25-35, 1940.

BURNS, E. L., and SCHENKEN, J. R. Spontaneous primary hepatomas in mice of strain C3H: II. The influence of breeding on their incidence. *Cancer Research 3:* 691-692, 1943.

CARR, J. G. Production of mutations in mice by 1:2:5:6-dibenzanthracene. *Brit. J. Cancer 1:* 152-156, 1947.

CLOUDMAN, A. M., and LITTLE, C. C. The genetics of tumor formation in mice, in relation to the gene T for brachyury. *J. Genetics 32:* 487-504, 1936.

COCKAYNE, E. A. *Inherited Abnormalities of the Skin and Its Appendages.* London, Oxford Univ. Press, 1933.

COLE, R. K., and FURTH, J. Experimental studies on the genetics of spontaneous leukemia in mice. *Cancer Research 1:* 957-965, 1941.

COLLINS, V. J., GARDNER, W. U., and STRONG, L. C. Experimental gastric tumors in mice. *Cancer Research 3:* 29-35, 1943.

COWDRY, E. V., CARRUTHERS, C., and SUNTZEFF, V. Influence of age on the copper and zinc content in the epidermis of mice undergoing carcinogenesis with methylcholanthrene and a note on the role of calcium. *J. Nat. Cancer Inst. 8:* 209-213, 1948.

COWEN, P. N. Strain differences in mice to the carcinogenic action of urethane and its non-carcinogenicity in chicks and guinea pigs. *Brit. J. Cancer 4:* 245-253, 1950.

COWEN, P. N. Some studies on the action of urethane on mice. *Brit. J. Cancer 1:* 401-405, 1947.

CRAMER, W. On an antagonism in the development of malignancy in two different organs. *J. Path. & Bact. 43:* 77-89, 1936.

CRIPPS, H. Two cases of disseminated polypus of rectum. *Tr. Path. Soc. London 33:* 165, 1882.

DICKIE, M. M., and WOOLLEY, G. W. Spontaneous basophilic tumors of the pituitary glands in gonadectomized mice. *Cancer Research 9:* 372-384, 1949.

DERINGER, M. K., HESTON, W. E., and ANDERVONT, H. B. Estrus in virgin strain A (low tumor) mice and in the reciprocal (A×C3H) F_1 hybrids. *J. Nat. Cancer Inst. 5:* 403-405, 1945.

DMOCHOWSKI, L. Mammary tumor inducing factor and genetic constitution. *Brit. J. Cancer 2:* 94-102, 1948.

DOBROVOLSKAIA-ZAVADSKAIA, N., and ROUYER, M. Reaction à certains agents cancerigènes, d'une lignée de souris exempte du cancer spontané de la mamelle (lignée xxx). *Compt. rend. Soc. de biol. 127:* 383-385, 1938.

DUKES, C. Hereditary factor in polyposis intestini or multiple adenomata. *Cancer Rev. 5:* 241-256, 1930.

ENGELBRETH-HOLM, J. Acceleration of development of mammary carcinomas in mice by methylcholanthrene. *Cancer Research 1:* 109-112, 1941.

ENGELBRETH-HOLM, J., and LEFÉVRE, H. Acceleration of the development of leukemias and mammary carcinomas in mice by 9,10-dimethyl-1,2-benzanthracene. *Cancer Research 1:* 102-108, 1941.

FALLS, H. F. Inheritance of retinoblastoma. *J.A.M.A. 133:* 171, 1947.

FEDERLEY, H. Sex-limited hereditary cancer in Lepidopterous larvae. *Hereditas 22:* 193-216, 1936-37.

FEKETE, E. Observations on three functional tests in a high tumor and a low tumor strain of mice. *Am. J. Cancer 38:* 234-238, 1940.

FEKETE, E., and GREEN, C. V. The influence of complete blockage of nipple on the incidence and localization of spontaneous mammary tumor in mice. *Am. J. Cancer 27:* 513-515, 1936.

Fekete, E., and Little, C. C. Observations on the mammary tumor incidence of mice born from transferred ova. *Cancer Research 2:* 525-530, 1942.

Fekete, E., Woolley, G. W., and Little, C. C. Histological changes following ovariectomy in mice: I. dba high tumor strain. *J. Exper. Med. 74:* 1-8, 1941.

Fibiger, J., and Bang, F. Production experimentale du cancer du goudron chez la souris blanche. *Compt. rend. Soc. de biol. 83:* 1157-1160, 1920.

Foulds, L. Mammary tumours in hybrid mice; the presence and transmission of the mammary tumour agent. *Brit. J. Cancer 3:* 230-239, 1949a.

Foulds, L. Mammary tumours in hybrid mice: Growth and progression of spontaneous tumours. *Brit. J. Cancer 3:*345-384, 1949b.

Frantz, M. J., and Kirschbaum, A. Sex hormone secretion by adrenal cortical tumors of mice. *Cancer Research 9:* 596, 1949.

Frantz, M. J., Kirschbaum, A., and Casas, C. Endocrine interrelationship and spontaneous tumors of the adrenal cortex in NH mice. *Proc. Soc. Exper. Biol. & Med. 66:* 645-646, 1947.

Furth, J. Transmission of myeloid leukemia in mice. *Proc. Soc. Exper. Biol & Med. 31:* 923-925, 1934.

Furth, J. Neoplastic transformation of granulosa cells in grafts of normal ovaries into spleens of gonadectomized mice. *J. Nat. Cancer Inst. 8:* 7-16, 1947.

Furth, J., and Boon, M. C. Induction of ovarian tumors in mice by X-rays. *Cancer Research 7:* 241-245, 1947.

Furth, J., Boon, M. C., and Kaliss, N. On the genetic character of neoplastic cells as determined in transplantation experiments. *Cancer Research 4:* 1-10, 1944.

Furth, J., and Furth, O. B. Neoplastic disease produced in mice by general irradiation with X-rays: I. Incidence and types of neoplasms. *Am. J. Cancer 28:* 54-65, 1936.

Gardner, E. J., and Stephens, F. E. Cancer of the lower digestive tract in one family group. *Am. J. Hum. Genetics 2:* 41-48, 1950.

Gardner, E. J., and Woolf, C. M. The influence of high and low temperatures upon the expression of tumorous head in *Drosophila melanogaster*. *Genetics 35:* 44-55, 1950.

Gardner, W. U. The effect of estrogen on the incidence of mammary and pituitary tumors in mice. *Cancer Research 1:* 345-358, 1941.

Gardner, W. U. Testicular tumors in mice of several strains receiving triphenylethylene. *Cancer Research 3:* 92-99, 1943a.

Gardner, W. U. Spontaneous testicular tumors in mice. *Cancer Research 3:* 757-761, 1943b.

Gardner, W. U., and Allen, E. Malignant and non-malignant uterine and vaginal lesions in mice receiving estrogen and androgen simultaneously. *Yale J. Biol. & Med. 12:* 213-234, 1939.

Gardner, W. U., Dougherty, T. F., and Williams, W. L. Lymphoid tumors in mice receiving steroid hormones. *Cancer Research 4:* 73-87, 1944.

Gardner, W. U., Kirschbaum, A., and Strong, L. C. Lymphoid tumors in mice receiving estrogens. *Arch. Path. 29:* 1-7, 1940.

Gardner, W. U., and Pan, S. C. Malignant tumors of the uterus and vagina in untreated mice of the PM stock. *Cancer Research 8:* 241-256, 1948.

Gardner, W. U., Smith, G. M., Strong, L. C., and Allen, E. Experimental production of malignant growths in mice by estrogenic chemicals. *J.A.M.A. 107:* 656-657, 1936.

GARDNER, W. U., and STRONG, L. C. Strain limited development of tumors of the pituitary gland in mice receiving estrogens. *Yale J. Biol. & Med. 12:* 543-548, 1940.

GARDNER, W. U., STRONG, L. C., and SMITH, G. M. Mammary glands of mature female mice of strains varying in susceptibility to spontaneous tumor development. *Am. J. Cancer 37:* 510-517, 1939.

GATES, R. R. *Human Genetics.* New York, The Macmillan Co., 1946, pp. 1176-1180.

GEIST, S. H., GAINES, J. A., and POLLACK, A. D. Experimental biologically active ovarian tumors in mice: Histogenesis and relationship to similar human ovarian tumors. *Am. J. Obst. & Gynec. 38:* 786-797, 1939.

GORBMAN, A., and GORDON, M. Spontaneous thyroidal tumors in the swordtail *Xiphophorus montezumae. Cancer Research 11:* 184-187, 1951.

GORDON, M. Genetics of melanomas in fishes: V. The reappearance of ancestral micromelanophores in offspring of parents lacking these cells. *Cancer Research 1:* 656-659, 1941.

GORDON, M. The variable expressivity of a pigment cell gene from zero to melanotic tumor induction. *Cancer Research 11:* 676-686, 1951.

GORDON, M., and SMITH, G. M. The production of a melanotic neoplastic disease by selective matings: IV. Genetics of geographical species hybrids. *Am. J. Cancer 34:* 543-565, 1938.

GORER, P. A. The incidence of tumors of the liver and other organs in a pure line of mice (Strong CBA strain). *J. Path. & Bact. 50:* 17-24, 1940.

GOTTSCHALK, R. G. The susceptibility to carcinogens of adult and embryo tissues. *Heredity 2:* 284, 1948.

GOWEN, J. W. The inheritance of focal melanosis in *Drosophila. Arch. Path. 17:* 638-647, 1934.

GROSS, L., GESSLER, A. E., and MCCARTY, K. S. Electron-microscopic examination of human milk particularly from women having family records of breast cancer. *Proc. Soc. Exper. Biol. & Med. 75:* 270-276, 1950.

GROSS, J., and SCHWARTZ, S. The metabolism of thyroxine in C57 mice and C3H mice with and without the mammary tumor inciter. *Cancer Research 11:* 614-618, 1951.

HAAGENSEN, C. D., and RANDALL, H. T. Production of mammary carcinoma in mice by estrogens. *Arch. Path. 33:* 411-442, 1942.

HALDANE, J. B. S. The genetics of cancer. *Nature, London 132:* 265-267, 1933.

HALDANE, J. B. S. A search for incomplete sex-linkage in man. *Ann. Eugenics 7:* 28-57, 1936.

HARNLY, M. H., and GOLDSMITH, E. D. The effect of crowding on the penetrance of an hereditary melanoma of *Drosophila melanogaster. Cancer Research 9:* 604, 1949.

HESTON, W. E. Lung tumors and heredity: Susceptibility of 4 inbred strains of mice and their hybrids to pulmonary tumors induced by subcutaneous injection. *J. Nat. Cancer Inst. 1:* 105-111, 1940.

HESTON, W. E. Relationship between susceptibility to induced pulmonary tumors and certain known genes in the mouse. *J. Nat. Cancer Inst. 2:* 127-132, 1941.

HESTON, W. E. Genetic analysis of susceptibility to induced pulmonary tumors in mice. *J. Nat. Cancer Inst. 3:* 69-78, 1942a.

HESTON, W. E. Inheritance of susceptibility to spontaneous pulmonary tumors in mice. *J. Nat. Cancer Inst. 3:* 79-82, 1942b.

HESTON, W. E. Relationship between the lethal yellow (A^y) gene in the mouse and susceptibility to induced pulmonary tumors. *J. Nat. Cancer Inst. 3:* 303-308, 1942c.

HESTON, W. E. Role of heredity in tumor development. *J. Nat. Cancer Inst. 5:* 161-171, 1944.

HESTON, W. E. Importance of genetic influence on the occurrence of mammary tumors in virgin female mice. *J. Nat. Cancer. Inst. 4:* 403-407, 1944a.

HESTON, W. E. Genetics of mammary tumors. *Am. A. Advance Sc., Publ. No. 22,* pp. 55-84, 1945 (Moulton, F. R., Ed.).

HESTON, W. E. Paths of gene action in mammary tumor development in mice. *J. Nat. Cancer Inst. 7:* 79-85, 1946.

HESTON, W. E. Role of genes and their relationship to extra-chromosomal factors in the development of mammary gland tumors in mice. *Brit. J. Cancer 2:* 87-90, 1948a.

HESTON, W. E. "Genetics and cancer." In *Advances in Genetics* (Demerec, M., Ed.) *2:* 99-125, 1948b.

HESTON, W. E., and ANDERVONT, H. B. Importance of genetic influences on the occurrence of mammary tumors in virgin female mice. *J. Nat. Cancer Inst. 4:* 403-407, 1944.

HESTON, W. E., and DERINGER, M. K. Relationship between the lethal yellow (A^y) gene of the mouse and susceptibility to spontaneous pulmonary tumors. *J. Nat. Cancer Inst. 7:* 463-465, 1947.

HESTON, W. E., and DERINGER, M. K. Relationship between the hairless gene and susceptibility to induced pulmonary tumors in mice. *Cancer Research 9:* 603, 1949a.

HESTON, W. E., and DERINGER, M. K. Relationship between hairless gene and susceptibility to induced pulmonary tumors in mice. *J. Nat. Cancer Inst. 10:* 119-124, 1949b.

HESTON, W. E., DERINGER, M. K., and ANDERVONT, H. B. Gene-milk agent relationship in mammary tumor development. *J. Nat. Cancer Inst. 5:* 289-307, 1945.

HESTON, W. E., DERINGER, M. K., DUNN, T. B., and LEVILLAIN, W. D. Factors in the development of spontaneous mammary gland tumors in agent-free strain C3Hb mice. *J. Nat. Cancer Inst. 10:* 1139-1151, 1950.

HESTON, W. E., and DUNN, T. B. Tumor development in susceptible strain A and resistant strain L lung transplants in LA F_1 hosts. *J. Nat. Cancer Inst. 11:* 1057-1072, 1950.

HOGREFFE, G. Genetic studies on leukemia in mice. *Brit. J. Cancer 2:* 108-114, 1948a.

HOGREFFE, G. Experimental genetic studies on leukemia in mice. *Acta path. et microbiol. Scandinav. 25:* 80-86, 1948b.

HOLLANDER, W. F., and STRONG, L. C. Further studies on mutations from methylcholanthrene-treated mice. *Cancer Research 9:* 565, 1949.

HORN, H. W. The "milk factor" in carcinoma of the human breast: An analysis of 88 cases. *New England J. Med. 243:* 373-375, 1950.

HUSEBY, R. A., and BITTNER, J. J. Differences in adrenal responsiveness to post-castrational alteration, as evidenced by transplanted adrenal tissue. *Cancer Research 11:* 258-259, 1951a.

HUSEBY, R. A., and BITTNER, J. J. The development of mammary cancer in castrate A strain male mice bearing ovarian grafts. *Cancer Research 11:* 450-452, 1951b.

HUTT, F. B., and COLE, R. K. The development of strains genetically resistant to avian lymphomatosis. *Offical Rep. of the 8th World's Poultry Congress,* pp. 719-725, 1948.

HUTT, F. B., COLE, R. K., and BRUCKNER, J. H. Four generations of fowls bred for resistance to neoplasms. *Poultry Sc. 20:* 514-526, 1941.

JACKSON LABORATORY, STAFF OF. The existence of non-chromosomal influence in the incidence of mammary tumors in mice. *Science 78:* 465, 1933.

JACOBSON, O. *Heredity in Breast Cancer.* Busck, Copenhagen, 1946.

JEGHERS, H., MCKUSICK, V. A., and KATZ, K. H. Generalized intestinal polyposis and melanin spots of the oral mucosa, lips and digits: A syndrome of diagnostic significance. *New England J. Med. 241:* 993-1005, 1031-1036, 1949.

JEGHERS, H., MCKUSICK, V. A., and KATZ, K. H. The syndrome of generalized intestinal polyposis and melanin spots of the oral mucosa, lips and digits. *Ciba Clin. Symposia. 2:* 199-202, 1950.

JOHNSON, R. M., and ALBERT, S. Age and strain differences in phosphorus metabolism in various endocrine organs of mice. *Cancer Research 9:* 612, 1949.

JONES, E. E. The morphology of hyperplastic nodules in the mammary glands of C3H and C3Hb mice. *Cancer Research 11:* 260, 1951.

KAPLAN, H. S. Influence of age on susceptibility of mice to the development of lymphoid tumors after irradiation. *J. Nat. Cancer Inst. 9:* 55-56, 1948.

KIRBY, A. H. M. Studies in carcinogenesis with azo compounds; action of 4 azo dyes in mixed and pure strain mice. *Cancer Research 5:* 673-682, 1945a.

KIRBY, A. H. M. Studies in carcinogenesis with azo compounds; action of azo compounds in mice and the bearing thereof on theories of azo dye carcinogenesis. *Cancer Research 5:* 683-696, 1945b.

KIRSCHBAUM, A. Induction of mammary cancer with methylcholanthrene: II. Histologic similarity between carcinogen-induced tumors and certain mammary neoplasms occurring spontaneously. *Cancer Research 9:* 93-95, 1949.

KIRSCHBAUM, A., and BITTNER, J. J. The relation of milk influence to carcinogenic induction of mammary carcinoma in mice. *Proc. Soc. Exper. Biol. & Med. 58:* 18-19, 1945.

KIRSCHBAUM, A., FRANTZ, M., and WILLIAMS, W. L. Neoplasms of the adrenal cortex in non-castrate mice. *Cancer Research 6:* 707-711, 1946.

KIRSCHBAUM, A., and KAPLAN, H. S. Induction of leukemia in mice. *Science 100:* 360-361, 1944.

KIRSCHBAUM, A., and MIXER, H. W. Induction of leukemia in 8 inbred stocks of mice varying in susceptibility to the spontaneous disease. *J. Lab. & Clin. Med. 32:* 720-731, 1947.

KIRSCHBAUM, A., and STRONG, L. C. Leukemia in the F strain of mice: Observations on cytology, general morphology and transmission. *Am. J. Cancer 37:* 400-413, 1939.

KIRSCHBAUM, A., STRONG, L. C., and GARDNER, W. U. Influence of methylcholanthrene on the age incidence of leukemia in several strains of mice. *Proc. Soc. Exper. Biol. & Med. 45:* 287-289, 1940.

KOLLER, P. C. Inheritance of xeroderma and its chromosome mechanism. *Brit. J. Cancer 2:* 149-155, 1948.

KORTEWEG, R. Chromosale invloeden op den groei en extra-chromosomale invloeden op het outstaan van kanker bij muis. *Nederl. Tijdschr. v. geneesk. 79:* 1482-1490, 1935.

KORTEWEG, R. Hereditary factors predisposing to mammary cancer in mice. *Nederl. bij Tijdschr. v. geneesk. 80:* 4008, 1936.

KORTEWEG, R. Genetically determined differences in hormone production: A possible factor influencing the susceptibility to mammary cancer in mice. *Brit. J. Cancer 2:* 91-94, 1948.

KREBS, C., RASK-NIELSEN, H. C., and WAGNER, A. The origin of lymphosarcomatosis and its relation to other forms of leucosis in white mice. *Acta Radiol.* Supp. 10: 1-53, 1930.

KREYBERG, L. On the genetic factor in development of benign tar tumors in mice. *Acta path. et microbiol. Scandinav. 11:* 174-182, 1934.

KREYBERG, L. On susceptibility to cancer development in the skin and in the mammary gland in two lines of inbred mice. *Am. J. Cancer 24:* 554-565, 1935.

LACASSAGNE, A. Hormonal pathogenesis of adenocarcinoma of the breast. *Am. J. Cancer 27:* 217-228, 1936.

LACASSAGNE, A. Sarcomes lymphoides apparus chez des souris longuement traitées par les hormones oestrogènes. *Compt. rend. Soc. de biol. 126:* 193-195, 1938.

LACASSAGNE, A., and NYKA, W. Difference de reaction de l'hypophyse à l'administration prolongée de substances oestrogènes dans diverse lignées selectionnées de souris. *Compt. rend. Soc. de biol. 126* 1112-1115, 1937.

LATHROP, A. E. C., and LOEB, L. Tumor incidence and tumor age in various strains of mice. *J. Exper. Med. 22:* 646-673, 1915.

LAW, L. W., and MILLER, J. H. The effect of thymectomy on the incidence, latent period, and type of leukemia in high leukemia strains of mice. *Cancer Research 10:* 230-231, 1950a.

LAW, L. W., and MILLER, J. H. Observations on the effect of thymectomy on spontaneous leukemias in mice of the high-leukemic strains, RIL and C58. *J. Nat. Cancer Inst. 11:* 253-262, 1950b.

LEITCH, A. The effect of cessation of the irritant on the development of experimental tar tumors. *Brit. M. J. 2:* 1101-1103, 1922.

LI, M. H., GARDNER, W. U., and KAPLAN, H. S. Effects of X-ray irradiation on the development of ovarian tumors in intrasplenic grafts in castrated mice. *J. Nat. Cancer Inst. 8:* 91-98, 1947.

LI, M. H., and GARDNER, W. U. Influence of age of host and ovaries on tumorigenesis in intrasplenic ovarian grafts. *Cancer Research 10:* 162-169, 1950.

LITTLE, C. C. The role of heredity in determining the incidence and growth of cancer. *Am. J. Cancer 15:* 2780-2789, 1931.

LITTLE, C. C. Individuality and the hereditary process in mammals. *Rec. Gen. Soc. America 2:* 65, 1933.

LITTLE, C. C. The relation of coat color to the spontaneous incidence of mammary tumors in mice. *J. Exper. Med. 59:* 229-250, 1934a.

LITTLE, C. C. The bearing of genetic work with transplanted tumors on the genetics of spontaneous tumors in mice. *Am. J. Cancer. 22:* 578-585, 1934b.

LITTLE, C. C. The genetics of spontaneous mammary cancer in mice. *Occasional Publ., Am. A. Advance. Sc. 4:* 17-21, 1937.

LITTLE, C. C. Hybridization and tumor formation in mice. *Proc. Nat. Acad. Sc. 25:* 452-455, 1939.

LITTLE, C. C. A review of progress in the study of the genetics of spontaneous tumor incidence. *J. Nat. Cancer Inst. 1:* 727-736, 1941a.

LITTLE, C. C. "The genetics of spontaneous tumor formation." In *Biology of the Laboratory Mouse* (Snell, G. D., Ed.). Philadelphia, Blakiston Co., pp. 248-278, 1941b.

LITTLE, C. C. The genetics of cancer in mice. *Biol. Rev. 22:* 315-343, 1947.

LITTLE, C. C., and GORER, P. A. "The genetics of cancer in mice." Appendix I. in Gruneberg, H.: *Genetics of the Mouse.* New York, Cambridge Univ. Press, 1943.

LITTLE, C. C., and MCPHETERS, B. W. The incidence of mammary cancer in a cross between two strains of mice. *Am. Nat. 66:* 1-3, 1932.

LITTLE, C. C., and PEARSONS, J. The results of a functional test in a strain of mice (C57 Bl.) with a low breast tumor incidence. *Am. J. Cancer 38:* 224-233, 1940.

LOCKHART-MUMMERY, P. Cancer and heredity. *Lancet 208:* 427-429, 1925.

LOCKHART-MUMMERY, P., and DUKES, C. E. Familial adenomatosis of colon and rectum. *Lancet 237:* 586-589, 1939.

LOEB, L. Further investigations on the origin of tumors in mice: VI. Internal secretion as a factor in the origin of tumors. *J. Med. Research 40:* 477-496, 1919.

LOEB, L. The significance of hormones in the origin of cancer. *J. Nat. Cancer Inst. 1:* 169-195, 1940.

LORENZ, E., and STEWART, H. L. Squamous cell carcinoma and other lesions of the forestomach in mice, following oral administration of 20-methylcholanthrene and 1:2:5:6-dibenzanthracene. *J. Nat. Cancer Inst. 1:* 273-276, 1940.

LORENZ, E., and STEWART, H. L. Tumors of alimentary tract in mice fed carcinogenic hydrocarbons in mineral-oil emulsions. *J. Nat. Cancer Inst. 9:* 173-180, 1948.

LUCKÉ, B. Tumors of the nerve sheaths in fishes of the snapper family (*Lutianidae*). *Arch. Path. 34:* 133-150, 1942.

LYNCH, C. J. Studies on the relation between tumor susceptibility and heredity: II. The incidence of tar tumors in strains of mice having a differing incidence of spontaneous growths. *J. Exper. Med. 42:* 829-840, 1925.

LYNCH, C. J. Studies on the relation between tumor susceptibility and heredity: III. Spontaneous tumors of the lung in mice. *J. Exper. Med. 43:* 339-355, 1926.

LYNCH, C. J. Studies on the relation between tumor susceptibility and heredity: IV. The inheritance of susceptibility to tar-induced tumors in the lungs of mice. *J. Exper. Med. 46:* 917-933, 1927.

LYNCH, C. J. Studies on the relation between tumor susceptibility and heredity: V. The influence of heredity upon the incidence of lung tumors in mice. *J. Exper. Med. 54:* 747-760, 1931.

LYNCH, C. J. Strain differences in susceptibility to tar-induced skin tumors in mice. *Proc. Soc. Exper. Biol. & Med. 31:* 215-217, 1933.

LYNCH, C. J. Susceptibility of mouse strains to lung tumor and sarcoma induced by 1:2:5:6-dibenzanthracene. *Proc. Soc. Exper. Biol. & Med. 33:* 401-403, 1935.

LYNCH, C. J. Studies on the relation between tumor susceptibility and heredity: VI. Lung tumors in mice with respect to the phenomena of maternal influence. *Am. J. Cancer 31:* 77-84, 1937.

LYNCH, C. J. Influence of heredity and environment upon the number of tumor nodules occurring in lungs of mice. *Proc. Soc. Exper. Biol. & Med. 43:* 186-189, 1940.

LYNCH, C. J. On the method of inheritance of susceptibility to lung tumors. *Cancer Research 1:* 740, 1941.

LYNCH, C. J. Lung tumors following intraperitoneal injection of 1:2:5:6-dibenzanthracene into young mice of three strains. *Proc. Soc. Exper. Biol. & Med. 52:* 368-371, 1943.

MACDOWELL, E. C. Genetic aspects of mouse leukemia. *Am. J. Cancer 26:* 85-101, 1936.

MacDowell, E. C. The genetics of mouse leukemia. *J. Hered. 28:* 131-138, 1937.
MacDowell, E. C., Biesele, J. J., Taylor, M. J., and Laanes, T. Mouse leukemia. *Baltimore, Md., Carnegie Inst. Wash. Yearbook 44:* 134-139, 1945a.
MacDowell, E. C., Potter, J. S., and Taylor, M. J. Mouse leukemia: XII. The role of genes in spontaneous cases. *Cancer Research 5:* 65-83, 1945b.
MacDowell, E. C., Potter, J. S., Taylor, M. J., and Laanes, T. Genetics of leukemia in mice. *Baltimore, Md., Yearbook Carnegie Wash. Inst. 39:* 217-221, 1940.
MacDowell, E. C., Potter, J. S., Taylor, M. J., and Ward, E. N. A second backcross test for determiners of spontaneous leukemia. *Genetics 26:* 160, 1941.
MacDowell, E. C., Potter, J. S., Ward, E. N., and Laanes, T. Genetics of leukemia in mice. *Baltimore, Md., Carnegie Inst. Wash. Yearbook 42:* 126-129, 1943.
MacDowell, E. C., and Richter, M. N. Mouse leukemia: IX. The role of heredity in spontaneous cases. *Arch. Path. 20:* 709-724, 1935.
MacDowell, E. C., and Taylor, M. J. Mouse leukemia: XIII. A maternal influence that lowers the incidence of spontaneous cases. *Proc. Soc. Exper. Biol. & Med. 68:* 571-577, 1948.
Macklin, M. T. The hereditary factors in human neoplasms. *Quart. Rev. Biol. 7:* 255-281, 1932.
Macklin, M. T. Genetic aspects of human breast cancer. *Anat. Rec. 109:* 321, 1951.
Marsh, W. S. J. Spontaneous mammary cancer in mice. *J. Cancer Research 13:* 313-339, 1929.
Mercier, L. Hérédité du lymphosarcome de la souris dans les croisements d'hétérozygotes pour le couple de facteurs cancer-non cancer. *Compt. rend. Soc. de biol. 124:* 403-405, 1937.
Mercier, L. Étude comparative sur l'hérédité du lymphosarcome spontané de la souris et du lymphosarcome de greffe. *Compt. rend. Soc. de biol. 124:* 796-798, 1937.
Mercier, L. Hérédité du cancer à l'intérieur d'une lignée de souris. Notion de facteur plasmo-chromosomique. *Comp. rend. Soc. de biol. 127:* 92-94, 1938.
Mercier, L. Hérédité du lymphosarcome de la souris: Resultats comfirmatifs. *Compt. rend. Soc. de biol. 133:* 29-31, 1940.
Mercier, L., and Gosselin, L. Hérédité au lymphosarcome de la souris. Hypothése explicative de cette hérédité. *Bull. de l'Acad. Med.,* [*Paris*], *109:* 196, 1933.
Mercier, L., and Gosselin, L. Charactéristiques d'une lignée de souris atteintes de lymphosarcome. *Compt. rend. Soc. de biol. 119:* 18-20, 1935.
Mider, G. B., and Morton, J. J. The effect of methylcholanthrene on the latent period of lymphomatosis in dilute brown mice. *Am. J. Cancer 37:* 355-363, 1939.
Mider, G. B., and Morton, J. J. Relative importance of local and constitutional effects of methylcholanthrene in the production of skin tumors in the mouse. *J. Nat. Cancer Inst. 1:* 41-44, 1940.
Miller, E. W., and Pybus, F. C. The effect of oestrone on mice of three inbred strains with special reference to the mammary glands. *J. Path. & Bact. 54:* 155-168, 1942.
Miller, E. W., and Pybus, F. C. The inheritance of cancer in mice with special reference to mammary carcinoma. *Cancer Research 5:* 84-93, 1945.
Morgan, W. C. The relation of the lethal yellow (A^y) gene to pulmonary tumor formation and obesity in an inbred strain of mice. *J. Nat. Cancer Inst. 11:* 263-268, 1950.

MORRIS, H. P., DUBNIK, C. S., and DALTON, A. J. Effect of prolonged ingestion of thiourea on mammary tumors in adult C3H mice. *J. Nat. Cancer Inst. 7:* 159-169, 1946.

MORTON, J. J., and MIDER, G. B. Production of lymphomatosis in mice of known genetic constitution. *Science 87:* 327-328, 1938.

MORTON, J. J., MIDER, G. B., LUCE-CLAUSEN, E. M., and MAHONEY, E. B. The effect of visible light on the development in mice of skin tumors and leukemia induced by carcinogens. *Cancer Research 11:* 559-561, 1951.

MÜHLBOCK, O. On the susceptibility of different inbred strains of mice for oestrone. *Acta Brevia Neerlandica 15:* 18-20, 1947.

MÜHLBOCK, O. The oestrone-sensitivity of the mammary gland in female mice of various strains. *Acta Brevia Neerlandica 16:* 22-27, 1948.

MÜHLBOCK, O. The sensitivity of the mammary gland to oestrone in different strains of mice with and without mammary tumor agent. *Acta Endocrinol. 3:* 105-110, 1949.

MÜHLBOCK, O. Note on the influence of the number of litters upon the incidence of mammary tumors in mice. *J. Nat. Cancer Inst. 10:* 1259-1262, 1950.

MÜHLBOCK, O. Hormonale ovariumtumoren na rontgenbestraling. *Nederl. Tijdschr. v. geneesk. 95:* 915-919, 1951.

MULLER, H. J. Progress and prospects in human genetics. *Am. J. Human Genetics 1:* 1-18, 1949.

MURPHY, D. P. *Heredity in Uterine Cancer.* Cambridge, Mass., Harvard University Press, 1952.

MURRAY, J. A. Cancerous ancestry, and the incidence of cancer in mice. *Fourth Sci. Rep., Imp. Cancer Res. Fund,* pp. 114-130, 1911.

MURRAY, J. A. Tar-cancer induction in mice with spontaneous malignant new growths. *Ninth Sci. Rep., Imp. Cancer Res. Fund,* pp. 83-88, 1930.

MURRAY, W. S. Studies on the inheritance of mammary carcinoma in the mouse: Concentration of the extrachromosomal factor: Physiological stability of the individual. *Cancer Research 1:* 123-129, 1941.

MURRAY, W. S., and LITTLE, C. C. The genetics of mammary tumor incidence in mice. *Genetics 20:* 466-496, 1935a.

MURRAY, W. S., and LITTLE, C. C. Further data on the existence of extra-chromosomal influence on the incidence of mammary tumors in mice. *Science 82:* 228-230, 1935b.

MURRAY, W. S., and LITTLE, C. C. Extrachromosomal influence in relation to the incidence of mammary and non-mammary tumors in mice. *Am. J. Cancer 27:* 516-518, 1936.

MURRAY, W. S., and LITTLE, C. C. Chromosomal and extrachromosomal influence in relation to the incidence of mammary tumors in mice. *Am. J. Cancer 37:* 536-552, 1939.

NEEL, J. B., and FALLS, H. F. The rate of mutation of the gene responsible for retinoblastoma in man. *Science 114:* 419-422, 1951.

NETTLESHIP, A., and HENSHAW, P. S. Induction of pulmonary tumors in mice with ethyl carbamate (urethane). *J. Nat. Cancer Inst. 4:* 309-319, 1943.

ORR, J. W. Mammary carcinoma in mice following intranasal administration of methylcholanthrene. *J. Path. & Bact. 55:* 483-488, 1943.

ORR, J. W. The induction of pulmonary adenomata in mice by urethane. *Brit. J. Cancer 1:* 311-316, 1947.

PAN, S. C., and GARDNER, W. U. Induction of malignant tumors by methylcholanthrene in transplanted uterine cornua and cervices of mice. *Cancer Research 8:* 613-622, 1948.

PARODI, A. Sulla reagione individuale del topo all' azione encogena del catrame. *Bol. Soc. ital. di. biol.* Sp. No. 5, 1927.

PASSEY, R. D., DMOCHOWSKI, L., ASTBURY, W. T., and REED, R. Preliminary electron microscope investigations of some human material. *J. Path. & Bact. 61:* 492, 1949.

PASSEY, R. D., DMOCHOWSKI, L., ASTBURY, W. T., REED, R., and EAVES, G. Electron microscope studies of human breast cancer. *Nature 167:* 643-644, 1951.

PENROSE, L. S., MACKENZIE, H. J., and KARN, M. N. A genetical study of human mammary cancer. *Brit. J. Cancer 2:* 168-176, 1948.

PYBUS, F. C., and MILLER, E. W. Spontaneous bone tumors of mice. *Am. J. Cancer 33:* 98-111, 1938a.

PYBUS, F. C., and MILLER, E. W. A sex difference in the incidence of bone tumors in mice. *Am. J. Cancer 34:* 248-251, 1938b.

REINHARD, M. C., and CANDEE, C. F. Influence of sex and heredity on the development of tar tumors. *Am. J. Cancer 16:* 640-644, 1932.

ROBSON, J. M., and BONSER, G. M. Production of mammary carcinomas in mice of a susceptible strain by the synthetic oestrogen, triphenylethylene. *Nature 142:* 836, 1938.

RUSCH, H. P., and BAUMAN, C. A. Tumor production in mice with ultraviolet irradiation. *Am. J. Cancer 35:* 55-62, 1939.

RUSSELL, B. R. G. The experimental production of tar sarcoma in mice and rats. *Eighth Sc. Rep., Imp. Cancer Res. Fund, pp.* 66-70, 1923.

RUSSELL, E. S. A comparison of benign and "malignant" tumors in *Drosophila melanogaster. J. Exper. Zool. 84:* 636-685, 1940.

RUSSELL, E. S. The inheritance of tumors in *Drosophila melanogaster* with special reference to an isogenic strain of st sr tumor 36a. *Genetics 27:* 612-618, 1942.

SCHABAD, L. M. Les tumeurs primitives du poumon dans la descendance des souris badigeonnées au goudron. *Compt. rend. Soc. de biol. 99:* 1550-1551, 1928.

SCHABAD, L. M. Studien über primäre Lungenschwülste bei maüsen und ihr Verhalten zum Steinkohlenteer als kancerogenem Faktor. *Ztschr. f. Krebsforsch. 30:* 24-59, 1929.

SCHARRER, B., and LOCKHEAD, M. S. Tumors in the invertebrates: A review. *Cancer Research 10:* 403-419, 1950.

SEELIG, M. G., and COOPER, Z. D. A review of recent literature of tar cancer (1927-1931 Incl.) *Am. J. Cancer 17:* 589-667, 1933.

SHIMKIN, M. B., and ANDERVONT, H. B. Effect of foster nursing on the induction of mammary and testicular tumors in mice injected with stilbestrol. *J. Nat. Cancer Inst. 2:* 611-621, 1942.

SIEMENS, W., and KOHN, E. *Ztschr. Induct. Abstamm-u. Veerb. Lehre. 38:* 1, 1925.

SIEMENS, H. W., and KOHN, E. Studien über Verebung von Hautkrankheiten: Xeroderma pigmentosum (mit Mitteilung von 5 neuen Fällen). *Ztschr. f. indukt. Abstammungs-und Vererbungslehre 38:* 1-61, 1925.

SILBERBERG, M., SILBERBERG, R., and LEIDLER, H. V. Effect of anterior hypophyseal transplants on intrasplenic ovarian grafts. *Cancer Research 11:* 624-628, 1951.

SLYE, M., HOLMES, H. F., and WELLS, H. G. Spontaneous tumors of liver, associated frequently with other primary growths (mammary gland and lung). *J. Med. Research 33:* 171-182, 1915-16.

SLYE, M., HOLMES, H. F., and WELLS, H. G. Primary spontaneous tumors in the kidneys and adrenals of mice. *J. Cancer Research 6:* 305-336, 1921.

SMITH, F. W. The relationship of the inherited hormonal influence to the production of adrenal cortical tumors by castration. *Cancer Research 8:* 641-652, 1948.

SMITH, F. W., and STRONG, L. C. Studies on gastric neoplasia in mice: The histogenesis and influence of some endocrine factors. *J. Nat. Cancer Inst. 10:* 423-428, 1949.

SMITHERS, D. W. Family histories of 459 patients with cancer of the breast. *Brit. J. Cancer 2:* 163-167, 1948.

STARK, M. B. An hereditary tumor in *Drosophila. J. Cancer Research 3:* 279-301, 1918.

STARK, M. B. An hereditary tumor. *J. Exper. Zool. 27:* 509-529, 1919a.

STARK, M. B. A benign tumor that is hereditary in *Drosophila. Proc. Nat. Acad. Sc. 5:* 573-580, 1919b.

STARK, M. B., and BRIDGES, C. B. The linkage relations of a benign tumor in *Drosophila. Genetics 11:* 249-266, 1926.

STARK, M. B. The origin of certain hereditary tumors in *Drosophila. Am. J. Cancer 31:* 253-267, 1937.

STERN, K. Reticulo-endothelial activity in mice of inbred strains. *Cancer Research 9:* 554-555, 1949.

STEWART, H. L., and ANDERVONT, H. B. Pathologic observations on adenomatous lesion of stomach in mice of strain I. *Arch. Path. 26:* 1009-1022, 1938.

STRONG, L. C. The genetic appearance of spontaneous carcinoma of the mammary gland in C3H mice. *Am. J. Cancer 25:* 599-602, 1935.

STRONG, L. C. Genetic analysis of induction of tumors by methylcholanthrene, with a note on the origin of the NH strain of mice. *Am. J. Cancer 39:* 347-349, 1940.

STRONG, L. C. Genetic analysis of induction of tumors by methylcholanthrene: The influence of spindle cell sarcoma and of carcinoma of the skin upon each other. *Cancer Research 1:* 572-574, 1941.

STRONG, L. C. Genetic analysis of induction of tumors by methylcholanthrene: Absence of the sex influence when a large dose of the carcinogen is administered. *Arch. Path. 36:* 58-63, 1943.

STRONG, L. C. Genetic analysis of the induction of tumors by methylcholanthrene. *Arch. Path. 37:* 131-135, 1944.

STRONG, L. C. Genetic analysis of the induction of tumors by methylcholanthrene: XI. Germinal mutations and other sudden biological changes following the subcutaneous injection of methylcholanthrene. *Proc. Nat. Acad. Sc. 31:* 290-293, 1945a.

STRONG, L. C. Genetic analysis of the induction of tumors by methylcholanthrene: IX. Induced and spontaneous adenocarcinomas of the stomach in mice. *J. Nat. Cancer Inst. 5:* 339-356, 1945b.

STRONG, L. C. Genetic analysis of the induction of tumors by methylcholanthrene: VIII. Two mutations arising in mice following injection of methylcholanthrene. *Arch. Path. 39:* 232-236, 1945c.

STRONG, L. C. Further observations on the genetic nature of gastric cancer in mice. *J. Nat. Cancer Inst. 7:* 305-308, 1947.

STRONG, L. C. Test of correlation between the pink-eye gene and susceptibility to induced fibrosarcoma in mice. *Cancer Research 11:* 42-45, 1951.

Strong, L. C., and Hollander, W. F. Effects of methylcholanthrene in pregnant mice. *J. Nat. Cancer Inst. 8:* 79-82, 1947.

Strong, L. C., and Smith, G. M. Benign hepatomas in mice of the CBA strain. *Am. J. Cancer 27:* 279-284, 1936.

Strong, L. C., and Smith, G. M. The local induction of carcinoma of the mammary gland by methylcholanthrene. *Yale J. Biol. & Med. 11:* 589-592, 1939.

Strong, L. C., Smith, G. M., and Gardner, W. U. The induction of tumors by 3:4:5:6-dibenzcarbazole in male mice of the CBA strain which develops spontaneous hepatoma. *Yale J. Biol. & Med. 10:* 335-346, 1938.

Suntzeff, V., Burns, E. L., Moskop, M., and Loeb, L. The effect of injections of estrin on the incidence of mammary cancer in various strains of mice. *Am. J. Cancer 27:* 229-245, 1936.

Suntzeff, V., Burns, E. L., Moskop, M., and Loeb, L. On proliferative changes taking place in the epithelium and vagina and cervix of mice with advancing age and under the influence of experimentally administered estrogenic hormones. *Am. J. Cancer 32:* 256-289, 1938.

Trentin, J. J. Vaginal sensitivity to estrogen as related to mammary tumor incidence in mice. *Cancer Research 10:* 580-583, 1950.

Trentin, J. J. The effect of the presence or absence of the milk factor and of castration on mammary response to estrogen in male mice of strains of known mammary tumor incidence. *Cancer Research 11:* 286-287, 1951.

Tsutsui, H. Uber das künstlich erzeugte canceroid bei der maus. *Gann 12:* 17, 1918.

Twort, C. C., and Twort, J. M. Cancer susceptibility in relation to colour of mice. *J. Hyg. 32:* 557-572, 1932.

Vazquez-Lopez, E. The effects of thiourea on the development of spontaneous tumors on mice. *Brit. J. Cancer 3:* 401-413, 1949.

Wassink, W. F. Cancer et hérédité. *Genetica 17:* 103-144, 1935.

Waters, N. F. Breeding for resistance and susceptibility to avian-lymphomatosis. *Poult. Sc. 24:* 259-269, 1945.

Waters, N. F. Types of lymphomatosis among different inbred lines of chickens. *Poult. Sc. 25:* 501-508, 1946.

Waters, N. F., and Prickett, C. O. The development of families of chickens free of lymphomatosis. *Poult. Sc. 23:* 321-333, 1944.

Weller, C. V. The inheritance of retinoblastoma and its relationship to practical eugenics. *Cancer Research 1:* 517, 1941.

White, J., and Stewart, H. L. Intestinal adenocarcinoma and intra-abdominal hemangio-endothelioma in mice ingesting methylcholanthrene. *J. Nat. Cancer Inst. 3:* 331-347, 1942.

Wilson, I. T. Two new hereditary tumors in *Drosophila*. *Genetics 9:* 343-362, 1924.

Woglom, W. H. Experimental tar cancer. *Arch. Path. 2:* 533-576, 709-752, 1926.

Woolley, G. W. Unpublished data, 1951.

Woolley, G. W., and Chute, R. Effect of steroids on adrenal tumor formation in mice. *Conf. Metabol. Asp. Conval., Trans.* 16th Meeting, N. P., pp. 65-79, 1947.

Woolley, G. W., Fekete, E., and Little, C. C. Mammary tumor development in mice ovariectomized at birth. *Proc. Nat. Acad. Sc. 25:* 277-279, 1939.

Woolley, G. W., Fekete, E., and Little, C. C. Differences between high and low breast tumor strains of mice when ovariectomized at birth. *Proc. Soc. Exper. Biol. & Med. 45:* 796-798, 1940.

Woolley, G. W., and Little, C. C. The incidence of adrenal cortical carcinoma in gonadectomized female mice of the extreme dilution strain: I. Observations on the adrenal cortex. *Cancer Research 5:* 193-202, 1945.

Woolley, G. W., and Little, C. C. Prevention of adrenal cortical carcinoma by diethylstilbestrol. *Proc. Nat. Acad. Sc. 32:* 239-240, 1946.

Yamagiwa, K., and Ichikawa, K. Experimentelle Studie über die Pathogenese der Epithelialgeschwülste: I. Mitt. d. med. Fak. d. Univ. zu Tokyo *5:* 15, 1915.

Yamagiwa, K., and Ichikawa, K. Experimental study of the pathogenesis of carcinoma. *J. Cancer Research 3:* 1-30, 1918.

Zimmerman, H. M., and Arnold, H. Experimental brain tumors: II. Tumors produced with benzpyrene. *Am. J. Path. 19:* 939-956, 1943.

Zimmerman, H. M., and Arnold, H. Experimental brain tumors: Incidence in different strains of mice. *Cancer Research 4:* 98-101, 1944.

CHAPTER 12

Hormonal Factors in Experimental Carcinogenesis

William U. Gardner
Carroll A. Pfeiffer
John J. Trentin
J. T. Wolstenholme

The consideration of hormonal functions within the body implies two fundamental requirements: (1) a source of a particular hormone within the body (effector); and (2) an organ, or tissue, or tissues responding to the hormone (respondor or end organ). Unfortunately many hormone mechanisms are not as simple as these, that is, direct effector-end organ relationships. Effectors themselves are often "end organs." Factors such as augmentors or inhibitors, often other hormones, acting either on the effector or the end organ, sometimes intervene. Furthermore, the role of systems within the body for the destruction, inactivation or excretion of the hormones can alter the internal environment within which the effector-end organ systems function. Therefore at least four different and possibly variable factors must be considered in the analysis of hormonal responses:

1. variations in hormone production
2. variations in end organ sensitivity
3. differences in the utilization, destruction or excretion of hormones
4. presence or absence of augmenting or inhibiting influences.

In general the hormones are not species specific, although our information is limited because of the small amounts of these substances stored within the body, and hence the few sources from which they have been obtained. For example, even though estradiol was obtained from pigs' ovaries we assume that it is the estrogen produced by animals of other species. The same end organs in animals from different species usually respond similarily to specific chemicals. In both instances, however, exceptions to the specificity of production and of end organ responses can be cited. Furthermore, the mechanisms for the inactivation, destruction, or excretion of hormones may differ among animals of different species. Extrapolation of conclusions derived from observations on one species to another species must be considered carefully, and this point must be emphasized early in this discussion.

Again, hormones in general quantitatively regulate specific functions rather than establish qualitatively specific functions; in other words they control rates of reaction within the body rather than initiate reactions which cells, without hormones, could not effect. The body can consume oxygen in the absence of the thyroid, a wound can heal in the absence of the pituitary, but the thyroid and pituitary growth hormones are well-known regulators of metabolism and growth. This generalization may seem inadequate when other end organs are considered. For example, ovarian follicular growth is completed in the presence of gonadotropic hormones, by substances without other proven effects upon the body. Nevertheless, early follicular growth occurs in the absence of the pituitary gland. Through mechanisms regulating rates of response, the body adapts itself throughout ontogeny, and in a constantly altering internal and external environment.

Why consider general problems of endocrine physiology in an introduction to endocrines in relation to cancer? Endocrinology shares much in common with cancer; both endocrine reactions, for the greater part, and cancer are described by the end results produced rather than by specific processes involved in the attainment of these end results. But if the origin of cancer is not a potentiality of an organ or tissue of a body it seems improbable that modification of the endocrine environment could incite cancer. Conversely, if a potentiality for cancer exists, a suitable endocrine environment may accelerate or promote that potentiality or, on the other hand, prevent its expression. The possibility that abnormal endocrine environments can create or destroy cancer seems remote—the hypothesis that abnormal endocrine environments may result in the expression of potentialities of the tissues, less likely to be expressed under a "normal" environment, seems tenable. Such a hypothesis places endocrine influences as indirect causes of cancer. Proof that they are direct causes of cancer does not exist.

In the following presentation the estrogenic, progestational, androgenic, adrenal cortical hormones and certain hormones of the pituitary will be considered. The terms "estrogen" and "estrogenic" will refer to all substances to which the animal responds in at least one common manner—vaginal epithelial proliferation and cornification—irrespective of whether or not the substance is similar chemically to those which may be produced within a living organism—in other words, whether or not it is a hormone. Evidence exists that estriol, estradiol, and estrone are produced in animals of some species and these substances can be considered to be hormones. Estradiol benzoate, stilbestrol, hexestrol, triphenylethylene, and many other substances, possessing estrogenic activity, are not hormones, although they may be very difficult to distinguish physiologically from hormones. Occasional reference will be made to specific chemicals when this seems warranted. It is possible that the presentation should be more specific since qualitative differences in response to specific chemicals, not yet revealed, may still become apparent. The methods of administration of hormones or physiologically active chemicals will often be mentioned, perhaps to the point of boredom, but the methods, solvent, site of injection, concentration, and frequency of injection can determine the levels and continuity of concentration within the body. Quantitative aspects should probably be emphasized more but the information available, when considered with the other variables mentioned above, is too often inadequate.

Several extensive reviews on the action of hormones in carcinogenesis or tumorigenesis have been published in recent years,[28, 59, 115, 161, 231, 232, 250, 254, 287, 400] In part this review will be a duplication of these but less stress will be placed on the non-neoplastic or questionably neoplastic responses that have been reported. This does not mean that the metaplasia and the abnormal histologic changes that accompany prolonged exposure to some of the steroid chemicals are not of importance, but that an attempt has been made to emphasize tumorigenic or carcinogenic responses or their control. For brevity much data will be presented in tabular form. Tables can be misleading in that they may group data with hidden variables but they do permit rapid perusual of masses of data. For example, animals given different amounts of some chemical or castrated at different ages, may not be adequately differentiated in any one table without multiple headings, but a brief table may present qualitative effects of the chemical or of ovariectomy in general. Transmitted, genetic, strain-limited or species-limited qualities may seem to receive undue consideration. The differences afford, however, an excellent point of departure for inquiry into mechanisms of action or of response and thus seem to merit the emphasis given.

MAMMARY TUMORS

Spontaneous mammary tumors occur in significant numbers in experimental animals of relatively few species, notably the mouse, rat, dog, and rabbit. Those of the rat are usually benign but transplantable fibroadenomas (see Bryan *et al.*[42] for references). A degree of dependence upon hormonal environment is indicated by a greater frequency of successful transplantation in female than in male hosts.[170]

The mammary tumors of rabbits are of two types.[156, 157] One type arises as a benign papilloma in association with pre-existing cystic mastitis. The other arises as an adenoma in previously normal breast tissue. Members of both groups become progressively more autonomous with development of invasiveness, metastases, and transplantability.

Spontaneous mammary tumors in the dog exhibit a relatively wide range of morphology and malignancy.[291] They occur usually in old females, with a few breeds showing a definite predisposition.

The typical mouse mammary tumor is an adenocarcinoma of acinar origin. Growth is rapid, and of an expansive rather than invasive nature. The average survival time in the case of the A, C3H, and DBA strains varies from fifty-nine days to about seventy-five days.[387] Metastases occur by way of the blood vascular system and are found usually in the lungs. The frequency of metastases is low in the early stages but increases considerably in the terminal stages. One hundred

TABLE 3. ATTEMPTS TO INDUCE MAMMARY TUMORS IN CASTRATED MALE MICE OF HIGH TUMOR STRAINS BY MEANS OF OVARIAN TRANSPLANTS

Author	*Strain*	*Site of transplantation**	*Age at transplantation*	*No. of mice*	*No. with mammary tumors*
Loeb [253]	8½+328, English, English+European hybrids	SC	2.5–5 mo.	19	0
Cori [70]	Marsh	IP	2–6 mo.	not stated	0
Murray [297, 298]	DBA	SC	4–6 wk.	210	38
	"	unimplanted controls	—	241	0
DeJongh and Korteweg [79]	not stated	not stated	not stated	16	9
	"	unimplanted controls	—	4	0
Loeb, Blumenthal, and Kirtz [255]	A, C3H, D and others	not stated	not stated	not stated	Tumors appeared but numbers not stated
Huseby and Bittner [191]	F_1 hybrids of A×C3H	SC	4–6 wk.	31	27
		SC^a	4–6 wk.	39	1
Silberberg and Silberberg [368, 369]	A	SC	1 mo.	27	1
	"	SC^b	1 mo.	26	8
	"	SC	7 mo.	26	0
	"	SC^b	7 mo.	29	0

* SC, subcutaneous; IP, intraperitoneal; ^{a}, intact males; ^{b}, pituitaries as well as ovaries grafted.

and twenty tumor-bearing control female mice of the Strong A strain survived an average of fifty-nine days and metastases occurred in 48 per cent.[385]

Although the mouse mammary tumors require certain definite hormonal conditions for their inception, and some may show signs of early hormonal dependence,[99a, 99b] they eventually become largely independent of hormonal environment, continue to grow following ovariectomy or hypophysectomy,[215, 121] and transplant to either male or female mice of the same strain. Since mammary tumors of the mouse have been most extensively studied, the present review will be confined largely to this species.

MAMMARY TUMORS OF MICE

Natural History

The involvement of hormonal influences in the genesis of mammary tumors in mice was early indicated by the sex-limited nature of the spontaneous occurrence of such tumors. Although mammary tumors occur in 90 per cent or more of female mice of some inbred strains, they rarely, if ever, occur in males. (An exceptional strain will be mentioned later.) Hormonal involvement was again implicated by the early observation of Lathrop and Loeb[235, 236] that the incidence of mammary tumors among breeding female mice of most strains was significantly higher than among virgins of the same stock. In most inbred strains showing a high incidence of mammary tumors in breeding females, the virgins also have a high incidence of mammary tumors, although generally not quite as high as the breeders. The Strong A strain shows the greatest difference in incidence of mammary tumors among breeding females (83.6 per cent of 1093 mice) and virgins (4.9 per cent of 223 mice).[24]

Ablation and Transplantation of Ovaries

In 1916 Lathrop and Loeb observed that in mice with a mammary tumor incidence of 60 to 70 per cent, ovariectomy at or before the age of 6 months reduced the incidence to 9 per cent.[236] Ovariectomy at 3 to 4 months completely or almost completely prevented the appearance of mammary tumors, at 5 to 7 months it lowered the incidence and increased the age at appearance of tumors, while ovariectomy after 7 months of age had little effect on incidence of mammary tumors.[253] These findings have been essentially confirmed by others.[70, 297, 299, 300]

Despite initial failures, mammary tumors were eventually induced in castrated male mice of high tumor strains by means of ovarian transplants (Table 3). These experiments demonstrated that, in addition to an inherited susceptibility, ovarian activity was essential for the spontaneous development of mammary tumors in mice.

Endocrine Imbalance

Exception to the low incidence of mammary tumors among female mice of susceptible strains ovariectomized at an early age occurred in those strains that develop adrenal hyperplasia after early castration.[96, 118, 423, 425] The mammary tumors were always preceded by adrenal hyperplasia or tumor formation, and by uterine, vaginal, and mammary changes indicative of estrogenic stimulation.[96] Ovariectomized mice of the NH strain bearing adrenal tumors excreted four times as much estrogen as intact normal females.[84] What appeared at first to be a high incidence of mammary tumors in the absence of estrogenic stimulation proved to be the result of an induced endocrine imbalance involving substitution of ovarian secretory activity by an adrenal secretion of estrogen.

During a five-year period, 48 spontaneous mammary tumors occurred among male mice of the H strain.[8, 9] The incidence of mammary tumors among females of the strain was 54.9 per cent. This is in striking contrast to the usual sex-limited occurrence of mammary tumors. Males of the H strain also show Leydig cell hypertrophy of the testis, similar to that observed in males of certain other strains following estrogen treatment. The spontaneous occurrence in males of the H strain of two lesions which occur rarely in males of other strains except after injection of estrogen is suggestive of a spontaneous endocrine imbalance involving an abnormal secretion of estrogen.

Spontaneous mammary tumors occur rarely in rabbits and rats of most strains. However, Greene[156] developed strains of rabbits showing predisposition to cystic disease and cancer of the mammary gland. Associated changes in the uterine mucosa, pituitary, and adrenals, identical to those following prolonged estrogen administration, indicated a spontaneous endocrine imbalance as a probable factor in the genesis of the breast tumors.

In the Albany strain of rats there appeared over a period of years a spontaneous endocrine imbalance involving hyposecretion of the pituitary, failure of ovulation and of luteinization, with consequent prolonged estrus, decreased fertility, increased fetal resorption, prolonged gestation, and a reduced rate of body growth.[42, 44, 418, 429] During the same period there also appeared among the females of this strain a high rate of spontaneous benign fibroadenomas of the mammary gland. A positive correlation existed between the severity of the endocrine imbalance and the appearance of mammary tumors, suggesting a causal relationship.

Exogenous Hormones

1. *Estrogen.* Lacassagne first induced mammary tumors in male mice by means of the purified estrogens.[221] Many investigators have subsequently induced mammary tumors in male mice, or increased the incidence of tumors in non-breeding females, by means of estrogen administration.[26, 33, 50, 53, 71, 117, 144, 163, 205, 230, 278, 363, 392, 398] The incidences of mammary tumors appearing in male or non-breeding female mice of a susceptible strain following adequate estrogen treatment are generally comparable, and approach the spontaneous incidence among breeding females of the same strain. In the very low tumor strains, such as the C57, estrogen is ineffective in the induction of mammary tumors.

Weekly injections of 100 r. u. of estradiol benzoate into C3H male mice, starting at 2 weeks of age, did not result in mammary tumors unless continued for at least eight weeks. Two injections of 1500 r. u. each, representing a greater total dose, but given over three days, produced no tumors.[50]

With prolonged estrogen treatment the incidence of mammary tumors increases with daily or weekly doses until a toxic level of estrogen is reached, above which the incidence of tumors is lower and the mammary glands stunted.[115, 119]

The injection of numerous natural and synthetic estrogens has resulted in mammary tumors in mice; their relative effectiveness is in general directly proportional to their physiologic activity. (For review see Gardner[115, 126] and Shimkin.[360])

Estrogenic stimulation increases the number of breast tumors appearing in mice after exposure to the carcinogenic hydrocarbons. Tumors appear readily in females or estrogen-treated males, but not in males receiving the chemical carcinogen only. (For review see Dmochowski.[83]) The same relationship was observed in rats, although male rats receiving methylcholanthrene alone showed a low incidence of breast tumors.[359]

Because of the role of estrogen in the experimental initiation of mammary adenocarcinomas in mice, it is of interest to consider its effects in other species. Spontaneous mammary carcinomas are uncommon in rats of most stocks but such tumors have followed prolonged estrogen treatment.[66, 87, 89, 150, 151, 270, 308, 310] One mammary adenocarcinoma developed in an estrogen-treated rabbit.[151] Prolonged treatment with large doses of estrogen has not resulted in mammary cancer in monkeys.[91, 119, 151, 165, 331] In the estrogen-treated guinea pig, breast tumors are very rare.[250] The appearance of breast cancer in women following estrogen administration is difficult to interpret. More suggestive, but still open to question, are the reports of breast cancer in estrogen-treated men.[1, 189]

2. *Progesterone.* The higher incidence of mammary tumors in breeding female mice than in virgins, and the demonstration that pseudopregnancy increases the incidence of mammary tumors in virgin mice of the A strain,[239] suggest the possibility that progesterone in addition to estrogen enhances the development of mammary tumors. However, the similarities of some of the biologic actions of testosterone and progesterone suggest a possible tumor-inhibiting effect of progesterone. Progesterone has been variously reported (a) to have no effect on,[61, 115, 229] (b) to increase,[393] (c) to decrease[169] the mammary tumor expectancy of mice.

The relatively long intervals between injections, and low dosages of progesterone used in most instances, constitute an important limitation. Hooker and Forbes[178] have determined the blood level of progesterone in mice at different time intervals after the cessation of progesterone administration. In castrated mice receiving 6 or 7 daily subcutaneous injections of 0.5 mg. of progesterone in oil, the plasma progesterone level was relatively high at three, six, nine and twelve hours after the last injection. However, at twenty-four hours the plasma progesterone level had fallen considerably. The rapid removal of progesterone indicates the need of daily injections or of subcutaneous pellets of progesterone in experiments where prolonged exposure of tissues to effective amounts of progesterone is desired.

Virgin female mice of a susceptible stock given progesterone pellets, showed an earlier appearance of mammary tumors.[397] Two littermate controlled groups of young intact virgin female hybrid mice (C3H ♀ × A ♂) were set up, each containing 60 animals. One group received a 14±1 mg. pellet of progesterone every twenty-eight days. To date, after eighteen months of treatment, 46 of the 60 treated mice have had mammary tumors, while only 18 tumors have appeared in the control group. Since 40 mice of the control group and 9 of the progesterone-treated group are still alive and nontumorous, it is too early to know whether the ultimate incidence of mammary tumors will be significantly different in the two groups.

In virgin female rats receiving 2-acetylaminofluorene, the incidence of mammary carcinoma was not increased by simultaneous administration of estrogen but was increased significantly by progesterone.[65]

3. *Androgens.* Androgens administered in adequate amounts to female mice of tumor-susceptible strains lowered the incidence of mammary tumors.[168, 201, 233, 262, 301] Mice so treated possessed underdeveloped mammary glands and atrophic ovaries.[233] In mice treated with exogenous estrogen and large doses of testosterone propionate, the development of the mammary glands was partially inhibited, and the incidence of mammary tumors was lower than in estrogen-treated controls.[128, 234] It seems probable therefore that androgens suppress mammary tumor formation in mice both by inhibition of ovarian function and of the mammary-stimulating effect of estrogen.

Intact testes also suppressed mammary tumor formation in mice bearing ovarian grafts. Mammary tumors developed in 27 of 31 castrated males bearing ovarian grafts; a tumor developed in 1 of 39 noncastrated males bearing ovarian grafts.[191, 193]

TABLE 4. EFFECT OF CASTRATION AND AGE AT INITIATION OF TREATMENT ON MAMMARY TUMOR INCIDENCE OF MALE C3H MICE RECEIVING .03 MG. ESTRADIOL BENZOATE WEEKLY FOR FIVE MONTHS

Condition	*Age at start of treatment*	*No. reaching tumor age*	*Mammary tumors* (%)	*Mean tumor age* (mo.)	*Mean age at death* (mo.)
Castrated	4 wk.	18	44.4	9.7	12.9
Castrated	4 mo.	40	30.0	12.8	13.0
Castrated	7 mo.	34	13.8	13.0	
Intact	4 wk.	19	15.8	10.7	12.8
Intact	4 mo.	25	4.0	17.0	10.8
Intact	7 mo.	29	2.9	12.0	

From Silberberg and Silberberg.[366, 369a]

The incidence of mammary tumors in male mice of strains C3H and D was lower when the mice were older at onset of estrogen treatment. A smaller decrease in the incidence of tumors occurred in female mice of the C3H strain with increasing age at onset of treatment.[260] The extent of testicular participation in the observed effect was studied by injecting both intact and castrated C3H mice with 0.03 mg. of estradiol benzoate weekly for five months starting at 4 weeks of age and at 4 and 7 months of age (Table 4).[366, 369a] The castrated mice had a higher incidence of tumors than the intact mice. However, a difference in tumor incidence with age at start of treatment was observed even among the castrated mice. The authors concluded that the age factor was independent of testicular function but acted synergistically with it.

The higher incidence of tumors in estrogen-treated castrated mice than in treated intact males is of interest. A protective action by the testis might well be expected in those few strains such as the Strong A and JK, and the Andervont Strain C or hybrids thereof, which during continuous estrogen treatment show hypertrophy of the testicular interstitial cells and testicular tumors that often secrete androgen. Data suggestive of such an effect in the A strain and its hybrids under continuous estrogen stimulus are given in Tables 5 and 6. However, the level of estrogen used in Table 4 is sufficient to cause marked atrophy of the testes and accessories in the C3H strain for as long as treatment is continued.

TABLE 5. INCIDENCE OF MAMMARY TUMORS IN CASTRATED AND INTACT STRAIN A MALE MICE RECEIVING 3.0 MG. TRIPHENYLETHYLENE WEEKLY UNTIL DEATH

Condition	*Androgen available, estimated by pelvic organs*	*No. of mice living 43 weeks or more*	*Mammary tumors* No.	%
Intact	+ +	52	1	1.9
Castrated	–	36	5	13.9

From Armstrong and Bonser.[7]

TABLE 6. INCIDENCE OF MAMMARY TUMORS IN CASTRATED AND INTACT HYBRID MALE MICE DERIVED FROM THE A STRAIN AND BEARING A 25 PER CENT STILBESTROL IN CHOLESTEROL PELLET*

Hybrid	*Condition*	*Age at start* (mo.)	*No. of mice*	*Mammary tumors* (%)	*Mean age at death* (da.)	*Mean age of tumor development* (da.)
C3H ♀ × A ♂	Intact	1–5	14	57	448	426
"	Castrated	1–5	16	81	507	445
CBA ♀ × A ♂	Intact	4–4½	17	18	586	604
"	Castrated	4–4½	15	80	648	635

* Interstitial cell hypertrophy and testicular tumors occurred among the intact males of both hybrid groups.
From Trentin.[397]

It is interesting to speculate, therefore, that the lower incidence of mammary tumors in the intact C3H males may have been the result of the recovery of the testes which occurs following cessation of estrogen treatment, and that had continuous estrogen treatment been used no protective action by the testes would have been observed in this strain.

The limited data on the C3H×A hybrids (Table 6) when broken down on the basis of age at start of treatment, reveal no significant difference in incidence of mammary tumors between the animals started at 1–3 months of age and at 3–5 months of age (Table 7).

TABLE 7. BREAKDOWN OF C3H×A DATA OF TABLE 6, ON BASIS OF AGE AT START OF TREATMENT.

Hybrid	*Condition*	*Age at start* (mo.)	*Mammary tumors* +	–
C3H ♀ × A ♂	Intact	1–3	3	3
"	"	3–5	5	3
"	Castrated	1–3	5	2
"	"	3–5	8	1

From Trentin.[397]

ESTROUS CYCLE

The relationship between experimentally altered exposure to estrogens and the appearance of mammary tumors in mice prompted numerous studies to determine whether the estrous cycles of mice of different strains might show characteristics that could be correlated with a high incidence of mammary tumors and might indicate a high rate of estrogen production. With advancing age the estrous cycles of mice of the low tumor C57 strain were found to diminish more rapidly in frequency and intensity than in animals of the high tumor DBA strain.[213] Shortly thereafter a possible correlation between the incidence of mammary tumors and length and regularity of estrous cycles in mice of a high and a low tumor strain was reported.[164, 223] However, a third strain subsequently studied did not confirm the correlation.[226] The work of a number of other investigators also indicated that no significant and consistent correlation exists between the incidence of mammary tumors and the nature of the estrous cycle.[32, 41, 49, 80, 257, 286, 390] Subsequent studies of the estrous cycle dealing specifically with the effect of the presence or the absence of milk factor will be mentioned later.

ESTROGEN SENSITIVITY

A somewhat higher percentage of positive vaginal smears was obtained from mice of a low tumor strain than from a high tumor strain when both were injected with equal doses of estrogen.[32] Mice of the high tumor DBA strain required more estrogen for a comparable degree of vaginal stimulation than did mice of the low tumor C57 and 0-20 strains.[288, 289, 403] A lower vaginal sensitivity to estrogen existed in the high tumor C3H strain than in the low tumor C and C57 strains.[362] However, no consistent correlation between the incidence of mammary tumors and the vaginal sensitivity to estrogen was observed when mice of the high tumor C3H, CBA, and A strains and the low tumor C57, JK, and N strains were studied.[396]

Inherited Hormonal Influence

Mice of the Strong A strain differ from those of other high mammary tumor strains in that the virgins have a low incidence of mammary tumors.[24] The incidence of tumors among breeding mice of the A strain is directly proportional to the number of litters born.[200] The induction of pseudopregnancy by mating with vasectomized males also increases the incidence of tumors in nonparous mice of the A strain.[239] Thus the effect of breeding appears not to be the result of the bearing of young *per se*, or of lactation, but is probably associated with the hormonal changes of pregnancy. The incidence of mammary tumors in virgin mice of the A strain was increased by estrogen administration[115, 392] or by implantation of several pituitaries from male and female littermates. Pituitary transplantation in ovariectomized females or in males failed to induce mammary tumors.[255, 258, 368]

Bittner[27] suggested that the mammary tumor incidence in virgin mice of susceptible strains might depend upon: (1) rate of production of estrogenic hormones; (2) rate of destruction of these hormones; and (3) threshold of mammary sensitivity to neoplastic change.

The low incidence of tumors in virgin mice of the A strain is genetically determined. Reciprocal hybrids between the A and C3H strains both show a high incidence of tumors among the virgins, approaching that of the C3H strain.[30, 172] On the assumption that a high incidence of tumors in virgin mice is hormonally determined, the term "inherited hormonal influence" has been applied.[28, 30]

In an attempt to demonstrate a difference in hormonal stimulation, the estrous cycles of virgin A and C3H mice, and of both reciprocal hybrids were studied.[80] No difference existed in the average length of cycle, but vaginal opening occurred later in mice of the A strain. The authors point out, however, that the difference between mice of the A and C3H strains represents only two cycles, and that variations in genetic susceptibility to hormonal stimulus may be of greater importance.

Huseby and Bittner[192] transplanted ovaries from Z (C3H) and A mice, and from their F_1 hybrids, into ovariectomized F_1 hybrids. During the first ten months after transplantation no significant difference was observed in the percentage of positive vaginal smears (smears in which epithelial cells were numerically predominant) in the three groups. Beyond this time the percentage of positive smears decreased first in hybrids bearing ovaries from C3H mice, and next in those bearing ovaries from mice of the A strain. The incidence of mammary tumors in the three groups was not greatly different, but tumors developed at a later age in hybrids bearing ovaries of A-strain mice. Since 57 per cent of the latter group had mammary tumors, the A-strain mouse's ovary in itself is not the primary determining factor of a low incidence of tumors in virgin mice of the A strain.

Interesting changes in ovarian morphology were noted. Ovaries from A strain mice contained few adult eosinophilic corpora lutea, while ovaries from C3H mice retained a rather large number of such elements. However, three months after transplantation into F_1 hybrid females, ovaries from A-strain mice showed a considerable increase in number of corpora lutea, and could no longer be distinguished from similarly grafted ovaries from mice of the C3H strain.

Loeb and Kirtz,[258] in reporting an increased incidence of tumors in A-strain mice following pituitary transplantation, noted that the preservation of corpora lutea was distinctly better in the bearers of transplants than in the controls. They suggested the possibility that the function of the corpora lutea might be concerned in the results of transplantation of the anterior lobe of the hypophysis.

Progesterone, administered to virgin C3H×A hybrids, reduced the average age at which tumors appeared.[397] The possibility must be considered that the difference in incidence of tumors between virgin mice of the A strain and of the C3H and other high tumor strains may be due to differences in pituitary secretory activity, possibly related to hormones regulating the persistence or function of corpora lutea.

Mammary Tumor Inciter: Hormonal Implications

In reciprocal crosses between mice of a high tumor and a low tumor strain, the incidences of mammary tumors of the two groups of hybrids approximate that of the maternal strain.[23, 214, 237, 381] By appropriate foster nursing experiments, Bittner[22, 25] localized this extrachromosomal influence as a milk-transmitted mammary tumor inciter. Thus in addition to a genetic susceptibility, and adequate hormonal stimulus, the milk agent constitutes a third prerequisite for a high incidence of spontaneous mammary tumors.

Mice possessing the milk agent had a lower fecal 17-ketosteroid excretion than mice of the same strain free of the agent.[29, 346] This indicated the possibility that the mode of action of the milk agent might involve an alteration of a hormonal mechanism. To date the evidence in this regard is not conclusive.

Little difference was observed in the vaginal sensitivity to estrogen of reciprocal hybrids between the high tumor DBA strain and low tumor C57 strain.[403] No difference was found in the vaginal sensitivity to estrogen of mice of the C3H, C, and C57 strains with and without the milk agent as a result of foster nursing.[362] No effect of the presence or absence of milk agent on vaginal sensitivity to estrogen was observed in mice of the C3H and A strains and in reciprocal crosses between the low tumor C57 and high tumor CBA* strains.[396]

No significant difference in the age at onset of estrus and in the frequency and duration of estrous cycles was observed in mice of the C strain with and without milk agent.[360] The presence of the milk agent increased the number of positive vaginal smears to a considerable extent in both strain-A mice and in F_1 hybrids between mice of the A and C3H strains. The difference was not evident in mice of the C3H strain and was questionable in F_1 hybrids between the C3H and dilute brown strains.[190, 192]

Armstrong[6] foster-nursed mice of the high tumor RIII strain on mice of the low tumor CBA strain with a drop in incidence of tumors from 69 per cent to 27 per cent. Low tumor CBA mice fostered on high tumor RIII females showed an increase in incidence of tumors from less than 1 per cent to 50 per cent.*

* The CBA strain has appeared in the literature as both a high and a low mammary tumor strain. In the first two decades of inbreeding by Dr. Strong the CBA strain was a low tumor strain. In 1935 mammary tumors began appearing in this stock in Dr. Gardner's colony, and at present the CBA strain in both Dr. Strong's and Dr. Gardner's colony is a

Foster nursing had no significant effect on age of vaginal opening, average duration of estrous cycles and of heat in virgin or parous animals, incidence of atypical cycles, and on the menopause. A slight decrease in average duration of heat was observed in the fostered RIII mice when atypical cycles (diestrus longer than seven days or cornification longer than four days) were excluded from consideration.

No change in the sensitivity of the mammary gland to estrogen was found in castrated female mice of the DBA, A, and C57 strains with and without milk agent as a result of foster nursing.[290] Reciprocal fostering of the C3H and C57 strains failed to alter significantly the estrogen-responsiveness of the mammary glands of castrated males of either strain.[396a] Of reciprocal hybrids between the CBA (high-tumor) and C57 strains, castrated males with CBA maternal parents showed greater estrogen-responsiveness of the mammary glands than did the reciprocal hybrid mice.[397] The mammary glands of ovariectomized mice of strains Z (C3H), D2, and A possessing the milk agent showed more vigorous growth (as judged by microscopic sections) during the early stages of response to estrogen, than did those of the same strains without the agent.[369b]

UTERINE TUMORS

Few uterine or uterine cervical tumors have developed in experimental animals under conditions controlled adequately to permit an analysis of their possible humoral etiology. The only outstanding exception is the rabbit.[160] Eighty-three adenomatous tumors of the uterine mucosa were noted in rabbits that underwent prolonged reproductive disturbances. The tumors eventually metastasized and killed their hosts. Approximately 75 per cent of the rabbits 5–6 years of age had uterine adenomata.[158] Strain differences were observed, some lines showing a higher incidence of tumors than others. The tendency for uterine adenomata paralleled that for toxemia of pregnancy. Although rabbits in general acquire uterine tumors more frequently than tumors at other sites,[58, 60, 337] the high incidence in relation to a clinical syndrome involving mammary hypertrophy or mammary cancers, adrenal and pituitary hypertrophy, and hepatic and renal changes characteristic of toxemia of pregnancy is of great interest. Furthermore, the progression of abnormal uterine growth through stages of hyperplasia, dependent neoplasia, and autonomous neoplasia afforded an excellent example of successive stages in carcinogenesis.[159] [See also page 165]

Spontaneous uterine cervical epithelial tumors have been observed in mice of one strain.[140] Interestingly, this strain was lost because of the high incidence

---

high mammary tumor strain. In Dr. Bonser's colony, with which Dr. Armstrong worked, the CBA strain is still a low tumor strain. During the first fourteen years in that laboratory no breast cancers were observed, although in two littermates of the fifty-third generation mammary tumors appeared. However, as mentioned above, foster-nursing on RIII females raised the mammary tumor incidence of their CBA mice to 50 per cent. This suggests the possibility that the spontaneous increases in tumor incidence of this strain may have been the result of spontaneous acquisition of mammary tumor inciter. Such an interpretation must presuppose an original loss of milk agent, or fluctuations in concentration above and below effective levels, since the CBA and C3H strains trace back on the maternal side to common ancestors in which mammary tumors occurred.[382] It is also possible that dietary changes[383, 384, 387] may have been involved in the spontaneous increases in the incidence of mammary tumors in the CBA strain.

of sterility. Thirteen of 56 untreated female mice of the strain had tumors of the uterus, uterine cervix, or vagina; 5 epidermoid, 7 undifferentiated, and 1 spindle-cell sarcoma. Epithelial tumors of the uterus or cervix had not been noted in untreated mice of other strains in the same laboratory and very few have been reported.[140] Fibromata or fibrosarcomata develop occasionally in mice of most strains. The uterus and cervix, however, must be considered as susceptible to neoplasia, because tumors in these sites do occur following application of carcinogenic hydrocarbons[315] or estrogens (see p. 239).

EFFECTS OF INDUCED HORMONAL IMBALANCES ON UTERINE TUMORIGENESIS

Although the clinical history of cancer of the cervix in women does not seem to permit the association of cancer of the cervix with obvious endocrine dysfunction, some evidence does exist that cancer of the fundus is associated with such dysfunction.[400] Hofbauer[174] noted some similarities of leukoplakia of the uterine cervix of women to changes in the uteri of guinea pigs with experimental hypergonadal states.

Partial ablation of the gonads of guinea pigs has resulted in marked uterine hyperplasia, epitheliomatous proliferation of the uterine cervical mucosa, and squamous metaplasia.[47, 48, 249, 252] Partial removal of the pituitary of guinea pigs,[46] as well as roentgen irradiation of the ovaries produced similar results.[351] In all of these instances the pituitary-ovarian hormone balance was apparently altered so that the animals—usually only a part of the experimental animals—showed evidence of hyperestrogenism.

Attempts to produce similar abnormal hyperplastic responses in rhesus monkeys failed. Monkeys with a small part of one ovary remaining showed regular menstrual cycles and normal uterine mucosa.[75, 76, 406] Roentgen irradiation resulted in no abnormalities of the genital tract until at least 800 r were used.[75] The large doses produced genital atrophy.

Ovaries transplanted into male rats rarely show corpora lutea; they contain only follicles which may become large and cystic. Pfeiffer[326] demonstrated that the formation of corpora lutea was prevented in intact female rats if, at 1 day of age, a testis was transplanted subcutaneously. The immature female's pituitary assumed characteristics of a male's pituitary under such conditions—an irreversible change that persisted throughout life, even if the transplanted testis was subsequently removed. Four of 16 rats, so altered, that survived three years, had leiomyomas at death[329] and one had a metastatic uterine adenocarcinoma.[330] Female mice, into which testes had been transplanted at birth, had pyometra and glandular cystic hyperplasia.[327] Postnatal injection of testosterone propionate produced similar nontumorous, physiologic and morphologic abnormalities in rats.[412]

Extensive uterine hyperplasia occurs in intact rats in parabiosis with castrated animals[413] but such animals have not been observed in large numbers and for long periods of time.

Although the above experiments have not resulted in tumors or cancer in many instances, they are considered important in that they reveal that controlled and reproducible alterations in intrinsic hormone production can induce tumors, abnormal hyperplasia, and metaplasia of the female genital tract: changes that can be produced by the administration of extrinsic hormones in what have been too often considered abnormally large doses.

EFFECT OF EXOGENOUS HORMONES ON UTERINE TUMORIGENESIS

Malignant uterine lesions have been observed primarily in mice and rabbits to which estrogenic substances and other hormones or carcinogenic chemicals have been administered.

Mouse

Lacassagne[225] described an epithelioma of the uterine cornua of a mouse that had received estrone and a pituitary extract. The lesion occurred in a mouse of a low mammary tumor strain and was quite small, not extending beyond the organ of origin. Cervical carcinomas appeared in 3 of 27 mice given weekly injections of 62.5 or 125 r. u. of estrone and cutaneous applications of a benzene solution of 1,2,5,6-dibenzanthracene.[320, 321] The adjacent pelvic organs and tissues were involved in the mouse with the largest tumor. Mice to which the carcinogenic chemical alone was applied had no uterine cervical cancer.

A "carcinoma-like" lesion was found in the cervix of a mouse of the "Old Buffalo" strain that had received 15 to 30 r. u. of theelol or theelin (estriol or estrone) for twenty-four months.[256] The lesion, consisting of cords of epithelial tissue, had invaded the muscular and subserosal layers. Precancerous or cancer-like lesions developed in the cervices of 26 of 235 mice from seven different strains that had received estrogens or estrogens and other hormones or hormone-containing extracts for prolonged periods.[391] The tendency to acquire mammary tumors was not associated with the occurrence of the uterine tumors. Some abnormal hyperplasia was noted in the cervices of some untreated controls.

Infiltrative epithelial lesions, some of them extending to the subserosa, occurred in 5 mice of three different inbred strains that for prolonged periods of time had received injections of estrone or estradiol benzoate.[114] These lesions may not have been malignant or have grown progressively in the absence of further hormone treatment. Subsequently one tumor was found that had metastasized to the lumbar lymph nodes and grew progressively when transplanted to other mice of the same strain.[135] The tumor was a squamous cell carcinoma, apparently arising from the dorsal cervix. The smaller lesions that could be more accurately localized had developed in the cervical canal or the lateral or dorsal wall of the cervix.

Three carcinomas, and 23 precancerous lesions or smaller carcinomas (they appeared to be smaller and hence earlier lesions) appeared among 134 estrogen-treated mice of four different inbred strains.[134] Five of 12 mice from two inbred strains acquired malignant or premalignant invasive epithelial lesions of the uterine cervix or upper vagina after treatment with estradiol benzoate and testosterone propionate, and 1 of 6 mice given estradiol benzoate and progesterone had a large invasive epithelial lesion. Among all groups the animals that survived for the longer periods showed the highest incidence of cervical tumors. Tumors of the uterine cornua were never observed, although squamous metaplasia and the extension of glands to the serosa occurred in many animals.

From 50 to 62 per cent of hybrid mice (C57$\times$CBA) surviving treatment with estradiol benzoate (16.6 or 50 μg. weekly in oily solution) for periods in excess of one year had invasive epithelial lesions of their cervices or upper vaginas. In 8 of the 25 mice with lesions the neoplasia had extended beyond the organ of origin.[3] Mice that were older at the time when injections were started showed the uterine cervical lesions after shorter periods of exposure to extrinsic estrogens than did younger animals.[74] The age of the host, or age changes of the animal or its "end organ," as modified by months of exposure to the intrinsic hormones of the animal, intensified or augmented the response to extrinsic hormones.

Thirteen of 35 mice of the BC strain that had received estrogens (estradiol benzoate or stilbestrol) alone or estradiol benzoate and testosterone propionate simultaneously had uterine cervical carcinomas or infiltrative lesions at death. None of the 82 untreated controls had epithelial tumors but 5 had uterine fibromyomas.[316]

In only one of the reports referred to above has a malignant lesion of the uterine horn occurred in an estrogen-treated mouse.[225] Epidermoid carcinomas, and precancerous or infiltrative lesions of the uterine cervix or upper vagina have been observed many times in estrogen-treated mice, especially among those animals tolerating treatment for prolonged periods. The rarity of such lesions among untreated mice adds significance to their appearance. Testosterone propionate did not inhibit the action of estrogens.

Uterine fibrosarcomas or fibromyomata have been observed in mice of three strains given estrone.[278]

How estrogens act in uterine cervical carcinogenesis is not known. Strain-limited tendencies are of minor significance—only one strain of mice has shown what might be an unusual susceptibility, and animals of this strain often had imperforate vaginas. The experimental induction of imperforate vaginas in groups of mice susceptible to uterine cervical carcinomas subsequent to estrogen-treatment did not increase the incidence of uterine cervical cancers in untreated animals.[148] Hence it seems unlikely that this condition alone would result in cervical cancer. At least two groups of investigators have studied the preliminary changes of the "end organs."[134, 163, 259, 391] The vaginal epithelium and cervical epithelium does not respond indefinitely to estrogen. Although it does not show the atrophy of the castrate, the epithelium is not as thick or as abundantly cornified as in an animal treated more briefly. On the outer lateral walls of the cervix, the external os or the cervical canal, areas of very thin, hypotrophic epithelium frequently exist. The epithelium seems to have lost its capacity to respond normally. From such areas the smaller infiltrative epithelial lesions seem to arise. Insofar as it is possible to discern, these small lesions are early stages of the larger ones and of the carcinomas, although the latter, for the greater part, are more anaplastic. The tumors thus seem to arise in areas that have become relatively atrophic in the presence of amounts of hormone adequate to prevent, if ad-

TABLE 8. UTERINE LESIONS IN MICE APPEARING SPONTANEOUSLY AND AFTER TREATMENT WITH ESTROGENS AND OTHER SUBSTANCES

Investigator		*Strain*	*No. of mice*		*Hormones or chemicals**	*Weekly dose* (mg.)	*Methods of application*	*Duration* (wk.)	*No. of tumors*	*Description*
			Exp.	*Control*						
Lacassagne [225]	1935	several	40	—	Es	.03	Subcut.	11–29	1	Epidermoid
Loeb, *et al.*[256]	1936	Old Buffalo	1	—	E	.0063 .0135	"	104	1	Epidermoid cancer-like
Perry [320]	1936	—	27	—	E + dibenz.	?	Cutan.	<28	3	"
Perry, *et al.*[321]	1937	—	75	75	E + dibenz.	?	Cutan.	26–40	3	"
Suntzeff, *et al.*[391]	1938	several	235	128	Es	variable	Subcut.	<106	26	"
Gardner, *et al.*[135]	1938	"	100+	100+	EB	"	"	38–52	19	1 carcinoma, 18 invasive lesions
Loeb, *et al.*[259]	1938	"	324	177	Es	"	"	4–80	—	—
Gardner & Allen [134]	1939	8 diff.	134	104	Es Es + tp Es + p	"	"	4–55	3 23	cancer invasive lesions
Allen & Gardner [3]	1941	CC hybrids	44	52	EB	.00166 .0050	"	52+	25	carcinoma and invasive lesions
Miller & Pybus [278]	1942	3 diff.	151	—	Es	variable	"	—	36	fibromata, fibrosarcomata
Crossen & Loeb [74]	1944	CBA C57	16	—	Es	"	"	—	9	invasive, precancer
Pan & Gardner [316]	1948	BC hybrids	35	82	EB or Es EB + tp	"	"	29+	13	cancer, precancer
Gardner & Pan [140]	1948	PM	56	—	None	—	—	60–100	13	5 carcinoma, 7 undifferentiated, 1 fibrosarcoma

* E, estrone; dibenz., 3,4-dibenzanthracene; EB, estradiol benzoate; Es, estrogens; tp, testosterone propionate; S, stilbestrol; p progesterone.

ministered intermittently, such atrophy. The connective tissue of the mucosa also becomes hyaline or mucoid and the blood-vessel walls are often thickened. The stromal changes are not, however, as localized as the epithelial atrophy. Virgin female rats showed more fibrous tissue in their genital tracts than did multiparous animals; in both, collagenous tissue increased with advancing age.[45]

Squamous metaplasia of the uterine epithelium, hyalinization of the mucosa, and chronic general or localized pyometra all occur frequently. Whether uterine conditions affect the cervical response is unknown but infiltrative lesions did occur in mice from which the uterine cornua had been removed. Uterine cervices transplanted into the subcutaneous tissues of estrogen-treated mice did not show infiltrative epithelial lesions but they became greatly distended.[133] All uteri of estrogen-treated mice must be septic, at least for a part of the period. Within four days after a single injection of estrogen, bacteria were present in the uteri.[411]

Rat

Uterine cancer or precancerous lesions have appeared infrequently in rats subjected to prolonged treatment with estrogens. Cystic hyperplasia and squamous metaplasia, sometimes with pyometra, frequently occurred. One carcinoma of the upper vagina, 1 uterine cervical papilloma, and 1 uterine carcinoma occurred among 34 ovariectomized rats receiving estrone.[269] Uterine tumors are not rare in untreated rats; Bullock and Curtis observed 48, including 20 epithelial tumors (10 squamous epitheliomas, 4 adenocarcinomas, 1 adenoacanthoma, 1 carcinoma, and 4 carcinosarcomas) in several thousand rats studied.[43] Uterine tumors were the fourth most common class of tumors observed. Squamous metaplasia was often associated with diffuse or circumscribed abscesses.

Guinea Pig

Estrogen-treated guinea pigs show a marked endometrial hyperplasia, especially of the lower uterine glands and fibromuscular outgrowths from the uterine serosa that sometimes become very large.[304, 305, 319] Lipschütz and his associates have studied the fibromatogenic action of estrogens in guinea pigs most extensively (see Lipschütz[250] for references). The fibromatogenic responses of the abdominal serosa are not limited to the uterus or parametrium but involve other areas, the gastrosplenic ligament and omental areas being especially susceptible. Many different estrogens and their esters induce such reactions. Progesterone or testosterone, if given concurrently, prevent the peritoneal fibroids and fibrous reactions. Lipschütz and his associates have reported numerous quantitative experiments on the antifibromatogenic action of several steroids.

Although they may attain considerable size, show evidence of invasion of adjacent tissues and appear quite hyperplastic, the fibromatous growths regress after cessation of treatment, or after the administration of an antifibromatogenic chemical, and fail to grow subsequent to transplantation into other animals. The lesions apparently arise in subserosal areas that collect histiocytes and secondarily become areas of fibroplasia.

Rabbit

Pierson[335, 336] described some malignant growths in the uteri of rabbits that had received estrogens or pituitary gonadotropins for long periods. Hyperemia, and sometimes hemorrhage and glandular cystic hyperplasia, led to progressive asceptic necrosis and resulted in a destruction of the uterine cornua of some estrogen-treated rabbits.[432, 434] In some rabbits only the uterine cervices remained.[132]

Monkey

Squamous metaplasia of the uterine cervical glands of rhesus monkeys occurs following the injection of estrogens.[173, 313] These lesions are always reversible when treatment is discontinued. Treatment prolonged for many years[91, 331] failed to maintain the endometrium in a hyperplastic state and to initiate progressive abnormal growths of the uterine cervix. Progesterone prevented the squamous metaplasia of the uterine cervical glands so common in estrogen-treated monkeys.[173]

OVARIAN TUMORS

Spontaneous ovarian tumors are rare in mice; Slye, Holmes, and Wells[373] reported that 44 cases occurred among 22,000 mice; of these 38 were described as benign solid papillary adenomata; 1, a solid teratoma; 1, a papillary cystadenoma, and 4 were regarded as primary malignant tumors of the ovary.

The first hormone-producing ovarian tumor described occurred in a 490-day-old mouse of the CBA strain.[389] At autopsy the peritoneal cavity was found to be filled with a pale reddish fluid and the right ovary was replaced by a large solid tumor. The uterus was distended, as if in estrus. Histologically, this tumor resembled an adenocarcinoma with some folliculoid arrangement. The evidence of endocrine activity of this tumor was observed by the estrous type of vaginal smears of castrated females and the growth of the rudimentary mammary glands of males bearing transplants of the tumor.[388] Special hormonal environments were necessary for the growth of this tumor. Growth readily occurred in intact males, was inhibited by orchidectomy, and did not readily occur in intact females. The rate of growth of the transplanted tumor was increased in normal female mice receiving pregnant mare's serum.

One mouse with bilateral granulosa cell tumors also had multiple mammary tumors, cystic hyperplasia of the uterus, and a chromophobe adenoma of the pituitary gland.[146] The appearance of multiple tumors of interrelated organs permits conjecture as to etiologic relationships.

Ovarian tumors in rats have been described; some were of the granulosa cell type and were successfully transplanted into related hosts.[43, 196] In general, however, careful studies of animals with ovarian tumors do not indicate obvious hormonal disturbances in their preceding history. The clinical histories of women with granulosa cell tumors are probably more complete than any of laboratory animals that acquire such tumors without predetermined experimental manipulation.

HORMONAL FACTORS IN OVARIAN TUMORIGENESIS

Although ovarian tumors had been observed repeatedly in roentgen irradiated mice for many years (see below) such experiments did not demonstrate a hormonal etiology of such tumors. The first highly indicative experiment was reported by Biskind and Biskind in 1944.[19] Granulosa cell tumors developed within eleven months in 3 of 9 ovariectomized rats of the Sherman strain bearing intrasplenic ovarian grafts, the largest tumor measuring $15 \times 13 \times 10$ mm. Histologically, the granulosa cell tumors were fairly sharply demarcated from the theca cell masses that were also present in the graft. Mitotic figures were numerous in some regions and the granulosa cells were arranged as in the folliculoid type of tumor.

The experiments were interpreted in the light of the observations of others,[90, 94] who demonstrated an increase in the gonadotropic content of the pituitary gland of gonadectomized rats and the apparent increase in circulating gonadotropins in the bodies of castrated animals,[413] the action of gonadal hormones in the reduction of the gonadotropic content of the pituitary gland and blood,[275, 280] and the action of the hepatic tissue of rats and mice in the destruction and inactivation of estrogens.[154, 401, 430] All of the above observations permitted an interesting point of departure for further experimental work.

Ovarian tumors occurred in gonadectomized male or female mice bearing intrasplenic grafts for 200 days or more.[243, 244] Granulosa cell tumors occurred predominantly in the males and mixed granulosa cell tumors and luteomas in the females. Ovarian tumors did not develop in castrated mice carrying intrasplenic ovarian grafts if vascular adhesions from the graft to the body wall or uterus were present that permitted the ovarian hormones to by-pass the hepatoportal system and, therefore, to be inactivated before escaping into the general circulation. Ovarian tumors did not occur in intrasplenic transplants of ovaries in unilaterally gonadectomized mice, and among 25 castrated females with subcutaneous ovarian transplants only 1 showed a questionable granulosa cell growth. No tumors were observed among 9 castrated males with subcutaneous ovarian transplants. Because castrated male mice with intrasplenic ovarian transplants had granulosa cell tumors and castrated females with intrasplenic ovarian transplants had predominately luteomas and mixed tumors, it was postulated that this was due to a physiologic difference in the pituitary glands of males and females; the pituitary glands of males producing less luteinizing hormone than those of females. Ovaries transplanted into male rats and mice seldom show corpora lutea.[326, 328]

Although it was subsequently shown that some ovarian transplants in the subcutaneous tissue became tumors,[191, 244] this was a relatively rare occurrence.

Of a total of 43 castrated mice (32 females and 11 males) with fragments of ovaries transplanted into the spleen, Furth and Sobel[111] observed tubular adenomas and granulosa cell tumors in 67 per cent of 29 animals (21 females and 8 males). Insertion of crystals of methylcholanthrene did not significantly hasten their appearance. The tumors were thought to be relatively less malignant than those arising in irradiated mice.

Ovaries transplanted into the mouse's pancreas also became tumorous, demonstrating that the spleen *per se* contributed no specific carcinogenic environment.[241] Ovarian tumors did not appear in the intrasplenic ovarian grafts of gonadectomized mice given 16.6 μg. of estradiol benzoate weekly or 1.25 mg. of testosterone propionate.[246] The gonadal hormones thus prevented ovarian tumorigenesis under such conditions.

Ovaries of old mice transplanted into the spleens of young castrated animals gave origin to tumors at about the same incidence as young ovaries transplanted into young hosts.[247] Few tumors arose, however, when old ovaries were transplanted into the spleens of old mice. The environment of the old host was not as conducive to tumor formation as was that of the young host. Pituitary gonadotropin decreased in mice with advancing age.[375] Furthermore, thyroid-fed, castrated animals and castrated animals on a restricted food intake, all bearing intrasplenic ovarian transplants, had a reduced ovarian tumor incidence as compared with control castrates bearing intrasplenic ovarian transplants.[279] Experimental hyperthyroid mice showed the lowest incidence of ovarian tumors. Mice maintained on a calorie-deficient diet quickly acquired ovarian tumors when the diet was unrestricted.

Roentgen irradiation of intrasplenic ovarian grafts did not increase the incidence of cancers or reduce the time needed for tumor formation beyond that in nonirradiated, intrasplenic ovarian grafts.[242]

A luteoma induced in a mouse that received 175 r and was painted twice with a 1 per cent methylcholanthrene in benzene solution has been extensively studied.[111, 112] This tumor was carried through several transfer passages, grew readily in males and females; histologically it appeared to be a pure luteoma and gave evidence of secreting an androgenic hormone.

Influence of Gonadal and Gonadotropic Hormones on Tumorigenesis in Intrasplenic Ovarian Grafts in Mice

Tumorigenesis of intrasplenic ovarian grafts in castrated mice is prevented by the administration of estrogens or testosterone;[246] however, 5 granulosa cell and 2 mixed tumors occurred in intrasplenic ovarian grafts in 8 castrated mice that received 1 mg. of progesterone in oil for 9–19 weekly injections. Three granulosa cell tumors, 1 luteoma, and 1 mixed tumor appeared in 5 castrated female mice with intrasplenic ovarian grafts, treated with progesterone, 1 mg. in oil, for 14–19 weekly injections.

One granulosa cell tumor and 2 mixed tumors occurred in 5 castrated males and 3 mixed tumors occurred in 5 castrated females with intrasplenic ovarian grafts, treated with daily injection of a gonadotropic preparation (PMS).[246]

Ovarian Tumors or Responses of Ovarian Transplants in the Spleens of Other Species.

Castrated guinea pigs bearing intrasplenic ovarian transplants[251] had no ovarian tumors twenty-two months after transplantation; however, the ovarian transplants did show marked degrees of luteinization and irregular clusters of lutein cells; true tumorous growths were not observed in this species during the period of observations.

Six of 8 rabbits survived 11–533 days with viable intrasplenic ovarian transplants. Two of the animals that survived for 512 and 513 days showed definite tumor formation in the transplants. Both transplants were solid, yellow in color, and measured 0.6 to 0.64 cm. in diameter. Microscopically they were composed of cells of the granulosa type with evidences of partial luteinization.[318]

Ovariectomized monkeys (*Macaca mulatta*) with intrasplenic transplants of ¼ of one ovary gave external evidence of the presence of estrogenic hormone in the general circulation.[405] The animals had menstrual cycles and sex skin changes comparable to those of intact monkeys. Apparently the monkey's liver does not effectively inactivate estrogens.

Ovarian Tumors in Irradiated Mice

While studying the effects of roentgen irradiation on leukemia in mice, Furth and Butterworth[108, 109] observed that the incidence of ovarian tumors was fifteen times higher in the roentgen irradiated stock than in the control stock. Most of the tumors induced in the mouse's ovary following irradiation were of the granulosa cell type. A small number were luteomas and tubular adenomas; however, only the granulosa cell type and luteoma type were associated with hormonal production by the tumor cells. The granulosa cell tumors were associated with evidence of estrogen production and the luteoma with evidence of progestin production.[11]

After transplantation some of the tubular adenomas transformed into granulosa cell tumors and a granulosa cell tumor may transform into a luteoma; however, these processes are not reversible. In many instances tumors retain their individual cell characteristics for many serial passages, especially tumors of the granulosa cell type, which transplant more readily, grow more rapidly, and metastasize more frequently than the tubular adenomas or luteomas. Roentgen-ray–induced granulosa cell tumors possess different metastasizing properties; some metastasize readily, others rarely or not at all. Pre-irradiation or gonadectomy of the host does not influence the formation of metastases. The sites of such metastases are usually the lung and liver.

Probable Mechanism of Ovarian Tumorigenesis Following Roentgen Irradiation. The induction of ovarian tumors by irradiation is not a function of the dose rate or total dosage but is dependent upon the minimum dose.[263] Twenty-five r to 50 r, if given as a single dose, appears to be a minimum dose for the production of ovarian tumors in mice.[107, 296] Roentgen irradiation must induce a delayed effect in the nature of a hormonal imbalance because 33 per cent of female mice are sterilized when exposed to 150 r at one to three days of life while ovarian neoplasms will develop in 76 per cent.[105] The hormonal imbalance is such that there probably is a diminution of estrogen production following roentgen irradiation[18, 39, 149] and this diminished output of estrogen stimulates the pituitary gland to increase the production of gonadotropins. This effect is further substantiated by the work of Lick *et al.*[248] Roentgen irradiation of a single ovary did not result in tumor formation if the second ovary was not irradiated or removed.

Influence of Gonadal Hormones on Ovarian Tumorigenesis in Mice Following Roentgen Irradiation. Irradiated mice (280–380 r) given weekly subcutaneous injections of 16.6 μg. of estradiol benzoate did not develop ovarian tumors (42 mice); irradiated mice (280–380 r) treated with 1.25 mg. of testosterone propionate in weekly subcutaneous injections developed ovarian tumors (29 animals with ovarian tumors out of a total of 45 animals); and irradiated mice (280–380 r) treated with weekly subcutaneous injections of sesame oil developed ovarian tumors (24 animals with ovarian tumors out of a total of 45 animals). All the tumors in these animals except 2 tumors in 1 animal were of the granulosa cell type; 2 tumors in one mouse receiving testosterone propionate were luteomas.[130, 131, 143]

Hormonal Production and Secondary Effects of Experimentally Produced Ovarian Tumors. Some of the ovarian tumors produced by roentgen irradiation or by intrasplenic ovarian transplants into castrated animals are hormonally active. Granulosa cell tumors are usually associated with an estrogenic activity, as noted by an increase in uterine weight, increase in the height of the cells of the lining epithelium of the castrate's uterus, vaginal cornification, submaxillary changes, glomerular capsular changes in the kidney, and mammary gland stimulation. Luteomas are usually associated with progesterone-like activity as noted by changes in the uterine stromal nuclei. Androgenic activity of certain ovarian tumors is noted by the stimulation of accessory male sexual organs, histologic changes of the serous tubules of the submaxillary gland, and glomerular capsular changes in the kidney. Tubular adenomas do not appear to have any hormonal activity.[104]

Castrated animals bearing subcutaneous transplants of certain granulosa cell tumors show the effects of marked estrogenic stimulation from these tumors while progestin stimulation has been observed in only one granulosa cell tumor. Bali and Furth[11] have observed evidence of progestin associated with certain luteomas and androgenic-like activity has been noted in animals bearing a transplantable luteoma that originated in a roentgen-irradiated mouse.

The hormonal activity of the tumor is related to the size of the tumor but correlation of the biologic activity of the tumor with its rate of growth, the degree of cellular differentiation, and the amount of necrosis cannot be made from observations reported to date.

Increased blood volume and sinusoidal dilatation in the liver, spleen, and adrenal glands occurred in mice bearing certain granulosa cell tumors.[67, 106, 110, 378] These hypervolemic effects were not related to the estrogenic activity of the tumor. Studies have shown that there is a marked increase in the plasma volume of these animals, with only a slight increase in the total mass of red blood cells and no increase in the extracellular-extravascular fluid volume. The tumor mass apparently plays an insignificant role in the degree of hypervolemia noted; some animals with small tumors show marked hypervolemia and animals with other than granulosa cell tumors, of equal or much larger size, show little or no hypervolemia. Similar hypervolemic changes have been noted in animals bearing a transplanted testicular tumor.[421]

Hypervolemia occurs rarely in mice with other tumors. It is apparently associated with something produced in the tumors that is labile and produced in relatively small amounts. Mice in parabiosis with tumor-bearing hosts do not show hypervolemia[420] and attempts to induce hypervolemia by extracts of tumors have failed. Following the removal of a tumor the animals quickly recover.[420] The above observations would exclude coincident infections transmitted with the tumors.

Luteomas, on the other hand, are associated with a polycythemia with little or no increase in the volume of the plasma compartment.[155] Scrotal hernias have also been observed in 4 castrated male mice with intrasplenic ovarian grafts, another indication of simultaneous estrogen and androgen production.[279]

TABLE 9. OVARIAN TUMORS IN INTRASPLENIC OVARIAN GRAFTS IN CASTRATED RATS AND MICE AND SOME DATA INCIDENT TO THE CONTROL OF SUCH EXPERIMENTS

Investigator	*Strain or species*	*No. of animals castrated*	*Conditions of experiment*	*No. of ovarian tumors**
Biskind & Biskind [19]	rat	9 ♀	intrasplenic graft	3 large, 2 small gct
Li & Gardner [244]	mice, A, C3H, and hybrids	25 ♂	intrasplenic graft	5 gct, 1 L
		33 ♀	" "	4 L, 7 M
		19 ♀	" (adhesions)	1 L
		25 ♀	subcutaneous graft	1 gct ?
		12 ♂	" "	0
		34 ♂	intratesticular	0
Furth & Sobel [111]	mice, hybrids R × K	32 ♀	intrasplenic grafts and x-rays or methylcholanthrene	21 ovarian tumors
		11 ♂		8 " "
		10 ♀	ovarian cell suspension in spleen	0
		4 ♂	ovarian cell suspension in spleen	0
Li, *et al.*[242]	mice, several inbred strains and hybrids	8 ♂	intrasplenic and x-ray	5 gct, 3 M
		9 ♀	" " "	2 gct, 3 L, 2 M
		6 ♂	" " " to hypophysis	1 gct, 3 M
		6 ♀	intrasplenic and x-ray to hypophysis	3 gct, 1 L, 1 M
		4 ♂	x-ray in vitro & intrasplen.	1 M
		7 ♀	" " " " "	1 gct, 1 L, 1 M
		†4 ♂	" " " " "	1 L, 1 M
		2 ♀	" " " " "	1 L
Li & Gardner [246]	mice, inbred strains and hybrids	13 ♂	intrasplenic	10 gct, 2 M
		9 ♀	"	5 gct, 4 L
		10 ♂ ♀	" unilat. cast.	0
		16 ♂ ♀	" + estrogen	0
		14 ♂ ♀	" + androgen	0
		13 ♂ ♀	" + progesterone	8 gct, 1 L, 3 M
		10 ♂ ♀	" + PMS	1 gct, 5 M
Peckham, *et al.*[318]	rat	12 ♀	intrasplenic	12 gct, (surviving 265 + days)
		2 ♀	" & adhesions	0
Biskind & Biskind [21]	rat	50 ♀	intrasplenic	46 tumors after 157 days
	Long & Evans,	21 ♀	" & adhesions	0
	Sherman	22 ♀	in renal capsule	0

* gct, granulosa cell tumor; L, luteoma; M, mixed granulosa cell, luteoma.
† = 1 non-irradiated and 1 irradiated ovary transplanted intrasplenically in each animal.

Interpretation. The ovarian tumors that develop in the intrasplenic grafts in castrated hosts and in irradiated mice are thought to be due to abnormal secretion of pituitary gonadotropin. Castrated mice with intrasplenic ovarian grafts, when in parabiosis with normal female mice, produce enough gonadotropin to stimulate excessively the gonads of the intact parabiont,[280] and hence demonstrate a high gonadotropin titer in the circulation of the mice with the transplants. Furthermore, the gonadotropin levels of roentgen-irradiated mice are abnormally high as demonstrated by parabiosis.[31] Roentgen rays, as well, impair the production of hormones by the ovary and result in an increased level of pituitary gonadotropin in the irradiated animals. All of the evidence to date, except the failure of presumably adequate amounts of testosterone propionate to prevent such tumors in irradiated mice, indicates that the pituitary gonadotropins, probably the follicle-stimulating hormone, induces the ovarian tumors. Ovarian tumors have so far not been induced by the prolonged administration of gonadotropins,[332] but many of the gonadotropic preparations are antigenic when given over long periods.

TABLE 10. INCREASED PRODUCTION OF GONADOTROPINS IN MICE WITH INTRASPLENIC OVARIAN GRAFTS OR WITH IRRADIATED OVARIES AS DETERMINED BY THE RESPONSE OF THE OVARIES AND UTERI OF INTACT MICE IN PARABIOSIS WITH THEM

		Intact partner		*X-rayed or castrate partner*	
Investigator	*Treatment*	*Ovary* (mg.)	*Uterus* (mg.)	*Ovary* (mg.)	*Uterus* (mg.)
Miller & Pfeiffer [280]	Intrasplenic grafts in ☿; all operations on same day	7.8	41.9	—	33.9
Miller & Pfeiffer [280]	Intrasplenic grafts in castration 30–50 days before parabiosis ☿	10.7	73.3	—	30.4
Boddaert [31]	X-rayed 2 or more months before operation. Parabiosed 26–28 days	15.8	235.8	2.6	58.7

Obviously experiments using pure gonadotropins are desirable and necessary. We already know, however, that hormone imbalances involving increases of intrinsic gonadotropin result in ovarian neoplasia. The suggestion that ovarian tissue utilizes gonadal hormones is not entirely consistent with the above interpretation.

The histogenesis of the ovarian tumors is not discussed here, although it is of importance in the interpretation of the hormonal states. Detailed descriptions of the histogenesis of experimental tumors and of the post-irradiation effects have been written.[21, 39, 63, 244, 402] Monographs on ovarian tumors have also been published.[357, 407]

TESTICULAR TUMORS

Spontaneous interstitial cell tumors of the testis occur relatively rarely in most mammals, although the testicular tumors most frequently produced by experimental means are of interstitial cell origin. A careful study of these experimentally produced tumors might indicate that some of the spontaneous tumors diagnosed as other types may well have been interstitial cell tumors. The incidence of spontaneous interstitial cell tumors in the dog (see Table 11 for summary) is high compared with any other species. It varies from slightly over 1 per cent to almost 100 per cent depending on the age of the dog and the definition of an interstitial cell tumor. Animals over 12 years of age or showing the general physical characteristics of senility, may be expected to exhibit testicular hyperplasia, and the incidence of unequivocal tumors may reach 80 per cent or more. Spontaneous interstitial cell tumors have been described in the horse,[324] but their incidence in old age is questionable as the number of intact males which reach old age is extremely limited in most countries. Kimara[206] in Japan, where stallions are not regularly gelded, found 49 testicular tumors in 27,224 slaughtered horses but concluded that they were derived from the epithelium of the seminiferous tubules. Spontaneous interstitial cell tumors have also been described in the mouse.[124, 185, 372] One strain of mice has been developed with a very high incidence of spontaneous testicular tumors.[8, 9]

TABLE 11. SPONTANEOUS INTERSTITIAL CELL TUMORS IN DOGS

Author	*No. of dogs*	*Age yrs.*	*No. of testes studied*	*Interstitial cell tumors* *No.*	*Percentage*	*Other tumors*	*Hyperplasia (%)*
Goodpasture [153]	37	9–14	74	17?	50 to 63	4?	100
Smith [377]	15	10–20	30	10?	?	?	87
Kunze [220]	?	9–15	?	13	?	10	?
Pallaske [314]	107	mostly 8–13 (½ to 20)	214?	31	29	7	66
Peyron, Blanchard, & Salomon [324]	85	5 + (8–10)	170	32	39	5	35
Zuckerman & McGowan [437]	243	all ages	?	3	1	32	
Peyron, Blanchard, Pomeau-Delelle, & Salomon [324]	400	old	?	50	12.5		
Schlotthauer, McDonald, & Bollman [350]	48*	old	96	51	100*	31	?
Braun [40]	31	12+	62	12	38.7	?	?
Huggins & Pazos [195]	41*	old	58	33	80.5	31	
Hooker, Pfeiffer, & DeVita [181]	38	old	76	7	20.0	?	?
Hooker, Pfeiffer, & DeVita [182]	51	old	102	11	20.0	?	?

? The total figure not given or can only be guessed at.
* Only animals with some type of testicular tumor reported.

Table 12. SUMMARY OF INVESTIGATIONS OF TESTICULAR TUMORS IN MICE

Author	*Strain or stock*	*Estrogens used**	*No. of mice*	*Method of application*	*Dose*	*Duration*	*Tumors*	*Hypertrophy and hyperplasia*
Burrows [56]	Stock	7 different	162	percutaneous	variable	5–9 mo.	—	77
Gardner [113]	A	5 different	15	inj. in oil	variable	2.5–8 "	—	15
	C3H		8	" " "	"	4–9 "	—	1
	CBA		5	" " "	"	" "	—	0
	N		8	" " "	"	" "	—	0
	F		8	" " "	"	" "	—	0
Hooker, Gardner, & Pfeiffer [179]	A	STE	—	inj. in oil	—	1–9 mo.	1	?
	A	EB	—	" " "	—	1–9 "	1	?
Bonser & Robson [38]	A	TPE	23	inj. in oil	3 mg. wkly.	20–69 wk.	13	23
	RIII	TPE	30	" " "	" " "	20–89 "		
	RIII	EDP	31	" " "	50 μg. wkly.	" " "		slight hypertrophy one third of animals
	CBA	TPE	20	" " "	3 mg. wkly.	" " "		
	CBA	EDP	26	" " "	50 μg. wkly.	" " "		
Shimkin, Grady & Andervont [361]	C	STE	62	pellets	variable	6–11 mo.	13	
	A	STE	20	"	"	7 "	2	
Hooker & Pfeiffer [180]	A	EB	9	inj. in oil	16.6 μg. wkly.	6–14 "	3	
	A	EB	40	" " "	50 μg. wkly.	" "	7	
	A	STE	47	" " "	.25 mg. wkly.	" "	29	
Bonser [35]	A	TPE	10	inj. in oil	3 mg. wkly.	30–89 wk.	8	10
Gardner [123]	JK	TPE	13	inj. in oil	2.5 or 5 mg. wkly.	8–16 wk.	7	
	A	TPE	17	" " "		15–18 wk.	7	
	C3H	TPE	14	" " "	" " "	9–22 wk.	1	
	C12I	TPE	6	" " "	" " "	11–13 "	—	
	CBA	TPE	5	" " "	" " "	18–25 "	—	
	N	TPE	5	" " "	" " "	13–21 "	—	
Bonser [36]	A†	TPE	9	inj. in oil	3 mg. wkly.	20–99 wk.	8	9
	W.L.	TPE	39	" " "	" " "	" "	3	31
	IFS	TPE	20	" " "	" "	" "	4	14
Athias & Furtado Dias [9]	H	None	7	—	—	—	7?	
Athias [8]	H	None	109	—	—	—	42?	

* STE, stilbestrol; EB, estradiol benzoate; TPE, triphenylethylene; EDP, estradiol dipropionate.
† Foster nursed to RIII.

EXPERIMENTALLY PRODUCED TUMORS

The most pertinent findings concerning the experimentally produced interstitial cell tumors of the testis are listed in Table 12.

Estrogens

Almost all experimentally produced interstitial cell tumors have developed following prolonged estrogen treatment. Apparently the first of these was described by Burrows[57] in 1937 who two years earlier published an account of the initial interstitial cell hypertrophy after estrogen treatment[52] and of differences in organ response to the various estrogens[56] which are dependent on the estrogenic potency. Gardner[113] in 1937 showed that this primary hypertrophy in response to estrogen was strain-limited and occurred in the A strain but not in the C3H, CBA, N and F strains of the mice used in cancer work at Yale. With the ability to keep the mice alive longer under constant effects of tri-p-anisyl chloroethylene, the C57 ♀ × CBA ♂ strain not only developed the hyperplasia but the interstitial cell tumors as well.[136]

At about the same time three different laboratories reported the development of interstitial cell tumors of the testis following treatment with estrogens: Bonser and Robson[38] in England, and Hooker, Gardner, and Pfeiffer[179] at Yale, in 1940, and Shimkin, Grady and Andervont[361] at the National Cancer Institute in 1941. The tumors developed in the A strain of Strong in the English and Yale experiments and in the C albino (Bagg) strain at the National Cancer Institute. The C strain is a descendant of the mice used as one parent in the development of the A strain. Testicular tumors also develop in the JK,[123] CBA, white label, and IFS[36] strains. One tumor has been produced in the C3H strain.[123] Estradiol benzoate,[38, 180] stilbestrol,[180, 361] triphenylethylene,[35, 38, 123] and tri-p-anisyl chloroethylene[136] have all been used to produce interstitial cell tumors.

Other Steroids

Androgens[180] and progesterone[397] retard the formation of interstitial cell tumors by estrogens.

Gonadotropins

Pregnant mare serum enhances the effect of estrogen on the testis and is effective in producing tumors in mice which have received preliminary treatment with estrogen.[334] Nodular hyperplasia has been induced in some cases with pregnant mare serum (PMS) alone.[333] PMS and APL, presumably because of their high luteinizing hormone content, cause the production of androgen by the transplanted interstitial cell tumors.[177, 183]

Gonad Transplantation

The only experimental production of interstitial cell tumors of the testis of the rat has been accomplished by transplanting the testis into the spleen of the castrate.[20, 399] This technic gives very consistent results in the rat[399] but has so far failed to produce testicular tumors in mice, even those of the very susceptible A strain.[245] Nodular hyperplasia of the interstitial cells of a testis grafted into the neck of an otherwise normal female of the A strain has been described[328] and is thought to be due to the endocrine imbalance between the hypophysis and ovaries which exists in such animals.

Irradiation and Other Procedures

Other methods of producing experimental interstitial cell tumors in the mouse have not been successful, but in the rat these tumors have been reported to follow x-ray treatment[325] and injections of tissue from leprosy lesions.[322, 325] Foster nursing and the lack of the milk agent has no effect upon the development of the tumors in mice.[36, 361] Methylcholanthrene and benzpyrene, either injected or transplanted as pellets into the testes may produce tumors of the connective tissue elements but have never produced interstitial cell tumors of the testis.[176] An embryonal testicular tumor occurred in one of 63 Street mice which had received 9,10-dimethyl-1,2-benzanthracene in the testis eleven months previously; 2 spindle cell sarcomas and 1 squamous cell carcinoma also developed in the testes of these mice.[340]

Description of Tumors

The first response of the testis to estrogens is impairment of spermatogenesis and a general hypertrophy of the interstitial cells.[36, 113] These cells arise from the mesenchymal cells and transform into normal interstitial cells which become secretorily exhausted and thus are large and foamy in appearance. These foamy cells degenerate and for the most part are cleared out from the intertubular spaces before the beginning of the next stage, which is the focal development of interstitial cells from the primitive mesenchymal cells which still remain in the intertubular spaces.[180] The latter process gives rise to nodules in the testis which grow and displace the tubules to the periphery, where they undergo pressure atrophy. The interstitial cells in the nodules go through the same stages as do the interstitial cells present during the general hyperplasia so that the nodules come to be composed of the large foamy cells. The latter cells have been classified as the first generation tumor cells. Gradually, cells develop which do not proceed to the foamy stage but resemble the normal Leydig cell very closely. These are known as the second generation tumor cells. Finally, in focal areas of the second generation tumor cells there appears a third generation of cells which are small and hyperchromatic. These are interpreted to be more primitive and less differentiated cells than the functional interstitial cells. Brown cells are extremely numerous in the initial hyperplasia and in tumors composed primarily of Stage 1 cells and give the characteristic coloring to the tumors. There are two schools of thought as to the source of the brown cells. Hooker and Pfeiffer[180] and Hooker, Pfeiffer, and Williams[184] believe that they are macrophages which have phagocytized the pigmented material, while Gardner and Boddaert[136] and others[264] are of the opinion that they are simply degenerating Leydig cells. All stages of hematopoiesis are often found in these tumors.[123, 136]

Endocrine Imbalance Theory of Interstitial Cell Tumor Formation

All of the evidence indicates that the action of estrogen in the formation of interstitial cell tumors is indirect. The original hyperplasia of the interstitial cells appears to be mediated by a release of luteinizing hormone from the hypophysis, which is followed by an exhaustive secretory phase and destruction of the hypertrophied Leydig cells. After this, nodular development of interstitial cells begins in localized areas from primitive mesenchymal cells and continues into tumor formation. This is interpreted to be due to a differentiation hormone from the pituitary which may be follicle stimulating hormone. The latter is then followed by the release of a secretory hormone which may be luteinizing hormone and causes the secretory changes in the cells.

The spontaneous interstitial cell tumors in mice have the same developmental history as the experimental tumors following estrogen treatment.[9, 176, 185] This has also been shown to be true for the primary interstitial cell tumors that form in old dogs.[181, 182] The atrophy of the tubular elements before the tumor develops led many early workers to ascribe a specific etiologic function to it[88, 211, 219, 379] and this has caused its thorough discussion in more recent papers on interstitial cell tumors in man.[198] Spangaro[379] in 1902 was apparently the first to describe atrophic senile testes in contrast to normal senile testes. The interstitial cells of the atrophic senile testes show remarkable changes which he describes as proceeding in three stages: (1) hyperplasia of the interstitial cells; (2) nodular development; and (3) foamy type of cytoplasm. All of these characteristics are seen in the atrophy that takes place before formation of the experimental tumors. Spangaro also describes cells that are rich in pigment. Durch[88] stresses that atrophy of the tubules occurs when there is interstitial hyperplasia and states that an ectopic position of the testes need not be a primary factor. Collins[69] shows quite convincingly that there is no correlation between interstitial cell hyperplasia and carcinoma anywhere in the body. The apparent increase in interstitial cells accompanying and following atrophy of the seminiferous tubules has recently been shown quite definitely to be a relative and not an actual increase,[92, 93] indicating that while both may be caused by the same endocrine imbalance the tumor is not of necessity the result of the atrophy of the seminiferous tubules.

It is not intended to devote much discussion to interstitial cell tumors in man but it should be mentioned that they show a striking similarity to the experimental tumors in mice.[37, 264, 302, 343] The work of Sand and Okkels[347] indicates that the testes of normal men vary tremendously in histology; only 8 out of 33 showed the classical normal picture. Giant Leydig cells, with 4 to 30 (usually 8 to 10) nuclei, were found in 85 of 721 human testes 18 years or older.[303] Large collections of Leydig cells are not necessarily pathologic, nor do Leydig cells in the tunica albuginea and epididymis necessarily indicate invasive growth.[409]

Malignancy

Malignancy in the experimentally produced interstitial cell tumors apparently depends upon the cell type that comprises the tumor. Metastasis through the lymphatics is quite common and can occur with tumors composed only of cells of Stage 1.[35, 180] Blood-borne metastases are fairly common,[35] and invasiveness by direct extension is shown to a certain degree, in tumors composed of cells of Stages 2 and 3.[180]

TRANSPLANTATION

The interstitial cell tumors will not grow when transplanted into unrelated strains of mice and will grow in the same strain only if estrogen is present.[35, 123, 127, 180] Bonser[36] reported that some tumors grew in females and that one tumor grew equally well with or without estrogen after the first generation. Usually the transplant will persist, but will not grow, without estrogen for 51 to 204 days and then will grow when estrogen is supplied.[127] Once the transplant starts growing it continues to do so after the discontinuance of estrogen and persisted unchanged in hypophysectomized mice observed for periods up to 28 days.[127] The rate of growth and structure remains unchanged after 3 years of successive transplants.[127] After serial passage through ten or more generations interstitial cell tumors acquire the capacity to grow in untreated male and female hosts.[132]

SECRETORY ACTIVITY OF THE TUMOR

The interstitial cell tumor produces androgen in large enough quantity during its formation to overcome the estrogen effect on the accessories,[35, 57, 180] and the transplanted tumor may secrete androgen for several transplant generations.[132, 35] The nonsecretory tumor may be caused to produce androgen by treatment with gonadotropins containing large amounts of luteinizing hormone.[183] It is probable that the Stage 1 cells produce most of the androgen, and that as the tumor becomes more autonomous it loses its secretory ability. Cells resembling the Stage 2 cells are produced when the tumors with less differentiated cells of Type 3 are made to secrete androgen.[183] At least one transplanted testicular tumor induced hypervolemia in its hosts.[421]

OTHER TUMORS OF THE TESTIS

Seminomas and Sertoli cell tumors occur frequently in dogs,[166, 194 197] but little is known of their etiology, and they have not been produced experimentally. The Sertoli cell tumor is interesting in that it has been shown to secrete estrogen.[194] Thirteen of 29 testicular tumors produced by transplanting the testis to the spleen in rats[399] had other than interstitial cell components and were classified as mixed tumors or teratomas. They were undoubtedly produced by the endocrine imbalance which exists in such animals.

PITUITARY TUMORS

Pituitary tumors are relatively rare in the mammal; an occasional one has been described in the horse,[394] dog,[199] Indian buffalo,[100] and mouse.[371] The rat is an exception in that it shows an appreciable tendency toward chromophobe adenomas in old age.[97, 312, 348, 349, 415, 417] Pituitary tumors also occur spontaneously in birds[371] but again are extremely rare.

Table 13. PITUITARY TUMORS IN ANIMALS RECEIVING STEROID HORMONES

Authors	*Species or strain*	*No. of animals*			*Treatment*				*Tumors*	
		Exp.	Sex	Cont.*	*Hormone*	*Weekly dose* (mg.)	*Application*	*Duration* wk.	Number	Percentage
Cramer & Horning [71]	mouse	12	♂	—	E	?	Cutan.	44	3	25
Zondek [431]	rat	5	♂	5	Ed	0.1–0.2	Subcut.	16	? (26.08 mg.)a	?
Gardner, Strong, & Smith [146]	mouse EI	1	♀	—	b	—	—	99	1	—
Oberling, Guerin & Guerin [311]	rat	7	⚦	—	c	—	—	52+	4**	57.14
McEuen, Selye, & Collip [271]	rat	11	⚦ ♀̸	—	Ee	.021	Subcut.	47–49	5	45.4
Burrows [55]	mouse	567	♂	52	Ee	?	Cutan.	69	1	0.17
Wolfe & Wright [416]	rat	20	♀	143	E	.014	Subcut.	11?	? (33.3 mg.)a	?
		17	♂ ♀		”	”	”	25–61	9	52
Zondek [435]	rat	14	♂	—	EB	.2	Subcut.	18	? (22.4 mg.)a	?
		4	♂		”	”	”	28	3 (91.6 mg.)a	75
		23	♂ ♀		”	”	”	39	19 (149.3 mg.)a	82.6
McEuen, Selye, & Collip [272]	rat, hooded	—	—	—	E	.007–.0105	Oral	121	1 (84 mg.)	?
Deansely [78]	rat	32	♂	4	Ed	11.8–16.5	Pel.	36–39	3	9.37
Korenchevsky, Hall, & Burbank [216]	rat	14	♀̸	3	Es	.009	Subcut.	12–16	? (98.0 mg.)a	?
		13	♀̸	8	Es & An	.2–7.5	”		? (60.2 mg.)a	?
Bacsich & Folley [10]	rat, hooded	4	♀	6	EB	7	Subcut.	3	? (38.0 mg.)a	?
		3	♀̸	4	”	”	”	”	(42.9 mg.)a	?

Noble, McEuen & Collip [310]	rat, hooded	15	♀̸	—	Ee	4–10.5	Pel.	49	? (28.4 mg.)a	?
Gardner & Strong [147]	mouse, C57	68	♂ ♀	—	EB	.0083–.025	Subcut.	35.5–65	14	20.58
Nelson [306]	rat	28	♂ ♀	—	STE	.035	Subcut.	56+	9	32.1
Gardner [117]	mouse, CC_1, CC_2	105	♂ ♀	105	EB	.00166 or .005	Subcut.	45.7–63	62	59
Nelson [307]	rat	—	—	—	STE or EB	.034–.07	Subcut.	40–60	91 (105 mg.)	100
Selye [356]	rat	10	♂	10	Ed	0.035	Subcut.	60	? (189 mg.)	?
Vazques-Lopez [408]	hamster	13	♂ ♀	—	EB or STE	10	Pel.	16–47	9	46.1
Segaloff & Dunning, [353]	rat, Fischer,	69	♂̸	10	{Ed {STE, Ee	.175 7.0 & .035	Subcut.	8	? (84.4 mg.)a†	?
	AXC	21	♂̸		STE	7.0 & .175	"	"	? (35.5 mg.)a	?
Loeper [261]	rat	—	♀	—	STE	0.6	Subcut.	26	2	?
Koneff, Simpson, & Evans [212]	hamster	20	♂ ♀	15	STE	10	Pel.	58	5 (14.0 mg. max.)	25
Gardner [129]	mouse,	72	♂ ♀	—	EB	.00166 or	Subcut.	74a	15	20.83
	CC	41	♂ ♀			.0025			26	63
Dickie & Woolley [81]	mouse	252	♂̸ ♀̸	—	adt	—	—	60+	79	31.3

* No pituitary tumors developed in the control animals.

E, estrin; Ed, estradiol; Ee, estrone; Es, estrogen; An, androgen; Eb, estradio benzoate; STE, diethylstilbestrol; a, average; b, granulosa cell tumor in both ovaries; c, ovarian graft in castrate males; **, may have been spontaneous; adt, adrenal tumors; Pel., pellet; cut., cutaneous; subcut,. subcutaneous.

† Average for the group giving the best response.

EXPERIMENTAL TUMORS

The essential data concerning most of the experimentally produced pituitary tumors are listed in Table 13. The general aspects of these experiments will be discussed under the following headings:

Estrogen

An increase in the size of the hypophysis, due to an increase in the number of chromophobes, occurs following estrogen administration. Papers making special reference to this fact began to appear between 1934 and 1936.[175, 224, 266, 358, 414] The production of pituitary tumors by estrogen treatment was first reported in mice,[71] and almost simultaneously in rats,[271, 431] in 1936. One rat had a pituitary tumor weighing 250 mg. after only 28 weekly injections of 10,000 mouse units of folliculin.[431] Estrogens were soon shown to be equally effective in male and female mice and in castrates of both sexes in producing pituitary adenomas.[72] It had already been shown that these tumors developed in castrated rats.

All of the naturally occurring estrogens are effective in inducing pituitary tumors, the effectiveness depending on their estrogenic activity and on the amount administered. They are active in pellet form,[310] as are also the synthetic estrogens;[306] the latter producing similar changes in the pituitary. The immediate effect of estrogen is to cause the release of luteinizing hormone.[175] This is followed by a decrease in chromophils[73, 410, 414] and a corresponding increase in chromophobes which is responsible for the uniform hypertrophy of the pituitary gland. With prolonged treatment adenomas appear, of which three types have been described: diffuse adenomatous hyperplasia, nodular foci of cells, and adenomas associated with profound vascular changes.[416] There is no increase in the gonadotropic hormone content of the pituitary tumors,[435] and probably there is a reduction in anterior pituitary function.[73] Nelson[307] states that pituitary tumors are invariably produced in rats receiving 50 to 100 μg. of diethylstilbestrol or estradiol benzoate daily for a year or more. They are chromophobe adenomas which give the appearance of being benign and grow progressively through the first ten or eleven months with no evidence of serious effects. When symptoms appear, after the pituitary body reaches a weight of 150 mg. or more, they are dramatic, and the animal usually dies within fifteen days. The symptoms are those of pressure on the brain. Atypical and giant cells have been described in the adenomas occurring in old age[419] and in estrogen-induced tumors.[356]

The rabbit's hypophysis does not increase in size excessively with estrogen treatment, although moderate enlargement does occur in the endocrine imbalances that are associated with the uterine and mammary hyperplasias that often lead to cancer. The hypophysis increases in size two to three times during the noninvasive neoplastic state of the mammary glands and four to five times after the invasive stage of the mammary neoplasms. This enlargement is a usually widespread, chromophobic hyperplasia, but occasionally is localized, consisting of an adenoma-like mass.[156]

Progesterone

Progesterone causes early a slight hypertrophy of the hypophysis, and in combination with estrogen produces a greater effect than estrogen alone.[354] However, it has also been shown that progesterone inhibits the tumorigenic action of estrogen on the pituitary.[2] A combination of progesterone and androgen may be more effective in this respect than either alone.[2]

Androgens

There is no evidence that androgens produce pituitary tumors. Testosterone inhibits the hypertrophy of the pituitaries of estrogen-treated rats.[354] Furthermore, testosterone, methyltestosterone, Δ^5-androstene-3(β)-17(α)-diol, and Δ^5-androstene-3(β)-ol-17-one suppress the tumorigenic action of the estrogen on the pituitary;[2] the first two are very effective and the last two, less so. The dipropionate of Δ^5-androstene-3(β)-17(α)-diol is more effective than the free compound; Δ^4-androstene-3, 17-dione is the most active in suppressing the estrogen enlargement of the pituitary; Δ^4-androstene-3-one, 17(β)-ol(cis testosterone) is also extremely active, although practically inert with respect to other hormonal actions.[2]

Gonad Transplantation and Other Methods

There has been a report[311] that 4 of 7 castrated male rats that had received ovarian grafts developed pituitary tumors, but in one of these the graft had not persisted. Since all of the rats of this strain that had received benzpyrene intracranially had pituitary tumors and since spontaneous tumors were found in this colony of rats[312] it may be that these were all of the spontaneous type of old age. It seems probable that the hypophyseal tumors occasionally reported to have been induced by other chemicals were only chance occurrences.

The Endocrine Imbalance Theory of Tumor Formation

There seems to be fairly good agreement that an endocrine imbalance in the aging rat induces the hyperplasia of the chromophobe elements of the anterior hypophysis.[348, 415, 417] There are usually other characteristic evidences of endocrine imbalance in rats of those strains which show high incidences of spontaneous pituitary tumors.[355, 418, 429] This is also true of the reported cases of pituitary tumors in rabbits.[156]

The endocrine imbalance theory ties together the otherwise unrelated reports of Burrows[55] and Gardner, Smith, and Strong.[146] The former reported that one of 567 male mice receiving estrogens developed an extensive chromophobe hyperplasia of the pituitary, thyroid adenoma, and gynecomastia with lactation, accompanied by spermatogenesis, after 483 days of treatment. The latter reported a primary adenoma of the pituitary in a female mouse of the EI strain that also had bilateral ovarian granulosa-cell tumors and multiple mammary carcinomas.

The development of hypophyseal tumors following estrogen stimulation is definitely strain-limited in mice[147] and to probably a lesser extent in rats.[86, 87, 349, 353] However, inbred strains of rats are not as numerous as inbred strains of mice. In the mice in experimental use at Yale, only the C57 strain consistently produces hypophyseal tumors following estrogen treatment. The AC3H, CBA, C12I, JK, and N do not have tumors and the hypophysis never hypertrophies to more than three times normal size.[147] It seems clear that the development of pituitary tumors in the C57 strain is inherited in a Mendelian fashion.[117, 129] The mice of the CE strain also develop chromophobe adenomas following diethylstilbestrol treatment.[428]

REVERSIBILITY AND TRANSPLANTABILITY

In rats pituitary tumors that have been produced by prolonged treatment with estrogen slowly regress following the cessation of treatment,[309] even when the tumor is large enough to give pressure symptoms. However, there appears to be no evidence that such experimentally produced pituitary tumors regress after the cessation of estrogen treatment in mice.[132] These tumors may be transplanted into and grow in estrogen-treated hosts of the same strain. Serial subcutaneous transplants survive for about four generations and then become lost in both mice and rats. Serial intraocular transplantation of the tumor has been carried for eleven transfer generations in estrogen-treated rats.[352] Spontaneous pituitary tumors in rats have been grown as homologous intraocular transplants for three serial generations, but growth was not accelerated in succeeding generations. They grew better in males, but the strain of rats did not seem to be a factor.[349]

OTHER PITUITARY TUMORS

Two adenomata of the intermediate lobe were found in rats chronically treated with estrogen.[271, 272] One of these tumors was pigmented, but since it was found in a hooded rat this might be expected. The intermediate lobe of the pituitary of the hamster always responds to prolonged estrogen treatment by the formation of adenomata-like lesions.[212, 408] These first invade the posterior lobe and the pituitary stalk to the hypothalamus and wall of the third ventricle and only secondarily invade the anterior lobe, the cells of which are essentially normal. Their induction by estrogen would tend to indicate that they are also a result of an endocrine imbalance. Basophilic tumors of the anterior lobe of the hypophysis develop in castrated F_1 hybrids of DBA and CE strains of mice and to a lesser degree in the F_1 hybrids of these strains crossed with the C57 black strain and in C3H and A crosses. However, these pituitary tumors only develop after adrenal cortical tumors are present[81] and again indicate they are the result of an endocrine imbalance.

ADRENAL CORTICAL TUMORS

Adrenal cortical tumors apparently occur sporadically in animals of most species. Numerous studies of patients with such tumors have been reported because of the interesting endocrine syndromes associated with many of them.

Among intact normal mice few adrenal cortical tumors have been observed.[370] One malignant adrenal tumor was noted in a 24-month-old female mouse of the C strain.[77] Thirteen adenomas and 2 carcinomas occurred among mice of the NH strain or hybrid derivatives[209] and adenomas occurred in some mice of the Bagg albino strain.[102] These tumors occurred in mice over 1 year old.

Adrenal cortical adenomas were found in 2 old male guinea pigs that had been castrated shortly after birth.[380] These tumors tended to masculinize their hosts. Mammary tumors appeared in mice of the DBA strain that were ovariectomized shortly after birth[423] and that subsequently showed adenomatous proliferation of adrenal cortical tissue. Similarly male mice of the DBA strain showed hyperplasia of the adrenal cortices and growth of their mammary glands subsequent to castration at early ages.[424] Adrenal tumors occurred in female mice of the NH strain that were castrated when 43–65 days of age and permitted to live for 600–700 days.[118] All of the tumors produced estrogen as indicated by the conditions of the uteri and mammary glands. Four times as much estrogen was excreted from these as from intact females of comparable ages.[84]

Adrenal cortical carcinomas developed in mice of another imbred strain (CE) subsequent to castration at birth or within one or two days thereafter; all of the females when 6 months old and most of the males when 7 months old had such tumors.[427, 428] Some of the tumors were transplantable.[422] They produced either estrogenic or androgenic responses in their hosts. The tumors were prevented when castrated mice received adequate amounts of stilbestrol.[428]

Strain differences in the incidence and type of adrenal lesions in gonadectomized mice occur as indicated above; adenomas were found in mice of the DBA strain and carcinomas in mice of the CE strain. Castrated mice of the C57 strain showed slight adrenal hyperplasia.[424] Furthermore, gonadectomized mice of the A strain showed few adrenal adenomas and no carcinomas, and mice of the C3H strain many adenomas or hyperplastic areas but very few carcinomas.[374] Hybrids between the two strains had more adrenal carcinomas than did either of the parental strains but fewer adenomas than did mice of the C3H strain.

The adrenal cortical tumors produce either estrogenic or androgenic effects or both. One group of investigators has reported marked strain differences in the hormonal activities; tumors in castrated mice of the Bagg albino strain produced predominantly estrogen, those in mice of the C3H and CBA strains elaborated both estrogen and androgen, and those of the A strain only androgen.[102]

The appearance of adrenal adenomas or carcinomas in old female mice could be explained on the same basis as those occurring after castration, especially in those animals that show an early cessation of ovarian function.[103] It has been assumed that, in the absence of gonadal steroids, the pituitary-adrenal relationship is altered, in mice especially, with the result that adrenal cortical tumors occur. Proof of this hypothesis is not available but one very suggestive experiment has been done. Flaks[99] found a highly malignant adrenal cortical tumor in a castrated mouse of the Strong A strain that had received an adrenocorticotropic extract of sheep and ox pituitaries. Another tumor occurred in a castrated stock mouse similarly treated. Malignant adrenal tumors in castrated mice of the A strain have not been observed under other conditions.

Although castrated animals of various species have been observed for many years, the guinea pig and the mouse (only the latter has been adequately studied) appear to be the only ones in which the consequences of castration include unusual hyperplasia or cancer of the adrenal. Even among mice, presumably genetically determined, strain-limited factors determine the quality and extent of the adrenal

TABLE 14. ADRENAL TUMORS IN INTACT, CASTRATED, AND IRRADIATED MICE

Authors	*Strain*	*Number of exp. animals*	*Number of tumors*	*Treatment*	*Location of tumors*	*Number of controls*	*Number of tumors*
Woolley, Fekete,& Little [423]	DBA	82 ♀	82-nodules	Castrate at 1 da. age	Cortex		
Wooley, Fekete,& Little [425]	dilute brown	40 ♂	13-nodules	Castrate at 1 da. age	Cortex	40	0
Gardner [118]	NH	15 ♀	13	Castrate at 43–65 da.	Cortex		
Fekete, Woolley, & Little [96]	DBA	95 ♀	84-nodules	Castrate at 1 da. age	Cortex		
Woolley, Fekete, & Little [426]	CE	22 ♀	17	Castrate at 2 da. age	Cortex		
Dalton, Edwards, Andervont, & Briggs [77]	C	1 ♀	1	Spontaneous	Cortex		
Woolley & Little [427]	CE	41 ♀	41	Castrate at 1–3 da.	Cortex	(killed 13–24 months)	
						15	0
	CE	19 ♂	15	Castrate at 1–3 da.	Cortex	15	0
						(killed 1–12 months)	
	CE	21 ♀	21	Castrate at 1–3 da.	Cortex	26	0
						(killed 1–12 months)	
Fekete & Little [95]	CE	63 ♀	58 91.9(%)	Castrate at 2 da. age	Cortex	20	0
		51 ♂	51 72.5(%)	Castrate at 2 da. age	Cortex	23	0
Woolley & Little [428]	CE	10 ♂	0	Castrate at birth 4.8 mg. diethylstilbestrol subcut.		35	16
		11 ♀	0	Castrate at birth 4.8 mg. diethylstilbestrol subcut.		32	11
Kirschbaum, Frantz & Williams [209]	NH	14 ♀	13	Spontaneous	Cortex		
		9 ♂	1	"	"		
Frantz & Kirschbaum [101]	Bagg	10 ♂	10	Castrate at weaning age	Cortex		
	Albinos	4 ♀	4		"		
Smith [374]	A	33 ♀	4	Castrate at 4 wk.	Cortex		
	C3H	33 ♀	23	"	"		
	ZAF_1	14 ♀	7	"	"		
	AZF_1	14 ♀	11	"	"		
	ZBC	55 ♀	46	"	"		
	ZBC	24 ♀	17	,	"		

Frantz & Kirschbaum [102]	Bagg Albinos	10 ♀	10	Castrate at weaning age	Cortex	8	4
Smith, Gardner, Li, & Kaplan [376]	BRS	134 ♂	4	Castrated			
	sev. strs.	13 ♀	2	750 RoU-Sb	Medulla	19	1
	" "	13 ♀	0	750 RoU-EB	"		
	" "	10 ♀	0	750 RoU-P	"		
	" "	19 ♀	2	750 RoU-TP	"		
	" "	17 ♀	0	750 RoU-PMS	"		
Dickie & Woolley [81]	DBA ♀ × C57 ♂	19 ♀	9	Castrate 1–3 days	Cortex		
	" "	24 ♂	4	"	"		
	C57 ♀ × DBA ♂	24 ♀	10	"	"		
	" "	22 ♂	4	"	"		
	DBA ♀ × CE ♂	27 ♀	24	"	"		
	" "	32 ♂	25	"	"		
	CE ♀ × DBA ♂	29 ♀	27	"	"		
	" "	24 ♂	17	"	"		
	CE ♀ × C57 ♂	23 ♂	17	"	"		
	" "	23 ♀	9	"	"		
	C57 ♀ × CE ♂	28 ♂	24	"	"		
	" "	21 ♂	13	"	"		
	A ♀ × C3H ♂	22 ♀	14	"	"		
	" "	17 ♂	8	"	"		
	C3H ♀ × A ♂	14 ♀	12	"	"		
	" "	15 ♂	11	"	"		

x, 5 strains and s, hybrids, Sb, stilbestrol; RoU, Roentgen units; EB, 16.6 μg. estradiol benzoate; P, progesterone; TP, testosterone propionate; PMS, pregnant mare serum concentrate.

response. Up to this time just what is inherited, i.e., specific quality of adrenal cortex (end organ), or different type of pituitary hormones, is not known. Furthermore, it is difficult at this time to compare work done in different laboratories, because the impression is definite that a sharp distinction is often not made between hyperplasias, adenomas, and carcinomas.

Marked adrenal hyperplasia also occurs in the adrenal glands of mice of some stocks and of rats that have been subjected to prolonged treatment with estrogens.[117, 271] Castrated mice of some hybrid groups showed a high incidence of adrenal tumors and an associated tendency for pituitary basophilia or "basophile adenomas."[81] "Pituitary tumors" were not observed until the mice were at least 14 months old, whereas adrenal hyperplasias or tumors were noted in many mice 6–13 months old. The pituitary changes were assumed to be secondary to the adrenal changes. The morphological characteristics of an adrenal tumor were not well designated. Adrenal hyperplasia occurs frequently in mice of groups susceptible to pituitary chromophobe adenomas subsequent to estrogen treatment.[117]

Adrenal medullary tumors occur occasionally. One group of investigators[376] has described 5 pheochromocytomas of unknown etiology among groups of irradiated and castrated mice.

One adenoma of the adrenal cortex and one large adrenal medullary tumor were found among 15 female rats of the Long-Evans strain that had received growth hormone for periods up to 485 days. The adrenal medullas of all the animals showed hyperplasia, sometimes extending through the cortex.[282]

LYMPHOID TUMORS

The term lymphoma will be used to refer to lymphosarcoma or lymphatic leukemia, except under rare circumstances, and it will refer to a malignant neoplasm in so far as it causes the ultimate death of the animal and grows progressively following transplantation into related hosts, producing therein a similar disease. Some hyperplastic lymphadenopathies do not meet these criteria and will therefore be omitted from this review.

Lacassagne[228] and Gardner[114] first reported that lymphomas occurred in estrogen-treated mice, appearing predominantly in the thymus or upper mediastinum and usually spreading to involve other organs and tissues. The first more complete study, however, was conducted with mice of the C3H strain. Approximately 15 per cent of the mice given large doses of estrogen had lymphomas at death, and less than 0.5 per cent of the mice not treated with estrogen, or mice given small doses of estrogen, had lymphomas. Estrogen-treated mice had about thirty times more lymphomas than did the controls. Furthermore, the largest doses of estrogen were the most effective in causing lymphoma.[139]

A much more extensive study revealed rather marked strain differences in the leukemogenic action of estrogens.[138] About 15 per cent of mice of the C3H, CBA, and PM stocks died with lymphomas when estrogens were injected; about 25 per cent of the mice that had received the largest doses died with lymphoma. Mice of four other strains showed a smaller increase or no increase in the incidence of lymphomas when estrogens were injected. The hybrid offspring of the mice that were susceptible to estrogen-induced lymphomas and mice that were resistant to lymphomas showed an intermediate incidence of lymphomas following estrogen treatment.[137] The hybrid offspring of two strains susceptible to lymphomas under such conditions showed a marked increase in the incidence of lymphomas.

The action of estrogens in causing lymphomas has been observed in several laboratories and it is usually strain-limited, indicating the importance of genetic or otherwise unknown factors (Table 15). Only 2 of 2000 control mice of three different strains and 121 of 4026 estrogen-treated mice had mediastinal lymphomas.[205] The treatment of mice with large doses of estrogens for three months resulted in an even higher incidence of lymphomas than did continuous treatment.[138] Castrated male mice treated cutaneously from four to six months with estrone dissolved in chloroform had a higher incidence of lymphoid hyperplasia than did intact animals.[82] In this instance the lesions were not transplantable.

When testosterone propionate was administered simultaneously with estrogens the lymphomagenic action of the latter was significantly inhibited, at least in mice of three (C3H, CBA, and PM) inbred strains—only 9 of 245 animals so treated had lymphomas.[138] This indicates that estrogens are lymphomagenic through their physiologic activities, which are largely inhibited by at least this one androgen.

All estrogens seem to possess a similar lymphomagenic quality when administered in adequate amounts: estrone, estradiol, estradiol dipropionate, estradiol benzoate, stilbestrol, and equilin benzoate have all been effective in increasing the incidence of lymphoma.[138]

Some question has been raised concerning the malignancy of estrogen-induced lymphomas. In at least one laboratory, the tumors failed to grow when transplanted into presumably related hosts.[82] This has not been the case in another laboratory, where the only lymphoid gland tumors (including those appearing in the thymus) that have failed to grow when transplanted subcutaneously were those involving only the mesenteric nodes or those belonging to the histocytoma group.[138] Tumors of the former groups have never been classed among the lymphomas in this laboratory, however, as they have been considered to be hyperplasias rather than lymphomas.

CASTRATION AND SEX IN SPONTANEOUS LYMPHOMAS

If exogenous estrogens are effective in increasing the incidence of lymphomas and exogenous androgens in inhibiting the action of estrogens, it is possible that intrinsic hormones may modify the incidence of lymphomas. Numerous experiments have been undertaken to compare the incidence of lymphomas among intact and gonadectomized males and females. Female mice usually have a higher incidence of leukemia than do males although the difference is slight (see Cole and Furth[68] for early references). The more frequent appearance of lymphomas in females than in males occurs in many strains but not in all, the C58 strain being a notable exception. Lymphomas occur more frequently in orchidectomized males than in intact males and ovariectomy has resulted in contradictory results, probably depending upon the strain used. Too often inadequate numbers of animals have been used to permit broad conclusions (Table 16).

TABLE 15. LYMPHOID TUMORS AMONG ESTROGEN-TREATED MICE AND CONTROLS

Authors	*Strain or strains of mice used*	*No. of mice used*	*No. or percentage of lymphoid tumors*	*Treatment*	*No. of controls*	*No. or percentage of lymphoid tumors controls*	*Treatment of controls*
Gardner [114]	A, C3H, CBA	111	4	large doses estrogen	—	none	—
Lacassagne [228]	R3, 30, 39, 17	?	14	estrogen or estrogen and pituitary extract	—	none seen 5 yr.	
Gardner, Kirschbaum, & Strong [139]	C3H	136	22	large doses estrogen	191	1	no treatment or very small doses estrogen
Shimkin, Grady, & Andervont [361]	C	61	7	stilbestrol-cholesterol pellets in mice for 5 to 11 months	143	none in mice 8–16 mo. old, 15 in mice 24 mo. old or more	
Bischoff *et al.*[16]	Marsh-Buffalo	40–T* 80–E†	28–36% 30–50%	2,100 r. u. per mo. 3.3–4.2 mg. total	40 40	18% 10%	sesame oil sesame oil
Bischoff *et al.*[15]	Marsh-Buffalo	36 36	34% 8%	"toxic amounts" "toxic amounts"	43	5%	sesame oil
Gardner [120]	C3H, CBA	303	76	large doses of several different estrogens	481	9	no treatment or sesame oil
Shimkin & Wyman [364]	C3H ♂	97	2	stilbestrol and estrone pellets	320 ♂ ♀	2	

Gardner *et al.*[138]	C3H	747	109	several estrogens in dif. doses	481	5
	CBA	445	67	" " " " "	62	2
	PM	143	22	" " " " "	58	0
	A	94	3	" " " " "	82	0
	C57	170	3	" " " " "	59	3
	JK	64	3	" " " " "	37	1
	C12I	136	8	" " " " "	43	0
	TOTALS	1799	215		822	11
Gardner & Dougherty[137]	16 hybrid groups	1403	165	several estrogens	739	34
Silberberg & Silberberg[367]	D ⚥	57	38.6%	200 r.u. estrogen benzoate wkly.	?	2%
	D ♀	60	40.0%	" " " "		
	D ⚦	73	50.7%	" " " "		
	D ♂	68	45.6%	" " " "		
Dmochowski & Horning[82]	H ⚦	97	38	estrone 4–6 mo. in chloroform	84	0
	H ⚦	100	6	" " " " "		
	H × R ⚦	49	32	" " " " "		
	H ⚦	60	9	" " " " "		
Murphy & Sturm[295]	RIL ♂	116	71.5%	stilbestrol	89	42%
Silberberg & Silberberg[365]	C3H ♂	19	4	.03 mg. estrogen benzoate	95 ♂	0
	C3H ♂	19	6	" " "	178 ♀	2
	C3H ♂	14	1	" " "		
	C3H ⚦	34	2	" " "		

* Theelin. † Estradiol

TABLE 16. EFFECT OF INTRINSIC HORMONES ON THE INCIDENCE OF LYMPHOMAS AND LEUKEMIAS IN MICE

Authors	*Strain or stock of mice*	*No. of mice*	*Sex*	*Number or percentage lymphoma*
McEndy *et al* [267]	AK	56	♀̸	25 (45%)
		67	♀	50 (74%)
		83	♂̸	50 (60%)
		67	♂	35 (52%)
Murphy [292]	RIL	36	♀̸ + tp*	58.3%
		31	♀̸	90.3%
		26	♀	88.4%
		34	♂̸	97.0%
		28	♂	53%
Kirschbaum [208]	F	34	♂̸	17
		22	♀̸	10
		325	♂ & ♀	53%
Kirschbaum & Mixer [210]	DBA	64	♀	8 (12%)
		47	♂	5 (10%)
	CBA	50	♀	4 (8%)
		26	♂	1 (4%)
	BALB	50	♀	1 (2%)
		27	♂	0
	C3H	59	♀	0
		23	♂	0
	A	50	♀	0
		42	♂	0
	F	50	♀	31 (62%)
		42	♂	26 (55%)
Law [240]	C58	41	♂	18 (44%)
		42	♂̸	32 (76%)
		45	♀	27 (60%)
		37	♀̸	24 (65%)
Murphy & Sturm [295]	RIL	89	♂	42%
		40	♀	70%

* Testosterone propionate.

SEX AND SEX HORMONES IN LYPHOMAS OF IRRADIATED ANIMALS

Roentgen-irradiated mice of most strains acquire a higher incidence of lymphoid tumors than do the unirradiated. The original observations of Krebs[217] have been reaffirmed in many laboratories (Table 17). Reference will be made here only to those reports in which hormonal factors have been emphasized in relation to irradiation, that is, where the sex of the irradiated animals has been reported or where sex hormones have been given to irradiated animals.

In general, irradiated female mice acquire more lymphomas than do irradiated males, although in some strains the reverse seems true. In only one instance, however, where fairly large numbers of animals have been used, has the incidence of lymphomas in the irradiated males exceeded that of the females.[203] The tendency for the incidence of lymphomas to be lower in the irradiated males could indicate that the testes exert a lymphoma-inhibiting action. Because the ages at which the mice were irradiated differed greatly in the several laboratories, the endocrine

TABLE 17. EFFECT OF SEX ON THE INCIDENCE OF LYMPHOMAS IN ROENTGEN-IRRADIATED MICE.

Investigator	*Strain*	*Number*	*Percentage or number*
Furth & Furth [109]	A	175 ♂	10%
		165 ♀	26%
	R	84 ♂	3.6%
		81 ♀	11%
	S	148 ♂	14%
		134 ♀	25%
Henshaw [171]	C57	28 ♂	25%
		29 ♀	35%
Kaplan [203]	A	78 ♂	12.8%
		77 ♀	9%
Kirschbaum & Mixer [210]	DBA/2	54 ♂	11
		37 ♀	14
	CBA	33 ♂	18
		37 ♀	14
	BALB	5 ♂	1
		11 ♀	9
	C3H	14 ♂	1
		15 ♀	1
	A	27 ♂	1
		31 ♀	5
	NH	7 ♂	0
		24 ♀	7
	C57	26 ♂	9
		36 ♀	6
	F	55 ♂	17
		47 ♀	12
Gardner [130]	BC	39 ♂	5
		45 ♀	21
Kaplan [204]	C57	14 ♂	11
		18 ♀	15
		22 ♂̸	19
		20 ♀̸	16

* A wide range of doses and methods of applying irradiation was used by the different investigators and sometimes by the same investigator.

TABLE 18. LYMPHOID TUMORS IN MICE OF THE BC STRAIN GIVEN ESTRADIOL BENZOATE OR TESTOSTERONE PROPIONATE SUBSEQUENT TO TOTAL BODY IRRADIATION (380–280 R.)

No. in group	*Sex*	*Treatment*	*No. with lymphoid tumors*
39	♂	sesame oil	7
44	♂	test. prop.	6
40	♂	est. benz.	29
45	♀	sesame oil	21
45	♀	test. prop.	9
42	♀	est. benz.	23

Testosterone propionate, 1.25 mg. weekly; estradiol benzoate, 16.6 μg. weekly.
From Gardner [131] and Gardner and Rygaard.[143]

state of the animals at the time of irradiation presumably also differed and this factor may account for some of the variable results that have been reported.

Recent experiments have indicated that the presence of testes or the addition of testosterone propionate inhibits the lymphomagenic action of roentgen irradiation in mice of at least one strain.[130] Furthermore, the addition of estrogens augmented the lymphomagenic action of x-ray (Table 18).

INFLUENCE OF SEX ON THE LYMPHOMAGENIC ACTION OF CARCINOGENIC HYDROCARBONS

Mice of one strain (DBA—subline 212 now called DBA/2)* show a high incidence of lymphomas at a relatively early age when subjected to methylcholanthrene. Approximately twice as many female mice as male mice so treated had lymphomas, although the difference in the controls was less striking.[210] A more extensive study revealed similar sex differences,[340a] whereas other studies indicated no sex difference in the incidence of lymphomas (Table 19).[238, 285]

TABLE 19. INFLUENCE OF SEX ON THE INCIDENCE OF LYMPHOMAS IN MICE EXPOSED TO CARCINOGENIC HYDROCARBONS

Authors	*Strain*	*Sex*	*Number of animals*	*Percentage or number of tumors*	*Hydrocarbon*
Morton & Mider [285]	DBA/2	♂	156	98.7%	methylcholanthrene
		♀		98.6%	
Law [238]	DBA	♂	119	83.8%	9, 10, dimethyl, 1, 2, benz-anthracene in benzene
		♀		85 %	
Kirschbaum & Mixer [210]	DBA/2	♂	47	15	methylcholanthrene
		♀	95	27	
Rask-Nielsen [340]	ST	♂	258	13	9, 10, dimethyl, 1, 2, benz-anthracene
		♀	403	21	

The several lymphomagenic agents, x-rays, estrogens, and carcinogenic hydrocarbons, seem not to be equally effective on mice of different strains. It has been stated that x-rays are probably the most effective.[208] Whether all of these agents act through a common intermediary is not known but certainly it is possible. Furthermore, it seems quite probable that the demonstrated inhibiting action of testosterone propionate on the lymphomagenic action of estrogens and of x-rays may also apply to the carcinogenic hydrocarbons. The extent to which x-rays may be leukemogenic through the mediation of the hormonal imbalances induced is also unknown. The action of estrogen, properly administered prior to irradiation, upon the increased tolerance of mice to total body irradiation, first reported by Treadwell *et al.*,[395] has been confirmed and indicates a need of further careful work. Furthermore, the possible lymphomagenic action of the adrenal cortical steroids should be investigated extensively.

Both estrogens and x-rays produce a temporary atrophy of the thymus and lymphoid tissues when given in adequate amounts. Dogs given large doses of estrogens invariably die with an extreme myeloid aplasia, a response not noted

* The Committee on Standardized Nomenclature for Inbred Strains of Mice. Standardized Nomeclature for Inbred Strains of Mice. *Cancer Research 12:* 602-613, 1952.

in animals of other species. Up to this time, however, lymphomas have not been described in estrogen-treated dogs.

Furthermore, although rats have been given estrogens over long periods the incidence of lymphoid tumors has not been striking. McEuen[269] observed 4 lymphomas among 34 rats given daily injections of 30 or 120 μg. of estrone. One lymphosarcoma occurred among 106 control rats. The lymphosarcomas involved the mesenteric lymph nodes. Such tumors did, however, occur in some of the animals of the breeding colony (65 females and 10 males). Lymphomas are the most common of tumors in rats;[43] of deep-seated tumors 152 out of 286 were of this type. The mesenteric nodes were the most common site and they occurred more frequently in males than in females. The lungs were occasionally involved. Seventy-five rats, 68 from one strain, had lymphomas involving the thymus, and of these 51 were females.

GROWTH HORMONE

Five of 15 female rats given 6 weekly injections of purified growth hormone for periods up to 485 days had lymphosarcomas of the lung at autopsy and all showed peribronchial lymphoid hyperplasia. None of the tumors involved extrathoracic lymph nodes; in 4, thoracic nodes were involved.[281]

INFLUENCE OF THE ADRENAL GLAND

Direct experiments have not been reported on the possible lymphomagenic action of adrenal cortical hormones or adrenal cortical-like steroids although indirect evidence of their leukemogenic action exists. It is possible that x-rays and estrogens may exert part of their leukemogenic action through the adrenal.

The capacity of estrogenic hormones and adrenal cortical hormones to cause a regression of lymphoid tissues is well known. Several investigators have reported either a temporary regression of transplanted lymphoid tumors in rats and mice given adrenal cortical-like compounds or a decreased incidence of successful "takes".[167, 293] Adrenalectomized rats were more susceptible to transplanted lymphomas than were intact rats.[294] The numerous recent studies on the possible chemotherapeutic action of cortisone and related compounds and adrenocorticotropic preparations will not be discussed here.

RENAL TUMORS

Male hamsters treated with diethylstilbestrol for 250 days or more have had tumors of the kidney.[207, 265, 408] The tumors may be multiple, become very large and metastasize throughout the abdomen. The tumors appear to arise from the pelvic epithelium but their exact origin is not known. To date they have occurred only in male hamsters.

ACTION OF ESTROGENS OR SEX INFLUENCES ON BONE AND OSTEOGENIC TUMORS

Skeletal sexual dimorphism has been noted for many years (see Gardner and Pfeiffer[141] for review). The pelves of some mammals show marked gross sexual dimorphism of either a transitory type as in the guinea pig, or of a persistent type as in the mouse. Generalized osseous changes in birds are associated with reproductive activity.

Estrogenic hormones induce marked changes in the osseous tissues of birds and some mammals such as the rat[432] and mouse.[116, 122, 141] Space does not permit an adequate reference to investigations in this field. Mention of the unusual responses to estrogenic chemicals is made for two reasons: (1) because it demonstrates so well some morphologic and physiologic responses to sex hormones; and (2) because osteogenic tumors have been observed, in mice of one strain at least, predominantly in the females. Pybus and Miller[278, 338, 339] observed osteogenic tumors in 77.3 per cent of female mice of one strain [Pybus' and Miller's branch of Marsh's Strain 3] and only in 29.6 per cent of the males; a difference of more than 2.5 times. These tumors were often multiple, but not always, and were widely distributed throughout the body.[339] Mice of this same strain have not acquired osteogenic tumors, or have rarely had such tumors in other laboratories.[132]

The osseous tissues of mice of different strains respond somewhat differently to estrogens. The mice of the strain studied by Pybus and Miller show a more rapid endosteal proliferation of new bone and subsequently an osteoclastic response.[122, 125, 277] Similar responses were noted in hypothyroid mice of other strains.[125]

Most of the bone tumors were apparently of periosteal origin whereas estrogen had less effect on periosteal bone formation insofar as has been determined, but rather induces endosteal bone growth. Testosterone propionate prevents the development of the characteristic osseous response of estrogen-treated mice when the two hormones are given concurrently.[122]

HORMONES AND THE RESPONSE TO CARCINOGENIC HYDROCARBONS

A number of investigators have studied the differences in age of and rate of appearance of tumors in male and female mice treated in different ways with carcinogenic chemicals or with carcinogenic chemicals and sex hormones. The incidence of tumors, largely epidermoid, in mice given cutaneous applications of methylcholanthrene dissolved in benzene was similar in both sexes.[152] A slight sex difference occurred when methylcholanthrene was injected subcutaneously in large doses.[386] On the other hand some investigators have noted that papillomata occurred earlier and more frequently became malignant in female mice.[34, 218, 276] Others have noted no difference in the incidence of tumors between male and female mice but an earlier appearance of tumors among the females,[341] and still others have noted a higher incidence of tumors in male mice given carcinogens subcutaneously.[344] Mice of different strains have been used in the different studies. Because of the differences in strains of animals used, differences in concentration and composition of carcinogen, and differences in method of application it is difficult to draw any conclusion except that sex may modify the response to carcinogens.

Mice given cutaneous applications of estrogens and methylcholanthrene dissolved in chloroform had a higher incidence of tumors than mice given methylcholanthrene alone.[152] On the other hand large doses of testosterone propionate slightly delayed the time of appearance of subcutaneous tumors around pellets of methylcholanthrene.[98]

Female mice of all strains (*A*, C3H, C57, and hybrids) were much more susceptible to hepatomas when *o*-aminoazotoluene or *para*-dimethylaminoazobenzene was used.[4, 5] The incidence of hepatomas among untreated mice is usually higher in males.

Rats fed 0.03 per cent 2-acetylaminofluorene with their diet showed a higher incidence of hepatic tumors when estradiol dipropionate (.125 mg. three times weekly) or testosterone propionate (.5 mg. three times weekly) was injected in sesame oil. Animals fed thiouracil had no hepatic neoplasia.[64] Male rats (83.6 per cent) were more susceptible to such tumors than were females (46 per cent); the decreased incidence in males given thiouracil (22 per cent) was not reversed when testosterone propionate was also given (29 per cent) but was prevented by the simultaneous administration of thyroxin (72 per cent). Thiouracil, however, prevented the hepatoma-favoring action of testosterone propionate.[317]

Although the influence of sex or gonadal hormones on responses to carcinogenic chemicals has not been consistent in all of the studies reported the general indications are that testosterone propionate or intrinsic androgens lower the incidence of skin or epidermoid tumors. When carcinogens were injected subcutaneously into animals such irregular results have been obtained that no trends can be discerned.

THE ACTION OF ANTERIOR PITUITARY HORMONES ON TUMORIGENESIS AND TUMOR GROWTH

The appearance of lymphoid and adrenal tumors in rats given pure growth stimulating hormone for long periods of time has already been mentioned[281, 282] and the possible role of gonadotropic hormones in ovarian, testicular and mammary tumorigenesis has been discussed. The growth of spontaneous or transplanted tumors and the response to carcinogenic hydrocarbons has also been studied using hypophysectomized animals.

The Walker rat carcinoma[12, 273, 345] and the Jensen sarcoma[342] in rats grew only about one-third as rapidly in hypophysectomized as in intact rats. The ratio of tumor weight to body weight was not greatly different, however, because of the cessation of general body growth in hypophysectomized animals. Intact animals, pair-fed with hypophysectomized controls, showed a greater increase in tumor weight and a greater loss of body weight. The effect of inanition therefore did not seem to account for the entire decrease in rate of growth in the hypophysectomized animals.[14, 17] Other investigators stated that the inanition during pituitary deficiency was the cause of the slower growth rate,[274] and found that the presence of successful transplants was greater in hypophysectomized rats than in starved rats. The pituitary is apparently not required for protein additions to malignant tissues but it does increase the rate of such additions. Tumors induced in rats given repeated subcutaneous injections of 1,2,5,6-dibenzanthracene also grew more slowly after their bearers were hypophysectomized: 0.33 gm. per day in hypophysectomized rats and 2.45 gm. in the controls.[13]

The process of carcinogenesis is not necessarily related to the growth of autogenous or transplanted tumors. Because of the relatively weakened condition of hypophysectomized animals few studies on carcinogenesis in such animals have been undertaken. Korteweg and Thomas,[215] however, found that papillomas and carcinomas arising in hypophysectomized mice painted with a solution of 3,4-benzpyrene occurred at a much later age than in the intact controls similarly treated. The hypophysis was not necessary for carcinogenesis. Elsewhere the growth of mammary tumors and testicular tumors in hypophysectomized animals has been mentioned.

SEMINAL VESICLES AND PROSTATE

Numerous studies on the effect of steroids on the prostate have been reported[283] but malignant changes have not occurred. Squamous metaplasia of the epithelia of the coagulating glands and seminal vesicles occurs after prolonged treatment of mice with estrogens;[54, 62, 222] in some strains to a greater extent than in others. Estrogen treatment also results in a fibromuscular hypertrophy of the male accessory glands.

Carcinogenic hydrocarbons induce malignant changes in transplants of prostatic glands in mice: 54 tumors from 75 mice.[186, 187.] Ten of these were epidermoid carcinomas but 42 were glandular. The prostatic lesions were induced by carcinogenic hydrocarbons more frequently in prostatic tissue from young animals.[187] Subsequent to transplantation the tumors often showed squamous metaplasia after some time. Most of the glandular tumors regressed when transplanted into prepubertally castrated mice; some resumed growth after injections of testosterone propionate. The squamous tumors were not affected by an absence of androgen. The glandular tumors transplanted into mice subsequently given stilbestrol regressed and showed some squamous metaplasia but after some time again grew progressively. Rats of several strains, as well as mice, acquire squamous cell carcinomas of the prostate when exposed to benzpyrene or methylcholanthrene. [85, 188, 284]

Prostatic hypertrophy and metaplasia occur frequently in dogs,[162, 437] a condition that can be reproduced by the injection of estrogens;[437] testosterone administered with estrogens prevented the prostatic changes. In monkeys, estrogens induce a marked fibromuscular hypertrophy and squamous metaplasia of the urethral epithelium.[404, 436]

There is no evidence that exogenous steroids are related to carcinogenesis of the prostate. The rare occurrence of spontaneous tumors in the prostate of experimental animals affords no significant leads. That the tissues are capable of malignant change has been demonstrated by their response to carcinogenic hydrocarbons. Many of the tumors so induced, however, are squamous epitheliomas and quite unlike the disease as it exists in man.

TUMORS AT THE SITES OF APPLICATION OF ESTROGENS

Several investigators have described sarcomas, usually spindle-cell or fibrosarcomas, arising at the sites of injection of estrogens when the latter have been dissolved in oils.[51, 145, 227] At one time it was considered that estrogens in high concentrations in the subcutaneous tissues might be carcinogenic, that is, induce sarcomas at the sites of injection. Tumors, however, have appeared in animals given sesame oil, the solvent used for the estrogens in some experiments. Whether the physical presence of oil, repeatedly injected at weekly intervals, or whether some chemical component is carcinogenic, is of course unknown. The appearance of tumors in animals given repeated injections of fatty fractions of normal or malignant tissues must, however, be considered as a nonspecific response unless the solvents of these fractions are tested carefully. Up to this time the appearance of sarcomas in relation to pellets of estrogens or estrogen and cholesterol have not been reported, an indication that the chemicals themselves are not carcinogenic. (One fibrosarcoma that surrounded a pellet of one part of stilbestrol and 3 parts of cholesterol,[132] has been found in the animal colony of the writers' laboratory—an incidence of no more than 0.1 per cent.)

BIBLIOGRAPHY

1. Abramson, W., and Warshawsky, H. Cancer of the breast in the male, secondary to estrogenic administration: Report of a case. *J. Urol. 59:* 76-82, 1948.
2. Albert, S., and Selye, H. The effects of various pharmacological agents on the morphogenetic action of estradiol. *J. Pharmacol. & Exper. Therap. 75:* 308-315, 1942.
3. Allen, E., and Gardner, W. U. Cancer of the cervix of the uterus in hybrid mice following long-continued administration of estrogen. *Cancer Research 1:* 359-366, 1941.
4. Andervont, H. B., Grady, H. G., and Edwards, J. E. Induction of hepatic lesions, hepatomas, pulmonary tumors, and hemangio-endotheliomas in mice with *o*-aminoazotoluene. *J. Nat. Cancer Inst. 3:* 131-153, 1942.
5. Andervont, H. B., White, J., and Edwards, J. E. Effect of two azo compounds when added to the diet of mice. *J. Nat. Cancer Inst. 4:* 583-586, 1943.
6. Armstrong, E. C. Observations on the nature of the oestrous cycle and on the effect upon it of the milk factor, in mice of two inbred strains, differing in mammary cancer incidence. *Brit. J. Cancer 2:* 59-69, 1948.
7. Armstrong, E. C., and Bonser, G. M. Effect of castration upon the induction of mammary tumors by oestrogen in male mice of the Strong A strain. *J. Path. & Bact. 60:* 517-519, 1948.
8. Athias, M. Lésions testiculaires chez des souris non cancéreuses, appartenant à une lignée très sujette au cancer de la glande mammaire. *Arq. Pathol. 17:* 397-417, 1945.
9. Athias, M., and Furtado Dias, M. T. Lésions testiculaires chez des souris atteintes d'adénocarcinome spontané de la glande mammaire. *Arq. Pathol. 13:* 381-396, 1941.
10. Bacsich, P., and Folley, S. J. The effect of oestradiol monobenzoate on the gonads, endocrine glands and mammae of lactating rats. *J. Anat. 73:* 432-440, 1939.
11. Bali, T., and Furth, J. Morphological and biological characteristics of x-ray induced transplantable ovarian tumors. *Cancer Research 9:* 449-472, 1949.
12. Ball, H. A., Samuels, L. T., and Simpson, W. The relation of the hypophysis to the growth of malignant tumors: I. The effect of hypophysectomy on transplanted carcinoma in the white rat. *Am. J. Cancer 16:* 351-359, 1932.

13. BALL, H. A., and SAMUELS, L. T. The relation of the hypophysis to the growth of malignant tumors: III. The effect of hypophysectomy on autogenous tumors. *Am. J. Cancer 26:* 347-351, 1936.
14. BALL, H. A., and SAMUELS, L. T. The relation of the hypophysis to the growth of malignant tumors: IV. A study of the influence of nutritional factors on Walker tumor 256 on relation to the effect of hypophysectomy. *Am. J. Cancer 32:* 50-56, 1938.
15. BISCHOFF, F., LONG, M. L., RUPP, J. J., and CLARKE, G. J. Influence of toxic amounts of estrin upon intact and castrated male Marsh-Buffalo mice. *Cancer Research 2:* 198-199, 1942.
16. BISCHOFF, F., LONG, M. L., RUPP, J. J., and CLARKE, G. J. Carcinogenic effect of estradiol and of theelin in Marsh-Buffalo mice. *Cancer Research 2:* 52-55, 1942.
17. BISCHOFF, F., MAXWELL, L. C., and ULLMAN, H. J. Hormones in Cancer. VIII. The influence of the hypophysis. *Am. J. Cancer 26:* 329-345, 1936.
18. BISCHOFF, F., ULLMAN, H. J., and INGRAHAM, L. P. The influence of irradiation of the ovaries upon estrus and neoplastic development in Marsh-Buffalo mice. *Radiology 43:* 55-58, 1944.
19. BISKIND, M. S., and BISKIND, G. R. Development of tumors in the rat ovary after transplantation into the spleen. *Proc. Soc. Exper. Biol. & Med. 55:* 176-179, 1944.
20. BISKIND, M. S., and BISKIND, G. R. Tumors of rat testis produced by heterotransplantation of infantile testis to spleen of adult castrate. *Proc. Soc. Exper. Biol. & Med. 59:* 4-8, 1945.
21. BISKIND, G. R., and BISKIND, M. S. Experimental ovarian tumors in rats. *Am. J. Clin. Path. 19:* 501-521, 1949.
22. BITTNER, J. J. Some possible effects of nursing on mammary gland tumor incidence in mice. *Science 84:* 162-163, 1936.
23. BITTNER, J. J. Tumor incidence in reciprocal F_1 hybrid mice: A×D high tumor stock. *Proc. Soc. Exper. Biol. & Med. 34:* 42-48, 1936.
24. BITTNER, J. J. Breast and lung carcinoma in A stock mice. *Pub. Health Rep. 54:* 380-392, 1939.
25. BITTNER, J. J. Possible method of transmission of susceptibility to breast cancer in mice. *Am. J. Cancer 39:* 104-113, 1940.
26. BITTNER, J. J. The influence of estrogens on the incidence of tumors in foster nursed mice. *Cancer Research 1:* 290-292, 1941.
27. BITTNER, J. J. Possible relationship of the estrogenic hormones, genetic susceptibility, and milk influence in the production of mammary cancer in mice. *Cancer Research 2:* 710-721, 1942.
28. BITTNER, J. J. Inciting influences in the etiology of mammary cancer in mice. A.A.A.S.: Gibson Island Research Conference on Cancer, Lancaster, Pa., Science Press, pp. 63-96, 1944.
29. BITTNER, J. J. Some enigmas associated with the genesis of mammary cancer in mice. *Cancer Research 8:* 625-639, 1948.
30. BITTNER, J. J., HUSEBY, R. A., VISSCHER, M. B., BALL, Z. B., and SMITH, F. Mammary cancer and mammary structure in inbred stocks of mice and their hybrids. *Science 99:* 83-85, 1944.
31. BODDAERT, J. Unpublished data.

32. BONSER, G. M. A comparison of the normal oestrous cycle and of the response to the administration of oestrin in two strains of mice differing greatly in incidence of spontaneous mammary cancer. *J. Path. & Bact. 41:* 33-42, 1935.

33. BONSER, G. M. The effect of oestrone administration on the mammary glands of male mice of two strains differing greatly in their susceptibility to spontaneous mammary carcinoma. *J. Path. & Bact. 42:* 169-181, 1936.

34. BONSER, G. M. The hereditary factor in induced skin tumors in mice: establishment of a strain specially sensitive to carcinogenic agents applied to skin. *J. Path. & Bact. 46:* 581-602, 1938.

35. BONSER, G. M. Malignant tumors of the interstitial cells of the testis in Strong A mice treated with triphenylethylene. *J. Path. & Bact. 54:* 149-154, 1942.

36. BONSER, G. M. Mammary and testicular tumours in male mice of various strains following oestrogen treatment. *J. Path. & Bact. 56:* 15-26, 1944.

37. BONSER, G. M., and HAWKSLEY, L. M. Two cases of interstitial-cell tumour of the human testis. *J. Path. & Bact. 55:* 295-299, 1943.

38. BONSER, G. M., and ROBSON, J. M. The effects of prolonged oestrogen administration upon male mice of various strains: Development of testicular tumors in the Strong A strain. *J. Path. & Bact. 51:* 9-22, 1940.

39. BRAMBEL, F. W. R., and PARKES, H. S. Changes in the ovary of the mouse following exposure to x-rays. *Proc. Roy. Soc.,* London, s.B., *101:* 316-328, 1927.

40. BRAUN, H. Zwischenzelladenome des Hodens, Beobachtungen an Hunden und am Menchen. *Virchows Arch. Path. Anat. 304:* 106-114, 1939.

41. BRUNSCHWIG, A., and BISSELL, A. D. Estrus cycles in mice of cancerous and noncancerous strains. *Arch. Surg. 33:* 515-520, 1936.

42. BRYAN, W. R., KLINCK, G. H., and WOLFE, J. M. The unusual occurrence of a high incidence of spontaneous mammary tumors in the Albany strain of rats. *Am. J. Cancer 33:* 370-388, 1938.

43. BULLOCK, F. D., and CURTIS, M. R. Spontaneous tumors of the rat. *J. Cancer Research 14:* 1-115, 1930.

44. BURACK, E., DANZI, M. V., WOLFE, J. M., and WRIGHT, A. W. Incidence of spontaneous fibroadenoma in the Albany strain of rats. *Cancer Research 4:* 410-416, 1944.

45. BURACK, E., WOLFE, J. M., LANSING, W., and WRIGHT, A. W. The effect of age upon the connective tissue of the uterus, cervix, and vagina of the rat. *Cancer Research 1:* 227-235, 1941.

46. BURCH, J. C., MCCLELLAN, G. S., JOHNSON, C. D., and ELLISON, E. T. The diagnosis and classification of menstrual disorders. *J.A.M.A. 108:* 96-101, 1937.

47. BURCH, J. C., WILLIAMS, W. L., and CUNNINGHAM, R. S. The etiology of endometrial hyperplasia. *Surg. Gynec. & Obst. 53:* 338-345, 1931.

48. BURCH, J. C., WOLFE, J. M., and CUNNINGHAM, R. S. Experiments on endometrial hyperplasia. *Endocrinology 16:* 541-546, 1932.

49. BURNS, E. L., MOSKOP, M., SUNTZEFF, V., and LOEB, L. On the relation between the incidence of mammary cancer and the nature of the sexual cycle in various strains of mice. *Am. J. Cancer 26:* 56-58, 1936.

50. BURNS, E. L., and SCHENKEN, J. R. Quantitative studies on relationship between estrogen and mammary gland carcinoma in strain C3H mice. *Proc. Soc. Exper. Biol. & Med. 43:* 608-610, 1940.

51. BURNS, E. L., SUNTZEFF, V., and LOEB, L. The development of sarcoma in mice injected with hormones or hormone-like substances. *Am. J. Cancer 32:* 534-544, 1938.

52. BURROWS, H. Changes induced in the interstitial tissue of the testis of the mouse by certain estrogens. *J. Path. & Bact. 41:* 218-219, 1935.

53. BURROWS, H. Carcinoma mammae occurring in a male mouse under continued treatment with oestrin. *Am. J. Cancer 24:* 613-616, 1935.

54. BURROWS, H. Pathological conditions induced by oestrogenic compounds in the coagulating gland and prostate of the mouse. *Am. J. Cancer 23:* 490-512, 1935.

55. BURROWS, H. Pituitary hyperplasia in a male mouse after the administration of oestrin. *Am. J. Cancer 28:* 741-745, 1936.

56. BURROWS, H. A comparison of the changes induced by some pure oestrogenic compounds in the mammae and testis of mice. *J. Path. & Bact. 42:* 161-168, 1936.

57. BURROWS, H. Acquired resistance to oestrone in a male mouse. *J. Path. & Bact. 44:* 699-701, 1937.

58. BURROWS, H. Spontaneous uterine and mammary tumors in the rabbit. *J. Path. & Bact. 51:* 385-390, 1940.

59. BURROWS, H. *Biological Actions of Sex Hormones* (ed. 2). Cambridge, The University Press, 1949.

60. BURROWS, H., and BOYLAND, E. Neoplasia in rabbits following the administration of 1,2,5,6-dibenzanthracene. *Am. J. Cancer 32:* 367-382, 1938.

61. BURROWS, H., and HOCH-LIGETI, C. Effect of progesterone on the development of mammary cancer in C3H mice. *Cancer Research 6:* 608-609, 1946.

62. BURROWS, H., and KENNAWAY, N. M. On some effects produced by applying oestrin to the skin of mice. *Am. J. Cancer 20:* 48-57, 1934.

63. BUTTERWORTH, J. S. Observations on the histogenesis of ovarian tumors produced in mice by x-ray. *Am. J. Cancer 31:* 85-99, 1937.

64. CANTAROW, A., PASCHKIS, K. E., STASNEY, J., and ROTHENBERG, M. W. The influence of sex hormones on the hepatic lesions produced by 2-acetylaminofluorene. *Cancer Research 6:* 610-616, 1946

65. CANTAROW, A., STASNEY, J., and PASCHKIS, K. E. The influence of sex hormones on mammary tumors induced by 2-acetylaminofluorene. *Cancer Research 8:* 412-417, 1948.

66. CHAMORRO, A. Production par le benzoate d'oestrone d'adénocarcinome mammaire chez des rats. *Compt. rend Soc. de biol. 137:* 325-326, 1943.

67. CLIFFTON, E. E., and WOLSTENHOLM, J. T. Hypervolemia and associated changes in mice bearing a transplanted granulosa cell tumor. *Cancer Research 9:* 331-335, 1949.

68. COLE, R. K., and FURTH, J. Experimental studies on the genetics of spontaneous leukemia in mice. *Cancer Research 1:* 957-965, 1941.

69. COLLINS, E. E. Somatic carcinoma and the state of the interstitial cells of the testicle. *Arch. Path. 22:* 470-476, 1936.

70. CORI, C. F. The influence of ovariectomy on the spontaneous occurrence of mammary carcinomas in mice. *J. Exper. Med. 45:* 983-991, 1927.

71. CRAMER, W., and HORNING, E. S. Experimental production by oestrin of pituitary tumours with hypopituitarism and of mammary cancer. *Lancet 230:* 247-248, 1936.

72. Cramer, W., and Horning, E. S. Effects of oestrin on the pituitary gland. *Lancet 230:* 1056-1057, 1936.

73. Cramer, W., and Horning, E. S. Adrenal changes associated with oestrin administration and mammary cancer. *J. Path. & Bact. 44:* 633-642, 1937.

74. Crossen, R. J., and Loeb, L. Long-continued administration of an estrogen on the sex organs of mice. *Arch. Path. 37:* 202-212, 1944.

75. Dahl-Iversen, E., and Hamburger, C. Experimental studies on cystic, glandular hyperplasia of the endometrium. II. Inability of x-ray treatment of the ovaries to produce cystic glandular hyperplasia of the endometrium in Rhesus monkeys. *Acta obst. et gynec. Scandinav. 27:* 317-326, 1947.

76. Dahl-Iversen, E., Hamburger, C., and Jorgensen, H. Cystic glandular hyperplasia of the endometrium elucidated by therapeutic experiences in patients and by experiments on Rhesus monkeys. *Acta obst. et gynec. Scandinav. 21:* 315-350, 1942.

77. Dalton, A. J., Edwards, J. E., Andervont, H. B., and Briggs, V. C. A spontaneous, transplantable, adrenal cortical tumor arising in a Strain C2 mouse. *J. Nat. Cancer Inst. 4:* 329, 1943-44.

78. Deanesly, R. Depression of hypophyseal activity by the implantation of tablets of oestrone and oestradiol. *J. Endocrinol. 1:* 36-48, 1939.

79. DeJongh, S. E., and Korteweg, R. Der Einfluss von Ovar-implantationen auf die Genitalien der kastrierten männlichen Maus. *Acta brev. Neerland 5:* 126-127, 1935.

80. Deringer, M. K., Heston, W. E., and Andervont, H. B. Estrus in virgin strain C3H (high-tumor) and virgin strain A (low-tumor) mice and in the reciprocal (A×C3H) F_1 hybrids. *J. Nat. Cancer Inst. 5:* 403-405, 1945.

81. Dickie, M. M., and Woolley, G. W. Spontaneous basophilic tumors of the pituitary glands in gonadectomized mice. *Cancer Research 9:* 372-384, 1949.

82. Dmochowski, L., and Horning, E. S. Influence of oestrone on the lymphoid tissues of male mice. *J. Path. & Bact. 59:* 307-312, 1947.

83. Dmochowski, L., and Orr, J. W. Induction of breast cancer by oestrogens and methylcholanthrene in high- and low-breast cancer strain mice. *Brit. J. Cancer 3:* 376-384, 1949.

84. Dorfman, R. I., and Gardner, W. U. Metabolism of the steroid hormones. The excretion of estrogenic material by ovariectomized mice bearing adrenal tumors. *Endocrinology 34:* 421-423, 1944.

85. Dunning, W. F., Curtis, M. R., and Segaloff, A. Methylcholanthrene squamous cell carcinoma of the rat prostate with skeletal metastases, and failure of the rat liver to respond to the same carcinogen. *Cancer Research 6:* 256-262, 1946.

86. Dunning, W. F., Curtis, M. R., and Segaloff, A. Strain differences in response to diethylstilbestrol and the induction of mammary gland and bladder cancer in the rat. *Cancer Research 7:* 511-521, 1947.

87. Dunning, W. F., Curtis, M. R., and Segaloff, A. Strain differences in response to diethylstilbestrol and the induction of mammary gland, adrenal and bladder cancer in the rat. *Unio Internat. Contra Cancrum, Acta 6:* 109-123, 1948.

88. Dürch, H. Ueber die Zwischenzellenhyperplasie des Hodens. *Verhandl. d. deutsch. path. Gesellsch. 11:* 130-136, 1907.

89. Eisen, M. J. The occurrence of benign and malignant mammary lesions in rats treated with crystalline estrogen. *Cancer Research 2:* 632-644, 1942.

90. ENGLE, E. T. Effect of daily transplants of anterior lobe from gonadectomized rats on immature test animals. *Am. J. Physiol. 88:* 101-106, 1929.

91. ENGLE, E. T., KRAKOWER, C., and HAAGENSEN, C. D. Estrogen administration to aged female monkeys with no resultant tumors. *Cancer Research 3:* 858-866, 1943.

92. ESCHENBRENNER, A. B., and MILLER, E. Quantitative histologic analysis of the effect of x-radiation on the interstitial tissue of the testis of LAF_1 mice. *J. Nat. Cancer Inst. 6:* 343-348, 1946.

93. ESCHENBRENNER, A. B., MILLER, E., and LORENZ, E. Quantitative histologic analysis of the effect of chronic whole-body irradiation with gamma rays on spermatogenic elements and the interstitial tissue of the testes of mice. *J. Nat. Cancer Inst. 9:* 133-147, 1948.

94. EVANS, H. M., and SIMPSON, M. E. A comparison of anterior hypophyseal implants from normal and gonadectomized animals with reference to their capacity to stimulate the immature ovary. *Am. J. Physiol. 89:* 371-374, 1929.

95. FEKETE, E., and LITTLE, C. C. Histological study of adrenal cortical tumors in gonadectomized mice of the ce strain. *Cancer Research 5:* 220-226, 1945.

96. FEKETE, E., WOOLLEY, G., and LITTLE, C. C. Histological changes following ovariectomy in mice. I. DBA high tumor strain. *J. Exper. Med. 74:* 1-8, 1941.

97. FISCHER, O. Uber Hypophysengeschwülste der weissen Ratten. *Virchows Arch. f. path. Anat. 259:* 9-29, 1926.

98. FLAKS, J. Influence of testosterone propionate on the induction of subcutaneous tumours in mice by 20-methylcholanthrene. *Brit. J. Cancer 2:* 386-394, 1948.

99. FLAKS, J. Adrenal cortical carcinoma with metastases in an ovariectomized Strong A mouse. *J. Path. & Bact. 61:* 266-269, 1949.

99a. FOULDS, L. Mammary tumors in hybrid mice: A sex-factor in transplantation. *Brit. J. Cancer 1:* 362-370, 1947.

99b. FOULDS, L. Mammary tumors in hybrid mice: Growth and progression of spontaneous tumors. *Brit. J. Cancer 3:* 345-375, 1949.

100. FOX, H. Report of the Laboratory and Museum of Comparative Pathology of the Zoological Society of Philadelphia, Vol. 52, 1924, p. 23.

101. FRANTZ, M. J., and KIRSCHBAUM, A. Androgenic secretion by tumors of the mouse adrenal cortex. *Proc. Soc. Exper. Biol. & Med. 69:* 357, 1948.

102. FRANTZ, M. J., and KIRSCHBAUM, A. Sex hormone secretion by tumors of the adrenal cortex of mice. *Cancer Research 9:* 257-266, 1949.

103. FRANTZ, M., KIRSCHBAUM, A., and CASAS, C. Endocrine interrelationship and spontaneous tumors of the adrenal cortex in NH mice. *Proc. Soc. Exper. Biol & Med. 66:* 645-646, 1947.

104. FURTH, J. Transplantability of induced granulosa cell tumors and luteoma in mice. Secondary effects of these growths. *Proc. Soc. Exper. Biol. & Med. 61:* 212-214, 1946.

105. FURTH, J. Relation of pregnancies to induction of ovarian tumors by x-rays. *Proc. Soc. Exper. Biol. & Med. 71:* 274-277, 1949.

106. FURTH, J., and BOON, M. C. Liver changes associated with a transplantable granulosa-cell carcinoma in mice. *Proc. Soc. Exper. Biol. & Med. 58:* 112-114, 1945.

107. FURTH, J., and BOON, M. C. Induction of ovarian tumors in mice by x-rays. *Cancer Research 7:* 241-245, 1947.

108. FURTH, J., and BUTTERWORTH, J. S. Neoplastic diseases occurring among mice subjected to general irradiation with x-rays: II. Ovarian tumors and associated lesions. *Am. J. Cancer 28:* 66-95, 1936.
109. FURTH, J., and FURTH, O. B. Neoplastic diseases produced in mice by general irradiation with x-rays: I. Incidence and types of neoplasms. *Am. J. Cancer 28:* 54-65, 1936.
110. FURTH, J., and SOBEL, H. Hypervolemia secondary to grafted granulosa cell tumors. *J. Nat. Cancer Inst. 7:* 103-113, 1946.
111. FURTH, J., and SOBEL, H. Neoplastic transformation of granulosa cells in grafts of normal ovaries into spleens of gonadectomized mice. *J. Nat. Cancer Inst. 8:* 7-16, 1947.
112. FURTH, J., and SOBEL, H. Transplantable luteoma in mice and associated secondary changes. *Cancer Research 7:* 246-262, 1947.
113. GARDNER, W. U. Hypertrophy of interstitial cells in the testes of mice receiving estrogenic hormones. *Anat. Rec. 68:* 339-347, 1937.
114. GARDNER, W. U. Influence of estrogenic hormones on abnormal growths. "Some fundamental aspects of the cancer problem." *A.A.A.S. 4:* 67-75, 1937.
115. GARDNER, W. U. Estrogens in carcinogenesis. *Arch. Path. 27:* 138-170, 1939.
116. GARDNER, W. U. The breaking strength of femurs of mice receiving estrogens. *Proc. Soc. Exper. Biol. & Med. 45:* 230-232, 1940.
117. GARDNER, W. U. The effect of estrogen on the incidence of mammary and pituitary tumors of hybrid mice. *Cancer Research 1:* 345-358, 1941.
118. GARDNER, W. U. Estrogenic effects of adrenal tumors of ovariectomized mice. *Cancer Research 1:* 632-637, 1941.
119. GARDNER, W. U. Inhibition of mammary growth by large amounts of estrogen. *Endocrinology 28:* 53-61, 1941.
120. GARDNER, W. U. Lymphoid tumors in estrogen-treated mice. *Cancer Research 2:* 725, 1942.
121. GARDNER, W. U. Persistence and growth of spontaneous mammary tumors and hyperplastic nodules in hypophysectomized mice. *Cancer Research 2:* 476-488, 1942.
122. GARDNER, W. U. Influence of sex and sex hormones on the breaking strength of bones of mice. *Endocrinology 32:* 149-160, 1943.
123. GARDNER, W. U. Testicular tumors in mice of several strains receiving triphenylethylene. *Cancer Research 3:* 92-99, 1943.
124. GARDNER, W. U. Spontaneous testicular tumors in mice. *Cancer Research 3:* 757-761, 1943.
125. GARDNER, W. U. Report at 6th meeting of Conference on Metabolic Aspects of Convalescence Including Bone and Wound Healing. New York, Josiah Macy, Jr. Fund, pp. 84-88, 1944.
126. GARDNER, W. U. Tumors in experimental animals receiving steroid hormones. *Surgery 16:* 8-32, 1944.
127. GARDNER, W. U. Some influences of hormones on the growth and persistence of transplanted testicular tumors. *Cancer Research 5:* 497-505, 1945.
128. GARDNER, W. U. The incidence of mammary tumors and the structure of mammary glands of estrogen plus testosterone-treated mice. *Cancer Research 6:* 493, 1946.
129. GARDNER, W. U. Hormonal imbalances in tumorigenesis. *Cancer Research 8:* 397-411, 1948.

130. GARDNER, W. U. Effect of estradiol benzoate and testosterone propionate on x-ray induced leukemia in mice. *Cancer Research 10:* 219, 1950.
131. GARDNER, W. U. Ovarian and lymphoid tumors in female mice of the BC strain subsequent to roentgen-ray irradiation and hormone treatment. *Proc. Soc. Exper. Biol. & Med. 74:* 434-436, 1950.
132. GARDNER, W. U. Unpublished data.
133. GARDNER, W. U., and ALLEN, E. Some effects of estrogens on the uterus of the mouse. *Endocrinology 21:* 621-730, 1937.
134. GARDNER, W. U., and ALLEN, E. Malignant and non-malignant uterine and vaginal lesions in mice receiving estrogens and androgens simultaneously. *Yale J. Biol. & Med. 12:* 213-234, 1939.
135. GARDNER, W. U., ALLEN, E., SMITH, G. M., and STRONG, L. C. Carcinoma of the cervix of mice receiving estrogens. *J.A.M.A. 110:* 1182-1183, 1938.
136. GARDNER, W. U., and BODDAERT, J. Testicular interstitial cell tumors in hybrid mice given tri-p-anisyl chloroethylene. *Arch. Path. 50:* 750-764, 1950.
137. GARDNER, W. U., and DOUGHERTY, T. F. The leukemogenic action in hybrid mice. *Yale J. Biol. & Med. 17:* 75-90, 1944.
138. GARDNER, W. U., DOUGHERTY, T. F., and WILLIAMS, W. L. Lymphoid tumors in mice receiving steroid hormones. *Cancer Research 4:* 73-87, 1944.
139. GARDNER, W. U., KIRSCHBAUM, A., and STRONG, L. C. Lymphoid tumors in mice receiving estrogens. *Arch. Path. 29:* 1-7, 1940.
140. GARDNER, W. U., and PAN, S. C. Malignant tumors of the uterus and vagina in untreated mice of the PM stock. *Cancer Research 8:* 241-256, 1948.
141. GARDNER, W. U., and PFEIFFER, C. A. Skeletal changes in mice receiving estrogens. *Proc. Soc. Exper. Biol. & Med. 37:* 678-679, 1938.
142. GARDNER, W. U., and PFEIFFER, C. A. Influence of estrogens and androgens on the skeletal system. *Physiol. Rev. 23:* 136-165, 1943.
143. GARDNER, W. U., and RYGAARD, J. Unpublished data.
144. GARDNER, W. U., SMITH, G. M., ALLEN, E., and STRONG, L. C. Cancer of the mammary glands induced in male mice receiving estrogenic hormone. *Arch. Path. 21:* 265-272, 1936.
145. GARDNER, W. U., SMITH, G. M., STRONG, L. C., and ALLEN, E. Development of sarcoma in male mice receiving estrogenic hormones. *Arch. Path. 21:* 504-508, 1936.
146. GARDNER, W. U., SMITH, G. M., and STRONG, L. C. An observation of primary tumors of the pituitary, ovaries and mammary glands in the mouse. *Am. J. Cancer 26:* 541-547, 1936.
147. GARDNER, W. U., and STRONG, L. C. Strain-limited development of tumors of the pituitary gland in mice receiving estrogens. *Yale J. Biol. Med. 12:* 543-548, 1940.
148. GARDNER, W. U., and YOUNG, H. L. Unpublished data.
149. GEIST, S. H., GAINES, J. A., and POLLACK, A. D. Experimental biologically active ovarian tumors in mice. Histogenesis and relationship to similar human ovarian tumors. *Am. J. Obst. & Gynec. 38:* 786-797, 1939.
150. GESCHICKTER, C. F. Mammary carcinoma in the rat with metastasis induced by estrogen. *Science 89:* 35-37, 1939.
151. GESCHICKTER, C. F., and BYRNES, E. W. Factors influencing the development and time of appearance of mammary cancer in the rat in response to estrogen. *Arch. Path. 33:* 334-356, 1942.

152. Gilmour, M. D. An investigation into the influence of oestrone on the growth and on the genesis of malignant cells. *J. Path. & Bact. 45:* 179-188, 1937.

153. Goodpasture, E. W. An anatomical study of senescence in dogs, with especial reference to the relation of cellular changes of age to tumors. *J. Med. Research 38:* 127-190, 1918.

154. Golden, J. R., and Sevringhaus, E. L. Inactivation of estrogenic hormone of the ovary by the liver. *Proc. Soc. Exper. Biol. & Med. 39:* 361-362, 1938.

155. Gottschalk, R. G., and Furth, J. Polycythemia associated with a transplantable luteoma. *Cancer Research 9:* 594, 1949.

156. Greene, H. S. N. Familial mammary tumors in the rabbit: I. Clinical history; II. Gross and microscopic pathology; III. Factors concerned in their genesis and development. *J. Exper. Med. 70:* 147-184, 1939.

157. Greene, H. S. N. Familial mammary tumors in the rabbit. IV. The evolution of autonomy in the course of tumor development as indicated by transplantation experiments. *J. Exper. Med. 71:* 305-324, 1940.

158. Greene, H. S. N. Uterine adenomata in the rabbit: III. Susceptibility as a function of constitutional factors. *J. Exper. Med. 73:* 273-292, 1941.

159. Greene, H. S. N., and Newton, B. L. Evolution of cancer of the uterine fundus in the rabbit. *Cancer 1:* 82-99, 1948.

160. Greene, H. S. N., and Saxton, J. A. Uterine adenomata in the rabbit. I. Clinical history, pathology and preliminary transplantation experiments. *J. Exper. Med. 69:* 691-708, 1938.

161. Greene, R. R., and Brewer, J. I. Relation of sex hormones to tumors of the female reproductive system. *Am. J. Roentgenol 45:* 426-444, 1941.

162. Greulich, W. W., and Burford, T. H. Testicular tumors associated with mammary, prostatic and other changes in cryptorchid dogs. *Am. J. Cancer 28:* 496-511, 1936.

163. Haagensen, C. D., and Randall, H. T. Production of mammary carcinoma in mice by estrogens. *Arch. Path. 33:* 411-442, 1942.

164. Harde, E. Influence des hormones et des vitamines dans la production des adéno-carcinomes mammaires chez la souris. *Comp. rend. Soc. de biol. 116:* 999-1001, 1934.

165. Hartman, C. G., Geschickter, C. F., and Speert, H. Effects of continuous estrogen administration in very large doses. *Anat. Rec. 79:* 31, 1941.

166. Harvey, W. F., Dawson, E. K., and Innes, J. R. M. *Debatable Tumours in Human and Animal Pathology.* Edinburgh, Oliver and Boyd, 1940, chap. I, pp. 1-6.

167. Heilman, F. R., and Kendall, E. C. The influence of 11-dehydro, 17-hydroxycortisone (compound E) on the growth of a malignant tumor in the mouse. *Endocrinology 34:* 416-420, 1944.

168. Heiman, J. Effect of testosterone propionate on the adrenals and on the incidence of mammary cancer in the RIII strain of mice. *Cancer Research 4:* 31-34, 1944.

169. Heiman, J. The effect of progesterone and testosterone propionate on the incidence of mammary cancer in mice. *Cancer Research 5:* 426-430, 1945.

170. Heiman, J., and Krehbiel, O. F. The influence of hormones on breast hyperplasia and tumor growths in white rats. *Am. J. Cancer 27:* 450-473, 1936.

171. Henshaw, P. S. Leukemia in mice following exposure to x-rays. *Radiology 43:* 279-285, 1944.

172. HESTON, W. E., and ANDERVONT, H. B. Importance of genetic influence on the occurrence of mammary tumors in virgin female mice. *J. Nat. Cancer Inst. 4:* 403-407, 1944.
173. HISAW, F. L., GREEP, R. O., and FEVOLD, H. L. The effects of oestrin-progestin combinations on the endometrium, vagina and sexual skin of monkeys. *Am. J. Anat. 61:* 483-503, 1937.
174. HOFBAUER, J. Leucoplakia cervicis uteri and early carcinoma. *Am. J. Obst. & Gynec. 27:* 633-646, 1934.
175. HOLWEG, W. Veranderungen des Hypophysenvorderlappen und des Ovariums nach Behandlung mit grossen Dosen von Follikelhormon. *Klin. Wchnschr. 13:* 92-95, 1934.
176. HOOKER, C. W. The biology of the interstitial cells of the testis. *Recent Progress in Hormones Research 3:* 173-195, 1948.
177. HOOKER, C. W. Personal communication.
178. HOOKER, C. W., and FORBES, T. R. Personal communication.
179. HOOKER, C. W., GARDNER, W. U., and PFEIFFER, C. A. Testicular tumors in mice receiving estrogens. *J.A.M.A. 115:* 443-445, 1940.
180. HOOKER, C. W., and PFEIFFER, C. A. The morphology and development of testicular tumors in mice of the A strain receiving estrogens. *Cancer Research 2:* 759-769, 1942.
181. HOOKER, C. W., PFEIFFER, C. A., and DEVITA, J. Spontaneous interstitial cell tumors of the testis in dogs. *Cancer Research 5:* 590, 1945.
182. HOOKER, C. W., PFEIFFER, C. A., and DEVITA, J. The significance of the character of the interstitial cells of the testis in the aged dog. *Anat. Rec. 94:* 471-472, 1946.
183. HOOKER, C. W., PFEIFFER, C. A., and STRONG, L. C. Experimental alteration of the cells of a transplanted tumor. *Cancer Research 7:* 723, 1947.
184. HOOKER, C. W., PFEIFFER, C. A., and WILLIAMS, W. L. The identity of the pigmented cells in the testis of estrogen-treated mice. *Anat. Rec. 94:* 539, 1946.
185. HOOKER, C. W., STRONG, L. C., and PFEIFFER, C. A. A spontaneous transplantable testicular tumor in a mouse. *Cancer Research 6:* 503, 1946.
186. HORNING, E. S. Induction of glandular carcinomas of the prostate in the mouse. *Lancet 2:* 829-832, 1946.
187. HORNING, E. S. The effects of castration and stilbcstrol on prostatic tumours in mice. *Brit. J. Cancer 3:* 211-230, 1949.
188. HORNING, E. S., and DMOCHOWSKI, L. Induction of prostatic tumors in mice. *Brit. J. Cancer 1:* 59-63, 1947.
189. HOWARD, R. R., and GROSJEAN, W. A. Bilateral mammary carcinoma in the male coincident with prolonged stilbestrol therapy. *Surgery 25:* 300-303, 1949.
190. HUSEBY, R. A., and BITTNER, J. J. Comparative studies of the estrous cycles in relation to the mammary tumor milk agent. *Cancer Research 7:* 722-723, 1947.
191. HUSEBY, R. A., and BITTNER, J. J. Incidence of mammary tumors in castrate and non-castrate male mice bearing ovarian grafts. *Proc. Soc. Exper. Biol. & Med. 69:* 321-329, 1948.
192. HUSEBY, R. A., and BITTNER, J. J. Studies on the inherited hormonal influence. *Unio. Internat. Contra Cancrum, Acta 6:* 197-205, 1948.
193. HUSEBY, R. A., SMITH, F. W., and BITTNER, J. J. The incidence of mammary tumors in castrate and non-castrate mice following ovarian transplantation. *Cancer Research 6:* 494, 1946.
194. HUGGINS, C., and MOULDER, P. V. Estrogen production by Sertoli cell tumors of the testis. *Cancer Research 5:* 510-514, 1945.

195. HUGGINS, C., and PAZOS, R. JR. Studies on tumors of the testis. II. The morphology of testicular tumors in dogs. *Am. J. Path. 21:* 299-309, 1945.

196. IGLESIAS, R., STERNBERG, W. H., and SEGALOFF, A. A functional ovarian tumor occurring spontaneously in a rat. *Cancer Research 10:* 226, 1950.

197. INNES, J. R. M. Neoplastic diseases of the testis in animals. *J. Path. & Bact. 54:* 485-498, 1942.

198. JEMERIN, E. E. Hyperplasia and neoplasia of the interstitial cells of the testicle. *Arch. Surg. 35:* 967-998, 1937.

199. JOEST, E. Dresden tierärztl Hochsch. Ber. *8:* 87-96, 1913 (quoted by Slye[371]).

200. JONES, E. E. Tumor incidence in line A albino mice following injections of progynon-B. *Am. J. Cancer 39:* 94-99, 1940.

201. JONES, E. E. The effect of testosterone propionate on mammary tumors in mice of the C3H strain. *Cancer Research 1:* 787-789, 1941.

202. JUNGCK, E. C., HELLER, C. G., and NELSON, W. O. Regulation of pituitary gonadotrophic secretion: Inhibition by estrogen or inactivation by the ovaries. *Proc. Soc. Exper. Biol. & Med. 65:* 148-152, 1947.

203. KAPLAN, H. S. Observations on radiation-induced lymphoid tumors of mice. *Cancer Research 7:* 141-147, 1947.

204. KAPLAN, H. S. Influence of thymectomy, splenectomy, and gonadectomy on incidence of radiation-induced lymphoid tumors in strain C57 black mice. *Cancer Research 10:* 228, 1950.

205. KAUFMANN, C., MÜLLER, H. A., BUTENANDT, A., and FRIEDRICK-FREKSA, H. Experimentelle Beiträge zur Bedeutung des Follikelhormons für die Karzinomentstehung. *Ztschr. f. Krebsforsch. 56:* 482-542, 1949.

206. KIWURA, T. On "orchidoma" or "orchidoblastoma" of the horse. *Japan Ztschr. Krebsforsch. 11:* 38-46, 1917.

207. KIRKMAN, H., and BACON, R. L. Malignant renal tumors in male hamsters (Cricetus auratus) treated with estrogen. *Cancer Research 10:* 122-124, 1950.

208. KIRSCHBAUM, A. Recent studies on experimental mammalian leukemia. *Yale J. Biol. & Med. 17:* 163-185, 1944.

209. KIRSCHBAUM, A., FRANTZ, M., and WILLIAMS, W. L. Neoplasms of the adrenal cortex in non-castrate mice. *Cancer Research 6:* 707-711, 1946.

210. KIRSCHBAUM, A., and MIXER, H. W. Induction of leukemia in eight inbred stocks of mice varying in susceptibility to the spontaneous disease. *J. Lab. & Clin. Med. 32:* 720-731, 1947.

211. KOCH, K. Zwischenzellen und Hodenatrophie. *Virchows Arch. f. path. Anat. 202:* 376-406, 1910.

212. KONEFF, A. A., SIMPSON, M. E., and EVANS, H. M. Effects of chronic administration of diethylstilbestrol on the pituitary and other endocrine organs of hamsters. *Anat. Rec. 94:* 169-195, 1946.

213. KORTEWEG, R. Experimenteel onderzoek aangaande de erfelijkheid van kanker. *Nederl. tijdschr. v. geneesk 77:* 4038-4050, 1933.

214. KORTEWEG, R. Proefondervindelijke onderzoekingen aangaande erfelijkheid van kanker. *Nederl. tijdschr. v. geneesk 78:* 240-245, 1934.

215. KORTEWEG, R., and THOMAS, F. Tumor induction and tumor growth in hypophysectomized mice. *Am. J. Cancer 37:* 36-44, 1939.

216. KORENCHEVSKY, V., HALL, K., and BURBANK, D. R. The manifold effects of prolonged administration of sex hormones to female rats. *Biochem. J. 33:* 372-380, 1939.

217. Krebs, C., Rask-Nielsen, H. C., and Wagner, A. The origin of lymphosarcomatosis and its relation to other forms of leukosis in white mice. *Acta Radiol.*, Suppl. *10:* 1-53, 1930.
218. Kreyberg, L. "The genetic and constitutional aspects of spontaneous and induced tumors." In *A Symposium on Cancer.* Madison, Wis., Univ. Wisconsin Press, 1938, pp. 3-19.
219. Kryle, J. Über experimentelle Hodenatrophie. *Verhandl d. deutsch. path. Gesellsch. 14:* 240-247, 1910.
220. Kunze, A. Über Zwischenzellentumoren im Hoden des Hundes. *Virchows Arch. f. path. Anat. 240:* 144-175, 1922.
221. Lacassagne, A. Apparition de cancers de la mamelle chez la souris mâle, soumis à des injections de folliculine. *Compt. rend. Acad. d. sc. 195:* 630-632, 1932.
222. Lacassagne, A. Metaplasie épidermoïde de la prostate provoquée, chez la souris, par des injections répétées de fortes doses de folliculine. *Compt. rend. Soc. de biol. 113:* 590-592, 1933.
223. Lacassagne, A. Sur la pathogénie de l'adéno-carcinome mammaire de la souris. *Compt. rend. Soc. de biol. 115:* 937-939, 1934.
224. Lacassagne, A. A comparative study of the carcinogenic action of certain oestrogenic hormones. *Am. J. Cancer 28:* 735-740, 1936.
225. Lacassagne, A. Tumeurs malignes, apparues au cours d'un traitement hormonal combiné, chez des souris appartenant a des lignées réfractaires au cancer spontané. *Compt. rend. Soc. de biol. 121:* 607-609, 1936.
226. Lacassagne, A. Hormonal pathogenesis of adenocarcinoma of the breast. *Am. J. Cancer 27:* 217-228, 1936.
227. Lacassagne, A. Sarcomas fusocellulaires apparus chez des souris longuement traiteés, par des hormones oestrogénes. *Compt. rend. Soc. de biol. 126:* 190-192, 1937.
228. Lacassagne, A. Sarcomes lymphoides apparus chez des souris longuement traiteés par des hormones oestrogènes. *Compt. rend. Soc. de biol. 126:* 193-195, 1937.
229. Lacassagne, A. Tentatives pour modifier, par la progéstérone ou par la testostérone, l'apparition des adénocarcinomes mammaires provoqués par l'oestrone chez la souris. *Compt. rend. Soc. de biol. 126:* 385-387, 1937.
230. Lacassagne, A. Statistique des différents cancers constatés dans des lignées sélectionées de souris, après action prolongée d'hormone oestrogène. *Bull. Assoc. franç. p. l'étude du cancer 27:* 96-116, 1938.
231. Lacassagne, A. Les rapports entre les hormones sexuelles et la formation du cancer. *Ergebn. Vitamin u. Hormonforsch. 2:* 259-296, 1939.
232. Lacassagne, A. *Radiophysiologie experimentale, cancer et hormones. VII. Les cancers produits par des substances chimiques endogènes.* Paris, Hermann et Cie, 1950.
233. Lacassagne, A., and Raynaud, A. Sur le méchanisme d'une action préventive de la testostérone sur le carcinome mammaire de la souris. *Compt. rend. Soc. de biol. 131:* 586-588, 1939.
234. Lacassagne, A., and Raynaud, A. Apparition de carcinome mammaire chez des souris subissant un traitement combiné d'oestrone et d'une dose de testostérone 50 fois plus forte. *Compt. rend. Soc. de biol. 132:* 431-434, 1939.
235. Lathrop, A. E. C., and Loeb, L. The influence of pregnancies on the incidence of cancer in mice. *Proc. Soc. Exper. Biol. & Med. 11:* 38-40, 1913.

236. LATHROP, A. E. C., and LOEB, L. Further investigations on the origin of tumors in mice: III. On the part played by internal secretion in the spontaneous development of tumors. *J. Cancer Research 1:* 1-19, 1916.
237. LATHROP, A. E. C., and LOEB, L. Further investigations on the origin of tumors in mice: V. The tumor rate in hybrid strains. *J. Exper. Med. 28:* 475-500, 1918.
238. LAW, L. W. The induction of leukemia in mice following percutaneous application of 9,10-dimethyl-, 1,2-benzanthracene. *Cancer Research 1:* 564-571, 1941.
239. LAW, L. W. Effect of pseudopregnancy on mammary carcinoma incidence in mice of the A stock. *Proc. Soc. Exper. Biol. & Med. 48:* 486-487, 1941.
240. LAW, L. W. The effect of gonadectomy and adrenalectomy on the appearance and incidence of spontaneous lymphoid leukemia in C58 mice. *J. Nat. Cancer Inst. 8:* 157-159, 1948.
241. LI, M. H. Malignant granulosa cell tumor in an intrasplenic ovarian graft in a castrated male mouse. *Am. J. Obst. & Gynec. 55:* 316-320, 1948.
242. LI, M. H., GARDNER, W. U., and KAPLAN, H. S. Effects of x-ray irradiation on the development of ovarian tumors in intrasplenic grafts in castrated mice. *J. Nat. Cancer Inst. 8:* 91-98, 1947.
243. LI, M. H., and GARDNER, W. U. Tumors in intrasplenic ovarian transplants in castrated mice. *Science 105:* 13-15, 1947.
244. LI, M. H., and GARDNER, W. U. Experimental studies on the pathogenesis and histogenesis of ovarian tumors in mice. *Cancer Research 7:* 549-566, 1947.
245. LI, M. H., PFEIFFER, C. A., and GARDNER, W. U. Intrasplenic transplantation of testes in castrated mice. *Proc. Soc. Exper. Biol. & Med. 64:* 319-323, 1947.
246. LI, M. H., and GARDNER, W. U. Further studies on the pathogenesis of ovarian tumors in mice. *Cancer Research 9:* 35-41, 1949.
247. LI, M. H., and GARDNER, W. U. Influence of age of host and ovaries on tumorigenesis in intrasplenic ovarian grafts. *Cancer Research 10:* 162-165, 1950.
248. LICK, L., KIRSCHBAUM, A., and MIXER, H. Mechanism of induction of ovarian tumors by x-rays. *Cancer Research 9:* 532-536, 1949.
249. LIPSCHÜTZ, A. Croissance atypique des glandes du corps utérin. Epidermisation de la muqueuse cervicale, troubles de l'equilibre entre ovaire et préhypophyse après des interventions ovariennes. *Gynéc. et obst. 36:* 491-498; *35:* 408-426, 1937.
250. LIPSCHÜTZ, A. *Steroid Hormones and Tumors.* Philadelphia, The Williams & Wilkins Co., 1950.
251. LIPSCHÜTZ, A., DELEON, H. P., WOYWOOD, E., and GAY, O. Intrasplenic grafts in the guinea pig and the problem of neoplastic reactions of the graft. *Rev. canad. de biol. 5:* 181-185, 1946.
252. LIPSCHÜTZ, A., and IGLESIAS, R. Multiple tumeurs utérines et extragénitales provoquées par le benzoate d'oestradiol. *Compt. rend. Soc. de biol. 129:* 519-523, 1938.
253. LOEB, L. Further investigations on the origin of tumors in mice: VI. Internal secretion as a factor in the origin of tumors. *J. Med. Research 40:* 477-496, 1919.
254. LOEB, L. The significance of hormones in the origin of cancer. *J. Nat. Cancer Inst. 1:* 169-195, 1940.
255. LOEB, L., BLUMENTHAL, H. T., and KIRTZ, M. M. The effectiveness of ovarian and hypophysial grafts in the production of mammary carcinoma in mice. *Science 99:* 230-232, 1944.

256. LOEB, L., BURNS, E. L., SUNTZEFF, V., and MOSKOP, M. Carcinoma-like proliferation in the vagina, cervix and uterus of a mouse treated with estrogenic hormone. *Proc. Soc. Exper. Biol. & Med. 35:* 320-322, 1936.
257. LOEB, L., and GENTHER, I. T. Heredity and internal secretion on origin of mammary cancer in mice. *Proc. Soc. Exper. Biol. & Med. 25:* 809-811, 1928.
258. LOEB, L., and KIRTZ, M. M. The effects of transplants of anterior lobes of the hypophysis on the growth of the mammary gland and on the development of mammary gland carcinoma in various strains of mice. *Am. J. Can. 36:* 56-82, 1939.
259. LOEB, L., SUNTZEFF, V., and BURNS, E. L. Growth processes induced by estrogenic hormones in the uterus of the mouse. *Am. J. Cancer 34:* 413-427, 1938.
260. LOEB, L., SUNTZEFF, V., BURNS, E. L., and SCHENKEN, I. R. Incidence of mammary carcinoma in mice treated with estrogen: Effect of the age at which the treatment with estrogen begins. *Arch. Path. 38:* 52-59, 1944.
261. LOEPER, J. Hypertrophie et adénome de l'antéhypophyse sous l'effect du diethylstilbestrol. *Progr. med., Paris 74:* 245, 1946.
262. LOESER, A. A. Mammary carcinoma response to implantation of male hormone and progesterone. *Lancet 2:* 698-700, 1941.
263. LORENZ, E., HESTON, W. E., ESCHENBRENNER, A. B., and DERINGER, M. K. Biological studies in the tolerance range. *Radiology 49:* 274-285, 1947.
264. MASSON, P. Deux cancers leydigiens de l'homme: Leur comparaison avec les tumeurs interstitielles experimentales de la souris. *Rev. canad. de biol. 2:* 168-243, 1943.
265. MATTHEWS, V. S., KIRKMAN, H., and BACON, R. L. Kidney damage in the golden hamster following chronic administration of diethylstilbestrol and sesame oil. *Proc. Soc. Exper. Biol. & Med. 66:* 195-196, 1947.
266. MAZER, C., ISRAEL, S. L., and ALPERS, B. J. The time element in the pituitary-ovarian responses to large doses of estrogenic hormone. *Endocrinology 20:* 753-761, 1936.
267. MCENDY, D. P., BOON, M. C., and FURTH, J. On the role of thymus, spleen, and gonads in the development of leukemia in a high-leukemia stock of mice. *Cancer Research 4:* 377-383, 1944.
268. MCEUEN, C. S. Metaplasia of uterine epithelium produced in rats by prolonged administration of oestrin. *Am. J. Cancer 27:* 91-94, 1936.
269. MCEUEN, C. S. Occurrence of cancer in rats treated with estrone. *Am. J. Cancer 34:* 184-195, 1938.
270. MCEUEN, C. S. Observations on rats treated with the sex hormones estrin and testosterone. *Am. J. Cancer 36:* 551-566, 1939.
271. MCEUEN, C. S., SELYE, H., and COLLIP, J. B. Some effects of prolonged administration of oestrin in rats. *Lancet 230:* 775-776, 1936.
272. MCEUEN, C. S., SELYE, H., and COLLIP, J. B. A pigmented adenoma of the intermediate lobe in a rat chronically treated with oestrin. *Proc. Soc. Exper. Biol. & Med. 40:* 241-244, 1939.
273. MCEUEN, C. S., and THOMSON, D. L. The effect of hypophysectomy on the growth of the Walker rat tumour. *Brit. J. Exper. Path. 14:* 384-391, 1933.
274. MCEUEN, C. W., and THOMSON, D. L. The growth of the Walker rat tumour in young and old animals. *Brit. J. Exper. Path. 15:* 224-227, 1934.
275. MEYER, R. K. BIDDULPH, C., and FINERTY, J. C. Pituitary-gonad interaction in immature female parabiotic rats. *Endocrinology 39:* 23-31, 1946.

276. MIDER, G. B., and MORTON, J. J. Relative importance of local and constitutional effects of methylcholanthrene in production of skin tumors in the mouse. *J. Nat. Cancer Inst. 1:* 41-44, 1940.

277. MILLER, E. W., ORR, J. W., and PYBUS, F. C. The effect of oestrone on the mouse skeleton, with particular reference to the Newcastle bone tumor (NBT) strain. *J. Path. & Bact. 55:* 137-150, 1943.

278. MILLER, E. W., and PYBUS, F. C. The effect of oestrone on mice of three inbred strains, with special reference to the mammary glands. *J. Path. & Bact. 54:* 155-168, 1942.

279. MILLER, O. J. *Studies on granulosa cell tumors occurring in intrasplenic ovarian grafts of castrated mice.* Thesis, Yale Univ., 1950, unpublished.

280. MILLER, O. J., and PFEIFFER, C. A. Demonstration of increased gonadotrophic hormone production in castrated mice with intrasplenic ovarian grafts. *Proc. Soc. Exper. Biol. & Med. 75:* 178-181, 1950.

281. MOON, H. D., SIMPSON, M. E., LI, C. H., and EVANS, H. M. Neoplasms in rats treated with pituitary growth hormone: I. Pulmonary and lymphatic tissues. *Cancer Research 10:* 297-308, 1950.

282. MOON, H. D., SIMPSON, M. E., LI, C. H., and EVANS, H. M. Neoplasms in rats treated with pituitary growth hormone: II. Adrenal glands. *Cancer Research 10:* 364-370, 1950.

283. MOORE, C. R. "Biology of the testes." In *Sex and Internal Secretions.* Baltimore, Md., Williams & Wilkins Company, 1939, chap. 7, pp. 353-451.

284. MOORE, R. A., and MELCKIONNA, R. H. Production of tumors of the prostate of the white rat with 1,2-benzpyrene. *Am. J. Cancer 30:* 731-741, 1937.

285. MORTON, J. J., and MIDER, G. B. Some effects of carcinogenic agents on mice subject to spontaneous leukoses. *Cancer Research 1:* 95-98, 1941.

286. MOSKOP, M., BURNS, E. L., SUNTZEFF, V., and LOEB, L. Incidence of mammary cancer and nature of the sexual cycle in various strains of mice. *Proc. Soc. Exper. Biol. & Med. 33:* 197-199, 1935.

287. MOULTON, F. R. *Mammary Tumors in Mice.* Washington, D. C., A.A.A.S., 1945.

288. MÜHLBOCK, O. On the susceptibility of different inbred strains of mice for oestrone. *Acta brev. Neerland. 15:* 18-20, 1947.

289. MÜHLBOCK, O. The oestrone-sensitivity of the mammary gland in female mice of various strains. *Acta brev. Neerland. 16:* 22-27, 1948.

290. MÜHLBOCK, O. The sensitivity of the mammary gland to oestrone in different strains of mice with and without mammary tumor agent. *Acta Endocrinol. 3:* 105-110, 1949.

291. MULLIGAN, R. M. *Neoplasms of the Dog.* Baltimore, Md., The Williams & Wilkins Co., 1949.

292. MURPHY, J. B. The effect of castration, theelin and testosterone on the incidence of leukemia in a Rockefeller Institute strain of mice. *Cancer Research 4:* 622-624, 1944.

293. MURPHY, J. B., and STURM, E. The effect of adrenal cortical and pituitary adrenotrophic hormones on transplanted leukemia in rats. *Science 99:* 303, 1944.

294. MURPHY, J. B., and STURM, E. The effect of adrenalectomy on the susceptibility of rats to a transplantable leukemia. *Cancer Research 4:* 384-388, 1944.

295. Murphy, J. B., and Sturm, E. The effect of diethylstilbestrol on the incidence of leukemia in male mice of the Rockefeller Institute Leukemia Strain (R.I.L.). *Cancer Research 9:* 88-89, 1949.
296. Murray, J. M. A study of the histological structure of mouse ovaries following exposure to roentgen irradiation. *Am. J. Roentgenol. 25:* 1-45, 1931.
297. Murray, W. S. Ovarian secretion and tumor incidence. *J. Cancer Research 12:* 18-25, 1928.
298. Murray, W. S. Proceedings of the twenty-third annual meeting of the American Association for Cancer Research. *J. Cancer Research 14:* 526 (discussion), 1930.
299. Murray, W. S. Some effects of ovariectomy upon breeding females. *Science 75:* 646-647, 1932.
300. Murray, W. S. Some effects of ovariectomy during the period of declining reproductive powers in mice. *J. Exper. Med. 63:* 893-900, 1936.
301. Nathanson, I. T., and Andervont, H. B. Effect of testosterone propionate on development and growth of mammary carcinoma in female mice. *Proc. Soc. Exper. Biol. & Med. 40:* 421-422, 1939.
302. Neeve, R. H., and Marsh, F. Interstitial-cell testicular tumour. *J. Path. & Bact. 56:* 575-576, 1944.
303. Nelson, A. A. Giant interstitial cells and extraparenchymal interstitial cells of the human testis. *Am. J. Path. 14:* 831-841, 1938.
304. Nelson, W. O. Fibromyomatous nodules in guinea pig uterus by prolonged estrogen administration. *Anat. Rec. 68:* 99-102, 1937.
305. Nelson, W. O. Atypical uterine growths produced by prolonged estrogen administration. *Endocrinology 24:* 50-54, 1939.
306. Nelson, W. O. The occurrence of hypophyseal tumors in rats under treatment with diethylstilbestrol. *Am. J. Physiol. 133:* 398, 1941.
307. Nelson, W. O. Some effects of hypophyseal tumors induced by treatment with estrogens. *Cancer Research 2:* 728, 1942.
308. Nelson, W. O. The induction of mammary carcinoma in the rat. *Yale J. Biol. & Med. 17:* 217-228, 1944.
309. Nelson, W. O. Personal communication.
310. Noble, R. L., McEuen, C. S., and Collip, J. B. Mammary tumors produced in rats by the action of oestrone tablets. *Canad. M. A. J. 42:* 413-417, 1940.
311. Oberling, C., Guérin, M., and Guérin, P. La production expérimentale de tumeurs hypophysaires chez le rat. *Comp. rend. Soc. de biol. 123:* 1152-1154, 1936.
312. Oberling, C., Sannié, C., Guérin, P., and Guérin, M. Sur la relation apparente des tumeurs hypophysaires et du benzpyrène injecté dans le cerveau chez le rat. *Compt. rend. Soc. de biol. 131:* 455-457, 1939.
313. Overholser, M. D., and Allen, E. Atypical cervical epithelium of the monkey by prolonged ovarian hormone. *Surg., Gynec. & Obst. 60:* 129-136, 1935.
314. Pallaske, G. Beiträge zur Frage der "Zwischenzellentumoren" bei Tieren. *Virchows Arch. f. path. Anat. 281:* 856-870, 1931.
315. Pan, S. C., and Gardner, W. U. Induction of malignant tumors by methylcholanthrene in transplanted uterine cornua and cervices of mice. *Cancer Research 8:* 613-621, 1948.
316. Pan, S. C., and Gardner, W. U. Carcinomas of the uterine cervix and vagina in estrogen- and androgen-treated hybrid mice. *Cancer Research 8:* 337-345, 1948.

317. Paschkis, K. E., Cantarow, A., and Stasney, J. Influence of thiouracil on carcinoma induced by 2-acetaminofluorene. *Cancer Research 8:* 257-263, 1948.

318. Peckham, B. M., Greene, R. R., and Jefferies, M. E. Granulosa cell tumors in female rats and rabbits. *Science 107:* 319-320, 1948.

319. Perloff, W. H., and Kurzrok, R. Production of uterine tumors in the guinea pig by local implantation of estrogen pellets. *Proc. Soc. Exper. Biol. & Med. 46:* 261-265, 1941.

320. Perry, I. H. Production of carcinoma of the uterus in mice. *Proc. Soc. Exper. Biol. & Med. 35:* 325-326, 1936.

321. Perry, I. H., and Ginzton, L. C. Development of tumors in female mice treated with 1,2,5,6-dibenzanthracene or theelin. *Am. J. Cancer 39:* 680-704, 1937.

322. Peyron, A. Sur les stades de debut dans les néoformation experimentales de la glande interstitielle. *Compt. rend Soc. de biol. 135:* 926-928, 1941.

323. Peyron, A., Blanchard, L., Poumeau-Delille, G., and Salomon, L. Sur l'histopathologie des tumeurs de la glande interstitielle du testicule chez l'homme et les animaux. *Compt. rend. Soc. de biol. 128:* 338-340, 1938.

324. Peyron, A., Blanchard, L. and Salomon, L. Les tumeurs des cellules interstitielles du testicule. *Bull. Assoc. franç. Cancer 25:* 427-450, 1936.

325. Peyron, A., and Samsonoff, N. Sur la production experimentale des tumeurs de la glande interstitielle du testicule chez le rat. *Compt. rend. Soc. de biol. 135:* 922-925, 1941.

326. Pfeiffer, C. A. Sexual differences of the hypophysis and their determination by the gonads. *Am. J. Anat. 58:* 195-225, 1936.

327. Pfeiffer, C. A. The effects of an experimentally induced endocrine imbalance in female mice. *Anat. Rec. 75:* 465-491, 1939.

328. Pfeiffer, C. A. Interstitial cell stimulation and luteinization under the influence of male and female hypophyses. *Yale J. Biol. & Med. 14:* 619-630, 1942.

329. Pfeiffer, C. A. Development of leiomyoma in female rats with an endocrine imbalance. *Cancer Research 9:* 277-281, 1949.

330. Pfeiffer, C. A. Adenocarcinoma in the uterus of an endocrine imbalance female rat. *Cancer Research 9:* 347-349, 1949.

331. Pfeiffer, C. A., and Allen, E. Attempts to produce cancer in Rhesus monkeys with carcinogenic hydrocarbons and estrogens. *Cancer Research 8:* 97-127, 1948.

332. Pfeiffer, C. A., and Hooker, C. W. Early and late effects of daily treatment with pregnant mare serum upon the ovary of mice of the A strain. *Anat. Rec. 84:* 311-329, 1942.

333. Pfeiffer, C. A., and Hooker, C. W. Testicular changes resembling early stages in the development of interstitial cell tumors in mice of the A strain after long-continued injections of pregnant mare serum. *Cancer Research 3:* 762-766, 1943.

334. Pfeiffer, C. A., and Hooker, C. W. Unpublished data.

335. Pierson, H. Experimental production of uterine enlargement with cancer through ovarian hormone. *Ztschr. f. Krebsforsch. 41:* 103-138, 1934.

336. Pierson, H. Weitere Follikulinversuche: Perforierende Plattenepithel-wucherungen im Uterus des Kaninchens mit Knorpel-und Knochenbefunden. *Ztschr. f. Krebsforsch. 47*: 1-12, 1937.

337. Polson, C. J. Tumours of the rabbit. *J. Path. & Bact. 30:* 603-614, 1927.

338. Pybus, F. C., and Miller, E. W. A sex difference in the incidence of bone tumours in mice. *Am. J. Cancer 34:* 248-251, 1938.

339. Pybus, F. C., and Miller, E. W. The gross pathology of spontaneous bone tumours in mice. *Am. J. Cancer 15:* 47-61, 1940.

340. Rask-Nielsen, R. On the development of tumors in various tissues in mice following direct application of a carcinogenic hydrocarbon. *Acta path. et microbiol. Scandinav.* Suppl. No. *78:* 1-44, 1948.

340a. Rask-Nielsen, R. Investigations into the varying manifestations of leukemic lesions following injections of 9:10-dimethyl- 1:2-benzanthracene into different subcutaneous sites in Street mice. *Brit. J. Cancer 3:* 549-556, 1949.

341. Reinhard, M. C., and Candee, C. F. Influence of sex and heredity on the development of tar tumors. *Am. J. Cancer 16:* 640-644, 1932.

342. Reiss, M., Druckrey, H., and Hochwald, A. Tumor und Inkret system. *Klin. Wchnschr. 12:* 1049-1050, 1933.

343. Riopelle, J. Tumeurs des cellules interstitielles du testicule. *Union Méd. du Canada 73:* 903-905, 1944.

344. Sall, R. D., and Shear, M. J. Studies in carcinogenesis: XII. Effect of the basic fraction of creosote oil on the production of tumors in mice by chemical carcinogens. *J. Nat. Cancer Inst. 1:* 45-55, 1940.

345. Samuels, L. T., Ball, H. A., and Simpson, W. The relation of the hypophysis to the growth of malignant tumors: II. The response of hypophysectomized rats to inoculation with Walker transplantable mammary carcinoma. *Am. J. Cancer 18:* 380-382, 1933.

346. Samuels, L. T., Bittner, J. J., and Samuels, B. K. Excretion of steroids in the feces of mice of various strains with and without the mammary tumor milk agent. *Cancer Research 7:* 722, 1947.

347. Sand, K., and Okkels, H. Histopathologie du testicule et sexualité anormale: Variabilité du tissu testiculaire chez l'homme. *Compt. rend. Soc. de biol. 123:* 184-187, 1936.

348. Saxton, J. A. Jr. The relation of age to the occurrence of adenoma-like lesions in the rat hypophysis and to their growth after transplantation. *Cancer Research 1:* 277-282, 1941.

349. Saxton, J. A. Jr., and Graham, J. B. Chromophobe adenoma-like lesions of the rat hypophysis: Frequency of the spontaneous lesions and characteristics of growth of homologous intraocular transplants. *Cancer Research 4:* 168-175, 1944.

350. Schlotthauer, C. F., McDonald, J. R., and Bollman, J. L. Testicular tumors in dogs. *J. Urol. 40:* 539-550, 1938.

351. Schmidt, I. G. Changes in the genital tracts of guinea pigs associated with cystic and 'interstitial gland' ovaries of long duration. *Endocrinology 24:* 69-81, 1939.

352. Segaloff, A. Personal communication.

353. Segaloff, A., and Dunning, W. F. The effect of strain, estrogen, and dosage on the reaction of the rat's pituitary and adrenal to estrogenic stimulation. *Endocrinology 36:* 238-240, 1945.

354. Selye, H. Interaction between various steroid hormones. *Canad. M. J. 42:* 113-116, 1940.

355. Selye, H. Experimental investigations concerning the role of the pituitary in tumorigenesis. *Surgery 16:* 33-46, 1944.

356. Selye, H. Atypical cell proliferation in the anterior lobe adenomas of estradiol-treated rats. *Cancer Research 4:* 349-351, 1944.

357. Selye, H. "Ovarian tumors." In *Encyclopedia of Endocrinology.* Montreal, Richardson, Bond and Wright, 1946, sect. IV, vol. VII.
358. Selye, H., Collip, J. B., and Thomson, D. L. Effect of oestrin on ovaries and adrenals. *Proc. Soc. Exper. Biol. & Med. 32:* 1377-1381, 1935.
359. Shay, H., Aegerter, E. A., Gruenstein, M., and Komarov, S. A. Development of adenocarcinoma of the breast in the Wistar Rat following the gastric instillation of methylcholanthrene. *J. Nat. Cancer Inst. 10:* 255-266, 1949.
360. Shimkin, M. B. See Moulton,[287] pp. 85-122.
361. Shimkin, M. B., Grady, H. G., and Andervont, H. B. Induction of testicular tumors and other effects of stilbestrol-cholesterol pellets in strain C mice. *J. Nat. Cancer Inst. 2:* 65-80, 1941.
362. Shimkin, M. B., and Andervont, H. B. Effect of foster nursing on the response of mice to estrogens. *J. Nat. Cancer Inst. 1:* 599-606, 1941.
363. Shimkin, M. B., and Andervont, H. B. Effect of foster nursing on the induction of mammary and testicular tumors in mice injected with stilbestrol. *J. Nat. Cancer Inst. 2:* 611-622, 1942.
364. Shimkin, M. B., and Wyman, R. S. Mammary tumors in male mice implanted with estrogen-cholestrol pellets. *J. Nat. Cancer Inst. 7:* 71-75, 1946.
365. Silberberg, M., and Silberberg, R. Significance of the age factor and sex glands in experimental leukemia of mice. *Proc. Soc. Exper. Biol. & Med. 58:* 347-348, 1945.
366. Silberberg, M., and Silberberg, R. Age factor in estrogen-induced breast cancers of mice. *Proc. Soc. Exper. Biol. & Med. 69:* 438-441, 1948.
367. Silberberg, M., and Silberberg, R. Role of age in estrogen-induced lymphoid tumors of mice. *Arch. Path. 47:* 340-349, 1949.
368. Silberberg, R., and Silberberg, M. Mammary cancer in castrate male mice receiving ovarian and hypophyseal grafts at various ages. *Proc. Soc. Exper. Biol. & Med. 70:* 510-513, 1949.
369. Silberberg, M., and Silberberg, R. Mammary growth in orchidectomized mice grafted with anterior lobes of hypophyses and ovaries at various ages. *Arch. Path. 49:* 733-751, 1950.
369a. Silberberg, M., and Silberberg, R. Age and susceptibility of the mammary gland of mice to estrogen. *Cancer Research 11:* 279-280, 1951.
369b. Silberberg, R., Silberberg, M., and Bittner, J. J. Relative role of milk agent and tissue sensitivity in estrogen-induced mammary growth. *Proc. Soc. Exper. Biol. & Med. 77:* 473-477, 1951.
370. Slye, M., Holmes, H. F., and Wells, H. G. Primary spontaneous tumors in kidney and adrenal of mice. *J. Cancer Research 6:* 305-337, 1921.
371. Slye, M., Holmes, H. F., and Wells, H. G. Intracranial neoplasms in lower animals: Studies in the incidence and inheritibility of spontaneous tumors in mice. *Am. J. Cancer 15:* 1387-1400, 1931.
372. Slye, M., Holmes, H. F., and Wells, H. G. Primary spontaneous tumors of the testicle and seminal vesicle in mice and other animals: XII. Studies on the incidence and inheritibility of spontaneous tumors in mice. *J. Cancer Research 4:* 207-228, 1919.
373. Slye, M., Holmes, H. F., and Wells, H. G. Primary spontaneous tumors of the ovary in mice. *Tr. Chicago Path. Soc. 11:* 75, 1920.
374. Smith, F. W. Relationships of the inherited hormonal influence to the production of adrenal cortical tumors by castration. *Cancer Research 8:* 641-651, 1948.

375. SMITH, F. W., and GARDNER, W. U. Biological assay of mouse pituitary gonadotrophin. *Anat. Rec. 106:* 248, 1950.

376. SMITH, F. W., GARDNER, W. U., LI, M. H., and KAPLAN, H. Adrenal medullary tumors in mice. *Cancer Research 9:* 193-198, 1949.

377. SMITH, L. W. Senile changes of the testis and prostate in dogs. *J. Med. Research 40:* 31-51, 1919.

378. SOBEL, H., and FURTH, J. Hypervolemia in mice bearing granulosa cell growths: Time of onset and some associated physiological and chemical changes. *Endocrinology 42:* 436-447, 1948.

379. SPANGARO, S. Über die histologischen Veränderungen des Hodens, Nebenhodens und Samenleiters von Geburt an bis zum Greisenalter, mit besonderer Berücksichtigung der Hodenatrophie, des elastischen Gewebes und Vorkommen von Krystallen im Hoden. *Anat. Hefte* (Abt. 1) *18:* 583-771, 1902.

380. SPIEGEL, A. Über das Auftreten von Geschwülsten der Nebennierenrinde mit vermännlichender Wirkung bei frühkastrierten Meerschweinchenmännchen. *Virchows Arch. path. Anat. 305:* 367-393, 1939-40.

381. Staff, Jackson Memorial Laboratory, per LITTLE, C. C. The existence of non-chromosomal influence in the incidence of mammary tumors in mice. *Science 78:* 465-466, 1933.

382. STRONG, L. C. Production of the CBA strain of inbred mice: Long life associated with low tumour incidence. *Brit. J. Exper. Path. 17:* 60-63, 1936.

383. STRONG, L. C. The incidence of spontaneous tumors of mice of the CBA strain after a change of diet: Preliminary report. *Am. J. Cancer 32:* 80-84, 1938.

384. STRONG, L. C. The incidence of spontaneous tumors in female mice (breeders) of the CBA strain. *Am. J. Cancer 32:* 85-89, 1938.

385. STRONG, L. C. The effect of heptylaldehyde-sodium bisulfite on spontaneous tumors of the mammary gland in mice. *Cancer Research 1:* 473-476, 1941.

386. STRONG, L. C. A genetic analysis of the induction of tumors by methylcholanthrene: V. Absence of sex influences when a large dose of carcinogen is administered. *Arch. Path. 36:* 58-63, 1943.

387. STRONG, L. C. Personal communication.

388. STRONG, L. C., GARDNER, W. U., and HILL, R. T. Production of estrogenic hormones by transplantable ovarian carcinoma. *Endocrinology 21:* 268-272, 1937.

389. STRONG, L. C., HILL, R. T., PFEIFFER, C. A., and GARDNER, W. U. Genetic and endocrine studies on a transplantable carcinoma of the ovary. *Genetics 23:* 585-595, 1938.

390. SUNTZEFF, V., BURNS, E. L., MOSKOP, M., and LOEB, L. On the relation between the incidence of mammary cancer and the nature of the sexual cycle in various strains of mice. II. The relative constancy of the characteristics of the sexual cycle in these strains. *Am. J. Cancer 26:* 761-766, 1936.

391. SUNTZEFF, V., BURNS, E. L., MOSKOP, M., and LOEB, L. Proliferative changes in the epithelium of vagina and cervix of mice with advancing age and under the influence of experimentally administered estrogenic hormones. *Am. J. Cancer 32:* 256-289, 1938.

392. SUNTZEFF, V., KIRTZ, M. M., BLUMENTHAL, H. T., and LOEB, L. The incidence of mammary gland carcinoma and cancer age in mice injected with estrogen and in non-injected mice of different strains. *Cancer Research 1:* 446-456, 1941.

393. SYMEONIDIS, A. Mammakrebserzeugung bei Mäusen durch Progesteron verabreicht während der Gravidität. *Unio Internat. Contra Cancrum Acta 6:* 163-166, 1948.

394. Trautmann, A. *Joest's Spezielle pathologische Anatomie der Haustiere.* Berlin, R. Schoetz, 1924, vol. 3.
395. Treadwell, A. deG., Gardner, W. U., and Lawrence, J. H. Effect of combining estrogen and lethal doses of roentgen-ray in Swiss mice. *Endocrinology 32:* 161-164, 1943.
396. Trentin, J. J. Vaginal sensitivity to estrogen as related to mammary tumor incidence in mice. *Cancer Research 10:* 580-583, 1950.
396a. Trentin, J. J. The effect of presence or absence of the milk factor and of castration on mammary response to estrogen in male mice of strains of known mammary tumor incidence. *Cancer Research 11:* 286-287, 1951.
397. Trentin, J. J. Unpublished data.
398. Twombly, G. H. Production of mammary carcinomas in male mice with a single implantation of oestrone. *Proc. Soc. Exper. Biol. & Med. 40:* 430-432, 1939.
399. Twombly, G. H., Meisel, D., and Stout, A. P. Leydig-cell tumors induced experimentally in the rat. *Cancer 2:* 884-892, 1949.
400. Twombly, G. H., and Pack, G. T. *Endocrinology of Neoplastic Diseases: A Symposium by Eighteen Authors.* New York, Oxford University Press, 1947.
401. Twombly, G. H., and Taylor, H. C. Inactivation and conversion of estrogens in vitro by liver and other tissues from human cancer patients and from mice of strains susceptible to mammary carcinoma. *Cancer Research 2:* 811-817, 1942.
402. Van Eck-Vermande, G. J., and Freud, J. Structure and function of mouse ovaries after x-raying. *Arch. internat. de pharmacodyn. et de thérap. 78:* 49-62, 1949.
403. Van Gulik, P. J., and Korteweg, R. Susceptibility to follicular hormone and disposition to mammary cancer in female mice. *Am. J. Can. 38:* 506-515, 1940.
404. van Wagenen, G. The effects of oestrin on the urogenital tract of the male monkey. *Anat. Rec. 63:* 387-403, 1935.
405. van Wagenen, G., and Gardner, W. U. Functional intrasplenic ovarian transplants in monkeys. *Endocrinology 46:* 265-272, 1950.
406. van Wagenen, G., and Morse, A. H. Uterine and ovarian response to partial and subtotal ovarian resection. *Endocrinology 30:* 459-464, 1942.
407. Varangot, J. *Les Tumeurs de la granulosa (folliculomes de l'ovaire).* Paris, L. Arnette, 1937.
408. Vazquez-Lopez, E. The reaction of the pituitary gland and related hypothalmic centers in the hamster to prolonged treatment with estrogens. *J. Path. & Bact. 56:* 1-13, 1944.
409. Warren, S., and Olshausen, K. W. Interstitial cell growths of testicle. *Am. J. Path. 19:* 307-332, 1943.
410. Weil, A., and Zondek, B. The histopathology of the pituitary of the white rat injected with follicular hormone. *Endocrinology 25:* 114-122, 1939.
411. Weinstein, L., Gardner, W. U., and Allen, E. The effect of estrogenic hormones on the bacterial content of the uterus. *Yale J. Biol. & Med. 16:* 43-51, 1943.
412. Wilson, J. G., Young, W. C., and Hamilton, J. B. A technic suppressing development of reproductive function and sensitivity to estrogen in the female rat. *Yale J. Biol. & Med. 13:* 189-202, 1940.
413. Witschi, E. Comparative physiology of the vertebrate hypophysis (anterior and intermediate lobes). *Cold Spring Harbor Symposia on Quantitative Biology 5:* 180-190, 1937.

414. Wolfe, J. M. Reaction of ovaries of mature female rats to injections of oestrin. *Proc. Soc. Exper. Biol. & Med. 32:* 757-759, 1935.

415. Wolfe, J. M. The effects of advancing age on the structure of the anterior hypophysis and ovaries of female rats. *Am. J. Anat. 72:* 361-383, 1943.

416. Wolfe, J. M., and Wright, A. W. Histological effects induced in the anterior pituitary of the rat by prolonged injection of estrin with particular reference to the production of pituitary adenomata. *Endocrinology 23:* 200-210, 1938.

417. Wolfe, J. M., Bryan, W. R., and Wright, A. W. Histologic observations on the anterior pituitaries of old rats with special reference to the spontaneous appearance of pituitary adenomata. *Am. J. Cancer 34:* 352-372, 1938.

418. Wolfe, J. M., and Wright, A. W. A comparative histological study of the anterior hypophysis and the ovaries of two strains of rats, one of which is characterized by a high incidence of mammary fibroadenoma. *Cancer Research 3:* 497-508, 1943.

419. Wolfe, J. M., and Wright, A. W. Cytology of spontaneous adenomas in the pituitary gland of the rat. *Cancer Research 7:* 759-773, 1947.

420. Wolstenholme, J. T. The effects of a transplanted granulosa-cell tumor on mice in parabiosis. *Cancer Research 10:* 344-347, 1950.

421. Wolstenholme, J. T., and Gardner, W. U. Sinusoidal dilatation occurring in livers of mice with a transplanted testicular tumor. *Proc. Soc. Exper. Biol. & Med. 74:* 659-661, 1950.

422. Woolley, G. W. The adrenal cortex and its tumors. *Ann. New York Acad. Sc. 50:* 616-626, 1949.

423. Woolley, G. W., Fekete, E., and Little, C. C. Mammary tumor development in mice ovariectomized at birth. *Proc. Nat. Acad. Sc. 25:* 227-279, 1939.

424. Woolley, G. W., Fekete, E., and Little, C. C. Differences between high and low breast tumor strains of mice when ovariectomized at birth. *Proc. Soc. Exper. Biol. & Med. 45:* 796-798, 1940.

425. Woolley, G. W., Fekete, E., and Little, C. C. Effects of castration in the dilute brown strains of mice. *Endocrinology 28:* 341-343, 1941.

426. Woolley, G. W., Fekete, E., and Little, C. C. Gonadectomy and adrenal neoplasms. *Science 97:* 291, 1943.

427. Woolley, G. W., and Little, C. C. The incidence of adrenal cortical carcinoma in gonadectomized male mice of the extreme dilution strain. *Cancer Research 5:* 211-219, 1945.

428. Woolley, G. W., and Little, C. C. Prevention of adrenal cortical carcinoma by diethylstilbestrol. *Proc. Nat. Acad. Sc. 32:* 239-240, 1946.

429. Wright, A. W., Klinck, C. H., and Wolfe, J. M. The pathology and pathogenesis of mammary tumors occurring spontaneously in the Albany strain of rats. *Am. J. Path. 16:* 817-834, 1940.

430. Zondek, B. The fate of follicular hormone in the living body. *Lancet 227:* 356, 1934.

431. Zondek, B. Tumour of the pituitary induced with follicular hormone. *Lancet 230:* 776-778, 1936.

432. Zondek, B. The effect of long-continued large doses of follicle hormone upon the uterus of the rat. *Am. J. Obst. & Gynec. 33:* 979-989, 1937.

433. Zondek, B. Impairment of anterior pituitary functions by follicular hormone. *Folia clin. Orient 1:* 1-36, 1937.

434. ZONDEK, B. Menstruation-like haemorrhage in rabbits induced by gonadotropic hormone. *J. Obst. & Gynaec. Brit. Emp. 45:* 1-23, 1938.
435. ZONDEK, B. Hypophyseal tumors induced by estrogenic hormone. *Am. J. Cancer 33:* 555-559, 1938.
436. ZUCKERMAN, S. The effects of prolonged oestrogenic stimulation on the prostate of the Rhesus monkey. *J. Anat. 72:* 264-276, 1938.
437. ZUCKERMAN, S., and MCKEOWN, T. The canine prostate in relation to normal and abnormal testicular changes. *J. Path. & Bact. 46:* 7-19, 1938.

CHAPTER 13

Virus-Induced Tumors and the Virus Theory of Cancer

Francisco Duran-Reynals

The so-called virus theory of cancer aspires to explain most or all types of the disease as being induced by viruses.† Two working hypotheses support this theory: (1) viruses fulfill the requirements which a hypothetical cause of the disease would demand; (2) there are some cancers certainly induced by viruses, and consequently it is elementary logic to look for such agents when trying to find the cause of the remaining tumors of unknown etiology.

MAIN ATTRIBUTES OF CANCER COMPATIBLE WITH VIRUS THEORY

The main attributes of malignant disease which, in a purely theoretical sphere, could be explained as being the results of virus effects are as follows:

1. Indefinite growth of cells;
2. Result of most varied stimuli in the proper genetic background;
3. Constancy in its appearance in selective tissues, but variability in that many tissues can be involved though with different frequency;
4. Highest incidence in maturity;
5. Presence of agents other than cells which can reproduce the disease in some cases but not in others.

ATTRIBUTES OF VIRUSES THAT CAN EXPLAIN PROPERTIES OF CANCER

Corresponding to the above, the following are known characteristics of viruses:

1. They require living cells, and quite often stimulate them to grow before destroying them;

† The present paper is a further development of a review recently published (45) in an easily available periodical. For this reason some phases in our discussion have been omitted or just sketched, the reader being referred to the previous publication. Concerning fundamental concepts, however, avoidance of repetition has been impossible.

2. They may exert their effects after the most varied provocative stimuli and in the most strict genetic background;
3. They can show the most rigid specificity for this or that species or cell; yet they are capable of variation, and as a result of this process they can acquire new affinities for cells not previously affected. Thus, *specificity* and *variation* are in a way antagonistic to each other. Therefore, a *constant* lesion and a *great variety of lesions* can be explained as being due to the same but variable virus;
4. They can remain latent in tissues—to which they can find easy access early in infancy and not manifest their effects until very late in life or else, as we shall soon see, when infecting a tissue that age has changed, they may induce lesions different from those caused in tissues from young hosts;
5. They can manifest themselves in a free, overt form or in a *masked* form, and these two states are often interchangeable.

It would be superfluous to enter into a detailed analysis of each of the properties of the viruses just listed. Still, concerning the first point, it is to be questioned why the initial cell proliferation started by so many viruses is stopped by a host reaction at a given moment, after a process lasting a few hours, as with some strains of mammalian pox viruses; or several days, as with fowl pox virus; or several weeks, as with the rabbit fibroma virus. If this host reaction did not take place, the natural conclusion is that a cancer-like process would ensue, as is shown by the fact that some cancer viruses, such as those of chicken sarcomas for instance, may induce in a foreign species growths that inexorably regress, thus behaving like ordinary viruses. What is, then, the fundamental difference between the two types of viruses? Or what factors in the host determine either a limited or an unlimited cell proliferation?

With regard to the fourth point, no comments are needed to emphasize the capacity of viruses, such as those of choriomeningitis, mouse poliomyelitis, and salivary gland viruses, to remain latent in tissues. Some remarks, however, concerning the modification of the infection by the age of the host may be of interest. Studies on the relation of age to infection are numerous, most of them establishing experimentally the fact of the greater susceptibility of the young to infection. However, a fact that so far has not been studied seems to emerge from recent observations, namely, that *viral infection of the old and generally more resistant host may manifest itself preferentially by cell proliferation rather than by cell destruction.* This fact will be one of the main phenomena around which the present discussion on tumor viruses will turn. In the field of non-neoplastic ordinary viruses, the following instructive examples of what could well be termed *neoplastic* infection as opposed to *destructive* infection[45] may be quoted:

1. Sheep pox and allied viruses induce in the young essentially destructive pustular lesions in a disease pattern which is often lethal, whereas in the adult they induce typical mild papillomas. The identity of these lesions in the adult cannot be clearly established unless they are passed to young hosts which then react with typical pox;[21, 61]

2. Infection of the chick embryo by herpes virus is proliferative and but little necrotic in the late stages of development, the reverse being true in early stages;[3]

3. Myxoma virus is far less proliferative and more destructive in young than in old animals and the attenuated virus is more proliferative than fresh virus.[2]

In the case of the fibroma virus events are more complex. The virus inoculated *in large amounts* into newborn rabbits causes an acute, lethal disease with traits largely destructive and inflammatory. When injected *in small amounts*, or after storage, it induces progressively growing tumors, sometimes very large, which either regress leaving the animal immune or can in their turn generate satellite nodules and generalized fibromas, to all intents and purposes metastases. Virus secured from either the necrotizing or the tumorous lesions induces the usual mild fibromas in the adult, which always regress, leaving the rabbit immune.[41] It is important to correlate these findings with those of Ahlström and Andrewes,[1] who treated adult domestic rabbits with chemical carcinogens and then infected them with fibroma virus: tumor regression was much delayed, and the subcutaneous tumors grew progressively "*coming to resemble true neoplasms.*" Intravenous injections of virus produced tumors at the sites injected with the carcinogen, and, in addition, produced generalized fibromas closely resembling the generalized lesions observed by the writer after injection into the newborn rabbit. X-rays have been shown to have the same effects,[33] but noncarcinogenic compounds were ineffective.

Thus, there is a gradation in resistance linked to age, which, in both the young and the adult hosts can be broken down: in the newborn by the injection of large amounts of active virus and in the adult by treatment with carcinogens. The resistance of the young can be completely suppressed but that of the adult can be suppressed only to the extent of reducing it to the level of the young hosts injected with attenuated virus. The important conclusion is that, in both cases, neoplasia with traits of malignancy can only be induced by the fibroma virus when the host is endowed with a certain, critical degree of resistance. If no resistance is present, an essentially inflammatory condition develops; if a strong resistance is present, a mild disease or no disease at all results.

The above are not, however, the only ways of changing the effects of fibroma virus or of its variant, the myxoma virus: as discussed elsewhere[41] constitutional, endocrine, and immunologic factors leading to virus mutation or variation are also effective. Concerning the latter, it was observed, in the United States by Shope[106] and in England by Andrews,[10] that the ordinary fibroma variety changed into inflammatory and intermediate strains.

Other examples of duality of effects of infectious agents were given in another publication.[49] One of the most interesting cases is that of infection by *Bartonella bacilliformis*, the cause of the acute, often lethal Oroya fever which, following recovery, changes into a real fibroangiomatous tumor, *verruga peruviana.*

The fifth point concerning the masking of viruses regards a phenomenon, or rather a group of phenomena, which really deserve an exhaustive analytic scrutiny, since they appear to be of the utmost importance in the virus field in general, and are exceedingly interesting for the discussion of viruses in relation to cancer. The phenomenon of "masking," a term indicating the situation in which a virus may be present in an infected tissue or cell and yet not demonstrable by the means currently used, establishes a clear-cut difference between viral and bacterial infection, for in the latter case—so far as is known—if a tissue remains negative after microscopic study, cultures, and animal inoculation, it is considered free of bacteria.*

A tentative classification may be made of at least some of the specific instances recorded in the literature (see Duran-Reynals[45] for references).

1. A variety of neurotropic viruses, after having exerted their effects on the central nervous system, cannot be transmitted to other hosts by inoculation of the ground tissue. These cases were designated by Levaditi as "self-sterilizable neuro-infections." The intransmissibility of the protracted herpes infection in rabbits described by Perdrau probably falls in the same category, although in this case the virus can be unmasked by storage in glycerol, by electrophoresis, and by dilution of the extract.

2. Virus could not be demonstrated under some circumstances in extracts of viscera from chickens infected with the virus of avian pest or in organ extracts of rabbits recovering from vaccinial infection. In the last case the virus was unmasked by electrophoresis or by repeated passages (Lepine, Olitsky, and others).

3. Salivary gland virus of some strains of mice induces a rapid lethal infection when injected intraperitoneally. Extensive lesions with typical inclusion bodies are found in the liver and other viscera; yet injection of the extracts of these tissues consistently fails to reproduce the lesions in other mice (McCordock and Smith).

4. The virus of swine influenza carried by the hog lung worm does not become infectious unless the provocative stimulus of *Hemophilus influenzae* is at play (Shope).

5. In virus infection of plants, the virus of the sour cherry tree, together with other viruses of the group, can be transmitted only by grafting of infected tissues and not by direct inoculation of healthy plants with juice of infected ones. However, transmission by this method can be accomplished if extracts from young leaves of the cherry tree are inoculated into young leaves of cucumber. An analogous situation is found in the case of the wound tumor virus which is only transmissible when previously passed to leaf hoppers (Black *et al.*).

6. Tobacco mosaic and cucumber viruses form insoluble complexes with certain protamines and histones and possibly with trypsin. These complexes are dissociated by appropriate methods and active virus is liberated. In the presence of large amounts of trypsin, the infectivity of the virus was almost destroyed, but its serologic reactions were unaffected.[14]†

However, it is—from recent work in both France and the United States—in the field of bacterial viruses that the most enlightening examples for discussion here are to be found. The three groups of relevant facts are:

1. After infection of susceptible bacteria by bacteriophage there is a phase in which no recoverable virus can be demonstrated, despite the employment of the variety of means available today for the detection of the phage either by breaking the bacterial cells or by other procedures (Doerman, Luria, Latarjet). These facts, as Luria points

* The photoreactivation of ultraviolet-irradiated bacteria[73] is an exception.

† Two reviews by N. W. Pirie concerning these topics may be read with considerable profit. One is his contribution to the 6th International Congress of Experimental Cytology: "The association of viruses with other materials in the cells and in extracts." The other is the chapter on viruses in the 1946 Annual Review of Biochemistry. These papers contain a number of instructive examples of masking, unmasking and allied phenomena concerning plant viruses and also animal viruses such as PVM and influenza.

out, may be compared with what is known of so many animal viruses which cannot be recovered for a time after infection. The serologic work of Hoyle and the Henles on influenza virus is specially noteworthy in that it shows that there is virus immunologic specificity without overt virus activity.[84]

2. It has been known for a long time that bacterial strains can carry bacteriophage. In some strains signs of phage activity are frequently and obviously shown; in others signs of lysis are observed only occasionally with various degrees of this phenomenon between these two extremes. Often, the carried virus is shown only by tests on other sensitive, indicator strains. Further investigations have shown the following features of lysogenic strains:[86] (1) Lysogenicity is a property of all the bacteria or spores of the strain; (2) It persists after repeated passages in the presence of specific antiphage serum; (3) Bacteria from the lysogenic strain absorb the phage they can produce; (4) Lysis of the bacteria by an enzyme, lysozyme, does not liberate phage from potentially lysogenic bacteria; (5) Resistant lysogenic bacteria which can produce a phage identical to the original one can be obtained from strains sensitive to a given phage.

Recent studies by Lwoff, *et al.*[85] have shown that by means of a special "microdrop" technic one can follow bacteria (*B. megatherium*) through as many as nineteen divisions without production of free phage. However, if the bacteria are grown in a special medium containing yeast and are subjected to ultraviolet radiation, the totality of the bacterial population is lysed by the action of free phage liberated from the bacteria. Therefore, under ordinary circumstances (in which "spontaneous" lysis occurs only in a few bacteria), the bacteriophage in the lysogenic culture, although not detectable, multiplies "intrabacterially," but under exogenous influences becomes free in a number of bacteria and destroys the whole population.

In other studies by Luria,[84] it was first shown that if bacteriophage is irradiated by ultraviolet light *one* phage particle thus treated does not induce lysis, but such lysis is accomplished by *two or more* irradiated particles, as if a whole active, free particle were reconstructed by materials from the plurality of phages, each of which would be defective in this or that character. It may be added that, as in the case of bacteria,[73] the same reactivation is accomplished by means of ordinary light (Dulbecco). That interactions can take place between different phages had already been demonstrated in the experiments of Delbruck and Hershey, quoted in[84], which show that in the progeny of phages resulting from "mixed" infections new types are to be found, the result of a recombination of alternative characters present in the parental types. All these phenomena take place only among units of the same phage strain or of related strains.

In the studies reviewed above the reader will come across different terms used by the authors to designate the state of the bacterial virus when it cannot be manifested as a free entity, such as "prophages," "intermediate stages," "inactivated" or "damaged" phage. The term *masking*, no matter how loose, could be used to cover that state of the virus that may last either for only a few minutes, as in the initial stages of bacterial infection, or for much longer periods of time, involving many bacterial generations, as in lysogenic bacteria; and the term *unmasking* could be employed for the reversion of the impaired virus to its free form. There are good reasons to suppose that after irradiation (Luria) or in the lysogenic strains, the virus is in an imperfect, impaired state from which it can recover by combination or by other means. Let us add that there is evidence that a combination phenomenon takes place in at least one animal virus, since in the Berry-Dietrich phenomenon the injection of heated, inactive myxoma virus together with fresh fibroma virus results in the reconstruction of the very virulent, lethal myxoma virus.

VIRUS VERSUS MUTATION

Phenomena that can be used as proof against the existence of a cancer virus could also—as shown in the preceding discussion—be used as proof against the unreservedly accepted existence of other viruses. From these and from the other facts above reviewed, it may be concluded that the virus theory of cancer is intellectually plausible[10] as an explanation of the cause of all or many cancers.

However, judging by what is published and by what is heard, the virus theory of cancer is not professed by many, the majority of cancerologists being attracted by other hypotheses, all or most of which can be ultimately reduced to the so-called mutation theory. In another publication,[45] the writer constructed an imaginary controversy between a virologist and a mutationist, and much the same has been done recently by Andrewes.[10] If an attempt were made to summarize both points of view, the following might be said: There is agreement in that cancer is the result of a *change*, which for the mutationist is the disease itself, because such change—the mutation—would be of a peculiar kind inducing unrestricted cell multiplication. For the virologist, the change makes possible a virus effect, by making the tissue specially susceptible to a virus, either latent or newly arrived. This virus would induce the disease without previous mutation or following mutation, which could be caused directly by the carcinogen or indirectly by the new environment created by the changed tissue. And one or another of these events must take place at least in a number of cases leading to cancer *certainly induced by viruses*, which we will now review.

CANCERS CAUSED BY VIRUS

AVIAN CANCER

As is well known, Ellerman and Bang[5] discovered the viruses of leukoses in 1908, and Rous[102] the viruses of sarcoma in 1912. The main reason why this type of cancer is of a very special interest is that, when properly investigated, causative viruses have been demonstrated in all the naturally occurring mesodermal tumors and leukoses, that is, the malignant lesions most commonly observed in chickens.

Most of the work on avian cancer has been concentrated on chicken tumors. However, when the viruses causing these tumors are adapted to other species of birds, such as ducks, the tumors that result appear practically like those naturally occurring in the new species. Also, there are indications that the few tumors or leukoses studied for transmissibility, occurring in species other than chickens, are also virus-induced. These considerations lead to the suspicion that viruses could easily be demonstrated in many cases of malignancy in the class *Aves*—and there are 15,000 species of birds as against 5,000 species of mammals. For the same reason, the importance of a systematic study of tumors and leukoses which are known to occur in birds other than chickens becomes evident.*

In most cases the viruses of chicken tumors and leukoses exert their effects promptly, thus being ideal tools for approaching important theoretical problems. Also, for the first time in cancer research, we detect in avian tumors and leukoses phenomena of a clear, though complex, epidemiologic value. For all these reasons avian cancer will be first discussed, and from what is learnt an attempt will be made to derive general principles that will be applied later, not only to other virus-induced tumors but to malignancy in general.

As attested by excellent reviews on the subject,[25, 52, 53, 70, 79] the chicken is one of the species showing the highest incidence of naturally occurring cancer. Figures of 10 per cent to 20 per cent are certainly not uncommon, and they are sometimes much higher, especially if lymphomatosis is included. This disease is said to account for 50 per cent of malignancy in chickens. The age incidence is also comparable to that of mammals and men: rare in youth (except for some forms of lymphomatosis), frequent in adult age, and possibly rare again, with some tumors, in extreme old age. The cancers observed also duplicate quite often those occurring in mammals and in man, although the incidence of the different avian types varies from that found in other species. There are wide variations in the total incidence of avian malignancy, often in the same country and under apparently the same environmental circumstances, a fact certainly not surprising if the vagaries in the spreading and mutability of infectious agents are considered. Also, as in so many other infectious diseases, clear seasonal variations in susceptibility have been observed in relation to: (1) natural occurrence of leukoses and possibly other tumors;[53] (2) development of tumors following injection with chemical carcinogens and growths of transplants from these tumors;[99] (3) development of teratomas of testes following injection of zinc chloride;[12] and (4) growth of tumors and leukoses on injection of the corresponding viruses.[27, 53] The periods of higher resistance begin in late summer. Maturity of the host is indispensable for these effects to be shown, and since endocrine changes are known to occur in fowls in the course of the year, the above facts may be interpreted as indicating a hormonal influence on avian cancer. Let us add, perhaps superfluously, that our awareness about cancer in chickens exists not merely because the species is so easily available for observation; for another species, the pigeon, is equally accessible, yet cancer in pigeons is extremely rare.

Compared to what is known on the influence of hereditary factors on mouse tumors, knowledge in the field of avian cancer is indeed limited. However, inbred strains of chickens are being developed in which are observed pronounced differences of susceptibility to the viruses of sarcomas[28, 34] and of lymphomatosis[121] reaching the

* A case in point is that of parakeets, of which, according to Dr. Ratcliffe's theory (communicated to us by Dr. B. Lucké), about 15 per cent have tumors, mostly of internal organs. Jarma (quoted in Engelbreth-Holm[53]) reported in these birds a combination of sarcoma and erythroblastosis, the condition being transmissible by cells. In 1939, Dr. Lucké sent us two parakeets with breast sarcomas from the Philadelphia Zoo. The tumors had a morphology and texture identical with that of the filterable chicken sarcomas of the Rous type. Unfortunately, circumstances prevented us from carrying out the adequate tests to show the presence of causative viruses in the growths.

point of complete resistance, in some strains, as against extreme susceptibility in other strains. It is hoped that inbred strains may become easily available, as in the case of mice, for—as will be seen later—the constant demonstration of causative viruses in some forms of malignancy, e.g. lymphomatosis, was only possible by using special strains inbred for susceptibility.

It is an important fact that the genetic factor can discriminate between resistance to the virus and to the cell infected by this virus. Some results by Rous[103] pointed in this direction. Convincing evidence was found in lymphoid tumor R.P.L.12[22] which, when transmitted by filtrates in genetically receptive breeds, induces generalized lymphomatosis after several months, while injection of cells results in large local tumors in a few days, this being often followed by generalization. However, with ordinary heterozygous Plymouth Rock chicks, filtrates were utterly ineffective, whereas cells induced the same disease as in the inbred strains.[47]

Physical, Chemical, and Immunologic Properties of the Viruses

The viruses of sarcomas and of erythromyeloid leukoses are very similar in many of their physical properties.[53, 79] The viruses are easily filterable although, as it will be later seen, this property is conditioned by several host factors. They are characterized by: a particle size of about 75 mμ; a medium resistance to heating, being inactivated at 55°–60°C.; a great sensitivity to oxidation, being reactivated by some reducing agents; a stability in a frozen or dry state; and a remarkable resistance to glycerol, and to x-rays. The Rous sarcoma virus, the best studied in this respect, can be sedimented by high speed centrifugation. Analysis of the sediment has shown that it has a complex structure containing lipoid, carbohydrates, and nucleoprotein of the ribose type.[30] Also, electron microphotographs of this material or of infected cells have shown the presence of typical bodies which it seems can be identified with the virus itself.[32]

The viruses of avian leukoses and tumors are antigenic for both heterologous and homologous species. Potent immune sera have been obtained in ducks, rabbits, etc., which: (1) neutralize the viruses *in vitro*; (2) afford some protection to chickens against further virus infection; and (3) agglutinate viruses purified by centrifugation and fix the complement in its presence.[31, 79] The same is true for sera from birds in which lesions have regressed. Comparable antibodies are found against sarcoma[37] and leukosis-sarcoma viruses[64] in most normal adult chickens, and these antibodies increase during tumor growth.[59] Also, these homologous sera can protect chicks against a sarcoma virus injected intravenously.[48] It is possible, though difficult, to immunize chickens actively against strains of tumors or leukoses, although, as in so many virus diseases, it is not exactly known whether an initial lesion followed by regression is indispensable to induce resistance.[23, 24]

The existence of antigenic relationships between different strains of erythromyeloid leukoses viruses is shown by the fact that chickens immune to a given strain are also immune to other strains tested, or to sarcomas induced by some of these strains.[53] Also, heterologous immune sera against one strain neutralize several virus strains. These facts duplicate in erythromyeloid leukoses what happens in sarcomas and endotheliomas (Andrewes). Matters may perhaps be different in the case of lymphomatosis. Thus, judging by some results, artificial immunization against one transplantable strain cannot be predicted to protect against other transplantable strains, or against the naturally occurring disease.[24]

On the other hand, it is very probable, if not certain, that there are common antigens, first, between viruses from strains of lymphomatosis and the Rous sarcoma virus, and secondly, between sarcoma and leukosis viruses on the one hand and the viruses that induced the sarcomas provoked by chemical carcinogens on the other. The first supposition is supported by results from an investigation carried out in the writer's laboratory, in collaboration with the East Lansing Agricultural Experiment Station:[47, 121] (1) sera from 28 chickens reared in strict isolation and largely free of lymphomatosis had no antibodies against the Rous virus, whereas 23 chickens, of the contaminated flock, from the same lines (as well as hundreds of other chickens studied at random—see later) had the antibodies; and (2) treatment of 6 isolated chickens with a lymphomatosis antigen resulted in the development of antibodies to the Rous sarcoma. The second supposition is supported by the experiments to be described later showing that chickens, pheasants, and rabbits, immunized against sarcomas provoked in chickens by the injection of carcinogens, develop antibodies which neutralize several sarcoma and leukosis viruses.

Species and Cell Specificity

As already noticed by early workers on avian cancer and later confirmed by many others, while in some strains of leukoses and tumors only a given type of cell is affected, other strains are characterized by the proliferation of a great variety of cells. Among the former we have many or all strains of lymphomatosis, the so-called "pure" strains of erythromyeloid leukoses of different sorts (although probably not the ordinary small cell lymphomatosis), and also sarcomas and angioendotheliomas resulting when the infective material is injected into tissues. (Oberling, Engelbreth-Holm, Furth, etc.). Let us note, though, that with some strains, tumor growth is not due to a virus effect on the host cells, but to the local multiplication of cells present in the inoculum.[101] To the above we have to add endotheliomas of the Mill Hill 2 type, the first action of which is an effect on lymphocytes and macrophages before the endothelium of vessels is involved, and this initial effect on cells of the macrophage type seems to be also exerted by the viruses of the Rous sarcoma type.[54]

Thus, enlarging a sequence already pointed out by Foulds,[54] the following gradation from a "pure" tumor to a "pure" leukosis may be made:

Fibrosarcomas;
Sarcomas of the Rous type;
Endotheliomas of the MH2 type;
"Combined" erythromyeloid leukoses;
"Pure" erythromyeloid leukoses.

As Foulds states concerning his original sequence: "between members of this series there are convergences or overlappings in cellular composition, yet each member is a distinct pathological entity."[54] Whether ordinary epidemic lymphomatosis and still other neoplasms can be included as last members of the list will be discussed later.

On the other hand, when viruses or cells from leukoses and tumors are injected into adult individuals from foreign species of birds, with a few possible exceptions, no growths are induced, but if the individuals injected are immature, then lesions may frequently develop. The conditions determining whether either regression or adaptation of the virus to the new species—a process which involves virus variation—will take place is to be discussed later. Here, it will suffice to state: first, that the ability to infect cells from a foreign species without virus variation—even if the infected individual is young—indicates a certain degree of nonspecificity; and second, that when variation occurs, adaptation of the virus is never carried beyond the infection of mesodermal cells of species zoologically near to the chicken. Thus, one can range pheasants, turkeys, guinea hens and ducks, as being susceptible to the Rous virus during a period ranging from just one day after hatching to several months.[39, 40]

As pointed out by Engelbreth-Holm and Furth in their discussions on the "combined" strains of leukosis viruses, it can be imagined, on the one hand, that a strictly specific virus for a given cell could cause all the cells derived from it, presumably having the same "receptors," to turn malignant. Thus, if the primarily susceptible cell is an undifferentiated hemohystioblast, the spectrum of leukoses and tumors that the virus can induce would be very wide, whereas the opposite would be true if the primarily susceptible cell was more differentiated. On the other hand, it may be imagined that the virus is less specific and endowed with the power of attacking a variety of cells which precede and follow, in the cytologic genealogy, the cells primarily attacked.

Both explanations are probably right. As shown later, chicken tumor viruses are endowed with a great power of variation, and therefore, in avian cancer, an extremely interesting situation exists in which the two elements of the conflict, namely viruses and cells, are changing continuously, thus producing the great variety of lesions of the avian leukosis-tumor complex.[92, 93] Previous statements may be recalled dealing with the antagonistic nature of the two processes, specificity and variation. While avian cancer viruses can well be considered as fairly specific for a given cell, they can acquire, through variation, the power of infecting many other cells.

EPIDEMIOLOGY

In viewing the great number and variety of chicken tumors and leukoses induced by viruses, the first question suggested to the virologist is how these viruses are transmitted in nature. Naturally, this is a question that the mutationist would never ask, for he believes that these "viruses" get detached from cells under the impact of carcinogens and such a fundamental fact would, naturally, relegate to a secondary position the further spread of these detached components. Some support for this view could come from the undeniable fact that chickens of all ages living in close contact with others, undoubtedly infected experimentally with many strains of tumors and leukoses, never contract the disease.* However, the virologist may not be too surprised at this, since natural contagion, leading to manifest disease, differs in many ways from the experimental contagion. Nevertheless, that a form of natural contagion may somehow take place is indicated by an observation, from the writer's laboratory, in which it was shown that the titer of antibodies for the Rous virus increased many times during a period of five months in chickens living in the somewhat crowded animal room, where many other infected birds were kept.[59]

More important, however, than this last observation is the following fact†: the vast majority of adult chickens, at least in the United States, living under ordinary conditions, have in their blood specific antibodies which neutralize the viruses of the Rous and Fuginani sarcomas and the Mill Hill 2 endothelioma. These antibodies are absent at hatching and develop gradually with aging.[37, 64] In orthodox epidemiology one would conclude without much hesitation that there must be some means of transmission of the tumor viruses to account for these antibodies. If this is assumed, only one step is required to give an explanation of the appearance of tumors, taking into account the many factors, ponderable or imponderable, that change an infection from latent to manifest. If to the facts above reviewed are added important newer contributions in the domain of lymphomatosis, the whole natural history of avian cancer may begin to come to light.

Lymphomatosis or lymphogenous leukemia (although aleukemic in most cases) is the most common form of malignancy in chickens, being also observed in other species of birds. The disease, either tumoral or infiltrating, manifests itself in many tissues, the three main forms currently accepted being the ocular, neural, and visceral; these forms are considered today to be the manifestation of effects of the same group of viruses. As attested by the many failures reported, lymphomatosis is far more difficult to transmit than other leukemias or tumors. Transmission, however, is readily accomplished if appropriate chickens inbred for susceptibility are inoculated; this fact indicates that the virus is far more exacting, genetically, than others of avian cancer. In most or all cases the disease is kept "pure" through the passages of the virus. Some strains affect the periosteum and endosteum inducing a curious condition called osteopetrosis or *marble bone*, comparable to Paget's disease of man.[22, 71]

By observing the ways in which the disease occurs naturally in flocks one could already suspect an epidemiologic pattern in lymphomatosis. This suspicion has been fully confirmed by the work carried out in East Lansing, Michigan, during the last twelve years.[119, 120, 122]

* However, authors like Patterson, Lee, and others cited in [53] reported infection by contact of a very wide leukoses complex, a conclusion doubted by some workers. The very facts now under discussion should counsel the keeping of an open mind on the point. For it might well be imagined that mutations occurring in some particular virus strains could lead, though exceptionally, to the acquisition of a frank contagious power.

† Andrewes,[10] who considers that neither cancer in general nor chicken sarcomas in particular are contagious, quotes several virus diseases, e.g. rabies, equine encephalitis, pseudorabies, as not being contagious among certain species: "Ready transmission of a virus disease happens very often, but often it does not."

1. By strict isolation during hatching and rearing, families of chickens have been raised either entirely free of lymphomatosis and other infectious diseases as well for several generations, or with an incidence far lower than that present in the ordinary infected flock.
2. The occasional failure to free these isolated birds from the disease may be due to passage of the virus to the progeny before hatching or in the process of hatching. This may be surmised from the fact that the virus has actually been found in apparently normal embryos and chicks by inoculation into susceptible birds reared in isolation. Also, tracheal and nasal washings from paralyzed birds (*neural* lymphomatosis) when instilled into the nasal passages and trachea of susceptible chicks induced a high incidence of *visceral* lymphomatosis.
3. If the isolated birds are mixed with the infected flock they may contract the disease *provided the exposure takes place at a very young age.*

To these facts may be added the results recorded above concerning the absence of antibodies for the Rous virus in the isolated chickens, and the development of such antibodies after treatment with lymphomatosis material.

Some authors do not accept the view that lymphomatosis is a true malignant disease. That the disease is epidemic, that it can be prevented by isolation, that in some forms it is not limited by age, that these viruses under certain conditions can destroy cells instead of stimulating them to grow (*vide infra*) are, no doubt, unusual features for cancer, but precisely because of these features the disease is of extraordinary interest, because it may help us to understand the mechanisms that lead to the establishment of the disease generally accepted as cancer. Do the facts disclosed on lymphomatosis serve to explain the mode of transmission of this particular disease, or can they be resorted to in trying to explain the propagation of other forms of avian cancer? Speculation on this point will be taken up again after surveying avian tumor viruses, and the influence upon their activities of a factor of the utmost importance in cancer: *the age factor.*

AGE AND NECROTIZING EFFECTS ON CELLS

When the viruses of the Rous sarcoma or other chicken sarcomas and of their variants in other species are injected into immature hosts, no tumors are induced, but hemorrhagic lesions appear which are the result of an effect of the virus on the small vessels.[38, 72, 89] This phenomenon is best shown in the case of a neurotropic or pseudoneurotropic duck variant of the Rous sarcoma, which induces in the central nervous system of ducklings lesions comparable in many ways to those induced by several ordinary viruses.[46] All these non-neoplastic lesions, which contain abundant free virus, can be maintained as such by passages through immature hosts, but if at every passage older hosts are injected, then tumors are induced.

Comparable facts were described by Blakemore and others in some strains of lymphomatosis.[18] The causative viruses when infecting chicks and embryos produced a mild, purely necrotizing disease (which highly increased in severity after repeated passages) involving the heart and liver of the bird, whereas the more resistant birds developed typical lymphoid neoplasia. Blakemore considers the latter to be the chronic state of an acute disease and he has recently[19] reiterated this conclusion in answering some objections by Asplin,[11] who pointed out that the necrotizing lesions might be due to another virus accompanying that of lymphomatosis. Pappenheimer *et al*,[96] in their important paper on neurolymphomatosis, had already stated that in field cases there was a clear transition between inflammatory lesions and neoplastic lesions.

Still another case is that of gliomas. Jackson in South Africa recently found that "in the fowl all gradations occur between lesions of chronic disseminated focal encephalitis and gliomas, often in the same brain." He states later: "I believe that glioma of the fowl will prove to be nothing but a proliferative response to a specific infectious agent."[69] Two points have to be remembered in this connection: the first is that the Rous virus is capable, through variation, of infecting the central nervous system of ducklings.[46] The second is that, as shown by Vazquez-Lopez,[117] the Rous virus injected intracerebrally into chickens induces sarcomas constituted by accumulations of corpuscles derived from microglia cells, from which, later, tumor cells appear. It is the belief of Vazquez-Lopez that these cells are the originating element of the so-called ameboid cells, the malignant cells of the tumor.

Thus, it seems well established that avian cancer viruses like those of fibroma, sheep pox, and others, can behave as destructive viruses under certain circumstances.

Age, Tumor Growth, Formation of Metastases and Transmissibility by Cells

To analyze the influence of age upon these features of the Rous sarcoma we must consider both the age of the host and the age of the tumor. As to the age of the host, it is responsible for basic differences such as the following: In the young a minimal amount of virus will induce rapidly growing tumors, often generating metastases and hemorrhagic lesions, and transmission either by cells or by filtrates is usually successful. In the adult host the reverse is true: larger amounts of virus are required to induce tumors, their growth is slow, hemorrhagic lesions are a rarity, metastasis formation diminishes and transmission is not always feasible either by cells or by filtrates. The influence of the age of the tumor becomes evident in the following manner: transmissibility of the tumor by cells, which is somewhat inhibited in the adult host, becomes much more difficult if the tumor is old. If such old tumors are transmissible by filtrates, that is, by the virus, the incidence of metastases is significantly less in the second generation of hosts than if the filtrate came from a young tumor.[37, 50, 57]

Thus, it seems clear from the above that (apart from possible variations in quantity) the quality of the virus changes fundamental features in malignancy, for alterations in these features, such as diminution of metastases, persist in a tumor induced in a second host by *virus alone*. It is clear that under the influence of the age factor *the virus has changed*. This alteration is of the greatest importance to the discussion of the following subject.

Age and Variation of Viruses

As stated before, it might be possible, under certain conditions, to infect heterologous species with the viruses of chicken tumors and leukoses. However, with the possible exception of Jarmai's strain of myeloid leukemia infecting turkeys, cited in[53], adaptation to the foreign species has never been achieved. It has been shown in the writer's laboratory that such adaptation is possible and even easy but—most important—that every time it is accomplished the virus varies or mutates.[39, 40]

Analysis of the conditions under which this adaptation takes place is most instructive: adaptation of the Rous sarcoma virus to a foreign species, namely ducks, is only possible, first, when the duck is no more than a few days old, and second, when the chicken virus is in that *changed* state discussed in the foregoing section, that is, the state found in aging chickens. As attested by literally hundreds of tests, it was not possible to adapt to ducks a virus from a tumor growing in a chick: if filtrates were injected into ducklings, no tumors at all resulted; if cell suspensions were used, then tumors—even very large—may develop, but these growths could not be maintained beyond a second or at best a third passage; they never induced generalized lesions; and when injected back into chickens reproduced the typical original Rous sarcoma.[44] However, if ducklings a day old were injected with filtrates or cells from a tumor grown in an adult chicken—say from 3 to 10 months old—tumors developed in which signs of variation could frequently be detected at once, and from these changed tumors stable lines could be obtained by passages into other ducks, even if these were several months old. On the other hand, if the tumors had been grown in chickens 19 to 20 months old, injections of filtrates were always unsuccessful, while injection of cell suspension was only rarely successful, but in the 2 cases in which growth was achieved adaptation followed.*

In the light of modern knowledge of bacterial and virus variation, it does not seem difficult to interpret the results just noted: the immature chick offers a splendid terrain for the virus which grows in the defenseless host practically unopposed, whereas the adult chicken—a far more resistant host—offers an adverse ground to the virus. It is in such ground that certain virus units produced by random mutation will be selected because they are better adapted than others to thrive, and they will soon take the upper hand over the rest of the virus population. Therefore, it is not that the virus varies as a result of the infection of the foreign species, the duck, but rather that ducks are infected by easily adaptable viruses because these viruses have previously been changed in the chicken. The phenomenon is in many ways comparable to the appearance of bacterial variants in an aging culture which becomes more and more adverse to the vast majority of the bacterial population. Thus, adaptation of the chicken sarcoma virus to foreign species depends on factors linked with the age of both the donor and recipient hosts, and also, as before stated, on factors depending on the position of the recipient species in the zoologic scale in relation to the donor species.

There are two points of great interest in the described experiments for the general thesis that viruses may be the cause of many cancers. The first is that whenever the virus varies, it acquires new properties, one of which is that of infecting new cells, and therefore of inducing new types of cancer. Thus, by

* The specificity of the age factor in discriminating between tumors grown in hosts 10 months old and tumors grown in hosts 18-22 months old should be pointed out: the former grow frequently in a foreign species, the duckling; the latter rarely.

variation of the Rous virus, a great variety of sarcomas have been obtained in ducks and other species, each different from the other, such as a hystiocytoma, a lymphocytoma, and probably a leukosis.[39, 40] It is no longer necessary to invoke the presence of a different latent virus for each type of cancer: through variation of one or a few viruses a great variety of tumors and leukoses can be rationally explained (see further comments in Duran-Reynals[45]).

The second point is that the inoculation of chicks with viruses from the chicken variants in other species, induces the development, not of the original chicken sarcoma, but of the variant tumor, as if these tumors in the foreign species were the tumors which potentially could have developed in the chicken that supplied the virus.* This point will be emphasized later.

Masking of the Virus and Regression of the Tumor

As before stated, a *change* occurs in the virus present in the adult or old animal. Transmissibility of the tumor by cells becomes difficult, and by filtrates is often impossible. *The virus has become masked.*

It has been known for a long time that great differences are found in the transmissibility of naturally occurring cases of malignancy. Thus, only 13 out of 40 cases of erythromyeloid leukoses, as studied by three different workers,[53] could be adapted to transplantation, and the situation is the same in cases of naturally occurring sarcomas.[42]

The same state of affairs is found regarding the transmissibility by filtrates of tumors already adapted to transplantation by cells. The best known case is that reported by Gye and Andrewes,[65] who carried the Rous sarcoma through 9 successful cell passages in which filtrates were consistently negative; and much the same is true in chicken tumor C, a slow-growing fibrosarcoma.[42] In our naturally occurring sarcomas it was found that indefinite transmissibility by cells (and ultimately by virus) was definitely possible in 4 (possibly in 8) out of 10 tumors developing in chickens from a few weeks to 10 months old, but only in one out of 4 tumors developing in chickens from 12 to 18 months. These figures, of course, were only suggestive of an age effect. However, analysis of available data from other workers was also compatible with the hypothesis that the age of the host had an influence on the transmissibility of naturally occurring tumors. Concerning filterability of the Rous sarcoma, it was already known from the work of Carr[29] and Doerr *et al.*[35] that filterability was a property bearing an inverse relation with the age of the tumor.

In the writer's work with Freire,[50] it was found that masking of the sarcoma virus is conditioned by the age of the host, age of the tumor, and the source material—cells or filtrates—employed in inducing the tumor. Concerning the first factor, it was also found that masking occurred in 27 out of 45 Rous sarcomas grown in chickens about 15 months old, whereas it occurred in only 6 of 38 tumors grown in chicks inoculated at the age of 2 weeks. The age factor acted preferentially on the tumors induced by filtrates as if the virus, thus unprotected, was more vulnerable to it; but it also acted

* With some of the variants, immature hosts are indispensable for the experiments, for the viruses of these strains have lost the capacity of infecting the adult original host. It is quite probable that re-adaptation of the duck variants to chickens is only possible through further variation of the virus which may lead, not to the original Rous sarcoma, but to still other conditions, such as osteopetrosis. On the other hand, other duck variants of the Rous sarcoma keep the power of infecting chickens, and can also infect pigeons (Borges and Duran-Reynals).[45]

on the virus, in older tumors induced by cells. The diminution in transmissibility by cells and in the formation of metastases, already evident in the older host before masking, became definitely more pronounced when the virus became masked.

Is masking of the virus an irreversible phenomenon? Experiments showed that as long as the cells are active the virus is also active, for inoculation of cells into chicks results in tumors which generate hemorrhagic lesions—a manifestation of a free virus; and the tumors themselves yield active filtrates. Also, roentgen irradiation seems to be effective in restoring filterability to unfilterable tumors.[90] It is clear, then, that the masked, impaired virus can revert to a state of full vigor if the cells are freed from the influence of the age factor. Let us point out that the antibody response in chickens carrying tumors in which the virus is masked is the same as when the virus is free.[59] This suggests that the masked virus is antigenic.

Other facts, however, indicate that the age factor can proceed to regression of the tumor, with concomitant disappearance or stable neutralization of the virus. Let us examine the available data. Little is known about spontaneous regression of spontaneously occurring tumors in chickens. There are data, however, indicating that such regression does occur, and even frequently, in transmissible chicken leukoses and tumors induced by viruses, provided the host is mature. Thus, Rothe-Meyer, cited in,[53] reports 25 cases of regression of myeloid leukoses among 1060 adult chickens, but only 3 cases among 1900 young chicks. In our laboratory the Rous sarcoma regressed in at least 15 per cent of mature chickens without a single case of regression among 1400 chicks[58] and only in 1 case did it regress among 6000 chicks in the series of Gye and Purdy.[66] Solid immunity to reinfection is established after tumor regression.

The effect of the age factor on tumor regression is also manifest in the transplants of several tumors provoked by chemical carcinogens. In the writer's experience[47] such transplants are only successful when young hosts are inoculated. However, in these cell-transmitted chicken tumors, as well as in so many transplantable tumors from mice and other mammals, influences on the cells themselves play an important part, as has been so well studied by Gorer.[62] No such influences have been so far detected—although they may well be present—in the virus-induced tumors in which the cells are derived from the host. In these cases the age factor acts—as far as we can detect—primarily on the virus, and the cancer cell seems to follow the fate of its causative agent.

The lack of regression in naturally occurring avian malignancy, contrasted with the not infrequent regressions when the virus, after repeated tumor passages, has acquired a greater vigor and conceivably a greater power to elicit defensive responses from the aging host, is indeed a puzzling subject; the facts suggest a lack of either antigenicity or some sort of stimulating power in the viruses of the naturally occurring growths which may be of great importance in determining the inexorable course of the disease.

The forces operating in the aging host are not precisely known, hence the adoption of the noncommittal term of age factor to express them. That the specific antibodies against tumor viruses play a part would seem quite logical, for these antibodies—the result, as before stated, of subclinical infection against contagious tumor viruses—are absent at hatching and develop progressively with aging; they increase after tumor growth, and in the few cases when they are absent before and after tumor growth, the tumors are always filterable.[59] However, no quantitative relation was found between the antibody titer and other manifestations of resistance[59] and, as in so many other diseases induced by viruses, or other agents, the role of the specific antibody is not yet well defined.

Fibromas

These neoplasms of very low malignancy are frequent in chickens. In our series of 7, only 1 could be carried through 2 passages.[42] Often, these tumors give the impression of slow and poorly growing fibrosarcomas. Yet we know that, at least in one case, a tumor of the latter sort changed into a malignant, filterable sarcoma.[42]

Sarcomas Developing after the Injection of Chemical Carcinogens

This is a subject of very special interest, for if agents are found in these tumors capable of perpetuating them, the fact can be taken by both mutationists and virologists as precisely proving their respective points.

Carrel was the first worker who claimed to have obtained tumors like those of the Rous type by indole, arsenic, and tar, which could easily be maintained by filtrate passages. Comparable results were obtained by Des Ligneris and Fisher by adding the carcinogens to tissue culture (quoted in[95]). Several other authors failed to duplicate these results. Some of them suspected that accidental contamination by Rous virus had taken place. Fisher himself could not repeat his own results in strict conditions of isolation. Later, McIntosh and Selbie published, on two occasions, the results of extensive investigations in which, from a total of 10 tumors which developed after inoculation of tar or methylcholanthrene, 5 proved to be filterable. Isolated cases of filterability have been reported by several authors, such as Maisin, Haddow, Haagen, and, quite recently, by Oberling and Guerin, quoted in [95, 99].

It has been objected[99] that many of the tumors of the McIntosh series appeared at sites remote from the one injected and that they were often associated with leukoses. These filterable tumors, therefore, could well be naturally occurring ones. However, as admitted by Peacock,[99] remote carcinogenesis is a well-established fact, for example, in lung and breast tumors or leukemias in mice after application of the chemical by a variety of routes. Therefore, if the chemical activated a latent process of malignancy, which may or may not have manifested itself naturally, it would have proven its carcinogenic quality by awakening a latent virus.

Nevertheless, as attested in extensive studies by several workers, the tumors induced by injecting the carcinogen in the breast muscles, although they are in some cases indefinitely transmissible by cells, are undoubtedly not transmissible by filtrates. Is there any evidence that masked viruses are the proximal cause of these tumors which would thus have been *provoked* rather than induced by the carcinogens? There is, indeed, such evidence as may be derived from the work of Andrewes,[9] confirmed by Foulds, Dmochowsky, Gottschalk[56, 64] and others, indicating that neutralizing antibodies against sarcoma or leukoses viruses develop in pheasants and chickens bearing transplants of chemically provoked tumors, and in rabbits immunized against extracts of such tumors. A hypercritical mind may perhaps feel a bit uneasy when thinking either about the presence in so many normal chickens of those natural antibodies against tumor viruses which could perhaps be nonspecifically raised by the tumor growth, or about possible neutralizing effects on the virus by antibodies against normal tissue components. However, careful study of the protocols of each investigator would seem to be enough to dissipate these doubts.

The mutationist can accept the above evidence, both direct and immunologic, as indicating that "viruses" are the cause of these chemically provoked tumors, with the provision that these agents are not exogenous but products of the cell liberated by the chemical. In other words, he would extend to these agents the views he has on the "viruses" of the naturally occurring tumors, a point which has been discussed elsewhere.[45] Other workers may not be convinced by the evidence outlined above, and they would argue that the same type of sarcoma could be produced by entirely different means: the naturally occurring, by viruses (considered either as exogenous or endogenous); the chemically provoked, by other mechanisms. Something must be said about identifying, as has often been done, the naturally occurring and the chemically provoked chicken sarcoma. It is perfectly true that both types of growths, in the hosts that first develop them, may look alike, including the occurrence of widespread metastases. However, judging at least by our experience, matters are different when the behavior of both types of tumors on transplantation is studied; for then the following features of the chemically provoked tumors as distinguished from the naturally occurring ones may be listed:

1. They are much more difficult to adapt to indefinite transplantation;
2. They grow less well or not at all in mature hosts;
3. They cannot be adapted to foreign species such as ducks, although some of them did grow in ducklings for a number of passages[47] and also in pheasants (Andrewes);
4. They rarely induce metastases and never hemorrhagic lesions;
5. They lack the pronounced viscosity due to hyperproduction of mucopolysaccharides, especially hyaluronic acid. Peacock[99] has also insisted on this trait.

We can add to these the observation of Mellanby[88] who detected in these tumors a higher consumption of oxygen than in the Rous sarcoma.*

* In our laboratory, in the course of several years, we have studied the transplantability, by cells and filtrates, of 84 tumors induced by methylcholanthrene in the breast muscles of Plymouth Rock chickens of different ages. Chicks 1–3 weeks old were always used for transplantation tests. A summary of the experiments follows:

1. Twenty of the tumors were induced by injecting methylcholanthrene into chicks 1–35 days old, and were transplanted within the first three months after injection of the carcinogen: 80 per cent of them were maintained through one, two, or three passages, but indefinite transplantation was never achieved;
2. Sixty-four of the tumors were induced by injecting methylcholanthrene into a group of 52 chickens 1–35 days old, and another group of 12 chickens 2–8 months old. The tumors of the first group were transplanted from three to eighteen months after the injection of the carcinogen: 12 of them (23 per cent) were maintained through only one, two or three

In other words, the sarcomas developing after injection of chemicals are tumors of relatively low malignancy, their position being probably between that of naturally occurring fibromas and the slowly growing, irregularly filtering fibrosarcomas. If, as seems well established, the transplantability of tumors by cells and filtrates bears a direct relation to the vigor, and probably quantity, of the virus, then in the case of the sarcomas a scale suggests itself, starting with those of the Rous type growing in young hosts, passing into fibrosarcomas and chemically provoked sarcomas, and ending with fibromas.

Epithelial Tumors

As stated before, these tumors are less frequent in birds than the mesodermal ones. Except for rare instances they are not transplantable, which eliminates the most valuable means for the study of their cause. Probably, as in the case of lymphoid tumors or leukoses, epithelial tumors are genetically very demanding and it will not be possible to learn about them until inbred strains of fowls are easily available. However, the following observations could perhaps be compatible with a virus effect:

1. The only transplantable carcinoma so far known came originally from an old hen injected two and a half years before with the virus of Mill Hill 2 endothelioma. The tumor was carried for many passages but on the second a sarcoma developed, months after injection, at the site where the carcinoma had been injected. This sarcoma was transplanted and subsequently transmitted by filtrates.[43]

2. In work by us[43] on a series of embryonal nephromas of the kidney, distant growths from either the epithelial or the fibroblastic (fibroma-like) parts of the tumor were observed in some cases, while in others typical sarcomatous metastases were present. In one case a causative virus was shown in such metastases, which were easily and indefinitely transmissible by filtrates, whereas the primary tumor proved not to be transplantable at all. The gradation established by these observations, together with the well-known fact that embryonal nephromas in all species metastasize both as carcinomas and as sarcomas, may be taken as an indication that a change toward malignancy has occurred in the metastasizing process, involving a virus effect. The established fact of the sarcomatous transformation of the stroma of transplantable mouse carcinomas can perhaps be quoted in connection with these findings.

3. In a series of liver carcinomas, suddenly occurring in a strain of ducks, lesions

---

passages, but 3 of the tumors (5 per cent) proved to be indefinitely transplantable. In the second group, transplantability of the tumors was still lower, 16 per cent, and no indefinitely transplantable tumors were obtained;

3. In no case, despite numerous tests, were the tumors transmissible by cell free materials.

Thus, there is clearly an age factor in the transmissibility of the chemically provoked tumors which is manifested by the much lower incidence of growth when old tumors are transplanted into chicks as compared to young tumors, this incidence being still lower when the hosts were old when injected with the carcinogen. However, it may be significant that indefinite transplantation, although rare, was only achieved with old tumors, as if these growths alone had the power of adapting themselves to a new environment in a way perhaps comparable to the adaptation of the Rous sarcoma, growing in old chickens, to the new environment of a foreign species, the duck. However, contrary to what happens to this tumor in an old host, in which the virus becomes masked, growth of the chemically provoked sarcomas in young hosts—always used in this investigation—never did result in a liberation of free virus.

were observed in the chick embryos in which the tumors were cultivated, which could be interpreted as virus effects.[26]

To the above should be added other results to be reported later concerning the induction, in the skin of chickens, of epithelial tumors in which the presence of fowl pox virus was repeatedly demonstrated.

Summarizing the properties of the viruses of chicken tumors and leukoses it can be stated that they have an epidemiologic behavior, they exert both destructive and proliferative effects on cells, they are capable of varying or mutating, and they have the power to induce immune reactions conducive to solid resistance. These viruses, therefore, behave fundamentally like ordinary viruses. On the other hand, viruses of lesser virulence seem to be the cause of the sarcomas developing after injection of chemical carcinogens. These viruses are generally masked and they have antigens in common with those causing the naturally occurring tumors or leukoses. Practically nothing is known concerning epithelial neoplasia, but the scant data available are not incompatible with a virus effect.

MAMMARY GLAND CANCER OF MICE*

In the case of breast tumors of mice, there is the puzzling situation that a very common type of cancer is overtly induced by a virus, and that this cancer may coexist in the same species, strain, or even individual with many other types of malignancy in which, with the possible exception of leukemia, no causative viruses have been demonstrated. It is also found in the mouse, where by selective inbreeding a great variety of strains have been obtained, each strain showing a widely varying incidence of different cancers. It is thanks to these strains that the virus of breast cancer was discovered, and that the intricacies of its action became known.

The story of the discovery of the virus at the Jackson Memorial Laboratory is well known: reciprocal crosses between high and low tumor strains resulted in the discovery of the fact that only the progeny from mothers of high tumor strains showed the same high incidence of cancer, whereas few or no cancers developed in the progeny from fathers of high tumor strains and mothers of low tumor strains. It was clear that the maternal influence was not of a chromosomal nature, and that there were three possible explanations for the transmission of the influence: through the cytoplasm of the ovum; during intrauterine life; and through the milk. Bittner[15] by the simple expedient of foster-nursing mice from high tumor strains, (e.g., Strain A) by mothers from low tumor strains (e.g. Strain C57 black), obtained F_1 mice relatively or entirely free of cancer, and this situation was maintained in the descendants of these foster-nursed mice for many generations. The opposite can also be true. Thus, Andervont changed Strain C from a low into a permanently high tumor strain by foster-nursing newborn C mice by mothers of a high tumor strain, such as C3H.

The virus appears to be a component of high molecular weight which is totally sedimentable by high speed centrifugation. It is filterable through different kinds

* References on some of the data quoted in this summary of breast tumors in mice may be found in excellent reviews.[4, 6, 16, 17, 105]

of filter candles and has apparently been detected by electron microscopy in milk and tumor tissue of mice from high tumor strains. By simply considering the way of transmission of the natural disease it would appear quite obvious that the virus should be endowed with a resistance to digestive enzymes and changes in *p*H. In fact, it withstands the effects of trypsin and changes of *p*H from 5 to 10.2, and keeps its activity for a long time if desiccated under certain conditions. It is destroyed if heated at 65° C. for thirty minutes.[13, 98]

The virus is antigenic, the effects of the specific antibody being manifested in the following ways: (1) neutralization in vitro of the tumor-inducing properties of the virus when extracts of tissues containing it are incubated with the serum; (2) neutralization in vivo of the tumor-inducing properties of the virus, but only when injected shortly after treatment of the mouse with the antiserum; and (3) probable elicitation of complement fixing and agglutinating antibodies.[68]

It appears, so far, that the virus is strictly species-specific, but not strain-specific. However, some strains of mice are partly or totally resistant to the viruses of other strains, which may be, after all, the result of partial strain specificity or predilection that would explain discrepancies among authors concerning this question.

The virus also appears to be strictly tissue-specific, the tumors induced being always of a typical acinar type, a fact to be contrasted with what is observed in tumors developing after treatment with chemical carcinogens which show a great variety of histologic types. The virus is present not only in the milk, but also in the blood and some tissues of both males and females. However, it seems to be inactivated by the placenta,[67] an important fact which may perhaps account for the non-transmissibility of the virus during gestation. In some strains virus has been found by Andervont[7] and also by Foulds,[55] to be present in the seminal fluid of high tumor strain males, a finding which indicates that males can contribute to cancer of the progeny by ways other than their genetic contribution, and which can explain some paradoxes in reciprocal crosses between high and low tumor strains.

The search for active virus in suspected materials is a long process, which no doubt accounts for our scarcity of knowledge concerning several of its properties. The mice in which the test materials are inoculated are: (1) individuals from high tumor strains fostered by low tumor mothers; (2) hybrids from high tumor fathers and low tumor mothers; and (3) individuals from low tumor strains but highly susceptible to the virus. In all cases, results indicated by tumor development are generally not available till many months after inoculation.

Any route of inoculation will only lead to the specific lesion, breast cancer. The intraperitoneal route seems to be more effective than lactation, the natural path of transmission. As far as is known, contagion by body contact does not take place. Some females may transmit the disease without ever developing cancer themselves, thus behaving as carriers in the strict bacteriologic sense. In fact, as Andervont points out, to illustrate the capacity of the virus for latency, "if breeding females of certain strains of mice were killed after they had weaned their first litters, the *inciter* would pass from generation to generation without any manifestation of the disease."

The incidence of tumors and the promptness of their appearance is in direct relation to the dose of virus injected, which can be very small indeed and still produce tumors. Since virus is abundantly present in normal and malignant tissues of the infected mice, and since the experimental transmission can be carried out indefinitely, as is the case in the natural disease, by lactation, it is obvious that the agent, like any other virus, is self-perpetuating, repeating endlessly in new hosts the same lesions from which it was derived. The virus, then, infects the host from the very first hours or minutes after birth, yet cancer will not grossly develop till many months later, presumably when the ground has become favorable and enough virus multiplication has occurred. Does the virus manifest itself in some way during its long period of latency? It seems probable that, long before tumor development, the morphology of the mammary gland is changed and that the number of hyperplastic nodules increases in mice harboring the virus either naturally or after experimental administration. Bittner *et al.*[17] have reported that the excretion of 17-ketosteroids is considerably altered under the same circumstances.

As stated by Bittner, soon after his fundamental finding, two more factors, besides the virus, are indispensable for the induction of breast tumors: the appropriate genetic constitution and a hormonal stimulation. One can add to this, as conditioning factors of minor importance, diet, temperature, season, crowding, etc.[91] It is certainly not surprising that the genetic make-up closely conditions the disease, as it is known to condition any other infectious process. However, in breast cancer, owing to the great variety of inbred strains available, the long duration of the disease, and the fact that the disease has been mostly studied by geneticists, we have a real wealth of information on the point. Many steps can be imagined in the long process which starts with the first ingestion of infected milk and continues until the terminal stage of the disease. Such steps could include intestinal permeability, ability of tissues to support virus multiplication, hormonal secretion and susceptibility of breast tissue to the hormones, host reaction against the virus, and many others. Each of these steps require conditioning by the genetic constitution of the host.

The conditioning of the disease by endocrine factors takes us back to 1913, when Loeb and his co-workers found that ovariectomy suppressed the incidence of breast tumors, while breeding increased it. In 1930, Goormaghtigh and Amerlink induced cystic disease in mice by injection of follicular fluid, and the following year Lacassagne induced breast cancer in male mice by injection of estrogens. Since then, breast cancer in both sexes has been induced by a variety of natural or synthetic estrogenic hormones, or by provoking, by various means, a general endocrine imbalance involving estrogenic stimulation. As first shown by Bittner, cancer does not develop in virgin A strain mice, despite their having the virus.

We know nothing about the intricate mechanism through which estrogens prepare the mammary gland for the virus effect, either directly or through the pituitary-adrenal system.[94] This is certainly not a surprising situation, since we understand little about the physiologic effect of hormones, and next to nothing about what the bacteriologist calls a favorable ground for the action of a given infectious agent.

However, interesting information is at hand concerning the general effects of the estrogens:

1. They induce breast cancer in females in the same frequency in which the disease occurs naturally in the different strains; and in males, in a ratio proportionate to the incidence in females.

2. The breast cells from high tumor strains are more susceptible to exogenous estrogens than those from low tumor strains (Loeb and Suntzef).

3. Histologically, there is observed in mice treated with estrogens a gradual passage from normal to cancer cells, exactly the same as that to be seen in the natural disease.

Therefore, it can safely be stated that in every respect the experimental administration of estrogens repeats faithfully the events occurring in the natural disease. In other words, the natural and the experimental "carcinogens" may be the same.

It seems superfluous to point out that because breast tumors, like most cancers, do not develop in young hosts, there is an age factor conditioning the appearance of such tumors. Other data suggest that, as in the case of chicken tumors, there develops parallel to the growth of the individual a resistance against the virus, which may account for the following phenomena:

1. Immature mice are far more susceptible than older ones (Andervont), and the dose of virus has to be increased many times to achieve in the latter the same results as in the former (Dmochowski);

2. When mice from a high cancer strain were allowed to ingest infected milk from their mothers for only twenty-four to forty hours, free virus disappeared in the successive generations. When an old mouse died free of tumor, none of her descendants developed cancer, although they lived to late average cancer age;[5]

3. As also shown by Andervont, in some special hybrids derived from high cancer fathers (carrying virus in the seminal fluid) and low cancer mothers, a minority of tumors appear at a young age, such as 4–7 months, while the majority of growths do not develop till the age of 16–24 months. Other studies have shown that free virus is present in the tumors from young hosts but not in those from old hosts, a phenomenon close to that of the masking of chicken sarcoma viruses in older chickens.[6]

Practically nothing is known concerning antibody production against the virus by the aging mouse, which could be a factor in the age resistance. As stated before, the virus is antigenic for heterologous species but, excepting for a suggestive experiment of Gorer and Law,[63] we do not know how the mice, resistant or susceptible, react, immunologically, to the virus present in their tissues since birth. Nor do we know whether the virus declines or becomes masked in the tissues of normal aging mice, or whether virus, presumably masked, in some tumors is still antigenic.

A case of special interest is that of the breast tumors induced by treatment with chemical carcinogens by a variety of routes. The main features of these tumors are the following:

1. They can be induced in low cancer strains in which the administration of estrogens is little or not at all effective in raising the tumor incidence;

2. The tumors show a variety of histologic patterns, in most cases different from the pattern observed in naturally occurring tumors or those induced by estrogen inoculation;

3. No free virus can be detected in the tumors by the usual technics.[8, 76]

The above points, like those concerning possible masking of the virus, will be taken up later in the discussion.

PAPILLOMATOSIS OF RABBITS*

When compared to other species, such as chickens, mice, and dogs, domestic (although possibly not wild) rabbits[113] appear to be relatively refractory to cancer of internal organs, whether occurring spontaneously or after injection of chemical carcinogens. However, rabbits respond to chemical carcinogens applied to their skin—although far less than mice—by developing papillomas of various sorts and ultimately cancer. One must remember that a transplantable tumor widely used in cancer research, the Brown-Pearce tumor, was derived from a squamous cell carcinoma arising in the scrotum of a rabbit.

In line with this, rabbits develop papillomatosis, a typical representative of virus-induced conditions affecting several animal species, including man. The disease is quite common in the United States among wild rabbits, specially cottontails, and is characterized by the occurrence of warts and horns quite similar to those developing in rabbits treated with chemical carcinogens. The causative virus was demonstrated by Shope in 1933: filtrates from the original papillomas reproduced the disease in both wild and domestic rabbits, and this disease could be transmitted indefinitely through the former hosts.[106] The virus seems to be a homogeneous, large monomolecular protein (measuring 35–40 mμ) which can be demonstrated in this form only in tumors from wild rabbits (Beard, Bryan, Wykoff and others, quoted in [80]). It is fairly specific for the susceptible animal species and strictly specific in respect to the tissue affected. Thus, four species of wild American rabbits (genus *Sylvilagus*), two species of jack rabbits (*Lepus Californicus*) and many species of domestic rabbits (genus *Orychtolagus*) have been found to be more or less sensitive. On the other hand, the virus is exclusively dermotropic, not only the epithelia of all mucosas being refractory, but also the epithelia from the skin follicles and glands. In these respects the virus differs, first, from the virus of the oral papillomatosis,[97] which attacks exclusively the epidermal cells of the lingual mucosa of rabbits, and second, from many pox viruses which induce proliferative and destructive changes in the cells of both epidermis and the follicles. The epidermal cells can be infected by the papilloma virus either by direct inoculation after slight injury experimentally or fortuitously inflicted—the latter being the presumed mechanism of natural infection—or following localization of a circulating virus after injury of the skin by a variety of mechanical means, and also after treatment with chemical carcinogens.

Curiously enough, the epidermal cells from immature hosts do not become neoplastic under the effect of the virus. Thus, inoculation into rabbits of ground

* The facts quoted in this summary and their references are to be found in reviews[75, 80, 104] on the subject. The contributions from the Rockefeller Institute workers, Shope, Rous, Kidd, and others, are to be found in the *Journal of Experimental Medicine* from 1934 onwards.

embryonic skin mixed with virus does not result in the development of any lesions, whereas papillomatous formations develop when the experiment is repeated employing adult skin.[74] Also, virus inoculation by scarification of the skin of newborn rabbits is far less successful in inducing papillomas than is the inoculation of adult rabbits.[47] These facts suggest an age factor which brings the epidermal cells to the right degree of maturation to be attacked by the virus. The virus exerts only minimal effects when inoculated in the skin of hypophysectomized rabbits[78] and it is important to point out that painting the skin of such animals with chemical carcinogens is also almost ineffective.[77] Thus, we have in these facts the only known examples of hormonal influences on rabbit papillomatosis.

As in the case with other viruses, virus cannot be recovered later than 15–60 minutes after inoculation of the skin of either wild or domestic rabbits (Pankalen). The virus in its free form can not be demonstrated in wild rabbits until papillomas appear, a few weeks after injection.

Morphologically, the experimentally induced papillomas do not differ fundamentally in the wild and domestic rabbit, although in the latter they are far less dry and more vascularized than in the former. In the wild rabbit, regression of the naturally occurring lesions takes place in about 20 per cent of the animals during the first six months, and in 36 per cent after this period. For unknown reasons, almost no regressions occur in the experimentally induced papillomas.[116] Contrary to what was believed until recently, malignant transformation of the papillomas takes place in the wild rabbit in about 25 per cent of the cases, the process starting around the twelfth month.[115] Virus is regularly found in the early papillomas, but disappears when the older growths show signs of regression or of malignant transformation. This suggests an age effect on the masking of the virus in these hosts. Virus can be found in papillomas of rabbits also showing cancers in which virus is absent.[114]

In the domestic rabbit regression occurs (though infrequently) during the first six months and never after this period, at least in the series of Syverton *et al.*[116] There are two other interesting characteristics of papillomas in domestic rabbits: the intransmissibility of the lesions, to a second generation of rabbits, bespeaking the absence in them of free virus, and the very frequent malignant transformation of the papillomas into squamous cell carcinomas, an event that takes place several months earlier than in wild rabbits. In the first of these events, in contrast with what is to be observed in tumors from wild rabbits, no pellet containing virus can be obtained by high speed centrifugation from extracts of papillomas from domestic rabbits; no virus protein can be demonstrated, and no absorption of the specific antibody takes place.[60, 80] Yet a specific viral antigen is present in such growths, as is attested by the regular appearance of specific antibodies in rabbits bearing the tumors or treated with the noninfective tumor extracts (Rous *et al.*). Other experiments show that this virus antigen may well be no other than the virus itself in a form capable of reverting to a free, infective form. Thus, the inoculation of tumor extracts from domestic into other domestic rabbits can be successful, if the skin of the latter has been rendered hyperplastic and more sensitive by treatment with materials such as methylcholanthrene, turpentine, or acetone, or if the tumor extract has been subjected to tryptic digestion. However, in all these cases the virus does not seem to have been maintained beyond a second passage, as was also the case of other strains mentioned by Shope.

The situation, however, was different in other cases. When, as in the experiments of Selbie,[108] the virus of the wild rabbit papilloma was injected simultaneously with that of sheep dermatitis, the former virus could be recovered from the lesions many months later, and then passed into other rabbits, through 15 generations, without association with the dermatitis virus. In other words, the virus adapted itself to the domestic rabbit and behaved like the virus of another strain described by Shope, also maintained for 15 passages through domestic rabbits. Interestingly, a single passage of the Selbie strain through the wild rabbit made the virus lose its power to infect domestic rabbits serially.[109] Both the infectivity in the two strains referred to above and the power to stimulate antibody production is far less pronounced in the papillomas of the domestic rabbit than in those of the wild animal. These facts have led several authors to believe that the former growths contain much less virus or virus antigen than the latter growths, and that the fundamental difference between the infection of wild and domestic rabbits is that lesions in the latter are produced with much less virus multiplication than in the former.

Let us turn now to the transformation of the papillomatous into squamous cell carcinomas. The phenomenon is another manifestation of the age factor which is never observed before six months, although after this period it takes place in 70 per cent of cases.[116] However, the same result can be obtained in a few weeks by injecting the virus intravenously into rabbits, the skin of which has been submitted to previous treatment with chemical carcinogens (Rous and Kidd), or by treating virus induced papillomas with chemical carcinogens (Rous and Friedewald). Thus, it can be stated that, as in a comparable situation in rabbit fibroma,[1, 41] carcinogens and the age factor exert vicarious effects.

It is important to remember in connection with these results that the papilloma cells in themselves are, to use Rous' expression, on the brink of malignancy, as attested by the invasive character of the growths obtained when these cells are grafted into favorable hosts, in which epidermoid tumors of greater or lesser malignancy can be obtained. If the host inoculated is the wild rabbit, virus can be recovered from the growths (Rous and Beard).

It is difficult to make the malignant tumors derived from the papillomas grow in other domestic rabbits. However, one of the growths, carcinoma V2, was successfully transplanted into other rabbits for at least 46 passages. Pertinent studies on this material revealed that no free virus was present in the cancers, but that all the rabbits bearing the tumor during the first 22 passages, during a period of five years, developed antibodies against papilloma virus, and that when these cancers were grafted into young hosts free papilloma virus was obtained in 3 successive passages. However, when the antibodies were investigated again in the blood of rabbits after 46 passages of the tumor, the results were negative, as if the original papilloma virus antigen were no longer present in the tumor. In other cancers derived from papillomas in the wild rabbit, neither free virus nor virus antigen was demonstrated, the latter point being shown by the incapacity of tumor extracts to elicit immune responses in another wild rabbit.[75] The significance of these facts will be discussed later.

HUMAN WARTS

Recent investigations on human warts are important. The transmissibility by cells of these warts has been known since 1896, the lesions being later transmitted by Ciuffo and by Serra, as well as others[112] by means of filtrates. Strauss *et al*,[111, 112] have shown in a number of warts the presence in the epithelial cells of typical nuclear inclusion bodies and cytoplasmic masses. The elementary bodies demonstrable by electron microscopy were arranged in crystalline-like clusters or layers in a pattern similar to that of crystalline plant viruses These inclusion bodies have been found in 4 per cent of verrucae vulgaris and in 44 per cent of verrucae plantaris.[110]

An age factor seems to be effective in determining the number of warts showing the findings. Thus, 47 per cent and 95 per cent of warts of an estimated duration of not more than two months and five months respectively showed the typical bodies. On the other hand, there is a trend indicating that the age of the host also had an influence, since 18 per cent of the positive cases were from patients 5 to 35 years old, as against 5 per cent in older patients.

Data are lacking concerning a possible parallelism between transmissibility and presence of inclusion bodies. Such a study could lead to important deductions on the relation between the existence of free or masked viruses on the one hand and the presence or absence of the typical bodies on the other.

ADENOCARCINOMA OF THE KIDNEY OF THE LEOPARD FROG

This curious condition, described by Lucké,[82, 83] is characterized by the occurrence of neoplasms in the kidneys of a number of leopard frogs (*Rana pipiens*), ranging from benign adenomas to invasive and not infrequently metastasizing adenocarcinomas. Typical acidophilic inclusion bodies are found, with seasonal variations, in the nuclei of the cancer cells, but were never observed in normal kidney cells. In hundreds of tests, the grafting of cancer tissue into a variety of tissues never resulted in local growth, but these inoculations, as well as those of cell-free materials, result in the development—after a period of six months—of the same kidney tumors in 20 per cent of the frogs as against 2 per cent of naturally occurring growths in the controls. These results are only obtained in the leopard frog, all other types of frogs tried, as well as a number of other animals, remaining refractory.

In summary, we are dealing here with a highly species- and cell-specific, ubiquitous virus, which in all probability is the cause of these kidney cancers. Owing to the peculiar circumstances in the occurrence of the disease our knowledge of this virus is indeed limited.

In the domain of neoplasia of cold-blooded animals we could also describe what is known of tumors of fishes and other species (Weisenberg, Smith, Nigrelli). A summary of the data suggesting virus effects in the etiology of such tumors was given elsewhere.[45, 49] This seems to be an extremely promising field, unfortunately hardly explored. Finally, one also should review the enlarging knowledge in the field of plant tumor viruses, a field full of promise for the subject under discussion. A few data on these viruses were given above when reviewing the phenomenon of masking of viruses in general. Limitation of space excludes a detailed analysis of the problem.

SUMMARY AND DISCUSSION

The properties of the three main groups of cancer viruses reviewed above could be thus summarized:

1. They have a chemical composition either relatively simple, such as that of the rabbit papilloma, or complex, like those of avian cancer, and have sizes intermediate between the very large and the very small viruses. The viruses of avian cancer and breast cancer of mice appear to be visible only in electron micrographs;
2. They are all antigenic; those of avian cancer and rabbit papilloma for homologous and heterologous species; data are lacking on antigenicity of breast cancer viruses for homologous species;
3. They are all species and cell specific. Therefore, they are highly conditioned by genetic factors;
4. Those of avian cancer are frequently apt to vary or mutate under certain circumstances, while there are no indications so far that breast cancer or papilloma viruses can do so, at least in the sense of acquiring new cell or species affinities;
5. They all have a definite mode of transmission, which in avian cancer may be of a rather complex nature;
6. In those of avian and breast cancer of mice, immaturity of the host is not only highly favorable, but sometimes indispensable for infection to take place. Furthermore, avian viruses have a dual effect on cells, since in the young host they induce a non-neoplastic disease. No such effects are known to be exerted by the breast cancer and papilloma viruses.
7. Those of avian cancer and breast cancer remain latent in the hosts for a long period of time, till cancer develops;
8. They are conditioned by hormonal effects, most conspicuously in the case of breast cancer;
9. They are all susceptible of undergoing *masking,* that is of assuming a state in which they cannot be revealed as free infectious entities (although they can be shown in some cases by indirect serologic methods or other means). *Unmasking,* that is reversion to a free state, can easily be induced in some avian viruses.

Some of these points will now be taken up as a basis for a general discussion of the subject. The first is that of the epidemiology of cancer, a concept involving naturally those of *transmission* and *prevention* by isolation.

The mode of transmission of the breast cancer virus through the milk is exactly the same as it is in the case of mouse poliomyelitis induced by the Theiler virus. As shown by von Magnus,[118] foster-nursing (by rats) protects mice and their progeny against the disease, as it could conceivably protect against any other milk-borne infection. And, as in breast cancer, colony infection will be restored by intentional or unintentional infection of a few individuals. In papillomatosis, infection of rabbits presumably of any age, inflicted through skin injury, can satisfactorily explain the natural spread of the disease. In both papillomatous and breast cancer, and presumably also in leopard frog adenocarcinoma, there seems to be no necessity to postulate virus variation to start infection. In these cases, neoplasia would be the result of highly specific, immutable viruses transmitted along simple, well-known pathways, and always inducing the same lesions regardless of the route of inoculation.

Matters are more complex in the case of avian cancer. Here there are a great variety of malignant lesions induced by a group of highly mutable viruses, many or probably all of which are interrelated antigenically, and contagion has been clearly demonstrated to occur in an important group of these viruses, those of lymphomatosis. Here the discussion initiated when analyzing the effects of the age factor on tumor viruses, notably the Rous sarcoma, may be taken up again.

It has been seen that from embryonal life to old age the age factor suppresses, first of all, the destructive effects of the virus, changing it into a tumor virus. Later, it lowers the susceptibility of the host to minimal infective doses, inhibits tumor growth, and depresses its capacity to produce metastases and transmissibility by cells but, most important, it causes the virus to vary, as shown by the induction of different tumors in several foreign species, and when these variant viruses are injected back into chickens, they do not induce the original chicken tumor, but the variant tumor.

The epidemic viruses of avian cancer, whether those of lymphomatosis or of another type, infect the host from a very early age. Since these viruses can manifest themselves either shortly after exposure or much later in life, indicating a long period of latency, the virologist could venture the following hypothesis: in a number of the infected individuals the virus induces either a non-neoplastic disease, clinically recognizable or not, or a neoplastic disease with inflammatory features, such as lymphomatosis. Later in life, in the surviving birds, when the "soil" in the aging individual is conducive to such an event (as shown with the Rous sarcoma virus), the virus varies and induces in the hosts a variety of tumors comparable to those induced by the mutants of the Rous virus in other species.

In summary, a simple form of isolation such as foster-nursing protects mice against the breast cancer virus, and against at least one other virus, that of mouse poliomyelitis;[118] a more strict form of isolation protects chickens against lymphomatosis and conceivably against other forms of cancer also, as well as against practically all of the infectious diseases common in chickens. It would be extremely interesting to know how absolute isolation leading to germ-free chickens—and other animals also—such as has been obtained at Notre Dame University, affects the incidence of naturally occurring neoplasia in general, or that usually resulting after inoculation of chemical carcinogens. It is obvious that such a study could be decisive in the question of viruses in relation to cancer.

Other important points are that variation of the virus takes place in the aging host when the virus shows signs of degradation (manifested by lower transmissibility by cells and less power to induce metastases), and before the virus becomes masked. Following masking, the tumor may regress leaving the animal immune. Thus, all these phenomena are somehow related, and masking could perhaps be considered as a kind of variation. These problems were amply discussed elsewhere.[45]

Let us now examine in some detail the phenomenon of masking, possibly the one on which speculation can be most interesting. Somehow or other the age factor is frequently associated with the masking of cancer viruses, as is best shown in chicken sarcomas and also in those mouse breast cancers studied by Andervont. In the papilloma-carcinoma sequence in rabbits, the age factor is manifested by the unfilterability of old papillomas in the wild rabbit, and perhaps by other phenomena. However, the virus can be more rapidly masked by other factors, such as those present in the domestic rabbit. As in ordinary viruses, such as tobacco and cucumber mosaic, influenza, and probably many others, the masked tumor viruses keep their antigenic power, at least to a certain extent, as shown in the papilloma-carcinoma sequence in domestic rabbits and presumably in the case of the Rous virus in old chickens. However, in the case of the carcinomas derived from papillomas, the original papilloma antigen can no longer be recognized, after many passages, or can never be demonstrated.[75, 114] On account of these facts, are we going to conclude that the papilloma virus—that virus which, to use Rous' expression, before having changed "brings cells to the brink of malignancy"—is not the proximal cause of the carcinoma after having changed?* Are we going to conclude the same with those late breast cancers of mice in which no free virus is found while it is plentiful in the same tumors occurring earlier?

Before we dismiss viruses as the cause of these tumors it will be useful to remember the newer knowledge on viruses other than those of cancer, notably bacterial viruses. There, too, virus activity could not be detected by the great variety of means today available, after infection of the bacterium, after radiation, and in lysogenic bacteria. Yet, we know that the inactivated, degraded bacteriophage can be unmasked, and can revert to a free state. This can be accomplished by means, often quite simple, in a process comparable to: (1) the reversion of the Rous virus to a free state in the young host or following radiation; and (2) the demonstration of free papilloma virus, by inoculation of specially prepared tissues or as a result of the concomitant effect of another virus.

Comparisons between lysogenic strains of bacteria and virus-induced tumors are specially pertinent since there are obvious analogies between the gradient of filterability in the naturally occurring chicken tumors and the ease—or difficulty—with which free bacteriophage can be shown in different strains of lysogenic bacteria. This leads us to the tumors induced by chemical carcinogens, a really crucial point since so many cancers in so many species can be thus induced. First of all, we have to note a similar, if not identical, state of affairs between the sarcomas that develop in chickens and the breast tumors that develop in mice, after treatment with carcinogens, as compared with the corresponding naturally occurring tumors in both species: the latter tumors contain free virus, the former

* Concerning further speculation on this point the reader is referred to the original papers by Rous *et al.*

do not. Moreover, there are, in both species, histologic differences between the naturally occurring and the chemically provoked tumors, and, at least in chickens, the chemically provoked are far less malignant than those naturally occurring.

We know that in chemically provoked cancer of chickens, causative viruses can be demonstrated. These viruses, as bacteriophage in some lysogenic strains, would only occasionally be shown in a free form, as in the sporadic cases of filterability reported on these tumors. In other cases, though, the viruses are shown by indirect serologic means because of the fact that the masked virus in the tumors has an antigenic community with a given free virus cause of naturally occurring tumors. Does this not suggest that a similar state of affairs may exist in mouse tumors developing after treatment with carcinogens, or arising naturally under certain circumstances? Yet, failure to induce carcinogenesis by foster-nursing or failure to detect free virus by other means is often interpreted as proving absence of virus.

Analogous reflections come to mind in the case of carcinomas derived from papillomas in which papilloma antigen is no longer or has never been detected. A specific antigen, ultimately derived from the papilloma virus, but no longer possessing its immunologically reacting components, may well exist in the carcinoma. Analogies with the situation in different strains of the same but immunologically unrelated viruses, such as those of lymphomatosis and influenza, suggest themselves.

It might be added that if other cancers in man and animals were also induced by viruses that become masked, the corresponding antibodies would be found in the sera, but detection of these antibodies is not possible because we do not know which is the free virus: a vicious circle, and a tantalizing situation.

Future Research

How could the virologist orient his investigations in the future?

The presence of causative viruses is often sought in tumors by merely testing the effects of filtrates, and, the results being negative, it is concluded that viruses are absent. It may be useful in this respect to list here, first of all, what may well be called the *gradient of difficulty* in detecting viruses in cancers, in order of increasing difficulty.

1. Cases in which a simple passage by extract or filtrate of the original tumor reproduces the disease in non-inbred hosts of the same species: for example, the papilloma virus from wild rabbits injected into other wild rabbits; viruses from some naturally occurring chicken sarcomas; and the virus from the kidney adenocarcinoma of the leopard frog.

2. Cases in which previous cell passages and/or inoculation of inbred hosts are necessary, as in other naturally occurring chicken sarcomas (for instance the original Rous sarcoma) and most strains of chicken lymphomatosis.

3. Cases in which infection of a tissue specially prepared, or concomitant effects of another virus, are required: e.g., rabbit papilloma virus infecting the domestic rabbit.

4. Cases in which highly inbred strains of mice properly crossed, an adequate hormonal stimulation, and a careful study of the progenies is indispensable: e.g., breast tumor virus of mice;

5. Cases in which the virus can only be shown indirectly by serologic means, for example, chicken sarcomas induced by methylcholanthrene and papilloma derived from rabbit carcinoma.

It is to be seen, therefore, that detection of many cancer viruses has not been, by any means, an easy matter, but precisely for this reason the statement may be made that the greater the difficulties in showing the presence of causative viruses in some tumors, the more hopeful one should be of finding the same agents in other tumors.

More or less encouraged by this conclusion the virologist could recapitulate the properties listed above of the cancer viruses and arrive at the tentative conclusion that while all cancer viruses have *transmissibility*, *antigenicity*, *specificity*, and *ability to become masked*, those of avian cancer have, in addition, the properties of *mutability* and that of *dual action* (non-neoplastic and neoplastic) on cells; these two attributes apparently lacking or being reduced to a minimum in the viruses of breast cancer, papillomatosis, and possibly kidney adenocarcinoma.

The existence of these two tentative groups of viruses in the cancers, the cause of which is known, would suggest a quest for comparable groups for the cancers, the cause of which is not known. Therefore, as a way of approach, the virologist would search for immutable viruses exerting only proliferative effects. This should be done by duplicating and improving the methods that have led to the finding of the viruses reviewed above.*

The second approach presupposes a previous speculation on the nature of the avian cancer viruses. On analyzing their properties, it was seen that they behave fundamentally like ordinary viruses, including their power to induce inflammatory-necrotizing conditions. The question then arises whether the opposite could also be true, that is, whether some ordinary viruses—with which the bacteriologist is already familiar, or which still remain to be discovered—could behave like cancer viruses under certain circumstances. Behind this hypothesis is the fact of the stimulating power upon the cell shown by so many of these ordinary viruses, a property which could be brought to extreme limits, as a result of either environmental or mutational changes. Compatible with the hypothesis, and venturing an explanation of the phenomenon, would be the prevalence of cancer in the old individual, in the tissues of which the viruses would fully manifest their neoplastic potentialities with or without previous variation.

The duality of effects of some ordinary viruses quoted early in this paper, plus those of avian cancer, come to mind in this connection. To this could be added those conditions in which both inflammatory and neoplastic features are observed in the lesions. One of such conditions is the so-called *Jagziekte*,[36] a probable virus disease affecting the lungs of sheep. The resemblance of the lesions of *Jagziekte* and some cases of lung cancer in humans has been pointed out.[20] Other conditions are influenza in man and animals (Winternitz, Ascanazy),[107]†

* The results recently reported by Gye, Craigie, *et al.* 66a are now being so hotly debated that it is preferable to permit time to elapse before final conclusions are reached.

† In appropriate experiments infection of mice with influenza virus has not increased the incidence of lung tumors.[107]

Kaposi's sarcoma,[87] Hodgkin's disease, and still others. The constant finding of mumps virus in 6 cases of sarcoidosis[81] should also be mentioned.

No matter how speculative the above reasonings are, experiments have been undertaken trying to prove that ordinary virus infection can result in neoplasia.[47]

The essence of the most suggestive results will be summarized. If chicks a few days old are painted on the right side with a solution of methylcholanthrene, minute lesions develop, within several weeks, strictly limited to the treated side. These lesions are typical of fowl-pox, as shown by the characteristic histologic pattern and by easy transmission to other chicks. On continuation of the paintings other lesions appear such as large fibrous inflammatory ulcers, angiomata, and discrete epithelial neoformations often suggesting early malignancy, and finally typical squamous cell carcinomas followed sometimes by generalized metastases. Fowl-pox virus can be demonstrated in practically all of these lesions by passage of their extracts to other chicks. Histologically, there seems to be a gradual transition from the fowl-pox lesions to those of squamous cell carcinoma. Also, the scarification of skin, prepared by methylcholanthrene, with fowl-pox virus results in the development of invasive epithelial lesions.

In summary, the carcinogen brings out an ordinary virus known to exert a pronounced stimulating effect on normal epithelium, and known to be latent in most flocks of chickens, and this virus is found in the multiple skin lesions, ranging from purely inflammatory to purely neoplastic, that develop on continuing treatment with the carcinogen.*

It is perfectly true that these results, although suggestive, do not prove that fowl-pox virus, or a variant of it, is instrumental in the development of multiple skin lesions after treatment with the carcinogen, but it would seem that, even leaving aside the intrinsic value of the findings, what has been suggested by the experiments is enough to justify further efforts in the general direction of the hypothesis that some ordinary viruses can induce malignancy under certain conditions.

Whatever the approach, the most important point to be kept in mind is the nature of the factors leading to masking and unmasking of the cancer viruses; that is, the situation which prompts the investigator who believes that many other cancers are virus induced to ask himself this naïve but fundamental question: why are the causative viruses free in some cancers and masked in others? We do not know whether the investigator will be able to answer such a question in the near or distant future, but if he does answer it at all it will only be because he keeps in close touch with daily developments in all fields of infection, notably in that of viruses.

ADDENDUM

Recently new facts have been disclosed in the field of tumor viruses and allied subjects. Fortunately, practically all of the findings appeared in the volume of the Conference, *Viruses as Causative Agents of Cancer*, held at the New York Academy of Sciences on November 16 and 17, 1951, and also in the proceedings of the

* It may be of interest to point out that, in experiments similar to ours, the Peacocks[100] did not observe either pox lesions or tumors in the skin of chickens repeatedly treated with chemical carcinogens. One may well wonder whether the pox virus was not absent in the chickens used by these authors.

Second National Cancer Conference, section of Virology, held at Cincinnati on March 3-5, 1952. The contributions of J. W. Beard on erythromyeloblastic disease of fowls, those of Alice Moore on oncolytic viruses, the studies of B. R. Burmester on fowl lymphomatosis, those of S. Meryl Rose on transformation of tumor viruses in amphibia, and still others, complement and extend several points developed in the present article. Of a very special interest are the findings of L. Gross on the virus etiology of mouse leukemia which brought about so much stimulating discussion.

Other publications which would also be useful to consult are those by P. Borges and Duran-Reynals, *Cancer Research*, 1952, *12*:55; another by Duran-Reynals and Estelle Bryan on the significance of antibodies against tumor viruses naturally occurring in normal chickens, to be published soon, and the Eleventh Annual Report of the Regional Poultry Research Laboratory, East Lansing, Michigan, 1949-1950.

BIBLIOGRAPHY

1. Ahlström, C. G., and Andrewes, C. H. Fibroma virus infection of tarred rabbits. *J. Path. & Bact. 47:* 65-86, 1938.
2. Ahlström, C. G. On the anatomical character of the infectious myxoma of rabbits. *Acta path. et microbiol. Scandinav. 17:* 377-393, 1940.
3. Anderson, K. Pathogenesis of herpes simplex infection in chick embryos. *Am. J. Path. 16:* 137-138, 1940.
4. Andervont, H. B. "The milk influence in the genesis of mammary tumors." In *A Symposium on Mammary Tumors in Mice.* Publication of the A.A.A.S., 1945.
5. Andervont, H. B. Studies on the disappearance of the mammary-tumor agent in mice of strains C3H and C. *J. Nat. Cancer Inst. 10:* 201-214, 1949.
6. Andervont, H. B. The present status of the mammary tumor inciter problem. *Conference given at the Jackson Memorial Laboratory,* August 9, 1949.
7. Andervont, H. B., and Dunn, T. B. Mammary tumors in mice presumably free of the mammary-tumor agent. *J. Nat. Cancer Inst 8:* 227-233, 1948.
8. Andervont, H. B., and Dunn, T. B. Response of mammary-tumor-agent free strain DBA female mice to percutaneous applications of methylcholanthrene. *J. Nat. Cancer Inst. 10:* 895-925, 1950.
9. Andrewes, C. H. Evidence for the presence of a virus in a non-filterable tar sarcoma of the fowl. *J. Path. & Bact. 43:* 23-33, 1936.
10. Andrewes, C. H. The bearing of recent work on the virus theory of cancer. *Brit. M. J. 1:* 81-85, 1950.
11. Asplin, F. D. Observations on the aetiology of lymphomatosis (3 articles). *J. Comp. Path. & Therap. 57:* 116-143, 1947.
12. Bagg, H. J. Experimental production of teratoma testis in the fowl. *Am. J. Cancer 25:* 69-84, 1936.
13. Barnum, C. P., and Huseby, R. A. The chemical and physical characteristics of preparations containing the milk agent virus. *Cancer Research 10:* 523-529, 1950.
14. Bawden, F. C., and Pirie, N. W. The relationships between liquid crystalline preparations of cucumber viruses 3 and 4 and strains of tobacco mosaic virus. *Brit. J. Exper. Path. 18:* 275-291, 1937.

15. Bittner, J. J. Some possible effects of nursing on the mammary gland tumor incidence in mice. *Science 84:* 162, 1936.
16. Bittner, J. J. Inciting influences in the etiology of mammary cancer in mice. *A.A.A.S. Research Conference on Cancer,* 1944.
17. Bittner, J. J. Some enigmas associated with the genesis of mammary cancer in mice. *Cancer Research 8:* 625-639, 1948.
18. Blakemore, F. Further observations on the demonstration of an infective agent in the tissues of fowls affected with fowl paralysis (neurolymphomatosis). *J. Comp. Path. & Therap. 55:* 1-18, 1945.
19. Blakemore, F. Avian leukaemia. *Proc. Royal Soc. Med. 39:* 738-739, 1946.
20. Bonne, C. Morphological resemblance of pulmonary adenomatosis (*Jaagsiekte*) in sheep and certain cases of cancer of the lung in man. *Am. J. Cancer 35:* 491-501, 1939.
21. Bonnet, S. C. J., Horgan, E. S., and Mansur Ali Haseeb. The pox diseases of sheep and goats. *J. Comp. Path. & Therap. 54:* 131-160, 1944.
22. Burmester, B. R. Studies on the transmission of avian visceral lymphomatosis: II. Propagation of lymphomatosis with cellular and cell-free preparations. *Cancer Research 7:* 786-797, 1947.
23. Burmester, B. R., and Belding, D. V. M. Immunity and cross immunity reactions obtained with several avian lymphoid tumor strains. *Am. J. Vet. Research 8:* 128-133, 1947.
24. Burmester, B. R., Prickett, C. O., and Belding, T. C. The occurrence of neural and visceral lymphomatosis in chickens proven immune to transplants of lymphoid tumor strains. *Poultry Sc. 25:* 616-621, 1946.
25. Campbell, J. G. Neoplastic disease of the fowl with special reference to its history, incidence and seasonal variation. *Jour. Comp. Path. & Therap. 55:* 308-321, 1945.
26. Campbell, J. G. Spontaneous hepatocellular and cholangio-cellular carcinoma in the duck: An experimental study. *Brit. J. Cancer 3:* 198-210, 1949.
27. Carr, J. G. The absence of a seasonal influence upon the Rous No. 1 sarcoma in young chicks. *Brit. J. Exper. Path. 23:* 339-342, 1942.
28. Carr, J. G. Some investigations upon the nature of the resistance of an inbred line of fowls to the development of the Rous No. 1 sarcoma. *Brit. J. Exper. Path. 24:* 127-132, 1943.
29. Carr, J. G. The relation between age, structure, and agent content of Rous No. 1 sarcomas. *Brit. J. Exper. Path. 24:* 133-137, 1943.
30. Claude, A. Chemical composition of the tumor producing fraction of the chicken tumor 1. *Science 9:* 213-214, 1939.
31. Claude, A., and Murphy, J. B. Transmissible tumors of the fowl. *Physiol. Rev. 13:* 246-275, 1933.
32. Claude, A., Porter, K. R., and Pickels, E. G. Electron microscope study of chicken tumor cells. *Cancer Research 7:* 421-430, 1947.
33. Clemmesen, J. The influence of Roentgen radiation on immunity to Shope fibroma virus. *Am. J. Cancer 35:* 378-385, 1939.
34. Cole, R. K. Genetic resistance to the transmissible sarcoma of the fowl. *Cancer Research 1:* 714-720, 1941.
35. Doerr, R., Bleyer, L., and Schmidt, G. W. Über des Verhalten des Virus des Rous-Sarkoms in der Blutzirculation refractärer und empfänglicher Tiere. *Ztschr. f. Krebsforsch. 36:* 256-275, 1932.

36. DUNGAL, NIELS. Experiments with Jaagsiekte. *Am. J. Path. 22:* 737-759, 1946.
37. DURAN-REYNALS, F. Neutralization of tumor viruses by the blood of normal fowls of different ages. *Yale J. Biol. & Med. 13:* 61-76, 1940.
38. DURAN-REYNALS, F. A hemorrhagic disease occurring in chicks inoculated with the Rous and Fuginami viruses. *Yale J. Biol. & Med. 13:* 77-98, 1940.
39. DURAN-REYNALS, F. The reciprocal infection of ducks and chickens with tumor-inducing viruses. *Cancer Research 2:* 343-369, 1942.
40. DURAN-REYNALS, F. The infection of turkeys and guinea fowls by the Rous sarcoma virus and the accompanying variations of the virus. *Cancer Research 3:* 569-577, 1943.
41. DURAN-REYNALS, F. Immunological factors that influence the neoplastic effects of the rabbit fibroma virus. *Cancer Research 5:* 25-39, 1945.
42. DURAN-REYNALS, F. Transplantability and presence of virus in spontaneous sarcomas and fibromas of chickens in relation to the age of the tumor-bearing animal. *Cancer Research 6:* 529-534, 1946.
43. DURAN-REYNALS, F. On the transplantability of lymphoid tumors, embryonal nephromas and carcinomas. *Cancer Research 6:* 545-552, 1946.
44. DURAN-REYNALS, F. The age factor in adaptability of a sarcoma virus to other animal species. *Science 103:* 748-749, 1946.
45. DURAN-REYNALS, F. Neoplastic infection and cancer. *Am. J. Med. 8:* 490-511, 1950.
46. DURAN-REYNALS, F. The significance of the non-neoplastic lesions induced in the central nervous system of ducklings by the virus of a duck variant of the Rous sarcoma. *Yale J. Biol. & Med. 22:* 555-564, 1950.
47. DURAN-REYNALS, F. Unpublished observations.
48. DURAN-REYNALS, F., and ESTRADA, E. Protection of chick against Rous sarcoma virus by serum from adult chickens. *Proc. Soc. Exper. Biol. & Med. 45:* 367-372, 1940.
49. DURAN-REYNALS, F., and SHRIGLEY, E. W. Virus infection as an etiological agent of cancer. *A.A.A.S. Research Conference on Cancer.* 1944, pp. 1-23.
50. DURAN-REYNALS, F., and FREIRE, P. M. The age of the tumor-bearing hosts as a factor conditioning the transmissibility of a chicken sarcoma by filtrates and cells. (Tentative title of a paper in preparation.)
51. ELLERMAN, V., and BANG, O. Experimentelle Leukämie bei Hühnern. *Centbl. f. Bakt. 46:* 595, 1908.
52. ELLERMAN, V. *Leucosis of Fowls and Leucemia Problems.* London, Gyldendal, 1921.
53. ENGELBRETH-HOLM, J. *Spontaneous and Experimental Leukaemia in Animals.* Edinburgh, Oliver and Boyd, Ltd., 1942.
54. FOULDS, L. The filterable tumors of fowls: a critical review. *Imperial Cancer Research Fund (Great Britain) Eleventh Scientific Report,* 1934, (Supplement).
55. FOULDS, L. Mammary tumours in hybrid mice: the presence and transmission of the mammary tumour agent. *Brit. J. Cancer 3:* 230-239, 1949.
56. FOULDS, L., and DMOCHOWSKI, L. Neutralizing and complement-fixing properties of antisera produced by fractionated extracts of a non-filterable dibenzanthracene fowl sarcoma. *Brit. J. Exper. Path. 20:* 458-465, 1939.
57. FREIRE, P. M., and DURAN-REYNALS, F. A study of the generalized lesions from a chicken sarcoma in relation to some characteristics of the causative virus. (Tentative title of a paper in preparation.)

58. Freire, P. M., and Duran-Reynals, F. Growth and regression of a chicken sarcoma in relation to the age of the host. (Tentative title of a paper in preparation.)

59. Freire, P. M., and Duran-Reynals, F. Serum antibodies in relation to the masking of a chicken sarcoma virus and to the behavior of the tumor in hosts with different degrees of resistance. (Tentative title of a paper in preparation.)

60. Friedewald, W. F., and Kidd, J. G. Specific absorption of antibody with extracts containing the rabbit papilloma virus. *Proc. Soc. Exper. Biol. & Med. 41:* 218, 1939.

61. Glover, R. E. Contagious pustular dermatitis of the sheep. *J. Comp. Path. & Therap. 41:* 318, 1928.

62. Gorer, P. The significance of studies with transplanted tumours. *Brit. J. Cancer 2:* 103-107, 1948.

63. Gorer, P. A., and Law, L. W. An attempt to demonstrate neutralizing antibodies to the mammary tumour "milk agent" in mice. *Brit. J. Cancer 3:* 90-93, 1949.

64. Gottschalk, R. G. Le rôle des virus dans les tumeurs et leucémies avaires. *Bull. Assoc. franç. p. l'étude du cancer 35:* 329-350, 1948.

65. Gye, W. E., and Andrewes, C. H. A study of the Rous fowl sarcoma No. 1: I. Filterability. *Brit. J. Exper. Path. 7:* 81-87, 1926.

66. Gye, W. E., and Purdy, W. J. *The Cause of Cancer.* London, Cassel & Co. Ltd., 1931.

66a. Gye, W. E., Begg, A. M., Mann, I., and Craigie, J. The survival of activity of mouse sarcoma tissue after freezing and drying. *Brit. J. Cancer 3:* 259-267, 1949.

67. Hummel, K., Little, C. C., and Eddy, M. S. Studies on the mouse mammary tumor agent: II. The Neutralization of the agent by placenta. *Cancer Research 9:* 135-136, 1949.

68. Imagawa, D. T., Green, R. G., and Halvorson, H. O. A precipitin test for antigens present in mouse tissues containing the milk agent. *Proc. Soc. Exper. Biol. & Med. 68:* 162-166, 1948.

69. Jackson, C. Relationship of glioma to encephalitis in the domestic fowl, and associated parasitic agents. *Nature 161:* 441, 1948.

70. Jungherr, E. "The avian leukosis complex." In *Diseases of Poultry* (H. E. Biester, ed.). Ames, Iowa State College Press, 1943, chap. 18, pp. 367-414.

71. Jungherr, E., and Landauer, W. Studies on fowl paralysis: 3. A condition resembling osteopetrosis (marble bone) in the common fowl. *Storrs Agric. Exper. Station Bull. 222:* 1-34, 1938.

72. Karnofsky, D. A., Parisette, L. M., Patterson, P. A., and Jacquez, J. A. The behavior and growth of homologous and heterologous normal and neoplastic tissues in the chick embryo: and the influence of various agents on tumor growth. *Acta Unio. Internat. Contra Cancrum, Acta 6:* 641-651, 1949.

73. Kelner, A. Photo reactivation of ultraviolet-irradiated Escherichia coli, with special reference to the dose-reduction principle and to ultraviolet-induced mutation. *J. Bact. 58:* 511-522, 1949.

74. Kidd, J. G., and Parsons, R. J. Tissue affinity of Shope papilloma virus. *Proc. Soc. Exper. Biol. & Med. 35:* 438-441, 1936.

75. Kidd, J. G. The pathogenesis and pathology of viral diseases. *Symposia of the Section of Microbiology, The New York Acad. of Med.* New York, Columbia University Press, 1950.

76. KIRCHBAUM, A., WILLIAMS, W. L., and BITTNER, J. J. Induction of mammary cancer with methylcholanthrene: I. Histogenesis of the induced neoplasms. *Cancer Research 6:* 354-362, 1946.
77. LACASSAGNE, A., and NYKA, W. Influence de la privation d'hyphophyse sur le développement des tumeurs chez le lapin. *Compt. rendu Soc. de biol. 121:* 822-824, 1936.
78. LACASSAGNE, A., and YYKA, W. Faible réaction à l'injection intraveineuse du virus de Shope au niveau des papillomas obtenus par badigeonnages au benzopyrine chez des lapins à l'hypophyse détruite. *Bull. Assoc. Franç. p. l'étude du cancer 26:* 154-162, 1937.
79. LAFFORET-FURIET, J. "Tumeurs de la poule." In *Les ultravirus des maladies humaines.* Paris, Maloine, 1943.
80. LEPINE, P., and LAFFORET-FURIET, J. "Papillome de Shope." In *Les ultravirus des maladies humaines.* Paris, Maloine, 1943.
81. LÖFGREN, S., and LUNDBÄCK, H. Isolation of a virus from six cases of sarcoidosis. (Lymphogranulamatosis Benigna Schaumann). *Acta Med. Scandinav. 138:* 71-75, 1950.
82. LUCKÉ, B. A neoplastic disease of the kidney of the frog, Rana pipiens. *Am. J. Cancer 20:* 352-379, 1934.
83. LUCKÉ, B. Carcinoma in the leopard frog: its probable causation by a virus. *J. Exper. Med. 68:* 457-468, 1938.
84. LURIA, S. E. Bacteriophage: An essay of virus reproduction. *Science 111:* 507-511, 1950.
85. LWOFF, A., SIMINOVICH, L., and KJELDGAAR, N. Induction de la lyse bactériophagique de la totalité d'une population microbienne lysogène. *Comp. rend. 231:* 190-191, 1950.
86. LWOFF, A., and GUTMANN, A. Recherches sur un bacillus megatherium lysogène. *Ann. Inst. Pasteur 78:* 711-739, 1950.
87. MACKEE, G., and CIPOLLARO, A. C. Idiopathic multiple hemorrhagic sarcoma (Kaposi). *Am. J. Cancer 26:* 1-28, 1936.
88. MELLANBY, E. Eleventh Annual Report. *Brit. Empire Cancer Campaign 81,* 1934.
89. MILFORD, J. S., and DURAN-REYNALS, F. Growth of a chicken sarcoma virus in the chick embryo in the absence of neoplasia. *Cancer Research 3:* 578-584, 1943.
90. MISZURKI, B., PIKOVSKI, G., GOLDHABER, G., and DOLJANSKI, L. Effect of X-rays on the transmissibility of fowl sarcoma in its nonfilterable phase. *Cancer Research 5:* 422-425, 1945.
91. MORRIS, H. P. "Diet and some other environmental influences in the genesis and growth of mammary tumors in mice." In *A Symposium on Mammary Tumors in Mice.* Publication of the A.A.A.S., 1945.
92. OBERLING, C. "Leucoses transmissibles des oiseaux." In *Les ultravirus des maladies humaines.* Paris, Maloine, 1943.
93. OBERLING, C. *The Riddle of Cancer.* New Haven, Yale University Press, 1944.
94. OBERLING, CH., GUERIN, M., MME. LAPLANE DE SEZE, and MME. LACOUR. Production de tumeurs hypophysaires et mammaires chez le rat par injections de folliculine seule on associée à d'autres hormones. *Bull. Assoc. franç. p. l'étude du cancer 37:* 176-192, 1950.

95. Oberling, Ch., and Guerin, M. Sarcome de la poule par methylcholanthrene devenu filtrable. *Bull. Assoc. franç. p. l'étude du cancer 37:* 5-14, 1950.
96. Pappenheimer, A. W., Dunn, L. C., Cone, V., and Seidlin, S. M. Studies on fowl paralysis (neurolymphomatosis gallinarum): I. Clinical features and pathology. *J. Exper. Med. 49:* 63-86, 1929.
97. Parsons, R. J., and Kidd, J. C. Oral papillomatosis of rabbits, a virus disease. *J. Exper. Med. 77:* 233-337, 1943.
98. Passey, R. D., Dmochowsky, L., Reed, R., and Astbury, W. T. Biophysical studies of extracts of tissues of high and low breast-cancer-strain mice. *Biochimica & Biophysica Acta 4:* 391-409, 1950.
99. Peacock, P. R. The etiology of fowl tumours. *Cancer Research 6:* 311-328, 1946.
100. Peacock, A., and Peacock, P. R. Attempts to induce epithelial tumours in fowls. *Brit. J. Cancer 3:* 289-295, 1949.
101. Pikovski, M., and Doljanski, L. Studies on the relationship between sarcoma and leukosis in chickens: II. Histogenesis of tumors induced by intramuscular inoculation of cell-containing leukotic material. *Cancer Research 10:* 1-7, 1950.
102. Rous, P. Transmission of a malignant new growth by means of a cell-free filtrate. *J. A. M. A. 56:* 198, 1911.
103. Rous, P. Resistance to a tumor-producing agent as distinct from resistance to the implanted tumor cells. *J. Exper. Med. 18:* 416-427, 1913.
104. Rous, P. The nearer causes of cancer. *J.A.M.A. 122:* 573-581, 1943.
105. Shimkin, M. B. "Hormones and mammary cancer in mice." In *A Symposium on Mammary Tumors in Mice.* Publication of the A.A.A.S., 1945.
106. Shope, R. Infectious papillomatosis of rabbits. *J. Exper. Med. 58:* 607-624, 1933.
107. Steiner, P. E., and Loosli, C. G. The effect of human influenza virus (type A) on the incidence of lung tumors in mice. *Cancer Research 10:* 385-392, 1950.
108. Selbie, F. R. Shope papilloma and sheep dermatitis in the rabbit: mutual interference, superinfection and effects of chemical pre-treatment of the skin. *Brit. J. Exper. Path. 27:* 143-154, 1946.
109. Selbie, F. R., Robinson, R. H. M., and Shope, R. Shope papilloma virus: reversion of adaptation to domestic rabbit by passage through cottontail. *Brit. J. Cancer 2:* 375-380, 1948.
110. Strauss, M. J. Personal communication.
111. Strauss, M. J., Shaw, E. W., Bunting, H., and Melnick, J. L. "Crystalline" virus-like particles from skin papillomas characterized by intranuclear inclusion bodies. *Proc. Soc. Exper. Biol. & Med. 72:* 46-50, 1949.
112. Strauss, M. J., Bunting, H., and Melnick, J. L. Virus-like particles and inclusion bodies in skin papilloma. *J. Invest. Dermat. 15:* 433-443, 1950.
113. Syverton, J., Berry, G. P., and Dascomb, H. E. Studies on carcinogenesis of rabbits: 1. Malignant tumors induced in cottontail rabbits by the injection of methylcholanthrene in tricaprylin. *Cancer Research 2:* 436-444, 1942.
114. Syverton, J., Wells, E. B., Koomen, J., Dascomb, H. E., and Berry, G. P. The virus induced papilloma to carcinoma sequence: III. Immunological tests for papilloma virus in cottontail carcinomas. *Cancer Research 10:* 474-482, 1950.
115. Syverton, J. T., Dascomb, H. E., Wells, E. B., Kooman, J., and Berry, G. P. The virus induced rabbit papilloma-to-carcinoma sequence: II. Carcinomas in the natural host, the cottontail rabbit. *Cancer Research 10:* 440-444, 1950.

116. SYVERTON, J. T., DASCOMB, H. E., KOOMEN, J., WELLS, E. B., and BERRY, G. P. The virus induced papilloma to carcinoma sequence: I. The growth pattern in natural and experimental infections. *Cancer Research 10:* 379-384, 1950.
117. VAZQUEZ-LOPEZ, E. On the growth of the Rous sarcoma inoculated into the brain. *Am. J. Cancer 26:* 29-55, 1936.
118. VON MAGNUS, H., and VON MAGNUS, P. Breeding of a colony of white mice free of encephalomyelitis virus. *Acta path. Scandinav. 26:* 175-177, 1949.
119. WATERS, N. F. Natural transmission of avian-lymphomatosis. *Poultry Sc. 24:* 226-233, 1945.
120. WATERS, N. F. The contagious nature of a lymphoid tumor in chickens. *Science 106:* 246-247, 1947.
121. WINTON, B. *Eleventh Annual Report of the Regional Poultry Research Laboratory.* East Lansing, Michigan, 1950.
122. WINTON, B. *Ninth Annual Report of the Regional Poultry Research Laboratory.* East Lansing, Michigan, 1948.

CHAPTER 14

Transplantable Tumors

George D. Snell

DEFINITIONS

Since the demonstration by several investigators in the latter part of the nineteenth century that tumors will continue to grow when transferred in succession through several hosts, a vast volume of work has been carried out with tumors thus propagated. Early investigations were often handicapped by the inconsistent and fluctuating results usually obtained when tumors are transplanted into non-inbred and hence heterozygous animals. These difficulties were largely overcome when it was shown by Little and co-workers that, with certain exceptions to be discussed later, transplantable tumors originating in an inbred strain will: (1) grow progressively in all animals of that strain; and (2) fail to grow, or grow temporarily but later regress, when transplanted into a foreign strain. These conclusions had been foreshadowed by earlier experiments of Tyzzer and of Loeb with partially inbred stocks (see historical review in Little[177]). While important work continues to be done with transplantable tumors of fowl and rabbits, where inbred strains are not yet generally available, it is now standard practice in tumor transplant experiments with rats and mice to use only inbred strains or their hybrids.

Discussions of inbreeding and of inbred strains will be found in Russell,[239] Heston,[135] and in Chapter 11 of this volume.

It will be useful at this point to define certain terms.

An *inbred strain* is one resulting from matings of brothers with sisters for 20 or more consecutive generations. Some increase in homozygosity occurs after the 20th generation, but for most purposes inbreeding for 20 generations is adequate. An equivalent increase in homozygosity is produced by parent-offspring matings, provided that where consecutive parent-offspring matings are made the cross is always to the younger of the two parents.

An *autotransplant* is one in which an individual is grafted with its own tissue.

An *isotransplant* is a transplant from one individual of an inbred strain to another individual of the same inbred strain.

A *homoiotransplant* (or homotransplant) is a transplant between individuals of the same species but of different genotypes. Typically, it is a transplant from an individual of one inbred strain to an individual of a second inbred strain.

A *heterotransplant* is a transplant between different species, as from the rat to the mouse.

Loeb[180] uses the term syngenesiotransplant to mean transplants between sibs, but since nontwin sibs of random-bred strains are never identical, and may be of very diverse genotypes, the term has only limited usefulness.

The terms autograft or autoplastic graft, homograft or homoplastic graft, etc., are synonyms of the terms defined above, except that graft is more often applied to a normal tissue transplant than to a tumor transplant.

Tumor transplants may be divided into three categories according to the degree of growth observed: (1) *completely negative transplants* which show no growth whatsoever; (2) *regression transplants* which grow temporarily but later regress; and (3) *positive transplants* which grow progressively and kill the host. Since complete failure to grow and temporary growth followed by regression are both indicative of some degree of resistance on the part of the host, Groups 1 and 2 are frequently bracketed together as *negative* (−) transplants in contradistinction to Group 3, the *positive* (+) transplants.

The term "take" is sometimes used to indicate the degree of success of a transplant. Unless specifically defined by the author (and it frequently is not), it fails to distinguish between regressions and positive transplants. Its use, therefore, is to be avoided. We shall use it occasionally to mean that the final outcome of a graft was either not observed or not specified.

Latent period signifies the interval between tumor inoculation and the first appearance of palpable tumor growth.

TYPES OF TRANSPLANTABLE TUMORS

Neoplasms of many sorts and from many species have been successfully transplanted. Little[176] gives a list of transplantable tumors of the mouse. The list given below, taken from the literature of the last sixteen years, with emphasis on tumors of the mouse, will serve to convey some idea of the great variety of transplantable neoplasms, but is in no sense complete. Most of the tumors are merely listed, and a reference given; in the case of a few of the more interesting ones, a brief description is appended of the behavior of the transplants. The tumors are grouped according to the organ affected.

Adrenal cortical carcinoma.[280] This tumor arose in Strain CE mice, and was carried through four transplant generations in this strain with 1 failure to grow out of 29 mice inoculated. It grew slowly, forming medium to large masses at 90 to 404 days after inoculation. It originally consisted of two distinct types of tissue, but only "Type I" persisted in the later transplant generations. It probably secreted androgens, and possibly also estrogens.

Brain tumors induced in mice.[285] The types reported include astrocytoma, ependymoma, oligodendroglioma, and polar spongioblastoma.

Adenomatous gastric lesion of Strain I mice.[7] The lesions were successfully transplanted by intravenous inoculation, producing growths in the lung, but serial transplantation has not been reported.

Kidney carcinoma of the frog.[36]

Hemangioendothelioma of the liver. Spontaneous tumor arising in a C3H mouse.[82]

Hepatoma. Spontaneous tumor arising in a C3H mouse.[83]

Carcinoma of liver parenchyma cells. A spontaneous tumor from a C57L mouse.[61]

Reticuloendothelioma of the liver. A spontaneous tumor arising in a C57L mouse.[61] This tumor grew 100 per cent in mice of the C57L strain and in C57BL×C57BR hybrids. Originally it did not grow in other pure strains, but one subline was developed which gave 84 per cent positive growths in C57BL mice. Subcutaneous inoculations metastasized regularly and extensively in all susceptible hosts but the site of metastases varied with the host strain. In C57L mice, the liver, lung, and spleen were regularly involved; in hybrid mice it metastasized also to the kidneys and ovaries.

Carcinoma of the lung.[6, 262] Twenty-two transplantable lung carcinomas derived from several different inbred strains of mice are described. A number of them underwent sarcomatous transformation.

Lymphosarcoma from C3H mouse.[166]

Lymphatic leukemia and lymphosarcoma induced in Wistar rat.[220] This tumor was unusual in that its manifestation depended entirely on the site of the inoculation. When given intraperitoneally, the organs involved were blood, lymph nodes, and thymus. Subcutaneous inoculation, on the other hand, produced a local lymphosarcoma spreading only as far as the regional lymph nodes. In the later transplant generations, 90 per cent to 100 per cent of the hosts died in six to ten days after inoculation.

Myeloid leukemia of mice.[18]

Chloroleukemia of mice.[128]

Monocytoma. An induced tumor arising in a C57BL mouse.[167]

Mammary tumors of the rat.[77]

Melanoma "S91."[1, 279] Snell and Cloudman, unpublished data. A slow-growing tumor originating in the tail of an irradiated DBA mouse. Metastases are frequent. A line, largely lacking pigment, has been developed which grows in B alb C mice.

Embryoma of the mouse ovary.[141]

Granulosa cell tumors.[98] These tumors of the mouse ovary produce hypervolemia in the host.

Luteomas.[99] These tumors of the mouse ovary were induced by irradiation. They are slow-growing; five or more weeks usually elapse between inoculation and the appearance of a palpable mass. They cause obesity in the host, and other changes probably associated with the secretion of progestins.

Adenocarcinoma of the preputial gland.[264] A tumor from a Strain A mouse.

Skin carcinomas. Cooper,[64] *et al.,* described 3 tumors which arose in Swiss mice following treatment with methylcholanthrene. Two were keratinizing squamous cell carcinomas. Growth remained consistently slow; transplants were made only about every four to eight weeks. Engelbreth-Holm[88] has described transplantation of a spontaneous cornifying squamous cell carcinoma of mice.

Splenic tumor originating in reticular or endothelial cells of a hybrid mouse.[17] The hosts show profound anemia and extreme erythropoiesis in the spleen.

Splenic tumors rich in mast cells.[15] Three of 6 tumors arising in Ak mice or their hybrids were successfully transplanted. The growth was slow with palpable nodules appearing only after two to eight months. Metastases did not occur.

Testicular tumor.[138] Arose in Strong C strain mouse.

Thyroid tumors of the rat.[24]

Epithelioma of the uterus of the rat.[122] This tumor showed a high percentage of metastases to the lymph nodes.

METHODS

The commonest method of tumor transplantation in mice is by subcutaneous transplantation with a trocar consisting of a large needle and stilet. A suitable needle is "special needle No. 468LRT," manufactured by Becton, Dickinson and Co. This comes with a blunt point and should be sharpened before use. The stilet comes sharp-pointed and should be filed to a flat end.

Tumor tissue is removed under aseptic conditions from the donor mouse, placed on a slide, and snipped into fine pieces with curved scissors. A piece is loaded into the needle with the aid of forceps and suction produced by withdrawing the stilet. The needle is then inserted through the skin on the flank near the hind leg, pushed forward under the skin to the axilla, and the tissue forced out with the stilet. As the needle is withdrawn, the skin should be squeezed against it with thumb and finger as a precaution to prevent removal of the tissue. The suprascapular region is another favorable site for implantation and has the advantage that resulting tumors are in a particularly convenient location for palpation. Some workers favor simultaneous implantations in both axillae. It is usually necessary to have one person hold the mice while a second person performs the inoculations. Shaving and disinfecting the skin at the point of insertion of the needle is desirable but is sometimes omitted.

Another method that is sometimes employed is to homogenize 1 part minced tumor tissue in 4 parts chilled physiologic saline, using a Potter-Elvehjem type homogenizer, and then to inject subcutaneously. A suitable dose for mice is 0.2 cc. of the homogenate.

A useful method for the growth of transplantable tumors is their cultivation in the chick egg (see Chap. 21).

STORAGE OF TUMORS AT LOW TEMPERATURES

Tumor tissue will retain its viability for some time, in certain cases for as long as fifteen days,[210] when stored at temperatures just above the freezing point. Successful inoculations have been obtained following storage of ascitic fluid from the Ehrlich carcinoma for thirty days at 4° C.[124] More useful is the storage of tumor tissue in a dry ice (solid CO_2) refrigerator. Many, though not all, transplantable tumors can be stored by this method,[33, 212, 256] survival for over a year having been reported.[34] Why certain tumors survive freezing on dry ice while others do not, is not at present understood. Possibly the virulence and rate of growth are factors. Even with those that survive, there is an increase in the latent period. Also, with some tumors the percentage of successful transplants is lowered. Despite these limitations, storage on dry ice is a useful means of keeping many transplantable tumors.

There is some evidence that extremely rapid freezing is more damaging to the transplant than slow freezing. However, it is only by special technics, such as by direct immersion of the tumor in isopentane at –75° C., that damage can be produced by over rapid freezing.

A satisfactory procedure is to seal a piece of tumor in a small glass vial, which is then stored in the dry ice refrigerator. It is important that low temperatures be maintained; merely keeping the tissue frozen is not enough. When the tissue is to be used, thawing is accomplished at room temperature.

USEFUL SITES FOR TUMOR TRANSPLANTATION

Most transplantable tumors are routinely carried by subcutaneous inoculation. with the right axilla being the preferred site for transplantation. Experiments have been carried out, however, with implantations in many other areas, and some of these have proved to have special advantages for certain purposes.

deLong and Coman[70] have tested the kidney, liver, adrenal, spleen, and muscle of mice, rats, and rabbits as sites for inoculation. All gave good growth of homologous tumors; in the case of the rabbit, the spleen showed some advantage over other sites in so far as rate of growth was concerned. The percentage of takes was essentially the same in all cases. Intra-abdominal inoculation has been used routinely by Potter and Richter[230] for the transmission of leukemias. Intravenous inoculation has also been extensively employed.[7, 220, 272]

Some of the more unusual sites that have been tested are the ear,[140] the intestine,[204] the uterus,[126] areas in close proximity to bone,[217] the cheek pouch of the hamster,[188] and the interior of another transplantable tumor.[131, 214]

Two groups of sites are of interest for the reason that homoio- and heterotransplants are either retarded or favored as compared with their growth in the more common sites.

Intradermal inoculations have been used by Bessemans and Assert[22] and by Gross,[119] as a means of immunizing mice against tumors that give a high percentage of positive growths when inoculated subcutaneously. The use of a small immunizing dose is probably important. Another site useful for purposes of immunization is the tail.[4] This method has the advantage that the tumor can be completely removed at any stage after implantation simply by cutting off the tail. The immunization obtained by these procedures is discussed in later sections of this chapter.

In the testis, the brain, and the anterior chamber of the eye, transplants seem to be partly protected from the defense mechanisms of the host. Experiments with these sites are discussed in the last section of this chapter.

SOME NONGENETIC FACTORS AFFECTING SUCCESS OF TUMOR TRANSPLANTS

The degree and rate of growth of tumor transplants are influenced by a multiplicity of factors. The principal genetic factor, namely, those genetic differences between host and implant which cause the host to react to the implant as a foreign body or foreign protein, will be discussed in later sections. One nongenetic factor, the site chosen for the inoculation, has already been discussed. Some additional nongenetic factors will now be described.

There is considerable evidence that the number of cells inoculated may determine whether a homoiotransplant grows or fails to grow, and may in some cases make the difference between regression and positive growth. While isoplastic transplantation may be successfully accomplished with the inoculation of very few cells,[144] or even of a single cell in the case of leukemias,[97] relatively large numbers of cells, usually 100,000 or more, seem to be necessary for successful homoplastic transplantation. Early studies indicating this have been reviewed by deGaétani and Blothner.[69] More recently, Haagen and Seeger[124] found that transmission of the Ehrlich carcinoma with ascitic fluid required the presence of not less than 2250 cells, but only occasional mice showed growth with this dosage. For 100 per cent growth following intraperitoneal inoculation of ascitic fluid from this tumor, Klein *et al.*[160] reported that over 400,000 cells were necessary. Very similar results have been obtained with mouse sarcoma 180.[283] The Ehrlich carcinoma and sarcoma 180 arose in noninbred mice, hence any transplants made with them are homoplastic rather than isoplastic. Reinhard *et al.,*[235] using isoplastic transplants of a Marsh-Simpson tumor in Marsh-Simpson mice, obtained occasional takes with as few as 80 cells, but did not get 100 per cent takes with fewer than 9600 cells. The use of very small numbers of cells increased the latent period. Both Gross[119] and Connell and Munro[63] found an inverse relation between the number of cells inoculated and the number of regressions. Schrek[249] found no effect of a small inoculum on the number of regressions, but did note that it decreased the number of takes and lengthened the latent period. McCutcheon *et al.*[205] found that the number of metastases of the lung increased in proportion to the initial size of a subcutaneous implant.

A curious interaction of two grafts in the same animal, suggestive of some kind of dosage effect, has been reported by Russ and Scott.[238] These investigators used the Jensen rat sarcoma, and a breed of rats in which it grew very rapidly in about 90 per cent of the animals, but slower in the remaining 10 per cent. Rats were inoculated subcutaneously in one flank with tissue from a "slow" tumor, and then several days later in the other flank with tissue from a "fast" tumor. The presence of the second graft doubled the rate of growth of the first, as compared with control animals which received grafts in one flank only.

The quality as well as the size of the inoculum is important. Zahl and Drasher[283] found that seven-day growths of sarcoma 180 contained mostly viable cells, while two- and twelve-day growths contained a preponderance of necrotic cells. These microscopic observations were checked by measuring the growth of transplants. Seven-day old tissue gave more rapid initial growth in a new host than did two- and twelve-day old tissue.

Gross[118] reported a sex difference in susceptibility in mice. Small intradermal inoculations of sarcoma S37 more often failed to grow and more often regressed in females than in males. Likewise Greene[111] has noted a lower susceptibility in females than in males to a papillary type tumor transplanted in the anterior chamber of the rabbit's eye. Foulds[92] has also found a sex difference in susceptibility but in the opposite direction. Five of 8 mammary tumors originating in F_1 mice (♀C57BL × ♂R3) grew better in F_1 females than in F_1 males. When growth did occur in the males, the latent period was very prolonged. Administration of estrogen enhanced male susceptibility. These are special cases; with most tumors and under most experimental conditions the difference in susceptibility between the sexes is slight or entirely negligible.

Age is also a factor, young mice usually being more susceptible than old ones. Thus Bunting[40] found that mammary carcinoma 15091a (A strain origin) grew progressively in 77 per cent of DBA mice and 78 per cent of B alb C mice inoculated at the age of 1 to 2 days, but in only 33 per cent and 20 per cent respectively when the hosts were 6 to 8 weeks old. Likewise Gross[121] found that a transplantable lymphatic leukemia (Ak origin), inoculated in C3H mice, grew progressively in 97 per cent of mice aged 1 to 7 days, in 42 per cent of mice aged 8 to 15 days, in 17 per cent of mice aged 16 to 30 days, and no mice aged 2 to 6 months. Most of the inoculations were made subcutaneously, a few intraperitoneally.

Among the lower vertebrates, homoplastic grafts can be made between embryos with complete success; the immune reactions characteristic of the adult are apparently lacking in the embryo. There is now indirect but quite conclusive evidence that this is also true of mammals.

The evidence is provided by studies of the blood groups of dizygotic twins in cattle. Owen[223] has found that such twins almost invariably have identical blood types. Since there are a large number of genetically controlled erythrocyte antigens in cattle, the chance occurrence of such identity is ruled out. The explanation offered is that cells ancestral to the adult erythrocyte are exchanged by way of the vascular anastomoses known to occur in bovine twins, and become established in the opposite twin. Individuals of a twin pair have been shown by breeding tests to have blood cells normally incompatible with their genotype. Moreover, it has been demonstrated that there is a mixture of two distinct types of erythrocytes in certain twins. These foreign types of cells are not merely present at birth, but persist in the adult.

It is thus clear that tissues transferred at an early stage of development can become a permanent part of the host. Like the host's own tissues, they seemingly do not incite antibody formation even after the antibody-producing mechanism becomes established. Tissues grafted at one stage are accepted as native tissues even by the adult organism, while similar tissues grafted later in development are rejected as foreign. This is a basic fact that must be considered in any theory of tissue specificity.

Certain types of irritation or injury at the site of subcutaneous transplants seem to be favorable to the growth of homoiotransplants. Thus Jones[143] found that the implantation of a small piece of sterile flannel cloth at the same time as the tumor resulted in occasional temporary growths of tumor dbrB in black mice. Controls were completely negative. Likewise Zahl and Nowak[284] found that the growth of sarcoma 180 was accelerated in mice in which the skin at the site of implantation had been pulled away from the underlying muscle tissue. This was accomplished by forcing a small pair of scissors under the skin to the depth of the fulcrum and then spreading the points. At six to seven days, tumors in the experimental mice were over twice as large as those in the controls.

A contrary result was obtained when virulent tumors such as sarcoma 180 were mixed with starch grains prior to inoculation.[52] This produced inhibition. A possible explanation is found in the tendency of starch to attract leukocytes.

Blumenthal[31] found that homoplastic transplants of tissue from spontaneous tumors grew in about 22 per cent of mice themselves already bearing spontaneous tumors but grew rarely or not at all in control mice. This result may have no significance beyond the fact that healthy mice have more resistance than sick ones.

Wallace *et al.*[271] found a striking effect of temperature on the growth of subcutaneous isoplastic transplants. Mice of the C3H strain were inoculated subcutaneously with an induced C3H tumor and kept either in a room at 92° F. with a high humidity, or in a room at 65° F. with a variable humidity. In a typical experiment the size of the tumors at thirty days averaged about eight times larger in the warm room than in the cold one. There were also some regressions among mice in the cold room. When the tumor was implanted intramuscularly, it developed equally well in hosts in either room. This suggests that the effect of temperature is directly on the tumor itself rather than through the host.

Pearce and Van Allen[228] reported retardation of growth of the Brown-Pearce tumor in rabbits kept in continuous light or continuous dark.

Roentgen irradiation has frequently been used to lower the resistance of the host to homoiotransplants, see Bichel and Holm-Jensen.[23]

Chambers and Scott[54] were able to increase the frequency of regression of the Jensen rat sarcoma by cutting off its blood supply for two to four hours. This was accomplished by placing the tumors in a specially designed clamp while the hosts were under urethane anesthesia. There were 29 per cent regressions in the treated rats as against the less than 10 per cent usually found with this tumor.

INFECTIONS IN TRANSPLANTABLE TUMORS

Infections of various sorts are not infrequent in transplantable tumors and may cause alterations in the growth rate of such tumors. Diller[71] has reported the demonstration in transplantable tumors by special technics of spores and other fungal elements which in ordinary histologic preparations appear to be integral tumor cells or are mistaken for lymphocytes and other blood cells. The fungi were readily cultivated in appropriate media. Wyeth and Rahn[282] have described a *Treponema* which was regularly present in transplantable mammary adenocarcinoma dbrB, but not in other tumors examined. In suitable preparations under dark-field illumination, the *Treponema* could be seen as a spiral organism with 5 to 15 closely wound coils.

Areas of obvious bacterial infection are occasionally seen in transplantable tumors. Bacteria of various sorts may also be present without any gross alteration in appearance of the tumor tissue.[86, 234, 250] Rask-Nielsen and Rask-Nielsen[234] have noted that ulceration of subcutaneous tumors is not especially associated with infection, at least in the more profound parts of the tumor.

Woglom and Warren[277, 278] demonstrated the presence of a filterable agent in rat sarcoma 39. The agent was repeatedly recovered from this tumor, though its presence was not evident under ordinary circumstances of routine transplantation. The agent could be cultivated on media containing a high proportion of serum and was therefore bacterial rather than viral in nature.

Several instances of virus infections of tumors have been described. Pearce and

Rivers[226, 227] found a filterable agent, virus III, which proved to be indigenous to rabbits and which was also regularly present in the Brown-Pearce tumor. DeBruyn[68] found a filterable agent in a mouse lymphosarcoma which caused a lymphopenia in mice free of the tumor. A similar agent was found by Taylor and MacDowell[266] in line I leukemia of mice, though Taylor and MacDowell's agent produced a loss of weight and a rise in white cell count when inoculated into normal mice. Kritzler *et al.*[162] have identified a hitherto undescribed virus in mouse tumor E0771 and in its C57BL hosts.

Bittner[29] has reported the persistence of the mammary tumor milk agent in tumors originating in C57BL mice which carried the agent. After 10 transplant generations the agent was still present. Dmochowski[73] has confirmed this persistence of the milk agent in tumor transplants. A similar persistence was noted by Kidd[154] for Shope's rabbit papilloma virus and the V2 carcinoma. Evidently the causative agents for these tumors tend to be propagated with them.

Many experiments have been carried out in which transplantable tumors or their hosts have been artificially infected. These do not fall within the scope of this chapter, but it is worth noting that an infective agent introduced into the host may show an affinity for tumor tissue.[247] Hence a tumor may become infected by way of the host as well as through contamination during transplantation.

The effect of many, though not all, infections is to lower the growth potential of the parasitized tumor. This has been shown particularly in several of the studies of artificially infected tumors, but has also been evident in some spontaneous infections. Thus Schrek[250] found a longer latent period in infected than in uninfected tumors, an increase in the number of completely negative transplants, and possibly also a higher frequency of regression in the infected cases. Infection did not, however, affect the growth rate of those tumors that grew progressively. Opposite results were obtained by Pearce and Rivers,[227] who reported a slight increase in malignancy of the Brown-Pearce tumor when infected with virus III, and by Taylor and MacDowell,[266] who noted earlier death in animals with virus-infected tumors.

Various procedures have been employed to free tumors of infection. Aris[13] has reported the elimination of *Spirilla* from a mouse tumor by keeping a suspension of the tumor at a low temperature for three days. Schrek[248, 250] freed rat tumors of bacterial contamination by inoculating with minimal amounts of tumor suspension. The tumor was ground in a Latapie apparatus, filtered through an 80-mesh wire cloth, and diluted 1:1000 with saline. When 0.1 cc. of this suspension was injected, growth occurred in 34 per cent of the hosts as against 96 per cent in rats receiving 0.1 cc. of a 1:10 dilution. The resulting tumors were sometimes free of accompanying bacterial infection; if not free, the bacterial count was considerably reduced. After two successive transplants with minimal dose, contaminating micro-organisms were usually eliminated.

Gardner and Hyde[100] freed the Walker rat tumor of bacterial contamination by using tissue from metastases for transplantation. Metastases occur regularly with this tumor when inoculation is made into the tail of young susceptible animals.

Virus infections have been eliminated from tumors by passing the tumor through immune animals. Thus Andrewes[8] freed rabbit sarcoma RSI of virus III by transplantation in a rabbit immunized to virus III. Similar results were obtained with the Brown-Pearce tumor and vaccine virus, and the Brown-Pearce tumor and virus III, except that two transfers through immunized hosts were necessary in the latter case. Taylor and MacDowell[266] in like manner freed line I leukemia of mice from a parasitizing virus by passage through hosts that had recovered from virus infection. On the other hand, Kidd[154] was unable to free the V2 rabbit carcinoma from the Shope papilloma virus by this method. Kidd believes this may indicate that a more enduring partnership exists between tumor-inducing viruses and the host cell than is the case with "extraneous passenger viruses" and the host cell.

GENETIC BASIS OF SUSCEPTIBILITY AND RESISTANCE TO TRANSPLANTS

The genetic theory of transplantation was foreshadowed by Little[175] and elaborated and firmly established by the investigations of Little and co-workers during the two following decades. Reviews have been published by Bittner,[28] Little,[176, 177] and Snell.[254] The papers by Little should be consulted for a full bibliography. In this chapter only enough of the earlier studies will be cited to illustrate the basic points.

TABLE 20. RESULTS OF INOCULATION OF TUMOR 14905a (A STRAIN ORIGIN) IN A AND DBA MICE AND THEIR HYBRIDS

Case	*Inoculated mice*	*Parents*	*Number of mice* +	*Number of mice* −	*Percent* +
1	A	A	206	0	100
2	DBA	DBA	0	174	0
3	F_1	A×DBA	145	0	100
4	F_2	$F_1 \times F_1$	67	154	30.3
5	ABC	$F_1 \times A$	91	0	100
6	DBABC	$F_1 \times DBA$	6	81	6.9

From Cloudman.[58]

The investigations in this field have been based on the use of highly inbred strains of mice and the first filial (F_1), second filial (F_2), and backcross (BC) hybrid generations produced by crossing them. As a typical experiment, we may take one reported by Cloudman.[58] The strains used were the A and DBA. The tumor used was A strain mammary adenocarcinoma 14905a, inoculated subcutaneously by the trocar method. The results of the inoculations were classified as positive (+) or negative (−) according to whether or not the tumors grew progressively, killing the host, or failed to grow progressively. The latter class included some regressions. The results are given in Table 20. It will be seen that the tumor grew in 100 per cent of A, F_1 and ABC (backcross of F_1 to A) mice, none of the DBA mice, 30.3 per cent of F_2 mice, and 6.9 per cent of DBABC (backcross of F_1 to DBA) mice.

Numerous other experiments by Bittner, Cloudman, Little, MacDowell, Strong and Tyzzer (see Little,[176] for references) have given similar results, except that the percentage susceptible (+) in the F_2 generation, and the generations produced by backcrossing the F_1 to the resistant parent, have varied within wide limits according to the tumor and strains used.

With this introduction we may now: (1) state six laws of tumor transplantation; (2) give the explanation of these laws in terms of Mendelizing histocompatibility genes; and (3) point out and discuss certain exceptions to the laws.

The six laws summarizing the results of transplantation experiments with inbred strains of mice are as follows:

1. Transplants within a single inbred strain (isotransplants) grow progressively and kill all hosts. Example: Table 20, Case 1.

2. Transplants between strains (homoiotransplants) do not grow, or grow temporarily and then regress. Example: Table 20, Case 2.

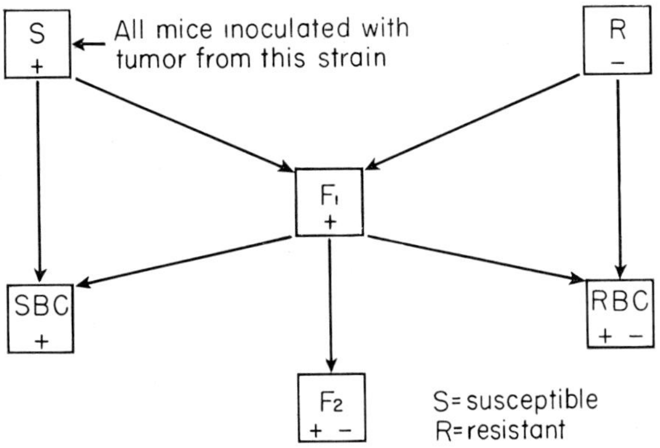

FIG. 51. The genetic laws of tumor transplant susceptibility in inbred strains and their hybrids. Animals which show progressive growth of the tumor are indicated by +, those which resist the growth by −. The F_2 generation and the backcross to the resistant parent (RBC) include both susceptible and resistant animals.

3. Transplants into hybrid animals, where one parent was inbred and susceptible, grow progressively and kill all hosts. Examples: Table 20, Cases 3 (F_1 mice) and 5 (ABC mice).

4. Transplants into F_2 mice, and into backcross mice from the mating $F_1 \times$ resistant parent, grow in a fraction of the hosts only. The susceptible percentage may vary within wide limits according to the strains of mice and the tumor employed. Examples: Table 20, Cases 4 (F_2 mice) and 6 (DBABC mice).

These four laws are illustrated in Fig. 51.

Two less important laws, representing somewhat special cases, are:

5. A tumor originating in an F_1 hybrid will grow in all F_1 hybrids but not in members of either parent strain. It will grow in a fraction of F_2 and BC mice. This law is based on 8 experiments by Bittner (see summary in Bittner[28]). Some exceptions will be discussed later.

6. A tumor originating in an animal of the F_2 or later hybrid generations will grow in all F_1 mice. This law can be deduced from the genetic theory of transplantation to be discussed later. Apparently it has been tested (and confirmed) in only 2 experiments (Bittner,[28] and Furth and Barnes[95]).

According to the classical genetic theory of tumor transplantation, these laws are explained by assuming that a transplant will grow if, and only if, the host carries certain dominant genes that were present in the animal in which the tumor originated. The number of dominant genes varies with the tumor and with the strains employed. We may illustrate first with a case where a single factor is required.

Assume a tumor originating in an A strain mouse, which is tested in the A strain, the DBA strain, and the F_1, F_2 and DBABC hybrid generations. Assume that the tumor will grow if, and only if, a dominant gene H is present. Progressive growth of the tumor is indicated by +, failure to grow progressively by −. $H-$ includes the two genotypes HH and Hh. Then:

A × DBA	HH +	×	hh −
F_1		Hh +	
F_2	3 $H-$ +		1 hh −
DBABC	1 Hh +		1 hh −

In the F_1 generation 100 per cent of the animals carry the gene H and are susceptible, in the F_2 generation 75 per cent, in the DBABC generation 50 per cent. Similarly if the growth of an A strain tumor requires the presence of two dominant genes, H and J:

A × DBA	$HHJJ$ +	×	$hhjj$ −	
F_1		$HhJj$ +		
F_2	9 $H-J-$	3 $H-jj$	3 $hhJ-$	1 $hhjj$
	9+		7−	
DBABC	1 $HhJj$	1 $Hhjj$	1 $hhJj$	1 $hhjj$
	1+		3−	

The percentage susceptible are: F_1 generation, 100 per cent; F_2 generation, 56.25 per cent; DBABC generation, 25 per cent. Or, in general, the ratio of animals susceptible to the total number of animals is

$$(3/4)^n \text{ for the } F_2 \text{ generation}$$
$$(1/2)^n \text{ for the DBABC generation}$$

where n is the number of dominant genes which must be present to produce susceptibility.

These theoretical expectations have been tested by Little and co-workers and by MacDowell and Richter[193, 195] against the results obtained with 36 different tumors, mostly mammary tumors, but including 1 melanoma and 2 leukemias.

Eight different inbred strains were used in the crosses. Furth, Boon and Kaliss[96] have published results with an additional group of tumors, including several induced sarcomas, and Gorer[104, 106] has tested a sarcoma and a leukemia. Data from 3 typical experiments are summarized in Table 21, and compared with the results expected according to genetic theory. The outcome of inoculations of A, DBA, and F_1 mice is not given in the table, but this conformed completely with expectations with two exceptions. Strain A tumor 17495a grew in 1 out of 94 DBA mice instead of being negative in all DBA mice as expected, and F_1 (A×DBA) tumor 19308A failed to grow in 2 out of 496 F_1 mice instead of being positive in all F_1 mice as expected. The table shows the results for the F_2 and backcross generations.

TABLE 21. OBSERVED NUMBER OF POSITIVE TRANSPLANTS FOR THREE MOUSE TUMORS, COMPARED WITH THE NUMBER EXPECTED ON THE BASIS OF THE GENETIC THEORY OF TUMOR TRANSPLANTATION

	F_2		*ABC*		*DBABC*	
	+	−	+	−	+	−
A strain tumor 14905a						
Observed	67	154	91	0	6	81
Expected (4 factors)	70	151	91	0	5	82
A strain tumor 17495a						
(prior to Jan. 1, 1930)						
Observed	70	58	67	0	27	60
Expected (2 factors)	72	56	67	0	22	65
(after Jan. 1, 1930)						
Observed	179	65			63	86
Expected (1 factor)	183	61			74.5	74.5
F_1 (A×DBA) tumor 19308A						
Observed	143	1434	28	874	131	799
Expected (8 factors)*	158	1419	28	874	116	814

Data for tumors 14905a and 17495a from Cloudman,[58] data for tumor 19308A from Bittner.[27]
* 3 dominants derived from the A strain, 5 from the dba strain.

In the case of tumor 14905a (strain A origin), an excellent agreement between observed and expected results is obtained if it is assumed that strain A carries 4 dominant genes which must be present if the tumor is to grow, and which are lacking in strain DBA (strain A is *HHJJKKLL* and strain DBA is *hhjjkkll*). With tumor 17495a a higher proportion of the animals was susceptible (66.9 per cent + in the F_2, 35.2 per cent + in the DBABC). This indicates a lower number of factors, but does not give a good fit with the expectations for either 2 factors (56.2 per cent + expected in F_2, 25 per cent + expected in DBABC) or 1 factor (75 per cent + in F_2, 50 per cent + in DBABC). If the data are broken down into two groups, however, according to the period when the inoculations were made, an excellent fit can be obtained. The tumors inoculated prior to January 1, 1930, conform closely to the expectations for 2 factors, the tumors after this date to the expectations for 1 factor. Evidently in the course of successive transplants the tumor underwent a change whereby fewer factors were necessary for its growth. This and other similar cases will be discussed further in the next section.

The third tumor listed in Table 21 arose in an F_1 (A×DBA) mouse. The results indicate that it required 8 factors of which the A strain contributed 3 and the DBA strain 5 (strain A is *HHJJKKmmnnoopp*, strain DBA is *hhjjkkMMNN-OOPP*).

While all experiments have not shown as close agreement between observed and expected results as the 3 cited, the deviations in general have been within the limits expected by chance alone. It is highly significant that, for each experiment, the results in both the F_2 and BC generations have conformed to expectations. Except in cases where the number of inoculated animals is large, a fit could be obtained for most possible observed values in one of these generations alone simply by juggling assumptions as to number of factors. It is unlikely, however, that fits could be obtained consistently for both F_2 and BC were the basic postulates of the theory invalid. In its essential features, then, the genetic theory of transplantation may be regarded as established.

The genes postulated in this theory may be called *histocompatibility genes*. The prefix "histo" is used because there is reason to suppose that the same genes determine susceptibility and resistance to both neoplastic and normal tissues (see, for example, Little and Johnson,[178] and Kaliss and Robertson[148]).

Snell[254] has discussed the evidence concerning the number of such genes present in the available inbred stocks of mice. In an early experiment by Little and Tyzzer,[179] involving a cross of Japanese waltzing and "common" mice, 14 or 15 segregating histocompatibility genes were indicated. The large number in this experiment is perhaps explained by the fact that the Japanese waltzing mouse is descended from *Mus bactrianus*, so that the cross-breeding brought in genes from two species. Crosses involving only strains of *Mus musculus* have indicated anywhere from 1 to 11 segregating loci. No one cross is likely to reveal all histocompatibility loci, for the reason that any two strains picked at random will be identical for some loci even though variability for these loci exists in the mouse population in general. The A strain might thus be *HHIIJJKKLLmmnnooppqqRRSSTTUUVVw-wxxyyzz* and the DBA strain *hhiijjkkllMMNNOOPPQQRRSSTTUUVVwwxxyyzz*. Only the histocompatibility genes *H* to *Q* will be revealed by an A×DBA cross. Other factors, such as the existence of tissue-specific antigens which might make tumors of diverse origin reveal different histocompatibility genes, bear on the estimated gene number. Snell concludes that 14 is a conservative estimate of the total number of loci determining susceptibility and resistance to tumor transplants. These are probably not equally important; some are "stronger" than others, in the sense that they play more of a role in stopping the growth of virulent tumors when transplanted homoplastically.

Early studies in the genetics of tumor transplantation were concerned with establishing the existence of histocompatibility genes, and with providing some evidence as to their number. Recently, more detailed evidence has been forthcoming about one locus. Linkage tests showed that in mice a histocompatibility locus, *H-2*, is closely linked with the dominant gene *Fu*, which causes a fusion of tail vertebrae.[109, 254, 259] Using this linkage, the existence of at least 4 alleles at the *H-2* locus was demonstrated. The demonstration rests on the use of a cross of the type (M×*Fu*)×N where M and N are any two inbred stocks, and *Fu* is a stock carrying the *Fu* gene. The mice from this double cross were inoculated with a tumor originating in Strain M. It can be shown by simple genetic reasoning that association in this cross between *Fu* and resistance proves that strain M and N carry *different H-2* alleles, whereas the absence of an association is evidence that they carry the *same* allele. By using this test on a variety of strains in different combinations, the number and distribution of such alleles can be determined.

By a series of such crosses, Snell and Higgins[259] demonstrated that there are at least 4 alleles, *H-2*, $H\text{-}2^d$, $h\text{-}2^b$, and $h\text{-}2^p$, at the *H-2* locus. The distribution of these alleles in several standard mouse strains is given in Table 22. Additional alleles may well be revealed by further crosses, since many stocks are still untested.

TABLE 22. H-2 ALLELE PRESENT IN SEVERAL STANDARD MOUSE STRAINS

Allele	*H-2*		$H\text{-}2^d$		$h\text{-}2^b$	$h\text{-}2^p$
Strain	A	*Fu*/C	B alb C	DBA/2	C57BL	P
Tumor	15091a	15091a	S621	P1534	C1498	S637

All strains except *Fu*/C are inbred. The tumor native to each strain which was used in the tests is also given.[259]

This information about the *H-2* locus bears in two important respects on the genetic theory of transplantation. First, this locus is apparently a "strong" histocompatibility locus, that is, it can stop the growth of old and virulent transplantable tumors not prevented by most or any other histocompatibility genes. Thus in the crosses reported by Snell and Higgins,[259] with infrequent exceptions, A strain tumor 15091a grew if, and only if, allele *H-2* was present; DBA strain tumor P1534 and B alb C tumor S621 grew if, and only if, allele $H\text{-}2^d$ was present; C57BL tumor C1498 grew if, and only if, allele $h\text{-}2^b$ was present, and P strain tumor S637 grew if, and only if, allele $h\text{-}2^p$ was present. There is every reason to suppose, however, that this concomitance between the presence of a particular *H-2* allele and susceptibility or resistance to transplants would not hold for many tumors of lower virulence, and that it would be less clear in the case of so-called nonspecific tumors such as sarcoma 180.

The second significant fact about the *H-2* locus is that none of the alleles so far detected behaves as a recessive. No strain carries an allele which is unnecessary for the growth of tumors originating in that strain. This is contrary to the classical genetic theory of transplantation, according to which one allele at each locus is recessive and hence should be without influence on tumor growth. This fact, however, brings the *H-2* locus in line with the blood group genes, where most alleles do express themselves in the heterozygote.

The *H-2* alleles are not only histocompatibility genes but also determine a series of erythrocyte antigens. Further details are given in the section on the antigenic basis for resistance to transplants.

SOME EXCEPTIONS TO THE LAWS OF TUMOR TRANSPLANTATION

The first law states that isotransplants always grow progressively and kill the hosts. There are many recorded exceptions to this law, where tumor transplants, particularly in the first transplant generation, grew only in some of the inoculated animals. Thus Edwards, Andervont and Dalton[82] reported a hemangioendothelioma of the liver arising spontaneously in C3H mice which grew progressively in only about 80 per cent of inoculated C3H mice. Likewise Stewart, Grady and Andervont[262] found that of 7 induced carcinomas of the lung, 5 grew 100 per cent in isoplastic grafts, but 2 failed to grow in a few mice in the early transplant generations, though they later also grew 100 per cent. Also MacDowell and Richter[194] obtained 4 negatives out of a total of 75 isoplastic transplants of line L leukemia. On the other hand, King and Lewis,[159] using the King A albino rats in generations 101 to 115 of brother × sister inbreeding, and Lewis and Lichtenstein,[173] using inbred mice, found that a large number of induced tumors without exception grew progressively in intrastrain transplants.

The probable explanation of the exceptions is that most inbred strains, even after many generations of brother × sister matings, are not completely homozygous. On rare occasions this may of course be due to contamination, but even ruling out such cases, a degree of heterozygosity may be expected to persist due to the occurrence of mutations. Haldane[125] has investigated this question theoretically and concludes that "most members of a mammalian pure line will be heterozygous for at least one gene as the result of mutation." Some of these mutant genes will never appear in the homozygous condition, and a still larger proportion will fail to become permanently established through the mating of a homozygous pair. Nevertheless, enough will become established to cause the rather rapid development of sublines within inbred strains. Even sibs will frequently have genetic differences. Of course many of these differences may have no bearing on susceptibility or resistance to transplants, but others will. This fact is probably adequate to explain all cases of failure of isoplastic grafts which are not due to contamination, insufficient inbreeding or faulty technics. Another possible explanation: that tumors carry tumor-specific antigens, cannot be ruled out as a factor in some cases.

That grafts between truly isogenic individuals should invariably succeed is indicated by the several reported cases of successful skin grafts between identical twins.[20, 37]

The second law of tumor transplantation states that homoplastic transplants are always either completely negative, or grow temporarily and then regress. Again there are many recorded exceptions, and in this case most of the exceptions are probably valid ones. Exceptions are particularly common in the case of transplants in the anterior chamber of the eye.[85] Of importance are the so-called nonspecific tumors, mostly old tumors originating in noninbred animals which have become so virulent that they kill a considerable percentage of hosts of all strains. An example is the Jensen rat sarcoma which in routine use in noninbred rats by Chambers and Scott[53] grew progressively in 98 per cent of

KC stock hosts, in 79 per cent of T stock hosts, in 79 per cent of home stock hosts prior to December, 1923, and in 35 per cent of home stock hosts subsequent to April, 1927. The low incidence in the last group was due to the fact that this stock had been bred for some generations from transplant survivors and hence had been selected for resistance.

Another exception, typical of a number of similar cases which could be cited, is provided by A strain tumor 15091a. This tumor is negative in most homoiotransplants, but has given 30 to 33 per cent positive growths in the DBA strain over an extended period of years (Fekete, Russell and Snell, unpublished data, Bunting[40] and Cloudman[59]). Such results may at first sight seem puzzling, since they are contrary to the frequently stressed uniformity of behavior of inbred strains. Actually, as has been pointed out very clearly by Russell,[239] inbred strains are occasionally quite variable with respect to certain characters.

The classical example is the observations by Wright[281] on polydactyly in 23 inbred strains of guinea pigs. In 12 of these 23 strains, all animals had normal 3-toed hind feet, in the remaining 11 strains a certain percentage of animals was polydactylous. This percentage varied from strain to strain, but was fixed within each strain once inbreeding was complete. The remaining intrastrain variability was entirely due to environmental factors. Thus inbreeding, where the genetic factors become fixed at a threshold such that they neither completely inhibit a trait nor induce a 100 per cent incidence thereof, becomes a means of demonstrating the role of environment in the trait's etiology.

In studies of tumor transplantation, there are not infrequently cases where, with a given combination of tumor and inbred host, the percentage of positive transplants is neither 0 nor 100 per cent, but some intermediate value. This emphasizes the importance of environmental factors in determining the outcome of homoiotransplants. Just what are the most important environmental factors is unknown, but they probably include some of the nongenetic factors (size of inoculum, presence or absence of infection in the tumor, health of the host, etc.) listed in previous sections of this chapter. These cases stand as exceptions to the general rule that tumor homoiotransplants do not grow progressively.

Occasional exceptions to the remaining laws of transplantation have been recorded. For example, Bittner[27, 28] found a few cases in which F_1 tumors failed to grow 100 per cent in F_1 mice. All such instances can probably be explained by the factors discussed above, namely, lack of complete homozygosity in many inbred strains, and the existence of a few particularly virulent tumors which do grow homoplastically in all or in a percentage of hosts of certain inbred strains, with the percentage in any given case being determined by a balance of genetic and environmental factors.

TRANSFORMATION AND MUTATION IN TRANSPLANTABLE TUMORS

It is an almost universal characteristic of transplantable tumors that they change during the course of repeated transfers. The changes may be grouped as (1) morphologic changes, and (2) physiologic changes. The latter are almost always in the direction of increased virulence as measured by: (a) rapidity of growth; (b) ability to kill hosts of genotypes previously resistant; and (c) increase in number of metastases. The types of change will be discussed in this order.

There have been many reports of the transformation of carcinomas into sarcomas. We select three that are particularly illuminating. Ludford and Barlow[183] studied the histology and the behavior in tissue cultures of 6 mammary carcinomas of mice through successive isoplastic transplants. All 6 underwent definite sarcomatous transformation. This histologic diagnosis was confirmed by the tissue culture studies. In the early carcinomatous stages the tissues *in vitro* grew in sheets with sharp boundaries; in the later sarcomatous stages they consisted of spindle-shaped cells becoming progressively more separated as they migrated peripherally. By growing embryonic mouse fibroblasts in cultures adjacent to each of the two types of tumor cells, it was shown that tumors in the carcinomatous stage stimulated fibroblast growth, while the sarcomatous tumors inhibited it. In 5 of the tumors the sarcomatous transformation was abrupt, probably occurring in one transplant generation; in the sixth it occurred more gradually.

Stewart, Grady and Andervont[262] noted fibrosarcomatous transformation in 11 of 22 pulmonary tumors of mice transplanted isoplastically. Twenty-one of the tumors were induced and one was spontaneous. Many of the tumors retained mixed carcinomatous and sarcomatous characteristics through a number of generations and only 4 ultimately became pure sarcomas.

Toolan and Kidd[269] found that sarcomatous transformation could apparently be induced in a transplantable C3H mammary carcinoma by four or more days' sojourn in the subcutaneous tissues of Strain A mice immune to them. In 13 out of 15 cases, the growths that resulted when the transplants were returned to C3H hosts were not mammary carcinomas but fibrosarcomas. One of these tumors was maintained through 25 transplant generations in C3H mice and retained its essentially sarcomatous nature, though with increased roundness of the cells.

Stewart *et al.*[262] have discussed four possible explanations of this type of change: (1) The tumors may originally have consisted of sarcomatous and carcinomatous elements. The transformation would then be simply a replacement of the dominant carcinoma cell by sarcoma cells. While there are a number of recorded instances in which distinct transplantable tumor types have been separated out from mixed tumors (e.g., Dunning *et al.*,[77] and Zimmerman and Maier[285]), the applicability of this phenomenon to sarcomatous transformations seems open to question. (2) The carcinoma cells could become transformed into sarcoma cells. This would constitute a true mutational process within the tumor. Kidd favors this interpretation. (3) Normal stromal cells derived from the animal in which the tumor originated could be carried along with the tumor through successive transplants and undergo, gradually or abruptly, neoplastic transformation. Ludford and Barlow point out that it is more plausible to expect such serial transfer of normal tissue to occur in isotransplantation than in homoiotransplantation. They note that earlier workers using homoiotransplants found evidence for the destruction of all transferred stroma and also observed sarcomatous transformation only infrequently. They also call attention to the probable presence of the tumor-inducing Bittner milk agent in their tumors. (4) Stroma composed of host cells could be the source of the sarcomas. It seems impossible at the present time to choose among these alternatives.

Histologic changes of other types have also been reported in transplantable tumors. Thus Cooper *et al.*[64] noted loss of the keratinizing tendency in one of two squamous cell carcinomas during the course of 20 to 21 subcutaneous passages, and Selbie[252] detected a carcinomatous transformation in a transplantable rat fibroadenoma. Likewise Algire[1] produced an almost pigment-free strain of DBA melanoma S91 by deliberate selection of paler portions of the tumors for successive transplants in B alb C hosts. This last case would seem of necessity to involve a mutation or series of mutations within the tumor.

The observation has been almost universal that tumors speed up their growth during successive transplants. As one example, Breedis *et al.*[35] found that formation of palpable masses of a transplantable lung tumor of an F_2 hybrid mouse required 131–135, 20–30, and 7–30 days in the first, second and third transfers respectively.

A particularly thorough study of changes in transplantable leukemias has been made by MacDowell.[190] In transplant line, M-liv, an abrupt acceleration of growth occurred during the seventeenth and eighteenth transfers. The interval to death was about 45 days at the first transfer, dropped gradually to about 15 days at the seventh transfer, held this level to the sixteenth transfer, and then dropped abruptly to 10 and then to 5 days during the seventeenth and eighteenth transfers. The tumor then remained stable for many transplant generations at this last level. For several generations prior to the sudden increase in virulence in the seventeenth to eighteenth generations, it was noted that the proportion of large, as compared with small, leukemic cells underwent a progressive increase. This reached its maximum at the nineteenth transfer and thereafter remained nearly constant. MacDowell also describes an unusual case in which there was a decrease in virulence at the sixty-seventh transfer of line M-kid with a later return to normal.

Miller and Taylor[213] found a decrease in the killing time of line U leukemia from 15 to 4 days during a long series of transfers and concomitantly a marked increase in the number of mitochondria per lymphocyte. This confirmed earlier observations of other workers. Biesele[25] found a two-fold to three-fold increase in volume of the chromosomes of transplanted leukemias.

The increase in rate of growth of transplantable tumors, at least in the early transplant generations may be due in part to the sorting out of tissues with different growth potentials. This is indicated, for example, by a study of Mottram[216] with tar warts in mice. Mottram found that autografts with different growth rates sometimes resulted when a single wart provided tissue for several grafts back onto the same mouse. However, if two cell lineages with even slightly different growth rates were included in one inoculum, the one growing more rapidly, because of the geometric nature of growth, would in only one transplant generation come to compose the greater part of the tumor. Further acceleration would be dependent on mutation.

That the presence of different structural areas in one transplantable tumor does not necessarily prove the presence of genetically different cell lineages is suggested by the observations of Jackson and Brues[141] on a transplantable embryoma of the mouse. This tumor maintained its highly pleomorphic nature through eleven serial transplants with no evidence that the different elements could be separated.

An example has already been given in the previous section of a transplantable tumor (17495a[58]) which during the course of successive transplants underwent a change, whereby instead of requiring two dominant genes in the host for successful growth it required only one. There have been other similar cases. Thus Strong[263] obtained from DBA tumor dBrD, which required 6 to 8 factors for successful propagation in F_2 (A×DBA) mice, 3 sublines, dBrDm, dBrDBl, and dBrDBs, which required two, two, and one factors respectively. The decreased number of requisite factors in the three mutant sublines was associated with an increased rate of growth.

Koch,[161] by using metastatic lesions for implantation, produced a strain of the Ehrlich mouse carcinoma with a high tendency to metastasize. This was accompanied by a shorter survival of the hosts and other signs of increased virulence.

Earle and co-workers[80] have made the important observation that fibroblasts from an adult C3H mouse cultivated over a period of time *in vitro*, and then inoculated back into C3H hosts, will grow progressively and can be transplanted serially, thus behaving in all respects like a transplantable sarcoma. Some of the strains of fibroblasts were treated with carcinogens, but these gave rise to a lower percentage of tumors than the untreated control strains.

Snell[255] has pointed out that hereditary changes in transplantable tumors, or the changes whereby normal fibroblasts *in vitro* develop malignant characteristics, need not trace back to gene mutations, but may equally well derive from mutations in mitochondria or microsomes or other self-reproducing cell entities.

INDUCED IMMUNITY

Induced Immunity to Tumor Homoiotransplants

It has been known for some forty-five years that regression of a tumor transplant renders a host immune to a second transplant of the same tumor. Other early investigations showed that implants of adult and embryonic normal tissue could also evoke immunity. The extensive work in this field has been reviewed by Woglom.[275] Recent studies have principally served to emphasize the specificity of induced immunity, and to show that, in certain cases at least, it can be produced with nonliving tissue. A few of the more significant findings are summarized below.

Lewis[168] investigated the immunity evoked in mice of the A, Bagg albino, C3H and C57BL strains by interstrain transplants of tumors induced in the last three of these strains. The tumors selected regularly showed some growth in the foreign strain but eventually regressed. The time required for immunity to develop was tested by removing the first transplant at varying intervals after inoculation. Mice in which the first transplant was removed after five days were regularly resistant to a second transplant of the same tumor. The immunity was, in considerable degree, strain-specific. Thus regression of a C57BL tumor in an A host usually did not confer immunity to a subsequent transplant of a C3H tumor. However, one C57BL tumor could immunize against a different C57BL tumor. Regression of a homograft did not render an animal resistant to an isograft.

The specificity of induced tissue immunity has been strikingly demonstrated by Medawar[206] with skin grafts in the rabbit. A preliminary immunizing homograft inhibited growth completely in a second graft from the same donor rabbit, but only partially in a second graft from any other donor rabbit.

Burmester and Prickett[42] have reported complete persistence for as long as 202 days of the immunity in fowl to the Olson fowl tumor produced by regression of this tumor.

There have been many attempts, most of them unsuccessful, to produce immunity to tumor homoiotransplants by injections of nonliving tissue. These have been reviewed by Snell *et al.*[257] Several cases of successful immunization without living cells will be described in the next two sections.

Induced Immunity to Tumor Isotransplants

In the past sixteen years there have been reported several cases in which mice of a given inbred strain have been immunized against a tumor which originated in that strain. Whatever may be the explanation of these cases, they are of unusual interest. It will be desirable, however, to precede our discussion with a word of caution.

As has already been pointed out in this chapter, inbred strains of mice are continually undergoing variation as a result of mutation. The variations are usually slight, and may be undetectable by ordinary means, but it may well be that an appreciable proportion of them can be detected by the methods of normal tissue and tumor immunity. If this be so, any two mice of the same inbred strain cannot necessarily be regarded as identical with respect to a tumor transplant. The larger the colony and the longer the interval between the origin of a tumor and its use in an immunization experiment, the greater are the chances of genetic difference between tumor and host. Not only do inbred strains change, but transplantable tumors also change. The process of mutation in tumors has already been discussed. Whether these changes are of such a nature as to permit the induction of resistance in an animal truly isogenic with the original donor is unknown, but it certainly cannot be ruled out as a possibility. Even when every precaution is taken, therefore, there exists in the case of isotransplants a possibility for genetic difference between tumor and host that is not found in autotransplants.

The first case of induced immunity to a tumor isotransplant was reported by MacDowell, Taylor and Potter.[196] These investigators used Line I leukemia, which originated in a C58 mouse and had been carried for 441 transplant generations before use in the experiment in question. This tumor when given intra-abdominally in "standard dose" (in the order of 80 million cells) killed all C58 hosts, but it was found that C58 mice regularly survived 1/524,000th of the standard dose. Moreover, by giving these survivors increasing doses an immunity was built up to the point where they were not killed by the standard dose. Later experiments [191, 192, 197] showed that complete immunity to Line I leukemia in C58 hosts could be induced by a single injection of embryo tissue from the unrelated Sto-li strain, but not with isogenic C58 embryo tissue, and that partial immunity could be induced by one to three injections of Line I tissue microsomes separated by high-speed centrifugation. There was a considerable degree of cross immunity between Line I leukemia and three other "old" leukemias, two of C58 origin and one of foreign strain origin, but immunization with Line I did not protect C58 mice against "new" C58 leukemias. MacDowell, in explanation of these results, stresses the immunologic changes that may occur in a tumor during a long series of transplants.

Marshak and Erf[201] succeeded in immunizing a small percentage (2.4–9.3) of Strong A strain mice against isotransplants of a lymphoma by a series of prior subcutaneous injections of fragmented lymphoma cells, isolated lymphoma nuclei, and isolated Strong A liver nuclei. The lymphoma employed had been carried through forty successive transfers and had grown progressively in 100 per cent of 2500 untreated A hosts.

Gross,[119, 120] using C3H mice and an induced C3H sarcoma (Sa 1) that had been carried through about twenty-four transfers made at seven- to ten-day intervals, succeeded in producing immunity by the use of small, intracutaneous inoculations. Of the mice that survived the first inoculation, 95 per cent resisted a second intracutaneous inoculation, and some of these in turn resisted subcutaneous inoculations.

Goldfeder[101, 102] immunized rats against isotransplants of a lymphosarcoma by prior transplants of irradiated tissue from the same lymphosarcoma. There was one regression in control animals. The lymphosarcoma was in the seventy-fifth transplant generation at the start of the experiment. Attempts at immunization with embryo skin were unsuccessful.

Aptekman and co-workers[11, 12, 169, 170] have carried out important studies in immunity to isotransplants in rats. An alcohol extract was prepared from spontaneous and transplanted sarcomas from several strains of rats. The extract contained nitrogen and some phosphorus. Nucleic acid and protein were probably present. This was then injected into tumor transplants growing in King A strain hosts. Sarcoma 231 (King A strain origin) was used in one series of experiments; in other cases it is merely stated that tumors native to the A strain and which grew progressively in all animals of this strain were employed. Following a series of two to ten injections, regressions were obtained in 96 per cent or more of the treated rats. Most of the cured rats resisted a second subcutaneous transplant of the same tumor. Offspring of the recovered rats were 100 per cent susceptible. Further experiments showed that immunity could be produced by injections of the alcoholic extract given prior to tumor inoculation. Fifty per cent of 94 rats given ten successive injections at two- to three-day intervals were tumor-immune. In three lines produced by continued inbreeding of survivors of this first test, the per cent of rats that could be protected by immunization rose to 87 per cent.

It may be noted that this effectiveness of selection, if real, indicates lack of homozygosity.

ENHANCING OR "XYZ" EFFECT

As was first shown by Flexner and Jobling,[91] injections of nonliving tumor tissue sometimes produce, not inhibition, but enhancement of growth in a subsequently inoculated tumor. This has been called the "enhancing" or "XYZ" effect. The literature in this field has been reviewed by Casey[44] and Snell[257] and we shall confine this summary to four series of investigations.

Casey and co-workers,[43, 44, 46, 49] and Drysdale and Casey[74] have prepared an enhancing or XYZ substance by storing tumor tissue or saline extract of tumor in the cold (−18° to 0° C.) for two to three weeks or more. Such tissue, after adequate storage, failed to give rise to tumors on inoculation. Casey tested the enhancing effect of such preparations on the Brown-Pearce tumor in rabbits and on several tumors in mice. The usual procedure was to give one injection of the killed tumor preparation and to inoculate the living tumor eight or more days later. In 58 treated rabbits, injected and inoculated subcutaneously, the incidence of tumors proven by autopsy was 76 per cent as compared with 31 per cent in untreated controls. The number of metastases was increased by the treatment and the volume of primary and metastatic tumors more than doubled. The XYZ substance could be injected 2 weeks after or as early as 7 months before tumor inoculation. It could be passed through a Berkfeld "V" filter, it withstood drying, and it was partially inactivated when heated to 52° C. and completely inactivated when heated to 56° C. for one hour. Growth of the Brown-Pearce tumor was not enhanced by preparations of a transplantable adenocarcinoma of the rabbit or of certain mouse tumors. Neither was it enhanced by extracts of rabbit testicle or by rabbit spleen that had been stored at −18° C.

In experiments with mice (strain not stated), one subcutaneous injection of enhancing substance prepared from the Bashford mouse carcinoma was followed twelve to eighteen days later by inoculation with living Bashford tumor. Of the treated mice, 67 per cent developed tumors with a mean volume of 3.2 cc., as compared with 57 per cent with a mean volume of 1.5 cc. in the controls. Sarcoma 180 likewise responded to its own enhancing substance. On the other hand, growth of the Bashford tumor was not influenced by a prior injection of the Brown-Pearce enhancing substance, and three different mouse tumors were not influenced by injection of enhancing substance from another mouse tumor.

In another series of experiments,[49] using inbred mice and several different mouse tumors, further evidence of the specificity of the effect was obtained.

Results seemingly in conflict with those of Casey have been reported by Kidd,[156] though the different outcome may have been due to the use of a different strain of rabbits. Kidd used "blue-cross" rabbits, and Casey used several strains other than the "blue-cross," including "New Zealand whites," "gray-browns," and "Chinchillas." In Kidd's experiments, 53 rabbits were given several injections of an extract of previously frozen Brown-Pearce tumor and inoculated with the living tumor at two or more sites seven to eight days after the last injection. Of these 53 animals, 17 were completely negative eleven to fourteen days after inoculation at one or more of the inoculation sites and a number of others had small tumors only, whereas all of 10 controls were positive with large tumors. The injections thus caused inhibition. This experiment is discussed further in the next section.

Snell and co-workers[146, 147, 149, 257, 258] have produced an enhancing effect on the growth of homoiotransplants in inbred mice by prior injections of lyophilized tissues. Two or more injections were given intra-abdominally, and the mice were inoculated with living tissue usually seven to fourteen days after the last injection. In a typical series of experiments using C57BR/cd mice and A strain tumor 15091a, 28 of 40 treated mice died with large tumors, while all of 28 controls survived. The results were found to be dependent in high degree on the particular tumor and host strain employed. Thus the growth of C57BL tumor C1498 tested in C57L mice was inhibited rather than enhanced by the injections, and C57BL tumor L946 showed little or no enhancing effect in B alb C mice but grew progressively and killed 100 per cent of treated C57BR/a mice. There were cross reactions between some tumors but not between others. The enhancing substance in fresh 15091a was not filterable through cellulose membranes. This result differs from the findings obtained by Casey with filtration of the XYZ substance, but this may be due to variations in method. Also, again in contrast to Casey's results, a pronounced enhancing effect was produced on the growth of 15091a in C57BL mice by lyophilized A strain liver, kidney, and spleen, and on the growth of E0771 in B alb C mice by lyophilized C57BL liver and kidney. Curiously enough, A red cells did not enhance the growth of 15091a nor did C57BL spleen enhance the growth of E0771. There was evidence that E0771 tested in B alb C mice responded to small prior injections (0.05–0.5 mg.) of lyophilized E0771 by inhibition whereas large doses (50 mg.) produced enhancement.

Lewis and Lichtenstein,[171, 172,] and Lewis[165] have shown that if repeated homoiotransplants are made into a single mouse, the mouse's resistance is finally broken down. Mice receiving seven to nineteen inoculations at about five-day intervals eventually grew tumors to which they were normally resistant. This phenomenon is possibly related to the enhancing effect.

A MATERNAL EFFECT ON SUSCEPTIBILITY TO HOMOIOTRANSPLANTS

There have been several reports indicating that mice reared by a mother or foster mother susceptible to transplants of a particular tumor can give rise to a strain with increased susceptibility to that tumor. There seems to be some question as to the consistency of this effect, which in any case is often slight rather than pronounced, but it is significant that it has been noted by three investigators in separate experiments.

Cloudman[59] used a line of DBA mice derived from ova grown in C57BL's, and a line of C57BL's derived from ova grown in DBA's. C57BL tumor L946 grew progressively in 51 per cent of the ova-transplant line of DBA's, in 25 per cent of the ordinary line. Conversely, DBA melanoma S91 grew in 37 per cent of the ova-transplant line of C57BL's in 12 per cent of the ordinary line.

Law[163, 164] obtained similar results with foster-nursing. Three leukemias grew better in foreign strain mice fostered on mothers of the susceptible or native strain than they did in nonfostered mice. The increased susceptibility was passed on to subsequent generations. Law showed, moreover, that the influence could be transmitted to resistant strain mice by feeding or injecting tissue of the susceptible strain, that the active factor could be dialyzed through parchment paper and was not entirely lost in Seitz filtration, that it remained stable for thirty days, in 50 per cent glycerol at $-4°$ C. that it was not entirely inactivated by heating at 85° C. for twenty minutes, and that partially digested milk from the stomach of nursing mice could transmit it. Two leukemias and several tumors other than leukemias did not respond to the influence. One of the tumors which failed to respond was S91, which Cloudman had found to grow better in his ova-transplant line of C57BL mice.

Barrett and Morgan[19] measured the rate of growth of a C3H mammary carcinoma transplanted in F_1 mice from reciprocal crosses between Strain C3H and Strain B alb C. The outcome of the inoculations was positive in every case, as expected, but the rate of growth was faster where the mother was a C3H and the father a B alb C than it was in the reciprocal combination.

REACTIONS OF THE HOST TO TUMOR TRANSPLANTS

Early transplantation studies were much concerned with changes in the organs of the host and with local reactions at the site of the implant in animals bearing foreign normal or tumor tissues. Attempts were made to relate these observations to the degree of natural or acquired resistance of the host. Loeb[180] has reviewed extensive experiments with normal tissues. Murphy,[218] in a series of investigations, found evidence implicating the lymphocyte as a factor in resistance to transplants. A review of the whole field up to 1929 has been published by Woglom.[275]

There are several pitfalls in interpreting this material. Since transplantable tumors may carry nonapparent infections, changes in the host may be due to an introduced infection rather than to the tumor. The fact that an animal carries a progressively growing tumor has frequently been taken as evidence that it lacks resistance. Actually, with homoiotransplants (and all work done with noninbred strains falls in this category) resistance is probably never lacking, though it may be insufficient to prevent progressive tumor growth. Some authorities have interpreted certain changes in organs, or local reactions around a regressing graft, as causes of the regression. Actually, unless they can be proved beyond question to have preceded the regressive changes, they may be an effect rather than a cause.

Perhaps partly because of these difficulties, results in this field have often been conflicting. We shall briefly review some of the more recent articles. For further details the reader is referred to the references given above.

Coman and Sheldon[62] have investigated the hyperemia which develops around tumor implants, sometimes as early as eighteen hours after implantation. Subcutaneous grafts of tumor, normal adult tissue, and normal embryonic tissue were made, isoplastically, homoplastically, or heteroplastically, onto the flank of mice. The mice were killed at appropriate intervals, the skin cut and pulled back to expose the graft, and the condition of the blood vessels observed. Hyperemia was found to be correlated with active growth. The authors conclude that the hyperemia around transplanted mouse tumors is due to the presence of proliferating cells.

Algire and co-workers[2, 3] studied the vascularization of transplants in especially designed transparent chambers in the skin of mice. They found, among other things, that rapidly growing tumors elicited capillary sprouts from the host in two to three days, whereas such sprouts usually did not appear with slow-growing tumors till after eight or more days.

Loeb[180] and Murphy[218] have stressed the accumulation of lymphocytes around grafts where the host is resistant. Kidd[157] has confirmed this phenomenon using inbred strains. In five- to seven-day homoiotransplants destined eventually to regress, but not in isotransplants, lymphocytes accumulated regularly and in force about the nodules of proliferating cancer cells. They migrated into the graft, and death of the cancer cells was observed where, but only where, they had penetrated. Darcy[66], using special stains, identified plasma cells in normal tissue homografts. They were few in number at four days, but numerous at eight days when breakdown of the graft was about to start. On the other hand, Potter and Findley[229] found that degeneration of a leukemia in mice with natural or induced immunity began before the invasion of normal host lymphocytes.

Symeonidis[265] has made a detailed histologic study of the reaction at the site of grafts in previously immunized hosts. While the grafts in immune hosts showed active growth and cell division for several days, differences were apparent from the reaction in normal hosts as early as eight hours after transplantation. At this time there was already an accumulation of monocytes and lymphocytes around the graft in the immune animals, and these cells became increasingly numerous. Controls showed numerous leukocytes at twenty-four hours, but no unusual accumulation of other cells. A fibrous capsule formed about the implant in immune hosts which the tumor cells did not succeed in penetrating. There was a complete failure to form a fibrovascular stroma.

A number of workers have reported an increased white cell count in the blood of tumor-bearing animals.[30, 78, 165] Murphy[218] found, following inoculation, a prompt and marked increase in lymphocytes in mice with tumors destined to regress and an even greater one in mice previously immunized, but none in mice with progressively growing tumors. Dunning and Reich[78] found a decrease in lymphocytes in the blood of rats with progressively growing tumors, even when of foreign origin, but an increase in polymorphonuclear leukocytes. Backofen,[14] using mice bearing the Ehrlich adenocarcinoma, found no change in the total white blood cell count, but like Dunning and Reich, noted a fall in lymphocytes and rise in polymorphonuclear leukocytes. The monocytes were high at ten days but later returned to normal.

In rabbits, a relationship has been shown between the pretransplantation level of hemoglobin, total white cell count, and eosinophil level, and the susceptibility to the Brown-Pearce tumor.[45, 47, 48] A group of apparently healthy animals of mixed breeds was selected and a series of determinations made of the level of blood platelets, of the eosinophil count, and of other blood characteristics. The animals were then given intratesticular tumor inoculations. It was found that rabbits with the optimal or modal values for hemoglobin, red cell count, and total white cell count were most resistant. Rabbits with high or low values tended to be susceptible. The correlation with modal red cell count was probably secondary to the correlation with hemoglobin level. Eosinophil level was also significant, high pretransplantation levels being associated with a lower incidence of metastases and a lower mortality. However, the effect of the eosinophil level did not appear till the seventh week after inoculation; during the first six weeks transplants in animals with high and low levels ran the same course. It is noteworthy that it is during the seventh week that signs of regression of the Brown-Pearce tumor first appear. No consistent relationship with other blood characteristics was found. It is not clear whether the observed differences in hemoglobin level and white cell count in the rabbits were hereditary or the result of unknown factors in the animals' earlier histories, but Casey and Drysdale regard the eosinophil level as hereditary.

Homburger,[137] and Savard and Homburger[244] found hyperplasia of the lymph nodes and atrophy of the thymus in CFW mice bearing sarcoma 180. Lymphoid hyperplasia was also observed with mammary adenocarcinoma E0771. Hypophysectomy did not prevent the changes. On the other hand, Murphy and Sturm[221] found a decrease in size of lymph nodes and spleen, as well as thymus, in rats with progressively growing subcutaneous transplants of a lymphosarcoma, though the weight of all these organs was increased in rats with regressing tumors. Homburger's data show a greater lymphoid hyperplasia at six days than at twelve days, suggesting a downward trend in the later stages of tumor growth. Murphy and Sturm killed many of their rats later than twelve days after inoculation. Moreover, as they point out, the fact that they used a lymphosarcoma may have caused an uneven competition between malignant and normal lymphoid cells for some essential nutritional factor.

Changes in the lymph nodes and spleen suggesting enhanced activity in mice with regressing tumors as contrasted with the condition in mice with progressively growing tumors were described by Murphy.[218]

Adrenal weight is increased in animals with transplanted tumors,[16, 221, 243] but this increase is prevented by hypophysectomy.[16] Pituitary weight, conversely, is decreased.[270]

Sibley and Lehninger[253] found that in tumor-bearing rats the level of serum aldolase may increase to as high as seven times the normal value and Euler and Pettersson[89] under similar conditions noted a rise of several hundred per cent in pyruvic acid.

CELLS AND TISSUES IN RELATION TO IMMUNITY

It is apparent from several of the studies reviewed in the preceding section that the growth or regression of transplants may be accompanied by cellular or tissue responses. There is a variety of additional evidence tending to show that certain cells and organs play a part in the phenomena of tumor immunity.

Woglom,[276] in confirmation of the work of earlier investigators, found that when the spleen of immunized rats was ground to a paste and mixed before inoculation with tumor tissue similarly prepared, it would retard or inhibit the growth of the tumor. Liver, testis, or kidney from immunized rats had little or no effect, nor did the spleen of nonimmunized rats. Three nonspecific tumors were used in this study, the Jensen sarcoma, Crocker Institute sarcoma 39, and the Flexner-Jobling carcinoma.

Kidd[157] has observed a similar inhibiting effect of minced immune lymph nodes on homoiotransplants in mice.

Potter *et al.*[231] and MacDowell[189] reported transfer of induced resistance to Line I leukemia by injecting minced spleen or liver from immunized mice. Animals of Strain C58 were immunized by giving increasing doses of leukemic cells (see p. 358.) Spleens and livers were then removed, minced, and injected into susceptible C58 mice. Three days later the mice were given a normally lethal dose of leukemic cells. One hundred per cent protection was obtained. Spleens so treated as to break up the cells were not effective, and spleens from mice immunized with normal tissue conferred no protection. It seems possible in this case that the protection of the hosts was due to the introduction of a few still living leukemic cells with the immune spleen or liver. No further reports on this phenomenon has appeared.

Murphy and Sturm[219] studied the growth of a mouse sarcoma implanted in the brains of mice and rats simultaneously with a fragment of spleen. It was found that autografts of spleen inhibited the growth of the tumor, though homografts of spleen were without effect. Testis grafts made autoplastically were also ineffective. In another series of experiments Murphy found a similar effect of spleen on tumors growing in the chick egg, but this effect has been disputed by other workers. These studies have been reviewed by Woglom.[275]

Centanni[51] investigated the growth *in vitro* of a mouse adenocarcinoma cultured on the same slide with fragments of muscle and viscera from normal and immune mice. Whereas the tumor cells grew out and infiltrated the tissues from normal mice, their growth was inhibited adjacent to the tissues from immune mice. Extracts of immune tissues also inhibited tumor growth. This very interesting finding has not been reported on further.

A number of experiments have established the fact that trypan blue and other substances that are taken up by the reticuloendothelial system lower the resistance of animals to tumor homoiotransplants. Thus Andervont[5] obtained progressive growth of A and C3H strain tumors in the majority of a group of DBA mice which received injections of trypan blue beginning six days prior to inoculation and continuing for several weeks after inoculation. The same tumors gave no growth in DBA control mice, but did grow occasionally when transferred from an injected to an uninjected DBA. Two spontaneous mammary gland tumors and one induced spindle-cell sarcoma were used. Meyer[209, 211] found a similar reduction in resistance to homoiotransplants in mice injected with trypan blue, lithium-carmine, pyrrol blue, or India ink.

Induced immunity, like natural immunity, can be abrogated by injections of substances which block the reticuloendothelial system.[4, 9, 182, 241]

Heiman[131, 132] found that antireticular cytotoxic serum was without effect on the growth of mouse sarcoma 180 or on that of several rat tumors.

ANTIGENIC BASIS OF RESISTANCE TO TRANSPLANTS

There is now a variety of evidence that the growth of transplanted tumors in resistant hosts is accompanied by the formation of antibodies. Some of the early work, mostly inconclusive, was reviewed by Woglom.[275] More recent but incomplete reviews will be found in Spencer[260] and in Stern and Willheim.[261]

Gorer[103, 104, 105, 107, 108] has shown that in certain tumor-host combinations in mice, the growth of tumor homoiotransplants results in the formation of iso-antibodies.* The formation of these antibodies, moreover, has been traced to specific gene differences between donor and host.

A number of inbred strains of mice were used in these studies, but two were particularly important, the A and the C57BL. Several tumors were employed, including one leukemia, all of A strain origin. It was found (Gorer[104]) that when C57BL mice were inoculated with one of the A strain tumors, they developed agglutinins for A strain erythrocytes (Fig. 52). The agglutinins could be absorbed

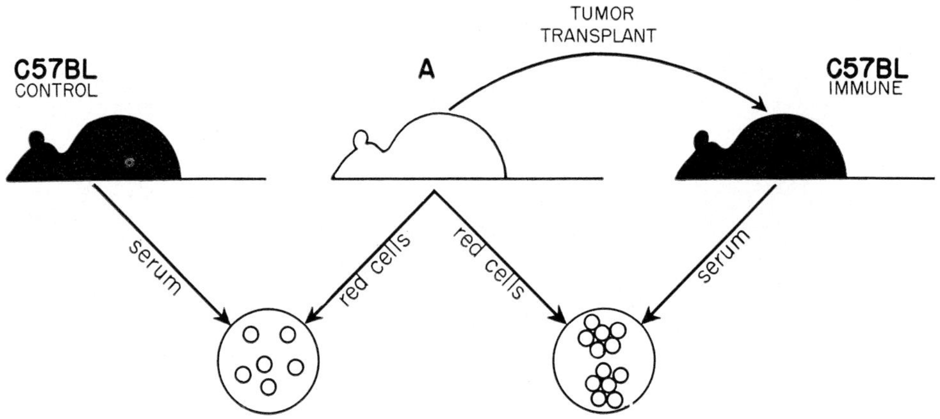

FIG. 52. Diagram illustrating the formation in C57BL mice of agglutinins against A red cells as a result of inoculation with an A strain tumor. (Gorer, 1937.)

by the A strain tumors; hence, it was concluded that A tumors and A erythrocytes shared a common antigen. This antigen was called Antigen II. The antigen could also be demonstrated with antisera produced in rabbits by the injection of A red cells. Such antisera, when absorbed with C57BL red cells, would specifically agglutinate A red cells. The identity of the antigen reacting with the antisera produced by these two methods was proved by testing the antisera against the erythrocytes of F_2 mice from the cross A × C57BL. In every case, if the erythrocytes of an F_2 mouse were agglutinated by the mouse antiserum, they could also absorb the antibodies from the rabbit antiserum. Those that were not agglutinated failed to absorb the antibodies.

To analyze the manner of inheritance of Antigen II and its relation to tumor susceptibility, a cross was made between the A and C57BL strains, and F_2 and

* The use of the term iso-antibodies to describe the antibodies formed in homoplastic transplantation provides a possibility of confusion. Presumably iso-antibodies are not formed in isoplastic transplantation, at least when host and donor are truly isogenic. If any antibodies are formed in this type of transplantation, they are identical with autoantibodies. The reader should be warned against this confusion, but all of the terms, except "isoplastic," which we have introduced, are too well established to allow any change.

backcross generations raised. These were tested for the presence of antigen II in their erythrocytes and then inoculated with an A strain tumor. The results are shown in Table 23. It will be seen that there is very close agreement with the results expected on the assumption that two histocompatibility genes were segregating, of which one determined Antigen II. Mice lacking Antigen II were always resistant; some of the mice with Antigen II were also resistant due to the lack of a second independently segregating factor. The gene determining Antigen II has been called *H-2*. Subsequent studies[109] showed it to be closely linked with the gene *Fu* (see pp. 351-352.) Gorer[108] has concluded from immunologic evidence that there may be a number of different alleles at the *H-2* locus, a conclusion confirmed by subsequent genetic studies.

TABLE 23. RESULTS OF RED CELL AGGLUTINATION TESTS AND TUMOR INOCULATIONS PERFORMED ON F_2 AND BACKCROSS MICE FROM THE CROSS A×C57BL.

	Number of mice			
	II +	*II* −	*Not II* +	*Not II* −
F_2 observed	35	13	0	17
F_2 expected, 2 factors	36.6	12.2	0	16.2
C57BC observed	17	17	0	44
C57BC expected, 2 factors	19.5	19.5	0	39

The tumor used was an A strain mammary carcinoma. Susceptible animals are indicated by +, resistant animals by −. The results are compared with those expected if susceptibility were due to two histocompatibility genes, of which one determines Antigen II.

From Gorer.[104]

The nature of the antibodies formed in C57BL mice inoculated with A strain tumors was further investigated. The possibility that agglutinin formation in resistant hosts was due to A red cells carried over in the transplant was tested and probably eliminated. However, injection of adequate doses of A red cells into C57BL mice did lead to the formation of agglutinins. Three types of iso-antibodies were found in immunized mice. These were: (1) ordinary iso-agglutinins; (2) antibodies requiring high concentrations of normal mouse serum to cause agglutination; and (3) blocking antibodies. Antibodies of Type 2 were sometimes found in the sera of normal C57BL animals. The proportions of the different types in immunized animals varied according to the conditions of immunization.

Caspari and Dalton[50] have detected an antigen or antigens associated with the *T* and *Ki* loci in mice that may bear some relation to the *H-2* series of alleles. *T* and *Ki* are closely linked with *Fu*.[76] Extracts of spleen and testis from *T*/+mice were injected into rabbits and the resulting antisera tested for precipitins and complement fixing antibodies against *T*/+, *Ki*/+ and +/+ extracts. The antisera were absorbed for the former test but not for the latter. Two tissue fractions were used, one containing the soluble proteins, the other probably including small particles. The antisera differentiated between *T*/+, *Ki*/+ and +/+ extracts when the particulate fraction was used but not with the soluble fraction. Whether the antigens revealed by these tests are the products of the *T* and *Ki* genes or of *H-2* alleles can only be determined by further tests, but in view of the close linkage of these loci, and of the proven role of *H-2* alleles in determining the antigenic structure of tissues, the second alternative seems not unlikely.

Lumsden,[185] using rats, confirmed Gorer's observation that immunization with a tumor (Jensen's rat sarcoma) will lead to the formation of red cell agglutinins. However, Lumsden's results were much less consistent than those of Gorer. The rats used were not inbred.

Kidd and co-workers[93, 151, 152, 153, 155, 198] have demonstrated the presence in several transplantable rabbit tumors of substances that fix complement when mixed with the sera of rabbits in which these tumors are growing or have regressed. Antisera were heated at 56° C. for thirty minutes, in later experiments at 65° C. for thirty minutes, before use. The latter temperature was found to inactivate the "natural tissue antibody."[158]

An active substance in the Brown-Pearce tumor was present in a protein fraction separable by high speed centrifugation. Experiments carried out with Claude showed it to be probably identical with the microsome fraction of this tumor. Complement fixing activity was absent from the supernatant fluid. The active substance was inactivated by alcohol, by acid (*p*H lower than 4.5), by alkali (*p*H higher than 11.5), by trypsin and chymotrypsin, and by heating at 65° C. for thirty minutes. It passed readily through collodion membranes with average pore diameters of 383 mμ, but was retained completely by those with average pore diameters of 348 mμ. As a routine procedure it was frequently stored at $-20°$ to $-25°$ C., or in glycerol.

This Brown-Pearce antigen reacted with sera of many, but not all, rabbits bearing the Brown-Pearce tumor or in which this tumor had recently regressed. It sometimes reacted with sera from rabbits which had borne the V2 carcinoma, but not with sera from control rabbits, or rabbits with virus-induced papillomas or several known types of infections.

Antisera produced by growth or regression of the Brown-Pearce tumor sometimes, though not always, reacted with extracts of various normal tissues, as well as with Brown-Pearce tumor extract. By absorption of antisera with normal and with Brown-Pearce tissue extracts it was shown that either or both of two different antibodies could be present. These were: (1) an *induced tissue antibody* that reacted with both normal and Brown-Pearce extracts; and (2) a specific *Brown-Pearce antibody* that reacted with Brown-Pearce extracts only. Kidd believes that the genetic constitution of the host was a factor in determining which antibodies were formed. Many blue-cross rabbits and all of a small group of chocolate-Dutch hybrid rabbits produced only the Brown-Pearce antibody. Other breeds of rabbits, if they produced any antibody, regularly produced both types.

In further tests it was shown that the Brown-Pearce antibody could be induced in many blue-cross rabbits by the intra-abdominal injection of cell-free extracts of the tumor. Occasionally the induced tissue antibody was present also. More than 50 rabbits of several other breeds were tested but failed to yield antibodies following injection of the extract. It was found, moreover,[156] that the presence of induced antibody and resistance to the tumor were correlated. Forty-two blue-cross rabbits were given three or four injections of extract. Seven to eight days after the last injection they were bled, the antiserum titered, and the rabbits inoculated with the Brown-Pearce tumor. Of 12 rabbits with a titer of 1:16 to 1:64, none grew the tumor, whereas all of 30 rabbits with a titer of 0 to 1:2 did grow the tumor. However, there was not a complete correlation between formation of the Brown-Pearce antibody and growth of the tumor, since other experiments with rabbits inoculated with the tumor but otherwise untreated showed that many animals without detectable antibodies in their sera at several successive bleedings nevertheless showed regression of the tumor.

Kidd believes that the Brown-Pearce antigen is specifically characteristic of the tumor and is not to be found in any normal rabbits. As evidence he states that antisera containing the Brown-Pearce antibody only have failed to fix complement in combination with extracts of various normal tissues of many different rabbits, including rabbits susceptible to the tumor, or to lyse or agglutinate red cells of such rabbits. It is difficult to rule out by such tests the possibility that it represents a rare but entirely normal antigen, or an antigen specific to certain normal tissues not included in Kidd's tests. The evidence would be clearer with a tumor which had arisen in an inbred strain of known genetic constitution. Should further studies substantiate the conclusion that the microsome fractions of tumors possess tumor-specific antigens, the fact would be of the utmost importance to an understanding of tumor etiology.

Friedewald and Kidd[93] also ran tests with the V2 carcinoma, with sarcoma RSI, and with the Kato sarcoma. Sera from rabbits (several breeds) with these tumors usually reacted with extracts of the corresponding tumor. With most sera, however, there were cross reactions, sometimes with extracts of other tumors, sometimes with kidney, liver, or spleen extracts. Several, but not all, V2 carcinoma antisera showed cross reactions with spleen and with Brown-Pearce tumor extracts. Four antisera were V2-specific, reacting with V2 extracts only.[155] With two exceptions, the sera reacted only with the sediments and not with the supernatants produced by a run of one hour at 25,000 R.P.M. on the high-speed centrifuge. The exceptions were a weak reaction of one of three V2 antisera with V2 carcinoma supernatant, and reactions of two Kato antisera with supernatants from several normal and neoplastic tissues. Several of the antisera reacted with a sedimentable fraction present in chick embryos.

In repetitions of Kidd's work, Cheever[55] obtained complement fixation with antisera of only 5 out of 35 rabbits inoculated with the Brown-Pearce tumor when tested against Brown-Pearce extracts, and Jacobs and Houghton[142] with only 3 out of 25. However, neither investigator used the blue-cross breed which Kidd found to be the best source of good antisera. Lippincott *et al.*,[174] Ellerbrook *et al.*,[87] and Thornton *et al.*,[267, 268] using a variation of Kidd's complement fixation technic, reported confirmation of his results. Maltaner[200] has called attention to the difficulty caused in tests such as those of Kidd by the anticomplementary action of tissue extracts. This is probably of more significance in connection with Kidd's "natural tissue antibody" than with the antibodies induced by tumor growth.

Bogdanovic[32] found some evidence that complement-fixing antibodies were formed in the sera of mice inoculated with the Ehrlich carcinoma. However, the results were complicated by the fact that the sera of normal mice of certain ages reacted with extracts of the tumor. Thus in tests with noninoculated mice, sera of 7 animals 3–5 weeks of age were all negative, sera of 13 out of 14 animals 4–6 months of age were all positive, and sera of mice 1 year of age were either negative or weakly positive.

Hoyle[139] demonstrated complement fixation between a lipoidal antigen obtained from sarcoma 37, and sera of mice bearing this tumor. Of the sera prepared individually from 216 tumor-bearing mice, 33 per cent gave positive reactions, the rest were either doubtful or negative. The antigen was extractable in absolute alcohol and in chloroform but not in ether. The antigen was not present in muscle, heart, kidney, or liver, or in 3 spontaneous breast tumors, but the same or a closely similar antigen was present in 2 out of 6 other transplantable tumors that were tested. The sera of all normal mice were negative. However, the sera of some mice bearing the 4 tumors without demonstrable antigen did react with sarcoma 37 antigen.

Dmochowski[72] was able to produce antisera in rats which would fix complement in combination with heated extracts of two transplantable rat tumors.

Several investigators have used parabiosis between pairs of mice or rats to study tumor immunity. Furth *et al.*[94] found that parabiosis between mice naturally immune and naturally susceptible to a transmissible leukemia did not protect the susceptible partner. Leukemic cells and other test substances passed freely between the parabionts, and death of the susceptible partner followed inoculation of either parabiotic twin. Cloudman,[60] in similar experiments using a reticuloendothelioma, found that parabiosis reduced the resistance of the naturally immune member of each pair. Harris[129] studied the effect of parabiosis on homoiotransplants where both members of the pair were from the same strain of mice. One parabiont was inoculated with a tumor that grew and then regressed; subsequently the other parabiont was inoculated with the same tumor. With rare exceptions the second transplant did not grow, showing that immunity had been transferred through the parabiotic union. Bichel and Holm-Jensen[23] used as the basis of their experiments the fact that rats can be rendered partially susceptible to heterotransplants of mouse tumors by exposure to x-rays. They found that parabiosis of an irradiated with a nonirradiated rat reduced this susceptibility. They conclude that some humoral influence which can be transferred between parabiotic partners is responsible for the resistance.

Marx[202] and Russ and Scott[238] have reported an increased resistance to transplants in the offspring of immunized rats. Marx used only a small number of animals so that his results are of doubtful value. Russ and Scott used adequate numbers but their animals were not inbred. This introduced the possibility that the increased resistance of the offspring was due to selection of the naturally more resistant rats as parents. Two of their experiments were designed to avoid this; nevertheless the enhanced resistance produced by the immunization of parents was passed beyond the first generation, thus suggesting some sort of selective action. In any case, passage of immune bodies through the placenta was not proved.

Woglom[276] found evidence that an inhibiting substance accumulated in minced tissue of rat sarcoma 39 during a sojourn of several days in immunized rats. Such tissue, when removed from the hosts and killed by repeated freezings and thawings, retarded the growth of fresh implants of sarcoma 39 with which it was mixed. The experiment was adequately controlled but the effect, though consistent, was slight.

Oster and Salter[222] found a drop of about one-third in urea nitrogen in mice immunized to sarcoma 180 and then given a dose of x-rays. There was no such response in irradiated, nonimmunized mice. The authors offer no explanation of the phenomenon.

Wharton[274] found that mice bearing transplantable tumors produced much lower titers of antibodies against several different antigens than did normal mice.

There have been numerous experiments in which antisera against transplantable tumors of the mouse or rat have been produced in rabbits or other alien species. Since the objective of these experiments usually has been tumor therapy or tumor diagnosis they are not reviewed here. Five references to investigations using this approach which have yielded interesting information about the antigenic characteristics of transplantable tumors are: D'Alessandro and Greco,[65] Green,[110] Maculla,[199] Dulaney *et al.*,[75] Werder *et al.*,[273] and Maver and Barrett.[203]

DEMONSTRATION OF CYTOTOXINS IN HOMOLOGOUS ANTISERA

There have been many experiments to determine whether or not serum from animals immunized against a transplantable tumor can inhibit the growth of the tumor either *in vivo* or *in vitro*. The possibility of such inhibition under appropriate experimental conditions can now be regarded as established.

Gorer[106] immunized C57BL mice by one or more inoculations of an A strain leukemia. Such immunization results in the formation of hemagglutinins (see preceding section). When a dilute suspension of leukemic cells was mixed with sera from such immune mice and injected immediately into susceptible strain A mice, growth of the leukemia was retarded or completely inhibited. Normal C57BL sera had no such effect. Absorption of the hemagglutinins with A red cells removed only a part of the protective antibody, but this antibody could be completely removed by absorption with leukemic cells.

Kidd[156] incubated Brown-Pearce tumor cells for two or three hours with rabbit sera containing the Brown-Pearce antibody (see preceding section) and inoculated the mixture into rabbits. Growth of the tumor was inhibited. Inhibition occurred also with sera heated to destroy complement. Incubation with normal serum, or with antisera against the V2 carcinoma or sarcoma I, had no effect on the subsequent growth of the tumor. Kalfayan and Kidd[145] described structural changes which appear in Brown-Pearce carcinoma cells incubated in the specific antiserum plus complement. Alterations were evident in the cytoplasm and viability was found to be lost after only five minutes exposure.

Burmester[41] studied the cytotoxic action of antisera produced by hyperimmunizing inbred chickens against an avian lymphoid tumor. The tumor employed normally gave rise to palpable masses in seven to fourteen days when whole cells were injected, but produced no tumors in less than ninety to one hundred and eighty days when filtrates were used. Incubation of the cells with antiserum for twenty-four hours at 20° to 37° C. reduced the tumor incidence at three weeks to 15.7 per cent as compared with 93.5 per cent in the controls. The cytotoxic action of the antiserum was not destroyed by heating to 66° C. for thirty minutes. Some effect on tumor growth could be produced by injecting the antiserum into birds inoculated with untreated tumor tissue. Cytotoxic antisera could be produced by the injection of killed tumor tissue but not normal lymphoid tissue.

Lewis *et al.*[169] were unable to demonstrate a protective action of sera or tissues from rats immunized against a tumor when mixed with the tumor prior to inoculation. Lewis and co-workers used tumors transplanted isoplastically, which may have some bearing on the negative outcome of their experiments. In the other three cases cited the tumor and the animals used to produce antiserum were from different strains or of different genotypes, and the presumption is that the reactions were strain specific in nature rather than tumor specific.

The independent demonstration by Gorer, Kidd, and Burmester of the presence of cytotoxins in the sera of tumor-immune animals establishes a presumption that antitumor cytotoxins should be demonstrable in tissue culture. Actually, while this has been attempted many times, the results have been very conflicting, particularly as regards to the specificity of the cytotoxins for tumors. Part of this conflict may be due to the use of non-inbred strains, part to differences or errors in technic. In any case, since the various claims have not been confirmed in independent investigations we shall give only a brief review of the subject.

Reports concerning cytotoxins capable of damaging tumor cells *in vitro* have been made by Lumsden and co-workers in numerous publications.[184, 186] Some of the antisera used were produced by immunization of rabbits against rat and mouse tumors. The clearest results, however, seem to have been obtained with rat antisera produced by homoiotransplants of rat tumors. It was found in this type of experiment that sera from rats in which a tumor had regressed were more apt to contain cytotoxins than were the sera of rats which grew the tumor progressively or which failed to grow it altogether.

Lumsden[184] found some evidence that cancer-specific cytotoxins could be produced. Rerrich and Wettstein[236] reached the same conclusion. On the other hand, Harris[130] found no specificity. Favorite and Cheever[90] found no cytotoxins in the sera of rabbits immunized to the Brown-Pearce tumor, Medawar[207] found no effect on rabbit skin cultures of sera from rabbits immunized to skin transplants, and Pybus and Miller[233] found stimulation rather than inhibition of mouse tumors cultured in mouse antisera.

GROWTH OF TRANSPLANTABLE TUMORS IN ALIEN SPECIES

There have been many attempts to grow transplantable tumors in alien species. With the exception of transplants in certain favored sites discussed in the next section, the results, even with highly virulent neoplasms, have usually been negative.* Temporary growth has occasionally been obtained, but there are only a few

* If the recent report by Toolan that pretreatment of rats by cortisone permits the growth and serial transplantation of human neoplasms into rats were to be confirmed this and some of the subsequent statements in this section would have to be modified. (Toolan, H. W.: Successful growth of human tumors in the subcutaneous tissues of laboratory animals treated with cortisone. Proc. Am. A. Cancer Research 1:56, 1953.)—EDITORS

reported cases where growth has been progressive, causing the death of the host, or where it has been possible to continue the heteroplastic transplants through successive generations. We are in general agrement with the statement of Selbie[251] that "Such . . . growth can be of no value in the study of cancer, particularly in therapeutic experiments." Studies of heterotransplantation have been reviewed by Woglom[275] and Kerguntal,[150] and we shall refer to only a few later publications.

Putnoky[232] has described a strain of the Ehrlich mouse carcinoma which was propagated by successive subcutaneous transplants in rats for seven years and which killed more than 50 per cent of the hosts (however, see Selbie[251]). Rats could be immunized against it by prior inoculations of mouse tissue. On the other hand, it appeared to have acquired some of the characteristics of a rat tumor, in that rats immunized to it showed a slight increase in resistance to rat tumors. DeBalogh[67] has also reported the development of a strain of the Ehrlich tumor capable of growth in rats, and Hall[127] has described an undifferentiated mouse carcinoma which grew in young rats with resulting death of the hosts in some instances. Hall's tumor, though it grew vigorously when transplanted back into mice, could not be propagated by successive transfers in rats.

Greene[115] has reported serial transfer of the Brown-Pearce rabbit tumor grown subcutaneously in DBA mice. All tumors eventually regressed. Transplantation in association with mouse embryonic tissue increased the percentage of takes in various mouse strains. C3H mice with large spontaneous tumors were much more susceptible than normal C3H mice.

The susceptibility of rats to mouse tumors can be increased by *in toto* exposure to strong roentgen irradiation.[57] Splenectomy is without effect.[132]

Success in heterotransplantation may be related to the use of a favorable strain as host. Possibly certain strains of mice and rats have haptenic groups in common which increase cross-compatibility. The distribution of the blood groups among the various primate species lends plausibility to such an assumption.

GROWTH OF TUMOR TRANSPLANTS IN TESTIS, BRAIN, AND ANTERIOR CHAMBER OF THE EYE

Homoio- and heterotransplants are more apt to grow in the testis, the brain, and the anterior chamber of the eye than they are in other locations. The last-named site is not only particularly favorable for growth of foreign tissues but has the added advantage that the growth can be directly observed at all stages because of the transparency of the eye.

Murphy and Sturm[219] have reported experiments with the transplantation of mouse tumors into the brain of noninbred rats and mice. Growth was obtained in a considerable percentage of the animals inoculated. However, when the heterografts, and probably also the homografts, attained such size that they came in contact with a ventricle, defensive reactions appeared and the tumors regressed. Spontaneous tumors not previously transplanted in other sites failed to grow in the brain, even in homologous hosts. Pearce and Brown[225] have reported that the Brown-Pearce rabbit tumor when inoculated into the brain will sometimes kill the host, whereas it fails to do so when inoculated subcutaneously. These authors[224] also found that the testis was a favored site for the growth of the Brown-Pearce tumor. More than 50 per cent of the hosts succumbed to intratesticular homoiotransplants, while subcutaneous inoculations were unsuccessful.

Greene[112, 114] and Greene and Murphy[117] have described the manner of growth of a variety of tumors in the anterior chamber of the eye of foreign strains and foreign species. As an example we may take the growth of the H-31 uterine carcinoma of the rabbit in the eye of the guinea pig. In a long series of experiments, made when the tumor was in the sixth to the fifteenth transplant generations, "takes" occurred in from 20 per cent to 100 per cent of the hosts. When the transplant was successful, a slight increase in size and a pinkish coloration was usually visible by the second week after transfer, and vascularization by the third week. However, a latent period of 110 days occurred in one instance. Usually by 40 or 50 days after inoculation, though sometimes earlier or later, the chamber was completely filled with tumor. Thereafter areas of degeneration appeared and the tumors underwent regression. However, regression was rarely complete; small nodules of healthy tumor tissue persisted and by continued growth again filled the chamber. Growth persisted in some cases for one or two years. No lesions in other organs were found which could be identified unequivocally as metastases, and Greene records no cases in which animals died from the tumor. In a later series of experiments with the same tumor, but in the twenty-sixth to the thirty-second transplant generations, all guinea pig hosts proved completely refractory.

Other tumors successfully transplanted heteroplastically in the anterior chamber grew faster or slower than H-31 or showed other quantitative differences, but followed a similar pattern. Rabbit breast tumor T-36 was carried successfully for two years or 48 successive generations in guinea pig's eye. This tumor occasionally caused rupture of the cornea, whereupon infection and spontaneous regression invariably ensued. No deaths directly attributable to the growth of the tumor were recorded, though a few animals with large protruding tumor masses succumbed to pneumonia. Growth continued throughout the life of the host in only 5 per cent of the cases. In several cases, successive transfer of tumors resulted in an increased percentage of takes.

Browning[38] found that regression was the ultimate fate of all homoiotransplants of spontaneous C3H mammary tumors in the anterior chamber of the eyes of C57BL and DBA mice, whereas isotransplants into C3H mice, with rare exceptions, would fill and burst the anterior chamber and thereafter continue their growth unchecked.

Normal tissues grown in the eye showed strain specificity to a high degree.[39]

Lucké and Schlumberger [181] studied the growth of frog carcinomas in the anterior chamber of the eye of a variety of alien species. The degree of growth was directly correlated with the degree of relationship.

In a number of studies, the success of transplants in the anterior chamber of the eye has been compared with various measures of the malignancy, virulence, or autonomy attained by a tumor.

Greene[111] removed fragments from 2 spontaneous tumors of the rabbit at different developmental stages and transplanted them into the anterior chamber of the eye of normal rabbits. There was a tendency for the percentage of takes to increase as the growth of the tumors progressed.

Browning[38] has confirmed the existence of such a tendency in an extensive series of experiments with mice. In these studies, C3H mammary tumors at various stages of development were transplanted into the anterior chamber of the eye of DBA and C57BL mice and other C3H mice. There was a distinct correlation between the size of the primary tumors at the time of transplantation and the occurrence and degree of growth in the alien strain hosts. Lung metastases were tested in the anterior chamber of C57BL mice, and in all cases gave takes in at least some of the hosts. In the case of isotransplants, there was a correlation between the size of the primary tumor and the time required to fill one half of the anterior chamber. Transplants from small primary tumors required twenty-five days to reach the specified size, transplants from medium tumors required eighteen days, transplants from large tumors required ten days, and transplants from metastases required eleven days. However, when two spontaneous tumors were available from one animal and this test was applied, the correlation between size of primary tumor and rate of growth often broke down completely.

No correlation was found between tumor histology and either rate of growth or capacity to grow in alien strains or species.

Greene[115] found that the Brown-Pearce rabbit tumor could be transplanted successfully to the eyes, testicles, and subcutaneous tissues of mice, hamsters, and rats, but would not grow at any site in guinea pigs. Since this is a virulent tumor which metastasizes freely,[224] this curious specificity establishes a lack of complete correlation between malignancy and heterotransplantability in one of the most favored test species.

Dyer and Kelly[79] tested 13 histologically and clinically proved cancers from mice, rats, and humans in the anterior chamber of the eye of guinea pigs. Growth in one or more of the guinea pig hosts was obtained with 6 of the tumors, no growth with the remaining 7.

Lushbaugh and Steiner[187] have reported negative results with the heteroplastic intraocular transplantation of a number of cases of malignant lymphoma. Hoffman and Rottino[136] were unsuccessful in attempts to transplant nodes from cases of Hodgkin's disease to the rat's eye. Eichwald[84] reported only 1 take in intraocular transplants in the guinea pig of 27 cancers of childhood. The one tumor successfully transplanted was a congenital fibrosarcoma. On the other hand, trophoblast obtained from human placentas grew rapidly in the anterior chamber of the eyes of rabbits and infiltrated the eye tissues.[123]

While there is undoubtedly some correlation between malignancy and the success of heteroplastic intraocular transplants, the correlation is evidently not close.

Several studies have been carried out to evaluate the usefulness of intraocular transplantation as a laboratory test for clinical malignancy. Schilling *et al.*[246] state that "this method is not reliable for the diagnosis of cancer because of the high incidence of failures (78 per cent) of growth in proved malignant tumors." Morris *et al.*[215] have reached a similar conclusion. On the other hand Greene[116] has reported results with intraocular transplantation of a series of human melanomas which showed close correlation with the clinical outcome of the disease. Even in these cases, however, the long latent period of some of the transplants must have limited their value as a diagnostic tool.

An interesting problem in connection with transplants in the testis, brain, and eye of foreign strains and foreign species is the reason for their relatively high degree of success. Several factors may be involved. We shall try to point out the significance of the experiments described but any final conclusions must await further studies.

The transplant may be shielded from the action of lymphocytes or other cells concerned in the defensive mechanisms of the host. Of significance in this connection are the experiments by Murphy and Sturm[219] already cited, in which it was found that heterotransplants to the brain were inhibited if accompanied by an autotransplant of spleen. Also possibly significant is the complete failure of intraocular heterotransplants of lymphomas and of nodes from cases of Hodgkin's disease.[136, 187]

Bisceglie[26] put pieces of the Ehrlich mouse tumor in small collodion sacs and implanted these in the peritoneal cavities of guinea pigs. If the sacs had a suitable degree of permeability, growth continued for some days. The sacs became surrounded by cells, particularly lymphocytes, and a small tear in the sac which permitted these cells to enter always prevented growth.

Medawar has pointed out that the brain lacks a lymphatic drainage system, and that this may limit the formation of antibodies against foreign tissues implanted in it. If antibodies are already present as a result of prior inoculations made in other sites, the brain provides no protection[208] (see, however, Murphy and Sturm,[219] and Ebeling[81]).

Saphir and Appel[240] found that vigorously growing intratesticular transplants of the Brown-Pearce tumor in rabbits could be made to regress by giving the rabbits an intracutaneous inoculation of the tumor. This suggests that testicular grafts, like intracerebral grafts, are susceptible to antibodies but are not efficient in generating them.

Several investigators have studied the growth of tumors in the anterior chamber of the eye of previously immunized rabbits. If the rabbit was immunized by intraperitoneal, intracutaneous, or intratesticular inoculation of the Brown-Pearce tumor, growth of tumor subsequently grafted into the anterior chamber of the eye was largely inhibited[21, 56] or was at least considerably delayed.[242] When the rabbit was immunized by intraocular inoculation of the Brown-Pearce tumor, growth of a second inoculation of the tumor was not inhibited.[56] However, with other perhaps less virulent tumors immunization against intraocular growth was obtained by prior inoculation of the other eye.[113, 245] It is thus apparent that rabbits can be immunized against intraocular transplants, and that sites other than the eye probably give the best immunization, at least in the case of the Brown-Pearce tumor.

Other studies shed further light on the mechanism of intraocular growth and immunity. Appel *et al.*[10] immunized rabbits by intracutaneous inoculation of the Brown-Pearce tumor and then tested the serum and aqueous fluid for complement fixing antibodies. Such antibodies were found to be present in the serum but not the eye fluid. However, a second test performed on previously tested eyes gave weak complement fixation, presumably because of change in the aqueous humor following damage to the eye caused in the process of the first test.

Medawar[208] determined the degree of growth of rabbit skin in the anterior chamber of the eye of rabbits immunized by a prior skin graft from the same donor. He found that the skin survived as long as it remained unvascularized, but that it was destroyed when vascularization occurred.

It thus appears that intraocular transplants grow in a favorable medium largely or entirely free of antibodies even in immunized hosts until they become vascularized. This favorable start may be an important factor in the success of intraocular transplants. Following vascularization the grafts presumably are exposed at once to the action of antibodies in immunized hosts, and soon generate antibodies in nonimmunized ones.

BIBLIOGRAPHY

1. ALGIRE, G. H. Growth and pathology of melanoma S91 in mice of strains DBA, A, and C. *J. Nat. Cancer Inst. 5:* 151-160, 1944.
2. ALGIRE, G. H., and CHALKLEY, H. W. Vascular reactions of normal and malignant tissues *in vivo*: I. Vascular reactions of mice to wounds and to normal and neoplastic transplants. *J. Nat. Cancer Inst. 6:* 73-85, 1945.
3. ALGIRE, G. H., and LEGALLAIS, F. Growth rate of transplanted tumors in relation to latent period and host vascular reaction. *Cancer Research 7:* 724, 1947.
4. ANDERVONT, H. B. Studies on immunity induced by mouse sarcoma 180. *Pub. Health Rep. 47:* 1859-1877, 1932.
5. ANDERVONT, H. B. Influence of trypan blue upon the resistance of mice to transplantable and induced tumors. *Pub. Health Rep. 51:* 591-600, 1936.
6. ANDERVONT, H. B. Pulmonary tumors in mice: III. The serial transmission of induced lung tumors. *Pub. Health Rep. 52:* 347-355, 1937.
7. ANDERVONT, H. B., and SHIMKIN, M. B. Intrapulmonary transplantation of the adenomatous gastric lesion of Strain I mice. *J. Nat. Cancer Inst. 2:* 151-155, 1941.
8. ANDREWES, C. H. Occurrence of virus III in rabbits in the lesion of infectious fibroma and of a transplantable sarcoma. *J. Path. & Bact. 50:* 227-234, 1940.
9. APPEL, M. Effect of trypan blue on immunity to the Brown-Pearce carcinoma. *Proc. Inst. Med., Chicago, 14:* 343, 1943.
10. APPEL, M., SAPHIR, O., JANOTA, M., and STRAUSS, A. A. Complement-fixing antibodies (Brown-Pearce carcinoma) in the blood serum and in the aqueous fluid of the anterior chamber of the eye. *Cancer Research 2:* 576-578, 1942.
11. APTEKMAN, P. M., LEWIS, M. R., and KING, H. D. A method of producing in inbred albino rats a high percentage of immunity from tumors native to their strain. *J. Immunol. 52:* 77-85, 1946.
12. APTEKMAN, P. M., LEWIS, M. R., and KING, H. D. Tumor-immunity induced in rats by subcutaneous injection of tumor extract. *J. Immunol. 63:* 435-440, 1949.
13. ARIS, H. A method for freeing transplantable tumors of spirilla. *Ztschr. f. Krebsforsch. 36:* 78-81, 1932.
14. BACKOFEN, O. A study of blood changes in mice with transplantable tumors. *Ztschr. f. Krebsforsch. 39:* 318-320, 1933.

15. BALI, T., and FURTH, J. A transplantable splenic tumor rich in mast cells: Observations on mast cells in varied neoplasms. *Am. J. Path. 25:* 605-619, 1949.
16. BALL, H. A., and SAMUELS, L. T. Adrenal weights in tumor-bearing rats. *Proc. Soc. Exper. Biol. & Med. 38:* 441-443, 1938.
17. BARNES, W. A., and FURTH, J. A transmissible malignant neoplasm of mice originating in reticular or endothelial cells. *Am. J. Path. 16:* 457-465, 1940.
18. BARNES, W. A., and SISMAN, I. E. Myeloid leukemia and non-malignant extramedullary myelopoiesis in mice. *Am. J. Cancer 37:* 1-35, 1939.
19. BARRETT, M. K., and MORGAN, W. C. A maternal influence on the growth rate of a transplantable tumor in hybrid mice. *J. Nat. Cancer Inst. 10:* 81-88, 1949.
20. BAUER, K. H. Homoiotransplantation of epidermis in identical twins. *Beitr. z. klin. Chir. 141:* 442-447, 1927.
21. BESREDKA, A., and BARDACH, M. Intracutaneous immunization of rabbits against an epithelioma inoculated in the eye. *Compt. rend. Acad. d. sc. 202:* 2193-2194, 1936.
22. BESSEMANS, A., and ASSERT, L. Attempts at immunization against the Ehrlich mouse sarcoma by the intradermal route. *Ann. Inst. Pasteur 58:* 130-139, 1937.
23. BICHEL, J., and HOLM-JENSEN, I. Parabiosis and resistance to transplantation: I. The influence of parabiosis on the growth of a mouse leukemia in irradiated rats. *Acta path. et microbiol. Scandinav. 24:* 531-533, 1947.
24. BIELSCHOWSKY, F., GNESBACH, W. E., HALL, W. H., KENNEDY, T. H., and PURVES, H. D. Studies on experimental goitre: The transplantability of experimental thyroid tumors of the rat. *Brit. J. Cancer 3:* 541-546, 1949.
25. BIESELE, J. J. Chromosomes in lymphatic leukemia of C58 mice. *Cancer Research 7:* 70-77, 1947.
26. BISCEGLIE, V. Studies on tumor immunity: II. On the growth in adult hosts of transplants enclosed in collodion sacs. *Ztschr. f. Krebsforsch. 40:* 141-158, 1933.
27. BITTNER, J. J. Genetic studies on the transplantation of tumors: VII. Comparative study of tumors 19308A, B, and C. *Am. J. Cancer 17:* 724-734, 1933.
28. BITTNER, J. J. A review of genetic studies on the transplantation of tumors. *J. Genetics 31:* 471-487, 1935.
29. BITTNER, J. J. Propagation of the mammary tumor milk agent in tumors from C57 black mice. *Proc. Soc. Exper. Biol. & Med. 67:* 219-221, 1948.
30. BLUMENTHAL, H. T. The effects of spontaneous and transplanted rat and mouse tumors on the red and white cells in circulating blood and bone marrow. *Cancer Research 1:* 196-204, 1941.
31. BLUMENTHAL, H. T. Homoiotransplantation of spontaneous tumors into mice bearing spontaneous tumors. *Cancer Research 2:* 56-58, 1942.
32. BOGDANOVIC, S. Complement fixation studies with malignant mouse tumors. *Ztschr. f. Immunitätsforsch. u. exper. Therap. 98:* 283-297, 1940.
33. BREEDIS, C. The action of extreme cold on leukemic cells of mice. *J. Exper. Med. 76:* 221-240, 1942.
34. BREEDIS, C., and FURTH, J. The feasibility of preserving neoplastic cells in the frozen state. *Science 88:* 531-532, 1938.
35. BREEDIS, C., ROBERTSON, T., OSENKOP, R. S., and FURTH, J. Character of changes occurring in the course of transplantation of two strains of lung tumors in mice. *Cancer Research 2:* 116-124, 1942.
36. BRIGGS, R. Transplantation of kidney carcinoma from adult frogs to tadpoles. *Cancer Research 2:* 309-323, 1942.

37. BROWN, J. B. Homografting of skin: With report of success in identical twins. *Surgery 1:* 558-563, 1937.
38. BROWNING, H. C. Heterologous and homologous growth of transplants during the course of development of spontaneous mammary tumors in C3H mice. *J. Nat. Cancer Inst. 8:* 173-189, 1948.
39. BROWNING, H. C. Homologous and heterologous growth of transplants of various tissues during the course of development in the mouse. *Cancer 2:* 646-672, 1949.
40. BUNTING, H. Studies in regression in a transplantable tumor in mice. *Yale J. Biol. & Med. 13:* 513-522, 1941.
41. BURMESTER, B. R. The cytotoxic effect of avian lymphoid tumor antiserum. *Cancer Research 7:* 459-467, 1947.
42. BURMESTER, B. R., and PRICHETT, C. O. Immunity reactions obtained with a transmissible fowl tumor (Olson). *Cancer Research 4:* 364-366, 1944.
43. CASEY, A. E. Experimental enhancement of malignancy in the Brown-Pearce rabbit tumor. *Proc. Soc. Exper. Biol. & Med. 29:* 816-818, 1932.
44. CASEY, A. E. Experiments with a material from the Brown-Pearce tumor. *Cancer Research 1:* 134-135, 1941.
45. CASEY, A. E., and DRYSDALE, G. R. Hereditary eosinophile levels in the acquired resistance of the rabbit to the Brown-Pearce tumor (abstract). *Cancer Research 7:* 728, 1947.
46. CASEY, A. E., MEYERS, L., and DRYSDALE, G. R. Selective blocking of host resistance to malignant neoplasm (Brown-Pearce tumor in New Zealand white rabbits). *Proc. Soc. Exper. Biol. & Med. 69:* 579-585, 1948.
47. CASEY, A. E., and PEARCE, L. Studies on the blood cytology of the rabbit: VIII. The blood of normal rabbits as an index of their resistance to a transplanted neoplasm. *J. Exper. Med. 54:* 475-492, 1931.
48. CASEY, A. E., PEARCE, L., and ROSAHN, P. D. The association of blood cell factors with the transplantability of the Brown-Pearce tumor. *Cancer Research 2:* 284-289, 1942.
49. CASEY, A. E., ROSS, G. L., and LANGSTON, R. R. Selective XYZ factor in C57 black mammary carcinoma EO771. *Proc. Soc. Exper. Biol. & Med. 72:* 83-89, 1949.
50. CASPARI, E., and DALTON, H. C. Genic action. *Carnegie Inst. of Washington Year Book 48:* 188-201, 1949.
51. CENTANNI, E. Investigations concerning the nature of tissue immunity against transplantable mouse carcinomas. *Ztschr. f. Krebsforsch. 28:* 47-56, 1928.
52. CHAMBERS, R., and GRAND, C. G. Neoplasm studies: II. The effect of injecting starch grains into transplanted tumors. *Am. J. Cancer 29:* 111-115, 1937.
53. CHAMBERS, H., and SCOTT, G. M. Variations in the growth of the Jensen rat sarcoma and the influence of technique. *J. Path & Bact. 33:* 553-561, 1930.
54. CHAMBERS, H., and SCOTT, G. M. On the effect of a temporary stoppage of the blood supply of rat tumors. *J. Path. & Bact. 42:* 265-269, 1936.
55. CHEEVERS, F. S. A complement-fixing antibody in sera of rabbits bearing Brown-Pearce carcinoma. *Proc. Soc. Exper. Biol. & Med. 45:* 517-522, 1940.
56. CHEEVER, F. S., and MORGAN, H. R. Mechanism of tumor immunity as investigated by means of the intraocular inoculation of the Brown-Pearce carcinoma. *Cancer Research 2:* 675-679, 1942.
57. CLEMMESEN, J. *The Influence of X-Radiation on the Development of Immunity to Heterologous Transplantation of Tumors.* London, Oxford Univ. Press, 1938.

58. CLOUDMAN, A. M. A comparative study of transplantability of eight mammary gland tumors arising in inbred mice. *Am. J. Cancer 16:* 568-630, 1932.

59. CLOUDMAN, A. M. The effect of an extra-chromosomal influence upon transplanted spontaneous tumors in mice. *Science 93:* 380-381, 1941.

60. CLOUDMAN, A. M. Reactions of hybrids and parabiotic pseudo-hybrid mice to inoculations of tumor C198. *Cancer Research 3:* 47-52, 1943.

61. CLOUDMAN, A. M. Organophilic tendencies of two transplantable tumors of the mouse. *Cancer Research 7:* 585-591, 1947.

62. COMAN, D. R., and SHELDON, W. F. The significance of hyperemia around tumor implants. *Am. J. Path. 22:* 821-825, 1946.

63. CONNELL, H. C., and MUNRO, L. A. A possible explanation of conflicting results in experiments with transplanted tumors. *Canad. M. A. J. 53:* 162-167, 1945.

64. COOPER, Z. K., FIRMINGER, H. S., and KELLER, H. C. Transplantable methylcholanthrene skin carcinomas of mice. *Cancer Research 4:* 617-621, 1944.

65. D'ALESSANDRO, G., and GRECO, A. Distribution and characterization of the species-specific lipoid antigen of the Jensen sarcoma and normal organs of rats. *Ztschr. f. Immunitätsforsch. u. exper. Therap. 94:* 147-170, 1938.

66. DARCY, D. A. Plasma cells in the reaction against rabbit tissue homografts. *Nature 163:* 98-99, 1949.

67. DEBALOGH, E. Investigations on a new heterologous tumor, "Budapest 1938," successfully propagated in Hungarian white rats. *Am. J. Cancer 39:* 45-55, 1940.

68. DEBRUYN, W. M. A lymphopenia-causing agent, probably a virus, found in mice after injection with tumor tissue and with cell free filtrates of lymphosarcoma T 86157 (MB). *Cancer Research 9:* 395-397, 1949.

69. DEGAËTANI, G. F., and BLOTHNER, E. A study of tumor transplantation with known numbers of cells. *Ztschr. f. Krebsforsch. 44:* 108-129, 1936.

70. DELONG, R. P., and COMAN, D. R. Relative susceptibility of various organs to tumor transplantation. *Cancer Research 10:* 513-515, 1950.

71. DILLER, I. C. Fungi associated with tumor tissues (abstract). *Anat. Rec. 105:* 504, 1949.

72. DMOCHOWSKY, L. Investigations on the serological specificity of experimental tumors. On the serological specificity of benzpyrene tumors of rats. *Am. J. Cancer 37:* 252-264, 1939.

73. DMOCHOWSKY, L. Survival of the milk factor in a transplantable breast tumour in mice. *Brit. J. Cancer 3:* 246-248, 1949.

74. DRYSDALE, G. R., and CASEY, A. E. Search for the Brown-Pearce tumor XYZ factor in rabbit spleen. *Proc. Soc. Exper. Biol. & Med. 69:* 306-308, 1948.

75. DULANEY, A. D., GOLDSMITH, Y., ARNESEN, K., and BUXTON, L. A serological study of cytoplasmic fractions from the spleens of normal and leukemic mice. *Cancer Research 9:* 217-221, 1949.

76. DUNN, L. C., and CASPARI, E. A case of neighboring loci with similar effects. *Genetics 30:* 543-568, 1945.

77. DUNNING, W. F., CURTIS, M. R., and MANN, M. E. Spontaneous malignant mixed tumors of the rat and the successful transplantation and separation of both components from a mammary tumor. *Cancer Research 5:* 644-651, 1945.

78. DUNNING, W. F., and REICH, C. Studies on the morphology of the peripheral blood of rats: II. Rats injected subcutaneously with carcinogenic hydrocarbons;

III. Rats with induced and transplanted tumors. *Cancer Research 3:* 258-274, 1943.

79. Dyer, H. G., and Kelly, M. G. Cultivation of tumors in the anterior chambers of the eyes of guinea pigs. *J. Nat. Cancer Inst. 7:* 177-182, 1946.
80. Earle, W. R., Shelton, E., and Schilling, E. L. Production of malignancy *in vitro*: XI. Further results from reinjection of *in vitro* cell strains into strain C3H mice. *J. Nat. Cancer Inst. 10:* 1105-1114, 1950.
81. Ebeling, E. Experimental brain tumors of the mouse. *Ztschr. f. Krebsforsch. 14:* 151, 1914.
82. Edwards, J. E., Andervont, H. B., and Dalton, A. J. A transplantable malignant hemangioendothelioma of the liver in the mouse. *J. Nat. Cancer Inst. 2:* 479-490, 1942.
83. Edwards, J. E., Dalton, A. J., and Andervont, H. B. Pathology of a transplantable spontaneous hepatoma in a C3H mouse. *J. Nat. Cancer Inst. 2:* 555-563, 1942.
84. Eichwald, E. J. Heterologous transplantation of cancer of childhood. *Cancer Research 8:* 273-274, 1948.
85. Eichwald, E. J., Evans, R. G., and Browning, G. M. The significance of the anterior chamber in tumor transplantation: I. Transplantation of mouse neuroblastoma C1300 to homologous hosts. *Cancer Research 10:* 483-485, 1950.
86. Eisen, M. J. A bacteriological study of mouse tumor. *Am. J. Cancer 28:* 512-521, 1936.
87. Ellerbrook, L. D., Rees, M., Thornton, H., and Lippincott, S. Complement fixation in animal neoplasia: II. Development of the reaction in New Zealand rabbits carrying the Brown-Pearce carcinoma (abstract). *Cancer Research 9:* 604-605, 1949.
88. Engelbreth-Holm, J. A transplantable cornifying squamous cell carcinoma in mice. *Acta path. et microbiol. Scandinav. 21:* 418-422, 1944.
89. Euler, H. v., and Pettersson, I. Observations on the blood of rats carrying transplants of the Jensen sarcoma. Ztschr. f. Krebsforsch. *51:* 193-198, 1941.
90. Favorite, G. O., and Cheever, F. S. Observations on the Brown-Pearce carcinoma in roller tube tissue cultures. *Cancer Research 1:* 136-143, 1941.
91. Flexner, S., and Jobling, J. W. On the promoting influence of heated tumor emulsions on tumor growth. *Proc. Soc. Exper. Biol. & Med. 4:* 156-157, 1907.
92. Foulds, L. Mammary tumours in hybrid mice: A sex-factor in transplantation. *Brit. J. Cancer 1:* 362-370, 1947.
93. Friedewald, W. F., and Kidd, J. G. Induced antibodies that react *in vitro* with sedimentable constituents of normal and neoplastic tissue cells: Presence of the antibodies in the blood of rabbits carrying various transplanted cancers. *J. Exper. Med. 82:* 21-39, 1945.
94. Furth, O. B., Barnes, W. A., and Browder, A. B. Studies on resistance to transmissible leukemia in mice by means of parabiosis. *Arch. Path. 29:* 163-174, 1940.
95. Furth, J., and Barnes, W. A. Differences between malignant blood cells from induced and spontaneous leukemias of mice. *Cancer Research 1:* 17-22, 1941.
96. Furth, J., Boon, M. C., and Kaliss, N. On the genetic character of neoplastic cells as determined in transplantation experiments with notes on the somatic mutation theory. *Cancer Research 4:* 1-10, 1944.

97. Furth, J., and Kahn, M. C. The transmission of leukemia of mice with a single cell. *Am. J. Cancer 31:* 276-282, 1937.

98. Furth, J., and Sobel, H. Neoplastic transformation of granulosa cells in grafts of normal ovaries into spleens of gonadectomized mice. *J. Nat. Cancer Inst. 8:* 7-16, 1947.

99. Furth, J., and Sobel, H. Transplantable luteoma in mice and associated secondary changes. *Cancer Research 7:* 246-262, 1947.

100. Gardner, R. E., and Hyde, R. R. A biological method for freeing Walker tumor No. 256 from contaminating bacteria. *Am. J. Cancer 34:* 442-445, 1938.

101. Goldfeder, A. Induced resistance in inbred homozygous rats to a lymphosarcoma autogenous to the strain. *Proc. Soc. Exper. Biol. & Med. 59:* 104-109, 1945.

102. Goldfeder, A. Failure of homozygous embryo skins to prevent growth of autogenous tumor-grafts in the rat. *Proc. Soc. Exper. Biol. & Med. 60:* 338-340, 1945.

103. Gorer, P. A. The detection of antigenic differences in mouse erythrocytes by the employment of immune sera. *Brit. J. Exper. Path. 17:* 42-50, 1936.

104. Gorer, P. A. The genetic and antigenic basis of tumor transplantation. *J. Path. & Bact. 44:* 691-697, 1937.

105. Gorer, P. A. The antigenic basis of tumor transplantation. *J. Path. & Bact. 47:* 231-252, 1938.

106. Gorer, P. A. The role of antibodies in immunity to transplanted leukemias in mice. *J. Path. & Bact. 54:* 51-65, 1942.

107. Gorer, P. A. Antibody response to tumor inoculation in mice with special reference to partial antibodies. *Cancer Research 7:* 634-641, 1947.

108. Gorer, P. A. The significance of studies with transplanted tumours. *Brit. J. Cancer 2:* 103-107, 1948.

109. Gorer, P. A., Lyman, S., and Snell, G. D. Studies on the genetic and antigenic basis of tumor transplantation: Linkage between a histocompatibility gene and "fused" in mice. *Proc. Roy. Soc. 135:* 499-505, 1948.

110. Green, R. G. Cytotoxic property of mouse cancer antiserum. *Proc. Soc. Exper. Biol. & Med. 61:* 113-114, 1946.

111. Greene, H. S. N. Familial mammary tumors in the rabbit: IV. The evolution of autonomy in the course of tumor development as indicated by transplantation experiments. *J. Exper. Med. 71:* 305-324, 1940.

112. Greene, H. S. N. Heterologous transplantation of mammalian tumors: I. The transfer of rabbit tumors to alien species: II. The transfer of human tumors to alien species. *J. Exper. Med. 73:* 461-486, 1941.

113. Greene, H. S. N. The participation of the eye in resistance phenomena related to tumor growth. *Cancer Research 2:* 669-674, 1942.

114. Greene, H. S. N. The heterologous transplantation of mouse tumors induced *in vitro*. *Cancer Research 6:* 396-402, 1946.

115. Greene, H. S. N. Heterologous transplantation of the Brown-Pearce tumor. *Cancer Research 9:* 728-735, 1949.

116. Greene, H. S. N. The heterologous transplantation of human melanomas. *Yale J. Biol. & Med. 22:* 611-620, 1950.

117. Greene, H. S. N., and Murphy, E. D. The heterologous transplantation of mouse and rat tumors. *Cancer Research 5:* 269-282, 1945.

118. Gross, L. Influence of sex on resistance to intraperitoneal inoculation of sarcoma in mice. *Proc. Soc. Exper. Biol. & Med. 49:* 67-71, 1942.

119. GROSS, L. The importance of dosage in the intradermal immunization against transplantable neoplasms. *Cancer Research 3:* 770-778, 1943.
120. GROSS, L. The specificity of acquired tumor immunity. *J. Immunol. 50:* 91-99, 1945.
121. GROSS, L. Susceptibility of newborn mice of an otherwise apparently "resistant" strain to inoculation with leukemia. *Proc. Soc. Exper. Biol. & Med. 73:* 246-248, 1950.
122. GUÉRIN, M., and GUÉRIN, P. Lymphotrophic and transplantable epithelioma from the uterus of the rat. *Bull. Assoc. franç. p. l'étude du Cancer 23:* 632-646, 1934.
123. GURCHOT, C., and KREBS, JR., E. T. Growth of trophoblast in the anterior chamber of the eye of the rabbit. *Science 103:* 25, 1946.
124. HAAGEN, E., and SEEGER, P. Studies on ascites tumor of the mouse: IV. The relation of the transplantability of the ascites tumor to the vitality of the cells and to the temperature. *Ztschr. f. Krebsforsch. 47:* 394-412, 1937.
125. HALDANE, J. B. S. The amount of heterozygosis to be expected in an approximately pure line. *J. Genetics 32:* 375-391, 1936.
126. HALL, B. V. Influence of the estrus cycle and the decidual reaction on the transplanted intra-uterine tumors in mice. *Yale J. Biol. & Med. 13:* 333-349, 1941.
127. HALL, B. V. Growth of an undifferentiated mouse carcinoma in the albino rat (abstract). *Cancer Research 10:* 223, 1950.
128. HALL, J. W., and KNOCKE, F. J. Transmission of chloroleukemia of mice. *Am. J. Path. 14:* 217-225, 1938.
129. HARRIS, M. The growth of alien strain tumors in parabiotic mice. *Cancer Research 3:* 546-549, 1943.
130. HARRIS, M. The role of humoral antagonism in heteroplastic transplantation in mammals. *J. Exper. Zool. 93:* 131-145, 1943.
131. HEIMAN, J. Implantation of rat carcinoma and sarcoma within benign fibroadenoma. *J. Cancer Research 12:* 73-82, 1928.
132. HEIMAN, J. Heterologous tumor transplants from mice to splenectomized rats. *Am. J. Cancer 23:* 282-288, 1935.
133. HEIMAN, J., and MEISEL, D. Antireticular cytotoxic serum (ACS): I. The effect of ACS on tumor growth in rats. *Cancer 2:* 329-334, 1949.
134. HEIMAN, J., and MEISEL, D. Antireticular cytotoxic serum (ACS): II. The effect of ACS in mice with transplanted and spontaneous mammary tumors. *Cancer 2:* 335-336, 1949.
135. HESTON, W. E. Development of inbred strains in the mouse and their use in cancer research. *R. B. Jackson Memorial Laboratory 20th Commemoration Lectures*, pp. 9-31, 1949.
136. HOFFMAN, G. T., and ROTTINO, A. Behavior of Hodgkin's disease nodes transplanted into the anterior chamber of the rat's eye. *Arch. Path. 48:* 230-233, 1949.
137. HOMBURGER, F. Studies on hypoproteinemia: III. Lymphoid hyperplasia and redistribution of nitrogen caused in mice by transplanted tumors (sarcoma 180 and breast adenocarcinoma EO771). *Science 107:* 648-649, 1948.
138. HOOKER, C. W., STRONG, L. C., and PFEIFFER, C. A. A spontaneous transplantable testicular tumor in a mouse (abstract). *Cancer Research 6:* 503, 1946.
139. HOYLE, L. A lipoidal antigen produced by certain malignant tumors of the mouse. *Am. J. Cancer 39:* 224-233, 1940.

140. HUMMEL, K. P., and LITTLE, C. C. Studies on the mouse mammary tumor agent: III. Survival and propagation of the agent in transplanted tumors and in hosts that grew these tumors in their tissues. *Cancer Research 9:* 137-138, 1949.

141. JACKSON, E. B., and BRUES, A. M. Studies on a transplantable embryoma of the mouse. *Cancer Research 1:* 494-498, 1941.

142. JACOBS, J. L., and HOUGHTON, J. D. Complement-fixation tests on rabbits with Brown-Pearce carcinoma. *Proc. Soc. Exper. Biol. & Med. 47:* 88-90, 1941.

143. JONES, E. The breakdown of hereditary immunity to transplantable tumor by introduction of an irritating agent. *J. Cancer Research 10:* 435-449, 1926.

144. KAHN, M. C., and FURTH, J. Transmission of mouse sarcoma with small numbers of counted cells. *Proc. Soc. Exper. Biol. & Med. 38:* 485-486, 1938.

145. KALFAYAN, B. and KIDD, J. G. Structural changes produced in Brown-Pearce carcinoma cells by means of a specific antibody (abstract). *Am. J. Path. 26:* 745-746, 1950.

146. KALISS, N., JONAS, G., and AVENT, N. L. Growth enhancement of tumor homoiotransplants in mice following injections of homogenates and ultrafiltration sediments of mouse tissues (abstract). *Cancer Research 10:* 228, 1950.

147. KALISS, N., and NEWTON, O. The effect of injection of dosage level of lyophilized mouse tissue on the subsequent growth of a tumor homoiotransplant (abstract). *Anat. Rec. 105:* 535, 1949.

148. KALISS, N., and ROBERTSON, T. Spleen transplantation relationships among two inbred lines of mice and their F_1 hybrids (abstract). *Genetics 28:* 78, 1943.

149. KALISS, N., and SNELL, G. D. The effects of injections of lyophilized normal and neoplastic tissues on the growth of tumor homoiotransplants in mice. *Cancer Research 11:* 122-126, 1951.

150. KERGUNTUL, R. *Inter-species Transplantation of Malignant Tumors. Monographie sur les Tumeurs.* Paris, Laboratorie du Professor Peyson, Inst. Pasteur, 1933.

151. KIDD, J. G. A complement-binding antigen in extracts of the Brown-Pearce carcinoma of rabbits. *Proc. Soc. Exper. Biol. & Med. 38:* 292-295, 1938.

152. KIDD, J. G. A distinctive substance associated with the Brown-Pearce rabbit carcinoma: I. Presence and specificity of the substance as determined by serum reactions. *J. Exper. Med. 71:* 335-350, 1940.

153. KIDD, J. G. A distinctive substance associated with the Brown-Pearce rabbit carcinoma: II. Properties of the substance: discussion. *J. Exper. Med. 71:* 351-371, 1940.

154. KIDD, J. G. The enduring partnership of a neoplastic virus and carcinoma cells: Continued increase in virus in the V2 carcinoma during propagation in virus-immune hosts. *J. Exper. Med. 75:* 7-20, 1942.

155. KIDD, J. G. Distinctive constituents of tumor cells and their possible relations to the phenomena of autonomy, anaplasia, and tumor causation. *Cold Spring Harbor Symposia on Quantitative Biology 11:* 94-112, 1946.

156. KIDD, J. G. Suppression of growth of Brown-Pearce tumor cells by a specific antibody: With a consideration of the nature of the reacting cell constituent. *J. Exper. Med. 83:* 227-250, 1946.

157. KIDD, J. G. The association of lymphocytes with cancer cells undergoing distinctive necrobiosis in resistant and immune hosts (abstract). *Am. J. Path. 26:* 672-673, 1950.

158. KIDD, J. G., and FRIEDEWALD, W. F. A natural antibody that reacts *in vitro* with a sedimentable constituent of normal tissue cells: II. Specificity of the phenomenon: general discussion. *J. Exper. Med. 76:* 557-578, 1942.
159. KING, H. D., and LEWIS, M. R. A study of the inducement and transplantability of sarcomata in rats. *Growth 9:* 155-176, 1945.
160. KLEIN, E., KURNICK, N. B., and KLEIN, G. The effect of storage on the nucleic acid content and virulence of mouse ascites tumors. *Exp. Cell Research 1:* 127-134, 1950.
161. KOCH, F. E. On the question of metastasis formation by transplantable tumors. *Ztschr. f. Krebsforsch. 48:* 495-505, 1939.
162. KRITZLER, R. A., MULLIKEN, B., and TURNER, J. C. A hitherto undescribed virus forming inclusion bodies in organs and experimental tumor of C57 mice. *Cancer 4:* 401-409, 1951.
163. LAW, L. W. Foster nursing and the growth of transplantable leukemias in mice. *Cancer Research 2:* 108-115, 1942.
164. LAW, L. W. Characterization of an influence affecting growth of transplantable leukemia in mice. *Cancer Research 4:* 257-260, 1944.
165. LEWIS, M. R. Myeloid hyperplasia brought about in mice by the growth of dibenzanthracene tumors and its relation to the transplantability of the tumor into mice of alien strains. *Am. J. Cancer 29:* 510-516, 1937.
166. LEWIS, M. R. Transplantable lymphosarcoma in mice. *Am. J. Cancer 34:* 399-406, 1938.
167. LEWIS, M. R. A transmissible monocytoma of the mouse. *Am. J. Cancer 36:* 34-43, 1939.
168. LEWIS, M. R. Immunity in relation to 1,2,5,6-dibenzanthracene-induced sarcomata. *Bull. Johns Hopkins Hosp. 67:* 325-344, 1940.
169. LEWIS, M. R., APTEKMAN, P. M., and KING, H. D. Inactivation of malignant tissue in tumor-immune rats. *J. Immunol. 64:* 321-326, 1949.
170. LEWIS, M. R., KING, H. D., APTEKMAN, P. M., and SEIBERT, F. B. Further studies on oncolysis and tumor immunity in rats. *J. Immunol. 60:* 517-528, 1948.
171. LEWIS, M. R., and LICHTENSTEIN, E. G. Breaking down the resistance of albino mice to the transplantation of tumors induced by 1,2,5,6-dibenzanthracene in a different strain of albino mice. *Am. J. Cancer 27:* 246-256, 1936.
172. LEWIS, M. R., and LICHTENSTEIN, E. G. Further studies on the breaking down of resistance of mice of one strain to the transplantation of tumors from mice of another strain. *Am. J. Cancer 28:* 746-751, 1936.
173. LEWIS, M. R., and LICHTENSTEIN, E. G. Studies on the transplantability of induced and spontaneous tumors occurring in mice of pure inbred stains. *Growth 1:* 375-383, 1937.
174. LIPPINCOTT, S. W., ELLERBROOK, L. D., THORNTON, H., and STOWELL, E. Complement fixation in animal neoplasia: III. Comparison of the Kidd technic with a more sensitive method for testing the sera from rabbits bearing the Brown-Pearce carcinoma (abstract). *Am. J. Path. 25:* 820-821, 1949.
175. LITTLE, C. C. A possible Mendelian explanation for a type of inheritance apparently non-Mendelian in nature. *Science 40:* 904-906, 1914.
176. LITTLE, C. C. "The genetics of tumor transplantation." In G. D. SNELL (ed.): *Biology of the Laboratory Mouse.* Philadelphia, The Blakiston Co., 1941.
177. LITTLE, C. C. The genetics of cancer in mice. *Biol. Rev. 22:* 315-343, 1947.

178. LITTLE, C. C., and JOHNSON, B. W. The inheritance of susceptibility to implants of splenic tissue in mice. *Proc. Soc. Exper. Biol. & Med. 19:* 163-167, 1922.
179. LITTLE, C. C., and TYZZER, E. E. Further studies on inheritance of susceptibility to a transplantable tumor of Japanese waltzing mice. *J. Med. Research 33:* 393-425, 1916.
180. LOEB, L. *The Biological Basis of Individuality.* Springfield, Ill., Charles C Thomas, 1945.
181. LUCKÉ, B., and SCHLUMBERGER, H. Heterotransplantation of frog carcinoma: Character of growth in the eyes of alien species. *J. Exper. Med. 72:* 311-320, 1940.
182. LUDFORD, R. J. Resistance to the growth of transplantable tumors: I. The influence of vital staining on induced resistance. *Brit. J. Exper. Path. 12:* 45-48, 1931.
183. LUDFORD, R. J., and BARLOW, H. Sarcomatous transformation of the stroma of mammary carcinomas that stimulated fibroblastic growth *in vitro.* *Cancer Research 5:* 257-264, 1945.
184. LUMSDEN, T. On cytotoxins lethal to nucleated mammalian cells normal and malignant. *Am. J. Cancer 31:* 430-440, 1937.
185. LUMSDEN, T. Agglutination tests in the study of tumor immunity, natural and acquired. *Am. J. Cancer 32:* 395-417, 1938.
186. LUMSDEN, T., and PHELPS, H. J. Serological observations on spontaneous regression of implants of Jensen's rat sarcoma. *Am. J. Cancer 29:* 517-521, 1937.
187. LUSHBAUGH, C. C., and STEINER, P. E. Intraocular transplantation of malignant lymphomas of the mouse, dog, and man in heterologous species. *Cancer Research 9:* 299-305, 1949.
188. LUTZ, B. R., FULTON, G. P., PATT, D. I., and HANDLER, A. H. The growth rate of tumor transplants in the cheek pouch of the hamster (abstract). *Cancer Research 10:* 231-232, 1950.
189. MACDOWELL, E. C. What and why is leukemia? A medico-biological study in mice. *Carnegie Inst. of Washington Pub. 501:* 353-367, 1938.
190. MACDOWELL, E. C. Variation in leukemic cells of mice. *Cold Spring Harbor Symposia on Quantitative Biol. 11:* 156-174, 1946.
191. MACDOWELL, E. C., POTTER, J. S., and TAYLOR, M. J. The influence of transplantation upon immunological properties of leukemic cells. *Proc. Nat. Acad. Sc. 25:* 416-420, 1939.
192. MACDOWELL, E. C., POTTER, J. S., TAYLOR, M. J., WARD, E. N., and LAANES, T. Mouse genetics. *Carnegie Inst. of Washington Year Book 40:* 245-250, 1940-41.
193. MACDOWELL, E. C., and RICHTER, M. N. Studies on mouse leukemia: II. Hereditary susceptibility to inoculated leukemia. *J. Cancer Research 14:* 434-439, 1930.
194. MACDOWELL, E. C., and RICHTER, M. N. Studies on mouse leukemia: IV. Specificity of susceptibility to different lines of inoculated leukemia. *Proc. Soc. Exper. Biol. & Med. 28:* 1012-1013, 1931.
195. MACDOWELL, E. C., and RICHTER, M. N. Studies on mouse leukemia: V. A. genetic analysis of susceptibility to inoculated leukemia of line I. *Biol. Zentralbl. 52:* 266-279, 1932.
196. MACDOWELL, E. C., TAYLOR, M. J., and POTTER, J. S. Immunization of mice naturally susceptible to a transplantable leukemia. *Proc. Soc. Exper. Biol. & Med. 32:* 84-86, 1934.

197. MacDowell, E. C., Taylor, M. J., and Potter, J. S. The dependence of protection against a transplantable mouse leukemia upon the genetic constitution of the immunizing tissue. *Proc. Nat. Acad. Sc. 21:* 507-508, 1935.
198. MacKenzie, I., and Kidd, J. G. Incidence and specificity of the antibody for a distinctive constituent of the Brown-Pearce tumor. *J. Exper. Med. 82:* 41-63, 1945.
199. Maculla, E. Antigenic analysis of embryonic, adult and tumor tissues. *Growth 13* (Suppl.): 33-60, 1949.
200. Maltaner, F. Significance of thromboplastic activity of antigens used in complement-fixation tests. *Proc. Soc. Exper. Biol. & Med. 62:* 302-304, 1946.
201. Marshak, A., and Erf, L. A. Effect of injections of nuclei on "take" of implants of a lymphoma in mice. *Proc. Soc. Exper. Biol. & Med. 46:* 428-430, 1941.
202. Marx, L. Lowered susceptibility to transplantable tumors in the young of tumor-bearing rats. *Ztschr. f. Krebsforsch. 35:* 170-171, 1932.
203. Maver, M. E., and Barrett, M. K. Serologic and anaphylactic reactions of the cathepsins of normal and neoplastic tissues. *J. Nat. Cancer Inst. 4:* 65-73, 1943.
204. Mazzacuva, G., and Santoboni, U. Experimental tumor research: 3. Behavior of the Galliera sarcoma in intestine and liver. *Pathologica 25:* 488-499, 1933.
205. Mc Cutcheon, M., Zeidman, I., and Coman, D. R. Factors affecting the number of tumor metastases. Experiments with a transplantable mouse tumor (abstract). *Am. J. Path. 26:* 673-674, 1950.
206. Medawar, P. B. Immunity to homologous grafted skin: I. The suppression of cell division in grafts transplanted to immunized animals. *Brit. J. Exper. Path. 27:* 9-14, 1946.
207. Medawar, P. B. Test by tissue culture methods on the nature of immunity to transplanted skin. *Quart. J. Mic. Sci. 89:* 239-252, 1948.
208. Medawar, P. B. Immunity to homologous grafted skin. III. The fate of skin homografts transplanted to the brain, to subcutaneous tissue, and to the anterior chamber of the eye. *Brit. J. Exper. Path. 29:* 58-69, 1948.
209. Meyer, J. R. Influence of reticulo-endothelial blockade on development of the transplantable lymphosarcoma of white mice. *Arch. Inst. Biol. Defesa Agric. & Animal 3:* 177-180, 1930.
210. Meyer, J. R. Experimental studies carried out with a second transplantable adenocarcinoma of the mouse found in S. Paulo. *Arq. Inst. Biol. (São Paulo) 13:* 127-136, 1942.
211. Meyer, J. R. Decrease of resistance to transplantable adenocarcinomata following injury to the reticulo-endothelial system. *Arq. Inst. Biol. (São Paulo) 14:* 97-104, 1943.
212. Mider, G. B., and Morton, J. J. The effect of freezing *in vitro* on some transplantable mammalian tumors and on normal rat skin. *Am. J. Cancer 35:* 502-509, 1939.
213. Miller, R. A., and Taylor, M. J. A concomitant change in mitochondria and virulence of a transplanted lymphoid leukemia. *Proc. Soc. Exper. Biol. & Med. 68:* 336-339, 1948.
214. Milone, S., and Vecchi, G. Implantation of one type of tumor into another type of tumor: Simultaneous transplantation of two types of tumors either in pieces or in the form of a mixture. *Gior. Accad. med. Torino 89:* 109-113, 1927.
215. Morris, D. S., McDonald, J. R., and Mann, F. C. Intra-ocular transplantation of heterologous tissues. *Cancer Research 10:* 36-48, 1950.

216. MOTTRAM, J. C. The relation between the growth rate of tar warts in mice and their corresponding autografts. *J. Path. & Bact. 42:* 79-90, 1936.

217. MUCCI, D. Behavior of bony tissue inoculated with experimental tumors. *Tumori 18:* 501-514, 1932.

218. MURPHY, J. B. The lymphocyte in resistance to tissue grafting, malignant disease, and tuberculosis infection: An experimental study. *Monographs of the Rockefeller Inst. for Med. Research 21:* 1-168, 1926.

219. MURPHY, J. B. and STURM, E. Conditions determining the transplantability of tissues in the brain. *J. Exper. Med. 38:* 183-197, 1923.

220. MURPHY, J. B. and STURM, E. The transmission of an induced lymphatic leukemia and lymphosarcoma in the rat. *Cancer Research* 1: 379-383, 1941.

221. MURPHY, J. B. and STURM, E. The effect of growth or retrogression of a transplantable lymphosarcoma of the rat on the lymphoid organs and the adrenals of the hosts. *Cancer Research 8:* 139-140, 1948.

222. OSTER, R. H. and SALTER, W. T. Immunization against neoplasm: Its effect on the nitrogen metabolism of the host. *Am. J. Cancer 32:* 422-433, 1938.

223. OWEN, R. D. Immunogenetic consequences of vascular anastomoses between bovine twins. *Science 102:* 400-401, 1945.

224. PEARCE, L., and BROWN, W. H. Studies based on a malignant tumor of the rabbit: II. Primary transplantation and elimination of a co-existing syphilitic infection. *J. Exper. Med. 37:* 631-645, 1923.

225. PEARCE, L., and BROWN, W. H. Studies based on a malignant tumor of rabbit: IV. The results of miscellaneous methods of transplantation, with a discussion of factors influencing transplantation in general. *J. Exper. Med. 37:* 811-828, 1923.

226. PEARCE, L., and RIVERS, T. M. Effect of host immunity to a filterable virus (virus III) on the growth and malignancy of a transplantable rabbit neoplasm. *J. Exper. Med. 46:* 65-80, 1927.

227. PEARCE, L., and RIVERS, T. M. Effect of a filterable virus (virus III) on the growth and malignancy of a transplantable neoplasm of the rabbit. *J. Exper. Med. 46:* 81-99, 1927.

228. PEARCE, L., and VAN ALLEN, C. M. Influence of light on the growth and malignancy of a transplantable neoplasm in the rabbit. *J. Exper. Med.* 45: 483-496, 1927.

229. POTTER, J. S., and FINDLEY, M. D. Histological observations on resistance to transplantable leukemia in immunized mice. *Proc. Soc. Exper. Biol. & Med. 32:* 1338-1340, 1935.

230. POTTER, J. S. and RICHTER, M. N. Mouse leukemia: VIII. Continuity of cell lineage in transmission lines of lymphatic leukemia. *Arch. Path. 15:* 198-212, 1933.

231. POTTER, J. S., TAYLOR, M. J., and MACDOWELL, E. C. Transfer of acquired resistance to transplantable leukemia in mice. *Proc. Soc. Exper. Biol. & Med.* 37: 655-656, 1938.

232. PUTNOKY, J. On immunity reactions of a heterotransplantable mouse carcinoma propagated in rats for seven years. *Am. J. Cancer 32:* 35-49, 1938.

233. PYBUS, F. C., and MILLER, E. W. On the existence of growth-promoting and growth-inhibiting properties *(in vitro)* of the sera and plasma of mice naturally immune, or with acquired resistance to a tar-sarcoma. *Brit. J. Exper. Path. 15:* 207-221, 1934.

234. RASK-NIELSEN, H. C., and RASK-NIELSEN, R. Further studies on a transmissible myeloid leukosis in white mice. II. *Acta path. et microbiol, Scandinav. 15:* 169-175, 1938.
235. REINHARD, M. C., GOLTZ, H. L., and WARNER, S. G. Further studies on the quantitative determination of the growth of a transplantable mouse adenocarcinoma. *Cancer Research 5:* 102-106, 1945.
236. RERRICH, E., and WETTSTEIN, V. Studies of tumor immunity. *Frankfurt. Ztschr. Path. 48:* 353-356, 1935.
237. RUSS, S., and SCOTT, G. M. Evidence to resistance to tumour grafts in the offspring of immunized rats. *Proc. Roy. Soc. s. B 128:* 126-137, 1940.
238. RUSS, S., and SCOTT, G. M. Experiments showing the influence of one growing tumour upon another. *Brit. J. Exper. Path. 23:* 127-133, 1942.
239. RUSSELL, W. L. "Inbred and hybrid animals and their value in research." In G. D. SNELL, ed.: *Biology of the Laboratory Mouse.* Philadelphia, The Blakiston Co., 1941.
240. SAPHIR, O., and APPEL, M. Regression of primary Brown-Pearce testicular carcinoma and metastases following intracutaneous transplantation with homologous tumor. *Am. J. Cancer 38:* 55-58, 1940.
241. SAPHIR, O., and APPEL, M. Attempts to abrogate immunity to the Brown-Pearce carcinoma. *Cancer Research 3:* 767-769, 1943.
242. SAPHIR, O., APPEL, M., and STRAUSS, A. A. Growth of Brown-Pearce carcinoma in the anterior chamber of the eyes of tumor-immune rabbits. *Cancer Research 1:* 545-547, 1941.
243. SAVARD, K. Adrenal changes in animals bearing transplanted tumors. *Science 108:* 381-382, 1948.
244. SAVARD, K., and HOMBURGER, F. Thymic atrophy and lymphoid hyperplasia in mice bearing sarcoma 180. *Proc. Soc. Exper. Biol. & Med. 70:* 68-70, 1949.
245. SCHILLING, J. A., and SNELL, A. C., Jr. Development of a state refractory to growth of a mouse tumor implanted in the anterior chamber of the guinea pig eye. *Arch. Path. 46:* 35-42, 1948.
246. SCHILLING, J. A., SNELL, A. C., Jr., and FAVATA, B. V. Heterologous ocular transplantation as a practical test for cancer. *Cancer 2:* 480-490, 1949.
247. SCHOEN, R. Tumors and ultraviruses: Studies of the lymphogranuloma virus. *Ann. Inst. Pasteur 60:* 499-510, 1938.
248. SCHREK, R. A quantitative study of the growth of the Walker rat tumor and the Flexner-Jobling rat carcinoma. *Am. J. Cancer 24:* 807-822, 1935.
249. SCHREK, R. The effect of the size of inoculum on the growth of transplantable rat tumors. *Am. J. Cancer 28:* 364-371, 1936.
250. SCHREK, R. A biological method for sterilizing contaminated transplantable tumors. *Am. J. Path. 12:* 531-543, 1936.
251. SELBIE, F. R. Early stages in the transplantation of the Ehrlich-Putnoky tumor into mice and rats. *Am. J. Cancer 28:* 530-539, 1936.
252. SELBIE, F. R. Carcinomatous transformation in a transplantable rat fibroadenoma. *Brit. J. Exper. Path. 23:* 62-68, 1942.
253. SIBLEY, J. A., and LEHNINGER, A. L. Aldolase in the serum and tissues of tumor-bearing animals. *J. Nat. Cancer Inst. 9:* 303-309, 1949.
254. SNELL, G. D. Methods for the study of histocompatibility genes. *J. Genetics 49:* 87-108, 1948.

255. Snell, G. D. Mutations in transplantable tumors. *Proc. First Nat. Cancer Conference* pp. 28-33, 1949.
256. Snell, G. D., and Cloudman, A. M. The effect of rate of freezing on the survival of fourteen transplantable tumors of mice. *Cancer Research 3:* 396-400, 1943.
257. Snell, G. D., Cloudman, A. M., Failor, E., and Douglass, P. Inhibition and stimulation of tumor homoiotransplants by prior injections of lyophilized tumor tissue. *J. Nat. Cancer Inst. 6:* 303-316, 1946.
258. Snell, G. D., Cloudman, A. M., and Woodworth, E. F. Tumor immunity in mice induced with lyophilized tissue, as influenced by tumor strain, host strain, source of tissue, and dosage. *Cancer Research 8:* 429-437, 1948.
259. Snell, G. D., and Higgins, G. F. Alleles at the histocompatibility-2 locus in the mouse as determined by tumor transplantation. *Genetics 36:* 306-310, 1951.
260. Spencer, R. R. Tumor immunity. *J. Nat. Cancer Inst. 2:* 317-332, 1942.
261. Stern, K., and Willheim, R. *The Biochemistry of Malignant Tumors.* New York, Macmillan and Co., 1943.
262. Stewart, H. L., Grady, M. D., and Andervont, H. B. Development of sarcoma at site of serial transplantation of pulmonary tumors in inbred mice. *J. Nat. Cancer Inst. 7:* 207-225, 1947.
263. Strong, L. C. Changes in the reaction potential of a transplantable tumor. *J. Exper. Med. 43:* 713-724, 1926.
264. Strong, L. C. The transplantation of an adenocarcinoma of the preputial gland in mice of the A strain. *Cancer Research 2:* 332-334, 1942.
265. Symeonidis, A. Experimental and morphological study of tumor immunity; the microscopic appearance and the nature of the tumor-immune reaction at the site of the implant. *Virchows Arch. f. path. Anat. 304:* 271-295, 1939.
266. Taylor, M. J., and Mac Dowell, E. C. Mouse leukemia: XIV. Freeing transplanted Line I from a contaminating virus. *Cancer Research 9:* 144-149, 1949.
267. Thornton, H., Ellerbrook, L. D., Lippincott, S. W. and Fong, C. Complement fixation in animal neoplasia: IV. The immediate and delayed anticomplementary effects of serum and antigen and their dependence upon the hemolysin concentration (abstract). *Cancer Research 10:* 245, 1950.
268. Thornton, H., Ellerbrook, L. D., Rhees, M., and Lippincott, S. W. Complement fixation in animal neoplasia: I. A study of technics for measurement of the reaction in rabbit serum with special reference to the temperature of inactivation (abstract). *Cancer Research 9:* 627-628, 1949.
269. Toolan, H. W., and Kidd, J. G. Sarcomatoid growths resulting from mammary carcinoma cells that had sojourned in immune mice (abstract). *Am. J. Path. 26:* 753-754, 1950.
270. Twort, J. M., and Lasnitzki, M. Studies in the pituitary weight of rats inoculated with transmissible tumor. *Endocrinology 23:* 87-90, 1938.
271. Wallace, E. W., Wallace, H. M., and Mills, C. A. Effect of climatic environment upon the genesis of subcutaneous tumors induced by methylcholanthrene and upon the growth of a transplantable sarcoma in C3H mice. *J. Nat. Cancer Inst. 3:* 99-110, 1942.
272. Warren, S., and Gates, O. The fate of intravenously injected tumor cells. *Am. J. Cancer 27:* 485-492, 1936.
273. Werder, A. A., Kirschbaum, A., and Syverton, J. T. The effects *in vitro* of specific antibodies on the cells of a transplantable mouse leukemia (abstract). *Cancer Research 10:* 248, 1950.

274. WHARTON, R. A. The effect of tumors on antibody levels in mice (abstract). *Cancer Research 9:* 628, 1949.
275. WOGLOM, W. H. Immunity to transplantable tumors. *Cancer Review 4:* 129-214, 1929.
276. WOGLOM, W. H. Absorption of the protective agent from rats resistant to a transplantable sarcoma. *Am. J. Cancer 17:* 873-893, 1933.
277. WOGLOM, W. H., and WARREN, J. A pyogenic filterable agent in the albino rat. *J. Exper. Med. 68:* 513-528, 1938.
278. WOGLOM, W. H., and WARREN, J. The nature of a pyogenic filterable agent in the white rat. *J. Hygiene 39:* 266-267, 1939.
279. WOODS, M. W., DUBUY, H. G., BURK, D., and HESSELBACH, M. L. Cytological studies on the nature of the cytoplasmic particulates in the Cloudman S91 mouse melanoma, the derived Algire S91A partially amelanotic melanoma, and the Harding-Passey mouse melanoma. *J. Nat. Cancer Inst. 9:* 311-323, 1949.
280. WOOLLEY, G. W., and LITTLE, C. C. Transplantation of an adrenal cortical carcinoma. *Cancer Research 6:* 712-717, 1946.
281. WRIGHT, S. An analysis of variability in number of digits in an inbred strain of guinea pigs. *Genetics 19:* 506-536, 1934.
282. WYETH, G. A., and RAHN, O. Regular occurrence of a treponema in live dbrB tumors of mice. *Fourth Internat'l Cancer Research Congress,* St. Louis, p. 60, 1947.
283. ZAHL, P. A., and DRASHER, M. L. Distribution and growth-potency of cells in a transplantable sarcoma. *Cancer Research 7:* 658-666, 1947.
284. ZAHL, P. A., and NOWAK, A., Jr. Effect of subcutaneous injury on tumor growth in the mouse. *Proc. Soc. Exper. Biol. & Med. 70:* 266-272, 1949.
285. ZIMMERMAN, H. M., and MAIER, N. The transplantation of experimentally induced brain tumors (abstract). *Am. J. Path. 25:* 801, 1949.

CHAPTER 15

Nutrition and Cancer

Albert Tannenbaum

Tumors develop from living cells and grow by assimilating nutrients from the host. Thus changes in the nutritional status of the host might be expected to modify both the development of a neoplasm and its subsequent growth. This obvious integration of cancer and nutrition was probably the basis for the early investigations regarding the possible effects of diet on tumors. It is not surprising, however, that the data and concepts resulting from these efforts do not, in general, stand up under present-day scrutiny—in the light of greatly increased knowledge of the biology of cancer, the biochemistry of nutrition, and the considerable advances in experimental technics. Nevertheless, it is of value, at least for historical purposes, to recognize the extensive and diversified investigations conducted by the early experimentalists and clinicians. These can be found in reviews by Stern and Willheim,[102] Waterman,[126] and Caspari.[23]

As in other facets of cancer research, the past two decades have seen a tremendous acceleration in investigations concerned with the relation of nutrition to cancer. This has been brought about by enhanced interest in the entire cancer problem, and by increased support and facilities for research. Furthermore, barriers to methodology have been removed by the greater availability of carcinogenic agents, inbred strains of animals that develop spontaneous tumors, and purified dietary components. Without the impressive advances in the science of nutrition much less would have been accomplished. Successively, the significance of energy requirements, proteins and amino acids, vitamins, enzymes, and intermediary metabolism has been comprehended and elucidated with increasing precision. These discoveries in nutrition, coupled with the advances in the knowledge of the biology of cancer, have resulted in a crude mosaic of the manner through which nutrition may modify the development and growth of tumors.

A summary and critical review is given in this chapter. In the hope that the final result will be helpful rather than confusing, no attempt has been made to be bibliographic or encyclopedic. The pertinent literature, qualified by the space available, is included, although some data of significance may have been omitted inadvertently or not recognized as important. At any rate, the reader may find other details and viewpoints in several fairly recent reviews,[5, 20, 41, 80, 91, 113] and in a collection of papers given at a symposium on the relation of nutrition to cancer and published by the New York Academy of Sciences.[57]

This presentation is divided into five sections. The first part concerns some of the complex problems of experimental design and interpretation that confront an investigator in the field of nutrition and cancer. The second is devoted to the effects of diet on the *origin* of neoplasms—the significance of caloric intake and of the proportion of dietary fat, protein, vitamins, and minerals. This is followed by a section concerned with the effects of a similar spectrum of dietary modifications on the *growth* of tumors. The fourth part deals with the implications and extensions derived from present knowledge. Lastly, the data suggesting that nutrition may play a role in the development of cancer in human subjects are discussed.

FACTORS OF EXPERIMENTAL DESIGN AND INTERPRETATION

Many problems present themselves to the investigator. These include the type of tumor, the diet, and other features of experimental design. How many animals should be employed? What controls are essential and what observations and measurements are imperative? Would chemical determinations and histologic examinations be helpful? There are no set rules, and the decisions are dependent on the facts available at the time, the experience of the research worker, and his personal judgment. The following brief discussion only scratches the surface, being in part factual, in part provocative. It may serve to make the reader cognizant of the difficulties and pitfalls which may be encountered and possibly give him a more critical attitude when considering the planning, results, and interpretations of the recorded investigations.

THE NEOPLASM

Neoplasm is a generic term encompassing many different kinds of tumors. Morphologically, functionally, and clinically, they are as diverse as the many diseases classified as infections or inflammations. The large variety of tumors, benign and malignant, need not be and generally are not affected in the same way by a particular dietary or nutritional change. It is possible, however, and this is evident in the discussion on caloric restriction, that many types of tumors respond in a similar manner to a specific dietary alteration. Such a consistent result invites investigation of the possible mode of action with the goal of understanding better the carcinogenic process. Dissimilarities are equally provocative. In any case, it is well to avoid generalization from the response of a single tumor-type, particularly one that is unusual or uncharacteristic. If possible, and if the project permits such a course, more than one kind of neoplasm should be investigated.

ORIGIN AND GROWTH

It is important to differentiate between the origin of spontaneously occurring or deliberately induced tumors and their subsequent growth. This dichotomy is not fully appreciated; even in the relatively recent literature on cancer one finds references to the effect of dietary variations on tumors (some concerned with origin, others with growth) with no attempt to separate these distinctly different problems. By this time, however, most investigators in this field and those concerned with other cancer problems, recognize that genesis and growth are separate processes and that a factor affecting the origin or genesis of a tumor may influence its growth in a different manner.

It is our thesis that a particular experimental procedure may affect the origin of a tumor—positively, negatively, or not at all—and have the same or another effect on its growth.

In this connection a comparable dichotomy applies to transplanted tumors. Again there are two separate processes, but in this instance they are the establishment, or "take," of the tumor implant, and its subsequent growth. To transplant a small amount of tumor or tumor mash, immediately apply an experimental procedure, and then draw conclusions regarding the growth rate is to overlook the possibility that the establishment of the implant may have been enhanced or delayed by the procedure. As with spontaneous and induced tumors, the experiment can be planned to yield a clearer result.

Entirely apart from the academic separation of the two processes, it is obvious that knowledge regarding the origin or establishment of tumors may suggest preventive means. Findings on growth characteristics may offer leads for therapeutic procedures.

NUMBER OF ANIMALS AND DURATION OF STUDY

Nutritional studies are usually directed toward determining the influence of dietary changes in increasing or decreasing the proportion of animals developing tumors, in accelerating or retarding the rate at which tumors appear, and in augmenting or depressing the growth of established tumors. The effects are rarely "all or none"—of a nature wherein all the control animals respond in one way, all the experimental animals in another. Consequently, the conclusions drawn from a study must depend on statistical evaluation of the data, whether or not this be done explicitly.

It is essential that attention be given from biologic viewpoints not only to the plan of the experiment but also to the statistical features. Too often the numbers of animals or of experiments are insufficient to support the conclusions drawn. With small groups of animals a real effect might be missed because differences do not attain statistical significance. In contrast, a biologic effect might be claimed when the differences observed could easily have occurred through chance alone. It is not intended to discuss Statistics, inasmuch as there are many good texts on statistical design and analysis. Nevertheless, either the numbers of animals or experiments should be sufficient to demonstrate the effects, or the inferences drawn from the experimental results should be limited.

An experimental effect may be one of retardation rather than of prevention. Early in an experiment a large difference in relative frequency or in growth of tumors may be evident, yet as the experiment progresses this difference may diminish or disappear. Undoubtedly an "effect" has been demonstrated, but it is necessary to recognize it as one of delaying the cancer process, not of preventing it. Thus although the duration of an experiment cannot be set by rule, it should be considered in evaluating the data obtained.

Needless disregard of these features of experimentation have resulted in a not inconsiderable amount of "poor" information, and of conclusions which, though possibly valid, cannot be readily accepted because the data presented do not constitute reasonably good proof.

KINDS OF DIET

Should commercial diets (made of natural foods) or semipurified diets of known components (so-called synthetic) be utilized? There is no single answer. Many accept the view that semipurified diets are preferable because more is known about their composition. However, in such diets:

1. The components are often only relatively purified. For example the fat component—hydrogenated cottonseed oil, lard, or others—is composed of many lipids. Casein, prepared to be vitamin-free, actually contains small quantities of the B vitamins.[21] Often, in long-term experiments, crude vitamin preparations such as liver powder or extract, yeast, or rice bran extract are used to supplement crystalline vitamins.
2. There is likely to be a less adequate quality, quantity, and balance of essential components than in many natural diets.

These conditions suggest the avoidance of a dogmatic attitude toward the choice of diets in nutritional investigations. Most often, the purpose of the study can be achieved through the use of a variety of diets. Some fundamental findings on the relation of nutrition to cancer have been disclosed through the employment of commercial diets. On the other hand, for the study of the effects of single dietary components the semipurified (synthetic) diet is often essential. Actually, there is no evidence that a particular dietary change, in caloric intake or essential nutrient, has an effect qualitatively dependent on the kind of diet.

Along these lines, the appraisal of caloric values of various components of the diet must be treated with reserve. Some accept the energy values for 1 Gm. of carbohydrate, protein, and fat as 4, 4, and 9 Calories, respectively, while others credit these components with slightly different values. Actual values for *particular* members of a class of components differ. What is more important is that even an accurate measure of the caloric content in a bomb calorimeter does not represent the calories available to the body. Such factors as digestibility, absorption, and balance in amount of essential components profoundly modify the caloric value of a foodstuff to the animal.

DIETS: AMOUNTS AND INTERRELATIONSHIPS

In view of the profound influence of caloric intake on the tumor process, another question that perplexes the investigator is the amount of ration to be fed to the control and experimental groups of a study. Should they be fed *ad libitum*? Or equicaloric amounts of food? An ideal situation would be one in which the animals in control and experimental groups were fed *ad libitum* and by free choice consumed equicaloric amounts of the different diets and in both groups, on the average, maintained approximately the same body weight. Under such conditions interpretation of the results would be uncomplicated. However, in actual experience such a fortunate situation rarely exists. The deletion, reduction, or increase of one particular component of the diet may result in a marked effect on voluntary food intake or on utilization of the ingested food. Diets low in protein, essential amino acids, or vitamins may be voluntarily consumed in lesser amounts than diets containing adequate proportions of these components. A ration with a high proportion of fat will be voluntarily eaten in amounts of greater caloric value than one with a lower proportion of fat. Thus diets fed *ad libitum* may result in considerable differences in caloric intake and body weight; it is usually quite difficult then to determine whether the observed effect on tumors is caused by the specific dietary change or is entirely a nonspecific consequence of the alteration in caloric intake. For this reason, in some studies rations are given in equicaloric amounts to experimental and control mice by such technics as force-feeding, paired feeding, or restricting the caloric values of all rations to a little less than that voluntarily eaten by the group with least appetite.

Even when diets are fed equicalorically there may yet be gross differences in utilization and consequently in body weight—a point also of some importance in the genesis and growth of tumors. In some investigations in our laboratory the control and experimental diets are fed in amounts which result in equal average body weights for the two groups. This is done since, so far as the animal is concerned, body growth is a better index of the nutritive value of a ration than is the caloric content as determined in a bomb calorimeter.

Still another consideration is bacterial synthesis of vitamins in the gastrointestinal tract. Control and experimental diets may produce a difference in intestinal flora, with resulting changes of which the investigator is not aware. That these factors may be of greater importance than is commonly realized is indicated by the conclusions of Johansson and Sarles[51] that "in all probability most animals, and human beings in particular, are rarely provided with a completely balanced diet, and apparently rely upon synthetic activities of their intestinal micro-organisms to provide many of the deficient growth factors."

INFLUENCE OF DIET ON DOSAGE OF CARCINOGEN

In interpreting the influence of a dietary procedure on the development of a tumor, consideration must be given to the possibility that the dietary change may have altered the *effective dosage of carcinogen.* Whether the carcinogen is applied to the skin, injected, or fed to the animals, the experimental diet may cause it to be absorbed or metabolized at a rate different from that occurring in the control group. The same general reasoning applies to the endogenous agents and conditions that produce spontaneous tumors, except that in this case the dietary modification may also affect the production of these carcinogenic factors.

On the other hand, the experimental procedure may have no influence on the actual amount of carcinogen that comes in contact with the target tissue, but rather it may exert its effect directly in the *carcinogenic process*, i.e., the actual tissue changes of neoplasia. If possible, these two separate influences should be differentiated.

SUMMARY

This brief survey of some of the considerations, problems, and dilemmas inherent in investigation on the influence of nutrition on neoplasms bespeaks the complexity of the field. The discussion indicates, with more or less rigor, the criteria that have been found of value in interpreting and appraising the studies reviewed in the following sections.

EFFECTS OF DIET ON THE ORIGIN OF TUMORS

In most investigations concerned with the influence of nutrition on the genesis of tumors, the diets—control and experimental—are initiated early, usually well before tumors are expected to appear. The control diets are designed, generally, to be adequate in quality and quantity for growth, maintenance, and function. As many studies are planned, the experimental and control diets differ in the proportion of only one component. It is true that to consider fats, proteins, vitamins, and salts single components is a gross breach of the recognition that each represents mixtures of substances of considerable heterogeneity. Nevertheless, experience in the field of nutrition validates discussing each class of components as a whole, except in those cases where a specific compound has been studied.

CALORIC INTAKE

Basic to the nutritional status of an animal is its ingestion of energy-supplying food, i.e., its caloric intake. As in human nutrition, there are no good means of ascribing "normal" values for either caloric intake or body weight. These are dependent on strain, age, kind of ration, method of caging, and amount of voluntary exercise. All this adds up to variable standards of normal caloric intake and body weight.

These comments serve as an introduction to the fact that in some laboratories, including the writer's, mice fed *ad libitum* often attain relatively high weights. Their fat depots are large and the animals appear somewhat obese. Some might consider them to have consumed more than the normal intake of calories, with resulting overweight. At any rate, there are no direct studies on the influence of supercaloric intakes (not complicated by other experimental procedures) on the genesis of tumors. Practically all the investigations on the effect of caloric intake have been concerned with underfeeding or caloric restriction.

Underfeeding and Caloric Restriction

Of all the dietary alterations investigated to the present time, caloric restriction has the most regular influence on the genesis of neoplasms in animals. Numerous thorough investigations have established the fact that chronic caloric restriction inhibits the formation of many types of tumors, decreasing the incidence of animals developing neoplasms and delaying as well the time at which the tumors appear.[16, 29, 58, 64, 71, 92, 93, 96, 97, 105, 107, 111, 112, 114, 117, 120, 133] An example of this inhibitory effect is given in Table 24 which summarizes an experiment on spontaneous mammary cancer in DBA female mice.[113] The mice of group N45 were restricted to 2.0 Gm. of a basic ration daily, their average body weight ranging from 19 to 21 Gm. during the course of the experiment. Group N42, the controls, received the same amount of the basic diet, but supplemented with cornstarch; these mice ingested an average of 3.0 Gm. daily and grew at a normal rate.

Table 24. Effect of a Calorie-Restricted Diet on the Formation of Spontaneous Mammary Carcinoma in DBA Virgin Female Mice

	N42: High calorie controls			*N45: Calorie-restricted group*		
Age (wk.)	*Mean weight* (Gm.)	*Animals alive and tumor-free*	*Cumulative tumor count*	*Mean weight* (Gm.)	*Animals alive and tumor-free*	*Cumulative tumor count*
10*	20	50	0	21	50	0
40	28	48	0	19	50	0
48	30	47	1	19	50	0
56	30	45	2	20	49	0
64	31	40	6	21	48	0
72	30	35	11	20	46	0
80	29	27	16	20	41	0
88	—	15	23	—	39	0
96	—	8	25	—	31	0
100	—	6	26	—	29	0

* Animals placed on experimental diets at 10 weeks of age.

By 100 weeks of age, 52 per cent of the 50 mice in the full-fed control group, N42, had developed spontaneous mammary cancer. None occurred in the calorie-restricted group. This striking effect is not attributable to any untoward sequelae such as earlier deaths or general debility in the restricted group. Actually these mice lived longer on the average than those of the group fed the high calorie ration, even when only the non-tumor mice are considered. Clinically, the restricted animals appeared to be in excellent condition, except that they were smaller than the full-fed controls. They were also more active, particularly before feeding. Furthermore, toward the end of the experiment, the restricted mice had fewer non-neoplastic pathologic changes in the heart, kidneys, liver, and other organs than the full-fed mice of the same age. This "improved" health and longevity of animals consequent to restriction of caloric intake is common to all the experiments we have undertaken and is a generally recognized phenomenon.[4, 70]

The diets of the two groups of the preceding experiment contained the same amounts and kinds of fats, protein, vitamins, and minerals. They differed only in their content of carbohydrate (cornstarch). Similar experiments have been performed, and with virtually the same effect on tumor formation, with diets in which the restricted ration had the same composition on a percentage basis as the control, i.e., all components of the diet were restricted in proportion to the over-all limitation of food intake. This procedure has been called "underfeeding," while restriction of carbohydrate only has been designated as caloric restriction. The latter term is, of course, not precise so far as metabolism is concerned; for when the total caloric intake is restricted sufficiently, there must be diversion of ingested protein and fat to meet energy requirements. Nevertheless, it has seemed a reasonable simplification to refer to carbohydrate restriction as caloric restriction, inasmuch as under the conditions usually employed in these experiments there were no concurrent changes (other than the reduced body weight) commonly associated with deficiencies of protein, fats, or vitamins. On this basis, and by inferences from direct experimentation with various essential dietary components, it seems likely that the main inhibitory effect on tumor formation obtained in the experiment described is attributable to the restriction of calories.

Tumors Responding to Caloric Restriction

The influence of chronic caloric restriction on tumor formation has been determined for many experimental neoplasms. Both natural and semipurified diets have been used and the restriction has been through underfeeding, or by limitation of carbohydrate or of carbohydrate and fat. Both mice and rats have been employed as experimental animals. Tumors that have been investigated are: spontaneous mammary carcinoma, skin tumors induced by carcinogenic hydrocarbons or ultraviolet light, induced sarcoma, spontaneous hepatoma, spontaneous lung adenoma, spontaneous and induced leukemia (all of the mouse); and lymphosarcoma and induced mammary carcinoma of rats. Some of the results, as presented in the literature, are summarized in Fig. 53. With all tumor types represented, the findings consistently reveal that long-term caloric restriction significantly inhibits the formation of tumors and, where the observations were made, delays the appearance of those tumors which do arise. Stated otherwise, caloric restriction decreases the incidence of tumors.

Although the caloric effect is evident with so many types of neoplasms that there is a temptation to regard it as a universal influence, there are two reports that counsel caution. One concerns the influence of this dietary alteration on the formation of hepatic tumors induced in rats by feeding *para*-dimethylaminoazobenzene. Attempts to ensure equal intake of the carcinogen resulted in increasing the concentration of the azo dye in the calorie-restricted diet to a point where these animals failed to survive its toxic action.[24] In another experiment the investigators found that caloric restriction of a carcinogen-free diet during a four-week interval—between two periods in which the rats were fed *ad libitum* diets containing the azo dye—actually enhanced carcinogenesis. As the authors point out, however, this approach permitted no definite conclusions regarding the caloric effect itself. The

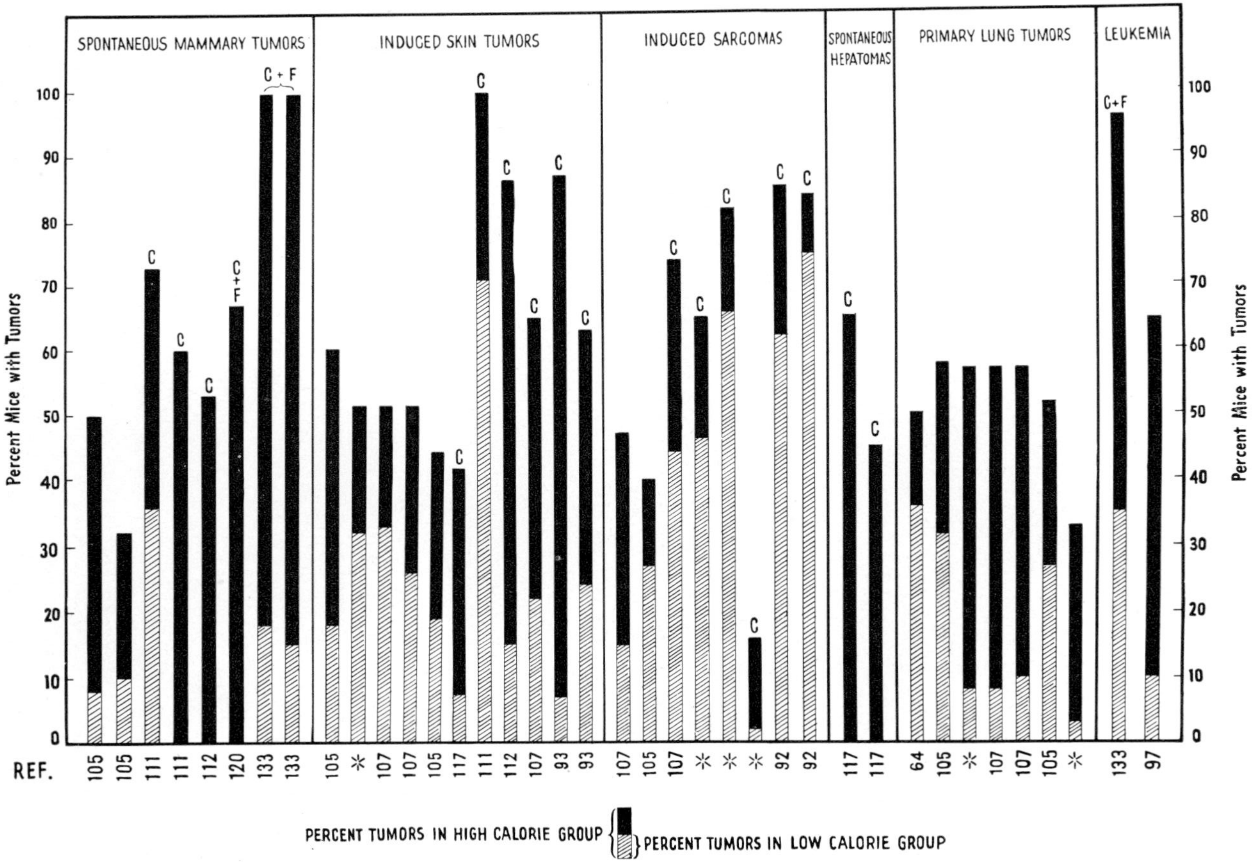

FIG. 53. Effect of restricted food intake on the incidence of various types of tumors in mice. Each bar represents an experiment: reference number below bar (* = unpublished experiments). The total height of the bar represents the incidence of tumors in the high-calorie group; the lower component of the bar (cross-hatched) represents the incidence of tumors in the low-calorie group. When there is no letter above a bar, caloric restriction was through underfeeding of all components of the diet; C above the bar indicates carbohydrate restriction only; C + F indicates restriction of both carbohydrate and fat.

second report deals with the formation of adrenal adenomata. C3H female mice castrated at weaning develop adrenal adenomata that assumedly produce estrogens. Caloric restriction had no effect on the incidence of these tumors.[58] The fact that all the mice, full-fed and calorie-restricted, developed the adenomata indicates the potency of the tumorigenic action. The question arises as to whether this might be another example of the overriding effect of a high dosage of carcinogen (see below).

As illustrated in Fig. 53, the actual extent of the decrease in the incidence of tumors varies from experiment to experiment. Without discussing the details of any particular study it seems that sarcomas induced by carcinogenic hydrocarbons are less inhibited by caloric restriction than are induced skin tumors; the latter are in turn less retarded than the mammary, lung, or hepatic neoplasms of spontaneous origin. The differential influence may be related to the potency of the carcinogenic agent and the malignancy of the tumor-type. Even for the same tumor there are differences of considerable magnitude. These are due in part to the extent of caloric restriction and to the kind and potency of the carcinogenic provocation.

Dosage of Carcinogen

As the dose or potency of the carcinogenic agent is increased there is an increase in incidence of tumors. Also, the neoplasms appear earlier. This occurs in calorie-restricted animals as well as in those that are full-fed. Consequently, as the carcinogenic response approaches its maximum the difference in tumor incidence between calorie-restricted and full-fed animals is likely to diminish. In fact, when a sufficiently high dose of chemical carcinogen is administered, almost all animals, whether calorie-restricted or not, develop tumors. Even under such conditions, however, the influence of caloric restriction manifests itself through a delay in the appearance of the tumors.[58, 114]

Degree of Caloric Restriction

In virtually all the studies listed in Fig. 53 the calorie-restricted mice ingested only 50 to 70 per cent as much food as the corresponding full-fed controls. Restrictions of this extent are about as great as can be maintained in the long period required for such experiments on carcinogenesis. It was of theoretical and possibly practical interest to determine whether less drastic calorie restriction also resulted in a reduced incidence of neoplasms. That lesser degrees of restriction actually do effect some inhibition of tumor formation has been shown in investigations where graded caloric intakes were utilized.[16, 111, 112, 117] It was found that successive small decreases from *ad libitum* levels produced successive decreases in the relative frequency of tumors. The nature of the quantitative relationship between the formation of neoplasms and caloric intake has been investigated for the spontaneous mammary carcinoma, the carcinogen-induced skin tumor, and the spontaneous hepatoma of the C3H male mouse. For each of the tumors studied (when the dosage of carcinogen or duration of the experiment was such that not all mice developed tumors) the incidence of tumors measured in probits* was a

* Probits are the transformation of the percentage incidences to areas of the normal distribution curve, these areas being measured in standard deviation units. The terminology and statistical technics applicable are outlined by Fisher and Yates.[32]

straight-line function of the logarithm of the caloric intake. Curves of actual data are given in Fig. 54. Similarly, the mean time of tumor appearance increased linearly with the logarithm of the decreasing caloric intake.

This relationship is of interest since it also represents the influence of successively increasing doses of drugs, poisons, etc. Plotting the incidence of tumors measured in per cent against the caloric intake on an arithmetic scale results in a ʃ shaped curve with the point of greatest inflection at the 50 per cent level of tumor formation. It may consequently be deduced from this relationship that a proportionate reduction in caloric intake has its largest inhibitory effect in the region of 50 per cent tumor incidence.[117]

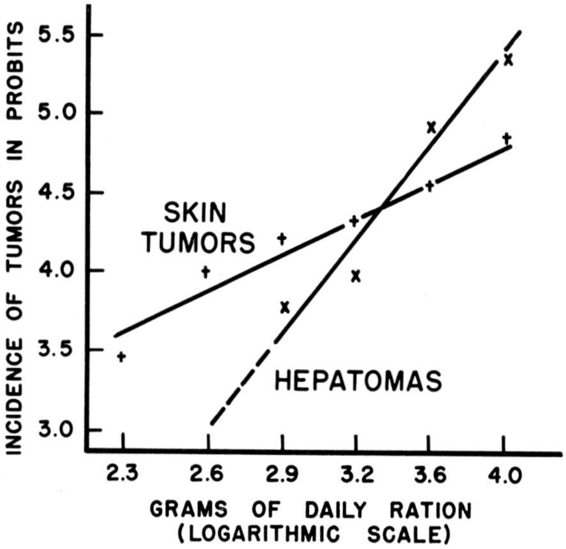

FIG. 54. Influence of the degree of caloric restriction on the formation of tumors. The figure indicates the linear relationship between the incidence of tumors in probits (32) and the logarithm of the caloric intake.

Both the data (Fig. 54) and their interpretation offer no evidence for the concept of a "critical level" of caloric intake relatively constant for all modes of carcinogenesis and all kinds of tumors. Rather it is likely that the critical amount of calories which controls whether or not an animal develops a cancer is dependent on the kind of tumor and the potency and nature of the carcinogenic agent, and, for any selected set of experimental conditions, varies with the individual animal.

STAGE OF CALORIC RESTRICTION

In studies with the spontaneous mammary carcinoma it was observed that institution of caloric restriction at any time (when the mice were 2, 5, or 9 months of age) before tumors began to appear, significantly inhibited their formation.[107] Indeed, if mice which characteristically develop multiple mammary carcinoma (such as C3H female mice) are employed and caloric restriction is begun after the first tumor has appeared, the proportion of animals with multiple tumors is significantly reduced (Tannenbaum, unpublished data). These studies imply that the main effect of caloric restriction occurs in what has been called the developmental stage of carcinogenesis.

The concept that carcinogenesis proceeds through several stages has been brought to fruition in recent years via a diversity of attacks, the most definitive of which have been the work of Rous[34, 69, 90] and of Berenblum.[8, 9] These investigators have utilized, in the main, skin tumors induced by carcinogenic hydrocarbons—a choice dictated by several factors. One is that the carcinogenic agent is well defined and its application readily terminated before detectable neoplasia occur. Another is that the tumors are external and their emergence is easily recognized. For this particular tumor, two stages of carcinogenesis are apparent: (1) a stage variously designated as initiation, inception, or latency, in which the carcinogen acts upon the normal cells, producing changes that render the cells biased toward tumor formation; these initial changes are self-limited and the cells do not become cancerous unless the conditions are favorable; (2) a stage of development, promotion, or formation, in which the initiated or biased cells develop into cancer cells that then grow.

The stage of initiation is produced by the action of a carcinogen, and these biased cells may lie dormant for as long as a year. The initiated cells may be developed or promoted by further applications of carcinogen or by the action of a cocarcinogenic agent such as croton oil.

The factors controlling and modifying the stage of initiation are probably different from those affecting the stage of development. For example, caloric restriction is a nutritional alteration that has little influence on initiation, whereas it distinctly inhibits development of tumors. This is illustrated in the following experiment.[109]

To the skin of mice of four equivalent groups, a benzpyrene solution was applied for a period of ten weeks. During this interval, considered to be the stage of *initiation*, no tumors appeared. At the end of the ten-week period, applications of carcinogen were discontinued. The mice were observed and examined for tumors for the following fifty-two weeks, considered to encompass the stage of *development*. Of the four groups, two were given a high caloric diet during the ten-week carcinogen period (initiation), and two were given a diet restricted in calories. At the termination of carcinogen application, one of the two groups on the high calorie diet was transferred to the calorie-restricted diet, and one of the two groups on the diet restricted in calories was transferred to the high caloric diet. Thus, one group of mice was maintained on a high caloric diet throughout the experiment, another on a restricted caloric diet throughout, while the other two groups had different sequences of diets during the two periods (stages of carcinogenesis). The results are given in Table 25.

Comparison of groups HH and LL clearly shows the significant inhibitory effect on tumor formation when there is caloric restriction throughout the entire period of carcinogenesis. The degree of inhibition in group LL must be regarded as the base line in considering the effect produced by restricting the diet in only one

TABLE 25. EFFECTS OF CALORIC RESTRICTION DURING THE TWO STAGES OF CARCINOGENESIS

Group	*Diet in period of carcinogen application (10 weeks)*	*Diet in period of tumor formation (52 wks.)*	*Tumor incidence (%)*
HH	high calorie	high calorie	69
HL	high calorie	low calorie	34
LH	low calorie	high calorie	55
LL	low calorie	low calorie	24

period. The two groups, HH and LH, that were given the high caloric ration during the period of tumor appearance, had a tumor incidence of about the same order, suggesting that the carcinogenic agent produced the initial fundamental changes regardless of the diet, low or high caloric, fed during the period of carcinogen application. Based on this conclusion it is of interest to make the following comparisons: HH and HL, showing that caloric restriction in the period of tumor appearance inhibits the genesis of tumors; HL and LL, indicating that the inhibition of tumor formation observed in the latter group was principally due to caloric restriction during the period of tumor appearance; and LH and LL, conversely revealing that high calories in the period of tumor appearance favored the genesis of tumors. Such data also give credence to the concept of stage-wise processes in carcinogenesis.

Intermittent Caloric Restriction

In all the preceding experiments (except the one just discussed) caloric restriction, once instituted, was maintained for the duration of the study; in other words, the conditions represented a chronic caloric restriction. The suggestion has been made that intermittent fasting, with *ad libitum* feeding between fasting, might have the same effect as chronic caloric restriction.[22] However, in a study utilizing the spontaneous mammary carcinoma of the DBA mouse,[118] twice-weekly fasts of twenty-four hours' duration with feeding *ad libitum* between fasts had no inhibitory influence on tumor formation. It is significant that the mice fasted intermittently, ate the same amount of food during the week, and grew as well as the control animals.

Mode of Action of Caloric Restriction

Inasmuch as restriction of caloric intake strikingly reduces the incidence of many different tumor-types, interest has been aroused as to the mechanism of this influence. Perhaps an understanding of the mechanism through which this dietary alteration produces its effects would also provide a clearer picture of the carcinogenic process.

When an animal is chronically restricted in calories many changes occur: in the relative weights of tissues and organs; in levels of tissue and body fluid constituents; in hormone levels, metabolism, and function. With regard to the mechanism of caloric restriction, which of the many alterations in the body are specifically related to the influence on tumor formation? When it was first recognized that caloric restriction inhibits tumor formation, the difficulty of explaining its mode of action also became evident.[107, 113] Emphasis was placed on the evidence that the effect had been obtained with many types of tumors of divergent tissue origin. Indeed, in one experiment the restricted group of mice revealed a reduction in incidence of two entirely different types of neoplasms: the induced skin tumor and the spontaneous tumor of the lung. Thus it was postulated that the caloric effect is caused by factors general in nature, present in all tissues of the body, and effective at all sites investigated. It was assumed that it must be related to a locally restricted nutritional supply.

It has been suggested that at least in the case of spontaneous mammary cancer the principal effect of caloric restriction is one of reducing the production of estrogen, assumed to be the primary carcinogen,[49] and in addition diminishing the response of the mammary gland to estrogen. Both effects are presumably the consequence of what has been called dietary pseudohypophysectomy.[84] There has been no attempt to extend this hypothesis to explain the effect of caloric restriction on other tumors. It might be considered, however, that significant inhibition of mammary tumor formation occurs with degrees of caloric restriction that have no serious effect on such critical functions as mating and fertility.

In contrast to the suggestion of pituitary insufficiency is the fact that in the restricted animal there is a relative adrenal hyperfunction. This is indicated by an increase in relative size of the adrenals, and an apparent increase in glyconeogenesis.[15] Boutwell and his co-workers state that perhaps these changes may explain the inhibiting effect of caloric restriction on tumor formation.

A third mechanism is that proffered by Bullough,[18] who postulates that the developmental stage of carcinogenesis is influenced by the mean mitotic activity of the tissue, inferentially including that of the latent cancer cells. Thus he finds that mitotic activity is definitely inhibited by caloric restriction and proportionately to the degree of the restriction. He concludes that the limiting factor in cell division is the amount of carbohydrate and carbohydrate intermediates available for the production of the energy required for mitosis.

Indirectly related to the understanding of the mode of action of caloric restriction are the results of experiments designed to evaluate the relative importance of caloric intake, metabolic turnover, and the resultant body-weight level. Such diverse procedures as the incorporation of sodium fluoride or dinitrophenol in the diet, or keeping the experimental mice in a cold room (at about 50° F.) on a caloric intake equal to that of control mice, markedly inhibited the formation of spontaneous mammary tumors.[116] Sodium fluoride caused a voluntary restriction of food intake. The other two procedures accelerated the metabolic rate; however, since food intake was not permitted to increase, there was a resultant imposed "restriction." In all three cases, the animals weighed decidedly less than the control mice. It is very likely that the decreased incidence of mammary carcinoma was not principally dependent on the sodium fluoride, dinitrophenol, or the low environmental temperature, but was mediated rather through their effects on food intake, food requirement, and body growth. These experiments, as well as others in which thyroid extract was incorporated into the diet,[99] support the conclusion that not only the level of caloric intake and total metabolic turnover but also the resultant body weight level may be significant factors in the genesis of tumors. These interrelationships require further elucidation.

The particulars of the above suggestions regarding the mode of action of caloric restriction are not mutually contradictory. It is likely that the actual detailed mechanism might be related to all of them. Work in this field offers promise.

FAT

In a pioneer investigation, Watson and Mellanby[127] found that feeding mice a diet containing from 12.5 to 25 per cent butterfat caused a definite increase in the incidence of skin tumors produced by tarring. The results obtained by the group of workers at the University of Wisconsin[6, 7, 50, 65, 66, 93] point in the same direction. In numerous experiments they have shown that skin tumors of the mouse, induced by either ultraviolet light or carcinogenic hydrocarbons, formed in greater numbers and at an earlier time in mice receiving a high-fat diet than in control mice consuming the basal ration. In contrast, the same investigators found that the formation of chemically induced sarcomas was not significantly altered by a high-fat diet.

Investigations in the author's laboratory utilized five different types of tumors: skin tumors and sarcoma induced by carcinogenic hydrocarbons, and the spontaneously occurring mammary carcinoma, lung adenoma, and hepatoma of the mouse. A number of experiments have been performed with each tumor.[100, 101,-108, 110, 112]

Spontaneous Mammary Carcinoma

The effect of a fat-enriched diet on the formation of spontaneous mammary carcinoma of the mouse is illustrated by the results given in Table 26. Although equicaloric feeding was not always achieved in the earlier experiments, there is no doubt that it was accomplished in this study.[100] The diets for the two groups contained a basal portion of casein, gelatin, salts, yeast extract, synthetic B vitamins, and a concentrate of A, D, and E vitamins. This basal portion was complemented by fat and cornstarch in different proportions. The diet for group AP 1 contained 2 per cent fat, that for group AP 4, 16 per cent. The daily ration for each mouse of the two groups, 10.9 Calories, was fed at slightly below the *ad libitum* level to insure equicaloric intakes.

The experiment was terminated when the few surviving mice were 2 years old. Correcting for deaths of nontumor animals, 89 per cent of the mice fed the fat-enriched diet developed tumors in comparison with 74 per cent of those on the low fat diet. The tumors in the fat-enriched group appeared when the mice were at a mean age of 69.4 weeks, compared with 76.3 weeks for the control group. Thus, more tumors developed in the mice on the fat-enriched diet, and these appeared significantly earlier than in the control group.

Although the effect is not large, comparable results have been obtained in numerous experiments: fat-enrichment of the diet results in a definite increase

TABLE 26. INFLUENCE OF THE PROPORTION OF DIETARY FAT ON THE FORMATION OF SPONTANEOUS MAMMARY CARCINOMA IN DBA VIRGIN FEMALE MICE

	Group AP1: 2% dietary fat			*Group AP4: 16% dietary fat*		
Age (wk.)	*Mean weight* (Gm.)	*Animals alive and tumor-free*	*Cumulative tumor count*	*Mean weight* (Gm.)	*Animals alive and tumor-free*	*Cumulative tumor count*
12*	21	60	0	21	60	0
40	30	60	0	31	58	1
50	30	56	1	30	54	3
60	31	49	8	31	38	17
70	32	40	16	32	26	28
80	33	32	24	30	13	39
90	31	19	31	—	6	44
100	—	10	38	—	1	48
104	—	4	40	—	1	48

* The experimental diets were initiated when the mice were 12 weeks old.

in the incidence and also in the earlier appearance of spontaneous mammary carcinomas.

The influence of dietary fat on the induction by diethylstilbestrol of mammary cancer in rats has been studied.[29] The fat contents of the diets were 6 per cent and 46 per cent. Although the experimental groups were small, a compounding of the data (on number of animals with tumors, number of neoplasms per animal, and latent periods) suggests an augmented tumor formation through the high fat ration.

SKIN TUMORS

There are many reports on the enhancement of the formation of tumors of the skin by means of high-fat diets. The neoplasms were induced by either tar, carcinogenic hydrocarbons, or ultraviolet light. Furthermore, the nature of the dietary fat employed appears to be relatively unimportant, increased tumor incidence having been observed with lard, butter fat, wheat germ oil, coconut oil, or hydrogenated cottonseed oil.[65]

In the experiments performed by the writer a small but consistent increase in the incidence of skin tumors and a reduction of the latent period were observed.[108, 110, 114] The diets utilized were mashes in which the fat was relatively well absorbed into the mixture, thus preventing greasiness of the animals' skins through contact with the ration.

The group at the University of Wisconsin has done extensive work in this field. At one time they reported large effects[65] but in later publications they showed these to have been partly due to oiliness of the skin brought about by physical contact with the ration. In excellent studies they prevented or minimized the skin greasiness by the use of special feeders, by emulsifying the fat in the drinking water,[66] or by adding special absorbents to the ration.[93] Currently there is general agreement that, among mice fed fat-enriched diets, induced skin tumors develop in only slightly greater number and somewhat earlier than in control animals.

Hepatic Tumors

Increasing the fat content of the diet from 2 to approximately 20 per cent resulted in a small enhancement in the rate of formation of the spontaneous benign hepatoma of the C3H male mouse.[101] In five of six experiments, the incidence of hepatomas was greater in the mice given the fat-enriched rations.

Much more attention has been accorded the influence of fat-enrichment of the diet on hepatic tumors (generally malignant) induced in the rat by *para*-dimethylaminoazobenzene. It has been reported that the formation of these tumors is accelerated by rations with moderate or high proportions of fat as compared with those containing little fat.[61, 85] However, this effect has not been found consistently.[76, 98] Furthermore, in these experiments the nature of the fat is at least as important as its amount in the diet.[61, 75, 76] Tumors developed less rapidly in rats fed rations containing olive oil than in those given corn oil, while the feeding of hydrogenated coconut oil retarded tumor formation significantly. The rate of tumor production in rats on diets containing either 20 per cent Crisco (partially hydrogenated cottonseed oil) or 20 per cent lard was no greater than that in rats fed rations with 5 per cent corn oil.

Other Tumors

In contrast to the augmenting influence of fat-enriched diets on the formation of the spontaneous mammary carcinoma and the induced skin neoplasms, and probably hepatic tumors, comparable increases in dietary fat did not increase the incidence of sarcoma induced by subcutaneous injection of carcinogenic hydrocarbons,[6, 66, 92, 108] of primary lung adenoma,[108] or of spontaneous and induced leukemia in mice.[67]

Characteristics of the Fat Effect

Several investigations have extended and refined our knowledge on the significance of high-fat diets. In one of these, the comparative influence of a fat-enriched diet on the formation of 3,4-benzpyrene induced skin tumors under conditions employing either a moderate or high dosage of carcinogen was determined.[114] The expected result occurred when moderate amounts of carcinogen were applied to the skin: more neoplasms developed, and these appeared at an earlier time. On the other hand, in both the control and fat-enriched groups practically 100 per cent of the mice receiving the high dosage of carcinogen developed tumors. Yet the neoplasms occurring in the mice of the high-fat group appeared at a significantly earlier time. Thus, although the massive dose of carcinogen obliterated or overrode the influence of fat-enrichment insofar as the incidence of tumors was concerned, the augmenting effect still manifested itself in the earlier time of appearance of the neoplasms.

In the section dealing with caloric restriction it was pointed out that this dietary change exerted its main effect in the developmental stage of carcinogenesis. The action of fat-enriched diets on the two stages of carcinogenesis of skin tumors, initiation and development, has also been studied.[65, 110] There is agreement that fat-enriched diets augment skin tumor formation more effectively when fed after the period of carcinogen application (during the developmental stage) than when fed only in the period of carcinogen application (during the initiatory stage).

Another question that arose in our laboratory was the quantitative relation between the degree of fat-enrichment of the diet and the formation of tumors, inasmuch as the enhancement of mammary and skin carcinogenesis appeared to be no greater in some experiments utilizing 30 per cent dietary fat than in others employing only 12 per cent. The influence of graded proportions of fat was appraised in studies with the spontaneous mammary carcinoma.[100] The concentration of dietary fat varied from 2 to 26 per cent; equicaloric diets were utilized and the mean body weights of the several experimental groups were similar. It was concluded that the rate of formation of mammary carcinoma, as measured by both incidence of tumors and average age at tumor appearance, tended to increase with increasing proportions of dietary fat. However, the effect was not arithmetically proportional to the level of fat: the enhancement of tumor formation resulting from increasing the dietary fat from 2 to 6 or 8 per cent was as great as that resulting from an increase from 6 or 8 per cent to 24 or 26 per cent. The effect appeared to reach a plateau with almost maximum augmentation at about 16 per cent. In agreement with this finding is the result of Boutwell, Brush, and Rusch[16] who found that a diet containing 61 per cent fat stimulated the formation of induced skin tumors to about the same extent as one containing 27 per cent.

With either the mammary or skin tumor, the enhancing effect of fat is demonstrable at various levels of caloric intake.[16, 112] Tumor formation was accelerated by fat enrichment of the diet whether the caloric intake (of both control and fat-enriched diets) was in the vicinity of 7 Calories per mouse daily or at near *ad libitum* levels (approximately 12 Calories).

Mode of Action of Fat-Enriched Diets

A wide variety of fats has been utilized in attempts to modify the production of skin tumors. The results were not related to the nature of the fat:[65] partially hydrogenated cottonseed oil, butterfat, corn oil, lard, etc. (glycerides of fatty acids of considerable variability, together with a small percentage of other substances). That the enhancement of tumor formation is due to the fatty acid fraction of the vegetable shortening utilized was demonstrated by hydrolyzing the fat, removing the unsaponifiable matter, reconstituting the fatty acids to glycerides, and feeding this material in place of the original fat.[66] Ethyl laurate produced about the same effect as hydrogenated cottonseed oil, whereas glycerol and the unsaponifiable fraction had less influence. The suggestion has been made that purified glycerides might be utilized in experiments of this nature, but it is questionable whether the cost and results would justify this refinement.

For many years we have been engaged in the intellectual pursuit of considering whether the "fat effect" might be mediated through the "caloric effect" or vice versa. Actual investigations to test those possibilities have not been performed as no clear and acceptable experimental designs were forthcoming. Recently it was suggested that the increased efficiency of utilization of diets with high proportions of fat might be the factor responsible for the action of fat-enriched diets in accelerating the formation of carcinogen-induced skin tumors.[16] This "saving" of net body energy might be regarded as equivalent to an increase in caloric intake. However, the results of our experiments do not support this interpretation.[100] The influence on the "caloric value" of the diet is not sufficient to account for any except a small part of the augmenting effect of a high-fat diet. In addition, if the augmenting effect on tumor formation were mediated mainly through the increased net body energy gain, it could be expected that high-fat diets would enhance the formation of all the types of tumors affected by the level of caloric intake. However, of the tumors of the mouse which respond to varying the level of caloric intake, only the following are accelerated by fat-enrichment of the diet: spontaneous mammary carcinoma, tumors of the skin induced by ultraviolet radiation or carcinogenic chemicals, and possibly liver tumors. The incidence of induced sarcoma, spontaneous lung adenoma, induced leukemia, and spontaneous leukemia, all influenced by caloric intake, are not affected by fat-enriched diets.

We have suggested [108, 113] that substituting fat for equicaloric amounts of carbohydrate in the diet may affect the genesis of tumors by at least two means: (1) a solvent action, brought about by increased fat content of the tissue involved, under which condition the rate of transfer or amount of carcinogen is altered; and (2) an independent effect of fat on the developing tumor cell. This hypothesis was offered to explain the augmenting effect of a fat-enriched diet on the formation of spontaneous mammary and induced skin tumors, and the slight retardation of the genesis of carcinogen-induced sarcoma. The lack of an effect of a high-fat diet on the incidence of spontaneous lung adenoma may be due to the fact that the lung is not a fat depot and is therefore unaffected by varying percentages of fat in the diet. The influence of a fat-enriched diet on tumor formation in a given tissue may depend upon the extent to which the amount of fat in that tissue is modified by the diet.

PROTEIN

The protein content of the diet, in both its qualitative and quantitative aspects, has a profound influence on the nutritional state of the animal. Inadequate protein intake results in many changes, notably a loss in growth rate or body weight. This can occur despite a caloric intake that would be more than sufficient for optimal growth were the dietary protein adequate in amount and quality. To some extent the following conditions are comparable: the mouse restricted in caloric intake does not have the necessary energy sources; the protein-deficient animal lacks the building materials for somatic growth. There are considerable differences in the metabolic states of these animals, but there are also many points of similarity.

It is convenient to discuss separately two approaches employed in studies on protein supply in relation to tumor formation. The first utilizes diets in which nutritionally adequate protein is varied within proportions that support optimal growth and longevity, or nearly so. The second examines the influence of protein deficiency; here the results may be confounded by the effects of altered caloric intake and body weight.

Dietary Protein in the Range Adequate for Growth

When mice are fed diets *ad libitum*, those containing casein at the level of 9 per cent support body growth almost as well as those with higher proportions. This level (9 per cent) of dietary casein is minimal, as evidenced by the fact that on restricted equicaloric rations mice ingesting this proportion of casein do not grow as well as those fed diets containing 18 per cent or more.[115]

In experiments in which semipurified rations containing 9, 18, 27, 36, or 45 per cent casein as the source of protein were employed, no noteworthy differences were observed in the formation of spontaneous mammary carcinoma in mice.[115] Neither was the incidence or time of appearance of benzpyrene-induced skin tumors influenced to any significant degree. Nor was the formation of sarcoma affected by increasing the proportion of dietary protein from 18 to 32 per cent;[115] and from 13 to 26 per cent in diets fed *ad libitum* or from 20 to 40 per cent in calorie-restricted diets.[92] Thus with three diverse tumor-types no significant influence was obtained on the rates of formation or final incidence of neoplasms. Yet the proportion of protein in the diets had been varied from 9 to 45 per cent.

The incidences of spontaneous benign hepatomas in mice given either 18 or 45 per cent casein were of about the same order (Silverstone and Tannenbaum, unpublished data).[115] However, when mice were fed diets containing 9 per cent casein, significantly fewer developed hepatomas as compared with those on an 18 per cent casein ration. This result has been observed in mice of two strains and in females as well as in males. The phenomenon is not dependent on differences in caloric intake or body weight. In fact, the differences in hepatoma incidence were obtained both in groups of mice fed equicalorically and in others maintained at equivalent body weight levels.

The diversity in hepatoma incidence on the 9 and 18 per cent casein diets was not due to the difference in the amount of protein ingested, inasmuch as a diet containing 9 per cent casein plus 9 per cent gelatin resulted in no higher incidence of hepatomas than the one containing only 9 per cent casein. On the other hand, supplementing a 9 per cent casein ration with small amounts of methionine and cystine augmented the hepatoma incidence to that observed in mice on an 18 per cent casein diet. It was inferred that hepatoma formation in mice is dependent on the level of adequate protein (casein is somewhat deficient in sulfur-containing amino acids). A less likely interpretation would relate the results to the total amount of sulfur-containing amino acids.

The rate of formation of malignant liver neoplasms induced in rats by the feeding of carcinogenic azo dyes may also be influenced by the proportion of dietary protein. With this tumor, however, increased protein generally retards the rate of formation.[56, 77, 91, 98] Despite extensive studies the relation is not entirely clear. A variety of factors is involved, such as the level of riboflavin in the diet,[78] and the concentration of riboflavin in the liver,[73] the latter being favored by high dietary protein[95] and decreasing with ingestion of carcinogenic azo dyes.[42, 55] Griffin, Clayton, and Baumann[44] recently reviewed the subject, added further data, and brought some clarification into this field. They concluded that increasing the dietary casein from 12 to 24 per cent usually effects a decreased rate of formation of these liver neoplasms. In their opinion "it is doubtful whether the beneficial effects of dietary protein in rats fed azo dyes involves the critical carcinogenic reaction. More probably they represent merely another example of the ability of dietary protein to increase the resistance of animals to such diverse toxic agents as benzene, chloroform, arsphenamine, selenium, and the carcinogenic hydrocarbons."

The complexity of the subject is not so great, however, as to obscure a significant point of divergence between the effects of dietary protein on the rate of formation of the benign hepatoma of the mouse and the malignant hepatic rat tumor induced by azo dyes. Increasing dietary casein from 9 to 18 per cent enhances the former, probably inhibits the latter. Considering this in the light of the lack of any noteworthy effect on the spontaneous mammary carcinoma, induced skin tumor, and induced sarcoma, it can be seen that the liver stands out as a unique tissue with regard to the influence of nutrition on tumor formation.

Dietary Protein in Proportions or Amounts Inadequate for Normal Growth

White and associates have employed diets containing inadequate amounts of protein or specific amino acids in studies in which leukemia was induced by methylcholanthrene in a subline of DBA mice.[135] The diets were deficient in either sulfur-containing amino acids (4 or 5 per cent dietary casein), tryptophane (peroxide-treated casein), or lysine (12 or 14 per cent gliadin). They compared the resulting incidences of leukemia with those in groups fed the respective rations supplemented with the deficient amino acid. A typical set of results is summarized in Table 27.

It would seem that the induction of leukemia is inhibited by low dietary cystine (through a low casein diet), whereas similar restrictions of the essential amino

Table 27. Effect of Diet on the Incidence in DBA Mice of Leukemia Induced by Methylcholanthrene

*Diet**	*Body weight† change* (Gm.)	*Mice‡ developing leukemia* (%)	*Mean latent period* (da.)
Cystine-deficient[a]	−0.2	55	113
" " +0.5% L-cystine	+4.5	92	97
Lysine-deficient[b]	+0.4	90	124
" " +0.62 L-lysine	+6.2	90	110
Tryptophane-deficient[c]	0.0	85	136
" " +0.1% L-tryptophane	+5.3	88	91

From White *et al.*[135]

* The diets were semisynthetic rations with the following protein sources: [a] Cystine-deficient: 5 per cent casein. [b] Lysine-deficient: 18 per cent gliadin. [c] Tryptophane-deficient: 3 per cent casein, 7 per cent peroxide-treated casein, and 0.28 per cent methionine.

† Mean change in body weight during first 60 days of experiment.

‡ There were 38 to 40 mice initially in each experimental group. Very few deaths occurred from causes other than leukemia except in the group fed the cystine-deficient diet. Here there were a considerable number of deaths with aortic sclerosis at an average latent period of 121 days.

acids lysine or tryptophane (through other deficient proteins) have no comparable effect, except for slight retardation in time of appearance. It is true that the animals on the deficient diets ate less and weighed less, and that caloric restriction alone effects considerable inhibition of leukemia formation.[133] The authors state, "if one considers this as a possible effect produced by caloric restriction, then it is difficult to rationalize the marked decrease in leukemia in the cystine-restricted group and not in the lysine-restricted and tryptophane-restricted groups."[135] They further conclude that "cystine played a role in the development of leukemia not associated with its properties as an essential amino acid for growth but with some other attribute not yet determined."

The effects of lysine- or cystine-deficient diets on the formation of spontaneous mammary carcinoma in C3H female mice were also investigated by the same group[131, 134] using diets similar to those employed in the leukemia study. In both cases there was a significant reduction of tumor incidence from nearly 100 per cent in mice fed adequate protein, to 25 per cent in those fed 18 per cent gliadin (low in lysine), and none in those fed 4 per cent casein (low in cystine). The difference in tumor formation produced by the two deficiency states can be attributed to dissimilarities in body weight—those in the low lysine group averaged 21 Gm., those in the low cystine group, 13 Gm. The effect is virtually identical with that expected if the animals had been calorie-restricted to those levels of body weight. In another study diethylstilbestrol pellets were implanted subcutaneously in C3H female mice being fed a low cystine diet.[130] Approximately 45 per cent of these animals developed mammary carcinoma, compared with none in the controls not receiving the pellets. It is our interpretation that this is another example of the overriding effect of a high dosage of carcinogen, as discussed in the section on caloric intake.

Larsen and Heston[64] examined the effects of a low cystine diet on the formation of spontaneous lung tumors in mice. They restricted the food intake of one group of mice on the cystine-supplemented ration to that of the mice on the cystine-deficient ration. Under these conditions there was no difference in the incidences of lung tumors.

The effects of rations containing 5 per cent casein as the source of protein on the formation of hepatic tumors induced by azo dyes, have also been studied.[132] When the food intake (and consequently the intake of azo dye) was adequately controlled, it was found that an increase in dietary cystine, while having no effect on the incidence of tumors, did cause some delay in their time of appearance. This is in agreement with the findings on the protective action of increased protein and methionine on the induction of these tumors.[44]

VITAMINS

With few exceptions the genesis of tumors is significantly affected by the level of ingested vitamins only when a deficiency state is maintained, i.e., if the vitamin content is lowered to the point where food intake and body growth are depressed. It is interesting to note that, as with dietary protein, the most prominent exception is liver neoplasia.

Induced Skin Tumors

Boutwell and co-workers[17] studied the formation of skin tumors induced with benzpyrene under conditions in which 10 of the B-vitamins were varied as a group from levels estimated to be just adequate for maintenance to amounts considerably above the optimal. All diets were fed equicalorically. Individual members, pairs, and sets of B-vitamins were also decreased to minimal levels in the presence of adequate amounts of the remaining vitamins. There were no noteworthy differences in the incidences of total skin tumors or of carcinomas at six months after beginning application of carcinogen, except for a somewhat lower incidence of carcinomas in the group fed all vitamins at the lowest level. These mice showed some evidence of pyridoxine deficiency, an acrodynia that was reversed by a single treatment with pyridoxine. The authors considered that the decreased tumor incidence might have been the result of a low level of pyridoxine. They did not press this point too strongly, however, since one group which was fed a ration adequate in all B vitamins except pyridoxine developed nearly as many tumors as the controls. These mice showed no clinical evidence of pyridoxine deficiency at any time. Kline *et al.*[62] observed a possible inhibition of skin tumor formation in mice fed a pyridoxine-deficient ration; caloric intake and body weight were maintained at equivalent restricted levels in both the control and deficiency groups.

We have performed experiments in which the B vitamin complex was supplied at maintenance levels and in three-fold or nine-fold greater amounts (Tannenbaum and Silverstone, unpublished data). The diets were fed at just below *ad libitum* levels in equicaloric amounts. There were no recognizable deficiency symptoms during the experiments, approximately twelve months, except that the animals given the lowest levels of vitamins weighed about 10 per cent less than the other two groups. The final tumor incidences were of the same order, though the rate of formation was possibly a little slower in the low vitamin group. With reference to pyridoxine, it should be stated that it was present in our low vitamin diet in amounts several times greater than the quantities utilized as maintenance by the Wisconsin group.

When the B vitamins are supplied beyond minimal needs, wide variation in dietary content has little influence on the formation of skin tumors. Certainly high levels have no influence as compared with amounts generally considered adequate for maintenance and growth.

Spontaneous Mammary Carcinoma

Two experiments comparable to the preceding, but with the spontaneous mammary carcinoma, have been performed (Tannenbaum and Silverstone, unpublished data). Here too, mice on the low vitamin diets weighed approximately 10 per cent less than those receiving three or nine times the minimal amounts employed. Among the three groups in each study, there were no differences in the incidence of tumors although, as with induced skin tumors, they appeared somewhat later in the groups on the low vitamin intake.

Morris and associates have conducted extensive experiments on the influence of vitamin deficiency states on the genesis of spontaneously occurring mammary carcinoma in mice.[81] They reported that a riboflavin deficiency, or partial deficiency, led to a reduced incidence of these tumors. Of importance, however, is the fact that body weights and food consumption of the deficient mice were also significantly lower.

Primary Lung Adenoma

Taylor and Williams[119] investigated the action of diets either high or low in B vitamins on the formation of spontaneous lung tumors in Strain A mice. At the time the experiment was discontinued the tumor incidences of the three groups were: control, 60 per cent; excess vitamin, 72 per cent; diluted vitamin, 47 per cent. The differences probably can be accounted for by the numbers of deaths not due to lung tumors. The authors state, "The data suggests that the higher tumor incidence in the 'excess vitamin' group was due to the fact that these animals were less susceptible to non-tumorous diseases, while the vitamin deficiency animals had a lowered tumor incidence because these mice were more susceptible to diseases other than cancer."

Brain Tumors

Russell has induced brain tumors by inoculating rats intracerebrally with pellets of methylcholanthrene.[94] Only a small number of animals was utilized, yet it appeared that periodic removal of thiamin and riboflavin from the diets accelerated the production of tumors of nervous tissue. On the other hand, the deficiency had no effect upon the induction time of fibrosarcomas derived from connective tissue.

Spontaneous Benign Hepatoma

In studies with the spontaneous benign liver tumor of the C3H male mouse, it was found that slight restriction of riboflavin or of total B vitamins, as compared with optimal or excess concentrations, had no great influence on the rate of formation of this neoplasm.[101] While hepatomas developed in slightly fewer of the animals on the restricted vitamin diets, this result could be attributed to their lower body weight.

Hepatic Tumors Induced by Azo Dyes

The early Japanese workers and others conducted extensive experimentation on the influence of dietary alterations on the development of liver tumors in rats fed *para*-dimethylaminoazobenzene ("butter yellow"). The field has already been reviewed to 1946.[86, 91] Only the effect of varying the proportion of vitamins is discussed here, with emphasis on the hindering action of low dietary riboflavin.

Kensler and associates focused attention on the importance of the level of riboflavin, in an otherwise adequate diet, on the development of liver tumors induced by azo dyes.[55, 56] An extensive study by the Wisconsin group, including a survey of 34 diets, indicated that supplements unusually rich in both protein and B vitamins, particularly riboflavin, inhibited tumor formation.[77]

Evidence has steadily accumulated that it is not the particular diet in itself, but rather the resultant concentration of riboflavin in the liver that is a pivotal factor in the genesis of liver neoplasms induced by carcinogenic azo dyes.[42, 43, 53] For example, it appears that increased protein in itself has little direct effect, but acts rather by altering the concentration of riboflavin in the liver.[27, 44, 95] Furthermore, it has been shown that riboflavin might be a coenzyme precursor or coenzyme in the systems that metabolize the azo dye.[54, 83]

Although riboflavin plays such an important role in the genesis of neoplasms of the liver of the rat induced by feeding azo dyes, its effect is not of the same order for all carcinogens of this class.[35] Furthermore, it seems to have little or no significance in the induction of hepatic tumors in rats fed acetylaminofluorene.[45]

Variations in the levels of other B vitamins, except for biotin and pyridoxine, are not considered to have any appreciable effect on the incidence of hepatic tumors induced by azo dyes. When rats were fed egg-white albumin as the principal source of protein the formation of the liver neoplasms was inhibited.[19] The retardation was considered to be the consequence of a biotin deficiency caused by the complexing of this vitamin with the avidin in the egg-white; the fact that the addition of excess biotin to this ration resulted in an increase in tumor incidence supported this interpretation. On the other hand, there is evidence that egg-white protein, independent of its avidin content or of the biotin supply to the animal, also inhibits the formation of liver neoplasia.[46, 60] Egg-white, as compared with casein, favors riboflavin storage in the liver, thereby protecting against the carcinogenic action of the dye.[74] With regard to pyridoxine, it has been shown that low dietary levels retard the genesis of azo-dye-induced hepatomas. The effect, however, is dependent on the previous nutritional history of the animal and on the protein content of the diet.[72, 78]

The following study is a good example of the common experience—that in general, adequate nutrition is a necessary prerequisite for the development of tumors.[78] Young mature rats were given a semipurified ration containing levels of B vitamins that, for the six-month period of study, just about maintained control animals (not given the azo dye) at their initial weight. Addition of *para*-dimethylaminoazobenzene to the diet of an experimental group caused them to lose weight; some died and none of the survivors at 6 months had liver tumors. In the rations of various groups, single vitamins were incorporated at decreased or very greatly increased levels without changing the others; nevertheless, on none of these did more than one of the surviving rats develop tumors. Under these conditions, even a low level of riboflavin, known to be a key factor in the genesis of these neoplasms, failed to evoke them.

Hepatic Tumors Induced by Choline Deficiency

Copeland, Salmon, and Engel[26, 31] have reported that among rats severely deficient in choline, liver tumors develop in a high proportion of the animals. This was accomplished in a special strain of rats having a high requirement for choline, and with diets so deficient in choline that periodic administration of this vitamin was necessary to prevent death from acute choline deficiency. The authors state that "the choline-deficient rats were in reasonably good condition for several months. Following this they gradually became unthrifty in appearance. There was marked loss of hair, muscular weakness, drowsiness, and lethargy. In some, the eyes became lusterless and opaque following earlier hemorrhage."

A great variety of pathologic changes were found in organs and tissues, some obviously of an inflammatory nature. Of main interest was the liver. Here advanced cirrhosis was found in all rats that received the choline-deficient diet for eight months or longer. In roughly 40 per cent of these animals hepatomas were found. To the reviewer many of these appear to be benign. These experiments indicate that tumors developed, in the absence of a known carcinogen, through the severe depletion of a single vitamin. They occurred in livers that were the seat of acute fatty and degenerative changes, and which under continued insult became cirrhotic.

It will be of interest and value to follow the development of this field. Are these hepatomas hyperplastic nodules of regenerating tissue in a severely damaged liver? Or are they true tumors, caused by injury due to dietary deficiency? And if the latter, do these findings support the often expressed view that tumors arise, not by stimulation of normal cells, but as an adaptation to conditions which injure and impair the growth of normal cells, whether these carcinogenic conditions be of physical, chemical, or parasitic origin? May severe dietary deficiencies, in special circumstances, be added to this list?

MINERALS

Several inorganic substances can be more or less directly implicated in the genesis of tumors, such as arsenic, beryllium, chromates, or radium and other radioactive elements. None of these, however, is a normal dietary constituent. There are conflicting reports on the influence of sodium, potassium, calcium, and magnesium salts on the genesis of tumors, a situation partly due to the small numbers of animals utilized.

Studies have been conducted on the influence of semipurified diets containing 2, 4, or 8 per cent of a relatively complete salt mixture (Tannenbaum and Silverstone, unpublished data). The tumors investigated were the benzpyrene-induced skin tumor and the spontaneous mammary carcinoma of the mouse. The salt mixture, Wesson's modification of the Osborne-Mendel formula, contained only inorganic substances. With each tumor-type two experiments were performed: in one the food was given *ad libitum*, in the second in equicaloric amounts. When the diets were fed *ad libitum*, the mice on the high salt diet consumed fewer calories and weighed about 10 per cent less than those given the intermediate salt ration, which in turn weighed about 5 per cent less than those on the lowest salt diet. The higher the salt content, the lower the caloric intake and body weight. The incidences of tumors and rates of appearance also decreased with increasing dietary salt but the differences were small. As an incidental finding, comparable results were observed with the spontaneous hepatoma. When the food intakes were kept equicaloric, the average body weights of the mice on 2 or 4 per cent salt were equivalent, while those of the animals receiving 8 per cent salt were about 10 per cent less. No differences in the ultimate incidences of tumors were observed. Thus, so far as induced skin tumors and spontaneous mammary carcinoma are concerned, modification of the proportion of dietary salts within limits supporting good body growth had no noteworthy effect on carcinogenesis.

SUMMARY

The genesis of neoplasms is in part dependent on the nutritional state of the host. Caloric restriction strikingly inhibits the formation of many tumor-types: spontaneous mammary carcinoma, skin tumors induced by carcinogenic hydrocarbons or ultraviolet light, induced sarcoma, spontaneous lung adenoma, spontaneous hepatoma, and spontaneous and induced leukemia, all of the mouse; and lymphosarcoma and induced mammary carcinoma of rats. With only slight reservation, it may be said that the retarding effect of restriction in caloric intake has been demonstrated with all tumor-types investigated. The magnitude of the inhibitory effect is modified by the type of tumor, dose and potency of the carcinogenic agent, and the degree of caloric restriction. The action appears to occur mainly in the developmental rather than in the initiatory stage of carcinogenesis.

In contrast to the arresting and relatively consistent inhibitory influence of caloric restriction are the effects of fat-enrichment of the diet. The genesis of the spontaneous mammary carcinoma and induced skin tumor is somewhat enhanced by high-fat rations. Hepatic tumors, spontaneous and induced, also appear to form more readily when the animals ingest these diets. Contrariwise, no noteworthy effect has been observed with the induced sarcoma, primary lung adenoma, and spontaneous and induced leukemia. Where fat enrichment favored carcinogenesis, the major effect occurred when the dietary fat was increased from very low proportions (2 per cent or less) to a level of approximately 8 per cent of the diet.

As with fat, the influence of dietary protein apparently varies with the nature of the tumor. The incidence of some tumor-types is not influenced by the level of dietary protein varied within ranges supporting normal or near normal growth. The formation of the spontaneous hepatoma of the mouse is inhibited, however, by low dietary protein whereas that of liver tumors induced in rats by azo dyes is generally enhanced. Retardation of the genesis of certain tumors through the feeding of diets deficient in total protein or an essential amino acid has been reported.

Increasing the proportion of B vitamins or of salts in the diet from minimal to many times optimal levels has no noteworthy influence on the formation of the spontaneous mammary or induced skin tumors, and of the spontaneous hepatoma of the mouse. Although diets deficient in vitamins generally depress the body weight and the genesis of tumors, extensive investigations have demonstrated that low proportions of dietary riboflavin enhance the formation of liver tumors induced in rats by *p*-dimethylaminoazobenzene. The induction of liver tumors in rats by means of a choline-deficient diet, without the presence of a known carcinogen, has been reported.

EFFECTS OF DIET ON THE GROWTH OF TUMORS

In investigations concerned with the influence of nutritional alterations on the *growth* of tumors, the term is properly confined to the enlargement of the tumor, regardless of whether it originally developed in the experimental animal or was implanted. With induced or spontaneous neoplasms, growth must be differentiated from origin. With transplanted tumors, growth should be considered apart from the processes involved in the establishment or "take" of the tumor; in interpreting the results of experiments in which such a separation is not achieved, either because of neglect or practical obstacles, it is frequently impossible to decide whether the experimental procedure modified the establishment of the implant or influenced its actual growth.

The significance of various nutrients, deficient or abundant, and of uncommon diets has been investigated, and a great variety of tumor-types and technics have been employed. Unfortunately and understandably, the number of conclusive findings is not commensurate with the time and effort expended. Contradictory findings are often reported for a specific nutrient—a variability arising from a great many factors. Different types of neoplasms might well respond in different ways. The magnitude of the deficiency or abundance of a nutrient maintained in the animal undoubtedly modifies the effect. The method of comparison employed often determines the emphasis which the investigator places on his data—for example, criteria of longevity, absolute increase in tumor volume in a specific time interval, or relative growth rate, may result in somewhat different "appraisals" of the same facts.

Despite, and because of, the paucity of definitive acceptable findings on the effects of nutrition on tumor growth, it is concluded in the following discussion that dietary alterations in animals bearing already established tumors have, in the main, relatively small effects. Or, when of appreciable magnitude, the practical value is negated by concomitant deleterious influences on the host.

CALORIC INTAKE

Available evidence suggests that overnutrition favors, while undernutrition inhibits, the growth of tumors. More specifically related to caloric intake are the many reports that underfeeding retards the growth of transplanted tumors.[13, 79, 89, 104] Bischoff and Long[12] demonstrated that the inhibition of growth was due to caloric restriction (restriction of either starch or fat only). In at least some of these studies, there was a clear separation between establishment and growth of the neoplasms.

The growth of mammary carcinomas that have arisen in full-fed mice is significantly diminished when the animals are transferred to a calorie-restricted diet (Tannenbaum, unpublished data).[105] However, there is only a small beneficial influence on the life span of the animal. Comparable effects on growth have been obtained with sarcomas that were induced by benzpyrene in full-fed mice.

Flory *et al.*[33] found with some strains of transmissible mouse leukemia that underfeeding, as compared with an *ad libitum* diet, prolonged the lives of animals previously given intravenous inoculations of leukemic cells. With myeloid leukemia 106 the average survival of underfed mice was 21 days, in comparison with 14 days for the control mice. The dietary restriction was begun the day after inoculation and the question arises as to whether the underfeeding delayed the establishment of the leukemia or actually inhibited subsequent proliferation (growth).

Moreover, with myeloid leukemia 1712 the average life span was unaffected or even somewhat shortened by underfeeding.

Underfeeding or calorie restriction alone is not a practical means of affecting the growth of tumors. A drastic decrease in food intake can retard the growth of a tumor, but at the same time the body weight of the host diminishes. It is questionable whether the life span of the tumor-bearing animal can be greatly increased by this procedure.

FAT

The level of fat in the diet has not been found to play a role in the growth of tumors. The rate of growth of sarcomas induced in mice fed fat-enriched diets did not differ from those arising in control mice given a diet low in fat.[6, 108] Transplanted tumors were also unaffected by a high-fat diet.[6] Growth rates of spontaneous mammary carcinoma and the longevity of the tumor-bearing mice were studied in experiments which utilized equicaloric diets containing different proportions of fat.[100] It was found that the average increase in size of the tumors formed in a group consuming a 2 per cent fat ration was virtually identical with that of a group receiving 24 per cent fat. Furthermore, the mean survival time of a mouse after the appearance of a tumor was unaffected by the proportion (2, 4, 8, 16, or 24 per cent) of dietary fat.

PROTEIN

Both the quality and quantity of dietary protein must be considered in relation to the growth of tumors. There is a difference in the effects when the protein is: (1) varied within limits that will yet permit good body growth and health; or (2) relatively complete but inadequate in amount, or in customary amounts but deficient in one or more essential amino acids. Diets in the first category have little effect upon the growth of tumors, whereas those in the second category may be inhibitory.

Adequate Protein

When groups of mice were fed diets containing varying proportions of casein (between 9 and 45 per cent) or mixed proteins within these proportions, they grew well and at relatively the same rate.[115] In three separate experiments, there was no regular association between the proportions of dietary protein and the average growth rates of the spontaneous mammary tumors that developed. In another experiment, in which C3H male mice were utilized, spontaneous hepatomas found at the termination of the study were of the same mean size in the several groups (receiving 9, 18, or 45 per cent dietary casein). It was inferred from this that the growth rates were similar. In a third investigation, sarcomas induced by subcutaneous injections of 3,4-benzpyrene grew at the same average rate in groups of mice consuming diets containing either 18 or 32 per cent protein. A similar result with induced sarcomas has been reported by others.[92]

Mild Deficiency

Moderate deficiency of dietary protein appears to have only a slight influence on the growth of tumors. Devik and co-workers[28] reported only a small inhibitory effect on the growth rate of transplanted Walker rat tumor 256. The body growth of rats maintained on a diet containing 5 per cent casein was considerably less than that of rats on 20 per cent casein. Nevertheless, the ultimate weight of the tumors averaged approximately 20 Gm. for the rats on 5 per cent, and 24 Gm. for those on 20 per cent casein. The tumors were transplanted into the hosts after they had been on the experimental diets for about one week, and were "harvested" fourteen days later. Strikingly similar results were obtained by Green and Lushbaugh,[40] utilizing the same tumor and approximately the same conditions. With rat hepatoma 31, Voegtlin and Thompson[124] also reported that restricting the protein to about 6 per cent casein caused the animals a loss in weight without greatly influencing the rate of tumor growth.

Severe Deficiency

In contrast to the above reports are the results obtained through the use of diets severely deficient in particular amino acids or in total protein. Voegtlin and associates[82, 121, 122, 123] have shown that diets insufficient in lysine or cystine and methionine retard the growth of spontaneous mammary tumors. Kocher[63] also investigated the effect of lysine deficiency on the same tumor type. He observed that when the inadequate diet was fed for a considerable period (the tumors were approximately 10 to 20 mm. in diameter initially) the inhibiting effect on growth was transient, the tumor resuming normal rapid growth after thirty to sixty days. When the lysine-deficient diet was given to animals with tumors approximately 25 mm. in diameter the inhibiting effect was either not apparent or of very short duration.

Florence White and Belkin,[129] in a model experiment of this kind, reported on the effect of a low-nitrogen diet on the establishment and growth of a transplanted mammary adenocarcinoma of the mouse. The protein of the experimental diet was restricted to that contained in the 5 per cent liver extract supplement, stated to be inadequate in at least four essential amino acids. The mice ingesting this diet remained in a state of continuous negative nitrogen balance and lost considerable body weight during the experiment. As compared with the controls, the establishment of the transplanted tumors was not affected by the experimental diet which had been instituted one week before inoculation. The effect of protein depletion on the growth of the tumor was evidenced in the somewhat slower growth rate (approximately 74 per cent of that in the controls) and the smaller mean volumes (less than 50 per cent of the controls) at the end of the 21-day experimental period. Green and associates[39] performed a somewhat similar experiment, utilizing the transplantable Walker rat tumor 256. One group of rats were protein-depleted for eight to twelve weeks and had lost 25 to 35 per cent of their pre-depletion body weight before being inoculated with the tumor. The establishment of the transplant was delayed. However, once the tumors became palpable they grew at essentially the same relative rate as those in the control group (although the absolute rate of growth was less). The animals were sacrificed fourteen days after implantation. The tumors in the rats fed the 1 per cent casein diet were only one-fourth the size of those in the rats fed the 22 per cent casein ration.

Mode of Action

Low dietary protein appears to retard the establishment of transplanted tumors. This conclusion is based on the following considerations. The remarkable investigations of Algire and Chalkley[3] have demonstrated the significance of the vascular reaction to the implantation of tumors. Growth of the implants did not become evident until the initial vascularization (of the implant) was accomplished, on about the fifth day. Complementary observations were made by Devik *et al.*[28] in their studies on the growth of the transplanted Walker tumor 256. They noted that the initial reaction of the host-tissues took place within the first forty-eight hours. An inflammatory exudate appeared around the graft, followed by the development of a primitive connective tissue network into which the tumor cells began to migrate. A rapid ingrowth of capillaries accompanied the organization of the connective tissue "capsule" and completed the *establishment* of the tumor graft by the fourth to seventh day. Then tumor cells migrated from the graft into the capsule of connective tissue and underwent mitosis; thus the tumor began to *grow* and spread.

The tissue reaction described is not peculiar to tumor transplants. Comparable changes were observed when normal tissues were injured or transplanted. What is of interest to us at this time, however, is the differential response of the host tissue depending upon the protein content of the diet. It was found that four days after grafting, the intensity of the inflammatory reaction around the implant was greater in rats maintained on the 5 per cent than in those on the 20 per cent casein diet. On the other hand, the capsule of connective tissue was much less distinct in the rats on the 5 per cent casein diet. Hence it appeared that as a consequence of low dietary protein there was a greater inflammatory reaction and less organization of the capsule. The differences were more clearly demonstrated by examination of the tumors seven, eight, and ten days after implantation. In rats on the high-protein diet, the migration of tumor cells was negligible and the tumors grew through the very high rate of cell proliferation at the periphery of the tumor parenchyma. With the low-protein diet, however, there was no definite tumor boundary and many isolated tumor cells could be seen in the loose, primitive network of connective tissue. The implants in the rats on the high-protein diet were already growing, while those in the rats on the low-protein diet had just been established.

Critical consideration of all the experimental work on the effects of dietary protein on the growth of transplanted tumors leads to the following impressions. Whether the dietary protein is high or low, there is at first a response of the host represented by an inflammatory exudate. This is followed in a few days by the development of connective tissue and a vascular bed, around and within the tumor implant. Diets adequate in protein permit these processes to occur at the "normal" rate, whereas diets low in protein inhibit them. Once established, however, the tumor grows—increases in size and weight—accumulating protein even while the host may be in marked negative nitrogen balance. Perhaps the most impressive feature is that the tumor grows at the expense of the host.

It is evident, therefore, that the actual growth of spontaneous, induced, and transplanted tumors is less affected by the proportion of protein in the diet than is the host. Moreover, in many instances the reported retardation of the "growth" of transplanted tumors through rations severely deficient in protein was in reality a combination of inhibition of establishment of the implant and of its subsequent growth.

VITAMINS

Tumors, as well as normal tissues, need vitamins for viability and growth. There has been the implicit hope, however, that the vitamin requirements of normal and neoplastic tissues would differ, at least quantitatively. Mainly as a consequence of this anticipated difference, there have been numerous investigations on the influence of vitamins on the growth of tumors. Some have utilized excess amounts of vitamins; most have been concerned with moderate to severe deficiencies. Virtually all the known vitamins have been studied.

In 1944, Burk and Winzler[20] published an extensive review of this subject. They pointed out the many difficulties specifically inherent in the planning, execution, and interpretation of investigations in this field. They felt that some criticism could be levelled at practically all the reports, but with great understanding refrained from doing so. They listed as complicating factors the need for: ascertaining the existence of alleged vitamin deficiencies; regulating caloric intake; employing more appropriate vitamin levels, and more exactly defined diets; recognizing the existence of multiple deficiencies; performing vitamin analyses of basal diet and pertinent tissues or body fluids; understanding the role of intestinal synthesis and destruction, absorption, detoxification, and coprophagy (principles of nutrition generally); using more animals in individual experiments, and purer stocks; extending results to several types of tumors; and distinguishing between tumor establishment and tumor growth.

Since Burk and Winzler's review there has been some improvement in experimental approach but no great advance in fundamental knowledge. It is intended here therefore, merely to mention a few examples of recent research.

Stoerck and Emerson,[103] in experiments with mouse lymphosarcoma C3H-ED, found that the induction of pyridoxine or riboflavin deficiencies caused tumor regression. The tumors were established before treatment was begun and deficiency was produced by the use of vitamin analogues as antagonists. The tumors recurred if the pyridoxine deficiency was corrected but not when the riboflavin deprivation was relieved. Analogues of thiamin, folic acid, or niacin had no influence on the growth of the neoplasm. The authors concluded that this lymphosarcoma probably has a high requirement for riboflavin, and that immunization processes probably play a role in the prevention of recurrences.

Little and co-workers[68] claim that the Rous chicken sarcoma has a relatively specific requirement for folic acid. Establishment of the tumor and possibly its growth were markedly inhibited by a folic acid deficiency, while deprivation of other vitamins had no effect except when the chicks were depleted to "dangerous" levels.

Folic acid antagonists have generally been reported to inhibit certain kinds of transmissible mouse leukemia and a few other mouse tumors. However, Kirschbaum, *et al.*[59] point out that therapy was usually begun shortly after inoculation of the tumor and that interference in some instances was possibly not with growth but with the initial tumor-host relation. In studies with four different transplanted leukemias, they found that if the leukemia were "established," i.e. allowed to proliferate for about ten days before treatment, neither aminopterin nor amethopterin were strikingly effective in prolonging the life of the animals.

Voegtlin and Thompson studied the influence of diet on established implants of hepatoma 31.[124] This is a transplantable liver tumor originally induced in a rat by means of *para*-dimethylaminoazobenzene. Large amounts of riboflavin and biotin promoted the growth of this tumor far beyond any effect on the animal's food intake or weight.

A report by Robertson and co-workers[88] on the influence of ascorbic acid deficiency is of interest. They examined the growth of a transplantable sarcoma in guinea pigs placed on a scorbutic diet about ten days after implantation. Tumor growth slowed down appreciably before any changes in food consumption or body weight were noted and the tumors attained a weight approximately one-fourth that in the control pigs. A significant finding was the greatly altered stroma and the decrease in the collagen of the tumors in the scorbutic animals.

SUMMARY

With regard to induced and spontaneous neoplasms, the major influence of dietary alterations is on genesis rather than on growth. In the case of transplanted tumors, both the establishment of the implant and its subsequent growth are affected by diet. However, referring specifically to growth, a perspective of the limited influence of nutritive changes is attained from the realization that a tumor may increase in size even while the host is losing weight.

Caloric restriction inhibits the growth of neoplasms, but the life span of the animal is not markedly lengthened. Increasing the fat content of the diet has not been found to influence the size of tumors. Variations in proportions of protein within limits that do not greatly affect the growth or weight of the host have no effect on the growth of neoplasms. Rations severely deficient in protein, however, hinder the growth of tumors, but it appears that the retardation may occur partly through voluntary caloric restriction. Such dietary measures also inhibit the establishment of transplanted tumors. The rate of growth of tumors is not significantly influenced by the vitamin intake except when the rations are deficient. Under the latter conditions there may be inhibition. Diets deficient in fats, proteins, vitamins, or minerals have not been shown to have a specific action on the growth of neoplasms.

IMPLICATIONS AND EXTENSIONS OF NUTRITIONAL STUDIES

Studies on nutrition in relation to the origin and growth of neoplasms have revealed many facts; refinements in this field and interdisciplinary approaches will yield further enlightenment. Particularly promising are the investigations directed toward elucidating the mechanisms of the effects produced by dietary alterations, and the attempts to combine dietary and chemotherapeutic approaches. The established principles, however, already have connotations for investigators not concerned primarily with nutritional studies. Caloric restriction or deprivation of particular nutrients may be part of the plan of an experiment but may also occur without the intention of the investigator. Irradiation, chemotherapeutic agents, or hormones, administered to experimental animals, may reduce their food consumption and body weight; or increase the dietary requirements for particular nutrients. An experimental procedure may induce diarrhea. Pulmonary or gastrointestinal infections may occur during the course of an investigation. All such procedures and conditions, as well as others, could result in altered metabolism, subnormal food consumption, or lower body weight of the experimental animal.

If, under any of the above conditions, the formation or growth of tumors is decreased (from normal expectations), it becomes necessary to decide whether the observed effect is consequent to the experimental procedure per se or to the accompanying undernutrition and decreased body growth. In no way is it implied that all experimental procedures mediate their influence through caloric intake or body weight; rather, for more exact interpretation, the nutritional states and body weights of both the control and experimental animals should be known.

Differentiation must also be made between the effect of an experimental procedure on the establishment of a transplanted tumor and on its subsequent growth. It is now known that the tissue changes necessary for the establishment or "take" of an implant require approximately four to seven days. The primitive connective tissue network and the primary vascularization process must be completed before the neoplastic cells can divide and migrate from the injection nidus—that is, begin to grow. It has also been demonstrated that the establishment of implants is delayed in animals ingesting low protein diets, and it is probable that rations with other inadequacies have the same influence. Possibly a similar effect on tumor establishment would follow if the effect of an experimental procedure resulted in either decreased food intake or a poorer nutritional state of the host.

This is emphasized since many investigators have administered chemotherapeutic compounds simultaneously with, or one or two days after, the implantation of a tumor suspension or fragment—and considered the resulting "tumor inhibition" indicative of the action of the agent on the growth of the neoplasm. Actually, under these conditions, the influence may be a combination of the effect on *establishment* and the effect on *growth*. This dichotomy must be recognized—and respected—for more exact interpretation. Possibly, with certain procedures, the influence is mainly on the rate of establishment, not on the rate of growth.

Not only have investigators sought information on the direct relation of nutrition to the genesis and growth of neoplasms but more recently the question as to whether nutrition may influence the action of another experimental procedure has been studied. Thus, some experiments on the growth of tumors have advanced from a single-factor approach (dietary alteration) to a two-factor approach (dietary alteration, other experimental procedure).

The following experiment by Elson and Haddow[30] illustrates this point. They found that the inhibiting action of intraperitoneally injected 1,2,5,6-dibenzanthracene on the growth of the transplanted Walker rat tumor 256 was dependent on the protein content of the diet. Growth inhibition increased with decreasing proportion of dietary protein. A similar relation was observed in experiments utilizing 2′-chloro-4-dimethylaminostilbene administered to groups of rats receiving diets containing either 20 or 5 per cent protein.

This latter finding has been confirmed by Green and Lushbaugh,[40] who used 4-dimethylaminostilbene and diets containing 22 or 5 per cent casein. They concluded that the inhibitory effect of the aminostilbene was in part dependent on the nutritional state of the rats.

The significance of the nutritional condition of the host on the response of a transplanted tumor to radiation has been studied by Devik and associates.[28] The initial "growth" of the tumor was inhibited by radiation to a greater extent in the rats on a 5 per cent casein diet as compared with those on a ration containing 20 per cent casein. In contrast, however, the slower growing tumors (of the 5 per cent casein group) continued to increase in size, whereas the faster growing ones (of the 20 per cent casein group) stopped, and even regressed.

These experiments have been briefly reviewed to indicate what may be expected of combining nutritional and other approaches in a single study. They draw attention to the significance of the nutritional state of the host as related to the cancer process.

ROLE OF NUTRITION IN HUMAN CANCER

Experimental observations on the relation of nutrition to cancer have been made mainly in animals. This section presents information implying that dietary deficiencies may play a definite, though at present unexplained, role in the production of some types of tumors in man. The subject has received attention in various textbooks on cancer and pathology and in a review by Hueper.[48] In contrast to these few instances are the data suggesting that neoplasms as a group occur more frequently in persons who overeat and are therefore overweight.

LIVER CANCER

In many areas of the world primary cancer of the liver accounts for a large proportion of all malignant neoplasms. A high incidence occurs among African Negroes, particularly Bantus, employed as miners in the gold mines near Johannesburg; and among natives of Southeastern Asia: China, Japan, Java, and Sumatra.[10, 14, 36] On the other hand, primary cancer of the liver is relatively rare among Caucasians,[10, 87] and among Negroes living under European or American standards.[52] The high rate of liver cancers among the affected populations has been variously ascribed to some special racial susceptibility, to endemic infection, or to nutritional deficiencies.

The major etiologic factor does not appear to be racial or infectious in nature. There remains the dietary theory, which has found an increasing number of supporters in recent years inasmuch as the neoplasms are associated with, or developed within, cirrhotic livers.[11] In this respect, it is an arresting fact that in one study cirrhosis of the liver was found in 4 out of every 5 autopsies performed on male Bantus at the Johannesburg General Hospital.[36]

A dietary origin for primary liver cancers is suspected, since: (1) the diet of the native groups susceptible to the tumors is of poor quality; (2) dietary deficiencies in protein and B vitamins are known to produce cirrhosis of the liver in experimental animals; and (3) cirrhosis of the liver in man is frequently associated with primary cancer of the liver. In excellent studies, Gillman and associates have shown that severe liver damage, ranging from diffuse fatty changes to multilobar cirrhosis, occurred in rats fed cornmeal mush and sour milk, the principal diet of the Bantus. Frank cirrhosis was found in about 20 per cent of the rats.[37, 38] These experimental observations, coupled with pathologic and clinical data on man, are circumstantial evidence in support of the view that in man diet may play a major role in the production of primary cancer of the liver.

It is becoming increasingly evident that one common denominator—among those groups prone to primary liver cancer—is malnutrition. The Bantus live almost exclusively on maize meal supplemented by fermented cow's milk, and consume very little meat—a diet lacking in protein and low in vitamins. For some, poverty dictates even limited supplies of this inadequate dietary. Comparably, the staple diet of the Far-Eastern races is rice; beri-beri, pellagra, and other forms of malnutrition are common among Javanese and Chinese.

Berman, in an excellent monograph,[11a] has carefully presented the known facts and—while cognizant that much more evidence and study are needed—suggests that primary hepatic cancer may be due to a sequence of events, a combination of environmental conditions. Malnutrition, by injuring the liver, may make it more vulnerable to a variety of infections and toxic substances that may have carcinogenic potentialities. In the light of present knowledge this appears to be a reasonable assumption. It is known that the ingestion of certain crude substances—chilli peppers, alkaloids of *Senecio jacobaea*, and wheat or maize containing selenium—may induce primary hepatic neoplasms in rats. To this list perhaps one may add other unknown carcinogens in foods and beverages, and the products of parasitic and bacterial infections. These might act individually in large amounts, or through the additive effects of small quantities of several of these agents.

PHARYNGEAL CANCER

Ahlbom has pointed out the frequency with which carcinoma of the oral cavity, pharynx, or esophagus in women is accompanied by the Plummer-Vinson syndrome.[2] The syndrome is characterized by anemia, achlorhydria, and general signs of atrophy of the mucous membrane, mouth, and pharynx; hyperkeratoses of the oral and nasapharyngeal mucosa develop later. Ultimately cancer may appear.[1, 2] Ahlbom, at the Radiumhemmet in Stockholm, found this syndrome in 65 per cent of 123 women with cancer of the mouth, pharynx, or esophagus. It is believed to be due to an unbalanced, possibly iron- and vitamin-deficient diet, such as that eaten by inhabitants of those parts of Sweden and Finland located within the Arctic Circle. Here the main dietary throughout the year consists of reindeer meat and salt fish. Only during the short summer are green vegetables available.[1, 2] The evidence and reasoning with regard to the pathogenesis of these tumors is suggestive.

THYROID CANCER

The incidence of cancer of the thyroid appears to be related to that of nodular goiter. Thus Bérard and Dunet, cited by Wegelin,[128] concluded on the basis of operative statistics that in endemic goitrous regions from 2.5 to 4.0 per cent of all malignant tumors arose in the thyroid, whereas in goiter-free areas the percentage is only 0.4 to 0.5. Wegelin noted the much greater relative frequency of thyroid cancer in necropsies in Berne, the center of a goitrous area, than in Vienna, Prague, or Berlin. Operative and autopsy statistics are in agreement that the incidence of these neoplasms is about ten times as frequent in Switzerland as in the United States. Studies in this country also suggest that the nontoxic nodular goiter is a precursor of malignancy.[25, 125] Some students of this subject have stated that as high as 90 per cent of thyroid carcinomas have been found to arise in pre-existing adenomas.

Where goiter is endemic, malignant tumors of the thyroid are present in significantly greater numbers, and endemic goiter appears in regions where there is an iodine deficiency in the soil, drinking water, and foodstuffs. Thus, thyroid cancer seems to be related to the occurrence of endemic goiter in population groups enduring a dietary iodine deficiency.

RELATION OF BODY WEIGHT TO CANCER INCIDENCE

In view of the striking influence of underfeeding on tumor formation in mice, the writer became interested in the possible significance of this finding with respect to cancer in man. The method of approach, the difficulties encountered, and the results have already been detailed.[106, 113] A brief summary follows.

For many years insurance companies have been studying the relationship of various social and biologic factors to the principal causes of death. Some of these studies throw light on the relationship of body weight to cancer mortality. Although the statistics refer to mortality, they also mirror incidence.

A review[106] of six available insurance studies and of one extensive study on dietary habits by Hoffman[47] indicates that individuals who overeat and are overweight when past middle age are more likely to die of cancer than are persons of average weight or less.

A typical study is that of Dublin, who used approximately 192,000 records (1887-1921) of the Union Central Life Insurance Company for an analysis of cancer mortality. The policy-holders, men who had bought insurance at 45 years of age and over, were classified according to weight *at issue of policy*. The analysis resulted in the distribution, shown in Table 28, of cancer mortality with regard to weight. There is a sufficiently consistent gradation in mortality rates to indicate that cancer incidence increases with increasing weight.

The findings in the insurance records represent summations or net effects for cancers of all types and sites. Obviously, certain neoplasms may be more vulnerable to the factors controlling body weight than others, just as calorie restriction of mice influences some tumor-types more than others. Actually, this is suggested in the few studies in which the cancers were classified according to site. The classifications of the tumors differed in details, and the conclusions were not always consistent. Yet the weight of evidence suggests that cancers of the intestines, liver and gallbladder, and genitourinary organs are correlated with body weight to a greater extent than are those in other sites.

TABLE 28. BODY WEIGHT AND CANCER MORTALITY

Weight at issue of policy	*Cancer mortality per hundred thousand*
25% or more overweight	143
15 to 25% overweight	138
5 to 15% overweight	121
normal weight	111
5 to 15% underweight	114
15 to 50% underweight	95

In a recently reported clinical study, it was found that cancer of the endometrium was present in greater frequency in overweight women than in women of lighter build. Of 389 patients with this disease, 44 per cent weighed more than 160 pounds; among women in the same age groups in the general population only 34 per cent weigh more than 160 pounds. Other observers have reported an abnormally high frequency of obesity in women with cancer of the uterus.

What is the practical significance of this apparent relationship between body weight and cancer incidence? Particularly because a similar inference had been derived from extensive animal experimentation, it was concluded that the avoidance of overweight might result in the *prevention* of a considerable number of some types of cancer in man, or at least, the neoplasms may be delayed in time of appearance. Such a regimen is already known to act prophylactically in other degenerative diseases, such as diabetes, heart disease, cerebral hemorrhage, and arthritis.

There are some who have raised the question of the difficulty—and the advisability—of attempting to keep an individual's weight at average or just below average levels. Others speak only of "drastic" dietary measures, and ignore the fact that both animal studies and insurance statistics indicate that the effects are in accord with a dose-response relationship: that even moderate continued caloric restriction or reduction in weight decreases the incidence of tumors.

It cannot be emphasized too strongly that the conclusions concerning the association between cancer and weight hold only for formation of tumors and not for the treatment of cancer once it has developed. Present evidence suggests that it is unlikely that underfeeding or caloric restriction alone is a practical means of affecting the growth of an established tumor.

CONCLUDING COMMENTS

The large number of diseases collectively termed cancer react in a variety of ways to the nutritional state of the host. Nevertheless, a degree of order and apprehension has been achieved.

The results of extensive animal investigations and available statistical and clinical data on man indicate that the *genesis* of tumors is enhanced by nutritional adequacy and abundance. Stated conversely and somewhat more specifically, caloric restriction strikingly inhibits the development of neoplasms; proportions of dietary fat, protein, and vitamins that are considered to be below the minimum for good nutrition also tend to repress tumor formation. On the other hand, there is evidence that the production of a few tumor-types is augmented by dietary deficiencies, particularly of proteins and vitamins. This occurs, in the main, in the liver, which from the viewpoint of carcinogenesis may be a unique organ.

Do dietary factors also play a role in modifying the *growth* of neoplasms? Probably to a lesser extent than in their genesis. Perhaps this is due to the greater growth potential of tumors in comparison with normal tissues: Neoplasms may increase in size while the animal is losing weight—in fact, at the expense of the host's normal tissues. Although deprivation in calories, protein, vitamins, or minerals may retard the growth of tumors, these dietary restrictions are deleterious to the host to the extent that the over-all benefit is limited.

The diet must be looked upon, in general, as a modifier of the cancer process, not as an initiator. Moreover, the diverse characteristics of the numerous types of neoplasms preclude the possibility that one particular dietary regimen would inhibit the genesis and growth of all of them. More facts on the relation of nutrition to cancer are obviously needed, as well as an understanding of the underlying mechanisms. These may well result in fundamental unifying concepts and comprehension of the cancer process.

BIBLIOGRAPHY

1. ADAIR, F. E. Prophylaxis of cancer. *Bull. New York Acad. Med. 23:* 383-393, 1947.
2. AHLBOM, H. E. Simple achlorhydric anaemia, Plummer-Vinson syndrome, and carcinoma of the mouth, pharynx, and oesophagus in women. *Brit. M. J. 2:* 331-333, 1936.
3. ALGIRE, G. H., and CHALKLEY, H. W. Vascular reactions of normal and malignant tissues in vivo: I. Vascular reactions of mice to wounds and to normal and neoplastic transplants. *J. Nat. Cancer Inst. 6:* 73-85, 1945.
4. BALL, Z. B., BARNES, R. H., and VISSCHER, M. B. The effects of dietary caloric restriction on maturity and senescence with particular reference to fertility and longevity. *Am. J. Physiol. 150:* 511-519, 1947.
5. BAUMANN, C. A. Diet and tumor development. *J. Am. Dietet. A. 24:* 573-581, 1948.
6. BAUMANN, C. A., JACOBI, H. P., and RUSCH, H. P. The effect of diet upon experimental tumor production. *Am. J. Hyg.* Sec. A., *30:* 1-6, 1939.
7. BAUMANN, C. A., and RUSCH, H. P. Effect of diet on tumors induced by ultraviolet light. *Am. J. Cancer 35:* 213-221, 1939.
8. BERENBLUM, I. The mechanism of carcinogenesis: A study of the significance of cocarcinogenic action and related phenomena. *Cancer Research 1:* 807-814, 1941.
9. BERENBLUM, I., and SHUBIK, P. An experimental study of the initiating stage of carcinogenesis and a re-examination of the somatic cell mutation theory of cancer. *Brit. J. Cancer 3:* 109-118, 1949.

10. Berman, C. Primary carcinoma of the liver in the Bantu races of South Africa. *South African J. M. Sc. 5:* 54-72, 1940.
11. Berman, C. The pathology of primary carcinoma of the liver in the Bantu races of South Africa. *South African J. M. Sc. 6:* 11-26, 1941.
11a. Berman, C. *Primary Carcinoma of the Liver.* London, H. K. Lewis, 1951.
12. Bischoff, F., and Long, M. L. The influence of calories per se upon the growth of sarcoma 180. *Am. J. Cancer 32:* 418-421, 1938.
13. Bischoff, F., Long, M. L., and Maxwell, L. C. Influence of caloric intake upon the growth of sarcoma 180. *Am. J. Cancer 24:* 549-553, 1935.
14. Bonne, C. Cancer and human races. *Am. J. Cancer 30:* 435-454, 1937.
15. Boutwell, R. K., Brush, M. K., and Rusch, H. P. Some physiological effects associated with chronic caloric restriction. *Am. J. Physiol. 154:* 517-524, 1948.
16. Boutwell, R. K., Brush, M. K., and Rusch, H. P. The stimulating effect of dietary fat on carcinogenesis. *Cancer Research 9:* 741-746, 1949.
17. Boutwell, R. K., Brush, M. K., and Rusch, H. P. The influence of vitamins of the B complex on the induction of epithelial tumors in mice. *Cancer Research 9:* 747-752, 1949.
18. Bullough, W. S. Mitotic activity and carcinogenesis. *Brit. J. Cancer 4:* 329-336, 1950.
19. Burk, D., Spangler, J. M., du Vigneaud, V., Kensler, C., Sugiura K., and Rhoads, C. P. Biotin-avidin balance in *p*-dimethylaminoazobenzene tumor formation. *Cancer Research 3:* 130-131, 1943.
20. Burk, D., and Winzler, R. J. "Vitamins and cancer." In *Vitamins and Hormones: Advances in Research and Applications.* New York, Academic Press, 1944, vol. 2, pp. 305-352.
21. Cannon, M. D., Boutwell, R. K., and Elvehjem, C. A. The vitamin content of casein. *Science 102:* 529-530, 1945.
22. Carlson, A. J., and Hoelzel, F. Apparent prolongation of the life span of rats by intermittent fasting. *J. Nutrition 31:* 363-375, 1946.
23. Caspari, W. *Nutrition and Cancer.* Paris, Hermann & Cie, 1938.
24. Clayton, C. C., and Baumann, C. A. Diet and azo dye tumors: Effect of diet during a period when the dye is not fed. *Cancer Research 9:* 575-582, 1949.
25. Cole, W. H., Slaughter, D. P., and Rossiter, L. J. Potential dangers of nontoxic nodular goiter. *J. A. M. A. 127:* 883-888, 1945.
26. Copeland, D. H., and Salmon, W. D. The occurrence of neoplasms in the liver, lungs, and other tissues of rats as a result of prolonged choline deficiency. *Am. J. Path. 22:* 1059-1079, 1946.
27. Czaczkes, J. W., and Guggenheim, K. The influence of diet on the riboflavin metabolism of the rat. *J. Biol. Chem. 162:* 267-274, 1946.
28. Devik, F., Elson, L. A., Koller, P. C., and Lamerton, L. F. The influence of diet on the Walker rat carcinoma 256, and its response to x-radiation: Cytological and histological investigations. *Brit. J. Cancer 4:* 298-314, 1950.
29. Dunning, W. F., Curtis, M. R., and Maun, M. E. The effect of dietary fat and carbohydrate on diethylstilbestrol-induced mammary cancer in rats. *Cancer Research 9:* 354-361, 1949.
30. Elson, L. A., and Haddow, A. The inhibitory action of 1:2:5:6-dibenzanthracene on the growth of the Walker carcinoma 256 in rats maintained on high and low protein diets. *Brit. J. Cancer 1:* 97-101, 1947.

31. Engel, R. W., Copeland, D. H., and Salmon, W. D. Carcinogenic effects associated with diets deficient in choline and related nutrients. *Ann. New York Acad. Sc. 49*, Art. 1: 49-67, 1947.

32. Fisher, R. A., and Yates, F. *Statistical Tables for Biological, Agricultural, and Medical Research* (ed. 2). London, Oliver and Boyd, Ltd., 1943, pp. 8-11.

33. Flory, C. M., Furth, J., Saxton, J. A. Jr., and Reiner, L. Chemotherapeutic studies on transmitted mouse leukemia. *Cancer Research 3:* 729-743, 1943.

34. Friedewald, W. F., and Rous, P. The pathogenesis of deferred cancer. A study of the after-effects of methylcholanthrene upon rabbit skin. *J. Exper. Med. 91:* 459-484, 1950.

35. Giese, J. E., Clayton, C. C., Miller, E. C., and Baumann, C. A. The effect of certain diets on hepatic tumor formation due to *m'*-methyl-*p*-dimethylaminoazobenzene and *o'*-methyl-*p*-dimethylaminoazobenzene. *Cancer Research 6:* 679-684, 1946.

36. Gilbert, C., and Gillman, J. Diet and disease in the Bantu. *Science 99:* 398-399, 1944.

37. Gillman, J. Effects on rats of prolonged feeding with the staple African diet. *Brit. M. J. 1:* 149-150, 1944.

38. Gillman, J., Gillman, T., Mandelstam, J., and Gilbert, C. The production of severe hepatic injury in rats by the prolonged feeding of maize-meal porridge (mealie-pap) and sour milk. *Brit. J. Exper. Path. 26:* 67-81, 1945.

39. Green, J. W., Benditt, E. P., and Humphreys, E. M. The effect of protein depletion on the host response to transplanted rat tumor Walker 256. *Cancer Research 10:* 769-774, 1950.

40. Green, J. W., and Lushbaugh, C. C. Histopathologic study of the mode of inhibition of cellular proliferation: Effect of 4-dimethylaminostilbene on the growth of Walker rat carcinoma 256. *Cancer Research 9:* 692-700, 1949.

41. Greenstein, J. P. *Biochemistry of Cancer.* New York, Academic Press, 1947.

42. Griffin, A. C., and Baumann, C. A. The effect of certain azo dyes upon the storage of riboflavin in the liver. *Arch. Biochem. 11:* 467-476, 1946.

43. Griffin, A. C., and Baumann, C. A. Hepatic riboflavin and tumor formation in rats fed azo dyes in various diets. *Cancer Research 8:* 279-284, 1948.

44. Griffin, A. C., Clayton, C. C., and Baumann, C. A. The effects of casein and methionine on the retention of hepatic riboflavin and on the development of liver tumors in rats fed certain azo dyes. *Cancer Research 9:* 82-87, 1949.

45. Harris, P. N. Production of tumors in rats by 2-aminofluorene and 2-acetylaminofluorene: Failure of liver extract and of dietary protein level to influence liver tumor production. *Cancer Research 7:* 88-94, 1947.

46. Harris, P. N. The effect of diet containing dried egg albumen upon *p*-dimethylaminoazobenzene carcinogenesis. *Cancer Research 7:* 178-179, 1947.

47. Hoffman, F. L. *Cancer and Diet.* Baltimore, Md., Williams and Wilkins, 1937.

48. Hueper, W. C. Environmental and occupational cancer. Supplement 209, *Public Health Reports,* pp. 26-28. Washington, U. S. Govt. Printing Office, 1948.

49. Huseby, R. A., Ball, Z. B., and Visscher, M. B. Further observations on the influence of simple caloric restriction on mammary cancer incidence and related phenomena in C3H mice. *Cancer Research 5:* 40-46, 1945.

50. Jacobi, H. P., and Baumann, C. A. The effect of fat on tumor formation. *Am. J. Cancer 39:* 338-342, 1940.

51. JOHANSSON, K. R., and SARLES, W. B. Some considerations of the biological importance of intestinal micro-organisms. *Bact. Rev. 13:* 25-45, 1949.

52. KENNAWAY, E. L. Cancer of the liver in the Negro in Africa and in America. *Cancer Research 4:* 571-577, 1944.

53. KENSLER, C. J. Effect of diet on the production of liver tumors in the rat by N,N-dimethyl-*p*-aminoazobenzene. *Ann. New York Acad. Sc. 49,* Art. 1: 29-40, 1947.

54. KENSLER, C. J. The influence of diet on the ability of rat-liver slices to destroy the carcinogen N,N-dimethyl-*p*-aminoazobenzene. *Cancer 1:* 483-488, 1948.

55. KENSLER, C. J., SUGIURA, K., and RHOADS, C. P. Coenzyme I and riboflavin content of livers of rats fed butter yellow. *Science 91:* 623, 1940.

56. KENSLER, C. J., SUGIURA, K., YOUNG, N. F., HALTER, C. R., and RHOADS, C. P. Partial protection of rats by riboflavin with casein against liver cancer caused by dimethylaminoazobenzene. *Science 93:* 308-310, 1941.

57. KING, C. J., *et al.* Nutrition in relation to cancer. *Ann. New York Acad. Sc. 49,* Art. 1: 1-140, 1947.

58. KING, J. T., CASAS, C. B., and VISSCHER, M. B. The influence of estrogen on cancer incidence and adrenal changes in ovariectomized mice on caloric restriction. *Cancer Research 9:* 436-437, 1949.

59. KIRSCHBAUM, A., GEISSE, N. C., JUDD, T., and MEYER, L. M. Effect of certain folic acid antagonists on transplanted myeloid and lymphoid leukemias of the F strain of mice. *Cancer Research 10:* 762-768, 1950.

60. KLINE, B. E., MILLER, J. A., and RUSCH, H. P. Certain effects of egg white and biotin on the carcinogenicity of *p*-dimethylaminoazobenzene in rats fed a subprotective level of riboflavin. *Cancer Research 5:* 641-643, 1945.

61. KLINE, B. E., MILLER, J. A., RUSCH, H. P., and BAUMANN, C. A. Certain effects of dietary fats on the production of liver tumors in rats fed *p*-dimethylaminoazobenzene. *Cancer Research 6:* 5-7, 1946.

62. KLINE, B. E., RUSCH, H. P., BAUMANN, C. A., and LAVIK, P. S. The effect of pyridoxine on tumor growth. *Cancer Research 3:* 825-829, 1943.

63. KOCHER, R. A. The effects of a low lysine diet on the growth of spontaneous mammary tumors in mice and the N balance in man. *Cancer Research 4:* 251-256, 1944.

64. LARSEN, C. D., and HESTON, W. E. Effects of cystine and calorie restriction on the incidence of spontaneous pulmonary tumors in Strain A mice. *J. Nat. Cancer Inst. 6:* 31-40, 1945.

65. LAVIK, P. S., and BAUMANN, C. A. Dietary fat and tumor formation. *Cancer Research 1:* 181-187, 1941.

66. LAVIK, P. S., and BAUMANN, C. A. Further studies on the tumor-promoting action of fat. *Cancer Research 3:* 749-756, 1943.

67. LAWRASON, F. D., and KIRSCHBAUM, A. Dietary fat with reference to the spontaneous appearance and induction of leukemia in mice. *Proc. Soc. Exper. Biol. & Med. 56:* 6-7, 1944.

68. LITTLE, P. A., OLESON, J. J., and SUBBAROW, Y. The effect of nutrition on the tumor response in Rous chicken sarcoma. *J. Lab. & Clin. Med. 33:* 1139-1143, 1948.

69. MACKENZIE, I., and ROUS, P. The experimental disclosure of latent neoplastic changes in tarred skin. *J. Exper. Med. 73:* 391-416, 1941.

70. McCay, C. M., Crowell, M. F., and Maynard, L. A. The effect of retarded growth upon the length of life span and upon the ultimate body size. *J. Nutrition 10:* 63-79, 1935.

71. McCay, C. M., Ellis, G. H., Barnes, L., Smith, C. A. H., and Sperling, G. Chemical and pathological changes in ageing and after retarded growth. *J. Nutrition 18:* 15-25, 1939.

72. Miller, E. C., Baumann, C. A., and Rusch, H. P. Certain effects of dietary pyridoxine and casein on the carcinogenicity of *p*-dimethylaminoazobenzene. *Cancer Research 5:* 713-715, 1945.

73. Miller, E. C., Miller, J. A., Kline, B. E., and Rusch, H. P. Correlation of the level of hepatic riboflavin with the appearance of liver tumors in rats fed aminoazo dyes. *J. Exper. Med. 88:* 89-98, 1948.

74. Miller, J. A. Studies on the mechanism of the effects of fats and other dietary factors on carcinogenesis by the azo dyes. *Ann. New York Acad. Sc. 49,* Art. 1: 19-28, 1947.

75. Miller, J. A., Kline, B. E., Rusch, H. P., and Baumann, C. A. The carcinogenicity of *p*-dimethylaminoazobenzene in diets containing hydrogenated coconut oil. *Cancer Research 4:* 153-158, 1944.

76. Miller, J. A., Kline, B. E., Rusch, H. P., and Baumann, C. A. The effect of certain lipids on the carcinogenicity of *p*-dimethylaminoazobenzene. *Cancer Research 4:* 756-761, 1944.

77. Miller, J. A., Miner, D. L., Rusch, H. P., and Baumann, C. A. Diet and hepatic tumor formation. *Cancer Research 1:* 699-708, 1941.

78. Miner, D. L., Miller, J. A., Baumann, C. A., and Rusch, H. P. The effect of pyridoxin and other B vitamins on the production of liver cancer with *p*-dimethylaminoazobenzene. *Cancer Research 3:* 296-302, 1943.

79. Moreschi, C. Relation between nutrition and tumor growth. *Ztschr. f. Immunitätsforsch. u. exper. Therap. 2:* 651-675, 1909.

80. Morris, H. P. Some nutritional factors influencing the origin and development of cancer. *J. Nat. Cancer Inst. 6:* 1-17, 1945.

81. Morris, H. P. Effects on the genesis and growth of tumors associated with vitamin intake. *Ann. New York Acad. Sc. 49,* Art. 1: 119-140, 1947.

82. Morris, H. P., and Voegtlin, C. The effects of methionine on normal and tumor growth. *J. Biol. Chem. 133:* lxix-lxx, 1940.

83. Mueller, G. C., and Miller, J. A. The reductive cleavage of 4-dimethylaminoazobenzene by rat liver: Reactivation of carbon-dioxide treated homogenates by riboflavin-adenine dinucleotides. *J. Biol. Chem. 185:* 145-154, 1950.

84. Mulinos, M. G., and Pomerantz, L. Pseudo-hypophysectomy: A condition resembling hypophysectomy produced by malnutrition. *J. Nutrition 19:* 493-504, 1940.

85. Opie, E. L. The influence of diet on the production of tumors of the liver by butter yellow. *J. Exper. Med. 80:* 219-230, 1944.

86. Opie, E. L. "The influence of diet on the production of hepatic tumors induced by *p*-dimethylaminoazobenzene." In *Approaches to Tumor Chemotherapy.* Lancaster, Pa., Science Press, 1947, pp. 128-138.

87. Pack, G. T., and LeFevre, R. G. The age and sex distribution and incidence of neoplastic diseases at Memorial Hospital, New York City. *J. Cancer Research 14:* 167-294, 1930.

88. ROBERTSON, W. VAN B., DALTON, A. J., and HESTON, W. E. Changes in a transplanted fibrosarcoma associated with ascorbic acid deficiency. *J. Nat. Cancer Inst. 10:* 53-60, 1949.
89. ROUS, P. The influence of diet on transplanted and spontaneous mouse tumors. *J. Exper. Med. 20:* 433-451, 1914.
90. ROUS, P., and KIDD, J. G. Conditional neoplasms and sub-threshold neoplastic states: A study of the tar tumors of rabbits. *J. Exper. Med. 73:* 365-390, 1941.
91. RUSCH, H. P., BAUMANN, C. A., MILLER, J. A., and KLINE, B. E. "Experimental liver tumors." In *A.A.A.S. Research Conference on Cancer.* Lancaster, Pa., Science Press, 1945, pp. 267-290.
92. RUSCH, H. P., JOHNSON, R. O., and KLINE, B. E. The relationship of caloric intake and of blood sugar to sarcogenesis in mice. *Cancer Research 5:* 705-712, 1945.
93. RUSCH, H. P., KLINE, B. E., and BAUMANN, C. A. The influence of caloric restriction and of dietary fat on tumor formation with ultraviolet radiation. *Cancer Research 5:* 431-435, 1945.
94. RUSSELL, W. O. The response of the central nervous system of the rat to methylcholanthrene: II. The effect of a diet deficient in thiamine and riboflavin on the induction of tumors derived from nervous tissue. *Cancer Research 5:* 152-156, 1945.
95. SARETT, H. P., and PERLZWEIG, W. A. The effect of protein and B vitamin levels of the diet upon the tissue content and balance of riboflavin and nicotinic acid in rats. *J. Nutrition 25:* 173-183, 1943.
96. SAXTON, J. A. JR. An experimental study of nutrition and age as factors in the pathogenesis of common diseases of the rat. *New York State J. Med. 41:* 1095-1096, 1941.
97. SAXTON, J. A. JR., BOON, M. C., and FURTH, J. Observations on the inhibition and development of spontaneous leukemia in mice by underfeeding. *Cancer Research 4:* 401-409, 1944.
98. SILVERSTONE, H. The levels of carcinogenic azo dyes in the livers of rats fed various diets containing *p*-dimethylaminoazobenzene: Relationship to the formation of hepatomas. *Cancer Research 8:* 301-308, 1948.
99. SILVERSTONE, H., and TANNENBAUM, A. Influence of thyroid hormone on the formation of induced skin tumors in mice. *Cancer Research 9:* 684-688, 1949.
100. SILVERSTONE, H., and TANNENBAUM, A. The effect of the proportion of dietary fat on the rate of formation of mammary carcinoma in mice. *Cancer Research 10:* 448-453, 1950.
101. SILVERSTONE, H., and TANNENBAUM, A. The influence of dietary fat and riboflavin on the formation of spontaneous hepatomas in the mouse. *Cancer Research 11:* 200-203, 1951.
102. STERN, K., and WILLHEIM, R. *The Biochemistry of Malignant Tumors.* New York, Reference Press, 1943.
103. STOERCK, H. C., and EMERSON, G. A. Complete regression of lymphosarcoma implants following temporary induction of riboflavin deficiency in mice. *Proc. Soc. Exper. Biol. & Med. 70:* 703-704, 1949.
104. SUGIURA, K., and BENEDICT, S. R. The influence of insufficient diets upon tumor recurrence and growth in rats and mice. *J. Cancer Research 10:* 309-318, 1926.
105. TANNENBAUM, A. The initiation and growth of tumors. Introduction: I. Effects of underfeeding. *Am. J. Cancer 38:* 335-350, 1940.

106. TANNENBAUM, A. Relationship of body weight to cancer incidence. *Arch. Path. 30:* 509-517, 1940.
107. TANNENBAUM, A. The genesis and growth of tumors: II. Effect of caloric restriction per se. *Cancer Research 2:* 460-467, 1942.
108. TANNENBAUM, A. The genesis and growth of tumors: III. Effects of a high-fat diet. *Cancer Research 2:* 468-475, 1942.
109. TANNENBAUM, A. The dependence of the genesis of induced skin tumors on the caloric intake during different stages of carcinogenesis. *Cancer Research 4:* 673-677, 1944.
110. TANNENBAUM, A. The dependence of the genesis of induced skin tumors on the fat content of the diet during different stages of carcinogenesis. *Cancer Research 4:* 683-687, 1944.
111. TANNENBAUM, A. The dependence of tumor formation on the degree of caloric restriction. *Cancer Research 5:* 609-615, 1945.
112. TANNENBAUM, A. The dependence of tumor formation on the composition of the calorie-restricted diet as well as on the degree of restriction. *Cancer Research 5:* 616-625, 1945.
113. TANNENBAUM, A. "The role of nutrition in the origin and growth of tumors." In *Approaches to Tumor Chemotherapy.* Lancaster, Pa., Science Press, 1947, pp. 96-127.
114. TANNENBAUM, A., and SILVERSTONE, H. Dosage of carcinogen as a modifying factor in evaluating experimental procedures expected to influence formation of skin tumors. *Cancer Research 7:* 567-574, 1947.
115. TANNENBAUM, A., and SILVERSTONE, H. The genesis and growth of tumors: IV. Effects of varying the proportion of protein (casein) in the diet. *Cancer Research 9:* 162-173, 1949.
116. TANNENBAUM, A., and SILVERSTONE, H. Effect of low environmental temperature, dinitrophenol, or sodium fluoride on the formation of tumors in mice. *Cancer Research 9:* 403-410, 1949.
117. TANNENBAUM, A., and SILVERSTONE, H. The influence of the degree of caloric restriction on the formation of skin tumors and hepatomas in mice. *Cancer Research 9:* 724-727, 1949.
118. TANNENBAUM, A., and SILVERSTONE, H. Failure to inhibit the formation of mammary carcinoma in mice by intermittent fasting. *Cancer Research 10:* 577-579, 1950.
119. TAYLOR, A., and WILLIAMS, R. J. Diet and spontaneous lung tumors in Strain A mice. *University of Texas Publication,* No. *4507:* 119-122, 1945.
120. VISSCHER, M. B., BALL, Z. B., BARNES, R. H., and SIVERTSEN, I. The influence of caloric restriction upon the incidence of spontaneous mammary carcinoma in mice. *Surgery 11:* 48-55, 1942.
121. VOEGTLIN, C., JOHNSON, J. M., and THOMPSON, J. W. Glutathione and malignant growth. *Pub. Health Rep. 51:* 1689-1697, 1936.
122. VOEGTLIN, C., and MAVER, M. E. Lysine and malignant growth: II. The effect on malignant growth of a gliadin diet. *Pub. Health Rep. 51:* 1436-1444, 1936.
123. VOEGTLIN, C., and THOMPSON, J. W. Lysine and malignant growth: I. The amino acid lysine as a factor controlling the growth rate of a typical neoplasm. *Pub. Health Rep. 51:* 1429-1436, 1936.
124. VOEGTLIN, C., and THOMPSON, J. W. Differential growth of malignant and nonmalignant tissues in rats bearing hepatoma 31: Influence of dietary protein, riboflavin, and biotin. *J. Nat. Cancer Inst. 10:* 29-52, 1949.

125. WARD, R. Malignant goiter. *Surgery 16:* 783-803, 1944.
126. WATERMAN, N. *Diet and Cancer: An Experimental Study.* Amsterdam, D. B. Centen's Uitgevers-Maatschappij, 1938.
127. WATSON, A. E., and MELLANBY, E. Tar cancer in mice: II. The condition of the skin when modified by external treatment or diet, as a factor in influencing the cancerous reaction. *Brit. J. Exper. Path. 11:* 311-322, 1930.
128. WEGELIN, C. Malignant disease of the thyroid gland and its relations to goitre in man and animals. *Cancer Rev. 3:* 297-313, 1928.
129. WHITE, F. R., and BELKIN, M. Source of tumor proteins: I. Effect of a low-nitrogen diet on the establishment and growth of a transplanted tumor. *J. Nat. Cancer Inst. 5:* 261-263, 1945.
130. WHITE, F. R., and WHITE, J. Effect of diethylstilbestrol on mammary tumor formation in Strain C3H mice fed a low cystine diet. *J. Nat. Cancer Inst. 4:* 413-415, 1944.
131. WHITE, F. R., and WHITE, J. Effect of a low lysine diet on mammary-tumor formation in Strain C3H mice. *J. Nat. Cancer Inst. 5:* 41-42, 1944.
132. WHITE, F. R., and WHITE, J. Effect of cystine per se on the formation of hepatomas in rats following the ingestion of *p*-dimethylaminoazobenzene. *J. Nat. Cancer Inst. 7:* 99-101, 1946.
133. WHITE, F. R., WHITE, J., MIDER, G. B., KELLY, M. G., and HESTON, W. E. Effect of caloric restriction on mammary-tumor formation in Strain C3H mice and on the response of Strain DBA to painting with methylcholanthrene. *J. Nat. Cancer Inst. 5:* 43-48, 1944.
134. WHITE, J., and ANDERVONT, H. B. Effect of a diet relatively low in cystine on the production of spontaneous mammary-gland tumors in Strain C3H female mice. *J. Nat. Cancer Inst. 3:* 449-451, 1943.
135. WHITE, J., WHITE, F. R., and MIDER, G. B. Effect of diets deficient in certain amino acids on the induction of leukemia in DBA mice. *J. Nat. Cancer Inst. 7:* 199-202, 1947.

PART II

Chemistry and Physics

CHAPTER 16

The Chemical and Genetic Mechanisms of Carcinogenesis

I. NATURE AND MODE OF ACTION

Alexander Haddow

NATURE AND VARIETY OF CARCINOGENIC AGENTS

The early history of carcinogenesis has been sketched elsewhere (Haddow and Kon, 1947), starting from Percival Pott's description of cancer of the skin in chimney-sweeps (cancer scroti), in *Chirurgical Observations*, 1775, and other accounts of the same disease by a long line of English surgeons including Earle, Astley Cooper, Hughes Bennett, Paget, and Butlin. The interest and importance of this condition lay in the proof which it brought of the environmental origin of at least one form of cancer, namely from contamination of the skin by soot. This by itself would without doubt have served as a sufficiently powerful stimulus to later investigation, but was reinforced, in the second half of the nineteenth century, by other and fresh accounts of cancer as an industrial hazard. Thus in 1875 von Volkmann discovered occupational skin tumors among the workers in the tar and paraffin industry at Halle. In the following year, Joseph Bell of Edinburgh described the earliest cases in the Scottish shalefield of "paraffin cancer," the natural history of which was to be related by Alexander Scott (1923) almost fifty years afterwards. Still later, in 1887, was found the first example of skin cancer affecting operatives in the Lancashire cotton-spinning industry, attributable to occupational contact with mineral oil used in lubrication—the so-called "mule-spinners' cancer."

All these phenomena were the outcome of one or other aspect of current industrialization. How frequent such environmental effects have been and still are, can be seen from the accounts of Henry (1947, 1950), and Cruickshank and Squire (1950), on cutaneous cancer in relation to occupation, of Woodhouse (1950) and Auld (1950) on the carcinogenic activity of petroleum fractions and extracts, and from the comprehensive surveys of Heller (1930) and Hueper (1948, 1950a,b), the last dealing with both present and potential cancer hazards in the operations of modern industry, and referring, among organic agents, to "anthracene oil," aromatic amines, benzol, "creosote oil," petroleum crudes and fractions, shale oil and lignite oil, tar, pitch, asphalt, and soot. Smith, Sunderland, and Sugiura (1951) have studied the carcinogenic activity of oils boiling above 370° C. obtained from petroleum by the fluid catalytic cracking process: the most potent material distils between 426° C. and 543° C., and within this range there is no great segregation of activity in narrow cuts, suggesting the presence of more than one carcinogen. Fischer, Priestley, Eby, Wanless, and Rehner (1951; see also Blanding, King, Priestley, and Rehner 1951, and Sunderland, Smith, and Sugiura 1951) have also examined the carcinogenicity of high-boiling catalytically cracked oils, indicating a scheme by which 6- (or 5-) *iso*propyl-1,2-benzanthracene and a methylchrysene were isolated from such material.*

NATURE OF THE CARCINOGENIC AGENT IN COAL TAR AND PITCH

Following the experimental production by Yamagiwa and Ichikawa in 1915 of malignant epithelial tumors by application of coal tar to the ears of rabbits, and the demonstration by Tsutsui (1918) of the advantage of painting the skin of mice as a method of biologic testing of carcinogenic tars, the first steps towards elucidation of the chemical nature of the active substance in coal tar came in 1921–26, when Bruno Bloch and Dreyfus and their collaborators in Zürich were able to show that the carcinogenic agent was concentrated in the higher boiling fractions as a neutral compound, that it was free from nitrogen, arsenic, or sulphur, and that it was capable of forming a stable complex with picric acid and probably belonged to the class of cyclic hydrocarbons (Bloch and Dreyfus, 1921). In 1924 and 1925 Kennaway succeeded in producing carcinogenic tars by the pyrolysis of petroleum, coal, skin, hair, yeast, and cholesterol, and by leading acetylene and isoprene ($H_2C{=}C(CH_3)CH{=}CH_2$) with hydrogen through strongly heated tubes. The tars so obtained showed an ascending order of biologic potency as they were prepared at successively higher temperatures (450° C.–1250° C.), and these results could be explained by assuming that acetylene was a common decomposition product, and that the carcinogenic material was actually formed from acetylene. Similar activity was found by Kennaway (1924, 1925) in the higher-boiling fractions of the mixture of hydrocarbons which Schroeter (1924) had obtained from tetrahydronaphthalene by treatment with aluminium chloride. There thus emerged the strong general conclusion that the carcinogenic agent was a complex hydrocarbon of the aromatic series.

Since the carcinogenic tars and oils usually showed a pronounced fluorescence, Mayneord in 1927 examined their fluorescence spectra, and discovered them to possess a characteristic spectrum consisting of three bands at low dispersions. This vital clue was developed by Hieger (1930) in an investigation of the fluorescence of a number of polycyclic aromatic hydrocarbons, particularly those related to anthracene. By a most fortunate chance, the known pure compounds which Hieger proceeded to examine included 1,2-benzanthracene (Fig. 55), and this substance was at once found to give a spectrum comparable with that of the carcinogenic mix-

* The reader is also referred to the chapter on occupational cancer (chapter 25).

tures. It was this circumstance which shortly led Cook to embark on the long series of synthetic studies on homologs of benzanthracene (Cook, Hieger, Kennaway, and Mayneord 1932), which founded our knowledge of the structural features underlying carcinogenic action so far as this type of compound is concerned, and has been dealt with, among other matters, in Cook's Pedler Lecture to the Chemical Society of London (1950).

About this time Erich Clar (1929) had just published various methods for the synthesis of certain slightly more complex hydrocarbons containing the benzanthracene system—in a classic series of papers on the aromatic hydrocarbons which still continues (e.g., Clar 1949a,b; Clar and Stewart 1951). These substances were at once tested for carcinogenic activity by Kennaway and Hieger (1930), who soon obtained positive results with the compound ultimately identified as 1:2:5:6-dibenzanthracene (Fig. 56). This was, therefore, the first known pure chemical compound manifesting pronounced carcinogenic properties. Later developments in its chemistry include the synthesis of a form labelled in the 9-position

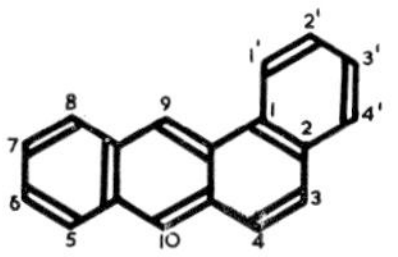

FIG. 55.
1:2-Benzanthacene.

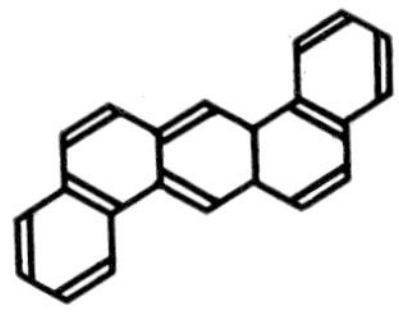

FIG. 56.
1:2:5:6-Dibenzanthracene.

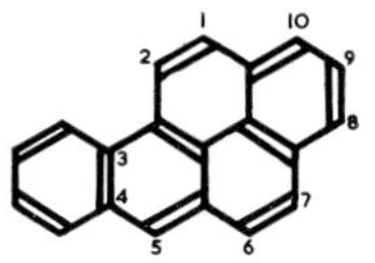

FIG. 57.
3:4-Benzpyrene.

with carbon[14] (Heidelberger, Brewer, and Dauben 1947), an early example of a technique which promises—and indeed in the hands of Heidelberger and his colleagues has already proved—to have the greatest value in elucidating the fate and action of such substances in the animal body.

The fluorescence spectrum—in Kennaway's words "the single thread that led all through this labyrinth"—was also used by Hieger (1933) in the concentration of the carcinogenic agent from coal tar pitch, culminating in the isolation of a pure hydrocarbon which showed the characteristic three-banded spectrum, and which proved to be strongly carcinogenic. At the time of its isolation this compound had not been elsewhere recorded, and it was therefore necessary to determine its molecular structure. Its properties suggested one of the two possible benzpyrenes, and these were synthesized by Cook and Hewett (1933), who were soon able to prove the identity of one of the compounds, (3:4-benzpyrene, Fig. 57), with the substance isolated from pitch. Tedious as the earlier extractions necessarily were, it was subsequently found by Berenblum and Schoental (1943), using a spectrographic method of estimation, that tar might contain as much as 1.5 per cent of benzpyrene, and Berenblum had also devised (1945) a relatively simple procedure (starting from the fact that sulfonation of benzpyrene does not readily occur with sulfuric acid alone in the cold), whereby as much as 75 mg. of almost pure benzpyrene can be recovered from 10 Gm. of a crude tar distillate.

Apart from its recovery from pitch and tar, benzpyrene (and related polynuclear aromatic hydrocarbons) are also detectable in other material by the methods of chromatography and spectroscopy, as for example in the atmosphere, in the "humus" from sewage effluents (Wedgwood and Cooper 1951), and in extracts of the barnacle species *Tetraclita squamosa rubescens* (Zechmeister and Koe 1952). In the last case the substances identified (e.g., anthracene, phenanthrene, chrysene, fluoranthene, and 3:4-benzpyrene), were regarded not as metabolic products but as originating probably from tarry materials floating along the Southern California coast.

BENZANTHRACENE HOMOLOGS

Cook's study of the benzanthracene homologs (Barry, Cook, Haslewood, Hieger, and Kennaway 1935), first disclosed the significance of position 5 in the parent hydrocarbon: whereas benzanthracene itself is only weakly active, methyl substitution in this position confers a high order of potency. This is probably a factor underlying the activity shown by compounds in which an additional ring finds one point of attachment in the same position, as, for example, in 1:2:5:6-dibenzanthracene. It was later shown that methyl substitution in positions 9 or 10 also leads to highly carcinogenic compounds, and indeed 10-methyl-1:2-benzanthracene is the most active of all the monomethyl derivatives of the parent substance. Of the remaining monomethyl isomerides, only the 6-methyl derivative exhibits notable activity (in the mouse), the others little or none. Proceeding to dimethyl-benzanthracenes, an important conception emerged when it was shown that substituents at any two favorable positions reinforce each other, so that the activity of the new compound is enhanced. Thus 5:6-dimethyl-1:2-benzanthracene is more active than the compounds possessing only one methyl group in positions 5 or 6, high activity is shown by 5:9- and 5:10-dimethyl-1:2-benzanthracene (Fieser and Newman 1936), and extreme potency is reached in 9:10-dimethyl-1:2-benzanthracene (Bachmann, Kennaway, and Kennaway 1938). It is possible that still greater augmentation is effected by methyl substitution simultaneously in *three* favorable positions, as in 5:9:10-trimethyl-1:2:-benzanthracene and 9-methyl-1:2:5:6-dibenzanthracene.

There is, however, a limit to advance in potency by increase in the number of substituted positions, since the compounds in which the four most favorable are substituted (5:6:9:10-tetramethyl-1:2-benzanthracene and 9:10-dimethyl-1:2:5:6-dibenzanthracene) show *decreased* activity. It should be noted that the nature of the substituent can be widely varied compatible with activity, as in many compounds with oxygen-, nitrogen-, and halogen-containing groups (cf. Lacassagne, Buu-Hoï, Hoán, and Rudali 1948), mostly in the positions 5, 9, and 10. These facts at once suggest the dependence of activity on an optimal molecular complexity, a conclusion which Cook (Barry *et al.* 1935) had stressed at an early stage in these investigations, and which has been upheld by many later examples. The limits of complexity compatible with activity are represented by two hexacyclic hydrocarbons, 1:2:3:4- and 3:4:8:9-dibenzpyrene. Apart from reduction in activity by increase in molecular size, substitution in a position not in itself favorable to activity, or only slightly so, simultaneously with substitution in a favorable position, greatly reduces the activity due to the latter. Finally, introduction of phenolic groups usually entails complete loss of carcinogenicity, and the same result follows the hydrogenation of individual rings.

CHRYSENES AND BENZPHENANTHRENES

Many of the above examples permit some degree of analogy with derivatives of 3:4-benzphenanthrene and chrysene, and it may be recalled that while Cook (Cook and Hewett 1933) regarded 3:4-benzpyrene as most nearly related to 1:2-benzanthracene, for other reasons Fieser (1941) suggested it should more suitably be formulated as a chrysene derivative. Marked progress was achieved on complete examination of the six possible hydrocarbons consisting of four condensed aromatic rings, and of the fifteen compounds having five such rings. This revealed carcino-

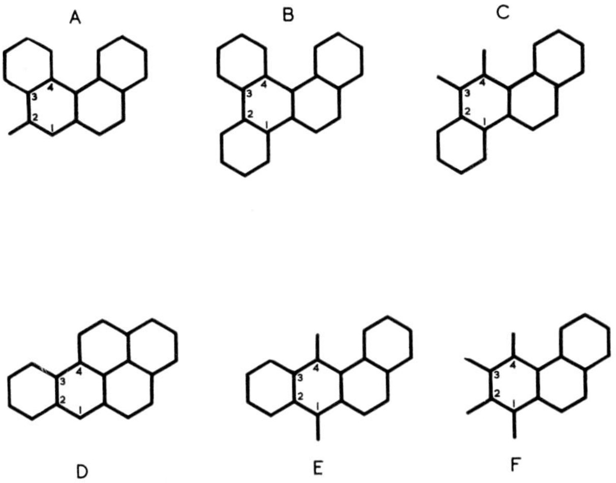

FIG. 58. Derivatives of phenanthrene (numbering indicates relation to phenanthrene).

genic activity in 3:4-benzphenanthrene and in 1:2:3:4- and 1:2:5:6-dibenzphenanthrene, and it also appeared that chrysene, as well as 1:2-benzanthracene and 3:4-benzphenanthrene, must be regarded as a parent compound of carcinogenic derivatives.

The next stage in this correlation was due to Hewett (1940). Each of these hydrocarbons is a derivative of phenanthrene, substituted in two of the 1-, 2-, 3-, and 4- positions. Further substitution in either or both of the remaining positions gives rise to highly carcinogenic hydrocarbons, as for example 2-methyl-3:4-benzphenanthrene (Fig. 58*A*), 1:2:3:4-dibenzphenanthrene (Fig. 58*B*), 1:2-dimethylchrysene (Fig. 58*C*), 3:4-benzpyrene (Fig. 58*D*) and 9:10-dimethyl-1:2-benzanthracene (Fig. 58*E*). Moreover, substitution is effective whether by two benzene rings or by one benzene ring and one or two methyl groups; this finally led Hewett and Martin (1940) to the synthesis of 1:2:3:4-tetramethylphenanthrene (Fig. 58*F*)—a key compound which is slightly carcinogenic, links the active derivatives of 1:2-benzanthracene, 3:4-benzphenanthrene, and chrysene, and may be regarded as the prototype of all these compounds.

POSSIBLE IMPLICATIONS FOR THE NATURAL CAUSATION OF CANCER

The possibility that compounds of the above types might play a part in the causation of "spontaneous" cancer was opened up by recognition, following the advances in sterol formulation due to Rosenheim and King in 1932, that many naturally occurring substances (including bile-acids and the sex hormones) have somewhat similar condensed polycyclic systems. Thus dehydronorcholene, a hydrocarbon prepared by Wieland and Schlichting from the desoxycholic acid of the bile, is a hydro-derivative of 1:2-benzanthracene, and in 1933 both Wieland and Dane, and Cook and Haslewood, obtained from it, by dehydrogenation with selenium, the fully aromatic hydrocarbon 20-methylcholanthrene (Fig. 59).

This compound soon proved to have carcinogenic potency of an extremely high order, as Cook (1933) had indeed predicted. The structure was rapidly established, confirmation provided by its synthesis (Fieser and Seligman 1935, cf. Cagniant and Cagniant 1948), and the compound also obtained starting from cholic acid (Fieser and Newman 1935). As for other outstandingly important carcinogens, a variant has now been prepared incorporating radioactive carbon (Dauben 1948).

There is as yet no proof that changes of the kind envisaged take place in vivo, and chemists are still divided, and the majority doubtful, as to their likelihood. In addition, the significance to be attached to them is inevitably affected first by the increasing range of chemical types now known to be carcinogenic, and secondly by recent views on the possible nature of the fundamental changes responsible for malignancy discussed below, changes which would certainly not be specifically dependent for their production upon a hydrocarbon whether introduced from without or originating through an aberration in steroid metabolism. However, both cholic acid and desoxycholic acid have a hydroxyl group in such a position as would promote the necessary cyclization (Kennaway and Hieger 1930). Further, from other cases in which there was no such special circumstance to favor ring-closure, Cook was of the opinion that certain sterol molecules might possess an inherent tendency to conversion into a methylcholanthrene derivative. Marked carcinogenic activity is not, however, generally found in compounds possessing hydrogenated rings—as already indicated—so that a further stage of dehydrogenation would be required. Important here is a finding by Ghiron, confirmed by Kennaway, (Cook, Kennaway and Kennaway 1940), that injection of desoxycholic acid itself may result in the production of connective-tissue tumors in mice: in such a case it would be of interest to know—although it is difficult to tell how the question might be solved—whether desoxycholic acid is intrinsically active, or is subject to transformation in vivo yielding minute traces of an active product. On the general problem of the aromatization of hydrogenated compounds in animal tissues much may be learned from such studies as those of Dickens (Dickens 1950, Beer, Dickens, and Pearson 1951).

Meanwhile one of the best analogies for the conversion of a hydrogenated ring-system into an aromatic one is provided by the estrus-producing hormone equilenin, possessing two aromatic rings and probably arising from a nonaromatic steroid precursor (Sandulesco, Tchung, and Girard 1933; Fieser 1941). In Fieser's view the rough structural analogy between equilenin and methylcholanthrene suggests that, if the latter does indeed arise by a process of abnormal sterol metabolism, this process may be closely associated with the normal one which results in the production of estrogenic hormones. He therefore invited consideration of the origin of carcinogens from the principles of the adrenal cortex, visualizing such reactions as might ensue from the condensation of dehydrocorticosterone with formaldehyde to give cholanthrene, and of estrone or equilenin with pyruvic acid, followed by aromatization, ring-closure to give the terminal benzenoid nucleus, and further dehydrogenation. A difficulty arises here (as also for desoxycholic acid, above), since the product, because of the persistence of the original hydroxyl group at C_3

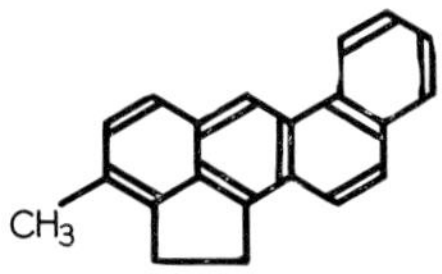

FIG. 59. 20-Methylcholanthrene.

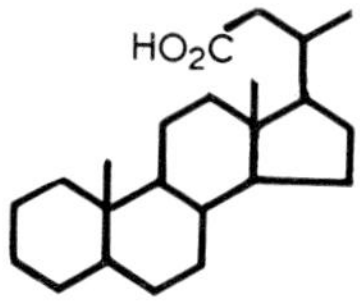

FIG. 60.

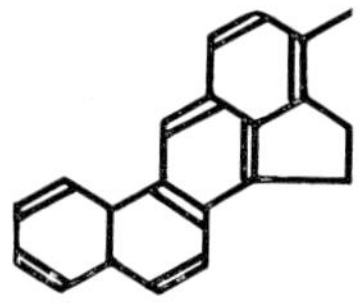

FIG. 61.

characteristic of all known natural partially-aromatic estrogens, would be a 3-hydroxy derivative and therefore unlikely to be carcinogenic, on analogy with the known inactivity of the synthetic compound 3-hydroxy-20-methylcholanthrene. A relevant observation was, however, made by Burrows, Cook, Roe, and Warren (1937) when they isolated from the urine of a male with an adrenal tumor a substance ($\Delta^{3,5}$-androstadiene-17-one) lacking this characteristic 3-hydroxyl group, and so showing that it may in certain circumstances be eliminated while the ring-

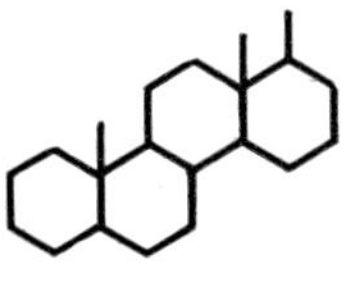

FIG. 62.

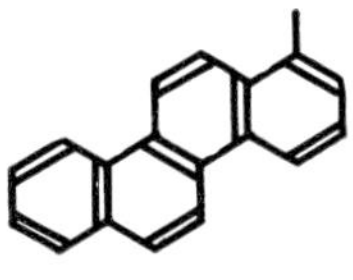

FIG. 63.

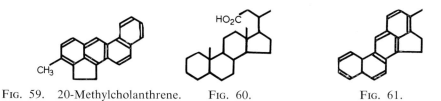

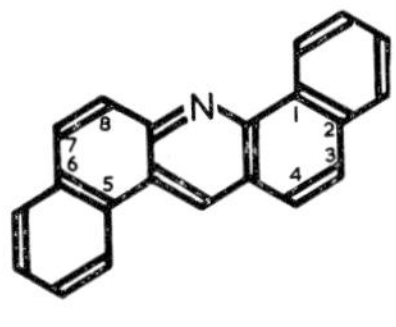

FIG. 64.
1:2:5:6-Dibenzacridine.

system is still nonaromatic. The same compound was later isolated by Wolfe (Wolfe, Fieser, and Friedgood 1941), from the urine of a female with adrenal tumor. Again in conformity with Fieser's opinion that the cortical steroids seem the more likely precursors of possible carcinogens in vivo, is an interesting suggestion by Shoppee, based on the fact that the structural analogy between a norcholanic acid (Fig. 60) and methylcholanthrene (Fig. 61), is paralleled by the even closer analogy between 17-methyl-D-homoandrostane (Fig. 62) and potentially carcinogenic methylchrysenes (Fig. 63). Experimental test of this possibility has so far not yielded any positive result.

NITROGEN- AND SULFUR-CONTAINING ANALOGS: 2-AMINO DERIVATIVES OF NAPHTHALENE, ANTHRACENE, AND FLUORENE

Carcinogenicity is by no means restricted to cyclic hydrocarbons, for it is found in certain nitrogenous analogs such as dibenzacridines and dibenzcarbazoles (e.g., Figs. 64 and 65). Lacassagne, Rudali, Buu-Hoï and Lecocq (1945), Lacassagne (1946, 1948) and Zajdela and Buu-Hoï (1950) have devoted attention to a series of methylated derivatives of the angular benzacridines and find a marked distinction, in that such derivatives of 1:2- (or 7:8-) benzacridine include many highly potent compounds, while similar derivatives of 3:4- (or 5:6-) benzacridine are for the most part inactive.

A specially interesting heterocycle is 3:4:5:6-dibenzcarbazole, to which attention was directed by Boyland (Boyland and Brues 1937), on account of its possible formation from 2-naphthylamine (Fig. 66), one of the intermediates believed to be

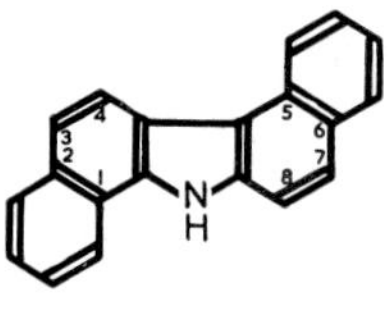

FIG. 65.
1:2:5:6-Dibenzcarbazole.

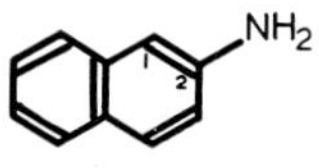

FIG. 66.
2-Naphthylamine.

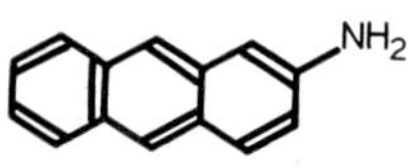

FIG. 67.
2-Anthramine.

responsible for occupational cancer of the bladder in dye-workers (Rehn 1895, Müller 1949, Truhaut 1949), and known to be able to induce this disease in dogs (Hueper and Wolfe 1937, Bonser 1943). 3:4:5:6-Dibenzcarbazole has the property of inducing tumors not only locally, but in the liver as well, and this type of carcinogenic action at a distance tends to be a feature of many such nitrogenous analogs, in contrast with the polycyclic hydrocarbons, the effects of which are more usually confined to the point of application or injection. The effects of N-methylation and ethylation in reducing the carcinogenic activity of 3:4:5:6-dibenzcarbazole have been studied by Kirby and Peacock (1946) and Kirby (1948) respectively.

The above and other polynuclear heterocyclic systems have also been studied by Badger, Pearce, and Pettit (1951a,b); Badger, Seidler, and Thomson (1951); and Badger and Pettit (1951), as also in a long series of papers from the French school, e.g., Lacassagne, Buu-Hoï, Royer, and Zajdela (1947); Buu-Hoï (1948); Buu-Hoï, Hoán, and Khôi (1949, 1950a,b); Buu-Hoï, Hoán, Khôi, and Xuong 1949, 1950, 1951); Buu-Hoï and Royer (1950); Buu-Hoï, Cagniant, Hoán, and Khôi (1950); Buu-Hoï and Hoán (1951), (mainly on carbazoles); Buu-Hoï (1949, 1950a,b) (on acridines); Buu-Hoï and Royer (1951); Buu-Hoï and Hoán (1951); Buu-Hoï (1951); and Buu-Hoï and Jacquignon (1951).

In experimental studies of the cause of industrial bladder cancer, Bonser, Clayson, and Jull (1951) have identified 2-amino-1-naphthol conjugates in the urine of dogs and other species after the administration of purified 2-naphthylamine. An approximate correlation between the amounts of the conjugates in the urine and the incidence of bladder tumors seeming to suggest a possible explanation of the observed differences in species susceptibility, 2-amino-1-naphthol hydrochloride was then tested for its local action on the bladder epithelium of the mouse, and found to be a carcinogen of the same order of potency as methylcholanthrene.

2-Naphthylamine is in turn related to 2-anthramine (Fig. 67), which was originally observed by Shear (1938) to produce multiple hepatomas in mice, and this to 2-aminofluorene (Fig. 68), the acetyl derivative of which was discovered by Wilson, De Eds, and Cox (1941), following its use as an insecticide, to possess carcinogenic activity of an exceptionally diversified type.

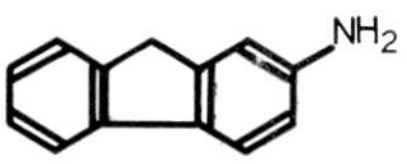

FIG. 68. 2-Aminofluorene.

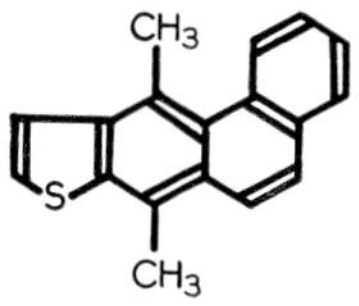

FIG. 69.

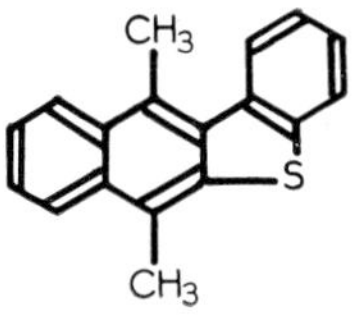

FIG. 70.

This compound is able to produce such varied growths as squamous keratinizing carcinomas, basal-cell carcinomas, mammary cancer, adenomas and carcinomas of the lung, benign and malignant tumors of the liver, and tumors of the bladder and kidney (Bielschowsky 1947; Engel and Copeland 1948; Morris, Dubnick, Dunn, and Westfall 1948; Lacassagne, Buu-Hoï, Royer, Rudali, and Zajdela 1948), and shows activity not only in the rat but in the mouse (Armstrong and Bonser 1944), the fowl (Bielschowsky and Green 1945), and in the cat (Bielschowsky 1947). The compound labeled with carbon^{14} in the 9-position has been described by Ray and Geiser (1949).

Finally, as additional examples of the manner in which the polycyclic hydrocarbon pattern can be modified, while still retaining carcinogenic potency, may be quoted the sulfur isosters (Fig. 69, Sandin and Fieser 1940; and Fig. 70, Tilak 1946, 1951), in each of which a benzene ring of the 9:10-dimethyl-1:2-benzanthracene system is replaced by a thiophene nucleus.

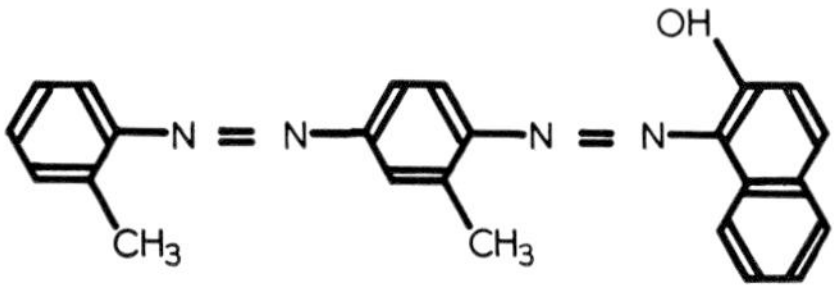

FIG. 71. "Scarlet red."

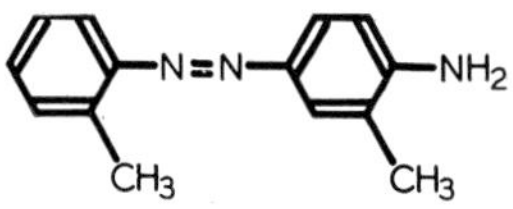

FIG. 72. 4′-Amino-2:3′-azotoluene.

These substances have proved of much help in deciphering the structural features most closely linked with biologic activity, as will be described below.

AZO COMPOUNDS

As early as 1906, B. Fischer described epithelial proliferation (in the ears of rabbits) following the injection of scarlet red (Biebrich Scarlet R medicinal) (Fig. 71). Although the growths were nonmalignant, Fischer rightly claimed his discovery as the first case of the induction of tumor-like proliferation by a chemical compound. A few years later, Hayward (1909) found that the active part of the scarlet red molecule was represented by 4′-amino-2:3′-azotoluene (Fig. 72).

In 1924, Schmidt, during a study of "Sudan" dyes in vital staining, noted that feeding of scarlet red produced epithelial proliferation (adenoma) in the livers of mice. This observation remained largely neglected, and little progress was made before 1931, when Yoshida (1934) observed the production by means of 4′-amino-2:3′-azotoluene of liver-tissue proliferation in mice. Varying his technic Yoshida was able to report liver tumors in rats which had been given the same compound over long periods in the diet. Kinosita (1940) later examined many other derivatives of azobenzene, and found an isomer of aminoazotoluene—4-dimethyl-aminoazobenzene (Fig 73)—to be highly active in producing liver tumors. This substance, with 4′-amino-2:3′-azotoluene and 2:3′-azotoluene, is also capable of producing connective tissue growths. Yoshida also noted, in a few of his animals, papilloma formation in the stomach and bladder, and bladder tumors were later obtained with 2:3′-azotoluene.

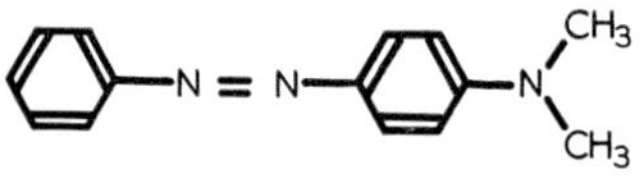

FIG. 73. 4-Dimethylamino-azobenzene ("butter yellow").

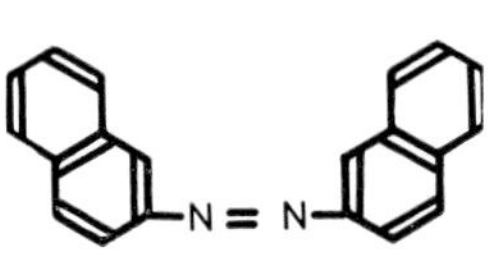

FIG. 74. 2:2′-Azo-naphthalene.

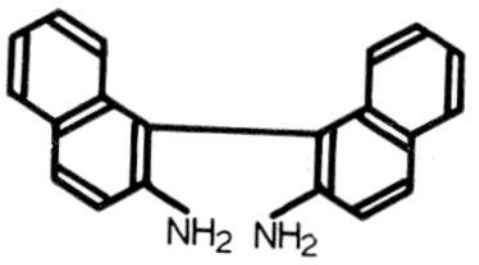

FIG. 75. 2:2′-Diamino-1:1′-dinaphthyl.

Miller and Miller (1948) tested the carcinogenic action of forty compounds either structurally similar to or possible metabolites of 4-dimethylaminoazobenzene, and suggested that two conditions are essential for high activity, first, that at least one methyl group must be attached to the amino group (cf. Kirby 1944), and secondly that the rings must bear either no substituents or only certain substituents in the 3′ position. Other studies on the carcinogenicity or hepatotoxic action of azo dyestuffs have been carried out by Cook (1947), Orr and Price (1948), Kuhn and Quadbeck (1949), Hackmann (1951) and Kirby and Peacock (1949), the last dealing with the carcinogenicity in mice of Oil Orange E or benzene-azo-β-naphthol. Labeled compounds have been synthesized by Salzberg, Nye, and Griffin (1950; 3′-methyl-(^{14})4-dimethylaminoazobenzene), and by Fones and White (1949); 4-dimethylaminoazobenzene containing N^{15} in each of the three possible positions).

In other attempts to produce bladder cancer, Cook, Hewett, Kennaway, and Kennaway (1940) selected the three azonaphthalenes, on the supposition that these might arise by oxidation of mixtures of naphthylamines, and so be present in the crude bases, exposure to which is a factor in the occupational incidence of the disease in chemical workers. No tumors of the bladder were obtained, but liver changes in mice, similar to those induced by the azobenzene derivatives, resulted from treatment with 2,2′-azonaphthalene (Fig. 74). Since azo compounds may be reduced in the body to amines by way of the hydrazo compound, and since this is susceptible to rearrangement, Cook and his colleagues then made tests with the compound which might thus be expected, viz., 2:2′-diamino-1:1′-dinaphthyl (Fig. 75). This induced liver tumors with even greater facility than 2:2′-azonaphthalene, a finding of interest since the diaminodinaphthyl readily undergoes deamination to 3:4:5:6-dibenzcarbazole which, as noted, itself produces liver tumors as well as skin cancer and connective tissue tumors in mice.

The suggestion has also been made, and has been very carefully considered by Miller, Miller, and Sapp (1951), that the carcinogenicity of 4-dimethylamino-azobenzene in the rat may similarly depend on the benzidine rearrangement of the hydrazo derivative to form, in this case, 2:4′-diamino-5-dimethylaminobiphenyl. The latter compound is, however, noncarcinogenic, and the carcinogenicity of 4-dimethylaminoazobenzene is increased by substitution of fluorine in the 2, 2′, 3′ or 4′ positions. The presence of the strong C-F bond in these positions should *decrease* activity if a rearrangement of a hydrazo metabolite was involved in the carcinogenic process. Only one of the five possible benzidine or semidine rearrangements could possibly occur in the case of the active 2′:4′:6′-trifluoro-4-dimethyl-aminoazobenzene, namely semidine rearrangement to the 2-position, and even this possibility is rendered unlikely by the activity of the 2-fluoro derivative. Thus while such rearrangements may occur in the metabolism of 4-dimethylaminoazobenzene, it is doubtful whether they play any role in carcinogenesis, and these authors regard the initial carcinogenic reaction as much more probably involving the azo linkage and at least one N-methyl group.

DERIVATIVES OF 4-AMINOSTILBENE

Haddow, Harris, Kon, and Roe (1947) have described the manner in which attention became directed to 4-aminostilbene and 4-dimethylaminostilbene (Fig. 76), as the parent compounds in a whole new series of carcinogenic derivatives. The tumors produced by these compounds in the rat include sarcomas at the point of injection; basal-cell carcinomas; squamous-cell carcinomas, particularly arising from the epithelium of the external acoustic duct, but also occurring on the face and in other regions; distant and multiple subcutaneous fibromas; cholangiomas of the liver; multiple mammary fibroadenomas in females; adenomas of the lung; and a few examples of intestinal carcinoma and hypernephroma. The nature of these tumors, and their distribution, is reminiscent of the variety of neoplasms produced by 2-acetylaminofluorene, and it is particularly striking that squamous keratinizing carcinomas of the acoustic duct should be produced by 2-acetylaminofluorene, 2-aminoanthracene, derivatives of 4-aminostilbene, and also by benzidine (Spitz, Maguigan, and Dobriner 1950), since this species of tumor had not been previously described. There are of course differences in detail between the carcinogenicity of 2-acetylaminofluorene and that of the aminostilbenes, as in the facility with which sarcomas are produced by the latter, and the relatively benign character of the mammary tumors induced with aminostilbenes. But the general biologic similarity is undoubtedly striking, and may reflect a certain degree of affinity between the two chemical types.

In the aminostilbenes, biologic activity would appear to depend essentially upon a basic group in the *p*- or *o*-position, an ethylene bridge in which neither hydrogen atom must be substituted, a free *p*′-position, and the *trans* configuration of the molecule as a whole.

For studies of the immunochemistry of carcinogen-protein conjugates it is of interest that Creech and Peck (1952; Peck and Creech 1952) have prepared isocyanates of 4-dimethylaminostilbene and 2-acetylaminofluorene conjugated with horse and bovine serum albumins: variations in experimental conditions produced conjugates containing from thirteen to sixty-two carcinogen groups per molecule of protein.

ENDOCRINE-INDUCED TUMORS

Fieser's suggestion referred to above, that the adrenal cortical steroids are the most likely precursors of carcinogens in vivo, has a particular significance for the remarkable case of the CE strain of mice, in which either ovariectomy or castration shortly after birth leads to the development of adrenal-cortical carcinomas—conceivably arising from a response on the part of the adrenal to compensate for the absence of the gonads (Fekete and Little 1945, Woolley and Little 1945, 1946). The same phenomenon has been observed by Houssay in a strain of rats (personal communication), while Dickie (1948) has described similar tumors of

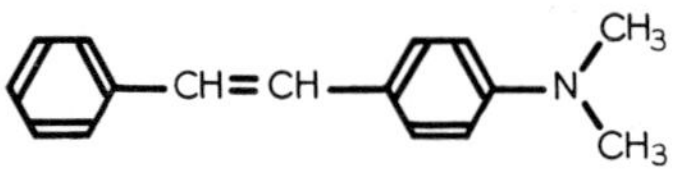

FIG. 76.
4-Dimethylaminostilbene

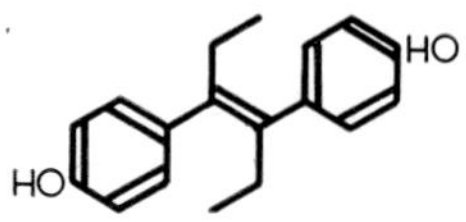

FIG. 77.
Diethylstilbestrol

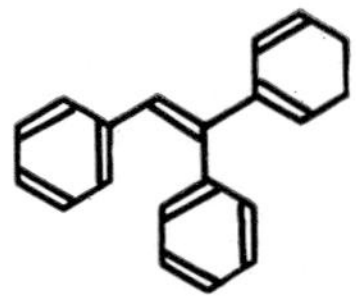

FIG. 78.
Triphenylethylene

the adrenal cortex in F_1 reciprocal hybrid mice between the DBA and CE pure lines, following castration at birth. In this case Woolley (1948; Dickie and Woolley 1949) showed that pituitary tumors might be observed after the appearance of such adrenal tumors, and that the former were in turn associated with extensive alveolar development of the mammary glands.

Even more direct connections between carcinogenesis and endocrine physiology were discovered by Lacassagne in 1932 (see also Lacassagne 1950), when he found that injection of the female sex hormone produces cancer of the breast in male mice, under certain favorable conditions, and by Cook and Dodds (1933) when they showed that individual polycyclic aromatic hydrocarbons—including, for instance, 3:4-benzpyrene—might show slight estrogenic as well as carcinogenic activity. We now know that the appearance of breast cancer in mice is determined by a number of predisposing and conditioning factors. Also, the carcinogenic action of the estrogens is mainly confined to tissues which are highly responsive to their physiologic action. Nevertheless, Lacassagne's experiment was the first in which cancer was produced by a naturally occurring compound, although there are now numerous accounts of the production of pituitary, mammary, uterine, testicular, adrenal, subcutaneous, leukotic, and osseous tumors in mice and other species with both natural and synthetic estrogens (see Burrows and Horning, 1947, 1952, Oberling, Guérin *et al.* 1950, Fels, 1950; also Kirkman and Bacon

[1950] on multiple malignant estrogen-induced tumors of the renal cortex in male hamsters [*Cricetus auratus*]).

It was the observation of Cook and Dodds which eventually led to the synthesis of artificial estrogens of high potency (Dodds, Goldberg, Lawson, and Robinson 1938), and among such compounds discovered later, diethylstilbestrol (Fig. 77) and triphenylethylene (Fig. 78) (Robson and Schönberg 1937) are specially capable of inducing breast and testis tumors in mice of susceptible strains. These structures are also of interest as showing some degree of structural resemblance to chrysenes and benzanthracenes.

In the elucidation of the role of hormones in carcinogenesis an important observation was made by Biskind and Biskind (1944), namely that implantation of ovaries into the spleens of adult gonadectomized female rats is followed several months later by the development of tumor-like masses of granulosa-cells. These experiments were based on two considerations; first the ability of the liver to inactivate ovarian hormones when these circulate through the hepatic portal system; and second the increase of pituitary gonadotropins subsequent to castration.

The observations themselves were confirmed and extended in mice by Li and Gardner (1947a,b), who also noted that the development of ovarian tumors in intrasplenic ovarian grafts could be inhibited by the administration of estradiol and testosterone. Of the principles emerging from Gardner's work as a whole (see Gardner 1952 and p. 244), two are of special interest, namely that the appearance of tumors following continuous hormone administration occurs after the period of growth response, when the tissue has become relatively refractory, and secondly the important role of gonadotropin in carcinogenesis. The latter factor was a determining one in the important experiments of Bielschowsky and Hall (1951 a,b), in which tumors were induced by 2-acetylaminofluorene in normal male rats joined in parabiosis to castrated litter-mates. Neoplasms were only obtained in animals receiving the carcinogen—never in their untreated litter-mates—and included adenocarcinomas of the seminal vesicles which were considered due to the carcinogenic action of acetylaminofluorene upon the hyperplasia induced in the seminal vesicles by high levels of androgens, due in turn to hormonal imbalance created by gonadotropin in the normal partner.

Benign and malignant tumors were also induced by acetylaminofluorene in intact female rats joined in parabiosis to gonadectomized litter-mates. Ovarian tumors, most of granulosa-cell type, occurred in 50 per cent, and follicle-stimulating hormone secreted in excess by the pituitary of the gonadectomized litter-mate was similarly regarded as the factor essential to their development. Pituitary tumors observed in intact parabiotic females were attributed to excess of estrogen secreted by their stimulated ovaries, and occurred independently of acetylaminofluorene.

In the investigation of the role of gonadotropin in carcinogenesis another procedure has been of interest, namely administration of the plant *Lithospermum ruderale*, the medicinal use of infusions of which, by the Indian tribes of Nevada, had been known to induce sterility in man.* Cranston (1945) first described that feeding the plant to

* See *Medicinal use of plants by Indian tribes of Nevada.* (Division of Plant Exploration, U. S. Dept. of Agriculture, Washington, 1941.)

mice abolished the estrous cycle, reduced fertility, and produced atrophy of the sex organs, thymus, and pituitary (see also Cranston and Robinson 1949, Draster and Zahl 1946, Zahl 1947). Noble and Plunkett (1950) found that the dried root caused irregularity of the estrous cycle in rats, although this species appeared more resistant. The action of estrogens was unaffected by administration of *Lithospermum*, and the plant itself was said to contain small amounts of an unidentified water-soluble estrogen. The evidence indicates that *Lithospermum* either inactivates gonadotropins or renders the target organs insensitive to their action (Plunkett and Noble 1950). Such findings are clearly relevant to reports by Cranston, Kucera, and Bittner (1950), and Zahl and Nowak (1951), of a decreased incidence of spontaneous mammary tumors in C3H mice so treated, although the latter authors believed that inanition and other factors still required to be evaluated, apart from a more specific effect of the *Lithospermum*-induced diestrus.

A fascinating example of tumor production due to a hormonal stimulus, or at least dependent upon it, is provided by experimental cancer of the thyroid. Griesbach, Kennedy, and Purves (1945) had shown that in rats a diet containing rape-seed led first to a uniform hyperplasia of the thyroid, and later to the occurrence of discrete and often multiple adenomas. Rape-seed contains an antithyroid substance belonging to the thiourea series, and the New Zealand workers were able to show that both the initial diffuse hyperplasia and the later adenomas were the results of increased production of thyrotropic hormone, induced by a relative deficiency of thyroxine in the circulating blood (see also Purves and Griesbach 1947). Later, Bielschowsky, Griesbach, Hall, Kennedy, and Purves (1949) found that such tumors could be grafted into other rats, provided the recipients had been rendered thyroxine-deficient either by thyroidectomy or by the administration of an antithyroid substance. While these tumors of the thyroid can be attributed to thyrotropic stimulation, other agents are known which can increase and accelerate such stimulation. Thus Bielschowsky (1944) showed that although acetylaminofluorene alone did not affect the thyroid, when given before or together with an antithyroid drug it resulted in the appearance of adenomas much sooner and in greater numbers than with such a drug alone. Bielschowsky (1949) also made the important observation in rats that although acetylaminofluorene will not induce tumors in the intact thyroid it will do so in the remnant left after subtotal thyroidectomy, presumably through the resultant stimulation of thyrotropic hormone, even without administration of an antithyroid drug. Secondly, the process is accelerated by radio-iodine, as appears from the work of Doniach (1950), the results of which show that radio-iodine, as well as acetylaminofluorene, can reinforce the thyrotropic stimulus and so increase the incidence of thyroid tumors. Pituitary tumors have also been described following damage to the thyroid by radio-iodine (Furth and Burnett 1951), and it is of much interest that these are transplantable only into animals with thyroids rendered deficient by radio-iodine pretreatment.

The particular role of thiouracil in the induction, growth and transplantability of thyroid tumors has been studied in the mouse by Morris and Green (1951) and Morris, Dalton and Green (1951): long-continued exposure of thyroid tissue to excessive amounts of thyrotropic hormone by means of serial transplantation of such tissue to mice ingesting thiouracil resulted in the transformation of hyperplastic thyroid tissue into malignant autonomous thyroid neoplasms.

MISCELLANEOUS CHEMICAL SUBSTANCES

URETHANE

Among other types of chemical carcinogens, special interest attaches to urethane, which was shown by Nettleship and Henshaw (1943) to have the property of greatly increasing the incidence of lung adenomas in mice. In confirmation, Jaffé (1944) found that all animals, in a strain not showing lung tumors spontaneously, had developed such tumors after 157 days from the first of fifteen injections of a 10 per cent urethane solution, or after 119 days on a diet containing 0.2 per cent of urethane. Larsen and Heston (1945; also Larsen 1947a, 1948) have brought forward evidence of the chemical specificity of the effect, which is largely confined to urethane itself.

Thus the relative potencies of the ethyl, *iso*propyl, and *n*-propyl esters of carbamic acid, as determined by the mean number of pulmonary tumors which they elicited, was found to be of the order of 84:4:1, the methyl, monochloroethyl, *n*-butyl, and *iso*amyl carbamates being inactive. However, Hidalgo and Whitehead (1951) have described two substances, namely 2,2′-dichloro *iso*propyl-N-ethyl (and diethyl) carbamate, more carcinogenic than urethane. Again the action was largely confined to the lungs, but since these compounds incorporate in the same molecule features of urethane and the nitrogen mustards, it may be that some of their activity is due to this circumstance, and therefore linked with the carcinogenicity of the mustards and other alkylating agents, which will be discussed in Chapter 17.

Larsen (1947b) also showed, in the offspring of strain A mice injected with urethane late in term, significant increases in the incidence and multiplicity of pulmonary tumors at 6 months of age, a sharp rise in the susceptibility of fetal mouse lung to the agent occurring during the last twenty-four hours of gestation. Orr (1947) believed that chronic inflammation might play a part in the pathogenesis of these lesions, and in some cases suggested they might be derived from proliferation of the bronchial epithelium. He also noted some evidence of regression when treatment was discontinued. On the other hand, Rogers (1951), in a study of the age of the host and other factors affecting the production by urethane of pulmonary adenomas in mice, showed (in agreement with Larsen) that young rapidly growing mice are greatly more responsive to the adenoma-producing influence of urethane than those just arriving at maturity, and suggested that the natural proliferative activity of the alveolar cells plays a major part in the formation of the tumors. That the tumors arise from the alveolar structure, and not from bronchiolar epithelium, atelectasis and inflammation playing no part in their development, was also the opinion of Mostafi and Larsen (1951a,b).

INDUCTION OF LIVER TUMORS BY CARBON TETRACHLORIDE, TANNIC ACID, *p*-PHENETYLUREA, AND *Senecio* ALKALOIDS

Apart from the azo compounds and carbazoles already considered, other and diverse agents are capable of inducing liver cancer specially, as for example carbon tetrachloride (Edwards 1941, Rudali and Mariani, 1950), and tannic acid (Korpássy and Kovács 1949, Korpássy and Mosonyi 1950, 1951). In the latter case the cirrhogenic and carcinogenic action of tannic acid shows some evidence of being increased by a low protein diet, as for tumors induced by many azo compounds. Another interesting example is the production of liver tumors in rats fed dosage levels of 0.1 per cent of the synthetic sweetening agent "dulcin" (*p*-phenetylurea) during their lifetime (Fitzhugh and Nelson 1950). Here the compound could conceivably be degraded in vivo to yield a product known to occur in the metabolism of 4-dimethylaminoazobenzene. Last is the description by Cook, Duffy, and Schoental (1950) of liver tumors in rats surviving intermittent feeding with the alkaloids of *Senecio jacobaea*. In the light of the indiscriminate medicinal use of such *Senecio* plants in South Africa, these results may conceivably have a bearing on the etiology of the primary liver tumors frequent among the Negro population there (Berman 1950, 1951).

Plastics and Polymers

An unusual observation was made when Turner (1941) accidentally found that bakelite discs implanted for long periods in albino rats eventually produced fibrosarcomas. The observation remained isolated for some years until Oppenheimer, Oppenheimer, and Stout (1948a,b), in the course of experiments performed on rats to produce hypertension by wrapping regenerated cellulose fibre (cellophane) around one kidney, again quite unexpectedly recorded sarcoma development in the neighborhood of the cellophane. The same result was later found to follow subcutaneous implantation in the abdominal wall, and pursuing the observation these authors (1952) have been successful in producing sarcomas in rats by imbedding various plastic films—of cellophane, alcohol-extracted cellophane, commercial polyethylene, pure polyethylene, and vinyl chloride—in the subcutaneous tissues.

Sarcomas have also been produced in mice, although in a smaller proportion, by imbedding cellophane and pure polyethylene film. The effect is apparently not due to additives or other impurities, or to trauma or chronic irritation, and while no adequate explanation has as yet been found, it may conceivably have some relation to carcinogenesis by various polyfunctional compounds to be described later, a number of which, although not all, are capable of polymer formation in vivo. As pointed out by the authors, the matter is also of some possible practical interest in connection with the tissue reactions to be expected to the plastics now being used in surgery (cf. LeVeen and Barberio 1949).

Trypan Blue

Yet another unusual experimental finding is that by the Gillmans and their collaborators, (Gillman, Gilbert, Gillman, and Spence 1948, Gillman, Gillman, and Gilbert 1949, Gillman and Gillman 1949), of hepatosplenomegaly, lymphomas and reticulum-cell sarcomas, and a Hodgkin's-like sarcoma, in a proportion of rats surviving protracted administration of trypan blue. This vital dye has also been described by Hamburgh (1952) as producing malformations in the embryos of treated mice (cf. Waddington and Carter 1952), and these authors draw attention to the similarities between the morphology of the embryonic stages of the malformations produced by trypan blue, and of those related malformations which are genetically determined.

Inorganic Carcinogens

As has been pointed out by Hueper (1952a), arsenicals were for more than a century the only metallic chemical substances showing, upon occupational, environmental, or medicinal exposure, a causal relationship to cancer in man; and an excellent review of the subject has been provided by Neubauer (1947). Later observations in the field of occupational carcinogenesis have, however, incriminated several additional metals or metallic compounds—with varying degrees of certainty—such as chromates, nickel carbonyl and asbestos, while, experimentally, beryllium, selenium, and nickel (Hueper 1952b) have been proved carcinogenic for certain species.

The production of bone sarcoma in rabbits by the intravenous injection of beryllium compounds was described by Gardner and Heslington (1946; see also Nash 1949, 1950; Barnes 1950), and Cloudman, Vining, Barkulis, and Nickson (1949), Dutra and Largent (1950), Dutra, Largent, and Roth (1951), Hoagland, Grier, and Hood (1950) and Sissons (1950) obtained similar results. In the case of nickel, Hueper (1952) injected the pure metallic powder into the femur, pleura, and nasal sinus of rats, and observed tumors (osteogenic sarcomas and tumors arising from the connective tissue and abdominal lymph nodes) in 30 per cent of animals dying after seven to sixteen months.

The metals have come into special prominence as possible causative agents in cancer of the lung, as for example in nickel, arsenic, and chromate workers. However, Bidstrup (1950) found any evidence that arsenic causes cancer of the lung in workers exposed to dust in its extraction, or use in manufacture, to be unconvincing, and Snegireff and Lombard (1951) employed a similar critical approach, and reached a negative conclusion, in considering the general cancer risk from arsenic in the metallurgical industry. Bidstrup, however, believed the occurrence of the disease among workers engaged in the smelting of ores containing arsenic, as well as in the manufacture of sheep dip, to be strongly suggestive.

Since 1932, carcinoma of the lung has been scheduled as an occupational disease in the chromate-producing industry in Germany (cf. Letterer, Neidhardt, and Klett 1944). In a survey of cancer of the respiratory system in the chromate-producing industry in the United States, Machle and Gregorius (1949) found that mortality rates for lung cancer at ages over 50 years ranged from ten to forty times that for a comparable industrial group, the fraction of deaths reported as due to cancer of the respiratory system ranging from thirteen to thirty-one times normal. In another study, Mancuso and Hueper (1951) found the death rate from lung cancer among chromate workers to be approximately fifteen times that in the general population, with a mean latent period of 10.6 years, and gave epidemiologic, biochemical, and histologic evidence suggesting chromate dust, chromic oxides, and other insoluble chromium compounds as the causal agents (cf. Bourne and Yee 1950).

Workers exposed to inhalation of such dusts may develop various acute and chronic injuries to the tissues of the respiratory system, and the origin of bronchiogenic carcinoma is associated with retention of the particles over long periods, and with pneumoconiotic changes (Mancuso 1951). Baetjer (1950a,b) also found death from lung cancer to be more frequent among chromate-producing workers than among the population as a whole. Bidstrup (1951) on the other hand did not find it possible to assess the true incidence of carcinoma of the respiratory system in the chromate-producing industry in Great Britain, but believed there might be some increase, although not to the high levels recorded in the United States.

From the above, it is clear that metals represent one possibility to be weighed seriously in identification of the unknown carcinogen in lung cancer associated with high consumption of tobacco (Wynder and Graham 1950, 1951, Levin, Goldstein, and Gerhardt 1950, Doll and Bradford Hill 1950). Equally, however, there may be not one but several environmental causes (Hueper 1951), and Graham (1951) presents evidence that epidermoid carcinoma of the bronchus is of different etiology from adenocarcinoma, oat-cell carcinoma, or round-cell carcinoma, the former being due to epithelial metaplasia under the influence of one or more carcinogens, and the latter arising in a latent embryonic bronchial bud.

ELECTROMAGNETIC AND CORPUSCULAR RADIATION

Radiation as a carcinogenic agent can be considered as comprising infrared, ultraviolet, roentgen and gamma-radiation, α- and β-radiation, and protons and neutrons. Latarjet (1951) has dwelt upon the possible role of the organism's isothermic radiation, and of thermal agitation, pointing out the intensity reached by the infrared flux of long wavelength, to which each cell is constantly exposed. In spite of the low value of the mean quantum energy of this infrared radiation, he feels it not impossible, in view of its intensity and permanence, that it should occasionally produce molecular accidents, especially in view of the low activation potentials of some of the biomolecules involved.

The case of cancer induction by ultraviolet radiation has been most excellently studied by Blum (1950), who points out that quantitative studies of carcinogenesis by this agent are more complete than for any other: he believes them to be explicable by a simple theory based on the assumption that the proliferation of certain cells is progressively accelerated by successive doses, but admits that a satisfactory explanation in terms of real mechanism is not yet apparent.

For roentgen rays, accounts continue to appear of both epithelioma and sarcoma arising in irradiated tissue (Cahan, Woodard, Higinbotham, Stewart, and Coley 1948, Spitz and Higinbotham 1951, Auerbach, Friedman, Weiss, and Amory 1951, Walter 1950, Deller 1951), and of the experimental production of ovarian tumors—granulosa cell, luteoma, and arrhenoblastoma (Mühlbock 1951). Carcinogenesis is described by Lorenz and his co-workers as the predominant picture of radiation injury, on the basis of their studies of the effects of long-continued roentgen and gamma-radiation in several animal species (Lorenz, Eschenbrenner, Heston, and Deringer 1949, Lorenz 1950, Lorenz, Eschenbrenner, Heston, and Uphoff 1951).

The most important remaining class is that of the radioactive elements and isotopes, and a voluminous and ever-growing literature testifies to their carcinogenic potency. The carcinogenic action of radium paints has long been recognized as an important and preventable industrial risk, from the work of Martland and Humphries (1929) and Martland (1931, 1939), and microscopic and autoradiographic studies of the active substances in bone (chiefly radium and its disintegration products), have been carried out by Hoecker and Roofe (1951). Late injuries, tumor formation, and other sequelae to the use of thorotrast have been described by Fleming and Chase (1936), Bauer (1948), Amory and Bunch (1948), Birkner (1949), and Zollinger (1949). In early reports, Brues, Lisco, and Finkel (1947; Lisco, Finkel, and Brues 1947) recounted the sequelae in different animal species of exposure to plutonium and various radioactive products of uranium fission. Radioactive strontium (Sr^{89}), with a 55-day half-life, has a marked tendency to concentrate in the skeleton and to produce tumors of bone in mice. Bone sarcomas are also produced by radioactive cerium-presyodymium (Ce^{144}-Pr^{144}) and by plutonium (Pu^{239}; see also Bloom and Bloom 1949). Following subcutaneous administration of 1 μg. of the last element, fibrosarcomas also appear at the site of injection. The carcinogenic effect in rats and mice of high-energy radiations associated with the uranium chain-reaction are also described by Henshaw, Riley, and Stapleton (1947). With penetrating radiations, the main terminal effects are generalized atrophy, the appearance of neoplasms of the hemopoietic tissues, and mediastinal lymphomatosis. When nonpenetrating radiations were used, the changes were limited mainly to the skin. Several months after single massive doses, in animals which rarely showed spontaneous skin lesions of any type, the incidence of carcinoma was raised to 100 per cent and the number of tumors per animal was as great as 50–100.

The beta rays from P^{32} contained in a phosphorus-impregnated plastic were applied by Henshaw, Snider, and Riley (1949) to rats, either in single massive doses (4,000–6,000 rep) or repeated small daily doses: tumors of diverse types from the skin and connective tissues appeared ten to twelve months after treatment whether single or repeated. The carcinogenicity of P^{32} has also been studied by Koletsky, Bonte, and Friedell (1950; also Koletsky and Christie 1951), and has been compared with that of roentgen radiation by Brues, Sacher, Finkel, and Lisco (1949). Koletsky *et al.* found that neoplasms (osteogenic sarcoma and squamous cell carcinoma) appeared in 40 per cent of a group of rats which had received a single LD_{50} dose of P^{32} (average latent period 290 days) or repeated doses of 1.5 μc (average latent period 165 days). Atypical proliferative lesions were usually found in these rats, and appeared to have acted as a precursor to the malignant change. Apart from the instances already mentioned above of thyroid and pituitary tumors produced by radio-iodine, tumors of the pituitary and trachea were obtained by Gorbman (1949) in mice, following doses of I^{131} sufficient to cause destruction of most or all of the normal thyroid gland. A similar response was described by Goldberg and Chaikoff (1951, 1952), carcinoma of the thyroid developing in 7 of 25 rats which had received intraperitoneal injections of 400 μc of I^{131}.

It is clear that modern developments in atomic physics, by rendering available radioactive isotopes in increasing variety and abundance, must greatly add to the scientific and practical problems which the potential carcinogenicity of such substances creates. This and other radiation hazards have been considered in the proceedings of a conference on the biologic hazards of atomic energy held in

London in 1950 (Haddow 1952), and also by Brues (1949, 1951), who points out that it is not strictly known whether a threshold amount of irradiation is necessary, or whether background irradiation alone may play a part in the etiology of cancer in man. Radiation hazards arising from the atomic energy program have been considered by Eisenbud (1951), and the pathologic effects of high levels of instantaneous radiations on humans at Nagasaki and Hiroshima by Warren (1946).

PROBLEMS OF THE MODE OF ACTION

From the preceding section, and from other reviews of experimental carcinogenesis (e.g., Salter 1948, Truhaut 1949b, Hartwell 1951, Wolf 1952), the number, range, and variety of carcinogenic agents is clearly such as to throw doubt on the likelihood of any underlying chemical specificity of their action. Nevertheless, the center of interest has naturally changed, so as to concentrate attention upon problems of mode of action—that is, the intimate details of the manner in which given carcinogenic types induce malignancy, and the question whether, in spite of their diversity, they may not bring about, by devious initial routes, biologic end results essentially similar in the principle of their causation. The question has been well expressed by Gavaudan and Poussel (1948): "Aussi n'est-il pas interdit de se demander devant la variété structurale des composés cancérigènes si la cancérisation chimique n'est pas . . . une réponse univoque à des perturbations initialement très différentes. Il serait évidemment difficile de parler d'une relation générale entre structure et pouvoir cancérigène si les étiologies physio-chimiques étaient différentes."*

Although these problems have been longest studied in the case of physical agents, the cyclic hydrocarbons, the azo compounds, and the aminostilbenes which will be considered first, a great impetus has arisen from the more recent discovery of carcinogenic activity in whole new series of biologic alkylating agents—the nitrogen mustards, epoxides, ethyleneimines and dimesyloxyalkanes—to be dealt with later.

PHYSICAL PROPERTIES

The great majority of the chemical carcinogens so far considered are lipoid-soluble but virtually insoluble in water. There is, however, no direct relation between the solubility properties and carcinogenic action, nor perhaps would any be expected since the laws governing them are clearly so different; for example, Klevans (1950) finds the logarithm of the solubility of the condensed polycyclic hydrocarbons in water to decrease linearly with molecular length. A quite different situation is found with the carcinogenic alkylating agents still to be described, where many are readily soluble in water and this feature is of importance in the pharmacology of their action.

For the polycyclic hydrocarbons and the aminostilbenes, no specific differences have been disclosed between carcinogens and noncarcinogens, by means of fluorescence or ultraviolet absorption spectroscopy, or from infrared spectroscopy

* "Is one not justified in asking—in view of the structural diversity of cancerogenic compounds—whether chemical cancerogenesis is not . . . a uniform response to a large variety of initial stimuli? It would obviously be difficult to speak of a general relationship between structure and cancerogenic potency if the physicochemical etiology varied."

(cf. Thompson, Vago, Corfield, and Orr 1950; Orr and Thompson 1950). Latarjet had suggested that the infrared-absorption properties of carcinogens might be of unique importance since infrared radiation is the only radiation acting continuously on all the tissues in vivo (*supra*), with the exception of the relatively unimportant radioactivity of potassium. Might these properties of a carcinogen strongly adsorbed to a self-duplicating protein fiber impress a deforming field long enough to allow modification and duplication of the new form? Pacault and Lecomte (1949) had also entertained some hope of relating carcinogenicity with infrared absorption properties, but after a study of various acridine and anthracene derivatives found no sign of any such systematic connection, although they did not entirely exclude the possibility at longer wavelengths. Iversen and Arley (1950; Iversen 1949), have suggested a possible correlation between certain ultraviolet absorption levels and the carcinogenicity of various benzanthracenes, in a general theory which appears nevertheless to require much further test. Cook, Schoental, and Scott (1950) have described an interesting simple relationship between the number of quinonoid rings and the maximum of the longest ultraviolet (or the shortest fluorescence) band of polycyclic aromatic hydrocarbons, which seems to reflect some fundamental connection between their chemical reactivity and spectra. Schoental and Scott (1949) had noticed a close relation between the position of the maximum of the first (shortest) fluorescence band and the minimum number of quinonoid rings in the molecule, so as to conform to the Fries rule that as many rings as possible should have Kekulé structures. These authors also found that for this series of compounds the shortest fluorescence band coincides approximately in wavelength with the longest absorption band. In a comparison between the values expressed in wave numbers of the longest ultraviolet absorption bands of a series of polycyclic aromatic hydrocarbons and the minimum number of quinonoid rings contained in their molecules, Cook, Schoental, and Scott subsequently found that the hydrocarbons fall into series of groups related to this number of quinonoid rings.

STRUCTURE AND ACTION

From the foregoing it is obvious that carcinogenicity is shared by substances of widely different features in the purely chemical sense, as for example anthracenes and fluorenes, aminostilbenes, acridines and carbazoles, and other heterocyclic analogs and isosters. It was this which led Cook to suggest the importance, in themselves, of general molecular shape and dimensions (Barry *et al.* 1935), and a somewhat similar opinion was held by F. Bergmann (1942), who conceived the molecule functioning as a whole, and its activity as being determined by shape and size. Bergmann suggested that all the carcinogenic hydrocarbons might be absorbed by a single receptor, and that all such compounds might be regarded as parts of an "ideal" carcinogenic structure. According to this view, geometrical conformity of carcinogen and receptor is a necessary condition for activity, although not a sufficient one. Inevitably we recall the molecular flatness of the carcinogenic hydrocarbons and aminostilbenes, and the occurrence of biomolecular flatness elsewhere, and especially in the furanose ring of the ribose residue with its possible importance in the construction of the long chains of nucleotides (Astbury, cited in

Hirst 1949). But we have still no knowledge of the site in the cell at which the action of the hydrocarbons and aminostilbenes takes place.

In an endeavor to define the structural requirements essential for carcinogenicity, Robinson (1946) suggested reaction at an activated phenanthrene-type bridge as a likely mechanism in the majority of cases. There are apparent exceptions, more than one mechanism may be concerned, and Robinson himself was unwilling to advance even a provisional hypothesis until more facts had been gathered. Equally,

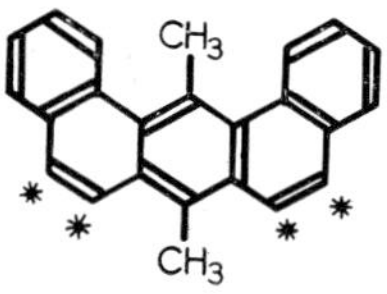

FIG. 79. 9:10-Dimethyl-1:2:7:8-dibenzanthracene (active).

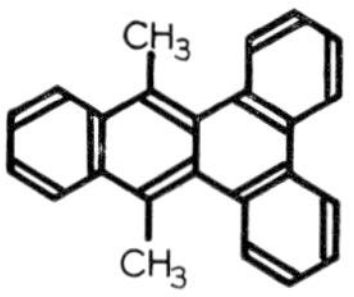

FIG. 80. 9:10-Dimethyl-1:2:3:4-dibenzanthracene (inactive).

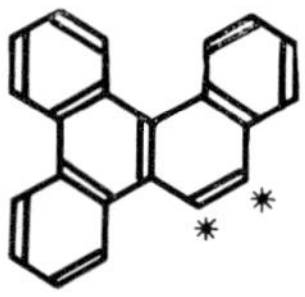

FIG. 81. 1:2:3:4-Dibenzphenanthrene (active).

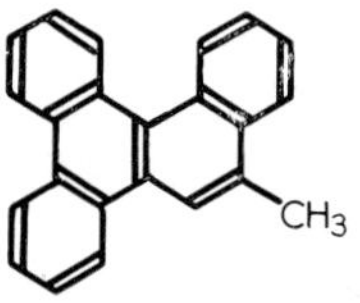

FIG. 82. 9-Methyl-1:2:-3:4-dibenzphenanthrene (inactive).

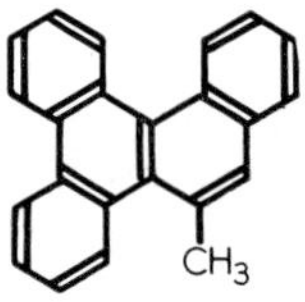

FIG. 83. 10-Methyl-1:2:-3:4-dibenzphenanthrene (inactive).

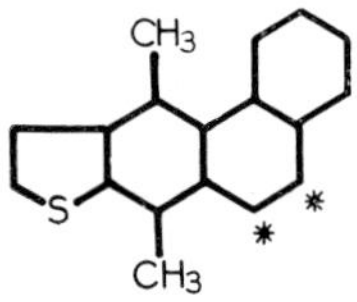

FIG. 84.

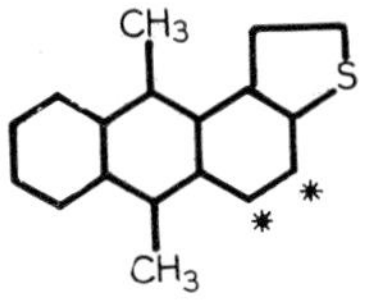

FIG. 85.

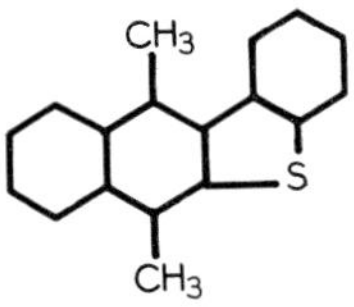

FIG. 86.

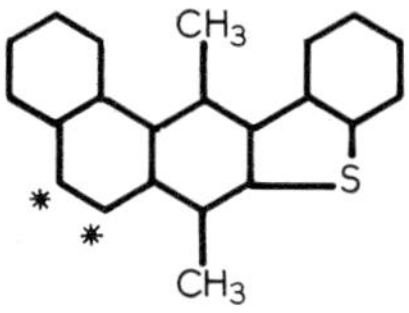

FIG. 87.

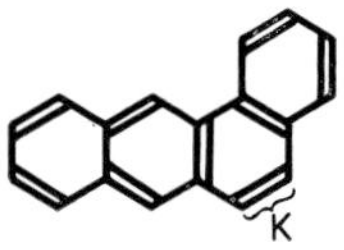

FIG. 88.

however, there are several examples, not merely consistent with such a view, but affording it striking support. The extreme carcinogenicity of 9:10-dimethyl-1:2-benzanthracene is a clear proof that unsubstituted *meso* positions are not essential for activity, and in the present connection it is of much interest that 9:10-dimethyl-1:2:7:8-dibenzanthracene (Fig. 79) containing two phenanthrene-type bonds, is markedly carcinogenic (Berenblum 1946), in contrast with 9:10-dimethyl-1:2:3:4-dibenzanthracene, (Fig. 80), containing none, which is completely inactive.

Other critical cases are provided by the contrast between the activity of 1:2:3:4-dibenzphenanthrene (Fig. 81) and the inactivity of derivatives substituted in either the 9- or 10-positions (Figs. 82 and 83, Harris and Bradsher 1946); and by a series of hydrocarbons in which a benzene ring is replaced by the isosteric thiophene nucleus. In 9:10-dimethyl-1:2-benzanthracene there are three benzene nuclei which can be replaced in this way, and two of them (Figs. 84 and 85, Fieser 1941) are carcinogenic. The third isomeride in which the phenanthrene bridge is replaced by sulfur (Fig. 86, Tilak 1946) is noncarcinogenic by subcutaneous injection in mice, and seems to be only weakly active on painting. Even more suggestive is the high potency which reappears in the benzoderivative (Fig. 87), in which the phenanthrene double bond is once again a feature.

These examples are in keeping with the view that an essential requirement may be the phenanthrene double bond or its equivalent, and that the 9- and 10- positions (shown in the formulae by *) must be unsubstituted. It also appears that the reactivity of these positions may be enhanced, or competitive reactivity reduced, by appropriate substitution elsewhere. The apparent importance of the phenanthrene double bond finds a parallel in the ethylene bridge of the aminostilbenes. Between these structures there is a high degree of similarity not merely on purely chemical grounds, but also in the way in which substitution, modification, or total replacement, annuls the biologic activity of the molecule as a whole. So far as the biologic effects of the aminostilbenes are concerned, such activity disappears when the ethylene bridge is extended to three or four carbon atoms, when it is reduced, when either or both hydrogen atoms are substituted, when either =CH- group is replaced by a nitrogen atom, or when the whole bridge is replaced by oxygen or sulfur. The hypothesis put forward by Haddow, Harris, Kon, and Roe (1948), that such compounds show biologic activity only when the stilbene system is coplanar, is supported by the polarisation studies of Everard and Sutton (1951). Boyland (1950a) has suggested that the phenanthrene double bond and the stilbene double bond are chemically reactive groups (capable for example of reacting with perbenzoic acid, see later), which so far as these molecules are concerned can be regarded as "carcinogenophores," and other examples of which may be the azo group, the nitrogen atom of certain carbazoles and acridines, and the aromatic amino group of the aminostilbenes and amino-azo compounds. It is, however, a question whether the general conception can apply so widely.

CHEMICAL AND METABOLIC REACTIVITY OF THE HYDROCARBONS

It has been supposed that the carcinogenic hydrocarbons, which on the whole are stable and comparatively inert, may exert their biologic effects through conversion into active metabolic products. Fieser (1941) laid stress on the fact that the most potent are endowed with a remarkable susceptibility to substitution reactions, and surpass all other known aromatic hydrocarbons in this type of reactivity. Using the reactions of diazo coupling, oxidation with lead tetra-acetate or perbenzoic acid, and condensation of the hydrocarbons with sulfur monochloride, he found in general that the order of reactivity was essentially the same for a given group of compounds, in such a sequence as indicated the possibility of a causal association between chemical reactivity and carcinogenesis, subject to other requirements such as solubility, absorbability, and molecular size.

These considerations suggested that the carcinogenic molecule undergoes a substitution reaction as the first stage in the production of its biologic effects, with the introduction of a hydroxyl, sulfydryl, or basic group yielding a functional derivative which might then enter into other changes possibly involving conjugation with cell constituents. A more direct action was suggested by the condensation of sulfur monochloride with carcinogenic hydrocarbons: with the most potent and reactive hydrocarbons, introduction of a sulfur substituent occurs at room temperature without catalyst, and Fieser suggested that the carcinogen might similarly combine with cell proteins by the opening of an S-S linkage.

The possibly specific role of sulfur metabolism in carcinogenesis by the polycyclic hydrocarbons has been extensively studied by Crabtree (1947), who showed that carcinogenesis might be impeded first by certain chlorine compounds which could act through condensation with SH-containing components so as to impair enzyme systems dependent on intact SH groups; by bromobenzene; by another class typified by the unsaturated maleic and citraconic acids, which form addition products with SH-containing compounds and disturb the sulfur metabolism of mouse skin by fixation of glutathione; and by naphthalene, anthracene, and phenanthrene, which are excreted as mercapturates—all suggesting that if sulfur is not concerned in the detoxication of carcinogens, it may be closely involved in their mechanism of action.

Boyland and Weigert (1947) have described how a carcinogenic hydrocarbon may combine with tissue constituents through the positions of prime reactivity, and how a hydrocarbon can be altered in the body to give neutral water-soluble substances by addition of the elements of hydrogen peroxide at positions of only secondary reactivity. Apart from such perhydroxylation of potential double bonds, the biologic oxidation of aromatic rings may also lead to other types of products, for example, phenols as in the conversion of 1:2:5:6-dibenzanthracene by rats and mice to the 4′:8′-dihydroxy-derivative (Dobriner, Rhoads, and Lavin 1942, Cason and Fieser 1940), and acids by ring-fission. In addition there may be other types of intermediates which have so far escaped detection, as for instance the di-epoxides, which have recently acquired a special significance and will be discussed in more detail later.

Isolation of the metabolic products of the polycyclic hydrocarbons, mainly by Boyland, Berenblum and Schoental, and Young, revealed the surprising fact that biologic oxidation does not attack the centers in the molecule which chemical agents show to be the most reactive. Work in this field has therefore been directed to two ends, first elucidation of the mechanism of the biologic oxidation process, and secondly the discovery of methods of chemical oxidation which would simulate the biochemical oxidation. In this connection Cook and Schoental (1948a,b) examined the oxidation of ten polycyclic aromatic hydrocarbons, including some of the most potent cancer-producing compounds, by osmium tetroxide in benzene-pyridine to diols which undergo facile dehydration to hydroxy-derivatives of the original hydrocarbons. This process represented the closest parallel thus far achieved to the biochemical oxidation of the hydrocarbons, although the positions of attack were still different in the two cases. The use of osmium tetroxide to determine the relative reactivity of aromatic double bonds was also described by

Badger (1949), Badger and Reed (1948), and Badger and Lynn (1950), in studies of the influence of methyl substitution in the benzanthracene molecule in increasing the rate of addition to the 3:4-bond, and of other substituent groups on the density of π electrons in the same region. In the work of Cook and Schoental the products of osmium tetroxide oxidation were similar in type to some of the compounds isolated from the excreta of animals to which the hydrocarbons were administered (Boyland and Levi 1935; Boyland and Shoppee 1947; Boyland and Wolf 1948, 1950; Booth and Boyland 1947, 1949; Cook, Ludwiczak, and Schoental 1950; Beale and Roe 1951), and the metabolic glycols are probably intermediates in the formation of the phenols which have been isolated in other cases (Weigert and Mottram 1946, Berenblum and Schoental 1946, 1949).

In another endeavor to find a reagent which would provide a still closer parallel to the biochemical hydroxylations, Cook and Schoental (1950) studied the products formed by oxidation of a series of aromatic hydrocarbons with Milas' reagent (hydrogen peroxide in *tert*-butanol, catalysed by osmium tetroxide). As early as 1912 Dakin (*Oxidations and Reductions in the Animal Body*, N. Y.) pointed out that hydrogen peroxide, alone of all the known chemical oxidizing agents, could bring about the same types of oxidation of a variety of compounds as do enzyme systems, and the widespread occurrence of catalase and peroxidases is also a pointer to the importance of hydrogen peroxide in some types of biochemical oxidation. Cook and Schoental regard their later results as to some extent bridging the gap between the biochemical and purely chemical oxidation of the hydrocarbons. The earlier findings had shown that it is possible to bring about selective chemical attack at positions in the molecule which are not normally the most reactive, and to simulate the perhydroxylation reactions which are a characteristic feature of the biochemical oxidations. It is important that the diols and phenols isolated in metabolic experiments represent only a small proportion of the hydrocarbon administered, and that most of the material undergoes more extensive degradation. Thus Heidelberger and his collaborators (Heidelberger and Jones 1948; Heidelberger, Kirk, and Perkins 1948; Heidelberger and Wiest 1951 also Heidelberger and Weiss 1951), using 1:2:5:6-dibenzanthracene labeled with radiocarbon, have shown that acids are formed by ring-fission of the hydrocarbon and also that some of the compound is completely oxidized to carbon dioxide. To this extent oxidation by the Milas' reagent imitates the metabolic oxidation, for prolonged treatment leads to extensive conversion of the hydrocarbons into acidic degradation products, only some of which have been identified.

The oxidation of various polycyclic aromatic hydrocarbons has also been studied by Roitt and Waters (1949) by the use of perbenzoic acid in chloroform at 0°C. In this connection the report of Eckhardt (1940), that only carcinogenic hydrocarbons are significantly attacked by perbenzoic acid under these conditions, was of interest: while the results accorded with those of Eckhardt generally, it was however found that, given sufficient time, perbenzoic acid appreciably attacked many noncarcinogenic hydrocarbons in addition. From the complicated sequence of consecutive reactions which appeared to be involved in these oxidations, no simple connections between structure, rates of oxidation, and carcinogenicity could clearly be traced, and in particular there was no evidence of oxidation in the phenanthrene positions which are prone to attack by osmium tetroxide.

Much importance attaches to the configuration of the metabolic diols, as *trans*, (in contrast with the *cis* configuration of the glycols obtained by Cook and Schoental with osmium tetroxide), in determining the reaction mechanism. Boyland and Levi (1935) showed that anthracene fed to rats and rabbits is converted in part into diols of levorotatory and inactive forms, while Young (1947) isolated a levorotatory form of the corresponding diol from the urine of rats dosed with naphthalene. According to Booth and Boyland (1949) these diols are obtained in each case as a mixture of an optically active and an inactive form, the dextrorotatory predominating in the metabolites from rabbits, the levorotatory in those from rats. Theoretically the diols can exist in *cis*- and *trans*- modifications and to each modification there will be *dextro*-, *levo*- and inactive forms. While Boyland and Shoppee (1947) originally inferred a *cis*-configuration for the anthracene metabolites, Booth and Boyland later preferred the *trans*-configuration for both the anthracene and naphthalene products (see also Cook, Loudon, and Williamson 1950), and with Turner, (Booth, Boyland, and Turner 1950) completed a proof that the biologically produced phenanthrene diol also has the *trans*-configuration.

If it cannot be claimed that these chemical and metabolic studies afford any clear picture of the carcinogenic process as yet, the facts disclosed are often complementary to those revealed by other methods, and will no doubt lead to a unified interpretation in due time. As already indicated, it is possible that a hitherto undiscovered metabolite may be of preponderant importance, even if produced in small amount, and the epoxides especially, which are a feasible case, will be further discussed below. Another possibility is that biochemical perhydroxylation may be effected by free hydroxyl radicals, in view of the fact that free radicals may play an important part in biologic oxidations (Waters 1946). In this case the question arises whether the free radical oxidations of carcinogenic hydrocarbons, in contrast with ionic oxidations, attack at different positions in the molecule, and if so whether these are the positions of the biochemical attack.

ACTION AND METABOLISM OF THE AZO CARCINOGENS

An outstanding advance in cancer research was made when it became recognized that the carcinogenic action of dimethylaminoazobenzene and other azo compounds is greatly influenced by the diet (Mori and Nakahara 1940, Mori 1941, Sugiura 1944) and is specially dependent upon its content of protein. That the protective role of protein is not entirely confined to azo carcinogenesis, but may also be an important factor in the induction and inhibition of tumors, is indicated by the later work of Elson (1949), with its suggestion that many different carcinogens may interfere with the normal channels of protein synthesis, and lead to tumor formation through the development of alternative synthetic routes.

Rhoads (1940, 1942a,b), and Rhoads and Kensler (1941), in a study of the induction of hepatic cancer by administration of dimethylaminoazobenzene to rats taking a diet of brown rice and carrots, found that supplementing this diet with yeast or liver-extract in adequate amounts completely prevented the development of tumors, the protective factor being none of the constituents of the vitamin B complex then described. The effect of feeding the carcinogen to animals taking the unsupplemented diet was an inhibition of the activity of at least two enzyme systems, cocarboxylase and cozymase, thus producing what these authors considered a conditioned or secondary deficiency disease. On the other hand, the development of the mutation which characterizes the malignant cell was accompanied by the appearance of an oxidising system insusceptible to the inhibitory effect of the toxic metabolic products of the carcinogen, and Rhoads and Kensler regarded their results as the first demonstration that cancer tissue evoked by a chemical carcinogen possesses an oxidative system immune to the inhibitory action of that carcinogen or of its metabolic products. This interesting result is consonant with views earlier developed by the writer from the purely biologic or physiologic aspect and summarised below, with the interpretation of the Madison school that the azo carcinogens may lead to the elimination of a specific hepatic protein, and with much new evidence from studies of biologic alkylating agents as carcinogens, still to be described.

Miller, Miller, Kline, and Rusch (1948) drew attention to an important correlation between the level of hepatic riboflavin and the appearance of liver tumors, in rats fed amino-azo dyes. Rats fed diets accelerating tumor induction had average hepatic riboflavin levels significantly lower than those of control and protected animals. Conversely, for various compounds the rate and extent of riboflavin loss were greatest with the more carcinogenic members. This correlation raised the question whether riboflavin-containing enzymes are responsible for the destruction of the dyestuff in the liver, and Miller and Miller (1947) had already indicated that the protein-bound dyes are metabolized more rapidly by rats receiving high levels of dietary riboflavin. On the other hand, if riboflavin or 4-dimethylaminoazobenzene or their derivatives compete for a protein involved in carcinogenesis, increased amounts of riboflavin would protect the protein and slow down the process.

The most detailed study of the metabolism of dimethylaminoazobenzene and related compounds has been made by the Millers and their associates (Miller and Miller 1946, 1947, 1948; Miller and Baumann 1945; Miller and Baumann 1946; Miller, Miller, and Baumann 1945; Miller 1947; Miller, Kline, and Rusch 1946; Mueller and Miller 1948, 1949, 1950). The azo carcinogens are subject to at least three metabolic reactions in the intact rat, namely stepwise demethylation of the N-methyl groups, reductive cleavage of the azo linkage, and hydroxylation principally at the 4′-position. One of the initial steps is a reversible demethylation of 4-dimethylaminoazobenzene to 4-monomethylaminoazobenzene, which has the same carcinogenic activity, and an irreversible demethylation to 4-aminoazobenzene, an essentially inactive compound. Boissonnas, Turner, and du Vigneaud (1949) described the metabolism in the rat of dimethylaminoazobenzene containing radiocarbon in the methyl groups, the rate of oxidation of the latter being shown by the rate of appearance of radioactivity in the expiratory CO_2. The significance of labile methyl groups in carcinogenesis by the azo dyes has also been studied by Kirby (1948b), who found N-demethylation related to species, strain, and diet but probably not to the carcinogenic property itself. Both demethylation and 4′-hydroxylation of dimethylaminoazobenzene were found by Mueller and Miller (1948) to be effected by liver homogenates fortified with diphosphopyridine nucleotide, nicotinamide, magnesium ion, and hexose diphosphate, and reduction cleavage, to yield the corresponding monophenylamines, has been shown by the same authors (1949, 1950) to be catalysed by a flavoprotein containing riboflavine-adenine-dinucleotide as the prosthetic group.

Another approach to the mechanism of action of the carcinogenic amino-azo dyes is provided by the observation that these and other carcinogens inhibit the autoxidation of unsaturated lipids (Rusch and Kline 1941, Deutsch, Kline, and Rusch 1941, Rusch 1948). Only very rough correlations were obtained between anti-oxidant effect and carcinogenic activity (Rusch and Miller 1948), but the matter may be of more general interest since destruction of various carcinogenic hydrocarbons was also shown to occur in the course of such oxidations, (Mueller, Miller, and Rusch 1945). The facts recall various suggestions of free radical mechanisms, already made and still to be considered, and Waters' studies of the action of hydrocarbons in autoxidation systems.

Perhaps the most important finding of the Madison group is that the liver of rats, after feeding dimethylaminoazobenzene, contains a protein-bound amino-azo dye (Price, Miller, and Miller 1948, Miller, Sapp, and Miller 1948). Pursuing this observation, the Millers were able to correlate the degree of such protein binding with carcinogenesis according to species, (thus the dye is chemically combined with tissue in which it produces tumors [e.g. mouse liver] but not in tissue to which it is not carcinogenic [e.g. rabbit liver]); with carcinogenesis according to rat tissues; with the influence of riboflavin level; with the differing biologic activity of individual dyes; and with the level of dyestuff administered. Moreover, and perhaps most important, the carcinogenic compound does not combine with the tissue of the tumor induced, suggesting a chemoresistance based possibly on the elimination in the tumor cell of the protein originally concerned.

That the principle is not necessarily confined to azo carcinogenesis is supported by Miller's (1951) studies of the formation of protein-bound derivatives of 3:4-benzpyrene in the epidermal fractions of treated mouse skin, and Heidelberger's confirmation (personal communication) of a similar fixation to protein of both dibenzanthracene and benzpyrene. On the assumption of a causal relationship between the formation of these derivatives and carcinogenicity, Miller discusses the question (relatively unimportant at this stage if the structures involved are autosynthetic) whether the proteins concerned occur in the nuclear genes, the cytoplasmic genes, or in enzymes. Whatever the detailed nature of the process, these views are of much interest as being identical with those reached from entirely different evidence in the case of carcinogenesis by the nitrogen mustards, di-epoxides, polyethyleneimines, and related compounds, namely that malignancy may be produced by the alteration or deletion, following chemical combination with the carcinogen, of some genetically critical self-duplicating protein (see later).

ENERGY STATES IN THE CARCINOGENIC MOLECULE

Investigation of the problems of chemical reactivity and carcinogenicity has been greatly stimulated by endeavors to relate this quality to a characteristic electron distribution in the molecules concerned. Otto Schmidt (1938, 1939a,b, 1941a,b) was the first to compare the electron density of the *meso* regions of certain carcinogenic hydrocarbons with that in noncarcinogens, and on the basis of this comparison he postulated, as a necessary condition of carcinogenic activity, that the density of such regions should exceed $0.44e/\text{Å}^2$; in particular he suggested that the activity of a carcinogen is due to the electro-affinity of its excited state facilitating a quantal change in neighboring molecules.

This new conception was extended and developed in a long series of studies by the Pullmans and Daudels and their schools (A. Pullman 1945, 1946a,b, 1947a,b; B. Pullman 1946; A. and B. Pullman 1946, 1948, 1949; Pullman, Berthier, and Pullman 1950; Martin 1946, 1948; Daudel 1946a,b, 1948a,b,c; P. and R. Daudel 1948; P. and R. Daudel, Buu-Hoï, and Martin 1948; P. and R. Daudel and Buu-Hoï 1950), who obtained supporting evidence for it through a quantum mechanical treatment which permits a calculation of the density of π electrons for a given structure, and by means of which a relation could be formulated between carcinogenicity and the electronic density of the region K (Fig. 88), the density threshold below which a substance ceases to be carcinogenic being 1.292e. Pacault (1946, 1951), by measurements of magnetic susceptibility, has also indicated certain electromeric structures which appear to be correlated with the property of carcinogenicity. Like Schmidt, Daudel (1946a,b, 1948, 1950; P. and R. Daudel 1949, 1950), has envisaged the molecular alterations which might result from the proximity of a region rich in π electrons to certain regions of protein molecules, and has attempted a semi-quantitative treatment of a hypothetical example, whereby a carcinogenic hydrocarbon might facilitate the first reactions of the carcinogenic process. In this example the first stage consisted in the formation of an addition complex between the carcinogen and the tissue elements, and the second in the interaction between the π electrons of a biologic amine and those of the hydrocarbon: although the theoretical approach must have its place in elucidating what Daudel calls the catalytic effects of carcinogenic hydrocarbons on chemical reactions, it is perhaps a question to what extent it can do so directly, apart from exploring possibilities already known to exist, or stimulating the discovery of new facts by experiment.

Nevertheless the French school can claim to have brought forward evidence of a concordance between the effects on the one hand of alkyl substitution on biologic activity in the hydrocarbons, and on polarisability on the other, to show the preponderant role of charge concentration in the transition state characterising the interaction of carcinogen and cell, and the electrophilic character of the cellular receptor or element which may be the seat of malignant change. The carcinogenic activity of the hydrocarbons would hence appear to be a function, not only of their static structure, but equally of the dynamic changes to which this is subject through polarisability (Pullman 1947c; Buu-Hoï, P. and R. Daudel, and Vroelant 1949).

While these relationships were claimed to be sufficiently sound to act as the basis for a certain degree of prediction (Buu-Hoï, P. and R. Daudel, Lacassagne, Lecocq, Martin, and Rudali 1947; Sandorfy, Vroelant, Yvan, Chalvet, and Daudel 1950), they were clearly subject to much further scrutiny and test. The results are of much interest, and have been surveyed to date by Coulson (1952). The validity of the resonance description of these molecules not being completely established, it was necessary that alternative calculations should be made, using a different type of approximation to the molecular wave function. Such an approximation was found in the method of molecular orbitals, (Lennard-Jones, Huckel, Mulliken, Coulson), and at an early stage such calculations did indeed appear to show that potent carcinogenic hydrocarbons possess anomalously high "fractional bond orders" in the K- region, (see also Coulson, Daudel, and Daudel 1947; Berthier, Coulson, Greenwood, and Pullman 1948; Daudel, Daudel, and Vroelant 1948; Baldock, Berthier, and Pullman 1948). Badger (1949), as an outcome of his studies of the relative reactivity of aromatic double bonds by measurements of the rate of addition of osmium tetroxide to carcinogenic and related noncarcinogenic hydrocarbons, concluded that his data appeared to support the Pullman calculations at least qualitatively; on the other hand it seemed to him that in assessing the validity of any correlation between the electronic charge on the K- region and carcinogenic activity, too little account had been taken of rather numerous exceptions (see also Badger 1950). Discussing the reactivity of aromatic bonds with reference to the carcinogenic benzanthracenes, Greenwood (1951) also believed his results to confirm those obtained by the Pullmans and the Daudels with simpler but less accurate technics, although he too drew notice to anomalies which seemed to have been ignored. He concluded with due provisos but as a not altogether unwarrantable deduction: "if we suppose that though the evidence is not decisive, the K region may play some role in the carcinogenic action of these molecules, then the most important conclusion to be deduced from the present results is that the K region may act by a largely heterolytic mechanism involving attack by two electrophilic centres."

In a study of the electronic structure of various aminostilbene derivatives in relation to their carcinogenicity, Pullman (1948), while unable to reach any final conclusions, believed his data to be not inconsistent with a relation between biologic activity and the extent of the charge concentrated on the ethylenic bond. The charge distribution and bond orders in various aminostilbenes were also calculated, using the method of molecular orbitals, by Coulson and Jacobs (1949), who found the charge distribution in the ethylenic bond to be markedly asymmetric. The extension of the Pullman hypothesis of optimum electronic charge to the azo linkage (called the K′ region), was examined by Badger and Lewis (1951), by observing the rate of addition of electrophilic reagents to this region in the three azonaphthalenes and azobenzene. The reaction rates indicated that the total charge on the two nitrogen atoms forming the K′- position in 2:2′-azonaphthalene must be greater than that in any of the other compounds, it being possibly significant that of these compounds only 2:2′-azonaphthalene produces liver tumors.

Whatever the outcome, the theory of Otto Schmidt, in the form which has been given it by the French, is believed by Daudel to have coordinated many facts, allowed a degree of prediction which test has confirmed, suggested fresh experiment, and above all stimulated the application of theoretical chemistry and physics in the field of molecular structure in biology.

RELATIVE STABILITIES OF THE NORMAL AND MALIGNANT CELL STATES

Both the normal and the malignant cell states have their levels of stability, as is shown respectively by a certain resistance to malignant change, and by the permanence of the new cellular properties once malignant change has occurred. Once a carcinogen has effected malignant transformation, its continued presence would appear to be no longer necessary for the subsequent growth of the tumor. Taken together, these facts suggest that the role of a given carcinogen is to induce a new (and stable) configuration of properties, and the question arises whether the relationship between the old and new configurations can be expressed in terms of different energy-levels. That the change is from a higher to a lower level is suggested by the relative ease with which the normal cell may be converted into a malignant form, in contrast with the impossibility, thus far, of effecting reversion. While the normal and malignant cell types have their own levels of stability, and are therefore discontinuous in their properties, transition from the former to the latter may on occasion be apparently continuous, or by way of intermediate forms of high instability. The latter phenomenon has frequently been noted in the histopathology of skin carcinogenesis, where the early stages may be reversible (even in some cases to the extent of regression of papillomas when the carcinogen is withdrawn), in contrast with the later steps, which are quite irreversible and take place whether exposure to the carcinogen is continued or not.

That the complete autonomy of malignant tumors is an extreme, reached by way of less stable or more responsive states, is shown by many recent examples, including the contributions of Greene (1951) on heterotransplantability of tumors, the initial estrogen-dependence of certain interstitial-cell tumors of the testis (Gardner 1945), and the conditioned pituitary growths described by Furth and Burnett (1951), which are induced by thyroid-destructive doses of radio-iodine and are transplantable only in mice whose thyroid glands have been similarly destroyed. In a study of the inception and development of mammary cancer in mice, Foulds (1951) has described the phenomenon of "progression," and defined it as a tendency towards an ultimate stage of growth unresponsive to hormonal and other regulation, and one which may possibly be inherent in the neoplastic process.

The writer (1947) had already drawn attention to the bearing on these problems of cell stability, of Schrödinger's application of quantum theory in relation to biology and genetics (1944). Schrödinger was led to suggest, from the stability and durability of the gene material on the one hand and its discontinuous mutation on the other, that such mutation might in fact be due to quantum jumps in the gene molecule; and he also emphasized the importance for biology of "isomeric" transitions betwen two configurations which are not neighboring and between which transition can take place only over intervening configurations which have a greater energy than either. Figure 89 shows in schematic fashion, and after Schrödinger, the energy-barrier (*X*) interposed between the stable states *I* (normal) and *II* (malignant), with the minimum energy (*A*) required to effect the change *I*→*II*.

It is clear first that amounts of energy less than this minimum will produce only impermanent changes which revert to the normal, secondly that transition from malignant to normal may be achieved, at least in theory, by application of a minimum amount of energy, greater than that required to change from the higher to the lower level. As to how much greater, nothing is known, and all experience very obviously points to the extreme difficulty or improbability of effecting such reversion: while cancer can be induced almost equally well by any one of a large variety of chemical and physical agents, it is possible that true reversal could be brought about only by macromolecules of extreme specificity, comparable perhaps with those responsible for pneumococcal transformation. At the same time, much might still no doubt be learned from rare events, such for

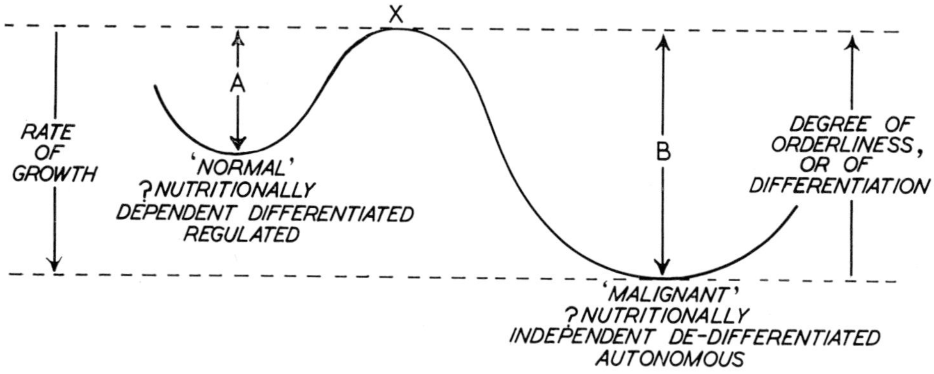

FIG. 89. Application of Schrödinger's quantum theory of biology and genetics to the transition from the normal to the malignant cell.

example as the regressive changes which occasionally take place in the leukemias of childhood with superadded nonspecific infections, and in such pathologic curiosities as multiple primary self-healing squamous epithelioma of the skin (Smith 1948, Charteris 1951).

Figure 89 also indicates other antithetic qualities associated with the normal and malignant states, as for instance nutritional dependence and independence respectively, following Lederberg's correlation (1946) on the one hand between normal tissue cells and nutritionally deficient mutants of *Neurospora*, and on the other hand between malignant cells and variants having a newly acquired or re-acquired capacity to synthesize an essential metabolite otherwise only available in regulatory amounts. While this correlation is no doubt well-founded in principle, there is an apparently paradoxical situation, to be dealt with below, in that many of the more recently discovered biologic alkylating agents are at once carcinogenic, and nevertheless produce biochemically dependent mutations in bacteria and moulds. Secondly, the transition from normal to malignant is frequently marked not only by an increased growth-rate, but also by loss of cellular differentiation:

this inverse relation is also indicated in Fig. 89, although it is far from being simple or invariable. Plainly the energy curves can equally well be regarded as referring to orderliness or structure, while other workers and especially Rondoni (1946), have dwelt on the increase of entropy on passing from normal to malignant, or from a less likely to a more likely state. In a discussion of the energetics of mutation, and of unstable states, Pauling (1949) has used a similar curve to illustrate the manner of occurrence of mutation, relating energy, or some other property associated with the self-duplicating power of a gene, with a parameter describing the gene configuration; while Stearn (1949) has shown the applicability of the Eyring formulation of rate theory (Eyring 1935) to a large variety of processes in the kinetics of biologic reactions, complex as well as simple. In this case Eyring stresses the free energy of activation rather than the heat or energy of activation, and has replaced the concept of reactive molecules by the "activated complex," the configuration and energy of which can be calculated from knowledge of the configuration of the normal reactant molecules together with the distribution of energy among their degrees of freedom.

Much of the work on the metabolism of the carcinogenic hydrocarbons, which has already been considered, suggests that it is not the hydrocarbon or a metabolite which is the proximate carcinogenic agent, but rather the energy released during the transformation from one metabolite to another. Similarly Anderson (1950) has adduced a certain amount of experimental evidence for this concept, that the proximate causal agent in chemical carcinogenesis is the energy liberated during oxidation of the carcinogen applied. This hypothesis may also provide a link between the carcinogenic action of roentgen rays, gamma rays, ultraviolet radiation, and chemical compounds, since all these agents may be, as has been suggested by Daudel (1946b), sources or carriers of energy in such a form as may readily interfere with the normal growth of the cell. A similar argument was used by Latarjet (1946), from a comparison between ionization and molecular activation in the action of radiations on microorganisms. Ionizing radiations on the one hand, and ultraviolet radiation on the other, are found to produce lesions so similar that it is impossible to decide the nature of the stimulus which provoked them, and it is suggested that what they perform in common is to deliver to the appropriate location in the cell an amount of energy sufficient to produce an identical primary effect. More recently, Latarjet (1951) has extended and generalized his interpretation, suggesting that the function of carcinogenic substances may be to increase the frequency of so-called molecular accidents by lowering the activation potentials of biologic macromolecules: in coupling with such a macromolecule, they would lower, by a kind of catalysis, the potential barrier corresponding to a given reaction. The carcinogenic potency of a molecule would thus be linked to two successive functions, first an elective fixation to a cellular substrate, and secondly the induction, by catalysis, of a certain reaction involving the substrate. A merit of this conception would be to establish some community of mechanism between carcinogenic chemical agents and radiations. The latter deliver energy to the molecules which absorb them, and in so doing activate them and then induce, with varying probabilities, reactions which would otherwise be only remotely likely. Hence, radiations and chemical carcinogens would favor the same primary reactions, highly improbable otherwise, in consequence of an access of energy of different types. It was this general notion which had already been vaguely formulated by Schmidt, and which led to the efforts of the French theoretical school to determine which were the structural features of carcinogenic molecules underlying their peculiar capacity for this special kind of catalysis.

CHAPTER 17

The Chemical and Genetic Mechanisms of Carcinogenesis

II. BIOLOGIC ALKYLATING AGENTS

Alexander Haddow

It is a remarkable circumstance, in view of the great volume of experiment which has been devoted to the mechanism of action of the cyclic hydrocarbons, the azo dyestuffs, the aminostilbenes, and other carcinogens, that so little should be known of the precise site in the cell at which such action takes place. Only of late have there been obtained the first hints—and for the moment they remain no more—as to the likely site of action of at least one class of chemical carcinogen, from the discovery of carcinogenic activity in a series of nitrogen mustards and (later) of other agents—the di-epoxides, polyethyleneimines and dimethanesulfonoxyalkanes—all of which are capable of alkylating various cell components and receptors (Haddow 1949, 1950, 1951). In this case observation of the carcinogenic properties of these compounds came long after their investigation as potential agents of chemical warfare (cf. Winternitz 1920), so that a vast literature already exists describing their effects in many other connections and upon a wide diversity of biologic systems.

The history and pharmacology of the bis (2-haloethyl)-amines and sulfides have been well described by Philips (1950; Hunt and Philips 1949), and a host of papers relates their specialized inhibitory effects upon cell division both normal and malignant, as in fertilization and development (Bodenstein 1947, 1948; Bodenstein and Goldin 1948; Barron, Seegmiller, Mendes, and Narahara 1948; Haskin 1948; Hutchens and Podolsky 1948; Hettig, Robertson, and Cline 1950); regeneration (Landing, Seed, and Banfield 1949); hemopoiesis, (Cameron, Courtice, and Jones 1947; Jacobson, Marks, Gaston, and Block 1949); the growth of tumors (Bass and Freeman 1946; Gilman and Philips 1946; Karnofsky 1950); and the treatment of leukemia (Burchenal 1948)—to mention only a few amongst innumerable applications to experimental pathology in general. From the biochemical aspect may be quoted studies of the reaction of the sulfur or nitrogen mustards with proteins (Kinsey and Grant 1946; Banks, Boursnell, Francis, Hopwood, and Wormall 1946; Peters and Wakelin 1947; Wood, Rachele, Stevens, Carpenter, and du Vigneaud 1948; Carpenter, Wood, Stevens, and du Vigneaud 1948; Stevens, Wood, Rachele, and du Vigneaud 1948; Stevens, McKennis, and du Vigneaud 1948; Bacq and Desreux 1948; Burnop, Richards, Watkins, and Wormall 1951), with carboxyl groups and with the amino groups of amino acids and peptides (Moore, Stein, and Fruton 1946), and with methionine (Stein and Moore 1946), and other amino acids (Boursnell, Francis, and Wormall 1946; du Vigneaud, Stevens, McDuffie, Wood and McKennis 1948); and the effects upon nucleic acid metabolism (Lowrance and Carter 1950), respiration and glycolysis (Needham, Cohen, and Barrett 1947), and the synthesis of urea, (Barron, Bartlett, Miller, Meyer, and Seegmiller 1948; McKinney 1949, 1950, 1951). Other properties of the mustards, which may conceivably depend upon the same qualities of reactivity as are responsible for their carcinogenic action, include the capacity to suppress many immunologic responses, as for instance to inhibit the Schwartzman phenomenon (Becker 1948, Schlang 1950, Good and Thomas 1951), to inhibit the development of humoral antibodies and of hypersensitivity (Bukantz, Dammin, Wilson, and Johnson 1948; Bukantz, Dammin, Wilson, Johnson, and Alexander 1949), and to inactivate complement (Watkins and Wormall 1948); and lastly a remarkable virucidal action (e.g. Rose and Gellhorn 1947), which is possibly related to the inactivation by the mustards of the cytoplasmic K factor in *Paramecium* (Geckler 1949), and of the pneumococcal transforming factor, and which can be applied in the sterilization of blood and plasma, (Hartman and Mangun 1949; Mangun, Kelly, Sanders, Pèpes, Wallbank, and Hartman 1951).

The discovery of carcinogenic activity in this new chemical class, in substances of relatively high reactivity, simple in structure, and yet possessing molecular features highly suggestive as to their mechanism, has led to speedy progress and to a theory of action which has in turn stimulated many later developments. Whether the suggested mechanism is at all applicable to other carcinogens, even in principle, remains of course an open question.

PROPERTIES OF THE NITROGEN MUSTARDS, AND THEIR RADIOMIMETIC CHARACTER

In an extension of work from the aminostilbene series, Haddow, Kon, and Ross (1948) carried out experiments to decide first in what types of aromatic amine the N,N-di-2-chloroethyl side chains, characteristic of the nitrogen mustards, could still contribute their specific cytotoxic properties, and secondly whether any enhancement of the therapeutic property might be achieved in these aromatic derivatives, in comparison with those members of the aliphatic series to which attention hitherto had been almost entirely confined. (Shortly afterwards, substituted mustards containing the benzanthracene, and phenanthrene and diphenylethane structures respectively, were described by Friedman and Seligman [1948] and by McKay and Brownell [1950].) At once it became apparent that marked cytotoxic and inhibitory activity, as judged against the growth of various animal tumors, is a feature of the N,N-di-2-chloroethyl derivatives of aniline, *o-*, *m-* and *p*-toluidine, *o-* and *p-* anisidine, *p*-aminobenzoic acid, *a-* and *β*-naphthylamine, as well as of many other amines. Certain compounds, for example N,N-di(2-chloroethyl)-β-naphthylamine, showed possible advantages, (as compared with the aliphatic mustards), in reduced toxicity and effectiveness by oral administration, and were made the subject of extensive clinical trial by Galton at the Royal Cancer Hospital, and by Matthews (1950) and Gardikas and Wilkinson (1951), among others, elsewhere, with particular reference to the leukemias, Hodgkin's disease, and allied lymphadenopathies and reticuloses.

While clinical usefulness has proved difficult to enhance in this series, the possibility is by no means excluded in view of the almost limitless chemical modifications still to be explored. Meantime, however, a great mass of more fundamental information has accrued, in a way which could not perhaps have been readily foreseen, and which has already shed much light upon the carcinogenic process.

The action of the aliphatic series upon the cell appeared to be highly direct, and not to be mediated by any specific organ system, including (in agreement with Bass and Feigelson [1948] and Karnofsky, Graef, and Smith [1948]) the adrenal. For the aromatic and aliphatic series equally, the cytologic alterations in both normal and malignant proliferating cells comprised chromosome fragmentation, bridge formation at anaphase, and other morphologic changes in chromosome structure interpreted as due to defects in the process of spiralization. Following chromosome "breakage" by these agents—a phenomenon which has lately been studied with much success by Revell (1952, below)—the fragmented chromatin is ejected into the cytoplasm, where it can be recognized in the form of so-called "micronuclei." These structures had already been described by others, as for example by Hughes and Fell (1949) in studies of the abnormal mitosis produced by mustard gas in tissue cultures, and they also occur in other circumstances, as in the triploid *Lilium tigrinum*, in which chromosomes which lag and are left in the cytoplasm upon the appearance of the nuclear membrane form micronuclei or microcysts which eventually degenerate (Chandler, Porterfield, and Stout 1937).

From all the evidence available it appears that the main primary action of the nitrogen mustards is exerted during the "resting stage," that the resulting damage becomes cytologically manifest only during mitosis, and that such damage may accumulate in successive cell divisions, as indicated by the presence of micronuclei of different ages, until the cell is in many cases no longer viable. Both the clinical effects which these substances are capable of producing, and the cytologic changes which form their basis, fully justify the description of such agents as "radiomimetic" (Dustin 1947), even though there may be profound differences between them and ionizing radiations in the details of their action. The striking similarity in at least their biologic end results is also shown in other phenomena which can be induced by radiation and the mustards equally.

Examples of this similarity are as follows: (1) local greying or bleaching of hair in mice, described by Hance and Murphy (1926; Hance 1928) as produced by roentgen irradiation, and extensively studied by Chase and his co-workers (Chase 1949, 1951; Chase, Quastler, and Skaggs 1947; Chase and Smith 1949; Chase and Rauch 1950), and for the case of chemical agents by Boyland and Sargent (1951); (2) characteristic acute and chronic degenerative changes in the bone-marrow and testis.

essentially similar whether produced by roentgen irradiation or the mustards (e.g., Landing, Goldin, and Noe 1949, Kindred 1951, Goldeck and Hagenah 1951); (3) the production by nitrogen mustard of a coagulation defect identical with that caused by roentgen irradiation, (Smith, Jacobson, Spurr, Allen, and Block 1948); (4) the ability to suppress antibody formation; and (5) mutagenic activity—to be discussed later.

Not surprisingly, this strong biologic parallelism between ionizing radiations and the nitrogen mustards has led to attempts to relate their action quantitatively, through the concept of the radioequivalence of radiomimetic chemical agents in their effects on cells both in vitro and in vivo, and in their reaction with desoxyribonucleic acid. Thus it had been noted by Boyland (1948) that in mice a dose of 1 mg. per kg. body weight of HN2 produces similar effects to a total body irradiation of 300—400 r, and it may be significant that this ratio is of the same order as that observed by Butler, Gilbert, and Smith (1950), using much greater doses, in the relative action of the mustards and of roentgen rays on nucleic acid. Similarly, Read (1950) observed that immersion of *Vicia faba* roots in a solution of one micromolar strength for one hour produced about the same response as 50 r of roentgen rays delivered under aerobic conditions.

CARCINOGENICITY OF THE NITROGEN MUSTARDS, AND OF MUSTARD GAS

The marked cytotoxic and growth-inhibitory capacity of the mustards in general, and their radiomimetic quality in particular, raised the question whether these agents might not, in common with other chemical and physical agents possessing these properties, also prove to be carcinogenic. This possibility was tested by Haddow and others in the mouse, rat, and hamster, and with abundantly positive result, since pronounced carcinogenic activity (mainly after subcutaneous injection but also following feeding), was shown by several compounds (Figs. 90-94), all representative of the new aromatic series.

Independently of the above, Boyland and Horning (1949) had also observed tumors (mainly of the lung) in mice receiving the aliphatic compounds HN2 and HN3, and Heston (1949) had described the induction of pulmonary tumors in Strain A mice treated with HN2. In further confirmation, Griffin, Brandt, and Tatum (1950, 1951) observed adenocarcinoma of the lung, leukemia, lymphosarcoma, angiosarcoma, and osteogenic sarcoma, in rats and mice given HN2 and HN3 by the intravenous, intraperitoneal, and subcutaneous routes, in some cases after a single dose. The case of mustard gas itself was of particular interest on several counts. First, Fell and Allsopp (1948), in studies of the histologic effect of repeated applications of minute quantities (2.5 and 12.5 γ) of mustard gas on the skin of mice, recorded certain similarities to treatment of the skin with 3:4-benzpyrene—for example, alternation of degeneration and repair, nuclear abnormalities, and hyperplasia. The effects differed however from those of benzpyrene in that no tumors were observed, and that the nuclear disturbances appeared more drastic and the hyperplastic regions more differentiated. In the authors' view the response most closely resembled that to a single massive dose of roentgen rays: since the period of observation was only one year, it is a question whether tumors might have appeared had the experiment been continued longer. Secondly, Strong (1949a) had commented upon the apparently exceptional position of mustard gas in compounds of this general class, since no carcinogenic activity had been reported although the substance is mutagenic. Thirdly, the writer and his colleagues, in attempting a correlation between the biologic properties of the mustards and their chemical reactivity (see later), had observed that mustard gas, although not at that time described as carcinogenic, occupies a

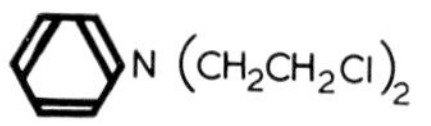

FIG. 90. N,N-di-2-Chloroethylaniline

FIG. 91. N,N-di-2-Chloroethyl-*p*-toluidine

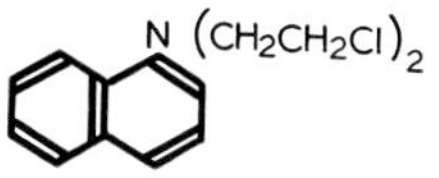

FIG. 92. 1-Naphthyldi-2′-chloroethylamine

position, so far as its reactivity is concerned, which is intermediate between that of certain aliphatic and aromatic mustards which were already known to be carcinogenic. For these various reasons, the writer carried out an experiment to test the carcinogenic action of mustard gas by subcutaneous injection in the rat, and obtained a clearly positive result. Meantime, Heston (1950a,b) had also obtained evidence of the carcinogenicity of sulfur mustard on the lung in Strain A mice.

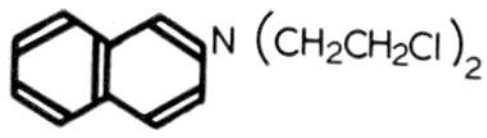

FIG. 93. 2-Naphthyldi-2′-chloroethylamine

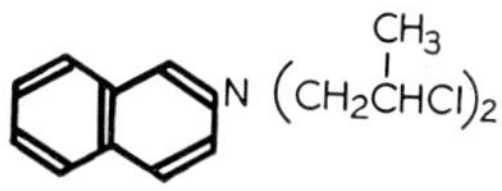

FIG. 94. 2-Naphthyldi-2′-chloro-*n*-propylamine

At an early stage in the investigations by the writer and his colleagues, it became obvious that the tumors induced by the aromatic nitrogen mustards showed an exceptional incidence of nuclear abnormalities—chromosome fragmentation, bridge formation at anaphase, and polyploidy—similar in character to the well-recognized abnormalities produced by the same compounds on dividing cells. While it seemed possible that some of these effects could be attributable to traces of the compound remaining at the tumor site, this appeared unlikely as a general explanation, since in a few cases at least the abnormalities persisted for a considerable time in the serial transplantation of these tumors (cf. Koller 1952), and hence suggested that the malignant cells in such cases bore the imprint of the carcinogen which had induced their appearance, in the form of a self-propagating structural change. While this situation still remains difficult to interpret, and is not confined to the carcinogenic mustards since somewhat similar nuclear abnormalities are also encountered, although on a smaller scale, in tumors induced by the cyclic hydrocarbons, it inevitably recalls the repeated observation of nuclear imbalance in tumors generally (e.g., Hauschka and Levan 1951 on tumor polyploidy), and serves once more to direct attention to the nucleus as the possible primary site of carcinogenic action. At the same time, it should be recognized that such gross changes are very probably not causal, but merely associated events, and that the essential alteration underlying malignancy is almost certainly much more specific and elusive. This is perhaps best shown by the fact that certain agents (e.g., 8-ethoxycaffeine, Kihlman 1950), while outstandingly capable of inducing structural chromosome change, appear devoid of the characteristic cytostatic effects of the mustards.

IMPLICATIONS AND INFERENCES: THE CROSS-LINKAGE HYPOTHESIS

For the first time in the study of carcinogenesis, the mustards provided agents of relatively high chemical reactivity, comparatively simple in structure, and with characteristic molecular features immediately suggestive of possible mechanisms of action. In efforts to establish the optimal requirements for biologic activity, and to correlate such with chemical reactivity, it became clear that biologic activity is associated with the haloalkyl chains exclusively, that a certain concentration of reactive halogen compound must be reached in order to permit biologic activity, and thirdly that a prominent feature, for both the aliphatic and aromatic series, is dependence of activity upon a minimum of two haloalkyl groups (Haddow, Kon, and Ross 1948).

The last feature had early been suspected by R. A. Peters at Oxford (personal communication), and was meantime emerging as a valid conclusion from the work of others. Thus Burchenal and co-workers (Burchenal, Lester, Riley, and Rhoads 1948; Burchenal and Riley 1949; Burchenal, Riley, and Lester 1949; Burchenal, Burchenal, and Johnston 1951), found that for chemotherapeutic activity against mouse leukemia the nitrogen mustard molecule must possess at least two β-halogenated alkyl groups, which might however be on the same or separate nitrogens; while Landing and others (Landing, Goldin, Noe, Goldberg, and Shapiro 1949; Landing and Eisenberg 1949) observed that the nitrogen mustards with two or more haloalkyl side chains are those most cytotoxic to rapidly proliferating cells.

Seeking the explanation for this bifunctional or polyfunctional requirement, Goldacre (considering reversible denaturation and the folding and unfolding of chromosome chains in relation to cell division, and the possible adsorption of carcinogenic molecules to the unfolded state), Loveless (from the aspect of chemical cytology), and Ross (from a study of the kinetics of reaction of such two-armed compounds), suggested that the two groups might be required to permit the molecule to react at two distinct points, lying either on a single surface or fiber, or, more especially, on two contiguous fibers (Goldacre, Loveless, and Ross 1949, see also Loveless 1950).

The possibility that cross-linking may play a part in the action of mustard gas on the nucleic acids had earlier been considered by Elmore, Gulland, Jordan, and Taylor (1948), in an investigation which these authors believed might provide an explanation of the cytologic effects of mustard gas as described by Koller (1943a), Robson (1943), and Fell and Allsopp (1943). In one product from thymus nucleic acid, the mustard molecules had reacted with two titratable groups, either in the same molecule or by a process of cross-linking between polynucleotide chains; also, comparison of solutions of the nucleic acid before and after treatment with the mustard afforded additional evidence in favor of a measure of intermolecular cross-linkage, in view of the increased viscosity of the treated sample.*

Of the various possibilities, cross-linkage between the constituent macromolecular fibers of the chromosome itself was of particular interest when considered in the light of the growing assumption that reaction of the mustard carcinogens might well be directly with genetic material. The latter had already been postulated in respect of chemical mutagenesis (Auerbach and Robson 1947), while the cell was known to be susceptible to the effects of the mustards at a time when there exists within it a system of parallel identical fibers, the gene strings of the sister chromatids. Moreover, the fibers are extended in the process of re-duplication and could, by analogy with stretched elastic polymers, be at their highest energy. Nevertheless, the cross-linkage hypothesis, which was first suggested as perhaps the most valid interpretation of the available facts (in spite of certain difficulties of probability and kinetics), is now known to be unduly simple.

First, it is exceptionally refractory to test, in view of the great difficulty in defining reliable criteria for cross-linking even in model systems, the fact that demonstration of cross-linking capacity in a model system provides no proof of such a mechanism within the cell, and conversely that a cross-linking mechanism is not excluded through inability to demonstrate it in some external or artificial system (cf. Alexander, Fox, Stacey, and Smith 1952). Second, other possibilities are known to be equally likely, as for example combination not with a genetic determiner directly, but with a precursor or substrate (Ross, Loveless); the anchoring of one arm followed by attachment of the second to some less accessible centre on the same fiber; polymerisation of the agent within the cell (Rose, below); a more random ramification or internal polymerisation, bringing about what is essentially an "anti-crease" effect due to prevention of the movement and slipping of molecular chains (Astbury); and finally the blanketing of receptors by a high concentration of monofunctional analogs.

In actual experience, little direct evidence of cross-linkage has so far been obtained. From the extensive work of Butler on the reaction between nitrogen

* It is of interest to find what kinds of cross-linkages are utilised in physiologic processes, especially those which bind polypeptide chains together during the hardening of proteins into skeletal structures (Brown 1950a,b). Increase in stability of fibrillar linkages is conferred by the act of tanning, for example by the vegetable tannins or by formaldehyde and *o*- or *p*-benzoquinone. The demonstration of tanning as a biologic process was due to Pryor (1940), who showed that the hardening of the protein oothecae of the cockroach is brought about by the addition to the protein of an orthodiphenol (protocatechuic acid, Pryor, Russell, and Todd 1946), which on oxidation to orthobenzoquinone forms covalent links between itself and the protein. It appears that the sulfide link and the quinone bond are the only types of covalent link so far known to occur in skeletal proteins. It was also of interest to find that the *tris* nitrogen mustard HN3 had been included in a patent application as early as 1934 (Schlack 1938), for the treatment of textiles so as to vary their affinity, and that Lautsch (1944) had been able to bring about cross-linking between lignin and polyethyleneimine by reacting them with di(chloroethyl)methylamine or HN2. Cross-linking by mustard gas had also been demonstrated by Deuel and Neukom (1949) for sodium alginates, pectates, and pectinates, with rapid increase in viscosity and the formation of primary valence gels.

mustard and nucleic acid (Butler and Smith 1950; Butler and Conway 1950; Conway, Gilbert, and Butler 1950), it would indeed appear that the effect of the agent may be depolymerizing rather than polymerizing, since desoxyribonucleic acid solutions so treated are degraded, losing their intrinsic viscosity and breaking down to molecular weights which are markedly less than those of the original nucleic acid and exhibit a considerable degree of polydispersity. While it is doubtless true that most complex molecules are subject to breakdown if they come under the influence of a wide range of agents, such as elevated temperatures, visible, ultraviolet and shorter wave radiations, and the action of specific chemical substances (see Melville 1950), chain breaking and cross-linkage are not necessarily mutually exclusive properties, since for protein, and possibly the nucleic acids, the latter process might also induce the former.

Further, many of the experiments of Butler and his co-workers were carried out with dilute solutions of nucleic acid, when in fact cross-linkage might only occur in concentrated preparations, in an analogous fashion, as Goldacre has suggested, to the varying effect of heat on concentrated and dilute solutions of egg albumen: certain later evidence confirms that this may indeed be so. The cross-linkage hypothesis was recapitulated by Goldacre in a jocular tag: *ut religet, sic carcinogenit.* If this is no more than an ideal simplification, and admitting the insufficiency of the hypothesis, and its perhaps too mechano-chemical flavor, the working hypothesis itself nevertheless remains an endeavor to explain the polyfunctional requirement for the action of the nitrogen mustards in vivo. In any event there can be no doubt of the powerful stimulus which the brief paper by Goldacre, Loveless, and Ross has exerted, or of the value of the new findings which have come about as the direct result.

STRUCTURE, CHEMICAL REACTIVITY, AND BIOLOGIC ACTION

While many more nitrogen mustards have been tested for cytotoxic activity than for carcinogenicity, the association between these properties would appear to be intimate, if not, as indeed the writer would suggest, essential. Hence, the great mass of work which has been carried out on the structure and chemical reactivity of these compounds, in relation to their biologic action, can reasonably be expected to shed light not only upon the mechanism of production of their acute cytotoxic effects, but upon the carcinogenic mechanism as well. From Ross's studies of the reactions of the haloalkylamines in aqueous solutions under mild conditions, it has been shown that these compounds should be regarded as alkylating agents—the first indeed of a whole series of biologic alkylating agents which includes epoxides, ethyleneimines, and sulfonic esters with radiomimetic and carcinogenic properties (Ross 1952). When such compounds enter into chemical reactions, these can be interpreted on the assumption of the formation of a carbonium ion as the reactive intermediate (Fig. 95). In tests with a considerable range of mono- and polyfunctional alkylating and esterifying agents for radiomimetic action in *Vicia*, Loveless (1951) also found that only those compounds are active which are capable of reacting by a carbonium ion mechanism.

In the case of the chloroethylamines the carbonium ion is produced by the elimination of the chloride ion under the electron-repelling influence of the nitrogen atom: for aliphatic derivatives (but not aromatic [Ross 1949a]) this carbonium ion may be stabilized by passing into the ethyleneimonium ion. The reactions of these agents involve nucleophilic displacements on a carbon atom, the reaction being unimolecular in the case of the mustards (that is, practically independent of the concentration of reacting centers), and bimolecular in the case of the epoxides, imines and sulfonic esters still to be considered. A carbonium ion is electrophilic and will react with any nucleophilic center, the main such centers to be found in biologic systems being organic and inorganic anions and bases, when the products are esters, ethers, alkylated amines, and ammonium and sulfonium cations. Clearly, however, whether a particular group is in a form capable of reacting at physiologic *p*H will depend upon its dissociation constant. On this consideration, the groups most likely to react with the cytotoxic alkylating agents are the carboxyl group and the terminal α-amino and histidine amino groups in proteins,

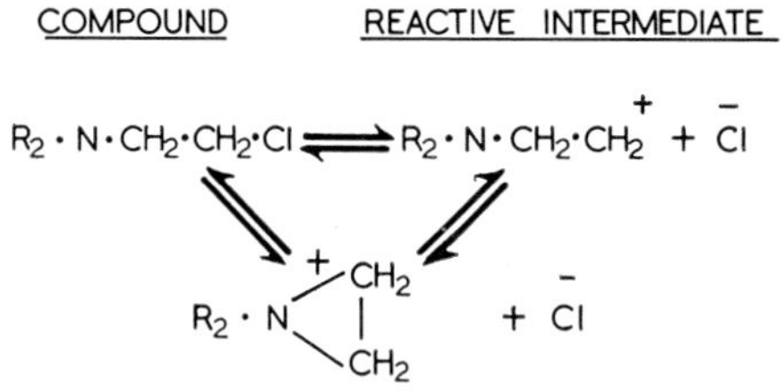

FIG. 95. Formation of carbonium ion as reactive intermediate.

and the phosphoryl and so-called aromatic type amino groups of the nucleic acids (Ross 1950a). Even in their reactive forms, however, the various groups may exhibit appreciable differences in their ability to react with an electrophilic center. This ability, which is a measure of their nucleophilic capacity, can be regarded as an "affinity" factor, and it is this which is measured by Ogston (1948) in his determination of competition factors. Thus the extent to which any component in a biologic system will react with a radiomimetic compound is proportional to a trinomial expression containing factors related to affinity, activity, and concentration (Ross 1950b). Ross has also drawn attention to the high competition factor of the mustards in the case of compounds of high molecular weight. For example, the ionised carboxyl groups in polymethacrylic acid appear to be more reactive than such groups in simple organic acids. While the mechanism is not clear, the phenomenon would explain why the mustards are effective in biologic systems at relatively high dilutions.

So far as the relations between structure and activity are concerned, it appears essential that a minimum of two haloalkyl side-chains should be present, and that the halogen atoms should not be separated from the nitrogen by more than two carbon atoms. As is shown in Table 29, the biologic activity of such compounds can be satisfactorily related to the ease of hydrolysis of the halogen atoms in aqueous acetone (Ross 1949b). Since these compounds react by an S_N1 mechanism in which the rate-determining step is the separation of the chloride ion, it would

Table 29. MUSTARD COMPOUNDS: CHEMICAL REACTIVITY AND BIOLOGIC ACTIVITY

Compound	*Percentage hydrolysis in half hour in 50 per cent acetone at 66° F. (Ross)*	*Biologic activity (Haddow)*
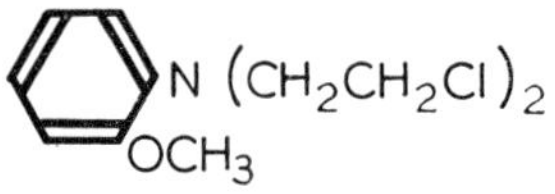	89	+
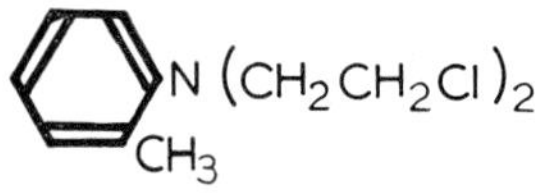	83	+
	58	+
	41	+
	38	+
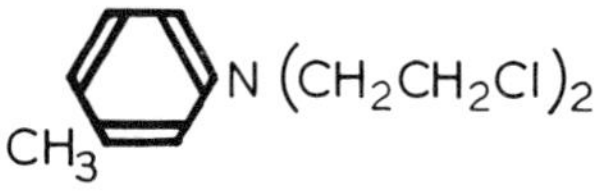	21	+
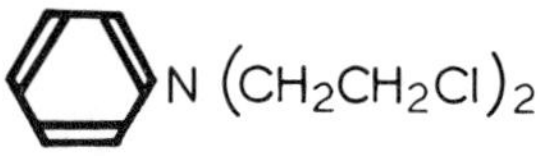	20	+
	12	−
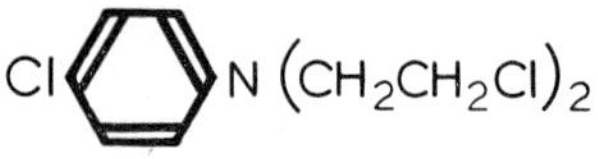	9	−
	1	−
	<1	−
	<1	−

be expected that electron-repelling substituents in the benzene ring would facilitate the reaction, whilst electron-attracting groups would retard it: the proposed reaction mechanism is in fact supported by the results obtained. The dependence of biologic activity on chemical reactivity is also shown by many other examples, as for instance when both are reduced by lengthening the chloroalkyl side-chains, or increased by the substitution of bromine or iodine for chlorine.

Although there must always be a proportion of the reaction of radiomimetic substances at sites other than acidic groups (as for example in the evidence of Press and Butler [1952] that reaction of nitrogen mustard with thymus nucleic acid and with the purine nucleosides involves the alkylation of adenosine or guanosine), Ross (1952) is of opinion that the more nearly do the conditions approach those likely to be realized in the treatment of living tissues with such agents, the more significant does the reaction with carboxyl groups become. This view, and the evidence upon which it is based, is further supported by studies of the action of mustard gas by many other investigators, e.g., upon hemoglobin (Ball, Davis, and Ross 1943), upon a range of proteins (Herriott, Anson, and Northrop 1946), upon collagen (Pirie 1947), and upon skin proteins (Ormsbee, Henriques, and Ball 1949), in all of which reactions the carboxyl groups were prominently involved.

While it is not of course claimed that the acid groups in the biologic reaction are necessarily those in nucleoproteins, such possibilities are clearly attractive, and Butler, Gilbert, James, and Ross (1951) have for example suggested that the loss in structural viscosity of desoxyribonucleic acid preparations, after treatment with mustards, might be connected with the formation of unstable tri-substituted phosphoric esters by reaction of the primary phosphoryl groups in the nucleic acid. Also, Davis and Ross (1952) indicate that more stable linkages may be formed by the reaction of chloroethylamines with primary phosphoryl groups in nucleic acids than with carboxylic groups in proteins. Alexander (1952) found that the phosphate groups of the sodium salt of thymus nucleic acid in dilute solution are esterified at similar rates by various mono- and polyfunctional compounds, so that it appears unlikely that it is this reaction alone which is biologically significant. However, in studying the influence of this prior combination of nucleic acid and radiomimetic agent on the subsequent combination with salmine, he found the affinity for protamine to be reduced, and speculated whether the biologic effects could be ascribed to interference with the normal formation of the nucleoprotein complex, or possibly to a change in shape of the nucleic acid molecule alone, since coiling of the macromolecule would be expected to interfere with protein synthesis if the suggestion of Haurowitz (1950) is accepted, that the role of nucleic acid is to maintain the "template protein" in an expanded state during biosynthesis.

Whatever the true explanation, it must also be considered whether the action of the mustards and other radiomimetic and carcinogenic agents may not be to block the synthesis of desoxyribonucleic acid itself, a conclusion which would be in agreement with that reached by many other investigators employing widely varied material. Thus Young and Campbell (1947) believed one of the major effects of mustard gas to be combination with and precipitation of the nucleoproteins of the cell, so inhibiting the natural processes of cell regeneration. Herriott (1948) observed that of various viruses examined, those containing desoxyribonucleic acid were inactivated faster than those containing ribonucleic acid, while following exposure to dilute solutions of mustard gas, suspensions of E. *coli* failed to produce desoxyribonucleic acid although pentose nucleic acid continued to be formed in nearly normal amount (Herriott 1951). Further evidence of the interruption of desoxyribonucleic acid synthesis by nitrogen mustard has been adduced by Bodenstein and Kondritzer (1948) and Griffin, Brandt, and Setter (1951), in the case of amphibian embryonic development and liver carcinogenesis respectively.

Impressed by the broad similarity of the effects produced by the nitrogen mustards and other cytotoxic agents reacting by a carbonium ion mechanism, and those produced by roentgen rays and peroxides, which react by a free radical mechanism, Ross (1950c) drew attention to two points of similarity in these processes. First, free radicals, like carbonium ions, are electrophilic reactants; second, the reaction of a carbonium ion derived from a mustard molecule with a nucleophilic center in a biologic system yields a product which is still electrophilic owing to the reactivity of the second halogen atom. Likewise, the reaction of a free radical can also lead to the production of an electrophilic center. The new electrophilic center formed in either case could react further in many ways, for example with a nucleophilic group on the same, or on a different, "surface." The former possibility had already been implied by Butler, Gilbert and Smith (1950, Butler and Smith 1950b), in discussing the action of roentgen rays and nitrogen mustard on nucleic acids, in which case the reaction would result in breaking down the nucleic acid structure, while the latter possibility represents a cross-linkage reaction. Butler (1950, Butler, Conway, Gilbert, and Smith 1951) was also led to inquire what features there might be in common in the actions on desoxyribonucleic acid of the mustards on one hand and free hydroxyl radicals on the other. While finding it difficult to establish a plausible mechanism which would yield simple free radicals such as hydrogen and hydroxyl, he suggested that the immediate reaction products of the mustards with water might themselves possess free radical properties, and furthermore that the ability to form bi-radicals might well be shared by many other carcinogenic substances, thereby allowing the possibility of an eventual community of action in carcinogens of widely different chemical type.

DI-EPOXIDES

It would seem that the characteristic feature of the radiomimetic mustards so far considered is their ability to act as bifunctional electrophilic reagents under mild conditions in aqueous solution (Davis, Everett, and Ross 1950). Since epoxides also were known to act as electrophilic reagents under the same conditions (Hammett 1940), and since it had been demonstrated that they react readily with proteins at physiological *p*H (Fraenkel-Conrat 1944), Ross (1950c) was led to include them for investigation. Before they could be examined, however, the same suggestion was made to the writer by J. B. Speakman, as an immediate outcome of the cross-linking hypothesis, and because of the application of various di-epoxides as cross-linking agents in textile practice (Speakman 1948). It appeared that the simplest member of the series, namely 1:2,3:4-diepoxybutane (Fig. 96), had already been investigated in textile research in Germany, in the treatment of wool (Alexander and Whewell), and cross-linking by di-epoxides was later studied by Deuel (1947).* Capp and Speakman (1949) showed that when animal fibers, such as wool and hair, are treated with an acid solution of 3:4-*iso*propylidene-1:2,5:6-dianhydromannitol for twenty-four hours at 50° C., cross-linkages are formed between the carboxyl groups of neighboring peptide chains, and following this observation attention turned to the possibility of cross-linking wool with simpler di-epoxides, for example 1:2,3:4-diepoxybutane, which again is capable of forming new cross-linkages between the peptide chains of animal fibers (Fearnley and Speakman 1950). In a patent application (1948), Speakman, Chamberlain, and Dorkin had also described the preparation of alkali-resistant alginic material by the treatment of alginic acid or a metal alginate, having at least a part of its carboxyl groups free, with di-epoxy compounds so as to produce cross-linkages thereof with the hydroxyl and carboxyl groups.

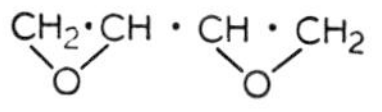

1:2:3:4-Diepoxybutane.

FIG. 96.

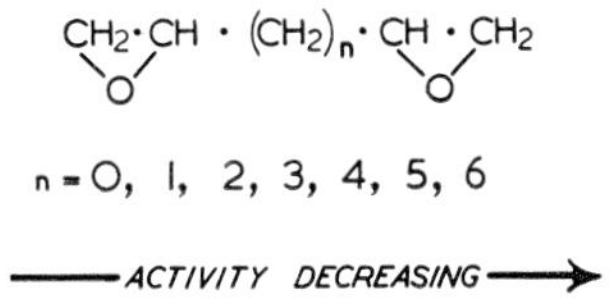

FIG. 97.

No sooner had the above suggestion been put to the test than it became obvious that a series of di-epoxides (Everett and Kon 1950), were indeed capable of producing biologic effects largely indistinguishable from those due to the radiomimetic mustards, as for example the same types of cytologic abnormality, greying of hair in mice, and retardation of the growth of experimental tumors. Such activity decreased in the series as is shown in Fig 97. More recently, the parent substance 1:2:3:4-diepoxybutane has also been shown to be carcinogenic.

As for the nitrogen mustards, no monofunctional epoxide appears to be biologically effective, and even among the di-epoxides it would appear that a certain minimum reactivity—as measured by the rate of reaction with the thiosulfate ion—must be exceeded before the compound is biologically active, although this level of reactivity is not, in itself, sufficient. The epoxide ring is readily opened, and the compound can then react with nucleophilic reagents in a manner similar to that of the carbonium ions derived from the halogenoalkylamines (Fig. 98).

Fraenkel-Conrat (1944) has shown that water-soluble epoxides such as ethylene oxide and propylene oxide readily react with crystalline egg albumen and with β-lactoglobulin under mild conditions, producing effects on the protein properties consistent with the esterification of a high proportion of the carboxyl groups: evidence was also obtained for the reaction of the epoxides, when present in large

* 1:2,3:4-Diepoxybutane has long been known, but the published method of preparation was tedious and did not easily afford a pure product (S. Przbytek, *Ber. d. deutsche chem. Gesellsch. 17:* 1091, 1884): it is now prepared by the epoxidation of butadiene monoepoxide (Everett and Kon 1950).

excess, with phenolic, primary amino, and sulfydryl groups. Ross (1950c) also confirms that epoxides react with ionised acid groups, and not with undissociated acids, and that their characteristics are such as would be expected if they react through a carbonium ion mechanism. While this is so, an important difference between the epoxides and mustards lies in the fact that, whereas the latter react by an S_N1 mechanism, and the extent of reaction is largely independent of the concentration of reacting centers, the former react by a bimolecular mechanism, with the extent of reaction dependent upon the availability of such centers. This is possibly of some significance in the reactions of epoxides with biologic systems where the concentration of reacting groups will vary from site to site: since nucleic acids contain a high proportion of ionised phosphate groups, reaction with epoxides might be specially favored.

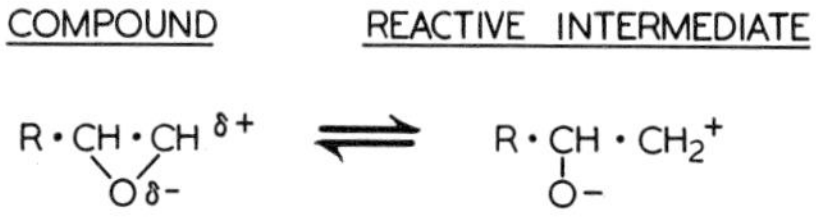
COMPOUND
REACTIVE INTERMEDIATE
R·CH·CH δ+
Oδ-
R·CH·CH2+
O-

FIG. 98.

+ O
O
+ H2O
ENZYME
H
OH
OH
H

FIG. 99.

Epoxides occur among the products of the autoxidation of unsaturated fatty acids (Ellis 1936), and of drying oils (O'Neill 1948), and it is possible they may take a significant part in various biologic oxidations. In the earlier discussion of the metabolic transformation of the carcinogenic hydrocarbons (p. 465), mention has already been made of the potential importance of hitherto unrecognized metabolites, such as epoxides, and in this connection Boyland and Wolf had earlier, unsuccessfully, attempted the synthesis of phenanthrene epoxide (cf. Boyland and Wolf 1950). Discovery of carcinogenic activity in the di-epoxides again drew attention to this point, since, according to Boyland (1950b), *trans*-diols are known to be formed not only by reduction of the corresponding quinone, or by Walden inversion of one hydroxyl group in a *cis*-diol, but also by hydrolysis of the corresponding epoxide. The last mechanism is perhaps more probable on account of the recognition of naturally occurring epoxides, e.g., of violaxanthin in the viola, iris, and gorse, and of an epoxide of carotene, hepaxanthin, in the liver (Karrer and Jucker 1947; cf. von Euler and Karrer 1950). The hypothetical process can be represented as in Fig. 99.

The oxygen atom of an epoxide group is also capable of migration, as for example when vitamin A epoxide or ionone epoxide is allowed to stand in acid solution. Although in this case the reaction may perhaps appear improbable, Boyland has suggested that if carcinogenic hydrocarbons react with oxygen first in the K region, the oxygen may then migrate to the adjacent double bond in the side ring (Fig. 100). The hypothesis of epoxide formation by the carcinogenic hydrocarbons is as yet supported by little evidence, but it would help to explain why the superficially unreactive polycyclic hydrocarbons produce such profound biologic effects, and would certainly effect a remarkable linkage between the action of carcinogens of apparently very diverse type. Boyland also points out, assuming the reaction proceeds through bond activation and the intermediate formation of an epoxide, that a number of routes to other products would then be possible, e.g., through oxygen, thiol, amino, or other groups (Fig. 101).

Completely independent of the above, the chemistry of the di-epoxides (e.g., of 4-vinyl-*cyclo*hexene dioxide, [Fig. 102] which has subsequently proved to be carcinogenic), had been intensively investigated in the laboratories of Canadian

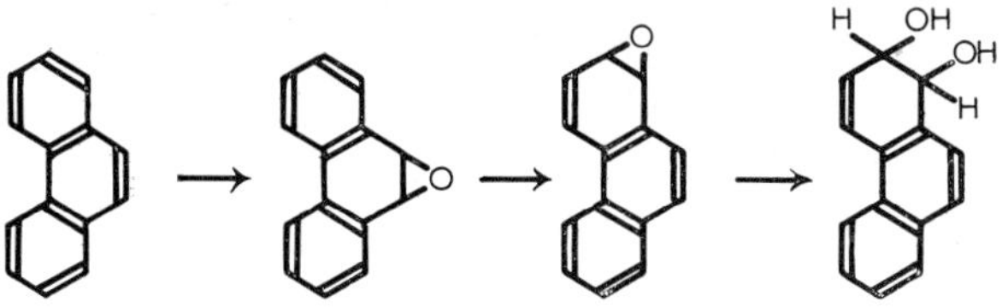

FIG. 100.

Industries Limited, Montreal, and this, with a consideration of the cross-linkage hypothesis, led Hendry, Homer, Rose, and Walpole (1951a) to a study of the cytotoxic activity of the di-epoxides, with special reference to the suggestion by Rose that these substances might produce their effects not essentially as individual molecules but rather as multi-reacting polymers. It had been known for some time that ethylene oxide readily polymerizes to produce linear structures having the repeating unit [-O-CH_2-CH_2-], and this property persists in more complex derivatives, including those with two oxide units. Since the polymerization is strongly

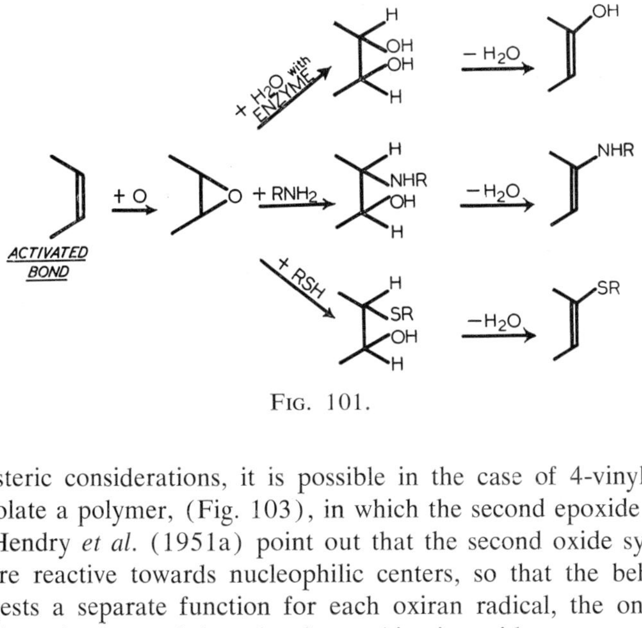

FIG. 101.

affected by steric considerations, it is possible in the case of 4-vinyl-*cyclo*hexene dioxide to isolate a polymer, (Fig. 103), in which the second epoxide ring remains unaffected. Hendry *et al.* (1951a) point out that the second oxide system is however the more reactive towards nucleophilic centers, so that the behavior of the dioxide suggests a separate function for each oxiran radical, the one being concerned in polymerization and the other in combination with centers carrying active hydrogens as in proteins and nucleoproteins. These authors also note that the dimensions of the -C-C-O- unit of the polyethylene glycol structure correspond closely with those of the -C-C-N- unit of polypeptides, so that in a polymer of the type of Fig. 103 a reactive epoxide group occurs along each side of the chain at intervals of every two α-amino-acid residues. If the biologic effects were due to bridges formed by individual di-epoxide molecules, either along or between protein or nucleoprotein units, then it would be necessary to admit a wide range of permissible distances between the two points of attachment of each molecule. If on the other hand these agents function not as individual molecules but as poly-reactive polymers of the form shown in Fig. 104, then the distance between adjacent reactive groups is constant at about 7.5 Å and theoretically independent of the conjunctive group X. Hendry *et al.* agree that the significance of these possibilities, in their relation to biologic action, must remain a matter of speculation, but suggest that after diffusion into the cell in monomeric form the di-epoxides may behave in one or both of two ways. First they may polymerize to give structures the side chains of which then react with protein or nucleoprotein of chromoso-

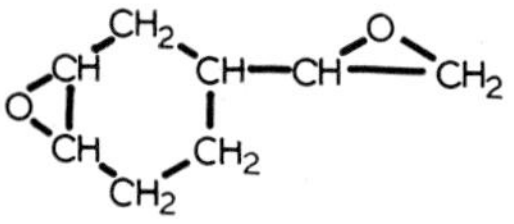

FIG. 102. 4-Vinyl-*cyclo*-hexane dioxide.

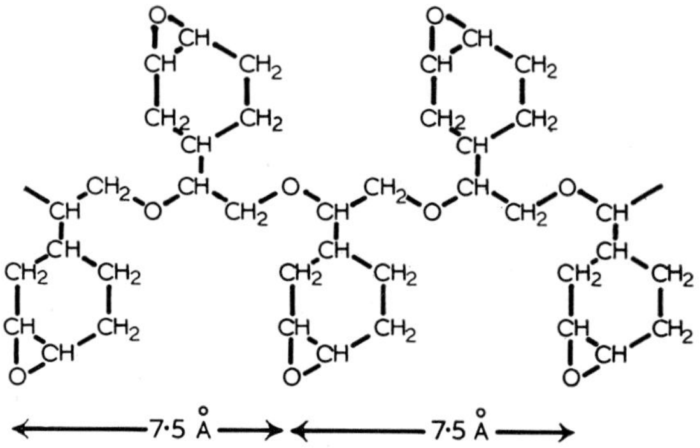

FIG. 103.

mal origin to produce, by cross-linkage with multipoint attachment, the observed aberrations of mitosis. Second, initial reaction of one of the epoxide groups of each monomeric molecule with the cell component may be followed by self-condensation of the free epoxide groups into a polyethenoxy structure similar to that already envisaged. While either sequence would lead to cross-linkage of high stability, these authors point out that cross-linkage in any form may not be strictly necessary, since serious impairment of function would result from the presence of even a single collateral polymer unit formed from the cytotoxic agent and held in position by numerous regularly spaced covalent bonds. These interesting speculations, and particularly the question whether they are likely to be valid generally, are further discussed below.

METHYLOLAMIDES

As a further example of cytotoxic activity of the nitrogen mustard type in a structurally related but halogen-free chemical class already in industrial use as cross-linking agents, Hendry, Rose, and Walpole (1951) described growth-inhibitory activity in compounds of the general formula shown in Fig. 105, with special reference to trimethylolmelamine (Fig. 106). In these authors' view the only obvious chemical property common to the methylolamides and mustards is their capacity to act as alkylating agents by interaction with groupings containing active hydrogen atoms. As with the mustards and epoxides, activity once more appears to be conditional upon the presence in the molecule of at least two alkylating groups. Again Hendry *et al.* point out that the groupings which occur in the methylolamides, the epoxides and the ethyleneimines (below), are characterized as much by the ease with which they polymerize as by their reactivity as alkylating agents, and as for the di-epoxides they raise the possibility that the active agent is not the monomeric material but a polymer formed therefrom within the cell. In the case of the methylolamides, the technical application of these substances ap-

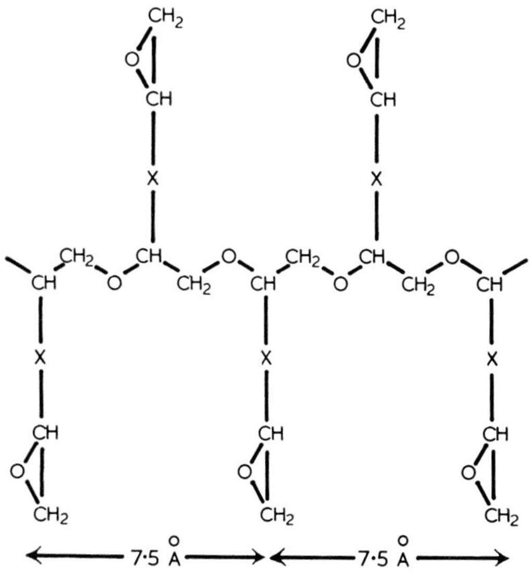

FIG. 104.

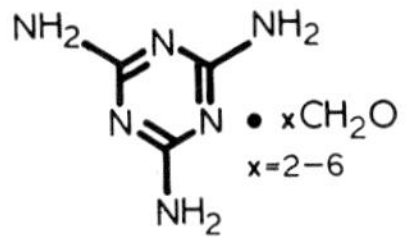

FIG. 105.

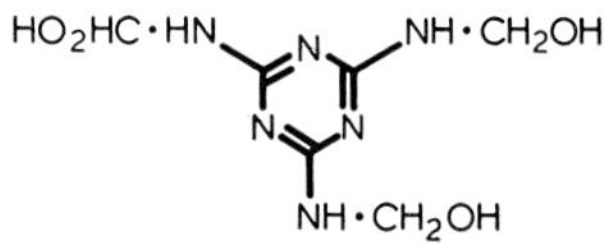

FIG. 106. Trimethylolmelamine.

pears dependent upon a combination of the two properties, leading to the formation of polymeric units with residual groupings capable of forming linkages between adjacent polymer chains, whether polypeptide as in wool, or poly-cellobiose as in cotton, with resultant modification in the structural and physicochemical properties of the amorphous region of such fibers.

According to Hendry *et al.* the exact nature of the polymer unit derived from trimethylolmelamine is not yet known, although Dixon, Christopher, and Salley (1948) have suggested that the triazine nuclei are arranged within it in lamellar form. Alternatively it may have an extended form, but in either case two of the methylol groups in each molecule of the monomer are required for the formation of the polymer chain, leaving one reactive side chain appended to each nucleus. Also, these reactive appendages will be spaced in line at distances apart which are approximate multiples of 3.7 Å, a distance corresponding very closely, as these authors point out, to the spacing of the purine and pyrimidine residues in the nucleic acids and of the amino-acids in extended polypeptides. Again, as for the epoxides, such polymers would be capable of forming an attachment along either protein or nucleic acid chains to give a much more stable type of cross-linkage than that provided by unassociated molecules.

Hendry and his colleagues also discuss the bearing on the question of affinity for fibers, of dyestuff substantivity, which is usually achieved by a pattern of repeat groupings capable of binding the linear dye molecule to the fiber by residual valency forces. In this case it would perhaps be possible to interfere with the mitotic process with a unit or polymer chain not linked covalently with, but merely adhering to, a vital cellular compound by such binding forces. This suggestion recalls that made earlier by Bradley (1936) on the possible relationship between carcinogenicity and substantivity, and his statement that the benzpyrene nucleus would appear to be equally potent whether regarded as a carcinogenic structure or as a unit in the structure of vat dyes.

Hendry *et al.* also mention the notion of the orientation of reactive groups as a factor of importance in interference with macromolecular function, possibly attained in the case of the active methylolamides by the formation of a polymer "backbone" carrying groupings at regularly spaced intervals. They also suggest that a similar orientation of prosthetic groups might be brought about solely by micelle formation, a factor which might perhaps equally well operate in the case of the polycyclic aromatic hydrocarbons and possibly of other carcinogens (see later).

While Rose's concept of polymer formation would assuredly prevent nucleic acid-histone combination (cf. Alexander, above), and could readily cause dissociation of nucleoproteins in accordance with evidence already mentioned, a polymerized structure would not on the other hand appear necessary to produce such blocking effects, in evidence of which may be quoted the undoubted activity of certain monofunctional imines (below), and of certain monofunctional mustards and other compounds in sufficiently high concentration in vitro. It is reasonable, where the combination between cytotoxic or carcinogenic agent is by salt linkages or hydrogen bonds, to suggest that the greater number of linkages offered by a polymer structure would result in a much more stable attachment, but in cases where the agent forms a covalent bond—for example, an ester linkage—the polymer structure would appear to offer no specific advantage. A critical factor is the unlikelihood, or indeed impossibility, of polymers with reactive chains being derived from many of the active mustards, and especially from the dimethanesulfonoxyalkanes still to be mentioned. While the formation of polymers might readily enhance the activity of certain types of carcinogenic agent, this last consideration, coupled with the conditions under which these compounds are administered in vivo—particularly a degree of dilution which would in itself be unfavorable to polymer formation—renders this mechanism unlikely as a general or essential requirement.

ETHYLENEIMINES

The application of bi- and polyfunctional agents to the treatment of rayon received particular attention by the I.G., Hoechst Farbwerke and other groups in Germany during the late war (see Hill *et al.* 1946, Evans 1949), and specially prominent among substances found to react with cellulose, on baking either in the presence of a catalyst or alone, were the compounds hexamethylene diamine diethyleneurea (Fig. 107) and triethyleneimine-1:3:5-triazine (triethylenemelamine) (Fig. 108)—representatives of a large class of polyethyleneimines with cross-

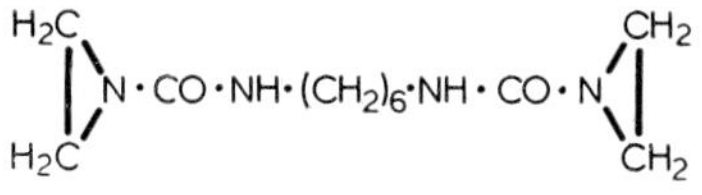

FIG. 107. Hexamethylene diamine diethyleneurea.

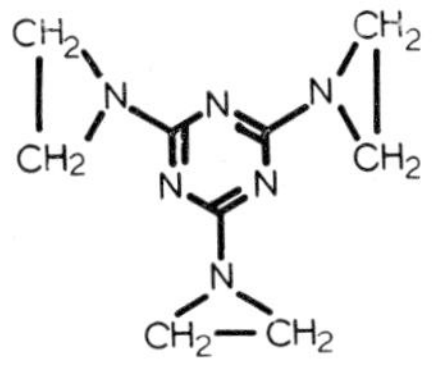

FIG. 108. Triethyleneimine-1:3:5-triazine.

linking ability and the capacity to effect a great reduction in the swelling properties of both artificial and natural fibers. While imines had earlier been considered in related technical applications (e.g., British Patent Specification 472.899, 1937), these later German developments, and the chemical work of Bestian (1950), unquestionably played a large part in directing the attention of several groups of workers independently to them, as cross-linking agents with a reactivity towards nucleophilic reagents similar to that of the mustards and epoxides (Fig. 109), and likely to manifest similar cytotoxic and carcinogenic action (e.g., Lewis and Crossley 1950; Burchenal, Crossley, Stock, and Rhoads 1950; Rose, Hendry, and Walpole 1950).

This surmise proved correct, and as for all the other examples so far considered, compounds possessing at least two reactive groups, in this case the ethyleneimine ring, showed greatest cytotoxic activity. Thus Burchenal, Johnston, Cremer, Webber, and Stock (1950) found that compounds showing the ability significantly

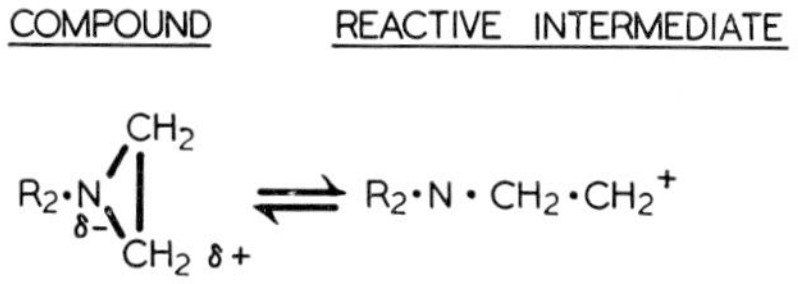

FIG. 109.

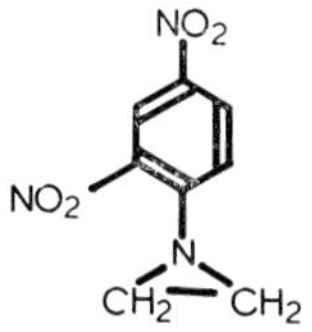

FIG. 110. 2:4-Dinitrophenylethyleneimine.

to prolong the survival time of mice with transplanted leukemia all possessed at least two ethyleneimine rings; while in a similar study of the Crocker mouse sarcoma Buckley, Stock, Crossley, and Rhoads (1952) observed monoethyleneimines to be much less effective than the *bis-* or *tris-* derivatives. At the same time, and to a degree not hitherto observed in a monofunctional compound. Philips, Walpole, and the writer independently observed growth-inhibitory activity in 2,4-dinitrophenylethyleneimine (Fig. 110). While a one-armed mustard could not be regarded as bifunctional, an ethyleneimine might, and consideration was given to the possibility of association of two such molecules in solution to yield a bifunctional agent, or that the nitro groups in Fig. 106 might act as auxochromes, forming an association with protein followed by reaction of the ethyleneimonium group at another site: this possibility was not however supported by experiments designed to test it.

Hendry, Homer, Rose, and Walpole (1951b) found the biologic activity of mono-ethyleneimines to be comparatively low, being no more than one-tenth to one-hundredth that of the nearest related *bis-* ethyleneimine derivatives, and the methods of preparation were such that the possibility could not be excluded that the latter were present as contaminants in amounts sufficient to produce the effects observed. Set against the likelihood of contamination was however the constancy of the effects produced by successive preparations of the same substance, an observation inconsistent with the expected variability in composition. These and other arguments apart, the activity found in 2:4-dinitrophenylethyleneimine, which on account of its mode of preparation must be regarded as essentially pure, compels acceptance of the occurrence of activity in monofunctional compounds. The hypothesis of cross-linking alkylation was also considered by Biesele, Philips, Thiersch, Burchenal, Buckley, and Stock (1950) in relation to yet another biologically active ethylene-imine, namely 2-ethyleneimino-4:6-dimethoxy-*s*-triazine (Fig. 111). These authors recognize that their results do not negate the possibility that the polyfunctional alkylating agents may act through a cross-linkage of fibrous molecules. Nevertheless, they regard it as more reasonable to attribute biologic activity to a common molecular feature, namely unstable three-membered heterocyclic radicals, while admitting, as against this view, Ross's inability to demonstrate ethyleneimonium moieties as intermediates in the reactions of the N,N-*bis*(2-chloroalkyl) arylamines.

In comment, Loveless and Ross (1950) refer to monofunctional compounds—such as 2-chloroethylsulfide and 2-chloroethyldimethylamine—which are able to produce chromosome breakage in plant material. However, the effect is elicited only by concentrations some fifty times that required of their bifunctional analogs, so that such monofunctional compounds, while active, are much less so. They also mention the case of 1:4-*bis*-methanesulfonoxybutane, synthesized by Timmis, which cannot form three-membered rings but can nevertheless react by a carbonium ion mechanism as also can the epoxides, ethyleneimines, and sulfur and nitrogen mustards. Loveless and Ross would therefore regard the ability to produce carbonium ions as a more general feature of all these agents than the ability to form compounds containing an unstable ring system, even though Timmis (below), brings forward still another mechanism for the special case of his *bis*-methanesulfonoxyalkanes. Perhaps the most striking example of biologic activity in monofunctional imines is the description by Hendry *et al.* of carcinogenic activity in stearoyl ethyleneimine ($C_{17}H_{35}CO.N(CH_2)$—a substance, incidentally, which was used by the Germans for waterproofing military uniforms*—and in myristoyl and caproyl ethyleneimine ($C_{13}H_{27}CO.N(CH_2)_2$ and $C_5H_{11}CO.N(CH_2)_2$): in this series, activity appears to be eliminated by branching of the chain.

Hendry *et al.* develop their theory of intracellular polymer formation for the case of the imines as for the epoxides and methylolamides, and in addition extend these notions to the carcinogenic hydrocarbons, azo compounds, and aminostilbenes. In the first case, two characteristics were selected as significant, namely the need for a planar structure of optimal molecular dimensions, and a degree of

* See *German Synthetic Fiber Developments.* (New York, Textile Research Institute, 1946.)

chemical reactivity sufficient to allow conjugation with protein. The synthesis was then visualized within the cell of a protein or nucleoprotein unit carrying the hydrocarbon moieties as side chains. The latter, by reason of their lipophilic nature, might then tend to associate into micelles, with the component flat molecules held together, perhaps in lamellar form, and possibly additionally interleaved by other hydrocarbon residues conjugated to a second peptide chain. The arrangement would resemble that provided by the reactive polymers derived from the epoxides, methylolamides, and ethyleneimines, the essential difference being the substitution of the covalent linkages between the repeating groups of the latter by

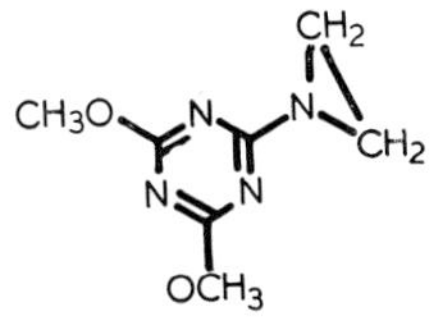

FIG. 111. 2-Ethyleneimino-4:6-dimethoxy-*s*-triazine.

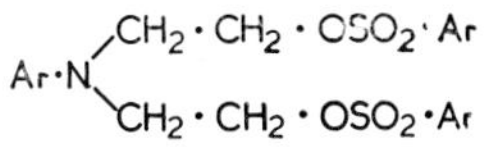

FIG. 112.

residual valencies. In essence, the carcinogenicity of the polycyclic hydrocarbons is regarded as a function of requisite chemical reactivity, together with the capacity of the molecules to pack into micellar units, and it may well be that some of the differences in biologic action between individual compounds could be explained by the influence of substitution and other changes on either or both of these factors.

Hendry *et al.* also draw notice to the suggestion of Mueller and Miller (1950), that the linkage of the carcinogenic azo-dyestuffs to protein may be through an intermediate methylolaminoazobenzene. Since the N-methylol group is capable of conferring cytotoxic activity upon other chemical systems, this, together with the occurrence of the azobenzene group in a number of typical micelle-forming dyestuffs (Vickerstaff 1950), might point to a mode of action whereby the attachment of the azobenzene residues to protein is followed by the orientation of the former into micelles analogous to those proposed for the polycyclic hydrocarbons. Similar arguments could be advanced in the case of the carcinogenic aminostilbenes, the stilbene group again being associated in dyestuff technology with special colloidal properties.

DIMETHANESULFONOXYALKANES

In the search for new types of bifunctional agents with cytostatic properties, biological activity was detected in various members of the series (Fig. 112) (Haddow and Timmis 1951), a result which led to the investigation of other structures bearing sulfonic acid ester groups, and in particular the $\alpha\omega$-methanesulfonoxyalkanes (Fig. 113) (Timmis 1951; Haddow and Timmis 1952).

While all members of this series exhibit activity where $n=2$–10, the degree of such varies considerably from one member to another, and in a highly regular manner. Thus it is maximal where $n=4$ or 5, less where $n=6$, 7, or 8, and very greatly reduced where $n=2$, 3, 9 or 10. Again the series is capable of acting through the carbonium ion mechanism (Fig. 114), although Timmis suggests that activity may be determined by the ability of these agents to form ring compounds with an amino or possibly a sulfhydryl group, variations in activity being attributed to variations in the stability of the ring or in the rate of its formation. The spatial configurations required to form such a ring, or (for instance) to esterify two adjacent phosphoryl groups, may however be similar, and the observed relationship between biologic action and the disposition of the functional groups could in fact lend support to either hypothesis. However, the activity of this series jeopardizes

$$CH_3SO_2O\,(CH_2)_n\,OSO_2CH_3 \qquad n = 2-10$$

FIG. 113.

COMPOUND — REACTIVE INTERMEDIATE

$$R \cdot CH_2 \cdot OSO_2 \cdot R' \rightleftharpoons R \cdot \overset{+}{CH_2} + \bar{O}SO_2 \cdot R'$$

FIG. 114.

Rose's theory of the formation of linear polymers with reactive side-chains, at least as a general mechanism, since it is impossible to derive such polymers from the dimethanesulfonoxyalkanes. The impressive strength of the correlation between tumor induction on the one hand and growth-inhibitory activity on the other, (and radiomimetic action in particular), is shown by the carcinogenicity of members of both the above series (Figs. 112 and 114), 1:4-dimethanesulfonoxybutane being outstandingly active in this respect.

NEWER INTERPRETATIONS OF THE BIOLOGIC MECHANISM

Whatever the precise chemical mechanism of the action of carcinogens, there can be little doubt of the importance of their combination with genetically determinant material, or its precursors, if this is, as seems likely, an essential part of the action of those at least which function through biologic alkylation. An older view (Haddow 1938), depicted the primary step in chemical carcinogenesis as an inhibition of the normal growth mechanism, leading to the adaptive formation of a new cell variant, released from the inhibitory influence of the agent which provoked it. The newer interpretation suggests that the primary step may be the inhibition of certain fundamental processes of genetic synthesis, followed by the generation of a new self-duplicating fiber or template, chemically, and hence genetically, modified. It is also a question whether the initial combination of the carcinogenic molecule with its genetic receptor may not lie at the basis of that primary, specific, and often irreversible change which, according to Berenblum and Shubik (1947, 1949a,b), gives rise, as a first stage in the carcinogenic process, to "latent tumor cells" (see also Berenblum 1948, 1949). Much other work supports the conception of a specific and early biochemical lesion, of such a kind that although no evidence of malignancy is immediately detectable, such very rapidly occurs when the cell is induced to regenerate (Rusch and Kline 1948; Glinos and Bucher 1949; Glinos, Bucher, and Aub 1951; Bullough 1950; Fritz-Niggli 1951; Brues and Sacher 1951).

The permanent re-orientation of genetic characters, under the impress of the chemical modification of an initial self-duplicating unit, recalls the manner in which the generation and secretion of a normal globulin may be replaced by that of an immune body, through the influence of a foreign antigen on the original surface, fiber or template. This immunologic parallel is supported by the views of many others, as for example of Tyler (1947), who regards the mechanism of the process of growth as essentially analogous to that in antibody formation, of Grabar (1947, 1950), who interprets antibody formation as a mechanism of adaptive synthesis, and of Laser (1951), who suggests that adaptive enzyme production results from a mechanism resembling an immunologic reaction, that is, in response to the formation of a conjugated antigen.

Most compelling, however, are the views of Burnet (Burnet and Fenner 1949), that antibody formation is the consequence of an inherited change in the pattern of synthesis of serum globulin in mesenchymal cells, namely a change which endures through repeated fissions long after the physical disappearance of the agent which in the first place brought it about. In this sense antibody formation, like malignant change itself, is the outcome of an inherited cellular transformation. Extracellular proteins are the reproductively inert by-products of the synthetic activity of an enzyme system undergoing continuous replication; antibody is serum globulin formed by an enzyme system which under the influence of antigen has submitted to an inherited change in many ways analogous with that responsible for the formation of adaptive enzymes in bacteria.

The relevance of the immunologic analogy to the problems of carcinogenesis cannot be gainsaid, and is further borne out by observations of the sensitivity of the antibody-producing mechanism both to roentgen-radiation and to radiomimetic and carcinogenic agents. In the first place, Hektoen's original classic researches on the effects of various leukotoxic agents on antibody formation (Hektoen 1915), which led him to conclude that antibodies might be produced in the spleen, the lymphatic tissues, and the bone marrow, and which showed that antibody formation is suppressed by total body roentgen-radiation, have been confirmed and extended by Jacobson, Robson and Marks (1950), while the sensitivity of the immune response both to roentgen rays and nitrogen mustards has been studied by Schwab, Moll, Hall, Brean, Kirk, Hawn, and Janeway (1950; for a general review see Taliaferro and Taliaferro 1951). Secondly, it is remarkable that the cell types (both normal and malignant), which are most sensitive to the cytotoxic action of the mustards and similar compounds, namely cells of the reticuloendothelial, lymphoid, and macro- and microphage systems, are precisely those believed to be involved in the cellular basis of immunity (Taliaferro 1949, Stallybrass 1950). Although the specific cell types most closely concerned are still a matter of controversy, and particularly whether they are lymphocytes (McMaster and Hudack 1935; Ehrich and Harris 1942; Harris, Grimm, Mertens, and Ehrich 1945; Harris and Harris 1949), or plasma cells (Fagraeus 1947, 1948 a, b; Bjørneboe, Gormsen, and Lundquist 1947; Ehrich, Drabkin, and Forman 1949; Forman, Drabkin, and Ehrich 1949; Moeschlin, Pelaez, and Hugentobler 1951), many workers are of opinion that antibody production is not the function exclusively of a single cell type but rather of any multipotent cell of the mesenchyme (Burnet and Fenner 1949, Campbell and Good 1949). In any event it is suggestive to find unusual sensitivity towards roentgen rays and radiomimetic chemical agents in cells specially active in the synthesis of protein and of desoxyribonucleoprotein (cf. Kabelitz 1951; Bing, Fagraeus, and Thorell 1945), and often having a striking ability to undergo rapid proliferation (cf. Hadfield 1949).

Last may be mentioned a possibility which is fraught with much potential significance for the "spontaneous" origin of cancer, especially in its relation to aging, and which arises from the fact that the alterations in cellular proteins which it is suggested are brought about by the biologic alkylating agents, whether by cross-linking or polymerization, are similar to or identical with those occurring in the aging of proteins (Bjorksten 1951), or of artificial and natural polymers such as rubber, vinyl, and diene polymers (Mesrobian and Tobolsky 1947), or cellulose nitrate (Campbell and Johnson 1950). In many such cases two processes are involved (as in the biologic situation), namely cross-linking, gelation, and polymerization on the one hand, and scission or degradation on the other, both of which may proceed by the same radical-activated chain mechanism. Bjorksten (1951) draws attention to the peculiar susceptibility of proteins to cross-linkage reactions, and to the point that most available information is so far empirical and gained from industrial practice, and that many phenomena have been ascribed to denaturation when in fact cross-linkage plays an important part. With reference to the theory of aging, the effects of cross-linking on proteins, and the changes which proteins undergo in the aging organism, appear to be identical, namely reduction of ability to retain bound water, brittleness, loss of elasticity, and reduced solubility or peptizability.

In Bjorksten's view it is surprising, in view of the cross-linking substances which could be formed in metabolism, that cross-linking of body proteins does not take place more rapidly than the aging phenomena observed, and he hazards the conclusion that the living organism must possess potent means of counter-action. All these considerations underline the desirability of the study of animal proteins in relation to age, and raise the questions whether specific carcinogens need in fact be involved in "spontaneous" carcinogenesis, whether the alkylating carcinogens may not simply expedite or facilitate aggregative or disaggregative changes in genetic protein which could in any event occur with age, and whether some such explanation may not underlie the occurrence not merely of cancer spontaneously, but of such phenomena as the production of malignancy in vitro (Earle, Schilling and Shelton 1950; Sanford, Earle, Shelton, Schilling, Duchesne, Likely, and Becker 1950), in the apparent absence of any extraneous carcinogen.

CYTOLOGIC ANALYSIS

It has already been made clear that the chromosomal abnormalities induced by the aromatic nitrogen mustards, whether acutely in normal cells or as a more lasting stigma in the cells of tumors induced by these agents, are almost certainly relatively gross effects, not essential to the carcinogenic process, and probably merely associated with, or accompanying, those more elusive alterations which are no doubt specifically responsible for malignant change. At the same time, it is not unlikely that all such effects are produced by a somewhat similar mechanism, and cytologic analysis of the nature and distribution of the visible changes has already yielded much information with a highly suggestive bearing on the problems of carcinogenesis and mutation.

Allusion has already been made to an important early concept, namely, that the initial combination of these agents with genetic material probably occurs in the so-called resting stage, and that the resulting abnormalities are merely revealed in the course of subsequent cell-divisions, their cause having been determined beforehand. That a similar principle may apply in other types of drug action is indicated, for example, by Mitchell's interpretation (1949) of the mode of action of penicillin. According to this, the effects of a toxic substance upon the cell are not always instantaneous, but frequently involve a course of events leading to the changes, reversible or otherwise, which are thus imposed. A first stage, in which the agent reacts with cellular components, is followed by a second in which the cell organization becomes altered through the impairment of function of the components directly affected earlier: so it may happen that only when the cell is disturbed from a state of rest may the effects of the agent become apparent or lethal.

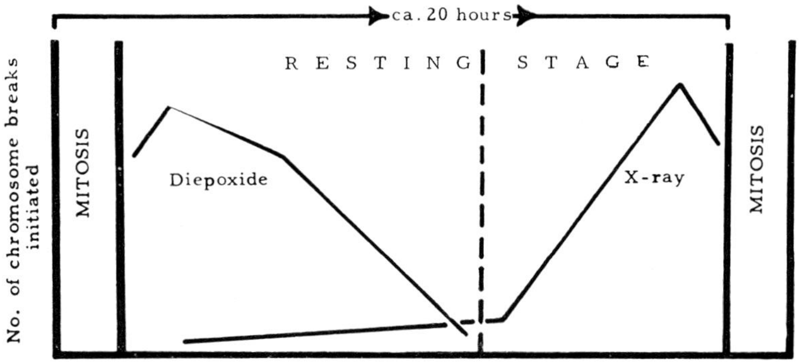

FIG. 115. Changes in cell sensitivity (in *Vicia faba*) to the initiation of breaks by di(2:3-epoxypropyl)ether and by X rays (Revell 1952).

Not only are the effects of nitrogen mustard determined in the resting stage, but there is a remarkable variation in the ease or likelihood of their production at different periods during this time. Thus Ford (1948), in a study of chromosome breakage in the root tip cells of *Vicia faba* treated with HN2, found that the production of breaks by this agent ceases prior to the onset of prophase, in contrast with ionizing radiation which can break the chromosomes in prophase itself. In work which has both confirmed and extended that of Ford, Revell (1952), studying a radiomimetic di-epoxide, observes that breaks are most frequent at the ensuing metaphase when the agent is administered early in the resting stage, that treatment at successively later stages gives progressively fewer breaks, and that none are produced in the last eight hours of the resting stage preceding mitosis. This last "insensitive" period corresponds, however, with that at which the cell is apparently most sensitive to roentgen-radiation (Fig. 115).

Revell draws attention to the misleading implications which can be introduced by the use of the term "break" to describe the consequence of chemical treatment. While there is ample evidence that ionizing radiations do in fact break chromosomes, and that the broken ends may afterwards rejoin, it is more difficult to visualize chemical compounds as acting in the same manner, at least in the sense implied, of breaking a preformed chromosome structure. There are, however, two ways in which such chemical agents might produce the equivalent of breakage. First, it is reasonable to assume that they might in some way act as inhibitors of chromosome synthesis, so as to produce a small deletion, where the normal linearly differentiated reproduction of the chromosome material is interrupted, either by the direct action of the agent or by its action on substrate required by the affected chromosome locus. Secondly, it is possible that the agent (or altered substrate), might induce apparent breaks at certain points on the chromosome length by preventing chromosome components from rejoining in the normal fashion. As Revell points out, this is not to say that the chromosome is an impermanent structure during the resting stage. At meiotic prophase, however, the chromosome is known to break and rejoin in the process of chiasma formation, and it seems inconceivable that this involves the complete severance of, perhaps, several hundred polypeptide linkages. If the chromosome is basically composed of polypeptide chains, it seems more likely these must be joined by other relatively labile linkages, at least during the stage when crossing-over occurs at meiosis. Such a stage might have its homolog during mitosis, when the chromosomes might be breakable and rejoinable at these labile points. On this view, Revell likens chemical breakage to a sort of illegitimate crossing-over.

It is of much interest that the second part of the resting stage, insensitive to di-epoxide, is also the stage at which Howard and Pelc (1951 a,b,c,d) observe a cessation in the synthesis of desoxyribonucleic acid by *Vicia* root tip material. Such synthesis, according to these authors, occurs during interphase, but ceases about six hours before the beginning of visible prophase: P^{32} is incorporated in this form only in nuclei which are preparing for division, and as such is inherited by the daughter cells. Obviously it is tempting to suspect from this correlation that a carcinogenic or mutagenic chemical agent may act by reason of its ability to interfere at some stage in desoxyribonucleic acid synthesis: yet Revell makes it clear that there is as yet no evidence for any causal correlation between these phenomena, save their coincidence in time. He also regards it as unjustifiable from our present knowledge, and perhaps misleading, to refer to chromosome sensitivity as though it were varying at different stages, since the observed variation may be due to a declining concentration of substrate in parts of the cell which are remote from the chromosomes themselves.

Apart from the distribution of the initial effects of the chemical agent in time, in relation to the cell cycle, much important information has also been derived from a study of the distribution of the resultant chromosome breakages in relation to the chromosome length. Investigation of the incidence of roentgen-ray–induced mutation, since its first demonstration by Muller in 1927, had failed to reveal any great linear selectivity in the action of roentgen rays on the chromosome. However, Ford (1948) found that the short chromosomes in *Vicia faba* were broken by nitrogen mustard much more frequently than the long chromosomes, and that the distribution of breaks was very markedly biased towards certain chromosome regions: such localization of breakage is in marked contrast with the more generally distributed breakage which follows roentgen-irradiation. These observations have again been extended by Revell (1952), who remarks that there is no *a priori* reason to suspect that radiomimetic effects should show the same random distribution as those produced by roentgen rays, since there is no reason to suppose that a mutagenic or carcinogenic chemical agent can "act on the chromosomes in the sort of randomly corrosive fashion that has sometimes been assumed."

Revell employed the terminology previously used by Darlington and Upcott (1941) and by Darlington and La Cour (1945) for scoring roentgen-ray data, which involves interpretation in terms of chromosome and chromatid breaks. The most frequently observed change is the simple chromosome break yielding a centric and an acentric fragment. Both chromatids are broken at the same level, and hence breakage is presumed to have occurred during the resting stage before longitudinal splitting. Breaks in single chromatids are also seen, giving an acentric chromatid, and these have been supposed to occur either after splitting, or alternatively to arise from a chromosome break (caused before splitting), in which one chromatid only has rejoined (after splitting). The broken ends of chromosomes may reunite as before (restitution), in which case the break cannot be detected, or, after splitting, the two chromatids of each fragment may unite with each other (sister chromatid reunion). If more than one break is caused in a nucleus, then the fragments may reunite in new combinations, part of one chromosome being translocated on to another, as in the chromatid interchange, or the more rarely occurring triradial. The maps constructed by Revell are of simple breaks only, and from these (e.g., Fig. 116) it is clear that breaks induced by nitrogen mustard and certain other agents in the L chromosome show a marked peak in the nucleolar organizer arm, near to the centromere, and in or near the larger heterochromatic region. There are no breaks shown in the smaller heterochromatic region on the other side of the centromere: while there appears to be a maximum here as well, nearly all these breaks are involved in translocations and are thus excluded. The roentgen-ray–induced breaks are fairly scattered, although there is a gap on either side of the centromere, again probably spurious since many breaks involving translocations are in this region, and are omitted.

POSSIBLE SIGNIFICANCE OF HETEROCHROMATIN

In a critical appraisal, Revell believes that the available data are too imprecise, and the criteria used too vague, for any conclusions to be drawn. In the first place, heterochromatin as defined in these experiments is an unsatisfactory concept, depending upon an empirical cytologic test (the cold-treatment method of Darlington and La Cour [1940]), the interpretation of which is itself highly controversial: nothing exact is known of the chemical differences which determine the linear differentiation of the chromosome as a whole, or of heterochromatin and euchromatin in particular. Second, the nature of the technic employed does not permit direct observation of the primary events causing breakage, but only their consequences at the next metaphase, that is, after other events have intervened.

Revell also stresses the difficulty of providing reliable evidence for or against a number of possibilities, first that the different chromosomes, and the regions of varying susceptibility in them, do in fact react with chemical agents to a greater or less degree, or that altered substrate is utilized predominantly in certain chromosome regions; second, that the reaction products concerned have different stabilities in different parts of the chromosomes, and that in some cases they are decomposed so rapidly that no break is produced; third, that the chemical agents effect breaks undergoing restitution much more readily at some points than at others, so that the irregular distribution later observed is, therefore, misleading. The difficulties of

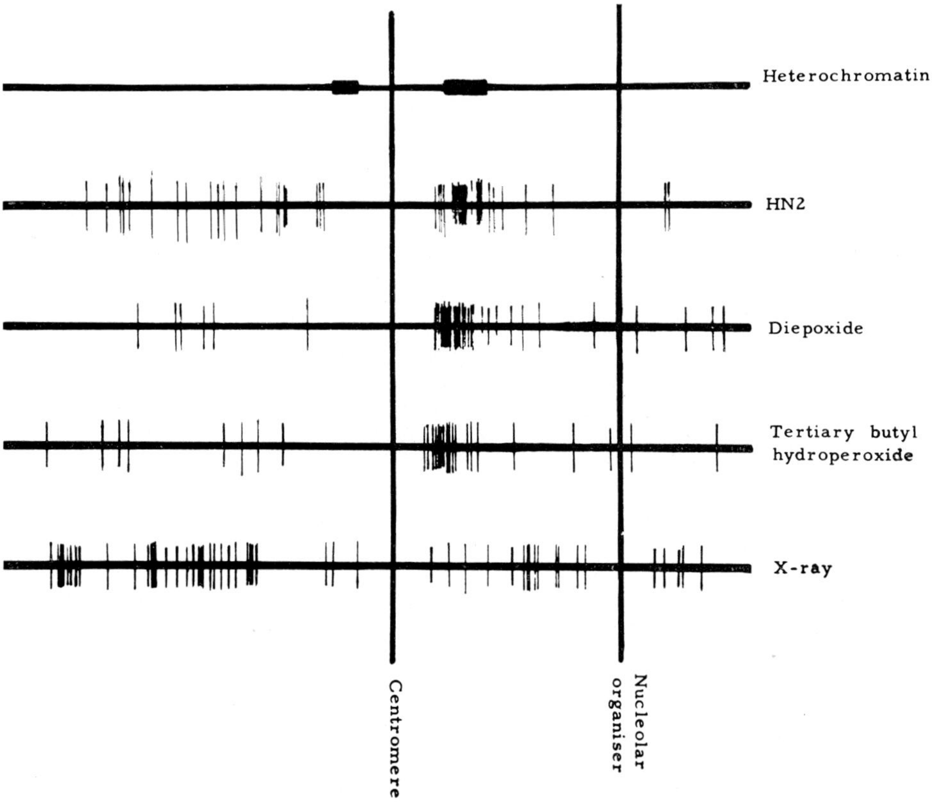

FIG. 116. Position of two heterochromatic segments and of a series of breaks induced by various agents in the L chromosome of *Vicia faba.* Each sample is of about 50 breaks, except in the case of tertiary butyl hydroperoxide where there are 27 only. The linear scale represents a magnification of 7700 (Revell 1952).

interpretation are further shown by the fact that chromosome breakage effectively confined to heterochromatin may be produced in *Vicia* by maleic hydrazide (Darlington and McLeish 1951), that is, by a substance which possesses none of the characteristic properties of the mustards and which is, so far as is known, not carcinogenic.

None the less, there is no denying that the agents studied by Revell induce chromosome breaks which occur predominantly, by whatever means, in regions correlated with heterochromatic behavior, and the finding may be significant in view of the facts that heterochromatin has a high nucleic acid charge in the resting nucleus, and that the same agents have, as already described, a special affinity for combination with acid groups. It may therefore at least be suspected (Loveless and Revell 1949), that the extrinsic agent is indeed combining with desoxyribonucleic acid at the resting-stage chromocentres, with breakage as a result.

Heterochromatin was originally described by Heitz (1928, 1932), as that part of the chromatin maintaining the condensed state, characteristic of the metaphase chromosome, throughout the nuclear cycle, and the segments starved by cold treatment of their nucleic acid at metaphase agree in number and position with the segments overcharged with nucleic acid in the resting stage (La Cour, 1951). On the other hand it seems impossible to provide any simple definition (Therman-Suomalainen 1948); in some cases it appears that the heterochromatin cannot be identified by any known technic (Mather 1949), and Baker and Callan (1950) have objected to the name itself on the ground that it suggests a substance or group of closely related substances with distinctive chemical characters, which is clearly not so. While Serra (1947a; see also Fernandes and Serra 1944; Fernandes 1948, 1949) believes that the heterochromatic condition may be permanent or transitory, and is not endowed with the great role in cell physiology which has been attributed to it, since many species occur with little or none, White on the other hand (1951) regards it as likely that no chromosomes exist which are completely euchromatic.

According to the original interpretation of Caspersson and Santesson (1942, and Caspersson 1947), heterochromatin regulates the formation of protein by the nucleus, and during the interphase seems to construct protein substances of a type rich in hexone bases, these forming the main part of the nucleolus and diffusing out towards the nuclear membrane, at the surface of which are built ribose nucleic acids, and, apparently by their mediation, the cytoplasmic proteins. Certainly the heterochromatin appears to have a marked influence upon the supply of nucleic acid, and other evidence indicates that an oversupply of the heterochromatic segments can accelerate the mitotic cycle (Darlington and Thomas 1941, Gulick 1944). Goldschmidt also expresses the view that heterochromatin may undergo a genetic change analogous to mutation in the euchromatin, the action being primarily concerned, however, with the processes of growth, especially with early differentiation, and possibly with the growth of the chromosomes themselves (Goldschmidt and Lin 1947, Goldschmidt 1948, 1949). Other useful accounts are given by Darlington (1945), Schultz (1947), and Vanderlyn (1949).

Bearing in mind these possibilities, and above all Mather's interpretation of the genetical activity of heterochromatin as the seat of quantitative and polygenic inheritance (1944, 1949), the impression remains, in spite of the difficulty and confusion of the literature as a whole, that heterochromatin may include a target of unique significance so far as concerns the chemical induction of variations in the timing and extent of growth and differentiation. It is not perhaps a coincidence that Koller (1943b), from a cytologic analysis of human tumors, indicated that the increased rate of division in their cells might be attributed to a quantitative change in nucleic acid synthesis resulting from alteration in the heterochromatic regions.

NUCLEUS AND CYTOPLASM

A primary action of carcinogenic agents on the cell nucleus would scarcely be surprising, and it can be recalled that tumor formation may, in certain favorable material, be initiated by purely genetic means alone, as in the melanoses and melanomas due to inter- and intraspecific genic imbalance in fishes (Gordon 1950 a, b), the plant tumors associated with various interspecific genome combinations in *Nicotiana* (Kehr 1950, 1951), and the production of ovular tumors and inhibition of embryo growth in incompatible crosses of *Datura* (Rappaport, Satina, and Blakeslee 1950). At the same time, nuclear changes of the kind envisaged as due to the alkylating carcinogens would unquestionably involve repercussions in the cytoplasm, so raising the whole problem of the mutual interdependence of nuclear genes and cytoplasm for their maintenance and functioning. Nothing is known of the alterations in the cytoplasm in the present case, and it is indeed still an assumption—although perhaps a reasonable one—that they are secondary. Most likely the particular question can be solved only through advances in the general biology of the nucleus-cytoplasm relationship, and much can meantime be gleaned from the existing literature, both older (Wilson 1906, Morgan 1934), and more recent (Brachet 1947). Cell behavior certainly appears to depend immediately upon the constitution of the cytoplasm, reflecting in turn the earlier action of the nuclear genes with which it has been associated (Mather 1948 a, b). Duryee (1939, 1949, a, b, 1950) goes so far as to claim that radiation damage to the chromosomes results primarily from the chemical products of the injured cytoplasm, typical nuclear damage in nonirradiated cells being produced by microinjection of cytoplasmic material withdrawn from irradiated (amphibian) eggs. However, Auerbach and Robson (1947) found the rate of lethal mutation not to be increased in untreated *Drosophila* chromosomes which had been introduced into cytoplasm treated with mustard gas, suggesting that this agent, like roentgen-radiation, acts on the chromosomes directly; and Whiting (1950) equally found no evidence of the mutagenicity of roentgen-rayed cytoplasm in *Habrobracon*. Brachet (1950; Linet and Brachet 1951) believes the synthesis of the cytoplasmic particles containing ribonucleic acid (in *Amoeba*), to be under nuclear control, but, contrary to the generally accepted view, found the presence of the nucleus not necessary for protein synthesis to continue for a considerable time, incorporation of CO_2 into protein, following enucleation, being far from negligible even after several weeks.

It will be recalled (above) that chromosome fragments produced by the mustards and similar agents are characteristically ejected from the nucleus into the cytoplasm, where they are recognized as so-called "micronuclei." Clearly these large structures are unable to function, and in due course they degenerate. It is however an interesting speculation (due to Loveless), whether, if the deleted particle were of sufficiently small, perhaps molecular, dimensions, it might then be capable of reproducing itself in the cytoplasm indefinitely. This and similar possibilities are very likely more than theoretical, and could lead to a situation with an important bearing on the problem of virus tumors, and consistent with much which is already known in the field of cytoplasmic inheritance and the action of plasmagenes (Sonneborn 1950 a, b; Schultz 1950; Michaelis 1949).

CARCINOGENESIS AND BIOLOGIC MUTATION

Almost as old as the experimental study of cancer is the question whether the process of carcinogenesis should not be regarded as a special case of biologic mutation more widely, and the attractiveness of the somatic mutation hypothesis is certainly not less because of the pronounced mutagenic properties of many of the carcinogens discovered recently. As in the case of the carcinogens, mutagens also include physical and chemical agents of great diversity, the effects of which have been investigated over a considerable range of biologic test-objects.

Thus Herskowitz (1951) has listed those substances which have been studied for their effects on *Drosophila*, while Demerec, Bertani, and Flint (1951) have likewise surveyed chemical agents tested for mutagenic action on *E. coli*. Individual mutagenic agents, chosen almost at random, include allyl*iso*thiocyanate (Auerbach and Robson 1944), ethylene oxide and propylene oxide (Rapoport 1948), formaldehyde (Rapoport 1946, Kaplan 1948, Burdette 1951), β-propiolactone (in *Neurospora*, Smith and Srb, 1951), radioactive phosphorus (in *Drosophila*, Bateman and Sinclair 1950; in barley, Thompson, Mackey, Gustafsson, and Ehrenberg 1950), mustard gas (Auerbach and Robson 1946; in *Zea mays*, Gibson, Brink, and Stahmann 1950), and nitrogen mustard (in *Penicillium notatum*, Stahmann and Stauffer 1947; in *E. coli*, Bryson 1948; in a basidiomycete, Fries 1948; in the mouse, Auerbach and Falconer 1949; in *Drosophila*, Burdette 1950a).

According to Latarjet (1948, 1951), there is a strict parallelism between carcinogenicity and mutagenicity so far as radiation is concerned, but not at all in the case of chemical agents. While Demerec, for example (1948 a, b, c) had earlier reported a number of carcinogenic compounds to be mutagenic, he was later led to revise his conclusions (1949). Special interest has centered on the case of methylcholanthrene, which Strong (1945) found to induce numerous variants, (involving coat-color changes and differences in susceptibility to tumors), in strains of mice treated with the hydrocarbon for a number of generations, but which Burdette (1949, 1950 a, b), and Bhattacharya (1948) reported inactive as a mutagen for *Drosophila*, although it is capable of elevating the tumor incidence (Burdette 1950c) in the same material. Strong (1949b) has raised the question whether every mutagen is a carcinogen, and every carcinogen a mutagen. Clearly both terms can only be used in a relative sense, and apart from the somewhat doubtful analogy of tumors in *Drosophila*, it is true to say that the mouse is the only species in which carcinogenesis and mutagenesis have been directly compared. As Fahmy and Bird observe (1952), it would be surprising if agents acting on growth-controlling genes in, say, the mouse, were also to act equally on those controlling morphogenesis and viability in *Drosophila*, and the absence of a strict parallelism of action between carcinogenesis and mutagenesis, in widely separate biologic material, clearly does not exclude the likelihood of an important relationship between the two properties.

The case is, however, stronger for mustard gas, nitrogen mustard, and the alkylating carcinogens discovered later. Thus Barratt and Tatum (1951), who found methylcholanthrene, 1:2:5:6-dibenzanthracene, and 9:10-dimethyl-1:2-benzanthracene and certain azo compounds to be active as mutagens for *Neurospora crassa*, with dimethylaminostilbene and acetylaminofluorene weaker or inactive, noted that even the most active of these was much less so than nitrogen mustard or radiation. Similarly Burdette (1949) recorded that the mutation rate of his *Drosophila* stocks was greatly increased simply by direct application of nitrogen mustard, in contrast with the negative results of his experiments using methylcholanthrene. It should be recalled that the discovery of the mutagenic action of mustard gas was originally due to the suggestion of Robson, based on his observation of the similarity of burns due to this agent and to roentgen rays.

Whatever the true relationship of the carcinogenic and mutagenic mechanisms, there is little doubt that each can shed light on the other. According to Auerbach (1949 a), all agents of high mutagenic efficiency have also been found to break chromosomes, and to interfere with mitosis, their toxic action being thus preferentially directed against dividing cells. In Auerbach's view, it is perhaps only to be expected that a substance which can react unspecifically with genes to produce mutations can also react with the chromosome thread to destroy its coherence, and the search for a substance which produces mutations but no chromosome breaks may prove identical with the search for a specific mutagen which reacts with only one or a few genes.

Much may be learned from a comparison of roentgen rays and chemical agents in mutagenesis. From analyses of the frequencies of sex-linked recessive lethals and of dominant lethals induced in the sperm of *Drosophila melanogaster* by nitrogen mustard, and comparison with the results obtained from roentgen-ray treatment, Wallace (1951) concluded that the modes of action of the two agents are similar, and that their greatest primary effect is probably on the chromosomal material. Auerbach (1950) also described, as similarities in the mutagenic action of mustard gas and of roentgen rays, the partial sterility of the treated flies, the zygotic lethality of their progeny, the production of recessive sex-linked lethals, the occurrence of visible mutations of the same types and in about the same frequency, the induction of chromosome breaks and translocations in plants, and of structural changes in the chromosomes of *Drosophila,* and the great increase in frequency of somatic crossing-over. But the same author also drew attention to certain notable differences in the action of the two agents in *Drosophila,* namely that the peak of sensitivity to the genetic action occurs during the development of the male germ cells in the case of mustard gas, and in the mature spermatozoa for roentgen rays; that there is a relative shortage of large re-arrangements among the chemically-induced mutations (see below); that visible mutations arising from mustard treatment show a high frequency of mosaics in their progeny; and that a mutagenic after effect accompanies the action of mustard gas but not that of roentgen rays.

Auerbach (1947) regards as the most plausible interpretation of these observations the assumption that chemical treatment, in contrast with roentgen-radiation, induces a labile pre-mutation which subsequently, after one or more cell divisions, may give rise to the actual mutation, or may revert to the old allelomorph. However, such delay in expression is not strictly limited to chemically induced mutants. (Newcombe and Scott 1949), and may apply to spontaneous mutation as well (Newcombe 1948). Auerbach's general viewpoint is nevertheless supported by other evidence, as for example in the experiments of Swanson, McElroy, and Miller (1949), in which pretreatment of the microconidia of *Neurospora crassa* with a relatively nonmutagenic concentration of nitrogen mustard so altered the stability of the genes as to increase significantly the effectiveness of ultraviolet radiation in inducing morphologic and biochemical mutation.

Muller (1948) had already considered the evidence that mutations are, in essentials, orthodox chemical reactions, and Auerbach (1949 a, b) concludes that the primary mutagenic action of mustard gas is a transfer of energy to a localized spot on the chromosome. Although more precise knowledge of the action is lacking, it is perhaps worthy of comment that one or two recognized mutagenic agents are also effective cross-linkers, e.g., formaldehyde (Fraenkel-Conrat and Mecham 1949, Middlebrook 1949), and allyl*iso*thiocyanate (Neish and Speakman 1949). That such cannot however be an essential requirement is shown by the mutagenic activity of various β-chloroethyl amines and sulfides containing only one reactive grouping (Stevens and Mylroie 1950, Auerbach and Moser 1950, Jensen, Kirk, and Westergaard 1950).

Examination by Bird (1950, 1952) of a number of arylhalogenoalkylamines and other alkylating agents suggests that the association between carcinogenicity and mutagenicity may be closer here than in any other class, as might perhaps be expected from their marked radiomimetic quality. Thus N,N-di(2-chloroethyl)-*p*-toluidine and -*p*-anisidine, and β-naphthyldi(2-chloroethyl)- and (2-chloropropyl)-amine, in sublethal doses sterilized, and produced larval "tumors" and other abnormalities in *Drosophila*, while all induced a significant increase in the number of sex-linked lethals, usually more frequently in sperm produced in the earlier days of adult life.

Bird and Fahmy (1952) have carried out a cytogenetic analysis of the action of carcinogens in *Drosophila melanogaster*, with special reference to 1:2,3:4-diepoxybutane. In this case the results are subject to the important reservation that the changes so detected in the salivary gland chromosomes are by no means the whole of the initial changes induced, since several cell divisions intervene between treatment and observation, and are likely to have a marked selective influence. Under these conditions, however, diepoxybutane is characterized by high potency in the production of small deficiencies, with only a small proportion of gross structural change. Of special interest are cases in which the bands at the deficiency locus show various "degrees of absence," varying from defects in staining properties to a complete elimination of the band, and Fahmy and Bird suggest that these "partial expression" deficiencies are the outcome of a modification in the molecular pattern of the gene which has prevented normal reproduction, the disabled gene reproducing itself either partially or erroneously, or not at all. The general conclusion is an important one, consistent with much other evidence, namely that while roentgen-radiation induces chromosome breaks and gross structural change, the radiomimetic mutagens and carcinogens tend rather to produce fewer breaks (and consequently fewer major re-arrangements), and interfere mainly with the synthesis and reproduction of genetic material.

CARCINOGENESIS AND ENZYME LOSS

The general biologic evidence has for some considerable time pointed, even if rather vaguely, to the probability that the cancer cell represents a somatic mutation by loss. The more recent advances would appear to enhance this probability—although not as yet conclusively—and to suggest that the deficiency is genetic or enzymic in nature. A difficulty might be thought to arise in the fact that the mutants induced in very varied biologic objects, for example by nitrogen mustard, represent biochemical deficiencies of such a kind as render the mutant cells nutritionally more dependent (e.g., Tatum 1946, Reaume and Tatum 1949), and not less so as is probable in the case of the malignant cell (cf. Lederberg, above). Nevertheless, the same agents are undoubtedly capable of causing the reversion of nutritionally deficient mutant cells to the nondeficient state (e.g., Stevens and Mylroie 1950), and it is entirely feasible that the loss of enzyme systems normally concerned in controlling the synthesis of substances essential to cell division could result in the unregulated synthesis of such substances, and so convert the normal cell from a state of nutritional dependence to one of self-sufficiency and unimpeded growth.

In spite of the great developments in knowledge of the nutritional control of growth in bacteria and fungi, little comparable information is available as to substances critical for the growth of animal cells. One such apparent example has, however, been encountered by the writer, in the case of the naturally occurring pigment xanthopterin, administration of which, in the rat and other species, induces an increase in kidney-size due to a direct stimulation of mitotic activity and cell-division in the tubular epithelium. This situation is highly suggestive of a device by which the normal growth and compensatory hypertrophy of the kidney may be regulated and controlled, by its dependence upon an essential factor which the organ is unable to synthesize and which must be supplied from elsewhere. It is also tempting to speculate—and indeed some evidence already exists in support of the proposition—whether the coexistent enzyme for which xanthopterin is the substrate, namely xanthopterin oxidase, may not play a part in regulating the concentration of the pterin at any given time, and whether inhibition or removal of the enzyme might not allow substrate accumulation and the release of cell division, in this specific tissue, from its normal control. Other agents which may conceivably play a similar role in the growth of specific cell-types are the unidentified substance detected by Bucher, Scott and Aub (1951) as associated with compensatory hypertrophy of the liver, and that responsible for the growth and protection of the bone-marrow (Jacobson 1952).

The mechanism proposed—the release of growth-promoting synthetic reactions or the accumulation of growth-promoting substrates by enzyme modification or loss—is by no means novel. Miller and Miller (1947) had already suggested that combination of an azo carcinogen and an autosynthetic protein could result in the gradual removal of this protein from the cell, the agent or its metabolites initiating the carcinogenic process through sublethal combinations with a critical protein in normal liver cells and their descendants: an autonomous tumor might thus be the outcome of a permanent alteration or loss of proteins essential for the control of growth. Potter (1950) also believes that there are certain enzymes of strategic importance in limiting the growth of normal cells, and postulates that it is the loss of these enzymes which marks the conversion from normal to malignant. Contrariwise, it appears not unreasonable to suppose that control can be effected by means of a self-imposed deficiency of a growth-factor, specialized cells thus preventing their own hypertrophy by a deficiency of building blocks which are also integral parts of the energy-transferring mechanism.

Potter (1944) had earlier considered cancer to result from the introduction of an abnormal protein, arising spontaneously in some cases, formed by the continued action of carcinogenic agents in others, and introduced into the cell in the case of tumors known to be of virus origin. This protein was assumed to be identical with an enzyme X except for the specific catalytic potency of the latter, this being regarded as a constituent of normally differentiated cells, possibly of the nature of a ribonucleoprotein complex of respiratory enzymes. The syntheses of both enzyme X and the new protein or virus were supposed to proceed autosynthetically, the results of competition between them being dependent on their relative concentrations. Potter's theory somewhat recalls the view that the essential change in carcinogenesis may not be enzyme elimination so much as the development of a "rogue" enzyme, and Rondoni's suggestion (1947; Rondoni and Barbieri 1950) that the interaction between carcinogen and cell protein may result, through a kind of denaturation, in transformation to an endogenous protein virus. Finally, Hoagland, Grier, and Hood (1950), discussing sarcoma production by beryllium in the light of the known effects of this metal in inhibiting alkaline phosphatase in vitro, raise the possibility that since the phosphatases control the level of organic phosphates which store energy for synthesis, any agent selectively inhibiting their hydrolytic action might be expected to increase synthetic activity.

Positive evidence of enzyme deficiency in tumor tissues is plentiful, although not infrequently misleading. As is pointed out by Rusch and Le Page (1948), loss of such enzymes as those of urea synthesis, in the transformation of liver cells to hepatoma, is not surprising since this represents a specialized system lost by the tumor. However, the absence of others cannot be explained on this basis. Thus Lan (1944) found no choline oxidase in an experimental hepatoma, and only a small fraction of the D-amino acid oxidase activity of liver; also, D-amino acid oxidase, choline oxidase, and uricase were absent in the Walker carcinosarcoma, and absence from tumors of cystine oxidase, exocystine desulfurase, and cysteine dehydropeptidase, has also been reported (Greenstein 1944, Greenstein and Leuthardt 1945). Again, Mitchell and Houlahan (1947) found an alternative pathway in *Neurospora* open to oxaloacetic acid, in which it is converted to a nucleic acid component (uracil) via orotic acid, a fact which might suggest, although there is no agreed evidence, that tumors could achieve increased pyrimidine synthesis through loss of the corresponding respiratory enzyme.

Before leaving the question of enzymatic deficiency in tumor tissues, it may be of value to recall—in view of the embryonic nature of tumors in general—Mendel and Mitchell's view that the absence or slow appearance during embryologic development of the oxidative and catabolic enzymes concerned in the transformation of the purines is a feature characteristic of active growth and synthesis (Needham 1931). Allfrey, Stern, and Mirsky (1952) have also compared enzyme distribution in embryonic and in adult tissues. In this work the most striking differences were found in fetal and adult intestinal epithelia, the cytoplasm of the adult mucosa cell, for example, having forty times the adenosine deaminase activity measured in the fetus. Increased activities in the adult cytoplasm were observed for all the enzymes studied. On the other hand, the relative nuclear activities were much higher in the fetal mucosa than in the adult. Such comparisons raise the problem as to which normal cell-type should be regarded as the precise homolog of the cancer cell, whether the differentiated adult cell, the differentiated embryonic cell, or the undifferentiated, pluripotent, or totipotent embryonic cell. Whichever viewpoint is most useful or most justified, there is no doubt of the urgent need for, or of the value which would accrue from, a more detailed and systematic study of enzyme distribution in embryonic and malignant cells than has been available hitherto.

Apart from observed enzyme deficiency in tumors, it is a question whether any clues may be derived from the inhibition of specific enzyme systems by carcinogens, and especially by the mustards. Needham (1948) found mustard gas not to be a general enzyme poison, out of some thirty enzymes examined only those of two well-defined groups being markedly inhibited—the phosphokinases (see also Bailey and Webb 1948), and a small group of proteinases. Of possibly special significance is the selective inhibition by nitrogen mustard of cholinesterases (Adams and Thompson 1948) and of other choline enzymes, in view of the claim by Barron, Bartlett, and Miller (1948) that in this case the mustards act as structural inhibitors, in contrast with their inhibition of other enzyme systems (including the phosphokinases), which requires greater concentrations and proceeds by combination with the various reactive groups of the protein moiety of the enzyme. According to these authors, inhibition of the oxidation of choline by choline oxidase, of the hydrolysis of acetylcholine by the esterase, or of the synthesis of acetylcholine by choline acetylase, is due in every case to structural inhibition, that is, inhibition through combination of the ethyleneimonium derivatives, structurally similar to choline, with the protein moiety of the enzyme at the same side chains where combination of choline or acetylcholine and protein normally takes place.

In the case of animal tumors there is, as yet, no evidence of the proposed substrate accumulation, or of overproduction of specific stimulants to growth, although Pullinger (1949) has suggested that mammary tumor cells may well produce an estrogen-like substance or "mammogen." Curiously enough, the clearest indication has so far come from the study of tumors in plants, even though the principle admittedly cannot be transferred to the case of animal tumors without some reserve. Nutritional studies indicate that bacteria-free crown gall tumor tissue possesses simpler requirements than do the tissues from which it is derived, and de Ropp (1951) offers three possible explanations, first that tumor tissue is equipped with a more nearly complete enzyme system, second that the process of tumor induction removes a growth inhibitor which limits the growth of healthy tissue, and lastly that the number of essential metabolites involved in the growth of tumor tissue may be smaller than in the case of normal tissue, the tumor being, therefore, less exacting. Furthermore, crown gall tumors produce many effects which are also shown by growth hormones such as indole acetic acid, and may exhibit "hyperauxiny." Estimations of the auxin content of *Helianthus tuberosus* and of *Scorzonera* by the *Avena* test showed substantial increases in the tumors as compared with the normal (Kulescha 1949, Kulescha and Gautheret 1948), and hence it seems possible (Braun 1947, Gautheret 1950) that enhancement of growth capacity may depend upon an ability to manufacture a growth hormone which may be either indole acetic acid or some kindred substance. It is of intense interest that the same result can follow prolonged treatment with a heteroauxin, through the phenomenon described by Limasset and Gautheret (1950) as *"accoutumance."*

Much of the above trend of reasoning, with specific reference to the genetic and enzymatic alterations responsible for the malignant transformation, finds its real basis in those studies of the genetic control of metabolism which are due to the schools of Fildes, Beadle, Tatum, and Ephrussi, and which have yielded almost innumerable examples of the relation of genes to the production of specific proteins or enzymes, with illustrations of deficiency or loss. Beadle (1952, also 1944-45, 1945, 1947, 1949) has concluded that the genetic or biochemical behavior of most mutant types in which biosynthetic processes are interrupted, is consistent with the hypothesis that enzymes, the specificities of which are gene-directed, serve as intermediaries between the genes and specific chemical reactions. While completely direct evidence is perhaps slight, enzyme modification or elimination could undoubtedly give rise to substrate accumulation of the kind envisaged, and as is indeed known to occur, as for example in the accumulation of 3-hydroxyanthranilic acid in *Neurospora* (see Bonner 1950, 1951.) In another classic case, indole was first shown to be converted to tryptophane in *Neurospora* in a single step by condensation with the amino-acid serine (Tatum and Bonner 1944), the condensation was then found to be governed by an enzyme requiring the presence of pyridoxal phosphate (Umbreit, Wood, and Gunsalus 1946), while finally Mitchell and Lein (1948) obtained a mutant blocked in the conversion of indole to tryptophane, and reported the enzyme, described by Umbreit *et al.,* to be lacking. The fact that single genes control single biochemical reactions led to the "1:1 hypothesis" (Horowitz, Bonner, Mitchell, Tatum and Beadle 1945, Horowitz and Leupold 1951), but in Bonner's view (1950) this tells us little concerning the mechanism of action, and is unsatisfactory on account of the cases in which enzyme production is influenced by several genes.

It will not have escaped the reader's attention that the possible role of enzyme deletion in carcinogenesis would indicate, for the first time, a specific difference between normal and malignant cells, with implications as to the means by which the process might ultimately be controlled, whether by enzyme substitution or the substitution of the reaction products of the substrate. That such a possibility is not wholly theoretical—even though it may be far from realization—is perhaps shown by three known examples of such substitution, one certainly referring to a situation simpler than the present, but all nevertheless capable of serving as suggestive and instructive models. The first, to which the writer's attention was directed by M. B. Goldblatt, refers to familial idiopathic methemoglobinemia, a condition belonging to the group of diseases, such as alcaptonuria and cystinuria, due to an inborn error of metabolism. In this disorder it has been possible to obtain evidence of a specific deficiency in the enzyme system of the erythrocytes, namely of coenzyme factor I, which is normally required, in addition to the enzymes and coenzyme I, for methemoglobin reduction through the oxidation of triosephosphate and lactate (Gibson 1948). The deficiency leads to an enzymatic reducing activity lower than that in normal cells, to a displacement of the normal hemoglobin:methemoglobin equilibrium, and to a consequent accumulation of abnormal amounts of methemoglobin in the blood. This failure is, however, restored by the addition of methylene blue, which, through cooperation with the coenzyme II dehydrogenases, brings about a great acceleration of methemoglobin reduction towards normal.

The second example arises from the genetic analysis of eye color in *Drosophila*, (Ephrussi and Beadle 1937, Ephrussi and Chevais 1937, 1938, Beadle, Clancy, and Ephrussi 1937, Ephrussi 1938, 1942 a, b), and in the flour-moth *Ephestia kühniella* (Butenandt). The wild form of the latter is marked by the dark brown pigmentation of the eyes of the moth and caterpillar, as well as of the skin and certain organs, due to the formation and deposition of the "ommochrome." By the spontaneous mutation of a single gene, a new race is formed which differs from the wild type in loss of the capacity to form pigment: the gene responsible for ommochrome formation is denoted as v^+, and the mutation defined as the change of this v^+ gene into its allele v. Butenandt (1951) has described how, if organs of the wild form, or, alternatively, ethanol-water extracts of the v^+-containing tissues, are transplanted or injected into the penultimate caterpillar stage of the pigment-deficient race, individuals are obtained capable of ommochrome formation, that is, the characters of the wild race reappear. Hence the tissues of the wild form contain an extractable substance, which is produced only under the influence of the v^+ gene, and which inserts itself between the gene and the external characteristic. It was next proved that this soluble pigment-forming substance is identical with the amino-acid kynurenin (Fig. 117; *o*-aminobenzoylalanine), already known as an intermediate product in the tryptophane metabolism of mammals. Since the degree of pigment formation was directly proportional to the kynurenin dose, it followed that kynurenin is not a catalyst in the process of pigment formation, but rather a building material or "chromogen" for the pigment molecule. In mammals, the degradation of tryptophane to kynurenin proceeds under the influence of the tryptophane-pyrrolase of the liver, this enzyme combining the function of a peroxidase and oxidase and probably transforming tryptophane *via* formyl kynurenin into kynurenin (Fig. 117).

An enzyme corresponding to tryptophane-pyrrolase also catalyses the change from tryptophane to the chromogen kynurenin in the wild form of *Ephestia*, a transformation which is hindered in the v mutant through enzyme deficiency. The function of the v⁺ gene would therefore appear to consist in rendering the active enzyme system available to the organism; mutation to v deprives the cell of the ability to achieve the normal enzyme-controlled degradation to kynurenin, and pigment formation is restored by artificial replacement of this single compound in

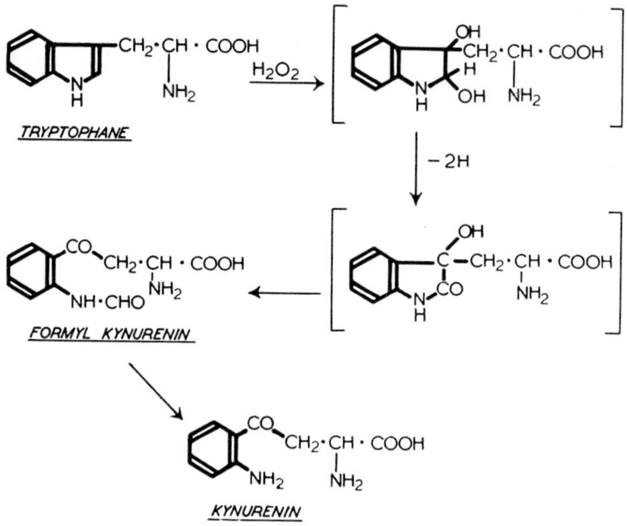

FIG. 117.

the reaction chain. These phenomena in the flour-moth have their exact parallel in *Drosophila* (Beadle, Ephrussi), where the red eye-color is controlled by the v^+ gene, and where the action is also dependent on kynurenin. A second gene in *Drosophila*, denoted by cn^+, has a similar effect, mutation to cn also leading to the loss of ommochrome formation. In this case, however, transplantation and injection

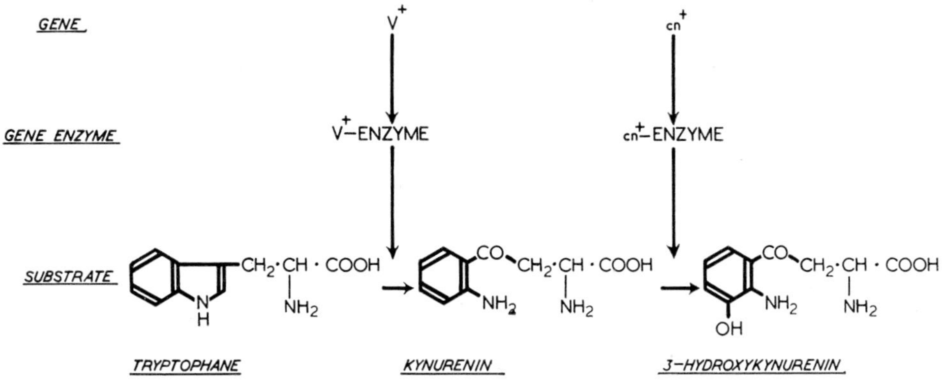

FIG. 118.

experiments have shown that the action of the cn^+ gene assumes the presence of the v^+ gene, and proceeds not through kynurenin but by way of 3-hydroxykynurenin (Fig. 118). Hence 3-hydroxykynurenin lies in a further part of the substrate chain tryptophane→pigment, and is produced from kynurenin only in tissues containing the cn^+ gene. It is therefore concluded that the gene reaction chain is as shown in Fig. 118, this scheme indicating not only how enzymes are influenced by genes in the stages of substrate modification, but also how various genes may cooperate in the development of a single phenotypic character. Butenandt emphasizes that many possibilities as to the detailed mechanism of gene action still remain open, first that the gene itself has the properties of an enzyme, and catalyses the dependent reaction, secondly that the gene produces the enzyme as a primary, secondary, or more distant product, and thirdly that the gene acts not on enzyme production but rather controls enzyme activity, as by the formation of specific activators or inhibitors. If none of these questions is as yet capable of an answer, and even though the genes and gene products concerned in malignant transformation remain completely unknown, there can be little doubt of the importance of these principles in our eventual understanding of the control and release of growth-promoting reactions.

The third example of the reconstitution of chemical, phenotypic, and, in this case, genetic characters, by the external supply of a specific chemical agent, arises from the induction by desoxyribonucleic acids of heritable change in bacteria and viruses, and had already been considered by the writer earlier (Haddow 1944). The phenomenon of the interconversion of types of *Pneumococcus* was first described by Griffith (1928), and depends upon the degradation of a given specific, virulent, "smooth" type (S), possessing the characteristic capsule with its polysaccharide antigens, into a nonspecific, avirulent, "rough" variant (R), lacking these features but convertible into the same or another specific and differentiated type (S) by growth in the presence of heat-killed S cells of the type to which conversion is desired. The transformation was afterwards achieved by means of sterile extracts of S cells (Alloway 1932, 1933), and represents one of the most striking examples of the artificial induction of heritable change.

The agent responsible for conversion was then recognized to be not the specific polysaccharide itself, but some other component of the S-type cell, and Avery and his co-workers (1944) isolated from type III pneumococci a desoxyribonucleic acid fraction capable of transforming unencapsulated R variants into fully encapsulated cells. Once transformation has occurred, the newly acquired characteristics are in this case transmitted, without any further addition of the transforming agent, and from the transformed cells a substance of identical activity can be recovered in amounts far in excess of that originally added, or needed, to induce the change.

The general principle has now been much extended (e.g., Alexander and Leidy 1950, 1951, Dianzani 1950, Ephrussi-Taylor 1951 a, b), and would seem to represent the incorporation of a gene product of one form into the genic material of another, and, effectively, directed mutation of the cell's enzymatic equipment by specifically oriented desoxyribonucleic acids. To what extent it can be applied in the transformation of animals cells is, of course, still quite unclear, although the possible involvement of desoxyribonucleic acids in the action of carcinogens suggests it may not be entirely without bearing. Certainly all these problems, whether involving animal cells or single-celled organisms, are essentially problems of re-differentiation, dependent for their solution on the possibility of bringing together complex compounds in such a way as to yield higher degrees of organization and complexity.

CONCLUSION

So far at least as the alkylating carcinogens are concerned, the theory of combination with genetic centers within the chromosome would, perhaps, appear to be that with the fewest assumptions, with the proviso that the action may be on elements shortly to be incorporated in the chromosome, through disruption of synthesis at sites rich in anions. As to the future, the conception of carcinogens as special kinds of "*Chromosomengifte*" will continue to be tested by more direct methods, amongst which the advances to be expected in micro-autoradiography should assist in defining with precision the sites of their action. More fundamentally, advance may largely depend upon growing knowledge of the macro- and micro-structure and molecular organization of the chromosome in relation to the cell cycle, and especially of the structure and permanence of the chromonema (Serra 1947 b, c, 1949; Ris 1947, Mirsky 1947, Ris and Mirsky 1949; Mazia *et al.* 1947; Kaufmann 1948; D'Angelo 1950; Mazia 1950; Pfeiffer 1950; Beams *et al.* 1950 a, b; Sedar and Wilson 1950; Manton 1950; Rozsa and Wyckoff 1950; Taylor 1951; Yasuzumi 1951, Yasazumi *et al.* 1951 a, b; Tomlin and Callan 1951; Barry 1952; Ambrose and Gopal-Ayengar 1952); of the relation between resting stage, prophase and anaphase chromosomes, and the known systems of protein folding and unfolding; of the basis for the specificity of attraction between chromosomes (Lindegren and Bridges 1938) and between identical molecules (Jehle 1950 a, b); of the nature of the intermolecular forces involved, and whether these act in autocatalytic reproduction between identical molecules (Jordan 1938, 1939 a, b, 1940), or by way of complementary structures (Pauling and Delbrück 1940); of the relation between the action of specific groups and bonds in proteins and the cooperative action of the whole molecule (Evans and Gergely 1949); and of the nature of the protein: nucleic acid association in replication, whether a function of nucleic acid may be to render rigid and insoluble the expanded monomolecular peptide layer of the template (Haurowitz 1949), or whether that of protein may be to protect the modulation of nucleic acid chains incorporating many different gene "codes" (Stern 1947). Much may be expected from a closer comparison of the enzyme equipment of embryonic, adult, and malignant cells, from studies of the influence of hormones on enzymes (cf. Dorfman, Goldsmith *et al.* 1951), and, no doubt by new technics, from investigation of the manner in which enzymatic deficiencies may be substituted or restored. Meantime, certain correlations are at any rate being approached, as for example between the chemical structure and properties of given carcinogens, their combination at certain chromosome regions, the cytologic effects so induced, and the genetic consequences to the cell which thus ensue. It is perhaps a measure of progress that while less than forty years ago the laboratory mouse was selected for the experimental study of carcinogenesis, on account of its high susceptibility, short life span, and ease of maintenance, the search should now be for biologic material with specially favorable cytology.

E. T. Whittaker's "postulates of impotence" referred to situations in which achievement is impossible, even though there be an infinite number of methods of approach, as for example the impossibility of obtaining work out of matter at a lower temperature than surrounding objects, or of measuring an absolute velocity in space. It might well be suspected whether the cancer problem falls in this category, representing as it does the case of a "natural" cellular adaptation of the most highly preferential kind. However, the advances of the past ten years indicate, with fair probability, that this is not so. That the action of certain carcinogens may be a fairly direct one on the gene, and that tumor production may be due to the resultant modification or elimination of the gene- or enzyme-mediated control of syntheses essential for cell-division and growth, opens up possibilities which may feasibly lead, in due time, to the chemical or enzymatic means of its reversal or control.

BIBLIOGRAPHY FOR CHAPTERS 16 AND 17

ADAMS, D. H., and THOMPSON, R. H. S. Selective inhibition of cholinesterases. *Biochem. J. 42:* 170-175, 1948.

ALEXANDER, H. E., and LEIDY, G. Transformation type specificity of *H. Influenzae. Proc. Soc. Exp. Biol. & Med. 73:* 485-487, 1950.

ALEXANDER, H. E., and LEIDY, G. Induction of heritable new type in type specific strains of H. influenzae. *Proc. Soc. Exper. Biol. & Med. 78:* 625-626, 1951.

ALEXANDER, P. Interference with the formation of a nucleoprotein complex by radiomimetic compounds. *Nature 169:* 226-227, 1952.

ALEXANDER, P., FOX, M., STACEY, K. A., and SMITH, L. F. The reactivity of radiomimetic compounds: I. Cross-linking of proteins. *Biochem. J. 52:* 177-184, 1952.

ALEXANDER, P., and WHEWELL, C. S. Some aspects of textile research in Germany. British Intelligence Objectives Sub-Committee, Final Report No. 1472, Item 22. London, H. M. Stationery Office, 1946.

ALLFREY, V., STERN, H., and MIRSKY, A. E. Some enzymes of isolated cell nuclei. *Nature 169:* 128-129, 1952.

ALLOWAY, J. L. Transformation *in vitro* of R pneumococci into S forms of different specific types by use of filtered pneumococcus extracts. *J. Exper. Med. 55:* 91-99, 1932.

ALLOWAY, J. L. Further observations on the use of pneumococcus extracts in effecting transformation of type *in vitro. J. Exper. Med 57:* 265-278, 1933.

AMBROSE, E. J., and GOPAL-AYENGAR, A. R. Molecular organizations in giant chromosomes. *Nature 169:* 652-653, 1952.

AMORY, H. I., and BUNCH, R. F. Perivascular injection of thorotrast and its sequelae. *Radiology 51:* 831-839, 1948.

ANDERSON, W. The emission of visible radiation from oxidation reactions of carcinogenic and related compounds. *Acta. Un. Int. Cancer 7:* 41-45, 1950.

ARMSTRONG, E. C., and BONSER, G. Epithelial tumours of the urinary bladder in mice induced by 2-acetyl-aminofluorene. *J. Path. & Bact. 56:* 507-512, 1944.

AUERBACH, C. The induction by mustard gas of chromosomal instabilities in *Drosophila melanogaster. Proc. Roy. Soc. Edin. s. B. 62:* 307-320, 1947.

AUERBACH, C. Chemical mutagenesis. *Biol. Rev. 24:* 355-391, 1949a.

AUERBACH, C. Chemical induction of mutations. *Proc. 8th Int. Congress of Genetics, Lund,* 128-147, 1949b.

AUERBACH, C. Differences between effects of chemical and physical mutagens. In *Pubbl. della Stazione Zoologica di Napoli. Suppl. Vol. 22:* 1-19, 1950.

AUERBACH, C., and FALCONER, D. S. A new mutant in the progeny of mice treated with nitrogen mustard. *Nature 163:* 678-679, 1949.

AUERBACH, C., and MOSER, H. Production of mutations by monochloro-"mustards". *Nature 166:* 1019-1020, 1950.

AUERBACH, C., and ROBSON, J. M. Production of mutations by allyl-*iso*-thiocyanate. *Nature 154:* 81, 1944.

AUERBACH, C., and ROBSON, J. M. Chemical production of mutations. *Nature 157:* 302, 1946.

AUERBACH, C., and ROBSON, J. M. The production of mutations by chemical substances. *Proc. Roy. Soc. Edin. s. B. 62:* 271-283, 1947a.

AUERBACH, C., and ROBSON, J. M. Tests of chemical substances for mutagenic action. *Proc. Roy. Soc. Edin. s. B. 62:* 284-291, 1947b.

AUERBACH, O., FRIEDMAN, M., WEISS, L., and AMORY, H. I. Extraskeletal osteogenic sarcoma arising in irradiated tissue. *Cancer 4:* 1095-1106, 1951.

AULD, S. J. M. Environmental cancer and petroleum. *J. Inst. Petroleum 36:* 235-253, 1950.

AVERY, O. T., MCLEOD, C. M., and MCCARTY, M. Studies on the chemical nature of the substances inducing transformation of pneumococcal types: Induction of transformation by a desoxyribonucleic acid fraction isolated from pneumococcus type III. *J. Exper. Med. 79:* 137-157, 1944.

BACHMANN, W. E., KENNAWAY, E. L., and KENNAWAY, N. M. Rapid production of tumours by two new hydrocarbons. *Yale J. Biol. & Med. 11:* 97-102, 1938.

BACQ, Z. M., and DESREUX, V. Action of vesicants and other war poisons on proteins and enzymes. In M. Polonovski, ed.: *Exposés annuels de biochimie médicale, Series 8*, 67-82. Paris, Masson, 1948.

BADGER, G. M. The relative reactivity of aromatic double bonds. *J. Chem. Soc.* 456-463, 1949a.

BADGER, G. M. An interpretation of some elimination reactions in disubstituted dihydro-derivatives of aromatic compounds. *J. Chem. Soc.* 2497-2501, 1949b.

BADGER, G. M. Addition of osmium tetroxide to dinaphthylethylenes. *Nature 165:* 647-649, 1950.

BADGER, G. M., and LEWIS, G. E. Rates of oxidation of azonaphthalenes. *Nature 167:* 403-404, 1951.

BADGER, G. M., and LYNN, K. R. The relative reactivity of aromatic double bonds: II. Addition of osmium tetroxide to substituted 1:2-benzanthracenes. *J. Chem. Soc.* 1726-1729, 1950.

BADGER, G. M., PEARCE, R. S., and PETTIT, R. Polynuclear heterocyclic systems: I. Introduction. *J. Chem. Soc.* 3199-3203, 1951a.

BADGER, G. M., PEARCE, R. S., and PETTIT, R. Polynuclear heterocyclic systems: II. Hydroxy-derivatives. *J. Chem. Soc.* 3204-3207, 1951b.

BADGER, G. M., and PETTIT, R. Polynuclear heterocyclic systems: IV. The linear pentacyclic compounds. *J. Chem. Soc.* 3211-3215, 1951.

BADGER, G. M., and REED, R. I. Relative reactivity of aromatic double bonds. *Nature 161:* 238, 1948.

BADGER, G. M., SEIDLER, J. H., and THOMSON, B. Polynuclear heterocyclic systems: III. The 3:4-benzacridine-5:10-dihydro-3:4-benzacridine complex. *J. Chem. Soc.* 3207-3211, 1951.

BAETJER, A. M. Pulmonary carcinoma in chromate workers: I. A review of the literature and report of cases. *Arch. Indust. Hyg. 2:* 487-504, 1950a.

BAETJER, A. M. Pulmonary carcinoma in chromate workers: II. Incidence on basis of hospital records. *Arch. Indust. Hyg. 2:* 505-516, 1950b.

BAILEY, K., and WEBB, E. C. Purification of yeast hexokinase and its reaction with ββ′-dichlorodiethylsulphide. *Biochem. J. 42:* 60-68, 1948.

BAKER, J. R., and CALLAN, H. G. Heterochromatin. *Nature 166:* 227-228, 1950.

BALDOCK, G., BERTHIER, G., and PULLMAN, A. The electronic structure of aromatic hydrocarbons with five adjoining benzene nuclei: Study by the method of molecular orbitals. *Compt. rend. Acad. d. sc. 228:* 931-933, 1948.

BALL, E. G., DAVIS, S., and ROSS, W. F. OSRD Formal Report No. 1630, June 7, 1943.

BANKS, T. E., BOURSNELL, J. C., FRANCIS, G. E., HOPWOOD, F. L., and WORMALL, A. Studies on mustard gas (ββ′-dichlorodiethyl sulphide) and some related compounds: 4. Their action on proteins (studied with the aid of radioactive sulphur). *Biochem. J. 40:* 745-756, 1946.

BARNES, J. M. Experimental production of malignant tumours by beryllium. *Lancet 1:* 463, 1950.

BARRATT, R. W., and TATUM, E. L. An evaluation of some carcinogens as mutagens. *Cancer Research 11:* 234, 1951.

BARRON, E. S. G., BARTLETT, G. R., and MILLER, Z. B. The effect of nitrogen mustards on enzymes and tissue metabolism: I. The effect on enzymes. *J. Exper. Med. 87:* 489-501, 1948.

BARRON, E. S. G., BARTLETT, G. R., MILLER, Z. B., MEYER, J., and SEEGMILLER, J. E. The effect of nitrogen mustards on enzymes and tissue metabolism: II. The effect on tissue metabolism. *J. Exper. Med. 87:* 503-519, 1948.

BARRON, E. S. G., SEEGMILLER, J. E., MENDES, E. G., and NARAHARA, H. T. The effect of nitrogen mustards on the respiration and fertilization of sea urchin sperm and eggs. *Biol. Bull. 94:* 267-274, 1948.

BARRY, G., COOK, J. W., HASLEWOOD, G. A. D., HEWETT, C. L., HIEGER, I., and KENNAWAY, E. L. Production of cancer by pure hydrocarbons: III. *Proc. Roy. Soc. s. B. 117:* 318-351, 1935.

BARRY, J. Chromosomes. *Biol. méd. Paris 41:* 1-84, 1952.

BASS, A. D., and FEIGELSON, M. The response of normal and malignant lymphoid tissue to methyl bis(β-chloroethyl)amine and ethyl carbamate in adrenalectomized and non-adrenalectomized mice. *Cancer Research 8:* 503-508, 1948.

BASS, A. D., and FREEMAN, M. L. H. Response of certain mouse tumours to mustard gas. *J. Nat. Cancer Inst. 7:* 171-176, 1946.

BATEMAN, A. J., and SINCLAIR, W. K. Mutations induced in *Drosophila* by ingested phosphorus^{32}. *Nature 165:* 117-118, 1950.

BAUER, K. H. Thorotrast injury and danger of sarcoma from thorotrast. *Chirurg. 19:* 387-389, 1948.

BEADLE, G. W. The genetic control of biochemical reactions. *Harvey Lectures, Series 40,* 179-194, 1944-45.

BEADLE, G. W. Biochemical genetics. *Chem. Rev. 37:* 15-96, 1945.

BEADLE, G. W. Genes and the chemistry of the organism. *Science in Progress 5:* 166, 1947.

BEADLE, G. W. Genes and biological enigmas. *Science in Progress 6:* 184-249, 1949.

BEADLE, G. W. Genetic control of metabolism. First *R. E. Dyer Lecture,* Federal Security Agency. Public Health Service Publication No. 142, National Institutes of Health. U. S. Government Printing Office, Washington, D. C., 1952.

BEADLE, G. W., CLANCY, C. W., and EPHRUSSI, B. Development of eye colours in *Drosophila*: Pupal transplants and the influence of body fluid on vermilion. *Proc. Roy. Soc. s. B. 122:* 98-105, 1937.

BEALE, R. N., and ROE, E. M. F. Ultraviolet absorption spectra of some metabolites of naphthalene, anthracene and phenanthrene. *J. Chem. Soc.* 2884-2888, 1951.

BEAMS, H. W., EVANS, T. C., VAN BREEMEN, V., and BAKER, W. W. Electron microscope studies on the structure of mitotic figure. *Proc. Soc. Exper. Biol. & Med. 74:* 717-720, 1950a.

BEAMS, H. W., EVANS, T. C., BAKER, W. W., and VAN BREEMEN, V. Electron micrographs of the amphiaster in the whitefish blastula (*Coregonus cluperformis*). *Anat. Rec. 107:* 329-345, 1950b.

BECKER, R. M. Suppression of local tissue reactivity (Schwartzman phenomenon) by nitrogen mustard, benzol and X-ray irradiation. *Proc. Soc. Exper. Biol. & Med. 69:* 247-250, 1948.

BEER, C. T., DICKENS, F., and PEARSON, J. The aromatization of hydrogenated derivatives of benzoic acid in animal tissues. *Biochem. J. 48:* 222-237, 1951.

BERENBLUM, I. 3:4-Benzpyrene from coal tar. *Nature 156:* 601, 1945.

BERENBLUM, I. In *Twenty-third Annual Report of the British Empire Cancer Campaign*, 106-109, 1946.

BERENBLUM, I. Mechanism of skin carcinogenesis. *Acta Un. Int. Cancer 6:* 16-19, 1948.

BERENBLUM, I. The biological mechanism of carcinogenesis. *Papal Academy Conference* 1-13, 1949.

BERENBLUM, I., and SCHÖNTAL, R. Carcinogenic constituents of shale oil. *Brit. J. Exper. Path. 24:* 232-239, 1943.

BERENBLUM, I., and SCHÖNTAL, R. The metabolism of 3:4-benzpyrene into 8- and 10-benzpyrenols in the animal body. *Cancer Research 6:* 699-704, 1946.

BERENBLUM, I., and SCHÖNTAL, R. The metabolism of chrysene: The isolation of 3-methoxy-chrysene by methylation of the phenolic metabolite of chrysene from rat faeces. *Biochem. J. 44:* 604-606, 1949.

BERENBLUM, I., and SHUBIK, P. A new, quantitative approach to the study of the stages of chemical carcinogenesis in the mouse's skin. *Brit. J. Cancer 1:* 383-396, 1947.

BERENBLUM, I., and SHUBIK, P. An experimental study of the initiating stage of carcinogenesis, and a re-examination of the somatic cell mutation theory of cancer. *Brit. J. Cancer 3:* 109-118, 1949a.

BERENBLUM, I., and SHUBIK, P. The persistence of latent tumour cells induced in the mouse's skin by a single application of 9:10-dimethyl-1:2-benzanthracene. *Brit. J. Cancer 3:* 384-386, 1949b.

BERGMANN, F. On the mechanism of tumour production by chemical agents. *Cancer Research 2:* 660-663, 1942.

BERMAN, C. Primary carcinoma of the liver among the Bantu mineworkers of the Witwatersrand. *Proc. Transvaal Mine Med. Officers' Assoc., 30:* 13-32, 1950.

BERMAN, C. *Primary Carcinoma of the Liver: A Study in Incidence, Clinical Manifestations, Pathology and Aetiology.* London, H. K. Lewis & Co. Ltd., 1951.

BERTHIER, G., COULSON, C. A., GREENWOOD, H. H., and PULLMAN, A. The electronic structure of aromatic hydrocarbons with four adjoining benzene nuclei. Study by the method of molecular orbitals. *Compt, rend. Acad. d. sc. 226:* 1906-1908, 1948.

BESTIAN, H. Some reactions of ethyleneimine. *Liebig's Annalen 566:* 210-244, 1950.

BHATTACHARYA, S. A test for mutagenicity of methylcholanthrene. *Nature 162:* 573, 1948.

BIDSTRUP, P. L. Cancer of the lung in nickel, arsenic and chromate workers. *Arch. belges Méd. Soc. 8:* 500-506, 1950.

BIDSTRUP, P. L. Carcinoma of the lung in chromate workers. *Brit. J. Indust. Med. 4:* 302-305, 1951.

BIELSCHOWSKY, F. Distant tumours produced by 2-amino- and 2-acetyl-aminofluorene. *Brit. J. Exper. Path. 25:* 1-4, 1944.

BIELSCHOWSKY, F. The carcinogenic action of 2-acetyl-aminofluorene and related compounds. *Brit. M. Bull. 4:* 382-385, 1947.

BIELSCHOWSKY, F. The role of thyroxine deficiency in the formation of experimental tumours of the thyroid. *Brit. J. Cancer 3:* 547-549, 1949.

BIELSCHOWSKY, F., and GREEN, H. N. An induced carcinoma in the fowl. *Nature 156:* 780, 1945.

BIELSCHOWSKY, F., GRIESBACH, W. E., HALL, W. H., KENNEDY, T. H., and PURVES, H. D. Studies on experimental goitre: the transplantability of experimental thyroid tumours of the rat. *Brit. J. Cancer 3:* 541-546, 1949.

BIELSCHOWSKY, F., and HALL, W. H. Carcinogenesis in parabiotic rats: Tumours of liver and seminal vesicle induced by acetylaminofluorene in normal males joined to castrated males or females. *Brit. J. Cancer 5:* 106-114, 1951a.

BIELSCHOWSKY, F., and HALL, W. H. Carcinogenesis in parabiotic rats: Tumours of the ovary induced by acetylaminofluorene in intact females joined to gonadectomized litter-mates, and the reaction of their pituitaries to endogenous oestrogens. *Brit. J. Cancer 5:* 331-334, 1951b.

BIESELE, J. J., PHILIPS, F. S., THIERSCH, J. B., BURCHENAL, J. H., BUCKLEY, S. M., and STOCK, C. C. Chromosome alteration and tumour inhibition by nitrogen mustards: the hypothesis of cross-linking alkylation. *Nature 166:* 1112-1113, 1950.

BING, J., FAGRAEUS, A., and THORELL, B. Studies on nucleic acid metabolism in plasma cells. *Acta physiol. Scandinav. 10:* 282-294, 1945.

BIRD, M. J. Production of mutations in *Drosophila* using four aryl-2-halogenoalkylamines. *Nature 165:* 491-492, 1950.

BIRD, M. J. Chemical production of mutations in *Drosophila*: Comparison of techniques. *J. Genet. 50:* 480-485, 1952.

BIRD, M. J., and FAHMY, O. G. Cytogenetic analysis of the action of carcinogens and tumour inhibitors in *Drosophila melanogaster*: I. 1:2,3:4-Diepoxybutane. *Proc. Roy. Soc. s. B. 140:* 556-578, 1953.

BIRKNER, R. Late injuries from thorotrast, judged from the oldest known case of such injury. *Strahlenther. 78:* 587-608, 1949.

BISKIND, M. S., and BISKIND, G. R. Development of tumors in the rat ovary after transplantation into the spleen. *Proc. Soc. Exper. Biol. & Med. 55:* 176-179, 1944.

BJORKSTEN, J. Cross-linkages in protein chemistry. In *Advances in Protein Chemistry 6:* 343-381, 1951.

BJØRNEBOE, M., GORMSEN, H., and LUNDQUIST, FR. Further experimental studies on the role of the plasma cell as antibody producers. *J. Immunol. 55:* 121-129, 1947.

BLANDING, F. H., KING, W. H., PRIESTLEY, W., and RAYNER, J. Properties of high-boiling petroleum products. Quantitative analysis of tumor-response data obtained from the application of refinery products to the skin of mice. *Arch. Indust. Hyg. 4:* 335-345, 1951.

BLOCH, B., and DREYFUS, W. The experimental production of carcinomata with lymph nodes and lung metastases, by means of coal tar components. *Schweiz. med. Wchnschr. 51:* 1033-1037, 1921.

Bloom, M. A., and Bloom, W. Late effects of radium and plutonium on bone. *Arch. Path. 47:* 494-511, 1949.

Blum, H. F. On the mechanism of cancer induction by ultraviolet radiation. *J. Nat. Cancer Inst. 11:* 463-495, 1950.

Bodenstein, D. Chemical alteration of development in *Drosophila. Anat. Rec. 99:* 590, 1947.

Bodenstein, D. The effects of nitrogen mustard on embryonic amphibian development: II. Effects on eye development. *J. Exper. Zool. 108:* 93-125, 1948.

Bodenstein, D., and Goldin, A. A comparison of the effects of various nitrogen mustard compounds on embryonic cells. *J. Exper. Zool. 108:* 75-91, 1948.

Bodenstein, D., and Kondritzer, A. A. The effect of nitrogen mustard on nucleic acids during embryonic amphibian development. *J. Exper. Zool. 107:* 109-121, 1948.

Boissonnas, R. A., Turner, R. A., and du Vigneaud, V. Metabolic study of the methyl groups of butter yellow. *J. Biol. Chem. 180:* 1053-1058, 1949.

Bonner, D. M. Genes and biochemical reactions. J. Alexander, ed.: In *Colloid Chemistry, Theoretical and Applied 7:* 277-294. New York, Reinhold, 1950.

Bonner, D. M. Gene-enzyme relationships in *Neurospora. Cold Spring Harbor Symp. Quant. Biol. 16:* 143-154, 1951.

Bonser, G. M. Epithelial tumours of the bladder in dogs induced by pure β-naphthylamine. *J. Path. & Bact. 55:* 1-6, 1943.

Bonser, G. M., Clayson, D. B., and Jull, J. W. An experimental inquiry into the cause of industrial bladder cancer. *Lancet 2:* 286-288, 1951.

Booth, J., and Boyland, E. Metabolism of naphthalene. *Biochem. J. 41:* xxix-xxx, 1947.

Booth, J., and Boyland, E. Metabolism of polycyclic compounds: V. Formation of 1:2-dihydroxy-1:2-dihydronaphthalenes. *Biochem. J. 44:* 361-365, 1949.

Booth, J., Boyland, E., and Turner, E. E. The optical resolution of (±)-trans-9:10-dihydroxy-9:10-dihydrophenanthrene. *J. Chem. Soc.* 2808-2810, 1950.

Bourne, H. G., and Yee, H. T. Occupational cancer in a chromate plant. *Indust. Med. 19:* 563-567, 1950.

Boursnell, J. C., Francis, G. E., and Wormall, A. Studies on mustard gas (ββ'-dichlorodiethyl sulphide) and some related compounds: 2. The action of mustard gas, ββ'-dichlorodiethyl sulphone and divinyl sulphone on amino-acids. *Biochem. J. 40:* 737-742, 1946.

Boyland, E. The pharmacology of chloroethylamines. *Biochem. Soc. Symp. No. 2* 61-70, 1948.

Boyland, E. The structure of chemical carcinogens. *Acta. Un. Int. Cancer 7:* 59-67, 1950a.

Boyland, E. The biological significance of the metabolism of polycyclic compounds. In R. T. Williams, ed.: *Biological Oxidation of Aromatic Rings. Biochem. Soc. Symp. No. 5*, Cambridge, pp. 40-54, 1950b.

Boyland, E., and Brues, A. M. The carcinogenic action of dibenzcarbazoles. *Proc. Roy. Soc. s. B. 122:* 429-441, 1937.

Boyland, E., and Horning, E. S. The induction of tumours with nitrogen mustards. *Brit. J. Cancer, 3:* 118-123 (1949).

Boyland, E., and Levi, A. A. Metabolism of polycyclic compounds: I. Dihydroxy-dihydro-anthracene from anthracene. *Biochem. J. 29:* 2679-2683, 1935.

Boyland, E., and Sargent, S. The local greying of hair in mice treated with X-rays and radiomimetic drugs. *Brit. J. Cancer 5:* 433-440, 1951.

Boyland, E., and Shoppee, C. W. The metabolism of polycyclic compounds: The configuration of the dihydroxy-dihydro-anthracenes produced from anthracene. *J. Chem. Soc.* 801-804, 1947.

Boyland, E., and Weigert, F. Metabolism of carcinogenic compounds. *Brit. M. Bull. 4:* 354-359, 1947.

Boyland, E., and Wolf, G. Metabolism of phenanthrene. *Biochem. J. 42:* xxxii, 1948.

Boyland, E., and Wolf, G. Metabolism of polycyclic compounds: VI. Conversion of phenanthrene into dihydroxy-dihydro-phenanthrenes. *Biochem. J. 47:* 64-69, 1950.

Brachet, J. Biochemical and physiological interrelations between nucleus and cytoplasm during early development. *Growth 11:* 309-324, 1947.

Brachet, J. A cytochemical study of nucleated and enucleated fragments of amoebae. *Experientia 6:* 294-295, 1950.

Bradley, W. Carcinogenic activity and substantivity. *Nature 137:* 404-405, 1936.

Braun, A. C. Recent advances in the physiology of tumor formation in the crown-gall disease of plants. *Growth 11:* 325-327, 1947.

Brown, Helen. *Nature 165:* 586, 1950.

Brown, C. H. A review of the methods available for the determination of the types of forces stabilizing structural proteins in animals. *Quart. J. Micr. Sc. 91:* 331-339, 1950.

Brues, A. M. Biological hazards and toxicity of radioactive isotopes. *J. Clin. Investigation 28:* 1286-1296, 1949.

Brues, A. M. Carcinogenic effects of radiation. In J. H. Laurence and J. G. Hamilton, eds.: *Advances in Biology and Medical Physics 2:* 171-191, 1951.

Brues, A. M., Lisco, H., and Finkel, M. P. Carcinogenic action of some substances which may be a problem in certain future industries. *Cancer Research 7:* 48-49, 1947.

Brues, A. M., and Sacher, G. A. The significance of time-dose relationships in carcinogenesis. *Cancer Research 11:* 240, 1951.

Brues, A. M., Sacher, G. A., Finkel, M. P., and Lisco, H. Comparative carcinogenic effects by X radiation and P-32. *Cancer Research 9:* 545, 1949.

Bryson, V. The effects of nitrogen mustard on *Escherichia coli. J. Bact. 56:* 423-433, 1948.

Bucher, N. L. R., Scott, J. F., and Aub, J. C. Regeneration of the liver in parabiotic rats. *Cancer Research 11:* 457-465, 1951.

Buckley, S. M., Stock, C. C., Crossley, M. L., and Rhoads, C. P. Inhibition of the Crocker mouse sarcoma 180 by certain ethyleneimine derivatives and related compounds. *Cancer 5:* 144-152, 1952.

Bukantz, S. C., Dammin, G. J., Wilson, K. S., and Johnson, M. C. The inhibitory effect of nitrogen mustard on the development of humoral antibodies, cutaneous hypersensitiveness and vascular lesions in rabbits following injections of horse serum. *J. Lab. & Clin. Med. 33:* 1463-1464, 1948.

Bukantz, S. C., Dammin, G. J., Wilson, K. S., Johnson, M. C., and Alexander, H. L. Inhibitory effect of nitrogen mustard (*bis* beta-chloroethyl amine) on experimental serum hypersensitiveness. *Proc. Soc. Exper. Biol. & Med. 72:* 21-26, 1949.

Bullough, W. S. Mitotic activity and carcinogenesis. *Brit. J. Cancer 4:* 329-336, 1950.

Burchenal, J. H. The newer nitrogen mustards in the treatment of leukemia. *Radiology, 50:* 494-499, 1948.

Burchenal, J. H., Burchenal, J. R., and Johnston, S. F. Chemotherapy of leukemia: III. Further studies on the effect of nitrogen mustards and related compounds on transmitted mouse leukemia. *Cancer 4:* 353-356, 1951.

Burchenal, J. H., Crossley, M. L., Stock, C. C., and Rhoads, C. P. The action of certain ethyleneimine (aziridine) derivatives on mouse leukemia. *Arch. Biochem. 26:* 321-323, 1950.

Burchenal, J. H., Johnston, S. F., Cremer, M. A., Webber, L. F., and Stock, C. C. Chemotherapy of leukemia: V. Effects of 2, 4, 6-triethyleneiminotriazine and related compounds on transplanted mouse leukemia. *Proc. Soc. Exper. Biol. & Med. 74:* 708-712, 1950.

Burchenal, J. H., Lester, R. A., Riley, J. B., and Rhoads, C. P. Studies on the chemotherapy of leukemia: I. Effect of certain nitrogen mustards and carbamates on transmitted mouse leukemia. *Cancer 1:* 399-412, 1948.

Burchenal, J. H., and Riley, J. B. Relation between structure and activity in the nitrogen mustards. *Cancer Research 9:* 553-554, 1949.

Burchenal, J. H., Riley, J. B., and Lester, R. A. Studies on the chemotherapy of transmitted leukemia in mice. *Acta Un. int. Canc. 6:* 448-450, 1949.

Burdette, W. J. The lethal mutation rate in *Drosophila melanogaster* following the administration of 20-methylcholanthrene and methyl-bis(β-chloroethyl)amine hydrochloride. *Cancer Research 9:* 594, 1949.

Burdette, W. J. Lethal mutation rate following serial administration of methyl-bis(β-chloroethyl)amine hydrochloride. *Genetics* 35: 99, 1950a.

Burdette, W. J. Tumors and mutations in *Drosophila. Tex. Rep. Biol. & Med. 8:* 123-133, 1950b.

Burdette, W. J. Comparison of mutation rate and tumor incidence in *Drosophila* treated with chemicals. *Genetics 35:* 658-659, 1950c.

Burdette, W. J. Tumor incidence and lethal mutation rate in *Drosophila* following treatment with formaldehyde. *Cancer Research 11:* 241, 1951.

Burnet, F. M., and Fenner, F. *The Production of Antibodies* (ed. 2). London, Macmillan, 1949.

Burnop, V. C. E., Richards, D. E., Watkins, W. M., and Wormall, A. Combination of nitrogen-15-labelled nitrogen mustard with proteins. *Nature 168:* 251-252, 1951.

Burrows, H., Cook, J. W., Roe, E. M. F., and Warren, F. L. Isolation of $\Delta^{3:5}$-Androstadiene-17-one from the urine of a man with a malignant tumour of the adrenal cortex. *Biochem. J. 31:* 950-961, 1937.

Burrows, H., and Horning, E. S. Oestrogens and neoplasia. *Brit. M. Bull. 4:* 367-377, 1947.

Burrows, H., and Horning, E. S. *Oestrogens and Neoplasia.* Oxford, Blackwell Scientific Publications, 1952.

Butenandt, A. The mode of action of hereditary factors. In *Jahrbuch der Max-Planck-Ges.* 160-174, 1951.

Butler, J. A. V. Nature of nucleotoxic substances. *Nature 166:* 18-19, 1950.

Butler, J. A. V., and Conway, B. E. The action of ionizing radiations and of radiomimetic chemicals on deoxyribonucleic acid: II. The effect of oxygen on the degradation of the nucleic acid by X-rays. *J. Chem. Soc.* 3418-3421, 1950.

Butler, J. A. V., Conway, B. E., Gilbert, L., and Smith, K. A. Chemical analogies in the action of ionizing radiations and of radiomimetic chemicals on nucleic acid. *Acta Un. int. Canc. 7:* 443-446, 1951.

BUTLER, J. A. V., GILBERT, L., JAMES, D. W. F., and ROSS, W. C. J. Degradation of deoxyribonucleic acid by a "nitrogen mustard." *Nature 168:* 985-986, 1951.

BUTLER, J. A. V., GILBERT, L., and SMITH, K. A. Radiomimetic action of sulphur and nitrogen "mustards" on deoxyribonucleic acid. *Nature 165:* 714-716, 1950.

BUTLER, J. A. V., and SMITH, K. A. The action of ionizing radiations and of radiomimetic chemicals on deoxyribonucleic acid: I. The action of some compounds of the "mustard" type. *J. Chem. Soc.* 3411-3418, 1950a.

BUTLER, J. A. V., and SMITH, K. A. Degradation of deoxyribonucleic acid by free radicals. *Nature 165:* 847-848, 1950b.

BUU-HOÏ, N. P. The chemistry of carcinogenic nitrogen compounds: III. Polysubstituted pyrroles and indoles as potential cocarcinogens. *J. Chem. Soc.* 2882-2888, 1948.

BUU-HOÏ, N. P. The chemistry of carcinogenic nitrogen compounds: II. Further derivatives of 1:2- and 3:4-benzacridines. *J. Chem. Soc.* 670-676, 1949.

BUU-HOÏ, N. P. The chemistry of carcinogenic nitrogen compounds: IV. New substituted angular benzacridines and dibenzacridines. *J. Chem. Soc.* 1146-1152, 1950a.

BUU-HOÏ, N. P. The chemistry of carcinogenic nitrogen compounds: V. Angular hydroxybenzacridines and hydroxydibenzacridines. *J. Chem. Soc.* 2096-2099, 1950b.

BUU-HOÏ, N. P. Carcinogenic nitrogen compounds: VIII. *J. Chem. Soc.* 2871-2873, 1951.

BUU-HOÏ, N. P., CAGNIANT, P., HOÁN, N., and KHÔI, N. H. Potential nitrogenheterocycle carcinogens: VI. Poly-substituted 1,2-benzcarbazoles, 1, 2, 5, 6- and 1, 2, 7, 8-dibenzocarbazoles. *J. Org. Chem. 15:* 950-956, 1950.

BUU-HOÏ, N. P., DAUDEL, P., DAUDEL, R., LACASSAGNE, A., LECOCQ, J., MARTIN, M., and RUDALI, G. An attempt at prediction of the carcinogenicity of chemical substances. *Compt. rend. Acad. d. sc. 225:* 238-240, 1947.

BUU-HOÏ, N. P., DAUDEL, P., DAUDEL, R., and VROELANT, C. Application of the method of molecular diagrams to the study of the reactivity of organic molecules: III. Some condensed aromatic hydrocarbons. *Bull. Soc. chim. Fr. 16:* 211-246, 1949.

BUU-HOÏ, N. P., and HOÁN, N. Potential nitrogen-heterocycle carcinogens: XII. 9-Ethylcarbazole-3-aldehyde and its derivatives. *J. Org. Chem. 16:* 1327-1332, 1951a.

BUU-HOÏ, N. P., and HOÁN, N. Carcinogenic nitrogen compounds: VII. *J. Chem. Soc.* 2868-2870, 1951b.

BUU-HOÏ, N. P., HOÁN, N., and KHÔI, N. H. Carcinogenic derivatives of carbazole: I. The synthesis of 1,2,7,8-, 1,2,5,6- and 3,4,5,6-dibenzocarbazole and some of their derivatives. *J. Org. Chem. 14:* 492-497, 1949.

BUU-HOÏ, N. P., HOÁN, N., and KHÔI, N. H. Potential nitrogen-heterocycle carcinogens: IV. Synthesis of 2, 3-benzocarbazoles and of indenoindoles. *J. Org. Chem. 15:* 131-134, 1950a.

BUU-HOÏ, N. P., HOÁN, N., and KHÔI, N. H. Potential nitrogen-heterocycle carcinogens: VII. Polycyclic carbazoles bearing ethyl groups, and thiophene isosters thereof. *J. Org. Chem. 15:* 957-961, 1950b.

BUU-HOÏ, N. P., HOÁN, N., KHÔI, N. H., and XUONG, N. D. Carcinogenic derivatives of carbazole: II. Isosteric compounds of carbazole containing a thiophene nucleus. *J. Org. Chem. 14:* 802-812, 1949.

BUU-HOÏ, N. P., HOÁN, N., KHÔI, N. H., and XUONG, N. D. Potential nitrogenheterocycle carcinogens: VIII. Polycyclic carbazoles with phenolic groups. *J. Org. Chem. 15:* 962-965, 1950.

BUU-HOÏ, N. P., HOÁN, N., KHÔI, N. H., and XUONG, N. D. Potential nitrogenhetero-cycle carcinogens: IX. Halogen-containing angular benzo- and dibenzcarbazoles, and their thiophene analogs. *J. Org. Chem. 16:* 309-314, 1951.

BUU-HOÏ, N. P., and JACQUIGNON, P. Carcinogenic nitrogen compounds: IX. *J. Chem. Soc.* 2964-2968, 1951.

BUU-HOÏ, N. P., and ROYER, R. Potential nitrogen-heterocycle carcinogens: III. New derivatives of N-ethylcarbazole. *J. Org. Chem. 15:* 123-130, 1950.

BUU-HOÏ, N. P., and ROYER, R. Carcinogenic nitrogen compounds: VI. Derivatives of 1:2- and 3:4-benzophenarsazines. *J. Chem. Soc.* 795-798, 1951.

CAGNIANT, P., and CAGNIANT, D. Research in the field of cholanthrene hydrocarbons: I. Some modifications in Fieser's and Seligman's method of synthesis of methyl-20-cholanthrene. *Bull. Soc. chim. Fr.* 1012-1014, 1948.

CAHAN, W. G., WOODARD, H. Q., HIGINBOTHAM, N. L., STEWART, F. W., and COLEY, B. L. Eleven cases in which osteogenic sarcoma developed in irradiated bones 6-22 years after roentgen or radiation therapy. *Cancer 1:* 3-29, 1948.

CAMERON, G. R., COURTICE, F. C., and JONES, R. P. The effects of $\beta\beta'$-dichlorodiethyl methylamine hydrochloride on the blood-forming tissues. *J. Path. & Bact. 54:* 425-435, 1947.

CAMPBELL, B., and GOOD, R. A. Antigen-antibody mechanisms in neurotropic virus diseases. *Ann. Allergy 7:* 471-481, 1949.

CAMPBELL, H., and JOHNSON, P. Aging of solutions of cellulose nitrate. *J. Polym. Sci. 5:* 443-463, 1950.

CAPP, C. W., and SPEAKMAN, J. B. The cross-linking of animal fibres: I. 3,4-Isopropylidene-1,2,5,6-dianhydromannitol. *J. Soc. Dy. Col. 65:* 402-406, 1949.

CARPENTER, F. H., WOOD, J. L., STEVENS, C. M., and DU VIGNEAUD, V. Chemical studies on vesicant-treated proteins. *J. Am. Chem. Soc. 70:* 2551-2553, 1948.

CASON, J., and FIESER, L. F. Synthesis of 4′, 8′-dihydroxy-1,2,5,6-dibenzanthracene and its relation to products of metabolism and hydrocarbon. *J. Am. Chem. Soc. 62:* 2681-2687, 1940.

CASPERSSON, T. The relations between nucleic acid and protein synthesis. *Symp. Soc. Exper. Biol. 1 (Nucleic acid)* 127-151, 1947.

CASPERSSON, T., and SANTESSON, L. Studies on protein metabolism in the cells of epithelial tumors. *Acta Radiol., Suppl. 46:* 1-105, 1942.

CHANDLER, C., PORTERFIELD, W. M., and STOUT, A. B. Microsporogenesis in diploid and triploid types of *Lilium tigrinum* with special reference to abortions. *Cytologia, Fujii Jubilee Vol.* 756-784, 1937.

CHARTERIS, A. A. Self-healing epithelioma of the skin. *Am. J. Roentgenol. 65:* 459-464, 1951.

CHASE, H. B. Greying of hair: I. Effects produced by single doses of X rays on mice, *J. Morphol. 84:* 57-79, 1949.

CHASE, H. B. Number of entities inactivated by X rays in greying of hair. *Science 113:* 714-716, 1951.

CHASE, H. B., QUASTLER, H., and SKAGGS, L. S. Biological evaluation of 20 million volt roentgen rays: II. Decoloration of hair in mice. *Am. J. Roentgenol. 57:* 359-361, 1947.

CHASE, H. B., and RAUCH, H. Greying of hair: II. Response of individual hairs in mice to variations in X radiation. *J. Morphol. 87:* 381-391, 1950.

CHASE, H. B., and SMITH, V. W. X ray-induced greying in the mouse with reference to melanoblasts. *Anat. Rec. 105:* 533-534, 1949.

CLAR, E. Polynuclear aromatic hydrocarbons and their derivatives: I. Dibenzanthracene and its quinones. *Ber. d. deutsch. chem. Gesellsch. 62:* 350-359, 1929.

CLAR, E. Aromatic hydrocarbons: LIII. 7:8-benzheptaphene. *J. Chem. Soc.* 2440-2442, 1949a.

CLAR, E. Aromatic hydrocarbons: LIV. The anellation principle and resonance in aromatic hydrocarbons. *Chem. Ber. 82:* 495-514, 1949b.

CLAR, E., and STEWART, D. G. Aromatic hydrocarbons: LIX. 1:2:3:4-dibenzpyrene. *J. Chem. Soc.* 687-690, 1951.

CLOUDMAN, A. M., VINING, D., BARKULIS, S., and NICKSON, J. J. Bone changes observed following intravenous injections of beryllium. *Am. J. Path. 25:* 810, 1949.

CONWAY, B. E., GILBERT, L., and BUTLER, J. A. V. The action of ionizing radiations and of radiomimetic chemicals on deoxyribonucleic acid: III. The molecular weights of deoxyribonucleic acid degraded by X rays and by treatment with a "nitrogen mustard." *J. Chem. Soc.* 3421-3425, 1950.

COOK, J. W. In *Discussion on experimental production of malignant tumours. Proc. Roy. Soc. s. B. 113:* 277, 1933.

COOK, J. W. Azo dyes and experimental liver tumours. *Brit. J. Nutrition 1:* 245-253, 1947.

COOK, J. W. Polycyclic aromatic hydrocarbons. Pedler Lecture to the Chemical Society. *J. Chem. Soc.* 1210-1219, 1950.

COOK, J. W., and DODDS, E. C. Sex hormones and cancer-producing compounds. *Nature 131:* 205-206, 1933.

COOK, J. W., DUFFY, E., and SCHÖNTAL, R. Primary liver tumours in rats following feeding with alkaloids of *Senecio Jacobaea C. Brit. J. Cancer 4:* 405-410, 1950.

COOK, J. W., and HASLEWOOD, G. A. D. The conversion of a bile acid into a hydrocarbon derived from 1:2-benzanthracene. *J. Soc. Chem. Ind. 52* (38): 758-759, 1933.

COOK, J. W., and HEWETT, C. L. The isolation of a cancer-producing hydrocarbon from coal tar. III. Synthesis of 1:2- and 4:5-benzpyrene. *J. Chem. Soc.* 398-405, 1933.

COOK, J. W., HEWETT, C. L., KENNAWAY, E. L., and KENNAWAY, N. M. Effects produced in the livers of mice by azonaphthalenes and related compounds. *Am. J. Cancer 40:* 62-77, 1940.

COOK, J. W., HIEGER, I., KENNAWAY, E. L., and MAYNEORD, W. V. Production of cancer by pure hydrocarbons. *Proc. Roy. Soc. s. B. 111:* 455-484, 1932.

COOK, J. W., KENNAWAY, E. L., and KENNAWAY, N. M. Production of tumours in mice by deoxycholic acid. *Nature 145:* 627, 1940.

COOK, J. W., LOUDON, J. D., and WILLIAMSON, W. F. Stereochemistry of metabolic diols from naphthalene and anthracene. *J. Chem. Soc.* 911-914, 1950.

COOK, J. W., LUDWICZAK, R. S., and SCHÖNTAL, R. Polycyclic aromatic hydrocarbons: XXXVI. Synthesis of the metabolic oxidation products of 3:4-benzpyrene. *J. Chem. Soc.* 1112-1121, 1950.

COOK, J. W., and SCHÖNTAL, R. Oxidation of carcinogenic hydrocarbons by osmium tetroxide. *J. Chem. Soc.* 170-173, 1948a.

COOK, J. W., and SCHÖNTAL, R. Oxidation of anthracene by osmium tetroxide. *Nature 161:* 237-238, 1948b.

COOK, J. W., and SCHÖNTAL, R. Catalysed hydrogen peroxide oxidation of aromatic hydrocarbons. *J. Chem. Soc.* 47-54, 1950.

COOK, J. W., SCHÖNTAL, R., and SCOTT, E. J. Y. Relation between bond structure and the longest ultra-violet absorption band of polycyclic aromatic hydrocarbons. *Proc. Phys. Soc., Lond.* A. *63:* 592-598, 1950.

COULSON, C. A. In *Advances in Cancer Research.* New York, Academic Press, 1952, Vol. 1.

COULSON, C. A., DAUDEL, P., and DAUDEL, R. Comparison between the two methods of constructing molecular diagrams. *Rev. sci. 85:* 29-32, 1947.

COULSON, C. A., and JACOBS, J. Charge distribution and bond orders in aminostilbene and related molecules. *J. Chem. Soc.* 1983-1986, 1949.

CRABTREE, H. G. Anti-carcinogenesis. *Brit. M. Bull. 4:* 345-348, 1947.

CRANSTON, E. M. Effect of *Lithospermum ruderale* on estrous cycle of mice. *J. Pharmacol. 83:* 130-142, 1945.

CRANSTON, E. M., KUCERA, G. R., and BITTNER, J. J. *Lithospermum ruderale* and the incidence of mammary tumors in mice. *Proc. Soc. Exper. Biol. & Med. 75:* 779-781, 1950.

CRANSTON, E. M., and ROBINSON, G. A. Effect of *Lithospermum ruderale* on the gonadotropic potency of the pituitary gland. *Proc. Soc. Exper. Biol. & Med. 70:* 66-67, 1949.

CREECH, H. J., and PECK, R. M. Conjugates synthesized from proteins and the isocyanates of certain systemic carcinogens. *J. Am. Chem. Soc. 74:* 463-468, 1952.

CRUICKSHANK, C. N. D., and SQUIRE, J. R. Skin cancer in the engineering industry from the use of mineral oil. *Brit. J. Indust. Med. 7:* 1-11, 1950.

D'ANGELO, E. G. Salivary gland chromosomes. *Ann. N. Y. Acad. Sci. 50:* 910-919, 1950.

DARLINGTON, C. D. The chemical basis of heredity and development. *Discovery 6:* 79-86, 1945.

DARLINGTON, C. D., and LA COUR, L. F. Nucleic acid starvation of chromosomes in *Trillium. J. Genet. 40:* 185-213, 1940.

DARLINGTON, C. D., and LA COUR, L. F. Chromosome breakage and the nucleic acid cycle. *J. Genet. 46:* 180-267, 1944.

DARLINGTON, C. D., and MCLEISH, J. Effect of maleic hydrazide on the cell. *Nature 167:* 407-408, 1951.

DARLINGTON, C. D., and THOMAS, P. T. Morbid mitosis and the activity of inert chromosomes in *Sorghum. Proc. Roy. Soc. s. B. 130:* 127-150, 1941.

DARLINGTON, C. D., and UPCOTT, M. B. Spontaneous chromosome change. *J. Genet. 41:* 297-338, 1941.

DAUBEN, W. G. The synthesis of 20-methylcholanthrene labeled in the 11-position with C^{14}. *J. Org. Chem. 13:* 313-316, 1948.

DAUDEL, P., and DAUDEL, R. On the physico-chemical theory of the mechanism of action of carcinogenic substances. *Acta Un. Int. Cancer 6:* 20-26, 1948.

DAUDEL, P., and DAUDEL, R. The possible formation of a complex between carcinogenic substances and the tissues. *Bull. Soc. Chim. biol. 31:* 353-360, 1949.

DAUDEL, P., and DAUDEL, R. Application of wave mechanics to the study of the mechanism of action of carcinogenic substances on the tissues. *Biol. méd. 39:* 201-236, 1950.

DAUDEL, P., DAUDEL, R., and BUU-HOÏ, N. P. The problem of predicting the carcinogenic property of chemical substances. *Acta Un. Int. Cancer 7:* 91-115, 1950.

DAUDEL, P., DAUDEL, R., BUU-HOÏ, N. P., and MARTIN, M. Molecular diagrams of mesomerism and reactivity of organic molecules. *Bull. Soc. Chim. Fr. 15:* 1202-1211, 1948.

DAUDEL, P., DAUDEL, R., and VROELANT, C. Approximate method of constructing molecular diagrams by the technique of molecular orbitals. *Compt. rend. Acad. d. sc. 227:* 1033-1034, 1948.

DAUDEL, R. Influence of heterocyclic elements and methyl substituents on mesomerism. *Compt. rend. Acad. d. sc. 222:* 797-799, 1946a.

DAUDEL, R. Physico-chemical theories of carcinogenesis. *Rev. sci. 84:* 37-42, 1946b.

DAUDEL, R. Electronic factors capable of playing a part in phenomena of carcinogenesis. *Compt. rend. Soc. de biol. 142:* 5-6, 1948a.

DAUDEL, R. Application of wave mechanics to the study of phenomena of carcinogenesis. *Bull. Ass. franç. Cancer 35:* 110-124, 1948b.

DAUDEL, R. The possible formation of an addition complex between carcinogenic hydrocarbons and a cellular component in the course of their metabolism. *Bull. Ass. franç. Cancer 35:* 319-328, 1948c.

DAUDEL, R. The mechanism of action of carcinogenic substances. *Compt. rend. Acad. d. sc. 231:* 493-495, 1950.

DAVIS, W., EVERETT, J. L., and ROSS, W. C. J. Aryl-2-halogenoalkylamines: VII. Some derivatives of β-naphthyl-di-2-halogenoalkylamines. *J. Chem. Soc.* 1331-1337, 1950.

DAVIS, W., and ROSS, W. C. J. Aryl-2-halogenoalkylamines: XI. The reaction of 2-naphthyl-di-2′-chloroethylamine with some phosphoric acid derivatives. *J. Chem. Soc.* 4296-4300, 1952.

DELLER, P. Fibrosarcoma of the tongue after interstitial irradiation. *Lancet 1:* 1159-1160, 1951.

DEMEREC, M. *Carnegie Institution Year Book.* New York, 1948a.

DEMEREC, M. Mutations induced by carcinogens. *Brit. J. Cancer 2:* 114-117, 1948b.

DEMEREC, M. Induction of mutations in *Drosophila* by dibenzanthracene. *Genetics 33:* 337-348, 1948c.

DEMEREC, M. Chemical mutagens. *Proc. 8th Int. Congr. Genetics, Lund* 201-209, 1949.

DEMEREC, M., BERTANI, G., and FLINT, J. A survey of chemicals for mutagenic action on *E. coli. Am. Nat. 85:* 119-136, 1951.

DEUEL, H. Glycolic esters of pectinic acid. *Helv. Chim. Acta 30:* 1523-1534, 1947.

DEUEL, H., and NEUKOM, H. Cross linking of sodium alginates by mustard gas. *J. Polym. Sc. 4:* 755-757, 1949.

DEUTSCH, H. F., KLINE, B. E., and RUSCH, H. P. Oxidation of phospholipids in the presence of ascorbic acid and carcinogenic chemicals. *J. Biol. Chem. 141:* 529-538, 1941.

DIANZANI, M. A. Mutation in the enzymatic equipment of *Esch. coli* and *proteus* OX-19 directed by desoxyribonucleic acid isolated from bacteria of the same and of different species. *Experientia 6:* 332-334, 1950.

DICKENS, F. Biological aromatization of hydroaromatic compounds. In R. T. Williams, ed.: *Biological Oxidation of Aromatic Rings. Biochem. Soc. Symp. 5:* 66-84, Cambridge, 1950.

DICKIE, M. M. Histological appearance of pituitary tumors in experimental F1 reciprocal hybrid mice. *Acta Un. Int. Cancer 6:* 252-253, 1948.

DICKIE, M. M., and WOOLLEY, G. W. Spontaneous basophilic tumors of the pituitary glands in gonadectomized mice. *Cancer Research 9:* 372-384, 1949.

DIXON, J. K., CHRISTOPHER, G. L. M., and SALLEY, D. J. Fundamental physical-chemical characteristics of melamine resin acid colloid. *Paper Tr. J. 127:* 455-463, 1948.

DOBRINER, K., RHOADS, C. P., and LAVIN, G. I. The spectroscopic study of biological extracts: II. The detection, isolation and biological effects of the metabolites of 1,2,5,6-dibenzanthracene. *Cancer Research 2:* 95-107, 1942.
DODDS, E. C., GOLDBERG, L., LAWSON, W., and ROBINSON, R. Oestrogenic activity of certain synthetic compounds. *Nature 141:* 247-248, 1938.
DOLL, R., and BRADFORD HILL, A. Smoking and carcinoma of the lung. *Brit. M. J. 2:* 739-748, 1950.
DONIACH, I. The effect of radioactive iodine alone and in combination with methylthiouracil and acetylamino-fluorene upon tumour production in the rat's thyroid gland. *Brit. J. Cancer 4:* 223-234, 1950.
DORFMAN, R. I., GOLDSMITH, E. D., *et al.* The influence of hormones on enzymes. *Ann. N. Y. Acad. Sci. 54:* 531-728, 1951.
DRASHER, M. L., and ZAHL, P. A. The effect of *Lithospermum* on the mouse estrous cycle. *Proc. Soc. Exper. Biol. Med. 63:* 66-70, 1946.
DURYEE, W. R. Does the action of X rays on the nucleus depend on the cytoplasm? *Biol. Bull., Wood's Hole 77:* 326, 1939.
DURYEE, W. R. The nature of radiation injury to amphibian cell nuclei. *J. Nat. Cancer Inst. 10:* 735-795, 1949a.
DURYEE, W. R. Interactions between nucleus and cytoplasm. *Anat. Rec. 105:* 574, 1949b.
DURYEE, W. R. Chromosomal physiology in relation to nuclear structure. *Ann. N. Y. Acad. Sci. 50:* 920-953, 1950.
DUSTIN, P. Some new aspects of mitotic poisoning. *Nature 159:* 794-797, 1947.
DUTRA, F. R., and LARGENT, E. J. Osteosarcoma induced by beryllium oxide. *Am. J. Path. 26:* 197-209, 1950.
DUTRA, F. R., LARGENT, E. J., and ROTH, J. L. Osteogenic sarcoma after inhalation of beryllium oxide. *Arch. Path. 51:* 473-479, 1951.
EARLE, W. R., SCHILLING, E. L., and SHELTON, E. Production of malignancy *in vitro*: IX. *J. Nat. Cancer Inst. 10:* 865-881, 1950.
ECKHARDT, H.-J. Action of perbenzoic acid on aromatic hydrocarbons. *Ber. 73:* 13-15, 1940.
EDWARDS, J. E. Hepatomas in mice induced with carbon tetrachloride. *J. Nat. Cancer Inst. 2:* 197-199, 1941.
EHRICH, W. E., DRABKIN, D. L., and FORMAN, C. Nucleic acids and the production of antibody by plasma cells. *J. Exper. Med. 90:* 157-168, 1949.
EHRICH, W. E., and HARRIS, T. N. The formation of antibodies in the popliteal lymph node in rabbits. *J. Exper. Med. 76:* 335-348, 1942.
EISENBUD, M. Radiation hazards in the atomic energy program. *Indust. Med. 20:* 7-11, 1951.
ELLIS, G. W. Autoxidation of the fat acids: II. Oxidoelaidic acid and some cleavage products. *Biochem. J. 30:* 753-761, 1936.
ELMORE, D. T., GULLAND, J. M., JORDAN, D. O., and TAYLOR, H. F. W. The reaction of nucleic acids with mustard gas. *Biochem. J. 42:* 308-316, 1948.
ELSON, L. A. Some effects of diet on toxicity: The influence of diet on the induction and inhibition of tumours. In *Selective Toxicity and Antibodies, 3rd Symp. Soc. Exper. Biol.* 1949.
ENGEL, R. W., and COPELAND, D. H. Mammary carcinoma in rats fed 2-acetylaminofluorene. *Science 108:* 336-337, 1948.
EPHRUSSI, B. Aspects of the physiology of gene action. *Am. Nat. 72:* 5-23, 1938.

EPHRUSSI, B. Chemistry of "eye color hormones" of *Drosophila*. *Quart. Rev. Biol. 17:* 327-338, 1942a.

EPHRUSSI, B. Analysis of eye color differentiation in *Drosophila*. *Cold Spring Harbor Symp. Quant. Biol. 10:* 40-48, 1942b.

EPHRUSSI, B., and BEADLE, G. W. Development of eye colors in *Drosophila*: Transplantation experiments on the interaction of vermilion with other eye colors. *Genetics 22:* 65-75, 1937.

EPHRUSSI, B., and CHEVAIS, S. Development of eye colors in *Drosophila*: Relation between pigmentation and release of the diffusible substances. *Proc. Nat. Acad. Sc. 23:* 428-434, 1937.

EPHRUSSI, B., and CHEVAIS, S. Development of eye colors in *Drosophila*: Relation between production, utilisation and release of the diffusible substances. *Bull. Biol. 72:* 48-78, 1938.

EPHRUSSI-TAYLOR, H. Allogenic transformations of the pneumococcus. *Exper. Cell Res. 2:* 589-607, 1951a.

EPHRUSSI-TAYLOR, H. Genetic aspects of transformations of pneumococci. *Cold Spring Harbor Symp. Quant. Biol. 16:* 445-455, 1951b.

VON EULER, H., and KARRER, P. On the vitamin A effect of β-carotene-di-epoxide and of luteochrome. *Helv. Chim. Acta 33:* 1481-1482, 1950.

EVANS, J. G. The fine structure of fibres in relation to dyeing and finishing. In J. M. Preston, ed.: *Fibre Science*, 248-272. Manchester, England, The Textile Institute, 1949.

EVANS, M. G., and GERGELY, J. A discussion of the possibility of bands of energy levels in proteins: Electronic interaction in non-bonded systems. *Biochim. Biophys. Acta 3:* 188-197, 1949.

EVERARD, K. B., and SUTTON, L. E. Polarisation in conjugated systems: Part II. Steric hindrance in derivatives of 4-dimethylaminostilbene. *J. Chem. Soc.* 2816-2817, 1951.

EVERETT, J. L., and KON, G. A. R. The preparation of some cytotoxic epoxides. *J. Chem. Soc.* 3131-3135, 1950.

EYRING, H. Activated complex in chemical reactions. *J. Chem. Phys. 3:* 107-115, 1935.

FAGRAEUS, A. Plasma cellular reaction and its relation to the formation of antibodies *in vitro*. *Nature 159:* 499, 1947.

FAGRAEUS, A. Antibody production in relation to development of plasma cells: *in vivo* and *in vitro* experiments. *Acta med. Scandinav., Suppl. 204:* 3-122, 1948a.

FAGRAEUS, A. The plasma cellular reaction and its relation to the formation of antibodies *in vitro*. *J. Immunol. 58:* 1-13, 1948b.

FEARNLEY, C., and SPEAKMAN, J. B. Cross linkage formation in keratin. *Nature 166:* 743-744, 1950.

FEKETE, E., and LITTLE, C. C. Histological study of adrenal cortical tumors in gonadectomized mice of the CE strain. *Cancer Research 5:* 220-226, 1945.

FELL, H. B., and ALLSOPP, C. B. Report to Ministry of Supply, 27th July 1943. London, H. M. Stationery Office.

FELL, H. B., and ALLSOPP, C. B. The effect of repeated applications of minute quantities of mustard gas on the skin of mice. *Cancer Research 8:* 177-182, 1948.

FELS, E. Pituitary tumours produced by diethyl stilboestrol. *Compt. rend. Soc. d. biol. 144:* 1226, 1950.

FERNANDES, A. On the distribution of a supernumerary heterochromatinosome in pollen. *Bol. da Soc. Broteriana 22:* 119-143, 1948.

FERNANDES, A. The problem of heterochromatinisation in *Narcissus bulbocodium* L. *Bol. da Soc. Broteriana 23:* 5-89, 1949.

FERNANDES, A., and SERRA, J. A. Euchromatin and heterochromatin in their relations with the nucleus and the nucleolus. *Bol. da Soc. Broteriana 19:* 67-125, 1944.

FIESER, L. F. Production of cancer by polynuclear hydrocarbons. University of Pennsylvania Bicentennial Conference, Philadelphia, 1941.

FIESER, L. F., and NEWMAN, M. S. Methylcholanthrene from cholic acid. *J. Am. Chem. Soc. 57:* 961, 1935.

FIESER, L. F., and NEWMAN, M. S. The synthesis of 1:2:benzanthracene derivatives related to cholanthrene. *J. Am. Chem. Soc. 58:* 2376-2382, 1936.

FIESER, L. F., and SELIGMAN, A. M. The synthesis of methylcholanthrene. *J. Am. Chem. Soc. 57:* 228-229 and 942-946, 1935.

FISCHER, B. The experimental production of atypical epithelial proliferation and the induction of maligant tumours. *München. med. Wchnschr. 53:* 2041-2047, 1906.

FISCHER, H. G. M., PRIESTLEY, W., EBY, L. T., WANLESS, G. G., and REHNER, J. Properties of high-boiling petroleum products: Physical and chemical properties as related to carcinogenic activity. *Arch. Indust. Hyg. 4:* 315-324, 1951.

FITZHUGH, O. G., and NELSON, A. A. Comparison of the chronic toxicities of synthetic sweetening agents. *Federation Proc. 9:* 272, 1950.

FLEMING, A. J., and CHASE, W. H. The effects of administration of thorium dioxide. *Surg., Gynec. & Obst. 63:* 145-148, 1936.

FONES, W. S., and WHITE, J. Preparation of *p*-dimethylaminoazobenzene containing isotopic nitrogen. *Arch. Biochem. 20:* 118-124, 1949.

FORD, C. E. Chromosome breakage in nitrogen mustard treated *Vicia faba* root tip cells. *Proc. 8th Int. Congr. Genetics, Lund* 570-571, 1948.

FORMAN, C., DRABKIN, D. L., and EHRICH, W. E. Nucleic acids and antibody production by plasma cells. *Am. J. M. Sc. 217:* 710, 1949.

FOULDS, L. Experimental study of the course and regulation of tumour growth. *Ann. R. Coll. Surg. Engl. 9:* 93-101, 1951.

FRAENKEL-CONRAT, H. The action of 1,2-epoxides on proteins. *J. Biol. Chem. 154:* 227-238, 1944.

FRAENKEL-CONRAT, H., and MECHAM, D. K. The reaction of formaldehyde with proteins: VII. Demonstration of intermolecular cross-linking by means of osmotic pressure measurements. *J. Biol. Chem. 177:* 477-486, 1949.

FRIEDMAN, O. M., and SELIGMAN, A. M. Derivatives of 10-methyl-1,2-benzanthracene related to the nitrogen and sulphur β-chloroethyl vesicants. *J. Am. Chem. Soc. 70:* 3082-3086, 1948.

FRIES, L. Mutations induced in *Coprinus fimetarius* (L) by nitrogen mustard. *Nature 162:* 846-847, 1948.

FRITZ-NIGGLI, H. Quantitative analysis of cancer induction by carcinogenic substances. *Oncologia 4:* 53-64, 1951.

FURTH, J., and BURNETT, W. T. Hormone-secreting transplantable neoplasms of the pituitary induced by I^{131}. *Proc. Soc. Exper. Biol. & Med. 78:* 222-224, 1951.

GARDIKAS, C., and WILKINSON, J. F. Trial of β-naphthyl-di-2-chloroethylamine in leukaemia, Hodgkin's disease and allied disorders. *Lancet 1:* 137-139, 1951.

GARDNER, L. U., and HESLINGTON, H. F. Osteo-sarcoma from intravenous beryllium compounds in rabbits. *Federation Proc. 5:* 221, 1946.

GARDNER, W. U. Some influences of hormones on the growth and persistence of transplanted testicular tumors. *Cancer Research 5:* 497-505, 1945.

GARDNER, W. U. The effect of steroid hormones on experimental pituitary and gonadal tumorigenesis. *Ciba Foundation Colloquia on Endocrinology 1:* 52-64. London, 1952.

GAUTHERET, R. J. Plant cancer. *Endeavour 9:* 21-25, 1950.

GAVAUDAN, P., and POUSSEL, H. Observations on theories of chemical carcinogenesis. *Gallica Biol. 1:* 111-113, 1948.

GECKLER, R. P. Nitrogen mustard inactivation of the cytoplasmic factor Kappa in *Paramecium aurelia* Variety 4[1]. *Science 110:* 89-90, 1949.

GIBSON, P. B., BRINK, R. A., and STAHMANN, M. A. The mutagenic action of mustard gas on *Zea mays. J. Hered. 41:* 232-238, 1950.

GIBSON, Q. H. The reduction of methaemoglobin in red blood cells and studies on the cause of idiopathic methaemoglobinaemia. *Biochem. J. 42:* 13-23, 1948.

GILLMAN, J., GILBERT, C., GILLMAN, T., and SPENCE, I. Experimental production of hepato-splenomegaly, reticulum-cell sarcoma and Hodgkin's disease. *S. Africa M. J. 22:* 783-784, 1948.

GILLMAN, J., and GILLMAN, T. Lymphomata (including Hodgkin's-like sarcomata): their experimental production: A study of their pathogenesis and etiology and a comparison with corresponding tumours in man. *Clin. Proc.* (J. Cape Town Post-Grad. M. A.), *8:* 222-361, 1949.

GILLMAN, J., GILLMAN, T., and GILBERT, C. Reticulosis and reticulum-cell tumours of the liver produced in rats by trypan blue with reference to hepatic necrosis and fibrosis. *S. Africa J. M. Sc. 14:* 21-84, 1949.

GILMAN, A., and PHILIPS, F. S. The biological actions and therapeutic applications of the β-chloroethyl amines and sulfides. *Science 103:* 409-415, 1946.

GLINOS, A. D., and BUCHER, N. L. R. Liver regeneration and carcinogenesis by *p*-dimethylaminoazobenzene. *Acta Un. Int. Cancer 6:* 713-719, 1949.

GLINOS, A. D., BUCHER, N. L. R., and AUB, J. C. The effect of liver regeneration on tumor formation in rats fed 4-dimethylaminoazobenzene. *J. Exper. Med. 93:* 313-325, 1951.

GOLDACRE, R. J., LOVELESS, A., and ROSS, W. C. J. Mode of production of chromosome abnormalities by the nitrogen mustards: The possible role of cross-linking. *Nature 163:* 667-671, 1949.

GOLDBERG, R. C., and CHAIKOFF, I. L. Development of thyroid neoplasms in the rat following a single injection of radioactive iodine. *Proc. Soc. Exper. Biol. & Med. 76:* 563-566, 1951.

GOLDBERG, R. C., and CHAIKOFF, I. L. Induction of thyroid cancer in the rat by radioactive iodine. *Arch. Path. 53:* 22-28, 1952.

GOLDECK, H., and HAGENAH, H. Influence of nitrogen mustard on fertility and spermiogenesis of laboratory rats. *Ztschr. f. d. ges. exper. Med. 117:* 467-480, 1951.

GOLDSCHMIDT, R. B. Heterochromatic inheritance. *Science 108:* 679, 1948.

GOLDSCHMIDT, R. B. Heterochromatic heredity. *Proc. 8th Int. Congr. Genetics, Lund* 244-255, 1949.

GOLDSCHMIDT, R. B., and LIN, T. P. Chromatin diminution. *Science 105:* 619, 1947.

GOOD, R. A., and THOMAS, L. Inhibition by nitrogen mustard of the generalized Schwartzman reaction and of bilateral renal cortical necrosis produced with *S. marcescens* toxin in cortisone-treated rabbits. *J. Lab. & Clin. Med. 38:* 815, 1951.

GORBMAN, A. Tumorous growths in the pituitary and trachea following radiotoxic dosages of I^{131}. *Proc. Soc. Exper. Biol. & Med. 71:* 237-240, 1949.

GORDON, M. Heredity of pigmented tumours in fish. *Endeavour 9:* 26-34, 1950a.

GORDON, M. Genetics, speciation and the origin of melanotic tumours in fishes. *Genetics 35:* 110-111, 1950b.

GRABAR, P. *Blood Serum Globulins.* Paris, Masson, 1947.

GRABAR, P. Origin and functions of globulins and antibodies. *Brit. M. J.* 1, 431-432, 1950.

GRAHAM, E. A. Primary cancer of the lung with special consideration of its etiology. *Bull. N. Y. Acad. Med. 27:* 261-276, 1951.

GREENE, H. S. N. A conception of tumor autonomy based on transplantation studies: A review. *Cancer Research 11:* 899-903, 1951.

GREENSTEIN, J. P. Note on the cystine oxidase activity in normal and neoplastic tissues of the mouse. *J. Nat. Cancer Inst. 5:* 39-40, 1944.

GREENSTEIN, J. P., and LEUTHARDT, F. M. Degradation of cystine peptides by tissues: III. Absence of exocystine desulfurase and dehydropeptidase in tumors. *J. Nat. Cancer Inst. 5:* 249, 1945.

GREENWOOD, H. H. The reactivity of aromatic bonds, with reference to carcinogenic compounds of 1:2-benzanthracene. *Brit. J. Cancer 5:* 441-457, 1951.

GRIESBACH, W. E., KENNEDY, T. H., and PURVES, H. D. Studies on experimental goitre: VI. Thyroid adenomata in rats on Brassica seed diet. *Brit. J. Exper. Path. 26:* 18-24, 1945.

GRIFFIN, A. C., BRANDT, E. L., and SETTER, V. Nitrogen mustard inhibition of azo dye carcinogenesis. *Cancer Research 11:* 868-872, 1951.

GRIFFIN, A. C., BRANDT, E. L., and TATUM, E. L. Nitrogen mustards as cancer-inducing agents. *J.A.M.A. 144:* 571, 1950.

GRIFFIN, A. C., BRANDT, E. L., and TATUM, E. L. Induction of tumors with nitrogen mustards. *Cancer Research 11:* 253, 1951.

GRIFFITH, F. Significance of pneumococcal types. *J. Hyg. 27:* 113-159, 1928.

GULICK, A. The chemical formulation of gene structure and gene action. *Advances in Enzymology 4:* 20-39, 1944.

HACKMANN, C. Carcinogenicity of azo dyes. *Krebsforsch. 57:* 530-541, 1951.

HADDOW, A. Cellular inhibition and the origin of cancer. *Acta Un. Int. Cancer 3:* 342-353, 1938.

HADDOW, A. Transformation of cells and viruses. *Nature 154:* 194-209, 1944.

HADDOW, A. Mode of action of chemical carcinogens. *Brit. M. Bull. 4:* 331-342, 1947.

HADDOW, A. Newer concepts in the chemistry of growth. *Proc. First Nat. Cancer Conference, Memphis* 88-94, 1949.

HADDOW, A. A new hypothesis concerning the mode of action of the nitrogen mustards. *Acta haematol. 3:* 117-118, 1950.

HADDOW, A. Advances in the study of chemical carcinogenesis. *Proc. Roy. Soc. Med. 44:* 263-266, 1951. (President's Address to the Comparative Medicine Section of the Royal Society of Medicine.)

HADDOW, A. In A. Haddow, ed.: *The Biological Hazards of Atomic Energy.* Oxford, Clarendon Press, 1952.

HADDOW, A., HARRIS, R. J. C., KON, G. A. R., and ROE, E. M. F. The growth-inhibitory and carcinogenic properties of 4-aminostilbene and derivatives. *Phil. Trans. Roy. Soc. A. 241:* 147-195, 1948.

HADDOW, A., and KON, G. A. R. Chemistry of carcinogenic compounds. *Brit. M. Bull. 4:* 314-326, 1947.

HADDOW, A., KON, G. A. R., and ROSS, W. C. J. Effects upon tumours of various halo-alkylarylamines. *Nature 162:* 824-827, 1948.
HADDOW, A., and TIMMIS, G. M. Bifunctional sulphonic acid esters with radiomimetic activity. *Acta Un. int. Cancer 7:* 469-471, 1951.
HADDOW, A., and TIMMIS, G. M. "Myleran," (1:4-dimethanesulphonyloxybutane), in the treatment of chronic myeloid leukaemia. *Lancet 1:*207-208, 1953.
HADFIELD, G. The general pathology of the lymphadenopathies. *Ann. R. Coll. Surg. Engl. 5:* 89-105, 1949.
HAMBURGH, M. Malformations in mouse embryos induced by trypan blue. *Nature 169:* 27, 1952.
HAMMETT, L. P. *Physical Organic Chemistry.* New York, McGraw-Hill, 1940, p. 301.
HANCE, R. T. Detection of heterozygotes with X rays. *J. Hered. 19:* 481-485, 1928.
HANCE, R. T., and MURPHY, J. B. Studies in X-ray effects: XV. Prevention of pigment formation in the hair follicles of colored mice with high voltage X rays. *J. Exper. Med. 44:* 339-342, 1926.
HARRIS, P. N., and BRADSHER, C. K. The carcinogenicity of 1,2,3,4-dibenzophenanthrene and its 9-methyl and 10-methyl derivatives in mice. *Cancer Research 6:* 487, 1946.
Observations on the carcinogenicity of 1,2,3,4-dibenzophenanthrene and its 9-methyl and 10-methyl derivatives. *Ibid. 6:* 671, 1946.
HARRIS, T. N., GRIMM, E., MERTENS, E., and EHRICH, W. E. The role of the lymphocyte in antibody formation. *J. Exper. Med. 81:* 73-83, 1945.
HARRIS, T. N., and HARRIS, S. Histochemical changes in lymphocytes during the production of antibodies in lymph nodes of rabbits. *J. Exper. Med. 90:* 169-180, 1949.
HARTMAN, F. W., and MANGUN, G. H. Nitrogen mustards as effective blood and plasma sterilizing agents. *Federation Proc. 8:* 357, 1949.
HARTWELL, J. L. *Survey of compounds which have been tested for carcinogenic activity.* U. S. Public Health Service Publication No. 149 (ed. 2). Washington, U. S. Government Printing Office, 1951.
HASKIN, D. Some effects of nitrogen mustard on the development of external body form in the fetal rat. *Anat. Rec. 102:* 493-512, 1948.
HAUROWITZ, F. Biological problems and immunochemistry. *Quart. Rev. Biol. 24:* 93-101, 1949.
HAUROWITZ, F. *The Chemistry and Biology of Proteins.* New York, Academic Press, 1950.
HAUSCHKA, T. S., and LEVAN, A. Characterization of five ascites tumors with respect to chromosome ploidy. *Anat. Rec. 111:* 467, 1951.
HAYWARD, E. Further clinical experience in the use of scarlet-red dyes and their components in hastening the formation of epithelial tissue in granulating surfaces. *München. med. Wchnschr. 56:* 1836-1838, 1909.
HEIDELBERGER, C., BREWER, P., and DAUBEN, W. G. Synthesis of 1,2,5,6-dibenzanthracene labeled in the 9 position with carbon 14. *J. Am. Chem. Soc. 69:* 1389-1391, 1947.
HEIDELBERGER, C., and JONES, H. B. The distribution of radioactivity in the mouse following administration of dibenzanthracene labeled in the 9 and 10 positions with carbon 14. *Cancer 1:* 252-260, 1948.
HEIDELBERGER, C., KIRK, M. R., and PERKINS, M. S. The metabolic degradation in the mouse of dibenzanthracene labeled in the 9 and 10 positions with carbon 14. *Cancer 1:* 261-275, 1948.
HEIDELBERGER, C., and WEISS, S. M. The distribution of radioactivity in mice follow-

ing administration of 3,4-benzpyrene-5-C^{14} and 1,2,5,6-dibenzanthracene-9-10-C^{14}. *Cancer Research 11:* 885-891, 1951.

HEIDELBERGER, C., and WIEST, W. G. The metabolic degradation in the mouse of 1,2,5,6-dibenzanthracene-9-10-C^{14}: II. 5-Hydroxy-1,2-naphthalic acid, a new metabolite. *Cancer Research 11:* 511-518, 1951.

HEITZ, E. Heterochromatin in mosses: I. *Jahrb. wiss. Bot. 69:* 762-818, 1928.

HEITZ, E. The origin of chromocentres. *Planta 18:* 571-635, 1932.

HEKTOEN, L. The influence of the X ray on the production of antibodies. *J. Infect. Dis. 17:* 415-422, 1915.

HELLER, I. Occupational cancer. *J. Indust. Hyg. 12:* 169-197, 1930.

HENDRY, J. A., HOMER, R. F., ROSE, F. L., and WALPOLE, A. L. Cytotoxic agents: II. Bis-epoxides and related compounds. *Brit. J. Pharmacol. 6:* 235-255, 1951a.

HENDRY, J. A., HOMER, R. F., ROSE, F. L., and WALPOLE, A. L. Cytotoxic agents: III. Derivatives of ethyleneimine. *Brit. J. Pharmacol. 6:* 357-410, 1951b.

HENDRY, J. A., ROSE, F. L., and WALPOLE, A. L. Cytotoxic agents: I. Methylolamides with tumour-inhibiting activity, and related inactive compounds. *Brit. J. Pharmacol. 6:* 201-234, 1951.

HENRY, S. A. Occupational cutaneous cancer attributable to certain chemicals in industry. *Brit. Med. Bull. 4:* 389-401, 1947.

HENRY, S. A. Cutaneous cancer in relation to occupation. *Ann. R. Coll. Surg. Engl. 7:* 425-454, 1950.

HENSHAW, P. S., RILEY, E. F., and STAPLETON, G. E. The carcinogenic effect of pile radiations. *Cancer Research 7:* 48, 1947.

HENSHAW, P. S., SNIDER, R. S., and RILEY, E. F. Aberrant tissue developments in rats exposed to beta rays. *Radiology 52:* 401-415, 1949.

HERRIOTT, R. M. Inactivation of viruses and cells by mustard gas. *J. Gen. Physiol. 32:* 221-239, 1948.

HERRIOTT, R. M. Nucleic acid synthesis in mustard gas-treated *E. coli* B. *J. Gen. Physiol. 34:* 761-764, 1951.

HERRIOTT, R. M., ANSON, M. L., and NORTHROP, J. H. Reaction of enzymes and proteins with mustard gas (*Bis*[β-chloroethyl]sulfide). *J. Gen. Physiol. 30:* 185-210, 1946.

HERSKOWITZ, I. H. A list of chemical substances studied for effects on *Drosophila*, with a bibliography. *Am. Nat. 85:* 181-199, 1951.

HESTON, W. E. Induction of pulmonary tumors in strain A mice with methyl bis(β-chloroethyl)amine hydrochloride. *J. Nat. Cancer Inst. 10:* 125-130, 1949.

HESTON, W. E. Carcinogenicity of sulfur mustard. *Cancer Research 10:* 224, 1950a.

HESTON, W. E. Carcinogenic action of the mustards. *J. Nat. Cancer Inst. 11:* 415-423, 1950b.

HETTIG, R. A., GORDON ROBERTSON, G., and CLINE, D. T. Effects of nitrogen mustard on the embryos of pregnant rats. *J. Lab. & Clin. Med. 36:* 833-834, 1950.

HEWETT, C. L. Polycyclic aromatic hydrocarbons: XXII. *J. Chem. Soc.* 293-303, 1940.

HEWETT, C. L., and MARTIN, R. H. Polycyclic aromatic hydrocarbons: XXVI. 1:2:3:4-Tetramethylphenanthrene. *J. Chem. Soc.* 1396-1402, 1940.

HIDALGO, J., and WHITEHEAD, R. W. Carcinogenicity of certain substituted carbamates. *J. Pharmacol. 103:* 347, 1951.

HIEGER, I. The spectra of cancer-producing tars and oils and of related substances. *Biochem. J. 24:* 505-511, 1930.

HIEGER, I. The isolation of a cancer-producing hydrocarbon from coal tar: I. Concentration of the active substance. *J. Chem. Soc.* 395-396, 1933.

HILL, R. *et al.* Synthetic fibre developments in Germany. File XXXIII-50. C.I.O.S. London, H. M. Stationary Office, 1946.

HIRST, E. L. The occurrence and significance of the pentose sugars in nature. *J. Chem. Soc.* 522-533, 1949.

HOAGLAND, M. B., GRIER, R. S., and HOOD, M. B. Beryllium and growth: I. Beryllium-induced osteogenic sarcomata. *Cancer Research 10:* 629-635, 1950.

HOECKER, F. E., and ROOFE, P. G. Studies of radium in human bone. *Radiology 56:* 89-98, 1951.

HOROWITZ, N. H., BONNER, D., MITCHELL, H. K., TATUM, E. L., and BEADLE, G. W. Genic control of biochemical reactions in *Neurospora*. *Am. Nat. 79:* 304-317, 1945.

HOROWITZ, N. H., and LEUPOLD, U. Some recent studies bearing on the one gene-one enzyme hypothesis. *Cold Spring Harbor Symp. Quant. Biol. 16:* 65-72, 1951.

HOWARD, A., and PELC, S. R. Nuclear incorporation of P^{32} as demonstrated by autoradiography. *Exper. Cell. Res. 2:* 178-187, 1951a.

HOWARD, A., and PELC, S. R. Synthesis of deoxyribosenucleic acid and nuclear incorporation of S^{35} as shown by autoradiography. In *Isotopes in Biochemistry*, Ciba Foundation Conference, 138-148. London, Churchill, 1951b.

HOWARD, A., and PELC, S. R. Nuclear incorporation of P^{32} as demonstrated by autoradiography. *Heredity 5:* 158, 1951c.

HOWARD, A., and PELC, S. R. Synthesis of nucleoprotein in bean root cells. *Nature 167:* 599-600, 1951d.

HUEPER, W. C. Environmental and occupational cancer. *U. S. Public Health Service Report, Suppl. 209:* 1948.

HUEPER, W. C. Present and potential occupational cancer hazards and carcinogenic operations in modern industry. *South M. J. 43:* 118-123, 1950a.

HUEPER, W. C. Carcinogens and carcinogenesis. *Am. J. Med. 8:* 355-371, 1950b.

HUEPER, W. C. Environmental lung cancer. *Indust. Med. 20:* 49-62, 1951.

HUEPER, W. C. Experimental studies in metal cancerigenesis: I. Nickel cancers in rats. *Tex. Rep. Biol. & Med. 10:* 167-186, 1952.

HUEPER, W. C., and WOLFE, N. P. Experimental production of aniline tumors of the bladder in dogs. *Am. J. Path. 13:* 656, 1937.

HUGHES, A. F. W., and FELL, H. B. Studies on abnormal mitosis produced in chick tissue cultures by mustard gas (ββ′-dichlordiethyl sulphide). *Quart. J. Mic. Sc. 90:* 37-56, 1949.

HUNT, C. C., and PHILIPS, F. S. The acute pharmacology of methyl bis(2-chloroethyl)-amine. *J. Pharmacol. 95:* 131-144, 1949.

HUTCHENS, J. O., and PODOLSKY, B. The effects of nitrogen mustards on cleavage and development of *Arbacia* eggs. *Biol. Bull., Wood's Hole 95:* 251, 1948.

IVERSEN, S. *A Possible Correlation between Absorption Spectra and Carcinogenicity.* Copenhagen, Munksgaard, 1949.

IVERSEN, S., and ARLEY, N. On the mechanism of experimental carcinogenesis. *Acta path. microbiol. Scandinav. 27:* 773-803, 1950.

JACOBSON, L. O. Evidence for a humoral factor (or factors) concerned in recovery from radiation injury: A review. *Cancer Research 12:* 315-325, 1952.

JACOBSON, L. O., MARKS, E. K., GASTON, E., and BLOCK, M. H. The effects of nitrogen mustard on induced erythroblastic hyperplasia in rabbits. *J. Lab. & Clin. Med. 34:* 902-924, 1949.

JACOBSON, L. O., ROBSON, M. J., and MARKS, E. K. The effect of X radiation on antibody formation. *Proc. Soc. Exper. Biol. & Med. 75:* 145-152, 1950.

JAFFÉ, W. Production of pulmonary adenomas in rats by the action of urethane, with observations on the localization of artificially produced tumours. *Rev. Policlin. Caracas 13:* 445-452, 1944.

JEHLE, H. Self duplication of genes and specific interaction between identical macromolecules. *Science 111:* 454, 1950a.

JEHLE, H. Specificity of interaction between identical molecules. *Proc. Nat. Acad. Sci. 36:* 238-246, 1950b.

JENSEN, K. A., KIRK, I., and WESTERGAARD, M. Mutagenic activity of some "mustard gas" compounds. *Nature 166:* 1020-1021, 1950.

JORDAN, P. Specific attraction between gene molecules. *Phys. Ztschr. 39:* 711-714, 1938.

JORDAN, P. Quantum-mechanical attraction and problem of immunity reaction. *Ztschr. f. Physiol. 113:* 431-438, 1939a.

JORDAN, P. On the problem of specific immunity. *Fundam. Radiol. 5:* 43-46, 1939b.

JORDAN, P. Hemistic theory of the phenomena of immunisation and anaphylaxis. *Z. Immunforsch. 97:* 330-344, 1940.

KABELITZ, H. J. The plasma cell and protein metabolism. *Acta Haematol. 5:* 232-242, 1951.

KAPLAN, W. D. Formaldehyde as a mutagen in *Drosophila*. *Science 108:* 43, 1948.

KARNOFSKY, D. A. Nitrogen mustards in the treatment of neoplastic disease. *Advanc. Internal Med. 4:* 1-75, 1950.

KARNOFSKY, D. A., GRAEF, I., and SMITH, H. W. Studies on the mechanism of action of the nitrogen and sulfur mustards *in vivo*. *Am. J. Path. 24:* 275-291, 1948.

KARRER, P., and JUCKER, E. Vitamin A-epoxide (hepaxanthin): II. *Helv. Chim. Acta 30:* 559-565, 1947.

KAUFMANN, B. P. Chromosome structure in relation to the chromosome cycle: II. *Bot. Rev. 14:* 57-126, 1948.

KEHR, A. E. A genetic explanation for tumor formation in *Nicotiana* hybrids. *Genetics 35:* 672-673, 1950.

KEHR, A. E. Genetic tumors in *Nicotiana*. *Am. Nat. 85:* 51-64, 1951.

KENNAWAY, E. L. The formation of a cancer-producing substance from isoprene (2-methyl-butadiene). *J. Path. & Bact. 27:* 233-238, 1924.

KENNAWAY, E. L. Experiments on cancer-producing substances. *Brit. M. J. 2:* 1-4, 1925.

KENNAWAY, E. L., and HIEGER, I. Carcinogenic substances and their fluorescence spectra. *Brit. M. J. 1:* 1044-1046, 1930.

KIHLMAN, B. 8-Ethoxycaffeine, an ideal inducer of structural chromosome changes in the root tips of *Allium cepa*. *Exper. Cell. Res. 1:* 135-138, 1950.

KINDRED, J. E. Some histochemical reactions of the testes of albino rats after intravenous injection of a nitrogen mustard *tris*(2-chloroethyl)amine. *Anat. Rec. 109:* 400-401, 1951.

KINOSITA, R. Studies on the cancerogenic azo and related compounds. *Yale J. Biol. & Med. 12:* 287-300, 1940.

KINSEY, V. E., and GRANT, W. M. Reaction of mustard gas with proteins; nutritional value of casein reacted with mustard gas. *Arch. Biochem. 10:* 303-309, 1946.
Reaction of mustard gas with proteins; biological assay of amino acids affected. *Ibid. 10:* 311-320, 1946.

KIRBY, A. H. M. Carcinogenic effect of aminobenzene. *Nature 154:* 668-669, 1944.

KIRBY, A. H. M. The carcinogenic activity of N-ethyl-3,4,5,6-dibenzcarbazole. *Biochem. J. 42:* lv, 1948a.

KIRBY, A. H. M. The significance of labile methyl groups in carcinogenesis by azo-dyes. *Acta Un. Int. Cancer 6:* 36-40, 1948b.

KIRBY, A. H. M., and PEACOCK, P. R. The influence of methylation on carcinogenic activity: I. N-methyl-3:4:5:6-dibenzcarbazole. *Brit. J. Exper. Path. 27:* 179-189, 1946.

KIRBY, A. H. M., and PEACOCK, P. R. Liver tumours in mice injected with commercial food dyes. *Glasgow M. J. 30:* 364-372, 1949.

KIRKMAN, H., and BACON, R. L. Malignant renal tumors in male hamsters (*Cricetus auratus*) treated with estrogen. *Cancer Research 10:* 122-123, 1950.

KLEVENS, H. B. Solubilization of polycyclic hydrocarbons. *J. Phys. Colloid Chem. 54:* 283-298, 1950.

KOLETSKY, S., BONTE, F. J., and FRIEDELL, H. L. Production of malignant tumors in rats with radioactive phosphorus. *Cancer Research 10:* 129-138, 1950.

KOLETSKY, S., and CHRISTIE, J. H. Biologic effects of radioactive phosphorus poisoning in rats. *Am. J. Path. 27:* 175-209, 1951.

KOLLER, P. C. Report to Ministry of Supply by J. M. Robson, October 1943, 1943a. London, H. M. Stationery Office.

KOLLER, P. C. Origin of malignant tumour cells. *Nature 151:* 244-246, 1943b.

KOLLER, P. C. Dicentric chromosomes in a rat tumour induced by an aromatic nitrogen mustard. *Heredity* (in press).

KORPÁSSY, B., and KOVÁCS, K. Experimental liver cirrhosis in rats produced by prolonged subcutaneous administration of solutions of tannic acid. *Brit. J. Exper. Path. 30:* 266-272, 1949.

KORPÁSSY, B., and MOSONYI, M. Carcinogenic activity of tannic acid: liver tumours induced in rats by prolonged subcutaneous administration of tannic acid solutions. *Brit. J. Cancer 4:* 411-420, 1950.

KORPÁSSY, B., and MOSONYI, M. Influence of dietetic factors on carcinogenic activity of tannic acid. *Lancet 1:* 1416-1417, 1951.

KUHN, R., and QUADBECK, G. Contributions to the study of carcinogenic azo dyestuffs. *Z. Krebsforsch. 56:* 242-245, 1949.

KULESCHA, Z. Relation between the capacity for spontaneous proliferation of the tissues of *Helianthus tuberosus* and their content of growth substance. *Compt. rend. Soc. de biol. 143:* 354-355, 1949.

KULESCHA, Z., and GAUTHERET, R. The production of growth substances by three types of *Scorzonera* cultures: Normal cultures, crown-gall cultures and cultures accustomed to hetero-auxin. *Compt. rend. Acad. d. sc. 227:* 292-294, 1948.

LACASSAGNE, A. Appearance of mammary cancer in the male mouse injected with folliculin. *Compt. rend. Acad. d. sc. 195:* 630-632, 1932.

LACASSAGNE, A. *Cancers Produced by Exogenous Chemical Substances.* Paris, Masson, 1946.

LACASSAGNE, A. Carcinogenic activity of some polycyclic nitrogen compounds. *Acta Un. Int. Canc. 6:* 9-15, 1948.

LACASSAGNE, A. *Cancers Produced by Endogenous Chemical Substances.* Paris, Hermann, 1950.

LACASSAGNE, A., BUU-HOI, N. P., HOÁN, N., and RUDALI, G. The carcinogenic activity of 10-halogeno- derivatives of 1,2-benzanthracene. *Compt. rend. Acad. d. sc. 226:* 1852-1853, 1948.

LACASSAGNE, A., BUU-HOI, N. P., ROYER, R., RUDALI, G., and ZAJDELA, F. Contributions to the study of the carcinogenic activity of 2-aminofluorene. *Compt. rend. Soc. de biol. 142:* 481-483, 1948.

LACASSAGNE, A., BUU-HOI, N. P., ROYER, R., and ZAJDELA, F. Investigation of the carcinogenic activity of some new polycyclic nitrogen compounds. *Compt. rend. Soc. de biol. 141:* 635-637, 1947.

LACASSAGNE, A., RUDALI, G., BUU-HOI, N. P., and LECOCQ, J. Carcinogenic activity of certain methyl derivatives of angular benzacridines. *Compt. rend. Soc. de biol. 139:* 955-957, 1945.

LA COUR, L. F. Heterochromatin and the organisation of nucleoli in plants. *Heredity 5:* 37-50, 1951.

LAN, T. H. The d-amino acid oxidase, uricase and choline oxidase in two transplanted rat tumors and in isolated nuclei of tumor cells. *Cancer Research 4:* 42-44, 1944.

LANDING, B. H., and EISENBERG, F. F. Nitrogen mustards: Statistical analysis of effects on sarcoma 180 and viscera of normal mice in relation to toxicity and structure. *Cancer 2:* 1083-1086, 1949.

LANDING, B. H., GOLDIN, A., and NOE, H. A. Testicular lesions in mice following parenteral administration of nitrogen mustards. *Cancer 2:* 1075-1082, 1949.

LANDING, B. H., GOLDIN, A., NOE, H. A., GOLDBERG, B., and SHAPIRO, D. M. Systemic pathological effects of nitrogen mustards, and a comparison of toxicity, chemical structure, and cytotoxic effect, with reference to the chemotherapy of tumors. *Cancer 2:* 1055-1066, 1949.

LANDING, B. H., SEED, J. C., and BANFIELD, W. G. The effects of a nitrogen mustard (*tris*[2-chloroethyl]amine) on regenerating rat liver. *Cancer 2:* 1067-1074, 1949.

LARSEN, C. D. Evaluation of the carcinogenicity of a series of esters of carbamic acid. *J. Nat. Cancer Inst. 8:* 99-101, 1947a.

LARSEN, C. D. Pulmonary-tumor induction by transplacental exposure to urethane. *J. Nat. Cancer Inst. 8:* 63-70, 1947b.

LARSEN, C. D. Pulmonary-tumor induction with alkylated urethanes. *J. Nat. Cancer Inst. 9:* 35-37, 1948.

LARSEN, C. D., and HESTON, W. E. Induction of pulmonary tumors in mice by anesthetic agents. *Cancer Research 5:* 592, 1945.

LATARJET, R. The primary biological effect of radiations and the structure of microorganisms. *Rev. Canad. Biol. 5:* 9-47, 1946.

LATARJET, R. Production of a bacterial mutation by carcinogenic and non-carcinogenic substances. *Compt. rend. Soc. de biol. 142:* 453-455, 1948.

LATARJET, R. Mode of action of carcinogenic agents on cells. *Paris méd. 8:* 105-110, 1951.

LASER, H. Adaptation of *B. subtilis* to fatty acids. *Biochem. J. 49:* lxvi-lxvii, 1951.

LAUTSCH, W. Ion exchangers on a lignin basis. *Ztschr. f. angew. Chem. 57:* 149-154, 1944.

LEDERBERG, J. A nutritional concept of cancer. *Science 104:* 428, 1946.

LETTERER, E., NEIDHARDT, K., and KLETT, H. Carcinoma of the lung after exposure to chromate and chromate dust: A clinical, pathological-anatomical and occupational study. *Arch. Gewerbepath. Gewerbehyg. 12:* 323-361, 1944.

LEVEEN, H. H., and BARBERIO, J. A. Tissue reaction to plastics used in surgery, with special reference to teflon. *Ann. Surg. 129:* 74-84, 1949.

LEVIN, M. L., GOLDSTEIN, H., and GERHARDT, P. R. Cancer and tobacco smoking. *J.A.M.A. 143:* 336-338, 1950.

LEWIS, M. A., and CROSSLEY, M. L. Retardation of tumor growth in mice by oral administration of ethyleneimine derivatives. *Arch. Biochem. 26:* 319-320, 1950.

LI, M. H., and GARDNER, W. U. Tumors in intrasplenic ovarian transplants in castrated mice. *Science 105:* 13-15, 1947a.

LI, M. H., and GARDNER, W. U. Granulosa cell tumors in intrapancreatic ovarian grafts in castrated mice. *Science 106:* 270, 1947b.

LIMASSET, P., and GAUTHERET, R. The cancerous nature of tobacco tissues accustomed to hetero-auxins. *Compt. rend. Acad. d. sci. 230:* 2043-2045, 1950.

LINDEGREN, C. C., and BRIDGES, C. B. Is agglutination an explanation for the occurrence and for the chromomere-to-chromomere specificity of synapsis? *Science 87:* 510-511, 1938.

LINET, N., and BRACHET, J. The production of ribonucleic acid and glycogen in nucleated and enucleated amine fragments. *Biochim. Biophys. Acta 7:* 607-608, 1951.

LISCO, H., FINKEL, M. P., and BRUES, A. M. Carcinogenic properties of radioactive fission products and of plutonium. *Radiology 49:* 361-363, 1947.

LORENZ, E. Some biologic effects of long continued irradiation. *Am. J. Roentgenol. 63:* 176-185, 1950.

LORENZ, E., ESCHENBRENNER, A. B., HESTON, W. E., and DERINGER, M. K. Carcinogenic activity of gamma and X rays. *Acta Un. Int. Cancer 6:* 818, 1949.

LORENZ, E., ESCHENBRENNER, A. B., HESTON, W. E., and UPHOFF, D. Mammary-tumor incidence in female C3Hb mice following long-continued gamma irradiation. *J. Nat. Cancer Inst. 11:* 947-965, 1951.

LOVELESS, A. *Factors influencing the mitotic cycle, with especial reference to the production of chromosome abnormalities.* Thesis submitted for the degree of Ph.D., University of London, 1950.

LOVELESS, A. Qualitative aspects of the chemistry and biology of radiomimetic (mutagenic) substances. *Nature 167:* 338-342, 1951.

LOVELESS, A., and REVELL, S. H. New evidence of the mode of action of "mitotic poisons." *Nature 164:* 938-944, 1949.

LOVELESS, A., and ROSS, W. C. J. Chromosome alteration and tumour inhibition by nitrogen mustards: the hypothesis of cross-linking alkylation. *Nature 166:* 1112-1114, 1950.

LOWRANCE, P. B., and CARTER, C. E. The effect of nitrogen mustards on the metabolism of nucleic acids in the hematopoietic tissues of the rabbit. *J. Cell. & Comp. Physiol. 35:* 387-401, 1950.

MCKAY, A. F., and BROWNELL, H. H. Syntheses of substituted ββ′-dichloro-diethylamines. *J. Org. Chem. 15:* 648-653, 1950.

MCKINNEY, G. R. The effect of a nitrogen mustard on certain synthetic reactions *in vitro. J. Pharmacol. 96:* 188-192, 1949.

MCKINNEY, G. R. The action of various drugs on certain phases of *in vitro* metabolism. *J. Pharmacol. 100:* 45-50, 1950.

MCKINNEY, G. R. The effect of certain compounds on the *in vitro* synthesis of urea and its precursors. *J. Pharmacol. 101:* 345-352, 1951.

MCMASTER, P. D., and HUDACK, S. S. The formation of agglutinins within lymph nodes. *J. Exper. Med. 61:* 783-805, 1935.

MACHLE, W., and GREGORIUS, F. Cancer of the respiratory system in the chromate-producing industry in the United States. *Proc. 9th Intern. Congr. Industr. Med., London, 1948*, pp. 463-468, 1949.

MANCUSO, T. F. Occupational cancer and other health hazards in a chromate plant. A medical appraisal: II. Clinical and toxicologic aspects. *Indust. Med. 20:* 393-407, 1951.

MANCUSO, T. F., and HUEPER, W. C. Occupational cancer and other health hazards in a chromate plant. A medical appraisal: I. Lung cancers in chromate workers. *Indust. Med. 20:* 358-363, 1951.

MANGUN, G. H., KELLY, A. R., SANDERS, B. E., PIEPES, S. L., WALLBANK, A. M., and HARTMAN, F. W. Virucidal action of mustards and imines. *Federation Proc. 10:* 220-221, 1951.

MANTON, I. The spiral structure of chromosomes. *Biol. Rev. 25:* 486-508, 1950.

MARTIN, M. Influence of the methyl group on the electronic configuration of benzanthracene. Applications to carcinogenic property. *Compt. rend. Acad. d. sc. 223:* 508-509, 1946.

MARTIN, M. Application of the method of molecular mesomerism diagrams to the study of cyclic nitrogen derivatives. *Compt. rend. Acad. d. sc. 227:* 1237-1239, 1948.

MARTLAND, H. S. The occurrence of malignancy in radio-active persons. *Am. J. Cancer 15:* 2435-2516, 1931.

MARTLAND, H. S. Occupational tumors. In I. L. O. Report: *Occupation and Health,* October 1939.

MARTLAND, H. S., and HUMPHRIES, R. E. Osteogenic sarcoma in dial painters using luminous paint. *Arch. Path. 7:* 406-417, 1929.

MATHER, K. The genetical activity of heterochromatin. *Proc. Roy. Soc. s. B. 132:* 308-332, 1944.

MATHER, K. Significance of nuclear change in differentiation. *Nature 161:* 872-874, 1948a.

MATHER, K. Nucleus and cytoplasm in differentiation. *Symp. Soc. Exper. Biol. 2:* 196-216, 1948b.

MATHER, K. *Biometrical Genetics.* London, Methuen, 1949.

MATTHEWS, W. B. A trial of β-naphthyldi-2-chloro-ethylamine (R.48) in leukaemia, Hodgkin's disease and allied diseases. *Lancet 1:* 896-899, 1950.

MAZIA, D. Fiber protein structure in chromosomes and related investigations on protein fibers. *Ann. N. Y. Acad. Sci. 50:* 954-965, 1950.

MAZIA, D., HAZASHI, T., and YUDOWITCH, K. Fiber structure in chromosomes. *Cold Spring Harbor Symp. Quant. Biol. 12:* 122-129, 1947.

MELVILLE, H. W. The breakdown of high polymer molecules. *Sci. Progr. 38:* 1-9, 1950.

MESROBIAN, R. B., and TOBOLSKY, A. V. Some structural and chemical aspects of aging and degradation of vinyl and diene polymers. *J. Polym. Sci. 2:* 463-487, 1947.

MICHAELIS, P. On the relation between cancer induction and plasmatic heredity. *Ztschr. f. Krebsforsch. 56:* 225-233, 1949.

MIDDLEBROOK, W. R. The irreversible combination of formaldehyde with proteins. *Biochem. J. 44:* 17-23, 1949.

MILLER, E. C. Studies on the formation of protein-bound derivatives of 3:4-benzpyrene in the epidermal fractions of mouse skin. *Cancer Research 11:* 100-108, 1951.

MILLER, E. C., and BAUMANN, C. A. The carcinogenicity of *p*-monomethylaminoazobenzene in various diets, and the activity of this dye relative to *p*-dimethylaminoazobenzene. *Cancer Research 6:* 289-295, 1946.

MILLER, E. C., MILLER, J. A., KLINE, B. E., and RUSCH, H. P. Correlation of the level of hepatic riboflavin with the appearance of liver tumors in rats fed aminoazo dyes. *J. Exper. Med. 88:* 89-98, 1948.

MILLER, J. A. Studies on the mechanism of the effects of fats and other dietary factors on carcinogenesis by the azo dyes. *Ann. N. Y. Acad. Sci. 49:* 19-28, 1947.

MILLER, J. A., and BAUMANN, C. A. The determination of *p*-dimethylaminoazobenzene, *p*-monomethylaminoazobenzene and *p*-aminoazobenzene in tissue. *Cancer Research 5:* 157-161, 1945.

MILLER, J. A., KLINE, B. E., and RUSCH, H. P. The inhibition of the carcinogenicity of *p*-dimethylaminoazobenzene by certain detergents, and the effect of diet on the levels of azo dyes in rat tissues. *Cancer Research 6:* 674-678, 1946.

MILLER, J. A., and MILLER, E. C. The metabolism and carcinogenicity of *p*-dimethylaminoazobenzene and related compounds in the rat. *Cancer Research 7:* 39-41, 1946.

MILLER, J. A., and MILLER, E. C. The presence and significance of bound aminoazo dyes in the livers of rats fed *p*-dimethylaminoazobenzene. *Cancer Research 7:* 468-480, 1947.

MILLER, J. A., and MILLER, E. C. The carcinogenicity of certain derivatives of *p*-dimethylaminoazobenzene in the rat. *J. Exper. Med. 87:* 139-156, 1948.

MILLER, J. A., MILLER, E. C., and BAUMANN, C. A. On the methylation and demethylation of certain carcinogenic azo dyes in the rat. *Cancer Research 5:* 162-168, 1945.

MILLER, J. A., MILLER, E. C., and SAPP, R. W. Evidence against the participation of benzidine and semidine rearrangements in carcinogenesis by 4-dimethylaminoazobenzene. *Cancer Research 11:* 269, 1951.

MILLER, J. A., SAPP, R. W., and MILLER, E. C. The absorption spectra of certain carcinogenic aminoazo dyes and the protein-bound derivatives formed from these dyes *in vivo*. *J. Am. Chem. Soc. 70:* 3458-3463, 1948.

MIRSKY, A. E. Chemical properties of isolated chromosomes. *Cold Spring Harbor Symp. Quant. Biol. 12:* 143-146, 1947.

MITCHELL, H. K., and HOULAHAN, M. B. Investigations on the biosynthesis of pyrimidine in *Neurospora*. *Federation Proc. 6:* 506-509, 1947.

MITCHELL, H. K., and LEIN, J. A *Neurospora* mutant deficient in the enzymatic synthesis of tryptophan. *J. Biol. Chem. 175:* 481-482, 1948.

MITCHELL, P. Some observations on the mode of action of penicillin. *Nature 164:* 259-262, 1949.

MOESCHLIN, S., PELAEZ, J. R., and HUGENTOBLER, F. Experimental investigations of the relationship between plasma cells and antibody formation. *Acta Haematol. 6:* 321-334, 1951.

MOORE, S., STEIN, W. H., and FRUTON, J. S. Chemical reactions of mustard gas and related compounds: II. The reaction of mustard gas with carboxyl groups and with the amino groups of amino acids and peptides. *J. Org. Chem. 11:* 675-680, 1946.

MORGAN, T. H. *Embryology and Genetics.* New York, Columbia Univ. Press, 1934.

MORI, K. Effect of liver feeding on liver cancer production by *o*-aminoazotoluol. *Gann 35:* 106-119, 1941.

MORI, K., and NAKAHARA, W. Effect of liver feeding on the production of malignant tumors by injections of carcinogenic substances. *Gann 34:* 48-59, 1940.

MORRIS, H. P., DALTON, A. J., and GREEN, C. D. Malignant thyroid tumors occurring in the mouse after prolonged hormonal imbalance during the ingestion of thiouracil. *J. Clin. Endocrinol. 11:* 1281-1295, 1951.

MORRIS, H. P., DUBNICK, C. S., DUNN, T. B., and WESTFALL, B. B. Some observations on carcinogenicity, distribution and metabolism of N-acetyl-2-aminofluorene in the rat. *Acta Un. Int. Cancer 6:* 47-51, 1948.

MORRIS, H. P., and GREEN, C. D. The role of thiouracil in the induction, growth and transplantability of mouse thyroid tumours. *Science 114:* 44-46, 1951.

MOSTOFI, F. K., and LARSEN, C. D. The histopathogenesis of pulmonary tumors induced in strain A mice by urethane. *J. Nat. Cancer Inst. 11:* 1187-1198, 1951a.

MOSTOFI, F. K., and LARSEN, C. D. Carcinogenic and toxic effects of urethane in animals. *Am. J. Clin. Path. 21:* 342-348, 1951b.

MUELLER, G. C., and MILLER, J. A. The metabolism of 4-dimethylaminoazobenzene by rat liver homogenates. *J. Biol. Chem. 176:* 535-544, 1948.

MUELLER, G. C., and MILLER, J. A. The reductive cleavage of 4-dimethylaminoazobenzene by rat liver: the intracellular distribution of the enzyme system and its requirement for triphosphopyridine nucleotide. *J. Biol. Chem. 180:* 1125-1136, 1949.

MUELLER, G. C., and MILLER, J. A. The metabolism of 4-dimethylaminoazobenzene and related carcinogenic aminoazo dyes by rat liver homogenates. *Acta Un. Int. Cancer 7:* 134-136, 1950.

MUELLER, G. C., MILLER, J. A., and RUSCH, H. P. The disappearance of carcinogenic hydrocarbons in autoxidising lipids. *Cancer Research 5:* 401-404, 1945.

MÜHLBOCK, O. Hormonal ovarian tumours after irradiation by X rays. *Ned. Tijdschr. Geneesk. 95:* 915-920, 1951.

MÜLLER, A. Survey of occupational vesical and renal lesions in the dyestuff industry. *Schweiz. med. Wschr. 79:* 445-449, 1949.

MULLER, H. J. *The Production of Mutations.* (1946 Nobel prizes.) Stockholm, Kungl. Boktryckeriet P. A. Norstedt and Söner, 1948.

NASH, P. H. *The Toxicology of Beryllium in Industry.* Thesis submitted for the degree of M.D., University of Cambridge, January, 1950.

NASH, P. H. Experimental production of malignant tumours by beryllium. *Lancet 1:* 519, 1950.

NEEDHAM, D. M. Reactions of mustard gas with enzymes in tissues and *in vitro. Biochem. J. 42:* xxv, 1948.

NEEDHAM, D. M., COHEN, J. A., and BARRETT, A. M. The mechanism of damage to the bone marrow in systemic poisoning with mustard gas. *Biochem. J. 41:* 631-639, 1947.

NEEDHAM, J. *Chemical Embryology.* Cambridge, Cambridge University Press, 1931, vol. 3, section 14, pp. 1289 ff, and 1326.

NEISH, W. J. P., and SPEAKMAN, J. B. Cross-linking reduced animal fibres. *Nature 164:* 708, 1949.

NETTLESHIP, A., and HENSHAW, P. S. Induction of pulmonary tumors in mice with ethyl carbamate (urethane). *J. Nat. Cancer Inst. 4:* 309-319, 1943.

NEUBAUER, O. Arsenical cancer: A review. *Brit. J. Cancer 1:* 192-251, 1947.

NEWCOMBE, H. B. Delayed phenotypic expression of spontaneous mutations in *Esch coli. Genetics 33:* 447-476, 1948.

NEWCOMBE, H. B., and SCOTT, G. W. Factors responsible for the delayed appearance of radiation-induced mutants in *Escherichia coli. Genetics 34:* 475-492, 1949.

NOBLE, R. L., and PLUNKETT, E. R. Effects of *Lithospermum ruderale* on sex organs of the rat. *Rev. Canad. Biol. 9:* 85-86, 1950.

OBERLING, C., and GUÉRIN, M. Chicken sarcoma produced by methylcholanthrene and become filtrable. *Bull. Ass. Franc. Cancer 37:* 5-14, 1950.

OGSTON, A. G. The replacement reactions of β-β′-dichlorodiethyl sulphide and of some analogues in aqueous solution: The isolation of β-chloro-β′-hydroxy diethyl sulphide *Trans. Faraday Soc. 44:* 45-52, 1948.

O'NEILL, L. A. *The Autoxidation of Drying Oils: Part II.* Research Association of British Paint, Colour, and Varnish Manufacturers, 1948.

OPPENHEIMER, B. S., OPPENHEIMER, E. T., and STOUT, A. P. Sarcomas induced in rats by implanting cellophane. *Tr. A. Am. Physicians 61:* 343-348, 1948a.

OPPENHEIMER, B. S., OPPENHEIMER, E. T., and STOUT, A. P. Sarcomas induced in rats by implanting cellophane. *Proc. Soc. Exper. Biol. & Med. 67:* 33-34, 1948b.

OPPENHEIMER, B. S., OPPENHEIMER, E. T., and STOUT, A. P. Sarcomas induced in rodents by imbedding various plastic films. *Proc. Soc. Exper. Biol. & Med. 79:* 366-369, 1952.

ORMSBEE, R. A., HENRIQUES, F. C., and BALL, E. G. The reaction of mustard gas with skin proteins. *Arch. Biochem. 21:* 301-312, 1949.

ORR, J. W. The induction of pulmonary adenomata in mice by urethane. *Brit. J. Cancer 1:* 311-316, 1947.

ORR, J. W., and PRICE, D. E. Observations on the hepatotoxic action of the carcinogen *p*-dimethylaminoazobenzene. *J. Path. Bact. 60:* 461-469, 1948.

ORR, S. F. D., and THOMPSON, H. W. The infra red spectra of carcinogens: II. Polynuclear hydrocarbons. *J. Chem. Soc.* 218-221, 1950.

PACAULT, A. Thesis presented to the Faculty of Science of the University of Paris. Series A, No. 2133, 1946.

PACAULT, A., and LECOMTE, J. Observations on infra red absorption and carcinogenic activity. *Compt. rend. Acad. d. sc. 228:* 241-242, 1949.

PAULING, L., and DELBRUCK, M. The nature of the intermolecular forces operative in biological processes. *Science 92:* 77-79, 1940.

PECK, R. M., and CREECH, H. J. Isocyanates of dimethylaminostilbenes and acetylaminofluorene. *J. Am. Chem. Soc. 74:* 468-470, 1952.

PETERS, R. A., and WAKELIN, R. W. Observations upon a compound of mustard gas and kerateine. *Biochem. J. 41:* 550-555, 1947.

PFEIFFER, H. H. Experiments with chromosomes isolated from intermitotic nuclei. *Experientia 6:* 334-335, 1950.

PHILIPS, F. S. Recent contributions to the pharmacology of *bis*(2-haloethyl)-amines and sulphides. *Pharmacol. Rev. 2:* 281-323, 1950.

PIRIE, A. The action of mustard gas on ox cornea collagen. *Biochem. J. 41:* 185-190, 1947.

PLUNKETT, E. R., and NOBLE, R. L. Effect of *Lithospermum ruderale* on anterior pituitary hormones. *Rev. Canad. Biol. 9:* 88-89, 1950.

POTTER, V. R. Biological energy transformations and the cancer problem. *Advances in Enzymology 4:* 201-256, 1944.

POTTER, V. R. *Enzymes, Growth and Cancer.* Springfield, Illinois, Charles C Thomas, 1950.

PRESS, E. M., and BUTLER, J. A. V. The action of ionizing radiations and of radiomimetic substances on deoxyribonucleic acid: IV. The products of the action of di-(2-chloroethyl)methylamine. *J. Chem. Soc.* 626-631, 1952.

PRICE, J. M., MILLER, E. C., and MILLER, J. A. The intracellular distribution of protein, nucleic acids, riboflavin and protein bound aminoazo dye in the livers of rats fed *p*-dimethylaminoazobenzene. *J. Biol. Chem. 173:* 345-353, 1948.

PRYOR, M. G. M. On the hardening of the ootheca of Blatta Orientalis. *Proc. Roy. Soc. s. B. 128:* 378-393, 1940.

PRYOR, M. G. M., RUSSELL, P. B., and TODD, A. R. Protocatechuic acid, the substance responsible for the hardening of the cockroach ootheca. *Biochem. J. 40:* 627-628, 1946.

PRZBYTEK, S. The second anhydride of erythritol: $C_4H_6O_2$. *Ber. 17:* 1091-1096, 1884.

PULLINGER, B. D. The significance of functional differentiation in mammary tumours. *Lancet 2:* 823-828, 1949.

PULLMAN, A. A relation between the distribution of electronic charges and the carcinogenic potency of a certain class of hydrocarbons. *Compt. rend. Acad. d. sc. 221:* 140-142, 1945.

PULLMAN, A. A method for calculating the influence of substituents on the distribution of electrons in an aromatic molecule. Application to certain carcinogenic hydrocarbons. *Compt. rend. Acad. d. sc. 222:* 392-394, 1946a.

PULLMAN, A. Electronic structure and carcinogenic activity of condensed aromatic hydrocarbons. *Bull. Ass. Franç. Cancer 33:* 120-130, 1946b.

PULLMAN, A. Electronic structure and carcinogenic activity of aromatic molecules. *Bull. Ass. Franç. Cancer 34:* 245-258, 1947a.

PULLMAN, A. Effect of the addition of saturated rings on the electronic structure and carcinogenic activity of polycyclic hydrocarbons. *Compt. rend. Acad. d. sc. 224:* 120-122, 1947b.

PULLMAN, A. On the electronic nature of cancer induction by organic molecules. *Compt. rend. Acad. d. sc. 225:* 738-740, 1947c.

PULLMAN, A. Electronic structure and carcinogenic activity of derivatives of 4-aminostilbene. *Compt. rend. Acad. d. sc. 226:* 486-488, 1948.

PULLMAN, A., BERTHIER, G., and PULLMAN, B. The energy characteristics of carcinogenic hydrocarbons. *Acta Un. Int. Cancer 7:* 140-148, 1950.

PULLMAN, A., and PULLMAN, B. Distribution of the electronic cloud and chemical reactivity of condensed aromatic hydrocarbons. *Experientia 2:* 364-367, 1946.

PULLMAN, A., and PULLMAN, B. A quantum mechanical study of the electronic structure of carcinogenic molecules. *Acta Un. Int. Cancer 6:* 57-63, 1948.

PULLMAN, A., and PULLMAN, B. A study of the electronic structure of biologically interesting organic molecules by means of wave mechanics. *Bull. Soc. Chim. biol. Paris 31:* 343-353, 1949.

PULLMAN, B. Electronic structure and carcinogenic activity of azoic compounds. *Compt. rend. Acad. d. sc. 222:* 1501-1509, 1946.

PURVES, H. D., and GRIESBACH, W. E. Studies on experimental goitre: 8. Thyroid tumours in rats treated with thiourea. *Brit. J. Exper. Path. 28:* 46-53, 1947.

RAPOPORT, I. A. Carbonyl compounds and the chemical mechanism of mutations. *Compt. rend. Acad. d. sc. URSS. 54:* 65-67, 1946.

RAPOPORT, I. A. The effect of ethylene oxide, glycide and glycols in genic mutation. *Doklady akademii nauk S.S.S.R. 60:* 469-472, 1948.

RAPPAPORT, J., SATINA, S., and BLAKESLEE, A. F. Ovular tumors and inhibition of embryo growth in incompatible crosses of Datura. *Science 111:* 276-277, 1950.

RAY, F. E., and GEISER, C. R. 2-Acetylamino-9-C^{14}-fluorene. *Science 109:* 200, 1949.

READ, J. In *Twenty-seventh Annual Report of the British Empire Cancer Campaign,* 1949, p. 116.

REAUME, S. E., and TATUM, E. L. Spontaneous and nitrogen mustard induced nutritional deficiencies in *Sacch. cerevisiae. Arch. Biochem. 22:* 331-338, 1949.

REHN, L. Bladder tumours in fuchsin workers. *Arch. klin. Chir. 50:* 588-600, 1895.

REVELL, S. H. A cytological investigation of the action of X-rays and radiomimetic chemicals. Thesis submitted to the University of London for the degree of Ph.D., October 1952.

RHOADS, C. P. Physiological aspects of vitamin deficiency. *Proc. Inst. Med. Chicago 13:* 198-205, 1940.

RHOADS, C. P. Carcinogenesis as a conditioned deficiency. *Bull. Johns Hopkins Hospital 70:* 330-331, 1942a.

RHOADS, C. P. Recent studies in production of cancer by chemical compounds; conditioned deficiency as mechanism. *Bull. N. Y. Acad. Med. 18:* 53-64, 1942b.

RHOADS, C. P., and KENSLER, C. J. Nutrition in carcinogenesis. *J. Nutrition 21:* Suppl. 1, 14, 1941.

RIS, H. The composition of chromosomes during mitosis and meiosis. *Cold Spring Harbor Symp. Quant. Biol. 12:* 158-160, 1947.

RIS, H., and MIRSKY, A. E. The state of the chromosomes in the interphase nucleus. *J. Gen. Physiol. 32:* 489-502, 1949.

ROBINSON, R. Some aspects of chemistry related to medicine. *Brit. M. J. 1:* 943-945, 1946.

ROBSON, J. M. Biochemical Subcommittee, Chemical Board, Ministry of Supply, 1st July, 1943. London, H. M. Stationery Office.

ROBSON, J. M., and SCHÖNBERG, A. Oestrous reactions, including mating, produced by triphenyl ethylene. *Nature 140:* 196, 1937.

ROGERS, S. Age of the host and other factors affecting the production with urethane of pulmonary adenomas in mice. *Cancer Research 11:* 275-276, 1951.

ROITT, I. M., and WATERS, W. A. The oxidation of some higher aromatic hydrocarbons with perbenzoic acid. *J. Chem. Soc.* 3060-3062, 1949.

RONDONI, P. *Il Cancro: Istituzioni di Patologia generale dei Tumori.* Milan, Casa Editrice Ambrosiana, 1946.

RONDONI, P. Proteins and enzymes in cancer. *Enzymologia 12:* 128-133, 1947.

RONDONI, P., and BARBIERI, G. P. The action of some carcinogenic compounds on SH-activated enzymes. *Enzymologia 14:* 10-14, 1950.

DE ROPP, R. S. The crown-gall problem. *Bot. Rev. 17:* 629-670, 1951.

ROSE, F. L., HENDRY, J. A., and WALPOLE, A. L. New cytotoxic agents with tumour-inhibitory activity. *Nature 165:* 993-996, 1950.

ROSE, H. M., and GELLHORN, A. Inactivation of influenza virus with sulphur and nitrogen mustards. *Proc. Soc. Exper. Biol. & Med. 65:* 83-85, 1947.

ROSS, W. C. J. Aryl-2-halogenoalkylamines: II. *J. Chem. Soc.* 1972-1983, 1949a.

ROSS, W. C. J. Aryl-2-halogenoalkylamines: I. *J. Chem. Soc.* 183-191, 1949b.

ROSS, W. C. J. Aryl-2-halogenoalkylamines: VI. Reactions with certain organic sulphur compounds. *J. Chem. Soc.* 815-818, 1950a.

ROSS, W. C. J. Biological action of X rays, nitrogen mustards, diepoxides and peroxides. *Nature 165:* 808-810, 1950b.

ROSS, W. C. J. The reactions of certain epoxides in aqueous solutions. *J. Chem. Soc.* 2257-2272, 1950c.

ROSS, W. C. J. The chemistry of cytotoxic alkylating agents. In *Advances in Cancer Research.* New York, Academic Press, 1952, vol. I.

ROZSA, G., and WYCKOFF, R. W. G. The electron microscopy of dividing cells. *Biochem. Biophys. Acta 6:* 334-339, 1950.

RUDALI, G., and MARIANI, P. L. On the production of liver tumours in the XVII Ivry mouse by means of carbon tetrachloride. *Compt. rend. Soc. de biol. 144:* 1626-1627, 1950.

RUSCH, H. P. The antioxidant effect of carcinogenic agents. In C. G. Mackenzie, ed.: *Biological Antioxidants: Transactions of the Second Conference.* New York, Josiah Macy Jr. Foundation, 1948, pp. 106-114.

RUSCH, H. P., and KLINE, B. E. Inhibition of phospholipid oxidation by carcinogenic and related compounds. *Cancer Research 1:* 465-472, 1941.

RUSCH, H. P., and KLINE, B. E. The influence of interrupted carcinogen treatment on tumor formation. *Proc. Soc. Exper. Biol. & Med. 69:* 90-95, 1948.
RUSCH, H. P., and LE PAGE, G. A. The biochemistry of carcinogenesis. *Ann. Rev. Biochem. 17:* 471-494, 1948.
RUSCH, H. P., and MILLER, J. A. Demethylation of carcinogenic aminoazo dyes by autoxidising linoleic acid. *Proc. Soc. Exper. Biol. & Med. 68:* 140-143, 1948.
SALTER, W. T. Chemistry of carcinogens. *Occup. Med. 5:* 441-465, 1948.
SALZBERG, D. A., NYE, W., and GRIFFIN, A. C. A labeled carcinogenic azo dye: 3′-methyl-(C^{14})4-dimethylaminoazobenzene. *Arch. Biochem. 27:* 243-244, 1950.
SANDIN, R. B., and FIESER, L. F. Synthesis of 9,10-dimethyl-1,2-benzanthracene and of a thiophene isolog. *J. Am. Chem. Soc. 62:* 3098-3105, 1940.
SANDORFY, C., VROELANT, C., YVAN, P., CHALVET, O., and DAUDEL, R. A comparison of static and dynamic methods for predicting the chemical properties of molecules from their molecular diagrams. *Bull. Soc. Chim. Fr. 17:* 304-311, 1950.
SANDULESCO, G. W., TCHUNG, W. W., and GIRARD, A. Contribution to knowledge of female sex hormones. *Compt. rend. Acad. d. sc. 196:* 137-140, 1933.
SANFORD, K. K., EARLE, W. R., SHELTON, E., SCHILLING, E. L., DUCHESNE, E. M., LIKELY, G. D., and BECKER, M. M. Production of malignancy *in vitro*: XII. Further transformations of mouse fibroblasts to sarcomatous cells. *J. Nat. Cancer Inst. 11:* 351-375, 1950.
SCHLACK, P. Treatment of materials for varying their affinity. U. S. Patent 2,131,146, September 27, 1938.
SCHLANG, H. A. The Schwartzman phenomenon: I. Inhibitory action of nitrogen mustard (HN2). *Proc. Soc. Exper. Biol. & Med. 74:* 749-751, 1950.
SCHMIDT, M. B. Vital fat staining in tissues and secretions by Sudan dye, and tumorous proliferation of the secretory glands. *Virchows Arch. f. Path. Anat. 253:* 432-451, 1924.
SCHMIDT, O. Relation between density distribution of definite valence electrons (*B*-electrons) and reactivity of aromatic hydrocarbons. *Ztschr. f. physikal. Chem. B39:* 59-82, 1938.
SCHMIDT, O. The characterisation of simple and carcinogenic aromatic hydrocarbons by the density distribution of definite valence electrons (*B*-electrons). *Ztschr. f. physikal. Chem. B42:* 83-110, 1939a.
SCHMIDT, O. Density distribution and energy spectrum of *B*-electrons: IV. Mechanism of the excitation process in cancerous and healthy cells. *Ztschr. f. physikal. Chem. B44:* 194-202, 1939b.
SCHMIDT, O. Characterisation and mode of action of the carcinogenic hydrocarbons. *Naturwiss. 29:* 146-150, 1941a.
SCHMIDT, O. The mechanism of action of carcinogenic organic substances. *Tumori 27:* 475-497, 1941b.
SCHÖNTAL, R., and SCOTT, E. J. Y. Fluorescence spectra of polycyclic aromatic hydrocarbons in solution. *J. Chem. Soc.* 1683-1696, 1949.
SCHRÖDINGER, E. *What Is Life? The Physical Aspect of the Living Cell.* Cambridge, Cambridge University Press, 1944.
SCHROETER, G. The chemical mechanism of reactions by means of aluminium chloride for synthesis and degradation. *Ber. d. deutsch. chem. Gesellsch. 57:* 1990-2003, 1924.
SCHULTZ, J. The nature of heterochromatin. *Cold Spring Harbor Symp. Quant. Biol. 12:* 179-191, 1947.
SCHULTZ, J. The question of plasmagenes. *Science 111:* 403-407, 1950.

SCHWAB, L., MOLL, F. C., HALL, T., BREAN, H., KIRK, M., HAWN, C. v. Z., and JANEWAY, C. A. Experimental hypersensitivity in the rabbit: Effect of inhibition by antibody formation, by X-radiation and nitrogen mustards on the histologic and serologic sequences, and on the behavior of serum complement, following single large injections of foreign proteins. *J. Exper. Med. 91:* 505-526, 1950.

SCOTT, A. The occupation dermatoses of the paraffin workers of the Scottish shale oil industry, with a description of the system adopted and the results obtained at the periodic examinations of these workmen. *8th Scientific Report, Imperial Cancer Research Fund* 85-142. London, 1923.

SEDAR, A. W., and WILSON, D. F. Electron microscopy study of mitosis in the onion root tip. *Anat. Rec. 108:* 531-532, 1950.

SERRA, J. A. Composition of chromonemata and matrix and the role of nucleoproteins in mitosis and meiosis. *Cold Spring Harbor Symp. Quant. Biol. 12:* 192-210, 1947a.

SERRA, J. A. Contributions to a physiological interpretation of mitosis and meiosis: I. The composition of the resting stage nucleus. *Portug. Acta Biol. 2:* 25-44, 1947b.

SERRA, J. A. Contributions to a physiological interpretation of mitosis and meiosis: II. The prophasic appearing of the chromonemata and the spiralization. *Portug. Acta Biol. 2:* 45-90, 1947c.

SERRA, J. A. The parallelism between the chemical and the morphological changes during mitosis and meiosis. Proc. 6th Int. Congr. Exper. Cytology. *Exper. Cell Res., Suppl. 1:* 111-122, 1949.

SHEAR, M. J. Carcinogenic activity of some anthracene derivatives. *J. Biol. Chem. 123:* Proc. cviii-cix, 1938.

SISSONS, H. A. Bone sarcomas produced experimentally in the rabbit, using compounds of beryllium. *Acta Un. Int. Cancer 7:* 171-172, 1950.

SMITH, J. F. Multiple primary self-healing squamous epithelioma of skin. *Brit. J. Derm. Syph. 60:* 315-318, 1948.

SMITH, H. H., and SRB, A. M. Induction of mutations with β-propiolactone. *Science 114:* 490-492, 1951.

SMITH, T. R., JACOBSON, L. O., SPURR, C. L., ALLEN, J. G., and BLOCK, M. H. A coagulation defect produced by nitrogen mustard. *Science 107:* 474, 1948.

SMITH, W. E., SUNDERLAND, D. A., and SUGIURA, K. Experimental analysis of the carcinogenic activity of certain petroleum products. *Arch. Indust. Hyg. 4:* 299-314, 1951.

SNEGIREFF, L. S., and LOMBARD, O. M. Arsenic and cancer: Observations in the metallurgical industry. *Arch. Indust. Hyg. 4:* 199-205, 1951.

SONNEBORN, T. M. Cellular transformations. *Harvey Lectures, Ser. XLIV,* 145-164, 1950a.

SONNEBORN, T. M. The cytoplasm in heredity. *Heredity 4:* 11-36, 1950b.

SPEAKMAN, J. B. Some practical applications of recent research on wool. *Medd. svenska Textilforskn. Inst. No. 7,* 1948.

SPEAKMAN, J. B., CHAMBERLAIN, N. H., and DORKIN, C. M. C. Production of alkali resistant alginate materials. U. S. Patent 2,536,893, January 2, 1951.

SPITZ, S., and HIGINBOTHAM, N. L. Osteogenic sarcoma following prophylactic roentgen-ray therapy: Report of a case. *Cancer 4:* 1107-1112, 1951.

SPITZ, S., MAGUIGAN, W. H., and DOBRINER, K. The carcinogenic action of benzidine. *Cancer 3:* 789-804, 1950.

STAHMANN, M. A., and STAUFFER, J. F. Induction of mutants in *Penicillin notatum* by methyl-*bis*(β-chloroethyl)amine. *Science 106:* 35-36, 1947.

STALLYBRASS, C. O. The mechanism of anti-body production. *Proc. Roy. Soc. Med. 43:* 137-141, 1950.

STEARN, A. E. Kinetics of biological reactions. *Advances in Enzymology 9:* 25-74, 1949.

STEIN, W. H., and MOORE, S. Chemical reactions of mustard gas and related compounds: III. The reaction of mustard gas with methionine. *J. Org. Chem. 11:* 681-685, 1946.

STERN, K. G. Nucleoproteins and gene structure. *Yale J. Biol. & Med. 19:* 937-949, 1947.

STEVENS, C. M., MCKENNIS, H., and DU VIGNEAUD, V. Studies on the effect of mustard-type vesicants on the phenol color reaction of proteins. *J. Am. Chem. Soc. 70:* 2556-2559, 1948.

STEVENS, C. M., and MYLROIE, A. Mutagenic activity of β-chloroalkyl amines and sulphides. *Nature 166:* 1019, 1950.

STEVENS, C. M., WOOD, J. L., RACHELE, J. R., and DU VIGNEAUD, V. Studies on acid hydrolysates of vesicant-treated insulin. *J. Am. Chem. Soc. 70:* 2554-2556, 1948.

STRONG, L. C. Genetic analysis of the induction of tumors by methyl cholanthrene: XI. Germinal mutations and other sudden biological changes following the subcutaneous injection of methyl cholanthrene. *Proc. Nat. Acad. Sci. 31:* 290-293, 1945.

STRONG, L. C. A new theory of mutation and the origin of cancer. *Yale J. Biol. & Med. 21:* 293-299, 1949a.

STRONG, L. C. The induction of mutations by a carcinogen. *Proc. 8th Int. Congr. Genetics, Lund* 486-499, 1949b.

SUGIURA, K. Effect of feeding dried milk on production of liver cancer by *p*-dimethylaminoazobenzene. *Proc. Soc. Exper. Biol. & Med. 57:* 231-234, 1944.

SUNDERLAND, D. A., SMITH, W. E., and SUGIURA, K. The pathology and growth behavior of experimental tumors induced by certain petroleum products. *Cancer 4:* 1232-1245, 1951.

SWANSON, C. P., MCELROY, W. D., and MILLER, H. The effect of nitrogen mustard pre-treatment on the ultraviolet induced morphological and biochemical mutation rate. *Proc. Nat. Acad. Sci. 35:* 513-518, 1949.

TALIAFERRO, W. H. Cellular basis of immunity. *Ann. Rev. Microbiol. 3:* 159-194, 1949.

TALIAFERRO, W. H., and TALIAFERRO, L. G. Effect of X-rays on immunity: A review. *J. Immunol. 66:* 181-212, 1951.

TATUM, E. L. Induced biochemical mutations in bacteria. *Cold Spring Harbor Symp. Quant. Biol. 11:* 278-283, 1946.

TATUM, E. L., and BONNER, D. Indole and serine in the biosynthesis and breakdown of tryptophane. *Proc. Nat. Acad. Sci. 30:* 30-37, 1944.

TAYLOR, J. H. Chromosome structure and behavior in relation to gene action. *Genetics, 36:* 579-580, 1951.

THERMAN-SUOMALAINEN, E. Heterochromatin and nucleic acid. *J. Sci. Agr. Soc. Finland 20:* 37-47, 1948.

THOMPSON, H. W., VAGO, E. E., CORFIELD, M. C., and ORR, S. F. D. The infra-red spectra of carcinogens: I. Derivatives of stilbene. *J. Chem. Soc.* 214-218, 1950.

THOMPSON, K. F., MACKEY, J., GUSTAFSSON, A., and EHRENBERG, L. The mutagenic effect of radiophosphorus in barley. *Hereditas 36:* 220-224, 1950.

TILAK, B. In *Twenty-third Annual Report of the British Empire Cancer Campaign,* 109-110, 1946.

TILAK, B. D. Sulphur isosters of carcinogenic hydrocarbons: I. *Proc. Indian Acad. Sci. 33A:* 131-141, 1951.

TIMMIS, G. M. Dimethanesulphonoxyalkanes: A new type of bifunctional radiomimetic compound. *Abstracts of Papers, XIIth Int. Congr. Pure and Appl. Chemistry* 334-335, 1951.

TOMLIN, S. G., and CALLAN, H. G. Preliminary account of an electron microscope study of chromosomes from newt oocytes. *Quart. J. Micr. Sci. 92:* 221-224, 1951.

TRUHAUT, R. Contribution to the study of occupational cancers: Bladder carcinogens. *Semaine d. hôp. Paris 25:* 3078-3084, 1949a.

TRUHAUT, R. Chemical factors in the induction of cancer. *Biol. med. 38:* 1-47; 89-115, 1949b.

TSUTSUI, H. Artificially-produced cancroid in the mouse. *Gann 12:* 17-21, 1918.

TURNER, F. C. Sarcomas at sites of subcutaneously implanted bakelite discs. *J. Nat. Cancer Inst. 2:* 81-83, 1941.

TYLER, A. An auto-antibody concept of cell structure in growth. Sixth Growth Symposium. *Growth 10:* 7-19, 1946.

UMBREIT, W. W., WOOD, W. A., and GUNSALUS, I. C. The activity of pyridoxal phosphate in tryptophane formation by cell-free enzyme preparations. *J. Biol. Chem. 165:* 731-732, 1946.

VANDERLYN, L. The heterochromatin problem in cytogenetics as related to other branches of investigation. *Bot. Rev. 15:* 507-582, 1949.

VICKERSTAFF, T. *Physical Chemistry of Dyeing.* Published for Imperial Chemical Industries Ltd., Edinburgh, 1950, pp. 57 ff., 172.

DU VIGNEAUD, V., STEVENS, C. M., MCDUFFIE, H. F., WOOD, J. L., and MCKENNIS, H. Reactions of mustard-type vesicants with α-amino acids. *J. Am. Chem. Soc. 70:* 1620-1624, 1948.

WADDINGTON, C. H., and CARTER, T. C. Malformations in mouse embryos induced by trypan blue. *Nature 169:* 27-28, 1952.

WALLACE, B. Dominant lethals and sex-linked lethals induced by nitrogen mustard. *Genetics 36:* 364-373, 1951.

WALTER, J. Epithelioma and papilloma arising on recently irradiated skin. *Brit. M. J. 1:* 273-274, 1950.

WARREN, S. The pathologic effects of an instantaneous dose of radiation. *Cancer Research 6:* 449-453, 1946.

WATERS, W. A. *Chemistry of Free Radicals* (ed. 2). Oxford, Clarendon Press, 1948.

WATKINS, W. M., and WORMALL, A. Inactivation of complement by nitrogen mustard. *Nature 162:* 535-536, 1948.

WEDGWOOD, P., and COOPER, R. L. The detection and determination of small quantities of polynuclear hydrocarbons by a combination of chromatographs and absorption spectroscopy. *Chem. Ind.* 1066-1067, 1951.

WEIGERT, F., and MOTTRAM, J. C. The biochemistry of benzpyrene: II. The course of its metabolism and the chemical nature of the metabolites. *Cancer Research 6:* 109-120, 1946.

WHITE, M. J. D. Nucleus, Chromosomes and Genes. In G. H. Bourne, ed: *Cytology and Cell Physiology* (ed. 2). Oxford, Clarendon Press, 1951, pp. 103-231.

WHITING, A. R. Absence of mutagenic action of X-rayed cytoplasm in *Habrobracon. Proc. Nat. Acad. Sci. 36:* 368-372, 1950.

WIELAND, H., and DANE, E. The constitution of the bile acids: LII. The place of attachment of the side chain. *Hoppe Seyler Z. 219:* 240-244, 1933.

WILSON, E. B. *The Cell in Development and Heredity.* New York, Macmillan, 1906.

WILSON, R. H., DE EDS, F., and COX, A. J. Toxicity and carcinogenic activity of 2-acetaminofluorene. *Cancer Research 1:* 595-608, 1941.

WINTERNITZ, M. C. *Collected Studies on the Pathology of War Gas Poisoning.* New Haven, Yale University Press, 1920.

WOLF, G. *Chemical Induction of Cancer.* London, Cassell, 1952.

WOLFE, J. K., FIESER, L. F., and FRIEDGOOD, H. B. Nature of the androgens in female adrenal tumor urine. *J. Am. Chem. Soc. 63:* 582-593, 1941.

WOOD, J. L., RACHELE, J. R., STEVENS, C. M., CARPENTER, F. H., and DU VIGNEAUD, V. The reaction of some radioactive mustard-type vesicants with purified proteins. *J. Am. Chem. Soc. 70:* 2547-2550, 1948.

WOODHOUSE, D. L. The carcinogenic activity of some petroleum fractions and extracts. *J. Hyg. 48:* 121-134, 1950.

WOOLLEY, G. W. Physiological relationships of pituitary tumors in experimental F1 reciprocal hybrid mice. *Acta Un. int. Cancer 6:* 265-267, 1948.

WOOLLEY, G. W., and LITTLE, C. C. The incidence of adrenal cortical carcinoma in male mice of the extreme dilution strain over one year of age. *Cancer Research 5:* 506-509, 1945.

WOOLLEY, G. W., and LITTLE, C. C. Prevention of adrenal cortical carcinoma by diethylstilbestrol. *Proc. Nat. Acad. Sc. 32:* 239-240, 1946.

WYNDER, E. L., and GRAHAM, E. A. Tobacco smoking as a possible etiologic factor in bronchiogenic carcinoma. *J.A.M.A. 143:* 329-336, 1950.

WYNDER, E. L., and GRAHAM, E. A. Etiologic factors in bronchiogenic carcinoma, with special reference to industrial exposures: Reports of 857 proved cases. *Arch. Indust. Hyg. 4:* 221-235, 1951.

YAMAGIWA, K., and ICHIKAWA, K. Experimental study of the pathogenesis of epithelial tumours. *Mitt. med. Fak. kaiserl. Univ. zu Tokio 15:* 295-344, 1915.

YASUZUMI, G. The microstructure of chromosome threads in the metabolic stage of the nucleus. *Chromosoma 4:* 222-231, 1951.

YASUZUMI, G., and MIYAO, G. Amino acid constituents of prochromosomes isolated from blood cells of various animals. *Science 114:* 38-39, 1951.

YASUZUMI, G., MIYAO, G., YAMAMOTO, Y., and YOKOYAMA, J. The microstructure and origin of the threadlike bodies isolated from the metabolic nucleus. *Chromosoma 4:* 359-368, 1951.

YOSHIDA, T. Development of experimental hepatoma by the use of *o*-amidoazotoluene, with particular reference to gradual changes in the liver up to the time of development of carcinoma. *Tr. Jap. Path. Soc. 24:* 523-530, 1934.

YOUNG, E. G., and CAMPBELL, R. B. The reaction of $\beta\beta'$-dichlorodiethylsulphide with proteins. *Canad. J. Res. 25:* 37-48, 1947.

YOUNG, L. The metabolic conversion of naphthalene to 1:2-dihydronaphthalene-1:2-diol. *Biochem. J. 41:* 417-422, 1947.

ZAHL, P. A. Some characteristics of the anti-estrous factor in *Lithospermum. Proc. Soc. Exper. Biol. & Med. 67:* 405-410, 1948.

ZAHL, P. A., and NOWAK, A. Incidence of spontaneous mammary tumors in mice with *Lithospermum*-induced diestrus. *Proc. Soc. Exper. Biol. & Med. 77:* 5-8, 1951.

ZAJDELA, F., and BUU-HOI, N. P. Carcinogenic activity of new angular benzacridines. *Acta Un. Int. Cancer 7:* 184-189, 1950.

ZECHMEISTER, L., and KOE, B. K. The isolation of carcinogenic and other polycyclic aromatic hydrocarbons from barnacles. *Arch. Biochem. 35:* 1-11, 1952.

ZOLLINGER, H. U. A spindle cell sarcoma of the kidney, 16 years after thorotrast pyelography. *Schweiz. med. Wchnschr. 79:* 1266-1268, 1949.

CHAPTER 18

The Chemistry of Cancer Tissue

Richard J. Winzler

The differences in histology and in growth behavior which distinguish malignant tissues from their normal counterparts must have a fundamental basis in the function and in the chemical composition of the individual cells and tissues. To what extent are such differences determinable? Is there any aspect of chemical composition which is characteristic of cancer? These are the major questions that confront the cancer chemist. It is from this viewpoint of the comparative chemistry of normal and malignant tissue that this discussion has been written. No attempt has been made to refer extensively to the vast literature pertaining to the chemistry of cancer tissue. This has, in large part, already been done in the excellent monographs by Stern and Willheim[64] and by Greenstein.[22] This discussion will be concerned with a few aspects of the problem which appear to the author to merit special consideration, and will be documented sparingly by reference to recent papers. Consideration of those aspects of the chemistry of malignant tissue pertaining to nucleic acids and to enzymatic constitution will be omitted here, since they are discussed in detail in Chapters 19 and 20 respectively.

SOME PROBLEMS OF COMPARISON

One of the knotty problems to be faced in comparing normal and malignant tissue is the selection of the basis on which comparisons should be made. This problem is not a simple one. The chemical composition of the various normal tissues may be very different, these differences reflecting, in part, the specialized functions of the tissue. To what tissue, then, should a cancer be compared? There appear to be a number of approaches to this problem, three of which merit special consideration.

Comparative studies of the chemical composition of normal and tumor tissues may be made by analyzing a large number of normal and malignant tissues. Application of statistical methods would then indicate whether or not any differences were significant and characteristic of cancer. Because of the varied chemistry of normal tissues, such studies would be unlikely to reveal anything but very gross alterations associated with cancer.

A second, more satisfactory method involves the comparison of a tumor with its tissue of origin. This avoids the complications associated with the study of completely unrelated tissues. However, problems still hinder interpretation of such comparative data. There is, for example, a considerable likelihood of changes in composition associated with the loss of the specialized structure or function of the normal tissue during the development of cancer. There is the further question as to whether comparisons should more properly be made between a tumor and the embryonic form of the tissue of origin, since, in many respects, the rapidly growing embryonic tissue more closely resembles cancer than does the more stable adult tissue.

The third, and perhaps most satisfactory approach, is the study of changes associated with the development of cancer from normal tissue. This is especially feasible in the case of chemical carcinogenesis. The problems mentioned above also pertain to this approach, but they become less troublesome since the intermediary "precancerous" stages between the normal and the malignant tissue can be studied.

Serious and fundamental objections can be found to each of these approaches. The variations between the chemistry of normal tissues are so great as to obscure any but the grossest changes that may be associated with cancer. The question of what normal and malignant pairs can be considered truly homologous is a most difficult one. Associated with this problem is the question of the relative contribution of normal and cancer tissue to the chemistry of a particular neoplasm, since tumors usually have a liberal complement of normal stroma or other tissue. In dealing with precancerous tissue it is not known whether all the cells are precancerous or whether the carcinogenic changes are associated with only a few isolated areas.

Still another problem complicating the comparative chemistry of malignant tissue is the selection of the best basis to which the concentration of any constituent should be referred. Most commonly, constituents have been expressed as grams per unit of either the wet or the dry weight of the tissues. Such expressions neglect the pronounced changes in water content, in extracellular inorganic (e.g., bone salts), or organic (e.g., collagen) constituents of the tissue that may be associated with the development of cancer. Other investigators have expressed concentrations on the basis of the total nitrogen or the total nucleic acid phosphorus. Perhaps the most accurate reference basis is the desoxyribose nucleic acid, since this is a nuclear constituent, and appears to be constant in any given type of cell (see, for example, Price and Laird[45]).

It is clear that the proper comparison of normal and tumor tissues from a chemical point of view is not just a matter of the application of simple analytic methods to tissue. Refined methods as well as careful control and selection of tissues must be applied if significance is to be attached to observed differences in chemical constitution.

GROSS CHEMICAL COMPOSITION

WATER, PROTEIN, CARBOHYDRATE, FAT, AND MINERALS

A large literature exists on the content of moisture, protein, carbohydrate, fat, and minerals in cancer tissue. Since all tissues, normal and malignant, contain these constituents in variable amounts, it is evident that only extreme changes will show significant trends. The monographs and recent reviews[4, 6, 21, 22, 57, 64] all contain references to such changes. In Table 30 is summarized, in a qualitative manner, the impression this reviewer has gained as to the comparative chemistry of normal and tumor tissue with respect to some of these gross constituents.

TABLE 30. COMPARATIVE CHEMICAL COMPOSITION OF NORMAL AND MALIGNANT TISSUE (Qualitative Impressions)

Constituent	*Comments*
Water	Increased significantly in most tumors as compared to homologous normal tissues.
Protein	A slight but definite decrease in most tumors. This is, in large part, referable to the increased water content.
Carbohydrate	The glycogen content of tumors arising from glycogen-poor tissues is usually increased over the homologous normal tissue.
Lipids	The lipid content frequently (but with many exceptions) appears to be increased in malignant tissue. This appears to be particularly true of the phospholipids and of cholesterol.
Nucleic acids	The nucleic acid content, especially the desoxyribose nucleic acid, appears to be increased significantly in tumor tissue as compared to the homologous normal tissue.
Potassium	A definite trend exists for the potassium to be increased in malignant tissue.
Calcium	A clear tendency exists for the calcium to be decreased in malignant tissue.

It should not be inferred from the condensation of the vast amount of work into the qualitative impressions of Table 30 that this work has been valueless. The suggestion is implicit, however, that it will be necessary to go much further into the more subtle chemistry of tissue to seek out those changes which are responsible for the special characteristics of tumor tissue.

Of the gross constituents mentioned in Table 30, the most constant difference between normal and tumor tissues is the increased water content of the latter. Most authors who have studied the chemistry of tumors have made the observation that the dry weight of tumor tissue is less than that of the corresponding normal tissue. The high water content of tumor tissue is shared by embryonic tissue, and therefore cannot be considered as uniquely characteristic of neoplasia. The significance of the increased water content is not known, but the suggestion has been made that it represents a tendency toward increased protein hydration.

The total amount of protein in tumors is usually somewhat less than in normal tissues, when expressed on a moist weight basis. However, this difference may disappear when the protein content is expressed on a dry weight basis.

Potassium is frequently high and calcium low in malignant tissue, giving an increased potassium-calcium ratio. This has been the subject of numerous studies, reviewed by Stern and Willheim.[64] deLong *et al.*[30] have recently suggested, on the basis of their analysis of the calcium and potassium content of normal and malignant human tissues and of normal and regenerating rat livers, that the decrease in the calcium content of tumor is more characteristic of malignancy than is the increase of potassium in such tissue. This suggestion was based on the observation that the potassium content is increased in regenerating rat liver, whereas the calcium is normal in this tissue. The suggestion was also advanced that the reduced calcium content of malignant tissue is a factor involved in the decreased mutual adhesiveness of cells observed in such tissue.[30]

The differences in the nucleic acid content of normal and of tumor tissues seem to be significant. This is discussed in detail in Chapter 19.

The inconstant changes in lipids and carbohydrates appear to lack special significance.

EPIDERMAL CARCINOGENESIS IN MICE

Most illuminating and extensive studies of the comparative chemistry of normal and malignant tissue have been made by the St. Louis group headed by Cowdry.[17] This group has investigated the histology, biochemical activities, and chemical composition of mouse epidermis in various stages of the development of squamous cell carcinomas following repeated painting with methylcholanthrene. In a recent review, Carruthers[7] has summarized the work of this laboratory. The chemical aspects of this work are gathered together in Table 31. The data, based on work carefully controlled and executed, may serve as a basis of discussion of the comparative studies of the gross chemical composition of a normal and homologous malignant tissue.

The results shown in Table 31 are in general accord with the observations and impressions summarized in Table 30, but can be considered as having greater validity, at least with respect to mouse epidermis and the corresponding carcinoma which arises from it under the influence of methylcholanthrene.

The water content of the epidermal tissue rises from a normal value of 60.9 per cent to 65.6 per cent in the hyperplastic tissue prior to the development of the carcinoma, and is still higher (81.7 per cent) in the cancer.[65] This increase in water content has been uniformly observed in cancer tissue.

Table 31 shows little change in protein nitrogen during the precancerous hyperplasia. This is followed by a distinct drop in the transplanted carcinomas derived from a methylcholanthrene-produced tumor.[53] If this protein nitrogen is expressed on a dry weight basis, however, the differences become insignificant. Of particular interest is the observation that the nonprotein nitrogen (trichloracetic acid-soluble nitrogen) drops from about 0.8 per cent or 0.9 per cent in the normal or precancerous tissue to 0.23 per cent in the tumor. This has led to the suggestion that the tumor is more efficient in utilizing nitrogenous intermediates of low molecular weight than are the normal tissues. Some of this nonprotein nitrogen is in the free amino acid fractions studied by Roberts *et al.*[54, 55, 56] and is discussed later.

Table 31 shows data by Wicks and Suntzeff[67] indicating that the total lipid

TABLE 31. CHANGES IN GROSS CHEMICAL COMPOSITION ASSOCIATED WITH EPIDERMAL METHYLCHOLANTHRENE CARCINOGENESIS IN MICE

Constituent	*Units**	*Normal epidermis*	*Benzene treated*	*Hyper-plastic†*	*Carcinoma‡*	*Reference No.*
Water	Gm./100 Gm.	60.9	—	65.6	81.6	65
Total N	Gm./100 Gm.	4.56	4.19	4.66	2.28	53
Nonprotein N	Gm./100 Gm.	0.79	0.92	0.95	0.23	53
Protein §	Gm./100 Gm.	23.6	20.4	23.2	12.8	53
Total lipid ‖	Gm./100 Gm.	19.27	16.65	7.79	—	67
Cholesterol ‖	Gm./100 Gm.	0.99	0.69	0.56	—	67
Phospholipid P ¶	mg./Gm.	1.63	1.53	1.20	3.11	16
Nucleoprotein P	mg./Gm.	1.24	1.19	1.30	0.75	
Potassium	μg./100 Gm.	347.	351.	346.	326.	7
Sodium	μg./100 Gm.	168.	163.	141.	141.	7
Calcium	μg./100 Gm.	44.	42.	19.	9.	7
Magnesium	μg./100 Gm.	19.	19.	22.6	18.0	7
Zinc	μg./100 Gm.	5.2	5.5	3.8	1.7	7
Copper	μg./100 Gm.	0.58	0.58	0.33	0.10	7
Iron	μg./100 Gm.	6.4	8.1	2.5	—	8
Biotin	μg./Gm.	0.196	0.194	0.125	0.149	51
Choline	mg./Gm.	2.47	2.18	2.65	6.24	51
Inositol	mg./Gm.	0.53	0.57	0.55	1.15	51
PABA	μg./Gm.	2.4	2.3	2.4	3.09	51
B_6 complex	μg/Gm.	2.45	2.88	3.05	4.10	51
Ascorbic acid	mg./Gm.	0.24	0.21	0.22	0.14	8

* Moist wet basis (unless otherwise indicated)
† Treated 10 to 20 days with methylcholanthrene in benzene
‡ Transplanted squamous cell carcinoma derived from methylcholanthrene-induced tumor
§ Protein N (by difference) × 6.25. The values are probably high due to phospholipid nitrogen etc.
‖ Calculated from lipid/protein N[67] and % protein N[53]
¶ Dry, fat: free tissue

and the cholesterol content falls during the first phases of methylcholanthrene carcinogenesis in mouse epidermis. This fall may largely reflect the disappearance of the sebaceous glands as a result of treatment with the carcinogen. The amount of phospholipid, however, shows a distinct increase as a result of carcinogenesis.[16] Evidence for a qualitative change in the lipids as a result of malignant changes in epidermis has been adduced by Carruthers and Suntzeff.[9, 10, 11] These investigators extracted the tissue lipids with ether and alcohol, and polarographed these lipids in a mixture of dioxane and water. The polarographic waves, given by electroreducible materials in the lipid extract, showed distinct differences between normal and hyperplastic mouse epidermis as compared to the homologous carcinoma. Appreciation of the significance of these lipids must await further study of their chemical character, but the results, if substantiated and if applicable to other tumors, will obviously be of considerable interest.

Strikingly reduced amounts of calcium, zinc, and copper were found in hyperplastic epidermis, and still further reductions were found in the carcinomas.[7] The significance of these observations depends on further clarification of the functions of these metals in the cell. Not only is the amount of calcium diminished, but there is some evidence that the physiologic state of the calcium may be altered during epidermal carcinogenesis. Thus, Lansing and co-workers[27] have studied the partition of calcium between ultrafilterable and nonultrafilterable forms in normal and hyperplastic epidermis and squamous cell carcinoma in mice. There appeared, in the tumor, to be a diminution in the percentage of the total calcium which was ultrafilterable. Distinct differences in the ability of normal or hyperplastic mouse epidermis and the homologous carcinoma to exchange intracellular calcium with extracellular calcium have been noted by Lansing, Rosenthal, and Kamen.[28] The carcinomatous tissues were unable to exchange this metal, suggesting that in cancer there may be alterations in the calcium-binding mechanisms, perhaps at the cell surface.

The B complex and ascorbic acid content of normal and hyperplastic epidermis, and the corresponding transplanted squamous cell carcinoma are shown in Table 31. These results will be discussed later.

COMPARATIVE STUDIES ON PROTEINS AND AMINO ACIDS

CELLULAR PARTICULATES

The application of differential centrifugation to the isolation of the cytoplasmic particulate constituents from tissue homogenates has resulted, in recent years, in a large amount of work on the chemistry, biochemistry, and cytology of the cell particulates and soluble proteins. It appears that extension of this work may be of special importance to the fundamental aspects of the cancer problem. The nuclei are first collected by low-speed centrifugation. Most workers refer to the fraction sedimented at 18,000 g for five minutes in isotonic salt or at 20,000 g for fifteen minutes in 0.88 M sucrose as large granules or mitochondria. The small granule or microsome fraction sediments at 18,000 g in ninety minutes in isotonic saline or at 20,000 g in four hours in 0.88 M sucrose. The supernatant proteins remain in solution under these circumstances. Claude, one of the pioneers in this field, has studied the chemical composition of the mitochondria, the microsomes, and the supernatant proteins of a number of normal and malignant tissues.[12, 13, 14, 15]

A striking feature of the cellular particulates is the elevated lipid content of both mitochondria and microsomes. Much of this is phospholipid in nature. The nucleic acid content is also high in both types of particulates, this nucleic acid being almost entirely of the pentose type. The chemical composition of the mitochondria and the microsomes is similar regardless of the tissue from which they were isolated. The mitochondria isolated from malignant tissue do not appear to differ appreciably from normal mitochondria (see also Dittmar[19]). It is of interest that the mitochondria and microsomes each account for about 15 per cent of the cytoplasmic solids of liver, the remainder being in the supernatant following removal of the microsomes. The relative amounts of the cytoplasmic constituents may vary from one tissue to another.

The similarity of cellular particulates to certain viruses has been pointed out, and the suggestion has been advanced that cancer may be a cytoplasmic disease due to the self-duplication of abnormal mitochondria.[68] Evidence has also been presented that the melanin of the Cloudman S-91 and the Harding-Passey mouse melanomas are associated with the mitochondria fraction of the tumor cells.[5, 69] The cytologic properties and biochemical activities of this fraction from the original S-91 melanoma and from a partially amelanotic tumor derived from it were closely similar, except for the high melanin content of the original tumor and the absence of DOPA oxidase in the amelanotic strain.

A reduction in the amount of protein, riboflavin, and ribose nucleic acid associated with the large granule fraction of livers from rats fed carcinogenic aminoazo dyes has been noted by two groups of workers.[18, 46, 47, 48, 49] The precancerous stages due to feeding of the aminoazo dyes appears to be associated with a disappearance of large granule or mitochondrial material. In hepatomas the amount of mitochondrial protein per cell is reduced to exceedingly low amounts.[45]

Not enough work has yet been carried out on the relation of the cellular particulates to cancer to assess their significance. However, extension of such studies, especially on the chemistry and metabolic activity of the mitochondria and microsomes may be of considerable importance in seeking out the biochemical characteristics which distinguish malignant from normal tissue. Differences between normal and tumor mitochondria or microsomes are more likely to be reflected in their enzymatic constitution than in their gross chemical composition or in their absolute amounts.

PROTEINS

The predominating position of the proteins from quantitative and from functional points of view has led naturally to the suggestion that "abnormal" proteins occur in cancer and are responsible for the altered growth potentialities of malignant tissue. While it can not be considered as supported or disproved by available evidence, this hypothesis certainly deserves continued consideration. An impressive amount of early work, carefully reviewed by Toennies,[66] has lent some credence to the suggestion that cancer tissue contains proteins distinct from those in normal tissue. Thus Mann and Welker[32, 33] have obtained evidence that certain substances from human tumor tissue might be immunologically different from those in normal tissues.

The amounts and properties of proteins extractable from various normal and tumor tissues, by a variety of extraction methods have been studied, the results in most cases suggesting that the extractable proteins may be altered in amount or kind in cancer tissue as compared to normal tissue (see review by Toennies[66]). In more recent studies Miller and his collaborators[36, 37] have attempted to control many of the variables present in older work. These workers have compared the proteins from a transplanted mouse rhabdomyosarcoma with normal mouse muscle with respect to their extractability in buffered KCl, their sedimentability, their viscosity, and their electrophoretic mobilities. The proteins of the rhabdomyosarcoma were more readily and completely extracted than those of normal muscle. The tumor extracts contained more material with a sedimentation rate characteristic of mitochondria, and less protein with the solubility properties characteristic of myosin than did the normal muscle extracts. Thus, very pronounced differences in the protein components of the rhabdomyosarcoma in comparison with its normal tissue of origin were apparent.

Electrophoretic examination of the extracts[37] demonstrated seven major components in the tumor extracts, and only three major components in the normal muscle extracts. Even proteins with analogous solubility characteristics were found to be different on the basis of electrophoretic behavior or specific viscosity. Thus the "myosin" fraction obtained from rhabdomyosarcoma was found to have an electrophoretic mobility which was distinct from that of normal muscle myosin, and its specific viscosity was appreciably lower. No identity between any of the major components of the two tissues could be demonstrated by electrophoretic methods. These results, while they in no way show that the proteins of the rhabdomyosarcoma are "abnormal," do demonstrate conclusively that the pattern of the major protein fractions of the tumor was completely different from that of the tissue of origin.

That the amounts of individual proteins associated with a normal tissue may be greatly reduced in the homologous tumor tissue is also shown in the work of Dunn *et al.*[20] Rat connective tissue was found to contain 5.4 Gm. of collagen per 100 Gm. of tissue, while the fibrosarcoma used for comparison contained only 0.47 per cent collagen. Similarly the amount of collagen and of elastin in a mouse squamous cell carcinoma is much less than in the normal mouse epidermis.[31]

Changes in the composition of the liver of rats during carcinogenesis due to the feeding of certain carcinogenic aminoazo dyes, have also indicated that the amounts of proteins and nucleic acids of the liver are significantly altered during the precancerous stages, and that these changes are followed by still further changes in the resulting hepatomas.[13, 23, 46, 47, 48, 49] The liver desoxypentose nucleic acid rises markedly in rats fed carcinogenic compounds. Griffin *et al.*[23] have shown that the globulin fraction of liver rose during azo dye carcinogenesis, whereas the total albumin fraction remained relatively constant.

An especially pertinent observation is that originally made by the Millers,[34, 35] who demonstrated that during aminoazo dye carcinogenesis a dye becomes firmly bound to the liver proteins. The amount of this dye reached a maximum in four to six weeks with diets containing 4-dimethylaminoazobenzene, and then fell progressively, until, when the hepatoma appeared, there was no bound dye associated with the proteins of the tumor tissue. This suggested the possibility that the process of carcinogenesis, in the case of the aminoazo dyes at least, involves the alteration or destruction of a normal protein or proteins essential for the control of growth, but not for the growth process. The possibility of such alterations of proteins as a result of carcinogenic stimuli had been proposed previously by Lavik *et al.*[29] from experiments in which subcarcinogenic effects of methylcholanthrene persisted for long periods of time and contributed to the subsequent carcinogenic effects of other carcinogens.

Price, Miller, and their associates have studied the distribution of protein-bound dye in the nucleus, mitochondria, microsomes, and supernatant proteins from livers of rats fed carcinogenic and noncarcinogenic azo dyes.[46, 47, 48, 49] No

TABLE 32. AMOUNTS OF SOLUBLE CYTOPLASMIC PROTEINS IN RAT LIVER AND RAT TUMORS

		Percentage of total area			
Component	*Mobility*	*Normal liver*	*Precancerous liver*	*Primary hepatoma*	*Metastatic hepatoma*
N	(−6.48 to −6.91)†	5.9 ± 1.5*	4.8 ± 2.5	19.5 ± 3.4	22.4
A	(−5.56 to −6.01)	10.0 ± 1.8	11.4 ± 2.1	20.9 ± 2.0	20.2
a_1	(−4.64 to −4.90)	20.3 ± 4.6	25.6 ± 7.6	22.4 ± 3.3	18.1
a_2	(−3.7 to −3.92)	17.9 ± 1.6	19.3 ± 5.0	14.1 ± 3.1	12.5
b	(−2.82 to −3.02)	13.8 ± 1.7	13.4 ± 2.3	9.9 ± 1.4	10.8
g	(−1.93 to −2.1)	15.0 ± 2.0	9.9 ± 1.6	6.6 ± 1.4	7.5
h_1	(−0.99 to −1.06)	8.9 ± 1.8	7.7 ± 1.5 }	3.1 ± 0.9	3.2
h_2	(−0.34 to −0.38)	8.0 ± 1.4	6.0 ± 1.2 }		
i	(+0.99 to +1.01)	1.7 ± 0.2	2.0 ± 0.5	—	—

From Sorof and Cohen[62]
* Standard deviation
† Mobility × 10^{-5} cm.^{2}/volt. sec.

correlation was found between the carcinogenicity of the dye and the amounts of the distribution of the bound dye in the proteins of cellular fractions.

In an especially important series of experiments, Sorof and Cohen have studied the electrophoretic patterns of soluble cytoplasmic proteins obtained from normal rat livers, the livers of rats fed 4-dimethylaminoazobenzene, and the hepatomas resulting from this diet. It was found that nine fairly well-defined components were present in the soluble proteins of normal[61] and precancerous[62] livers, and in the hepatomas.[62] No significant differences in the amounts or mobilities were apparent in the soluble proteins of normal or precancerous liver. The soluble proteins from the primary hepatomas and their metastases, however, showed a significantly different electrophoretic pattern, the relative amounts of two slow-moving components being markedly reduced, and those of two fast-moving components being increased.[62] Ultracentrifugal studies also indicated pronounced differences in the soluble proteins of the hepatoma as compared to the liver, the tumors showing an increase in the amounts of two rapidly sedimenting protein components. Especially significant was the fact that the soluble cytoplasmic proteins of primary 2-acetylaminofluorene-induced rat hepatoma, Jensen rat sarcoma, Flexner Jobling rat carcinoma, Walker 256 rat tumor, and chloroform-induced transplanted mouse hepatoma all gave electrophoretic patterns which were very similar to those obtained in the rat hepatoma mentioned above.[62] Work of Abrams and Cohen was cited which indicates that the soluble proteins of a number of human lymphoid tumors also gave electrophoretic patterns similar to those of rat hepatoma. These are also quite similar to the patterns obtained from the proteins of a transplanted mouse rhabdomyosarcoma studied by Miller *et al.*[37]

Table 32, condensed from work of Sorof and Cohen, shows the percentage areas and mobilities of nine components in the soluble proteins of normal rat liver, of precancerous livers from rats fed aminoazo dye, and of hepatomas induced by this diet, and their metastases.

It is seen that the fast components A and N are significantly increased in the tumors, while the slow h_1 and h_2 components are reduced markedly, at least as compared to liver.

The reduced amount of the h components in the primary aminoazo dye-induced hepatomas as compared to the liver is consonant with the protein deletion mechanism suggested by Miller and Miller.[34] However, the increase in the A and N components is compatible with the suggestion that there is an appearance or enrichment of particular proteins in neoplasms.

Perhaps the most striking aspect of these studies is the great similarity of the electrophoretic patterns of the soluble proteins from neoplasms of a number of species and tissues. This observation again supports the concept that tumor tissues, regardless of their origin, form a group of a common metabolic type.[22]

Sorof, Cohen, Miller, and Miller[63] have studied the electrophoretic distribution of protein-bound dye in the soluble cytoplasmic proteins of rats fed carcinogenic and noncarcinogenic aminoazo dyes. They found that 50 to 100 per cent of the protein-bound dye in this fraction migrated with the slow-moving h components, very probably with h_1. This component comprises only 6 to 10 per cent of the soluble cytoplasmic liver proteins (see Table 32). The appearance of the major portion of the dye with such a small proportion of the protein suggests that rather specific proteins may be involved in the dye-binding process. It is particularly interesting that the h components are the very ones which are low in the hepatomas produced by aminoazo dye feeding as well as in other tumors. Although the evidence is by no means complete or convincing, it would be tempting indeed to wonder whether the alteration or depletion of an h component is in some way associated with carcinogenesis, at least in the case of the aminoazo dyes.

How abnormal proteins might bring about cancer has been considered by Potter,[42, 43] who has advanced an enzyme-virus theory regarding carcinogenesis. The essential feature of Potter's hypothesis suggests that, during carcinogenesis, an abnormal enzyme or complex of enzymes appears in the organized cell. This protein, perhaps self-duplicating, was thought to lack the complete complement of enzymes in the original complex and to be derived from its normal counterpart under the influence of an exogenous or endogenous carcinogenic agent. The abnormal agent, then, may compete with the normal enzyme or complex for certain substrates or building blocks, and thus exert a redirecting effect on the metabolism and growth of the cell. Whether the abnormal agent would occur in the soluble proteins or among the cellular particulates is, of course, an open question, but it would be characteristic for the units of the complex to occur in relatively limited numbers per cell. However, if it were in the large or small granule fraction, the agent would, in many respects, resemble a virus. Although indirect evidence has been developed in support of this hypothesis, it has not been possible to bring direct proof to bear upon it. However, studies of mitochondria from liver and from hepatoma cells have revealed that the latter contain less of certain oxidative enzymes per unit of mitochondrial protein than do the former.[44, 59]

From the foregoing remarks it seems clear that specific proteins of a tumor may be considerably different from those in the tissue of origin. These changes may

TABLE 33. AMINO ACID COMPOSITION OF

Reference Method	*Dunn* et al.[20] Microbiologic		*Roberts* et al.[52] Microbiologic		*Sauberlich & Baumann*[58] Microbiologic	
Tissue	*Trans-planted rat fibrosarcoma**	*Normal rat connective tissue**	*Squamous cell mouse carcinoma†*	*Normal mouse epidermis†*	*Four rat tumors‡§*	*Normal rat tissues§ ‖*
Units	Gm./16 Gm. N	Gm./16 Gm. N	Gm./16 Gm. N	Gm./16 Gm. N	Gm./16 Gm. N	Gm./16 Gm. N
Arginine	5.9	2.8	5.7	5.6	5.4– 6.2	5.0– 6.0
Aspartic acid	8.6	10.0	—	—	—	—
Cystine	—	—	2.0	1.9	—	—
Glutamic acid	12.0	11.0	13.0	13.9	11.7–13.3	10.4–15.0
Alanine	—	—	—	—	—	—
Glycine	4.5	0	—	—	5.1– 6.3	4.9– 6.1
Histidine	2.5	4.0	2.0	1.9	1.9– 2.7	2.0– 2.4
Isoleucine	4.5	4.8	5.8	3.9	4.3– 5.6	4.8– 5.2
Leucine	7.5	8.5	8.0	6.1	7.2– 8.9	7.3– 9.1
Lysine	7.5	7.6	6.9	4.2	6.5– 8.3	6.5– 8.3
Methionine	1.8	2.5	2.0	1.5	1.9– 2.0	2.2– 2.5
Valine	5.2	4.8	5.2	3.7	4.4– 5.3	4.3– 6.1
Tyrosine	—	—	—	—	—	—
Phenylalanine	3.8	4.0	3.6	2.7	3.7– 4.4	3.4– 4.5
Proline	—	—	—	—	—	—
Serine	—	—	—	—	—	—
Threonine	3.8	2.8	4.3	3.3	3.1– 5.1	3.5– 4.1
Tryptophane	—	—	1.8	1.1	0.9– 1.0	1.2– 1.4

* Corrected for collagen and elastin content.

† Calculated from original data from total nitrogen content of 11.65 Gm. N/100 Gm. dry weight.

‡ Flexner-Jobling rat carcinoma, 4- and 3-dimethylaminoazobenzene-induced hepatomas, methylcholanthrene-induced sarcoma.

§ Extreme range of values.

‖ Normal and precancerous liver and normal muscle.

reflect a loss of specific function, and in no way represent a new "cancer protein." However, a field of importance for the future will be to apply refined methods of protein fractionation to the proteins of normal and malignant tissue in a search for a pattern of change which may characterize malignant tissue. In particular the possibilities of new "abnormal" proteins or the loss of specific proteins or enzymes involved in the control of the tissue growth by the whole organism should be considered.

AMINO ACID COMPOSITION

Any major change in the proteins associated with malignancy might well be reflected in changes in their amino acid composition. A great deal of the earlier work on this subject is critically reviewed by Toennies.[65]

A comparison of the amino acid composition of a number of tumors and their homologous normal tissues is gathered together in Table 33 from recent work by Dunn *et al.*,[20] Rafelson *et al.*,[50] Roberts *et al.*,[52] Sauberlich and Baumann,[58] Schweigert *et al.*,[60] and Zamecnik and Franz.[70]

NORMAL AND MALIGNANT TISSUE PROTEINS

Schweigert et al.[60] Microbiologic		*Zamecnik & Franz*[70] Starch chromatography		*Rafelson* et al.[50] Starch chromatography		Reference Method
Azo-dye induced rat hepatoma	*Normal rat liver*	*Azo-dye induced rat hepatoma*	*Normal rat liver*	*Mouse neuro-blastoma*	*Normal mouse brain*	Tissue
Gm./16 Gm. N	Gm./16 Gm. N	M/100 M AA	M/100 M AA	M/100 M AA	M/100 M AA	Units
6.3	6.4	7.2	6.5	5.5	5.5	Arginine
7.7	8.4	8.3	9.3	13.8	6.8	Aspartic acid
0.7	0.6	1.0	0.7	3.8	4.5	Cystine
11.1	9.9	19.2	17.6	11.0	9.4	Glutamic acid
—	—					Alanine
4.9	4.0	11.0	9.1	2.4	7.1	Glycine
2.8	3.2	2.7	2.8	4.1	5.5	Histidine
4.5	4.9	12.6	15.4	17.3	10.7	Isoleucine
9.5	10.7					Leucine
8.5	8.8	9.1	8.1	3.8	11.0	Lysine
2.0	2.9	10.1	10.6	2.8	9.1	Methionine
4.8	5.8					Valine
3.7	4.0			2.1	2.6	Tyrosine
3.7	5.0	3.3	4.0	4.5	2.3	Phenylalanine
4.1	4.0	5.4	5.3	15.5	11.7	Proline
4.3	3.8	5.8	5.7	7.6	6.5	Serine
3.9	4.3	4.3	4.9	5.8	7.5	Threonine
1.4	1.5	—	—	—	—	Tryptophane

Although significant differences between the concentrations of a few amino acids appear in each normal and malignant tissue pair, no general pattern of differences is apparent. Schweigert *et al.*[60] fractionated homogenates of normal liver, precancerous livers from rats fed 4-dimethylaminoazobenzene, and the hepatomas arising in these rats into nuclei, mitochondria, microsomes, and supernatant proteins, and studied the amino acid composition of each fraction. This sharpened significantly the distinction between the normal and malignant liver tissues.

The data so far accumulated would not support the thesis that a shift in the amino acid composition in any particular direction is characteristic of malignancy. Such differences as do occur may frequently be attributed to the reduction or increase of extracellular proteins, e.g. collagen in the malignant tissue.[20, 31, 58] The failure to observe in the amino acid composition significant trends associated with malignancy is, perhaps, not surprising in view of the fact that the amino acid composition of a mixture of a large number of proteins is involved. Consequently anything but the most extreme changes would tend to be obscured.

FREE AMINO ACIDS

Malignant tissue is capable of growing even when the nutritional state of the host is so poor as to cause a net loss in body weight. It has appeared possible, therefore, that cancer tissue may utilize nitrogenous substrates more efficiently than normal tissue. Presumably free amino acids constitute a major source of the protein building blocks of tissue, and consequently the concentration of the free amino acids in normal and tumor tissues assumes considerable interest.

Early investigations (such as those of Nakahara *et al.*[40]) did not show any great difference between nonprotein nitrogen or free amino nitrogen in certain tumors and their homologous normal tissues when expressed on a moist weight basis. However, the concentration of free arginine in certain tumor tissue has been found to be higher than in normal control tissue.[1, 26]

In the recent well-controlled experiments of Roberts and Frankel,[53] however, it was observed that the trichloroacetic-acid–soluble nitrogen was significantly lower in mouse squamous cell carcinomas than in normal or hyperplastic mouse epidermis. These workers also demonstrated that there was less total free amino acid in a number of tumor tissues than in the corresponding normal tissues.[54, 55, 56] They have shown that each normal tissue has a distribution of free amino acids which is distinctive and characteristic of that tissue, and tumor tissue also, regardless of its source, shows a recognizable and distinctive free amino acid pattern. These workers determined by means of two-dimensional paper chromatography the free amino acids in alcoholic extracts of homogenized tissues. The concentration of free arginine was too low to detect in both normal and tumor tissue, and so the relation of these results to the older work showing increased free arginine in tumor tissue cannot be assessed.

Although quantitative data have not been reported in these studies, it is clear from the qualitative results that the relative amounts of the free amino acids do not reflect the amino acid composition of the tissue as a whole.[55] Awapara *et al.*[2] have applied this same technic to the study of free aminoethylphosphoric ester in normal and malignant tissues. Although homologous tissues were not studied, there was no apparent tendency for tumors to be richer or less rich in this substance than normal tissues.

The considerable early work on the presence of glutathione in malignant tissue has been reviewed by Toennies.[66] Although the data have not been consistent, it has appeared that the glutathione content of cancer tissue is not markedly different from normal tissues.

In recent studies Zamecnik and Stephenson[71] have studied the glutathione in ultrafiltrates and trichloroacetic acid filtrates of normal, fetal, and regenerating rat liver, livers from aminoazo dye-fed rats, and the hepatomas from these livers. These experiments showed that the normal, the regenerating, and the control liver from the aminoazo dye-fed rats contained 0.83 to 0.95 mg. of glutathione per ml. of ultrafiltrate, whereas the fetal liver contained 0.2 mg./ml., and the hepatomas only 0.1 mg./ml. of ultrafiltrate. Since glutathione appears to be a major cathepsin-activating agent, the very low values in the tumor might be associated with a decreased activity of the protein-degrading mechanisms.

Continuation of these studies of the free amino acid concentration of tissues, and the relation of these to metabolic activity and growth rates should be of considerable importance in elucidating the role of such intermediates in protein synthesis. Since continued and unrestricted growth is characteristic of malignant tissue, such studies are of particular interest for the understanding of the chemistry and metabolism of cancer.

CONFIGURATION OF AMINO ACIDS

Amino acids may exist in either the L form or in the D form, the difference between these two forms depending upon the relative position in space of the amino group, the carboxyl group, the hydrogen atom, and the amino acid side chain about an asymmetric carbon atom. It has long been recognized that the amino acids of mammalian tissues occur in protein almost always in the L form. Most of the intermediate reactions of the amino acids in the metabolism of animal tissues are limited to the L isomers.

In 1939, however, Kögl and Erxleben[25] presented evidence that tumors contained certain amino acids, particularly glutamic acid, with the D configuration, and advanced the concept that the initiation and maintenance of these D amino acids in the cell proteins was an important aspect of malignancy. The importance of these suggestions led to experiments by many other investigators, the results almost uniformly failing to confirm Kögl's basic observation. However, the Utrecht group have continued to produce experimental evidence supporting their original claim (e.g., Kögl[24]), and the question must still be regarded as controversial. The extensive literature which has appeared as a result of these observations has been critically reviewed recently by Miller.[38] This excellent review of the evidence for and against Kögl's basic premise should be consulted for the details of the controversy. This reviewer, however, remains unconvinced that normal and tumor tissues differ in their content of the D or "unnatural" amino acids.

B-COMPLEX VITAMINS

The suggestion has been advanced that malignant tissues may, owing to their rapid growth, have a greater requirement for and a higher content of the water-soluble vitamins. Some aspects of the relation of vitamins to the cancer problem have recently been reviewed.[3]

The extensive work on the B vitamins in normal and tumor tissues carried out by R. J. Williams and his group at the University of Texas has been summarized in Table 25.[41]

The data of Table 34 suggest that the vitamin B complex content of tumor tissue tends to be generally lower than in the normal tissues used as a basis for comparison, although expression of the data on a dry weight basis reduces the differences. Pyridoxine, biotin, and perhaps riboflavin appear to be particularly low in malignant tissue, whereas the content of inositol and folic acid was either higher than normal or was not reduced to the same extent as the rest of the vitamin B complex in most tumor tissues. The significance of these observations is by no means clear as yet.

The Texas group has also expressed their analytic results in terms of a "profile" diagram, in which the vitamin content (in μg./Gm.) of the various vitamins in any tissue is referred to the vitamin content (in μg./Gm.) of the entire carcass.[39] The rat carcass was used as the reference basis for both rat and human vitamin profiles. This method of expression shows whether or not any or all of the vitamins of a particular tissue tend to be higher or lower than the average of the

TABLE 34. B VITAMIN LEVELS IN A GROUP OF NORMAL AND CANCER TISSUES FROM HUMAN AND RAT

Vitamin	Human			Rat		
	Normal tissue*	Cancer tissue†	$\frac{\text{Cancer}}{\text{Normal}} \times 100$	Normal tissue*	Cancer tissue	$\frac{\text{Cancer}}{\text{Normal}} \times 100$
Thiamin	1.80	1.28	71	3.7	1.54	42
Riboflavin	8.10	2.35	29	9.6	3.4	35
Nicotinic acid	31.20	23.50	75	87.0	23.6	27
Pantothenic acid	10.30	5.54	54	20.4	7.7	32
Pyridoxine	0.52	0.11	21	0.87	0.196	22
Biotin	0.18	0.038	21	0.22	0.05	23
Inositol	632.0	877.0	138	924.0	516.0	56
Folic acid †	1.4	2.86	200	3.7	3.54	96

From Pollack, Taylor, and Williams.[41]
All values expressed as micrograms per gram of moist tissue.
* The normal tissues used were lung, myocardium, spleen, renal cortex, brain, skeletal muscle, and whole adrenal.
† Micrograms of "potency" 40,000 units.

entire animal, and smooths out the quantitative differences in the amounts of the different vitamins.

It was observed that the various normal tissues had quite different vitamin profiles. Cancer tissues, however, had much more uniform vitamin profiles than the group of normal tissues used for comparison. The comparison of the uniformity of the vitamin content of different tissues was expressed by a value designated as the "vitamin uniformity." This value was calculated for any group of tissues by the relation:

$$\text{Vitamin uniformity} = 100 - \sqrt{\frac{(V-M)^2}{N}}$$

where $(V-M)^2$ is the sum of the squares of the deviation from the mean and N is the number of tissues

Table 35 shows the vitamin uniformity of normal and cancer tissues from the human and the rat.

It is evident from this table that the malignant tissues had higher vitamin uniformity values than normal tissue, and thus resembled each other to a greater extent than did the normal tissues. They formed, in effect, a group of a common tissue type with respect to their content of the B complex vitamins.

The changes in concentration of certain of the B complex vitamins during epidermal carcinogenesis in mice painted with methylcholanthrene have been determined by Rickey, Wicks, and Tatum,[51] their results being shown in Table 31. There was an increase in the choline and inositol content of the transplanted squamous cell tumors, which may perhaps be referable to the increased phospholipid content of the tumor.[18] Biotin was decreased and *p*-aminobenzoic acid and vitamin B_6 were increased in the transplanted carcinoma as compared to the normal or hyperplastic epidermis.

TABLE 35. VITAMIN UNIFORMITY IN NORMAL AND CANCER TISSUES FROM HUMAN AND RAT

Tissue	*Thiamin*	*Riboflavin*	*Niacin*	*Pantothenic*	*Pyridoxin*	*Biotin*	*Inositol*	*Folic acid*	*Average uniformity*
8 Normal human *	22	9	48	38	18	0	45	33	27
8 Cancer human †	29	87	80	73	81	39	59	80	66
8 Normal rat ‡	50	15	56	0	16	12	43	46	29.7
5 Rat cancers §	63	82	64	54	54	44	66	74	62.8

From Pollack, Taylor, and Williams.[41]
Calculated from the relation: $V.\ U. = 100 - \sqrt{\frac{(V-M)^2}{N}}$

where $(V-M)^2$ is the sum of the squares of the deviation from the mean, where N is the number of tissues.

* Striated muscle, spleen, renal cortex, myocardium, mammary gland, smooth muscle, ovary, and testis.

† Mammary carcinoma (2), spindle cell sarcoma, ovarian carcinoma, renal carcinoma, orbital melanoma, groin reticulum lymphosarcoma, and spindle cell myosarcoma.

‡ Liver, lung, heart, spleen, kidney, brain, skeletal muscle, and adrenals.

§ Walker rat carcinoma (3), and rat hepatoma (2).

The levels of particular B complex vitamins observed in tissues undoubtedly reflect, in most cases, the activities of the enzyme systems of which the vitamins are component parts. Thus tissues rich in transaminase activity may tend to have greater vitamin B_6 content, etc. When the functions of all the vitamins of the B complex are known completely, it may be possible to get a fair idea of the activity of certain tissue enzyme systems from their vitamin profiles. At the present time the evidence does not point toward any marked excess or deficit of the B complex vitamins in neoplastic tissue.

GENERAL DISCUSSION

What is the present status of the problem of the comparative chemistry of normal and malignant tissues? Are there any characteristic differences between the two types of tissue? The discussion in previous pages certainly does not give definitive answers to these questions. There are, however, a few generalizations that may be drawn from the material which has been presented.

Perhaps the most definite observation is the fact that these recent studies lend further support for the generalization that neoplastic tissues are rather closely related metabolically and chemically. They resemble each other far more than the normal tissues whence they came. The work of Warburg has emphasized this with respect to the aerobic and anaerobic metabolism of the tissues; the work of Greenstein has shown this phenomenon with respect to the presence and activities of a number of enzymes and enzyme systems; the work of Potter showed it with respect to some of the oxidative enzymes; the work of Williams has done likewise with respect to the B complex vitamins; the work of Sorof and Cohen has shown a similar relationship in the case of the soluble cytoplasmic proteins and the work of Roberts has shown the same trend with free amino acids. From every point of view thus far investigated, neoplastic tissues resemble each other more closely than do the corresponding normal tissues. This may represent a metabolic dedifferentiation toward a more primitive cell type.

This tendency of tissues to approach a common metabolic pattern as they become neoplastic makes it difficult to demonstrate possible characteristic differences between normal and tumor tissue. This depends upon the tissue of origin. Tumors arising from tissues high in a particular constituent may show a decrease in that constituent, whereas tumors arising from other tissue low in the constituent may contain it in greater amounts than the parent tissue. Thus there is no general direction of change characteristic of neoplastic tissue—only changes toward the common metabolic type. There is uniformity in the direction of change only when the tumor tissue type has chemical or metabolic values which lie outside the normal tissue range. This occurs, for example, in the case of water content, where cancer tissues regularly have higher percentages of moisture than normal tissues.

The survey of this problem by the author has failed to reveal a clear demonstration of any chemical characteristic which may account for the difference in growth behavior of normal and tumor tissue. This does not mean that such characteristics are nonexistent. It does mean, however, that more, and more refined, methods must be applied to the problem if such differences are to be found. Quantitatively very minor fractions of the tissue may be involved—components, the presence of which may not even yet be suspected. Could the fundamental difference, for example, be associated with a factor that responds to a humoral agent which governs the growth and differentiation of normal tissue but has no effect on neoplastic tissue? The composition studies with which we have so far been concerned may be far too gross to detect differences in such elusive agents. The differences which we have detected may not be fundamental characteristics, but simply the result of a reversion of malignant tissue to a more primitive type. Primitive tissues including neoplasms may be characterized by limited specialized function and as a consequence may present a uniform metabolic and chemical pattern.

Perhaps it is a mistake to seek a "characteristic change in cancer tissue." The fundamental changes associated with the development of cancer from one tissue may be completely unrelated to those involved in the development of cancer in a different tissue. In this connection, the study of the development of certain selected experimental cancers in great detail has a certain basic strength as compared to random analysis of various normal and malignant tissues. Thus the long-term studies on the chemical and biochemical changes associated with the development of squamous cell carcinomas in the skin of mice painted with methylcholanthrene, or the development of hepatomas in rats fed carcinogenic aminoazo dyes may elucidate the pathways of tumor formation in these particular cases. Similar long-term and intensive studies should be undertaken with other types of experimental tumors, e.g. spontaneous mammary carcinoma in mice, spontaneous and induced leukemia in mice, and the virus-produced chicken sarcoma. Detailed comparison of the changes associated with and factors controlling the development of these different neoplasms may eventually permit the determination of the chemical and metabolic changes most directly involved in the development of each neoplasm. Extension of this information to experimental or clinical cancer would then follow logically.

BIBLIOGRAPHY

1. ANNAU, E., and GÖZSY, B. Die Verteilung des Arginins im Jensen-Rattensarkom. *Zeitschr. f. Krebsforsch, 40:* 572-576, 1934.
2. AWAPARA, J., LANDUA, A. J., and FUERST, R. Free aminoethylphosphoric ester in rat organs and human tumors. *J. Biol. Chem. 183:* 545-548, 1950.
3. BURK, D., and WINZLER, R. J. Vitamins and cancer. *Vitamins and Hormones 2:* 305-352, 1944.
4. BURK, D., and WINZLER, R. J. The biochemistry of malignant tissue. *Ann. Rev. Biochem. 13:* 487-532, 1944.
5. DUBUY, H. G., WOODS, M. W., BURK, D., and LACKEY, M. D. Enzymatic activities of isolated amelanotic and melanotic granules of mouse melanomas and a suggested relationship to mitochondria. *J. Nat. Cancer Inst. 9:* 325-336, 1949.
6. CARRUTHERS, C. The biochemistry of malignant tissue. *Ann. Rev. Biochem. 19:* 389-408, 1950.
7. CARRUTHERS, C. Chemical studies on the transformation of mouse epidermis to squamous-cell carcinoma: A review. *Cancer Research 10:* 255-265, 1950.
8. CARRUTHERS, C., and SUNTZEFF, V. Influence of limited application of methylcholanthrene upon epidermal iron and ascorbic acid. *J. Nat. Cancer Inst. 3:* 217-220, 1942.
9. CARRUTHERS, C., and SUNTZEFF, V. A qualitative chemical change in carcinogenesis. *Science 108:* 450-454, 1948.
10. CARRUTHERS, C., and SUNTZEFF, V. Studies with the polarograph on the lipids of epidermis during normal and rapid growth. *Cancer Research 9:* 210-214, 1949.
11. CARRUTHERS, C., and SUNTZEFF, V. Further evidence for an alteration in the structure of a polarographically reducible substance in carcinogenesis. *Cancer Research 10:* 339-343, 1950.
12. CLAUDE, A. Particulate components of normal and tumor cells. *Science 91:* 77-78, 1940.
13. CLAUDE, A. Particulate components of cytoplasm. *Cold Springs Harbor Symposia on Quantitative Biology 9:* 263-271, 1941.
14. CLAUDE, A. The constitution of mitochondria and microsomes, and the distribution of nucleic acid in the cytoplasm of a leukemic cell. *J. Exper. Med. 80:* 19-29, 1944.
15. CLAUDE, A. Fractionation of mammalian liver cells by differential centrifugation: II. Experimental procedures and results. *J. Exper. Med. 84:* 61-89, 1946.
16. COSTELLO, C. J., CARRUTHERS, C., KAMEN, M. D., and SIMOES, R. L. The uptake of radiophosphorus in the phospholipid fraction of mouse epidermis in methylcholanthrene carcinogenesis. *Cancer Research 7:* 642-646, 1947.
17. COWDRY, E. V. "Experimental epidermal methylcholanthrene carcinogenesis in mice." In HOERR, N. L. (ed.): *Frontiers in Cytochemistry.* Lancaster, Pa., Jaques Cattell Press, 1943, pp. 131–162.
18. CUNNINGHAM, L., GRIFFIN, A. C., and LUCK, J. M. Effect of a carcinogenic azo dye on liver cell structure: Isolation of nuclei and cytoplasmic granules. *Cancer Research 10:* 194-199, 1950.

19. DITTMAR, C. Über den chemischen Aufbau von Mitochondrien normaler Zellen und von Tumorzellen und den Einfluss carcinogener Stoffe auf Mitochondrien. I. Die Zusammensetzung der Lipoide von Mitochondrien. *Zeitschr. f. Krebsforsch 52:* 46-56, 1941.

20. DUNN, M. S., FEAVER, E. R., and MURPHY, E. A. The amino acid composition of a fibrosarcoma and its normal homologous tissue in the rat. *Cancer Research 9:* 306-313, 1949.

21. GREENSTEIN, J. P. The biochemistry of malignant tissues. *Ann. Rev. Biochem. 14:* 643-664, 1945.

22. GREENSTEIN, J. P. *Biochemistry of Cancer.* New York, Academic Press, 1947.

23. GRIFFIN, A. C., NYE, W. N., NODA, L., and LUCK, J. M. Tissue proteins and carcinogenesis: I. The effect of carcinogenic azo dyes on liver proteins. *J. Biol. Chem. 176:* 1225-1235, 1948.

24. KÖGL, F. Chemische und biochemische Untersuchungen über Tumorproteine. *Experimentia 5:* 173-180, 1949.

25. KÖGL, F., and ERXLEBEN, H. Zur Ätiologie der malignen Tumoren. *Zeitschr. f. physiol. Chem. 258:* 57-95, 1939.

26. KLEIN, G., and ZIESE, W. Arginase und Arginin im Stoffwechsel der Tumoren. *Zeitschr. f. Krebsforsch. 37:* 323-346, 1932.

27. LANSING, A. I., ROSENTHAL, T. B., and AU, M. H. Ultrafilterable and non-ultrafilterable calcium in normal, hyperplastic epidermis, and squamous cell carcinoma. *Arch. Biochem. 16:* 361-365, 1948.

28. LANSING, A. I., ROSENTHAL, T. B., and KAMEN, M. Calcium ion exchanges in some normal tissues and in epidermal carcinogenesis. *Arch. Biochem. 19:* 177-183, 1948.

29. LAVIK, P. S., MOORE, P. R., RUSCH, H. P., and BAUMANN, C. A. Some additive effects of carcinogenic hydrocarbons. *Cancer Research 2:* 189-192, 1942.

30. DELONG, R. P., COMAN, D. R., and ZEIDMAN, I. The significance of low calcium and high potassium content in neoplastic tissue. *Cancer 3:* 718-721, 1950.

31. MA, C. K. Morphological and chemical investigation of dermal elastic, and collagenic tissue during epidermal carcinogenesis. *Cancer Research 9:* 481-487, 1949.

32. MANN, L. S., and WELKER, W. H. A specific antiserum for carcinoma protein. *A. M. J. Cancer 39:* 360-364, 1940.

33. MANN, L. S., and WELKER, W. H. Further studies of specific precipitin antiserums for the protein of cancer tissue: I, II. *Cancer Research 3:* 193-195, 196-197, 1943.

34. MILLER, E. C., and MILLER, J. A. The presence and significance of bound aminoazo dyes in the livers of rats fed *p*-dimethylaminoazobenzene. *Cancer Research 7:* 468-480, 1947.

35. MILLER, E. C., MILLER, J. A., SAPP, R. W., and WEBER, G. M. Studies on the protein-bound aminoazo dyes formed *in vivo* from 4-dimethylaminoazobenzene and its C-monoethyl derivatives. *Cancer Research 9:* 336-343, 1949.

36. MILLER, G. L., GREEN, E. U., KOLB, J. J., and MILLER, E. E. Studies on the proteins of rhabdomyosarcoma and normal muscle of mice: I. Gross composition, extractions with 0.5M KC1, and fractionations by differential centrifugation and dialysis. *Cancer Research 10:* 141-147, 1950.

37. MILLER, G. L., GREEN, E. U., MILLER, E. E., and KOLB, J. J. Studies on the proteins of rhabdomyosarcoma and normal muscle in mice: II. Electrophoretic and viscometric measurements. *Cancer Research 10:* 148-154, 1950.

38. MILLER, J. A. Do tumor proteins contain d-amino acids? A review of the controversy. *Cancer Research 10:* 65-72, 1950.
39. MITCHELL, H. K., and ISBELL, E. R. B vitamin content of normal rat tissues. *Univ. of Texas Publication* No. *4237:* 37-40, 1942.
40. NAKAHARA, W., KISHI, S., and FUJIWARA, T. Comparison of chemical composition between hepatoma and normal liver tissues. IV. Non-protein nitrogen, amino nitrogen, creatinine and creatine, urea, and uric acid. *Gann 31:* 355-362, 1937.
41. POLLACK, M. A., TAYLOR, A., and WILLIAMS, R. J. B vitamins in human, rat and mouse neoplasms. *Univ. of Texas Publication* No. *4237:* 56-71, 1942.
42. POTTER, V. R. Biocatalysts in cancer tissue. IV. An enzyme-virus theory regarding carcinogenesis. *Cancer Research 3:* 358-361, 1943.
43. POTTER, V. R. Biological energy transformations and the cancer problem. In *Advances in Enzymology*. New York, Interscience Publishers, 1944, vol. IV, pp. 201-256.
44. POTTER, V. R., PRICE, J. M., MILLER, E. C., and MILLER, J. A. Studies on intercellular composition of livers of rats fed various aminoazo dyes: IV. Effects on succinoxidase and oxalacetic acid oxidase. *Cancer Research 10:* 28-35, 1950.
45. PRICE, J. M., and LAIRD, A. K. A comparison of the intracellular composition of regenerating liver and induced liver tumors. *Cancer Research 10:* 650-658, 1950.
46. PRICE, J. M., MILLER, E. C., and MILLER, J. A. The intracellular distribution of protein, nucleic acids, riboflavin, and protein-bound aminoazo dye in the livers of rats fed *p*-dimethylaminoazobenzene. *J. Biol. Chem. 173:* 345-353, 1948.
47. PRICE, J. M., MILLER, J. A., MILLER, E. C., and WEBER, G. M. Studies on the intracellular composition of liver and liver tumor from rats fed 4-dimethylaminoazobenzene. *Cancer Research 9:* 96-102, 1949.
48. PRICE, J. M., MILLER, E. C., MILLER, J. A., and WEBER, G. M. Studies on the intracellular composition of livers from rats fed various aminoazo dyes: I. 4-aminoazobenzene, 4-dimethylaminoazobenzene, 4′-methyl-, and 3′-methyl-4-dimethylaminoazobenzene. *Cancer Research 9:* 398-402, 1949.
49. PRICE, J. M., MILLER, E. C., MILLER, J. A., and WEBER, G. M. Studies on the intracellular composition of livers from rats fed various aminoazo dyes: II. 3′-methyl-, 2′-methyl-, and 2-methyl-4-dimethylaminoazobenzene, 3-methyl-4-monomethylaminoazobenzene and 4′-fluoro-4-dimethylaminoazobenzene. *Cancer Research 10:* 18-27, 1950.
50. RAFELSON, M. E., PEARSON, H. E., and WINZLER, R. J. Studies on the amino acids of mouse brain and a mouse neuroblastoma. To be published.
51. RITCHEY, M. G., WICKS, L. F., and TATUM, E. L. Biotin, choline, inositol, *p*-aminobenzoic acid, and vitamin B_6 in transplantable mouse carcinomas and in mouse blood. *J. Biol. Chem. 171:* 51-59, 1947.
52. ROBERTS, E., CALDWELL, A. L., CLOWES, G. H. A., SUNTZEFF, V., CARRUTHERS, C., and COWDRY, E. V. Amino acids in epidermal carcinogenesis in mice. *Cancer Research 9:* 350-353, 1949.
53. ROBERTS, E., and FRANKEL, S. Arginase activity and nitrogen content in epidermal carcinogenesis in mice. *Cancer Research 9:* 231-237, 1949.
54. ROBERTS, E., and FRANKEL, S. Free amino acids in normal and neoplastic tissues of mice as studied by paper chromatography. *Cancer Research 9:* 645-648, 1949.

55. Roberts, E., Frankel, S., and Harman, P. J. Amino acids of nervous tissue. *Proc. Soc. Exper. Biol. & Med. 74:* 383-387, 1950.
56. Roberts, E., and Tishkoff, G. H. Distribution of free amino acids in mouse epidermis in various phases of growth as determined by paper partition chromatography. *Science 109:* 14-16, 1949.
57. Rusch, H. P., and LePage, G. A. The biochemistry of carcinogenesis. *Ann. Rev. Biochem. 17:* 471-494, 1948.
58. Sauberlich, H. E., and Baumann, C. A. The amino acid content of certain normal and neoplastic tissues. *Cancer Research 11:* 67-71, 1951.
59. Schneider, W. C., and Hogeboom, G. H. Intracellular distribution of enzymes: IV. The distribution of succinoxidase and cytochrome oxidase activities in normal mouse liver and in mouse hepatoma. *J. Nat. Cancer Inst. 10:* 969-975, 1950.
60. Schweigert, B. S. Guthneck, B. T., Price, J. M., Miller, J. A., and Miller, E. C. Amino acid composition of morphological fractions of rat livers and induced liver tumors. *Proc. Soc. Exper. Biol. & Med. 72:* 495-501, 1949.
61. Sorof, S., and Cohen, P. P. Electrophoretic and ultracentrifugal studies of soluble proteins of rat liver. *J. Biol. Chem. 190:* 311-316, 1951.
62. Sorof, S., and Cohen, P. P. Electrophoretic and ultracentrifugal studies on the soluble proteins of various tumors and of livers from rats fed 4-dimethylaminoazobenzene. *Cancer Research 11:* 376-382, 1951.
63. Sorof, S., Cohen, P. P., Miller, E. C., and Miller, J. A. Electrophoretic studies on the soluble proteins from livers of rats fed aminoazo dyes. *Cancer Research 11:* 383-387, 1951.
64. Stern, K., and Willheim, R. *The Biochemistry of Malignant Tumors.* New York, Reference Press, 1943.
65. Suntzeff, V., and Carruthers, C. The water content in the epidermis of mice undergoing carcinogenesis by methylcholanthrene. *Cancer Research 6:* 574-577, 1946.
66. Toennies, G. Protein-chemical aspects of cancer. *Cancer Research 7:* 193-229, 1947.
67. Wicks, L. F., and Suntzeff, V. Changes in epidermal cholesterol during methylcholanthrene carcinogenesis in mice. *Cancer Research 5:* 464-468, 1945.
68. Woods, M. W., and duBuy, H. G. Cytoplasmic diseases and cancer. *Science 102:* 591-593, 1945.
69. Woods, M. W., duBuy, H. G., Burk, D., and Hesselbach, M. L. Cytological studies on the nature of the cytoplasmic particulates in the Cloudman S-91 mouse melanoma, the derived Algire S-91A partially amelanotic melanoma, and the Harding-Passey mouse melanoma. *J. Nat. Cancer Inst. 9:* 311-323, 1949.
70. Zamecnik, P. C., and Franz, I. D. Peptide bond synthesis in normal and malignant tissues. *Cold Spring Harbor Symposia on Quantitative Biol. 14:* 199-208, 1950.
71. Zamecnik, P. C., and Stephenson, M. L. A comparison of activators of proteolytic enzymes and peptidases in normal rat livers and hepatomas. *Cancer Research 9:* 3-11, 1949.

CHAPTER 19

Nucleoproteins and Cancer

Gerhard Schmidt

Information concerning the chemistry and the metabolism of nucleoproteins in tumors is of interest because certain nucleoproteins are essential and quantitatively important constituents of the chromatin structures of the cell nucleus, while other nucleoproteins occur in considerable amounts in the cytoplasm as well as in the nucleus. Furthermore, it has been suggested that the ribonucleoproteins of the cytoplasm and of the nucleus participate in the biologic synthesis of proteins.

Histologic irregularities of the chromatin structures are characteristic phenomena of many malignant tumor cells. The interpretation of these irregularities will eventually depend on their correlation with chemical differences between the chromatin of normal and malignant cells.

Nucleoproteins are complexes consisting of basic proteins and of organic phosphoric acid compounds of high molecular weights, the nucleic acids. The nature of the linkages between the nucleic acid and the protein component of the nucleoprotein molecule is not yet clearly understood. Most of the nucleoproteins of higher animals are probably salts containing as cations the basic protein and as anions the nucleates: Even a brief description of the chemical structure of nucleic acids would exceed the available space. The reader is referred to the excellent recent monograph of Davidson.[R2*]

Most of the available observations concerning the role of nucleoproteins in malignant growth relate only to their characteristic prosthetic groups, the nucleic acids. Superficially, this approach would appear analogous to that of the histologic chromatin studies, because the staining of chromatin is based on the affinity of the acidic phosphoryl groups of the nucleic acids to basic dyes. Since histologic irregularities of the chromatin structures were found to be characteristic phenomena of malignant tumors, the question arises as to whether or not these irregularities are correlated with the distribution or the structure of nucleic acids in tumor cells.

It must be kept in mind, however, that the nucleic acids in stained histologic

* The letter *R* refers to items in the bibliography of review articles, at the end of the chapter.

preparations or in tissues studied by ultraviolet microscopy can only be considered as convenient "indicators" for the visualization of nucleoprotein structures. Visible alterations of those structures might be caused by chemical changes of the protein—as well as the nucleic acid-component of the nucleoproteins.

The present trend to limit cytochemical chromatin investigations to the chemistry of nucleic acids corresponds to the rapid progress of the analytic chemistry in this field. From the biologic point of view this trend has received encouragement by the discovery of Avery and of Boivin and their associates of mutagenic effects of bacterial desoxyribonucleic acids. There is good evidence in favor of the conclusion that the mutagenic effects of these "transforming factors" are inherent in certain desoxyribonucleic acid fractions: (1) The mutagenic effects were destroyed by incubating such factors with desoxyribonuclease. (2) Some of these factors were purified to a degree at which highly sensitive tests for the presence of protein gave negative results.[49, 49a, 114] It must be borne in mind, however, that the biologic functions of the chromatin are not inherent in the nucleic acids as such, but in compounds of nucleic acids with certain proteins. So far, it has not been possible to isolate nucleoproteins of the chromatin or of the cytoplasm of tissues or of tumors in pure form. The only pure nucleoproteins known are crystallized virus nucleoproteins. In these cases, quantitative biologic assay methods—the infectivity of the crystallized nucleoproteins—were available as guiding tests for the isolation. The isolation procedures of crystallized virus nucleoproteins could thus be developed on the basis of principles similar to those applied to the purification of enzyme proteins, which is also guided by quantitative activity tests. No qualitative or quantitative test for the biologic assay of nucleoproteins of chromatin or cytoplasm is as yet available. No criterion exists, therefore, by which one can establish the purity or the degree of denaturation of any nucleoprotein isolated from tissues.

Apart from the lack of biologic assay methods, some chemical properties of the nucleoproteins render it difficult to judge whether an isolated product was a cell constituent, or whether it was an artifact of the isolation procedure. One of these properties is the dissociating effect of alkali salts on the nucleoproteins.

Furthermore, the prosthetic groups of the nucleoproteins, the nucleic acids, are capable of forming complexes with many nonspecific proteins. It is thus possible that the original nucleoproteins dissociate during fractionation procedures involving the application of salt solutions in concentrations commonly used in the purification of proteins, and that the liberated nucleates recombine subsequently with nonspecific proteins of the tissue extracts. Even if, in the final product, the nucleic acids are combined with the same proteins with which they were associated in the living cell, it is a difficult problem to decide if the mode of their interlinking bonds was not altered during the preparation in view of the large number of groups capable of forming bonds between proteins and nucleic acids, and in view of the lability of such bonds.

An excellent and critical review on tumor nucleoproteins up to 1947 was given by G. Toennies.[R6] Since then, it has been increasingly recognized that the development of improved procedures for the extraction and isolation of nucleoprotein fractions is essential before this field of tumor biochemistry can benefit from the great advances of protein analysis.

The following brief survey of the procedures which have been used for the extraction of tissue nucleoproteins might illustrate some of the difficulties encountered in the correlation between extracted nucleic acid-protein complexes and the nucleoproteins of the cell.

1. *Extraction with dilute alkali and subsequent precipitation with acetic acid.* This is one of the oldest procedures and is considered as more or less obsolete at present. It was developed at a period in which it was assumed that the nucleic acids were tied to their protein components by relatively stable covalent bonds. The present trend is, however, to consider nucleoproteins as dissociable compounds. This is based on the classical preparations of yeast ribonucleic acid by Clarke and Schryver and of desoxyribonucleic acid by I. Hammarsten, involving the use of concentrated sodium chloride solution at neutral reaction. According to this concept, the process of solution of many nucleoproteins is probably accompanied by the separation of the nucleate anion from its protein component. The subsequent precipitation of the extract with acetic acid would thus result in a complex of nucleic acids with an undefined mixture of proteins. It is by no means certain, however, that all nucleoproteins are dissociable compounds. The separation of ribonucleic acid from crystallized tobacco mosaic virus, for example, requires rather drastic chemical treatment.

2. *Extraction with water at 100° C.* This method was introduced by Hammarsten[44] for the extraction of a pancreas ribonucleoprotein. It has not been used in recent investigations for the isolation of other nucleoproteins since the solubility of Hammarsten's nucleoprotein in boiling water is most likely a consequence of the enzymatic degradation of the genuine cell constituents.

3. *Extraction at low ionic strength near neutrality.* Extraction at low ionic strength (with water or very dilute salt solutions) had been introduced by Lilienfeld[63] for the preparation of thymus desoxyribonucleohistone. It is increasingly used in recent studies since it avoids alterations of the nucleoproteins by the solvent.[99] It is not easy, however, to prevent partial enzymatic hydrolysis of the protein as well as the nucleic acid components during the extraction. The slow rates of extraction under these conditions indeed suggest that such enzymatic effects play a part in the extraction of the nucleoproteins. Recent improvements of the extraction at low ionic strength have been introduced with the purpose of suppressing the action of desoxyribonuclease—for example by the removal of magnesium ions necessary for its activation. The application of low ionic strength extraction is limited, however, by the insolubility of many desoxyribonucleoproteins under these conditions.

4. *Extraction with potassium (or sodium) chloride solution.*[2, 64, 76, 80] Salt solutions of approximately molar concentration are the most efficient solvents for desoxyribonucleoproteins at neutral reaction. They were introduced by Mirsky for the isolation of sperm nucleoproteins. Their disadvantage is the dissociating effect on many nucleoproteins. The main field of application of this technic is the extraction of nucleoproteins from material in which nuclear structures are predominant, such as sperm cells, isolated chromosomes, or isolated nuclei. This limitation is advisable when the protein components of desoxyribonucleoproteins are the object of

the study; on the other hand this extraction method is widely applicable for the isolation of nucleic acids.

One of the most interesting results of recent studies on the isolation of desoxyribonucleoproteins is the observation that—according to K. G. Stern and his collaborators[99]—solutions of the undissociated nucleic acid–protein compounds do not exhibit the high values of viscosity and streaming bifringency which are characteristic for the sodium salts of highly polymerized desoxyribonucleic acid. This suggests that the highly asymmetrical shape of the free nucleate ions is profoundly influenced by their association with proteins in the form of nucleoproteins. Desoxyribonucleoproteins in salt solutions of molar concentrations are highly viscous, however, owing to the partial dissociation of the nucleoproteins under these conditions. On the other hand, the physicochemical properties of proteins are likewise influenced by nucleate ions. The presence of desoxyribonucleate in small concentrations prevents the heat coagulation of egg albumin, but not its denaturation.

Amino-acid analyses of tumor nucleoproteins have been reported by Greenstein, Thompson and Jenrette,[40] Bloom, Codgell and Lewis,[7] Khouvine *et al.*,[53, 54, 55] and Miller, Green, Kolb, and Miller,[73, 74] and Zbarski and Debov.[115] The results of these analyses do not show striking differences from the composition of the histones of nontumorous tissues. A detailed comparison between the composition of nucleoproteins of tumors and normal tissues will only be fruitful when a much larger amount of data, particularly on the composition of nucleoproteins of normal tissues, will be available (see also page 562).

The possible role of chromosomal proteins in the induction of cancer by nitrogen mustards[8] has been discussed by Haddow.[43] The effect might result from the intracellular formation of compounds between these proteins and the nitrogen mustards (see Chapter 17).

NUCLEIC ACIDS

COMPOSITION OF NUCLEIC ACIDS IN MALIGNANT AND NORMAL CELLS

Analysis of tissue nucleic acids has made remarkable advances during the past five years. In particular, it is now possible to determine quantitatively the two main fractions, desoxyribonucleic acid and ribonucleic acid, utilizing small amounts of tissue, and to characterize isolated nucleic acid samples by quantitative microanalyses of their individual purine and pyrimidine bases.

The isolation of each of the two nucleic acid fractions from small amounts of tissue has likewise made progress, although in the case of ribonucleic acid the procedures were developed very recently, so that the results of an extensive application of these methods to tumors are not yet available. One important difficulty has not as yet been completely overcome: It is possible to obtain desoxyribonucleic acid practically free of ribonucleic acid[113] (by the enzymatic destruction of the latter by ribonuclease), but it is not always possible to prepare genuine ribonucleic acid free of desoxyribonucleic acid. Attention should also be directed to a second problem: the necessity of preventing a partial degradation of ribonucleic acid samples by ribonuclease which is often not completely inactivated even by deproteinizing agents or by organic solvents. The possible influence of both factors on the results of the final analyses must be considered in each experiment.

Despite the fact that new experimental possibilities have been opened by the analytic advances just outlined, the biologic interpretation of the results is still severely limited because a fundamental analytic problem of nucleic acid chemistry is still unsolved: namely the question whether or not each of the two main fractions, DNA (desoxyribonucleic acid) and RNA (ribonucleic acid), consists of a number of different subfractions. Chromatography might eventually hold the key to the solution of this problem, but at present, no practical way for the further partition of DNA or RNA samples has as yet been found.

Pending further developments of fractionation procedures, the results of the available (not very numerous) analyses can be summarized by stating that the differences found between the composition of the DNA fraction of tumor tissue and that of normal tissues do not exceed those found between the DNA fractions isolated from different normal tissues of higher animals.

Woodhouse[112] reported that DNA from mouse and rat sarcoma and from fish sperm contained considerably higher amounts of guanine (13–15 per cent) than DNA from rat liver or calf thymus (8–9.6 per cent). Beale and his associates[3] analyzed ribonucleic acid isolated from fowl sarcoma G.R.C.H. 15 and found a purine : pyrimidine ratio 4.8:3.2 (in yeast and pancreas RNA this ratio approximates unity). The possibility cannot be excluded, however, that this ribonucleic acid was partially degraded by ribonuclease since the effect of this enzyme displaces the purine : pyrimidine ratio of the polynucleotide fraction in favor of the purines. Chargaff and his associates[18] found in pentose nucleic acids isolated from liver metastases of a colon cancer an appreciably higher content of guanylic acid than in the pentose nucleic acid from normal liver tissues. The purine pyrimidine ratio in these nucleic acid samples was close to unity.

QUANTITATIVE DISTRIBUTION OF DNA AND RNA

The desoxyribonucleic acids have, in regard to their distribution, a unique place in biologic chemistry, because they have so far been found exclusively in the chromatin structures of the cell nuclei. On the other hand, no cell nucleus is known in which desoxyribonucleic acids are missing.

Earlier studies have shown a considerable increase of the DNA content per gram of tissue of malignant tumors in comparison to that of the tissues from which the tumors originated. Quantitative figures computed on this basis, however, are difficult to interpret. It is difficult to decide whether an increase of the amount of DNA/Gm. of tissue is the result of the pathologic metabolism of the tumor cells or of the larger amounts of cells per weight unit of tissue. It is increasingly recognized that values for the amounts of DNA per cell represent far more adequate measurements than those of the amount of DNA per weight unit of tissue.

Chemical micro- or even ultramicromethods permit measurements of the DNA content per cell only in very favorable circumstances, namely, on homogeneous cell suspensions such as those of egg and sperm cells, or red or white blood cells. In sections of organized tissue such as liver, it is not easy to obtain reliable cell counts. Furthermore, in such material there is the basic difficulty of working with an inseparable mixture of heterogeneous cell types. This difficulty is not very serious for studies on metabolic functions which are characteristic or predominant in a certain cell type. Desoxyribonucleic acid, however, is a cell component which is of importance in the metabolism of all cells. This consideration shows the desirability of measuring the nucleic acid content of single cells. Such a procedure would have the additional advantage that the mitotic phase of the cell would be clearly defined.

Owing to the extremely small amounts of DNA in a single cell such measurements can only be accomplished by spectrophotometric technics. The requirements of such determinations have been set forth by Mirsky.[75] One of the requirements is the homogeneous distribution of the chromatin throughout the nucleus. So far, this requirement can be met only under very limited circumstances. In certain important conditions, for example, in mitotic phases with compact chromosomes, a homogeneous distribution of the chromatin cannot be achieved. Furthermore, reliable spectrophotometric determinations of DNA in single cells are so far only possible in cells with spherical nuclei.

Despite the principal difficulties just outlined, studies during the last three years on the DNA content per cell have already resulted in observations of far-reaching importance. According to studies carried out independently in the laboratories of the late A. Boivin[9] and of A. E. Mirsky[75] it appears that the amount of DNA per cell is a characteristic constant for the diploid somatic cells of a certain species. The value of the constant is different for each species. The DNA content of the mature germinal cells is approximately one half of that of the somatic cells. An apparent exception to this rule has been reported by Vendrely[106] and by Schmidt[89] and their associates who found in the sea urchin egg much higher DNA values than in the sperm cells. These data, however, which were included in a recent review by Davidson,[R2] require reinvestigation owing to the difficulty of determining DNA in unfertilized sea urchin eggs which contain a relatively enormous excess of RNA over the amount of DNA present.

Organs with relatively high numbers of polyploid cells contain larger amounts of DNA per cell than those calculated from the content of the reference cell.[62a]

The implications of the discovery of Boivin[9] and of Mirsky[75] are obviously of great biologic significance. The constancy of the amount of DNA per cell strongly suggests a correlation with that of the chromosome and gene number and represents at present the strongest support for the view that the DNA of the nucleus is an integral functional part of the chromatin structures. Apart from the principal significance of the constancy of the DNA content of each cell, this finding provides reference values for certain biologic studies. For example, the growth of tissue cultures can be measured by DNA determinations; changes in the composition of the liver could be referred to DNA values rather than to the weight or to the total nitrogen content of the organ.

Nucleic Acid Content of Tumor Tissue

The observations just discussed imply important consequences for investigations concerning the DNA content of rapidly growing tissues, in particular for those studies dealing with tumors. Since it can now be assumed that DNA formation takes place predominantly during mitosis, descriptions of the DNA content per cell must consider two phases: (1) The DNA content of the resting cell which is normally constant for the somatic cells of each species. It appears from cytochemical studies that the increase of DNA during mitosis begins when the biological appearance of the chromatin still resembles that of the resting nucleus. (2) The kinetics of DNA formation during mitosis.

Mark and Ris found the DNA content per nucleus in resting nuclei of mouse hepatoma to be similar to that of normal somatic cells.[68] Cunningham, Griffin, and Luck[22, 23] obtained similar results by analysis of isolated nuclei from rat tumors produced by feeding acetylaminofluorene and from precancerous lesions produced by 3-methyl 4-dimethylaminoazobenzene.

On the other hand, Klein, Kurnick and Klein[58] found the DNA content of mouse ascites tumor cells (20×10^{-6}) considerably elevated in comparison with that of normal cells and Davidson and McIndoe[26] found similarly elevated DNA values in a chicken sarcoma (G.R.C.H. 15) (5×10^{-6}, normal fowl cells 2.4×10^{-6}). Although these elevations were very high[58] it is not yet certain whether the mouse hepatoma behaves principally differently from the two last mentioned tumors since the DNA analyses of mouse hepatoma were carried out by spectrophotometry of simple resting cells, whereas those of the two other tumors were based on chemical determinations on cell suspensions. The latter figures represent, therefore, average values without consideration of the effects of polyploidy and mitosis. The results of Mark and Ris[68] demonstrate, at any rate, that malignant growth can occur with a normal DNA content of resting (nonmitotic) tumor cells. Klein[58] as well as Davidson,[26] attribute the elevated figures for the DNA content per tumor cell at least partially to polyploidy. The author of this review feels that this explanation in itself does not exclude the possibility that the kinetics of the increase of DNA during mitosis might differ in the cancer cell from that of normally growing tissues.

The amounts of DNA per nucleus in leukemic cells have been determined in spontaneous and in transplantable leukemia. A comparison between spontaneous and transplanted leukemia is instructive because of the much faster rate of the cellular multiplication in the latter type of leukemia. Métais and Mandel[71] as well as Davidson, Leslie, and White[26a] found that the DNA content of human leukemic blood cells and of normal leukocytes was closely similar. On the other hand, Petermann and her collaborators[81, 82] found a considerable increase of DNA per nucleus in spleen lymphocytes of mice with transplantable leukemia. According to Petermann the faster rate of mitosis in transplantable leukemia in comparison to that of spontaneous leukemia suggests the explanation that the higher DNA values in transplantable leukemia are an expression of more rapid cell divisions rather than of a specific malignant nucleic acid metabolism. In this respect, the behavior of the spleen in animals with transplanted leukemia resembles that of liver in the early stages of regeneration in which Price and Laird[85] demonstrated a considerable increase in the amounts of DNA per nucleus.

Amounts of Ribonucleic Acid in Tumors. In contrast to DNA, no satisfactory *cytochemical* procedure exists for the quantitative determination of ribonucleic acid in individual cells. Apart from the Unna-Pappenheim stain which permits a qualitative cytochemical differentiation between DNA and RNA, RNA cannot be identified histologically by a color reaction of specific, well-defined chemical groups such as Feulgen's test for DNA. Instead, RNA is identified in histologic sections or in cells by the decrease of the ultraviolet absorption following treatment with ribonuclease or with perchloric acid which selectively extracts RNA from sections. Such differences can be measured quantitatively in certain cell structures containing RNA in high concentration such as nucleoli, but owing to the heterogeneous distribution of RNA throughout the cytoplasm, it is so far not possible to obtain from histospectrophotometric data the total RNA content of the whole cell.

The lack of cytochemical methods for the determination of RNA in individual cells can be overcome to a certain degree by the application of chemical procedures when RNA and DNA are determined in the same sample.[90, 91, 92] The RNA:DNA ratio can then be used for the calculation of the average value of RNA per cell, if the DNA content per cell is known. It is evident that only tumors with a homogeneous histologic structure are suitable for such determinations. In particular, the absence of extensive interspersions of connective tissue or of necrosis is important. Petermann, Alfin-Slater, and Larack[79] reported that the RNA:DNA quotient rose from 0.5 in normal mouse spleen to 0.8–0.9 in leukemic mice. The RNA of the nuclei contributed more to this elevation than that of the cytoplasm.

Whereas the interpretation of the DNA values in resting cells of tumors is greatly facilitated by the fact that normal resting cells of a certain species contain very similar average amounts of DNA, the comparison of RNA figures of tumor and nontumor cells requires careful consideration of several factors: (1) the RNA contents of somatic cells in different tissues differ greatly and characteristically. In general the epithelial cells—particularly the glandular cells—have a much higher RNA:DNA ratio than the cells belonging to the mesenchyme group. For example, lymphocytes of spleen have an average RNA:DNA ratio of 0.5–0.8, liver 3–4, pancreas 8.2. The RNA content of normal cells is considerably dependent on external factors such as nutrition, whereas the DNA content is very little influenced by such factors.

Klein, Kurnick, and Klein[58] correlated the virulence and the RNA content of cells of the mouse ascites tumor.[57] They found that storage at 4° C. for twenty-four hours reduced the virulence of the tumor cells and was accompanied by a decrease of their RNA content whereas the amount of DNA per cell was not appreciably influenced. The decrease in virulence and that in the RNA content showed a remarkable parallelism.

The RNA:DNA ratio in fresh ascites tumor cells was five times higher than that of cells of an exudate obtained on the same animal strain during experimental aseptic peritonitis.[59] It cannot be concluded, however, that the high RNA:DNA ratio is characteristic of the malignant nature of the tumor cells since cells of the ascites tumor (Ehrlich carcinoma) are not comparable with the mesenchymatous cells of inflammatory exudations.

INTRACELLULAR DISTRIBUTION OF RNA AND DNA

Whereas in normal as well as in tumor cells, the occurrence of DNA is limited to the chromatin of the nucleus, RNA has been found in the cytoplasm as well as in the nucleus. In the nucleus, the nucleoli are particularly rich in RNA whereas the chromosomes contain only small amounts. The amounts of RNA present in the whole isolated nuclei have recently been found to be larger than those detected by Mirsky and Pollister[76] in the chromosomes. These two observations are not necessarily in contradiction, since it is possible that the presence of RNA in the nucleus is not limited to its chromatin structures. Petermann and Schneider[82] found that the RNA content of whole nuclei of leukemic spleen cells (transplantable leukemia) shows a much more striking increase in comparison to nuclei of normal spleen cells, than that found for the DNA fraction. The RNA:DNA ratio of the chromosomes shows also an increase which, however, is less marked than that of the ratio in the whole nucleus.

According to Petermann and Schneider[82] it is not as yet possible to decide whether the increase of the nuclear RNA content is specific for the leukemic cells or whether it is a general property of rapidly growing cells. The latter interpretation would be in agreement with the observations of Price and Laird[85] and of Johnson, Albert and Hoste[50] on regenerating livers, whereas in hepatomas a considerable decrease of the amount of RNA per nucleus in the nuclei, and in cytoplasmic structures such as the microsomes and the mitochondria and the total cell was observed.[78]

The increase of nuclear ribonucleic acid in some types of fast growing and malignant cells are possibly connected with the increase of the nucleolar heterochromatin observed by Caspersson and Santesson[17] in histospectrophotometric studies on malignant tumor cells. According to Pollister and Leuchtenberger[84] the nucleoli of meiotic sporocytes of Zeamays contain exclusively RNA. It remains to be seen whether or not this is a general property of nucleoli. A recent contradictory report by Litt, Monty, and Donnce[62b] who found predominantly DNA in isolated liver nucleoli is difficult to evaluate because the method of identification of the analyzed granules as nucleoli has not yet been described by the authors.

According to the interpretation of Caspersson and Santesson the nucleoli are the main site of the biologic synthesis of cytoplasmic proteins. If an increased amount of nucleolar heterochromatin could be correlated with an increased synthesis of cytoplasmic proteins, it would be plausible to consider the high nuclear RNA content of tumor cells as an essential phenomenon of malignant growth. It should be emphasized, however, that so far the evidence in favor of the connection between nucleolar ribonucleic acid and protein synthesis is circumstantial. Any concept based on this evidence remains a working hypothesis until such a connection will have been demonstrated by means of enzymatic experiments.

In the cytoplasm, RNA is a constituent of the microsomes and the mitochondria. A decrease of the relative amount of the mitochondria[78] as well as alterations of their histologic pattern[1] was found in rat and mouse hepatomas, and in liver cells of rats and mice fed 4-dimethylaminoazobenzene and sacrificed before the development of tumors.[86] Cunningham, Griffin, and Luck[23] observed similar cytoplasmic changes during the precancerous stage produced by 3-methyl,4-dimethylaminoazobenzene. They are inclined to consider the cytoplasmic alterations as effects secondary to the stimulation of mitoses.

EFFECT OF ANTIMETABOLITES ON THE NUCLEIC ACIDS OF TUMORS

Owing to the role of the nucleic acids in cell growth, studies of the effect of antimetabolites in the synthesis of nucleic acids are of particular interest.

It must be stated that the search for metabolic analogs with practical chemotherapeutic application is still in the initial stage of screening, and that probably none of the compounds studied so far are of decisive therapeutic value.[14, 45, 21, 83, 97, 100] Nevertheless, the study of antimetabolites of nucleic acid synthesis offers at present a rational pharmacologic approach to tumor therapy, and the importance of these efforts can hardly be overestimated.

It is not intended to present in this chapter a comprehensive review of the present development in this field. A brief discussion of some antimetabolites which have received particular attention during the past two years: azaguanine, 2,6-diaminopurine, and aminopterin, will illustrate the problems encountered in this field. The substances so far investigated were either analogs of purines and pyrimidines[48] or analogs of folic and folinic acids, which are probably factors required for the biologic synthesis of nucleic acids. (See also Chapter 22.)

AZAGUANINE

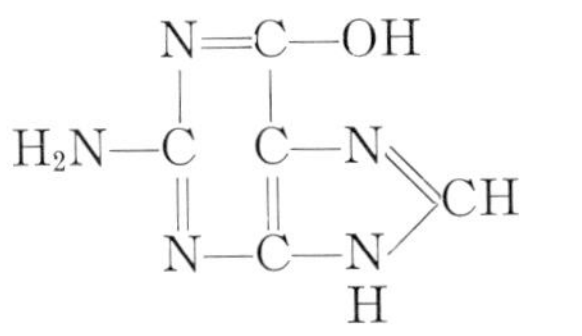

Guanine

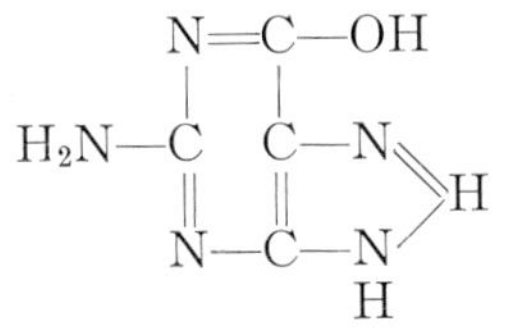

Azaguanine

5-Amino-7-hydroxy-1-*H*-*y*-triazolo pyrimidine (guanazolo, azaguanine) is a representative of the first group of compounds. This substance (and a number of pyrimidine analogs) was synthesized in 1947 by Roblin and his collaborators[88] with the purpose of finding effective antagonists of nucleic acid metabolism. Kidder and his group[56] studied the effect of such analogs on the growth of *Tetrahymena geleii,* a micro-organism whose metabolism exhibits remarkable similarities to that of higher animals. It was found that azaguanine had by far the strongest inhibitory effects of the analogs studied. The growth of a certain type of mouse adenocarcinoma was likewise prevented when the drug was administered during early phases of growth. These studies stimulated a considerable number of further investigations of the substance on various experimental tumors and leukemias. The observations of Kidder regarding the effect of azaguanine on mouse adenocarcinoma were fully confirmed, and it was found that another tumor (Brown-Pearce carcinoma) was likewise strongly inhibited in experiments in which the tumor was implanted in the anterior chamber of rabbits' eyes.

Spontaneous mammary cancers (C3H Bar Harbor strain, Swiss mice [Rockland farm]), mouse ascites tumor,[103] various experimental mouse and rat sarcomas however, remained unaffected by azaguanine.[101] Experimental lymphatic leukemias were likewise not influenced by this substance. The different behavior of different types of tumors towards azaguanine might be at least partially explained by varying degrees of its enzymatic deamination to the noncarcinostatic azaxanthine.[46]

Since azaguanine does not have any appreciable effects on the normal organs of such animals in which the strong inhibition of cancer growth was observed (see also Finkelstein *et al.*[31]) it was believed that the nucleic acid metabolism of the inhibited tumors differed in some way from the nucleic acid metabolism of normal tissues. This interpretation was supported by observations of Shapiro, Weiss and Gellhorn[95] who found that in tumor-bearing colchicinized animals which were treated with azaguanine the percentage of mitoses in the tumor cells was significantly lower than that of colchicinized controls, whereas no significant differences in the mitotic rates were found in other tissues of the animals such as jejunal crypts and testicles. According to the authors these observations suggest the conclusion that azaguanine specifically inhibits the tumor cells from entering into mitosis whereas it has no such effects on cells of normal tissues.

Other observations demonstrate, however, that the growth-inhibiting effect of azaguanine is not quite specific for tumor tissue, since Meyer, Henry and Weinman[72] reported that the eruption of the incisor tooth of 7–8 weeks' old mice was considerably retarded by azaguanine.

The mechanism of the growth-inhibiting effect of azaguanine is still conjectural. It is possible that azaguanine inhibits the incorporation of guanine into nucleic acids, since Brown and his collaborators[10, 11] demonstrated the incorporation of guanine in nucleic acids, by the breast carcinoma EO 771 (C57 black mice). Graff *et all.*[33] found no incorporation of guanine by the transplantable breast carcinoma 755 (C57 black mice) although adenine was utilized by the same tumor.

2,6-DIAMINOPURINE

$$
\begin{array}{c}
\text{N}=\text{C}-\text{NH}_2 \\
| \quad | \\
\text{H}_2\text{N}-\text{C} \quad \text{C}-\text{N} \\
\| \quad \| \quad \text{CH} \\
\text{N}-\text{C}-\text{N} \\
\text{H}
\end{array}
$$

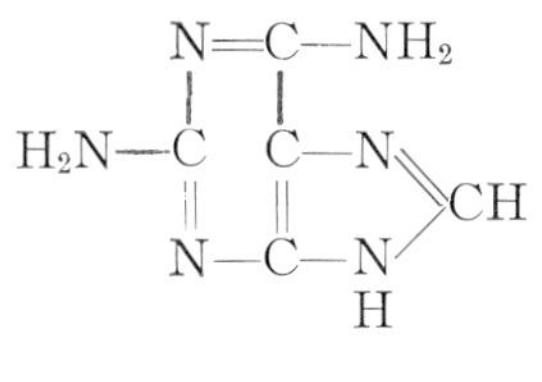

2,6-Diaminopurine was shown to be a potent inhibitor of cell multiplication, (vaccinia virus,[4] *Lactobacillus casei,*[47] the genital tract of the female chick, bone marrow).[83a]

Burchenal[13] and Skipper[96] and their associates found that 2,6-diaminopurine increased significantly the survival time in strain AK4 mouse leukemia.

Several substituted 2,6-diaminopurines inhibited the growth of mouse sarcoma 180.[28]

2,6-Diaminopurine[6] selectively damaged tissue cultures of the mouse sarcomas,

Crocker 180, T241, and Ma 387, whereas cultures of embryonic mouse heart remained almost unaffected. Embryonic rat skin cultures, however, were more sensitive to the agent than rat sarcoma or Walker carcinosarcoma.

The "antimetabolic" effect of 2,6-diaminopurine raises interesting problems of the mechanism of the action of antimetabolites, since Bendich, Furst and Brown[4] showed that this purine can be utilized by rats as precursors of nucleic acid guanine, but not of adenine. According to Bendich and his collaborators, the antimetabolic action of 2,6-diaminopurine could be explained either by interference with the formation of nucleic acid guanine from adenine or by the assumption that the "flooding" of the tissues with the specific precursor of one purine might upset the structural integrity of the nucleic acids. The first possibility is supported by the protective effect of adenine in the experiments on *Lactobacillus casei,* on the oviduct growth in chicks, and on tissue cultures; on the other hand, the effects on bone marrow and on transplantable leukemia have not been reversed by adenine.[13, 83a]

FOLIC ACID ANTAGONISTS

Definite inhibitory effects of injected aminopterin on the normal and malignant growth have been reported by several investigators who studied embryonic tissue,[52] R39 rat sarcoma, mouse sarcoma 180,[32, 93] mammary carcinoma EO771 (mouse), and Harding-Passey mouse melanoma.[102] Mouse ascites tumor was not affected by folic acid antagonists.[103] Tumor fragments kept in a solution of aminopterin lost their transplantability in the case of sarcoma R39 whereas those of sarcoma 180, adenocarcinoma EO771, and of the Harding-Passey mouse melanoma were hardly affected. Mouse C3H mammary tumors implanted into the yolk sac of embryonated eggs were inhibited by aminopterin to a much higher degree than the embryo.[104] The reversal of these effects by folic acid were reported by several authors[32, 34, 62] (see also [47]).

4-Amino-N[10]-methylpteroylglutamic acid (A-methopterin) considerably prolongs the survival time of leukemic mice.[15] This effect can be overcome either by large doses of folic acid[16] or of the citrovorum factor.

The correlation of those effects with the inhibition of nucleic acid synthesis is supported by the observation that aminopterin as well as A-methopterin inhibited the incorporation of isotopic formate and carbonate into the nucleic acid purines of the viscera of normal mice.[98] The incorporation of orotic acid into nucleic acids of liver and tumor slices was not inhibited by folic acid antagonists.[108]

ENZYMES OF NUCLEIC ACID METABOLISM

INCORPORATION OF PHOSPHORUS AND PURINES INTO TUMOR NUCLEIC ACIDS

Brues, Tracy, and Cohn[12] showed in 1944 that P^{32} is incorporated into the desoxyribonucleic acid fraction of rat hepatoma 31 at a faster rate than into that of normal liver and at a slower rate than into that of regenerating liver. The rates of incorporation of P^{32} are thus parallel to the growth rates of the three types of tissue. Once incorporated, the P^{32} remains for a considerable time in the DNA fraction, and the DNA fraction of hepatoma accumulates, therefore, a much larger amount of P^{32} than the surrounding liver tissue (see also [30, 67]).

Griffin and his associates[42] demonstrated that injected radiophosphorus is incorporated into the DNA of rat hepatoma to a much higher extent than into that of normal liver nuclei. These observations are of considerable interest because of their possible bearing on the clinical use of radiophosphorus for tumor diagnosis.[94] (See also Chapter 32.)

The incorporation of adenine and guanine into tumor nucleic acids has already been mentioned. Weed demonstrated the incorporation of orotic acid into nucleic acids by slices of Walker carcinoma 256 (rat) and human sarcoma and carcinoma.[108] In the RNA fraction, the incorporation occurred predominantly in the uridylic and to a much smaller extent in the cytidylic acid.[108]

DESOXYRIBONUCLEASE

Greenstein and Jenrette[37] found by determinations of viscosity and streaming bifringency that DNA was depolymerized much more rapidly by mammary tumors (spontaneous mammary carcinoma in C3H mice) than by hyperplastic or lactating mammary glands. On the other hand, hepatic tumors contained less DNA depolymerase than normal or regenerating liver (see also Kutscher[61]).

Recently, the presence of a specific inhibitor of desoxyribonuclease in extracts of the rapidly growing crop glands of brooding pigeons was discovered by Dabrowska, Cooper, and Laskowski.[24] No observations regarding the possible occurrence of this inhibitor in tumors are yet available.

RIBONUCLEASE

Daoust and Cantero[25] reported an increase of ribonuclease activity in rat livers during early precancerous stages following the ingestion of butter yellow. These observations might be correlated with the histochemical findings of Opie[78] who reported chromatolysis of basophilic cytoplasmatic granules under similar conditions.

XANTHINE DEHYDROGENASE

Since dietary riboflavin deficiency is one of the factors necessary for the production of hepatomas by the ingestion of *p*-dimethylaminoazobenzene, the studies of Greenstein[39] and of Westerfeld and their associates[109] on the behavior of xanthine-oxidase (a flavoprotein) during azo-dye carcinogenesis are of interest. A considerable decrease of liver xanthine oxidase was observed during the precancerous period, but a correlation with the development of hepatoma seems unlikely because of the unimpaired excretion of allantoin and uric acid and because of the fact that liver xanthine oxidase can be depleted by other dietary procedures without the subsequent development of tumors.

ALKALINE PHOSPHATASE

Alkaline phosphatase liberates inorganic phosphate from all mononucleotides but also from all ribonucleic acids and from depolymerized DNA. Undepolymerized DNA is not hydrolyzed by alkaline phosphatase. It acts, therefore, as phosphomonoesterase as well as phosphodiesterase against nucleic acids. It is not as yet clear if both activities are properties of one enzyme. The diesterase activity of alkaline phosphatase is specific for nucleic acids. It was recently found in our laboratory that a sample of highly purified alkaline phosphatase which was completely inactive against the phosphodiesters glycerylphosphorylcholine and glycerylphosphorylethanolamine formed rapidly inorganic phosphate from yeast ribonucleic acid.

A considerable increase of the amount of alkaline phosphatase during the development of rat hepatoma was first described by Greenstein and his collaborators.[35] Other investigators observed likewise intense alkaline phosphatase activity in liver tumors (see Woodard[111]). Pearson, Novikoff, and Morrione, however, found with histochemical staining with β-glycerophosphate as substrate that the most intense phosphatase activity was localized in the proliferating biliary ducts and in the infiltrating leukocytes rather than in the epithelial tumor cells.

The presence of alkaline phosphatase in the mitotic apparatus of normal and malignant cells was demonstrated by Biesele.[5]

On the other hand, Kabat and Furth[51] found, with histochemical methods, only little phosphatase in human breast cancers, whereas this enzyme is abundantly present in the normal lactating gland and also in nonmalignant fibroadenoma tumors of the mammary gland. Intense phosphatase staining was found in the osteoblastic portions of osteosarcoma.

RELATION BETWEEN TUMORS AND ENZYMES OF ORGANS OF THE HOST

Observations on the distribution of alkaline phosphatase in the organs of tumor-bearing animals have initiated a new and important concept in the physiopathology of tumors: the profound influence of tumors on the concentration of certain enzymes in other organs. The first observations were made in 1931 by Edlbacher and Kutscher[27] who found that minced striated muscle of tumor-bearing rats formed inorganic phosphate from DNA or RNA much more rapidly than muscle of normal animals.

More recently, the importance of the relation between tumors and enzymes of other tissues[20] and of blood has been emphasized by Greenstein[32, 34] who discovered the depression of catalase concentration in the liver of tumor-bearing animals, by Warburg[107] and by Sibley and Lehninger who found a significant increase of the aldolase content of the blood of tumor animals. Warburg suggested the possibility that tumors might directly or indirectly, utilize the abundant amounts of muscle aldolase in their own energy metabolism. The field of enzymes and cancer is reviewed in Chapter 20.

CONCLUSIONS

The study of nucleic acid metabolism in nonmalignant and in malignant cells is still in its initial phase—despite the intense work during the past few years and despite the wealth of data already available. A summary is therefore justifiable only for the orientation of the reader whose main interests are in other fields, but it should not be interpreted as an attempt to use the available information even for a new working hypothesis of the role of nucleic acids in normal and malignant growth.

The present working hypothesis is still the same which inspired the interest of the pioneer investigators—Miescher, Kossel, Schmiedeberg, Levene, Thannhauser—in nucleic acids, and it rests on the histologic observations suggesting the role of the chromatin in cell division and the striking abnormalities of the mitotic figures in malignant cells. This interpretation of the histologic stains has been convincingly supported by the observations of Hammarsten, Caspersson and their collaborators[17, 17a] in ultraviolet light. Furthermore, the scope of the biochemistry of nucleic acids has been extended by the comparatively recent information of the general occurrence of ribonucleic acids in the cytoplasm as well as in the nucleus.

Important advances in the chemical and cytochemical methods of nucleic acid analysis rendered it possible to approach the problem of nucleic acid metabolism in experimental biology and pathology during the past ten years. Nevertheless, no characteristic chemical abnormality of the nucleic acid metabolism of malignant tumors is so far discernible, perhaps with the exception of Davidson's observations regarding the decreased protein and the increased water content of malignant cells. (A detailed discussion of these findings is given in Chapter 18.)

This statement requires qualification, inasmuch as it is valid only for the very few aspects of nucleic acid metabolism which have been studied systematically and comparatively: the mutual proportion of the bases in each of the two nucleic acid fractions and the amount of the nucleic acid fractions per cell. The data concerning a third aspect, the intracellular distribution of the two nucleic acid fractions, are not as yet extensive enough to permit a summarizing appraisal.

It must be pointed out that these three topics comprise only a small sector of the intricate problems of nucleoprotein metabolism. It is not mere coincidence that the topics of tumor metabolism so far investigated are all problems of the "chemical anatomy" of the nucleic acids. This reflects on the unusual situation that the study of the biology of nucleic acids and nucleoproteins in higher animals depends at present to a large extent on histologic pictures rather than on functional or metabolic experiments. The successful and rapidly increasing use of microorganisms for many investigations of nucleic acid metabolism, and the use of isotopes for studies on higher animals are, however, promising and new biologic approaches to the problems of the intermediary metabolism of nucleic acids and, in particular, of their biologic synthesis.

The common "chemical denominator" postulated by Greenstein[R4] for the metabolism in malignant growth has so far not been found in the field of the nucleic acids despite their close relation to those structural processes which are common to all growing tissues, the mitoses.

This might not be surprising, however, in view of the highly specific growth effects and growth requirements of normal tissues and cells. It would indeed be surprising if the correlation of the enormous variety of intricate and highly specific chemical reactions, resulting in and hidden by a seemingly uniform and relatively simple anatomic pattern of growth and mitosis would find its chemical expression in an equally uniform and simple pattern of figures obtained by chemical analysis of one of the chromatin constituents.

Kossel and Schenck[60] uncovered the profound changes which the protein moieties of the nucleoproteins (certainly including those of the chromosomes) undergo during the maturation of the sperm cells. These observations suggest that the biologic interpretation of the nucleic acids in normal and malignant growth will only be possible after more refined methods for the study of the protein groups of the nucleoproteins will have become available.

BIBLIOGRAPHY

REVIEWS

1. Chargaff, E. Chemical specificity of nucleic acids and mechanism of their enzymatic degradation. *Experientia 6:* 201-209, 1950.
2. Davidson, J. N., *Biochemistry of the Nucleic Acids.* New York, Wiley, 1950.
3. Davidson, J. N., and Leslie, I. Nucleic acids in relation to tissue growth. *Cancer Research 10:* 587-594, 1950.
4. Greenstein, J. P. *Biochemistry of Cancer.* New York, Academic Press, 1947.
5. Schneider, W. C., and Hogeboom, G. H. Cytochemical studies on mammalian tissues: The isolation of cell components by differential centrifugation. *Cancer Research 11:* 1-22, 1951.
6. Toennies, G. Protein chemical aspects of cancer. *Cancer Research 7:* 193-229, 1947.

SPECIFIC REFERENCES

1. Annau, E., Manginelli, A., and Roth, A. Alterations of the mitochondrial pattern in the liver of tumor-bearing mice. *Cancer Research 11:* 404-405, 1951.
2. Bang, I. Chemical studies of lymphatic organs. *Hofmeisters Beitr. 4:* 331, 1903.
3. Beale, R. N., Harris, R. J. C., Roe, E. M. F., and Thomas, J. F. Nucleic acids of normal and cancerous tissues. The preparation and composition of a pentosenucleic acid from fowl sarcoma G.R.C.H.15. *J. Chem. Soc.* 1397-1407 1950.
4. Bendich, A., Furst, S. S., and Brown, G. B. On the role of 2,6-diaminopurine in the biosynthesis of nucleic acid guanine. *J. Biol. Chem. 185:* 423-433, 1950.
5. Biesele, J. J. Phosphatases of the mitotic apparatus in cultured normal and malignant mouse cells. *Proc. Natl. Canc. Conf.* 1949, pp. 34-41.
6. Biesele, J. J., Berger, R. E., and Hitchings, G. H. Tissue culture studies with 2,6-diaminopurine and related substances. *Cancer Research, 10:* 204, 1950.
7. Bloom, W. L., Codgell, B. and Lewis, G. T. The basic proteins of the cell nucleus. *Cancer Research 10:* 205, 1950.
8. Boyland, E., and Horning, E. S. The induction of tumors with nitrogen mustards. *Brit. J. Cancer 3:* 118-123, 1949.
9. Boivin, A., Vendrely, R., and Vendrely, C. Desoxyribonucleic acid as the site of hereditary characters in the cell nucleus: evidence by analysis. *Compt. rend. Acad. d. sc. 226:* 1061-1063, 1948.
10. Brown, G. B. In *Phosphorus Metabolism, A Symposium.* Baltimore, Md., The Johns Hopkins Press. Vol. II, 1952.

11. BROWN, G. B., BENDICH, A., ROLL, P. M., and SUGIURA, K. Utilization of guanine by the C 57 black mouse bearing adenocarcinoma EO771. *Proc. Soc. Exper. Biol. & Med. 72:* 501-502, 1949.
12. BRUES, A. M., TRACY, M. M., and COHN, W. E. Nucleic acids of rat liver and hepatoma: Their metabolic turnover in relation to growth. *J. Biol. Chem. 155:* 619-633, 1944.
13. BURCHENAL, J. H., BENDICH, A., BROWN, G. B., ELION, G. B., HITCHINGS, G. H., RHOADS, C. P., and STOCK, C. C. Preliminary studies on the effect of 2,6-diaminopurine on transplanted mouse leukemia. *Cancer 2:* 119-120, 1949.
14. BURCHENAL, J. H., BURCHENAL, J. R., and JOHNSTON, S. F. Chemotherapy of leukemia: III. Further studies on the effect of nitrogen mustards and related compounds on transmitted mouse leukemia. *Cancer 4:* 353-356, 1951.
15. BURCHENAL, J. H., BURCHENAL, J. R., KUSHIDA, M. N., JOHNSTON, S. F., and WILLIAMS, B. S. The chemotherapy of leukemia: II. The effect of 4-aminopteroylglutamic acid and 4-amino N^{10} methylpteroylglutamic acid on transplanted mouse leukemia. *Cancer 2:* 113-118, 1949.
16. BURCHENAL, J. H., KUSHIDA, M. N., JOHNSTON, S. F., and CREMER, M. A. Prevention of chemotherapeutic effects of 4-amino-N^{10}-methylpteroylglutamic acid on mouse leukemia by pteroylglumatic acid. *Proc. Soc. Exper. Biol. & Med. 71:* 559-562, 1949.
17. CASPERSSON, T., and SANTESSON, L. Studies on protein metabolism in the cells of epithelial tumours. *Acta Radiol. suppl. 46:* 1-105, 1942.
17a. CASPERSSON, T. Studies on the protein metabolism of the cell. *Naturwissenschafften 29:* 33, 1941.
18. CHARGAFF, E., MAGASANIK, B., VISCHER, E., GREEN, C., DONIGER, R., and ELSON, D. Nucleotide composition of pentose nucleic acids from yeast and mammalian tissues. *J. Biol. Chem. 186:* 51-67, 1950.
19. CORMAN, J. Cytological phenomena observed during selective and unselective injury to malignant cells in tissue culture with penicillium extracts and with nitrogen mustards. Univ. Microfilm, Ann Arbor, Mich. Pub. No. 1241, 79 pp. Microfilm Abstracts, 9, No. 2, 135-136, 1949.
20. CRUZ-COKE, E., PLAZA DE LOS REYES, M., and SCARELLA, A. Ribo- and desoxyribonucleic acids in transplantable sarcoma and liver of rats treated with tri-o-tolylphosphate. *Bol. Soc. Biol.*, Santiago, Chile, *7:* 71-76, 1950.
21. CUNNINGHAM, L., GRIFFIN, A. C., and LUCK, J. M. Polyploidy and cancer: The desoxypentosenucleic acid (DNA) content of nuclei of normal, precancerous and neoplastic rat tissues. *J. Gen. Physiol. 34:* 59-63, 1950.
22. CUNNINGHAM, L., GRIFFIN, A. C., and LUCK, J. M. Effect of a carcinogenic azo dye on liver cell structure: Isolation of nuclei and cytoplasmic granules. *Cancer Research 10:* 194-199, 1950.
23. CUNNINGHAM, L., GRIFFIN, A. C., and LUCK, J. M. The desoxyribonucleic acid content per nucleus in normal, precancerous, and cancerous tissues of the rat. *Cancer Research 10:* 211, 1950.
24. DABROWSKA, W., COOPER, E. J., and LASKOWSKI, M. A specific inhibitor for desoxyribonuclease. *J. Biol. Chem. 177:* 991-992, 1949.
25. DAOUST, R., and CANTERO, A. Ribonucleodepolymerase activity in the rat liver during the precancerous stage. *Rev. canad. de biol. 9:* 265-305, 1950.
26. DAVIDSON, J. N., and MCINDOE, W. W. Phosphorus compounds in the cell nucleus. *Biochem. J. 45:* 16, 1949.

26a. Davidson, J. N., Leslie, I., and White, J. C. The nucleic acid content of the cell. *Lancet 260:* 1287-1290, 1951.

27. Edlbacher, J., and Kutscher, W. Studies on tumor metabolism: II. *Ztschr. f. physiol. Chem.* 199, 200-216, 1931.

28. Elion, G. B., Buckley, S. M., Stock, C. C., and Hitchings, G. H. Effect of some substituted 2,6-diaminopurines on the growth of sarcoma 180. *Cancer Research* 11: 246, 1951.

29. Euler, H. von. The biochemistry of the nucleic acids and the nucleoproteins. *Deutsche med. Wchnschr. 73:* 265-271, 1948.

30. Euler, H. von, Hevesy, G., and Solodkowska, W. Turnover of ribonucleic acid in the Jensen sarcoma of the rat. *Arkiv. Kemi. Mineral. Geol. 26A:* 1-12, 1948.

31. Finkelstein, M., Winters, W. D., Thomas, P. A., Davison, C., and Smith, P. K. Effect of 8-azaguanine on growth and respiration of tumor tissue. *Cancer Research 11:* 247-248, 1951.

32. Goldin, A., Goldberg, B., Ortega, L. G., and Schoenbach, E. B. Reversal of aminopterin-induced inhibition of sarcoma 180 by folic acid. *Cancer 2:* 857-862, 1949.

33. Graff, S., Engelman, M., Gillespie, H. B., and Graff, A. M. Guanine in cancer. *Cancer Research 11:* 388-392, 1951.

34. Greenspan, E. M., Goldin, A., and Schoenbach, E. B. Studies on the mechanism of action of chemotherapeutic agents in cancer: V. Influence of the citrovorum factor and folic acid on the toxic manifestations of aminopterin in mice. *Cancer 4:* 619-625, 1951.

35. Greenstein, J. P. Distribution of acid and alkaline phosphatase in tumors, normal tissues and tissues of tumor bearing rats and mice. *J. Nat. Cancer Inst. 2:* 511-524, 1942.

36. Greenstein, J. P. Distribution of acid and alkaline phosphatase in tumors, normal tissues, and the tissues of tumor bearing rats and mice. *J. Nat. Cancer Inst. 2:* 511-524, 1943.

37. Greenstein, J. P., and Jenrette, W. V. The depolymerization of thymonucleic acid by an enzyme system in normal and cancerous hepatic and mammary tissues and in the milk and serums of several species. *J. Nat. Cancer Inst. 1:* 845-863, 1941.

38. Greenstein, J. P., Jenrette, W. V., and White, J. The liver catalase activity of tumor bearing rats and the effect of extirpation of the tumors. *J. Biol. Chem. 141:* 327-328, 1941.

39. Greenstein, J. P., Jenrette, W. V., and White, J. The relative activity of xanthine dehydrogenase, catalase and amylase in normal and cancerous hepatic tissue. *J. Nat. Cancer Inst. 2:* 17-22, 1941.

40. Greenstein, J. P., Thompson, J. W., and Jenrette, W. V. Chemical studies on the components of normal and neoplastic tissue: III. The composition and amphoteric properties of the nucleoprotein fraction of the Jensen rat sarcoma. *J. Nat. Cancer Inst. 1:* 367-376, 1940.

41. Griffin, A. C., Bloom, S., Cunningham, L., Teresi, J. D., and Luck, J. M. Uptake of labeled glycine by normal and cancerous tissues in the rat. *Cancer 3:* 316-320, 1950.

42. Griffin, A. C., Cunningham, L., Brandt, E. L., and Kupke, D. W. The incorporation of radioactive phosphorus, P^{32}, in the nucleic acids of normal and precancerous livers and of liver tumors. *Cancer Research 10:* 222, 1950.

43. HADDOW, A. Mode of action of the nitrogen mustards: A new working hypothesis and its possible relation to carcinogenesis. *Proc. Nat. Cancer Conf.*, 1949, pp. 88-94.
44. HAMMARSTEN, O. On nucleoproteins. *Ztschr. f. physiol. Chem. 19:* 19, 1894.
45. TAYLOR, S. G., HASS, G. M., CRUMRINE, J. L., and SLAUGHTER, D. P. Toxic reactions of 4-aminopteroylglutamic acid (aminopterin) in patients with far-advanced neoplastic disease. *Cancer 3:* 493-503, 1950.
46. HIRSCHBERG, E., GELLHORN, A., and KREAM, J. Enzymatic deamination of azaguanine by normal and neoplastic tissues. *Cancer Research 11:* 256-257, 1951.
47. HITCHINGS, G. H., ELION, G. B., VAN DER WERFF, H., and FALCO, E. A. Pyrimidine derivatives as antagonists of pteroylglutamic acid. *J. Biol. Chem. 174:* 765-766, 1948.
48. HITCHINGS, G. H., ELION, G. B., FALCO, E. A., RUSSELL, P. B., and VAN DER WERFF, H. Studies on analogues of purines and pyrimidines. *Ann. N. Y. Acad. Sc. 52:* 1318-1335, 1950.
49. HOTCHKISS, R. D. Chemical studies on the transforming factor of pneumococci. *Colloq. internat. d. centre natl. recherche sc. Unit. biol. douees contin. genet. Paris 8:* 57-65, 1948.
49a. HOTCHKISS, R. D. In *Phosphorus Metabolism: II. Symposium of the McCollum Pratt Institute.* Baltimore, Md., Johns Hopkins University, in press.
50. JOHNSON, R. M., ALBERT, S., and HOSTE, R. Phosphorus metabolism in regenerating liver. *Cancer Research 11:* 260, 1951.
51. KABAT, E. A., and FURTH, J. A histochemical study of alkaline phosphatase in various normal and neoplastic tissues. *Am. J. Path. 17:* 303-318, 1941.
52. KARNOFSKY, D. A., PATTERSON, P. A., and RIDGEWAY, L. P. Effect of folic acid, "4-amino" folic acids, and related substances on growth of chick embryo. *Proc. Soc. Exper. Biol. & Med. 71:* 447-452, 1949.
53. KHOUVINE, Y., and GREGOIRE, J. Desoxyribonucleoproteins of cancerous tissue (atypical epithelioma of the rat). *Compt. rend. Acad. d. sc. 228:* 1167-1169, 1949.
54. KHOUVINE, Y., and GREGOIRE, J. Histone of atypical epithelioma of the rat. *Compt. rend. Acad. d. sc. 231:* 1100-1101, 1950.
55. KHOUVINE, Y., and LÉVY-BORIS, M. L. Ribonucleoproteins of atypical epithelioma of the rat. *Compt. rend. Acad. d. sc. 228:* 870-872, 1949.
56. KIDDER, G. W., DOWEY, V. C., PARKS, R. E., JR., and WOODSIDE, G. L. Purine metabolism in tetrahymena and its relation to malignant cells in mice. *Science 109:* 511-514, 1949.
57. KLEIN, E., and KLEIN, G. Nucleic acid content of tumour cells. *Nature 166:* 832-833, 1950.
58. KLEIN, E., KURNICK, N. B., and KLEIN, G. The effect of storage on the nucleic acid content and virulence of mouse ascites tumor. *Exp. Cellular Research 1:* 127-134, 1950.
59. KLEIN, G. Use of the Ehrlich ascites tumor of mice for quantitative studies on the growth and biochemistry of neoplastic cells. *Cancer 3:* 1052-1061, 1950.
60. KOSSEL, A., and SCHENCK, E. G. Studies on the basic proteins, a contribution to the history of their formation. *Ztschr. f. physiol. Chem. 173:* 278-311, 1928.
61. KUTSCHER, W. Splitting of nucleic acid in malignant tissue. *Ztschr. f. Krebsforsch. 56:* 253-257, 1949.
62. LETTRÉ, H., and LANDSCHWITZ, C. Effect of folic acid on cancer cells. *Naturwissenschafften 34:* 345-346, 1947.

62a. LEUCHTENBERGER, C., VENDRELY, R., and VENDRELY, C. A comparison of the content of desoxyribonucleic acid (DNA) in isolated animal nuclei by cytochemical and chemical methods. *Proc. Nat. Acad. Sc. 37:* 33-38, 1951.

62b. LITT, U., MONTY, K. J., and DONNCE, A. Isolation and properties of rat liver cell nucleoli. *Cancer Research 12:* 279, 1952.

63. LILIENFELD, L. On the chemistry of the white blood cells. *Ztschr. f. physiol. Chem. 18:* 473, 1894.

64. LUCK, J. M. The liver proteins. *Cold Spring Harbor Symp. Quant. Biol. 14:* 153-160, 1949.

65. LUDFORD, R. J. Factors determining the action of colchicine on tumor growth. *Brit. J. Cancer 2:* 75-86, 1948.

66. MANDEL, P., MANDEL, L., and MONIQUE, J. Evolution of nucleic acids after compensated renal hypertrophy. C. R., *Compt. rend. Soc. de biol. 230:* 706-788, 1950.

67. MANN, W., and GRUSCHOW, J. Synthesis of nucleic acid and phosphoprotein in normal and cancer tissue slices studied with radioactive phosphorus. *Proc. Soc. Exper. Biol. & Med. 71:* 658-660, 1949.

68. MARK, D. D., and RIS, H. A comparison of desoxyribonucleic acid content in certain nuclei of normal liver and liver tumors. *Proc. Soc. Exper. Biol. & Med. 71:* 727-729, 1949.

69. MCKEY, D. G., and FARRAR, J. T. Basophilic substances in human liver cells. *Cancer 3:* 106-115, 1950.

70. MELLORS, R. C., and SUGIURA, K. Alkaline phosphatase activity and basophilia in hepatic cells following administration of butter yellow to rats. *Proc. Soc. Exper. Biol. & Med. 67:* 242-246, 1948.

71. METAIS, P., and MANDEL, P. Desoxypentosenucleic acid content of human leucocytes in normal and pathological states. *Compt. rend. Soc. de biol. 144:* 277-279, 1950.

72. MEYER, J., HENRY, J. L., and WEINMAN, J. P. The effect of 8-azaguanine on physiologic growth measured by the rate of eruption of the incisor of the mouse. *Cancer Research 11:* 437-441, 1951.

73. MILLER, G. L., GREEN, E. U., KOLB, J. J., MILLER, E. E. Studies on the proteins of rhabdomyosarcoma and normal muscle of mice: I. Gross composition, extractions with 0.5 N potassium chloride, and fractionations by differential centrifugation and dialysis. *Cancer Research 10:* 141-147, 1950.

74. MILLER, G. L., GREEN, E. U., MILLER, E. E., and KOLB, J. J. Studies on the proteins in rhabdomyosarcoma and normal muscle of mice: II. Electrophoretic and viscosimetric measurements. *Cancer Research 10:* 148-154, 1950.

75. MIRSKY, A. E., and RIS, H. The desoxyribonucleic acid content of animal cells and its evolutionary significance. *J. Gen. Physiol. 34:* 451-462, 1950-1951.

75a. MIRSKY, A. E., and RIS, H. The composition and structure of isolated chromosomes. *J. Gen. Physiol. 34:* 475-492, 1950-1951.

76. MIRSKY, A. E., and POLLISTER, A. W. Chromosin, a desoxyribose nucleoprotein complex of the cell nucleus. *J. Gen. Physiol. 30:* 117-148, 1946.

77. OLHAGAN, B., THORELL, B., and WISING, P. The endocellular nucleic acid distribution and plasma protein formation in myclomatosis. *Scandinav. J. Clin. & Lab. Investigation 1:* 49-59, 1949.

78. OPIE, L. E. Mobilization of basophilic substance (ribonucleic acid) in the cytoplasm of liver cells with the production of tumors by butter yellow. *J. Exper. Med. 84:* 91-106, 1946.

79. PETERMANN, M. L., ALFIN-SLATER, R. B., and LARACK, A. M. The nucleic acid distribution in normal and leukemic mouse spleen. *Cancer 2:* 510-515, 1949.
80. PETERMANN, M. L., and LAMB, C. M. The nucleohistone of beef spleen. *J. Biol. Chem. 176:* 685-693, 1948.
81. PETERMANN, M. L., and MASON, E. J. Nucleic acid content of chromosomes of normal and leukemic mouse spleen. *Proc. Soc. Exper. Biol. & Med. 69:* 542-544, 1948.
82. PETERMANN, M. L., and SCHNEIDER, R. M. Nuclei from normal and leukemic mouse spleen: II. The nucleic acid content of normal and leukemic nuclei. *Cancer Research 11:* 485-489, 1951.
83. PHILIPS, F. S., THIERSCH, J. B., and FERGUSON, F. C. Studies of the action of 4-aminopteroylglutamic acid and its congeners in mammals. *Ann. N. Y. Acad. Sc. 52:* 1349-1359, 1950.
83a. PHILIPS, F. S., and THIERSCH, J. B. Actions of 2,6-diaminopurine in mice, rats, and dogs. *Proc. Soc. Exper. Biol. & Med. 72:* 401-408, 1949.
84. POLLISTER, A. W., and LEUCHTENBERGER, C. Nucleotide content of the nucleolus. *Nature 163:* 360-361, 1949.
85. PRICE, J. M., and LAIRD, A. K. A comparison of the intracellular composition of regenerating liver and induced liver tumors. *Cancer Research 10:* 650-658, 1950.
86. PRICE, J. M., MILLER, J. A., and MILLER, E. C. The intracellular distribution of protein, nucleic acids and riboflavin in the livers of mice and hamsters fed 4-dimethylaminoazobenzene. *Cancer Research 11:* 523-528, 1951.
87. ROBERTSON, W. VAN B., and KRETSCHMER, N. Chemical changes in the liver during *p*-dimethylaminoazobenzene administration. *Cancer Research 9:* 564, 1949.
88. ROBLIN, R. O., JR., LAMPEN, J. O., ENGLISH, J. P., COLE, Q. P., and VAUGHAN, J. R., JR. Studies in chemotherapy: VIII. Methionine and purine antagonists and their relation to the sulfonamides. *J. Am. Chem. Soc. 67:* 290-294, 1945.
89. RUFFO, A. Competitive inhibition in chemotherapy and new substances of cancerolytic action. *Minerva med. 40:* 625-628, 1949.
90. SCHNEIDER, W. C. Nucleic acids in normal and neoplastic tissues. *Cold Spring Harbor Symp. Quant. Biol. 12:* 169-178, 1947.
91. SCHNEIDER, W. C., HOGEBOOM, G. H., and ROSS, H. E. Intracellular distribution of enzymes: III. The distribution of nucleic acids and adenosinetriphosphatase in normal mouse liver and mouse hepatoma. *J. Nat. Cancer Inst. 10:* 977-982, 1950.
92. SCHNEIDER, W. C., and KLUG, H. L. Phosphorus compounds in animal tissues: IV: The distribution of nucleic acids and other phosphorus compounds in normal and malignant tissues. *Cancer Research 6:* 691-694, 1946.
93. SCHOENBACH, E. B., GOLDIN, A., GOLDBERG, B., and ORTEGA, L. G. The effect of folic acid derivatives on sarcoma 180. *Cancer 2:* 57-64, 1949.
94. SCHULMAN, J. JR., FALKENHEIM, M., and GRAY, S. J. The phosphorus turnover of carcinoma of the human stomach as measured with radioactive phosphorus. *J. Clin. Investigation 28:* 66-72, 1949.
95. SHAPIRO, D. M., WEISS, R., and GELLHORN, A. The effect of azaguanine on mitosis in normal and neoplastic tissues. *Cancer 3:* 896-902, 1950.
95a. SIBLEY, J. A., and LEHNINGER, A. L. Aldolase in the serum and tissues of tumor-bearing animals. *J. Nat. Cancer Inst. 9:* 303-309, 1949.
96. SKIPPER, H. E., BENNET, L. L., EDWARDS, P. C., BRYAN, C. E., HUTCHINSON, O. L., CHAPMAN, J. B., and BELL, M. Antileukemic assays on certain pyrimidines,

purines, benzimidazoles and related compounds. *Cancer Research 10:* 166-169, 1950.

97. SKIPPER, H. E., CHAPMAN, J. B., and BELL, M. Studies of the role of folic acid in the leukemic process. *Cancer 3:* 871-873, 1950.
98. SKIPPER, H. E., MITCHELL, J. H., and BENNETT, L. L. Inhibition of nucleic acid synthesis by folic acid antagonists. *Cancer Research 10:* 510-512, 1950.
99. STERN, K. G., GOLDSTEIN, G., WAGMAN, J., and SCHRYVER, J. Studies on desoxyribonucleoproteins: Isolation and properties of geno-protein T. *Federation Proc. 6:* 296, 1947.
100. STOCK, C. C., BIESELE, J. J., BURCHENAL, J. H., KARNOFSKY, D. A., MOORE, A. E., and SUGIURA, K. Folic acid analogs and experimental tumors. *Ann. N. Y. Acad. Sc. 52:* 1360-1378, 1950.
101. SUGIURA, K., HITCHINGS, G. H., CAVALIERI, L. F., and STOCK, C. C. The effect of 8-azaguanine on the growth of carcinoma, sarcoma, osteogenic sarcoma, lymphosarcoma, and melanoma in animals. *Cancer Research 10:* 178-185, 1950.
102. SUGIURA, K., MOORE, A. E., and STOCK, C. C. Effect of aminopterin on the growth of carcinoma, sarcoma and melanoma in animals. *Cancer 2:* 491-502, 1949.
103. SUGIURA, K., and STOCK, C. C. Effect of various compounds on Ehrlich ascites tumor in mice. *Cancer Research 11:* 284-285, 1951.
104. TAYLOR, A., and CARMICHAEL, N. Folic acid analogs and the growth of embryo and tumor tissue. *Cancer Research 11:* 519-522, 1951.
105. THIERSCH, J. B. Bone marrow changes in man after treatment with aminopterin, amethopterin and aminoanfol. *Cancer 2:* 877-883, 1949.
106. VENDRELY, C., and VENDRELY, R. Sur la teneur individuelle en acide desoxyribonucleique des gametes d'oursins arbacia et Paracentrotus. *Compt. rend. Soc. Biol. 143:* 1386, 1949.
107. WARBURG, O. Enzyme chemistry of tumors. *Abhandl. deutsch Akad. Wiss. Berlin, Math. No. 3,* 1947.
108. WEED, L. L. The incorporation of radioactive orotic acid into the nucleic acid pyrimidines of animal and human tumors. *Cancer Research 11:* 470-473, 1951.
109. WESTERFELD, W. W., RICHERT, D. A., and HILFINGER, M. F. Studies on xanthine oxidase during carcinogenesis by *p*-dimethylaminoazobenzene. *Cancer Research 10:* 486-494, 1950.
110. WINNICK, T. Studies on the mechanism of protein synthesis in embryological and tumor tissues: II. Inactivation of fetal rat liver homogenates by dialysis and reactivation by the adenylic acid system. *Arch. Biochem. 28:* 338-347, 1950.
111. WOODARD, H. Q. The glycerophosphatase of rat liver cancer produced by feeding *p*-dimethylaminoazobenzene. *Cancer Research 3:* 159-163, 1943.
112. WOODHOUSE, D. L. Composition of nucleic acids: The guanine and thymine content of nucleic acids isolated from normal tissues and animal tumors. *Brit. J. Cancer 3:* 510-519, 1949.
113. WROBLEWSKI, F., and BODANSKY, O. Presence of desoxyribonuclease activity in human serum. *Proc. Soc. Exper. Biol. & Med. 74:* 443-445, 1950.
114. ZAMENHOF, S., LEIDY, G., ALEXANDER, H. E., FITZGERALD, P. L., and CHARGAFF, E. Purification of the desoxypentose nucleic acid of *Hemophilus influenzae* having transforming activity. *Arch Biochem. & Biophys. 40:* 50-55, 1952.
115. ZBARSKI, T. B., and DEBOV, S. S. Proteins of cell nuclei. *Doklady Akad. Nank, U.S.S.R. 63:* 795-798, 1948.

CHAPTER 20

Enzymes and Cancer

William H. Fishman

"One way of defining life is as an orderly functioning of enzymes. Disease manifests itself as a disorder, inhibition, or hyperfunction of enzymes."[65]

Cancer, with its characteristic disorganization of growth and bizarre manifestations, might be expected to reveal disturbances in the composition of enzyme systems. The discovery by Warburg[67] in 1933 of the high rate of anaerobic glycolysis of tumors first demonstrated that this was true. This observation, which coincided with the opening of our modern era of enzymologic research, was followed by many other studies that have provided an abundance of data. While many of these findings, it must be admitted, resist intelligent interpretation, a number of facts with practical clinical significance have been published, and recent attempts have been made to arrange the material concerning enzymes and cancer into an orderly scheme.

Greenstein has dealt extensively with enzymes and cancer in *The Biochemistry of Cancer*[33] and information on older work may be found in a book by Stern and Wilheim.[63] Detailed review articles have appeared in the *Annual Reviews of Biochemistry*[9, 32] and expositions have been published of *Biological Energy Transformations and the Cancer Problem*[52] and of *Enzymes, Growth and Cancer*[55] by Potter. The reader is referred to these publications for subject matter which, through limitation of space, will not be covered here. The purpose of this chapter will be to present a generalized account of enzymes and cancer with emphasis on those enzyme systems which appear to have some relation to human cancer.

CRITERIA OF COMPARISON OF ENZYMES IN TUMORS AND CONTROL TISSUES

Comparative studies of a given enzyme or of groups of enzymes in tumor tissues as contrasted with benign tissues are beset with difficulties. There are problems in the selection of homologous tissues for comparison, in evaluating differences in cellularity and nonmalignant pathology, in selecting the proper conditions for enzyme assay, and in defining criteria of significance.

HISTOLOGIC CHARACTERISTICS OF TUMORS AND BENIGN TISSUES

Ideally, tissues of the same histologic type as that of the tumor should be used for comparison. The following pairs of tissues may properly be studied: intestinal mucosa and intestinal adenocarcinoma, gastric mucosa and gastric adenocarcinoma, lymph nodes and lymphoma, liver and hepatoma, and skin and epithelioma. Examples of comparative studies in which one may not attribute specific characteristics to certain tumor components are the following: liver and metastases to liver from nonhepatic primary lesions, lymph node and lymph node metastases, and lung and metastases to it.

On the other hand, the tissue of origin may be composed of more than one cell type. For example, the kidney consists of the specialized structure, the nephron, arranged in the renal stroma, and the breast is formed by a network of ducts radiating through connective tissue. Comparison of the components of tumors of these organs with the same components of the kidney or breast is therefore difficult. Likewise, tumors of the same organ may differ markedly. Liver tumors induced in rats by aminoazo dye may be cholangiomas, hepatomas, or sarcomas.

SELECTION OF TISSUE FOR ENZYME STUDY

The question also arises which parts of the tumor should be selected for study. A malignant tumor which is entirely homogeneous in cell type is rarely found. As a rule, the edges of the tumor, while consisting of vigorously growing tissue, are surrounded by an inflammatory reaction of the vicinal tissues uninvolved with the tumor. Towards the central portions of the tumor, necrosis of varying degree is encountered. Even in an area of "healthy" tumor-tissue, necrosis may be detected. Should only obviously non-necrotic tissues be selected for study? If this is done, is this type of tissue truly representative of the tumor?

EXPRESSION OF ENZYME ACTIVITY

An important consideration is the selection of the index with which to relate enzyme activity. Some criteria which have been used are the computation of enzyme activity as a function of the wet weight, dry weight, nitrogen, nucleoprotein phosphorus, or the number of cancer cells of the tissue. Fresh tumor tissues possess a significantly greater water content than nontumor tissues. Accordingly, a comparison of the enzyme activities of tumor and benign tissues on the basis of wet weight would tend to yield figures for the tumor which are lower than they should be. Comparisons made on the basis of dry weight and nitrogen do not differentiate between the dry weight or nitrogen of the tumor cells and of the nontumor elements which may often be present in high proportions. Tissue figures based on wet weight, dry weight, or nitrogen, therefore, would be lower than would be obtained on the basis of tumor cells alone. However, there is the question of whether or not the dilution of the tumor cells by nontumor elements is comparable to the dilution of cells of healthy tissue by its stroma. There is great variation in the cellularity of tumors. Differences of enzyme activity based on any of the preceding criteria would possess only relative quantitative significance.

Nucleoprotein Phosphorus

Some investigators have employed measurements of the nucleoprotein phosphorus as a basis for expressing enzyme activity. This method may be criticized on the following grounds: (1) The nucleoprotein phosphorus of cells other than tumor, such as fibroblasts or leukocytes, will be included in the determination; (2) it is not known whether or not all tumor cells have the same nucleoprotein phosphorus content; (3) it is not certain that the nucleoprotein phosphorus determination may not include nitrogenous phosphorus compounds other than nucleoprotein. It is therefore probable that, in comparisons of enzyme activity based on nucleoprotein phosphorus, values obtained will be lower than they should be.

Cell Count

The most direct method of making comparisons of enzyme activity is that based on the number of tumor cells in the specimen. This technic as employed by Chalkley[11] and others[58] consists of counting the number of cells seen in the field which fall directly beneath a line in the eyepiece of the microscope. By this means, rather widely discrepant data on the cytochrome oxidase activity of thyroid adenoma were found to be consistent when expressed on the basis of the proportion of epithelial cells in the tissue. This technic has its limitations also. In view of the heterogeneous nature of tumor tissues, it is impossible to be certain that the block of tissue which is homogenized contains the same number of tumor cells as the section stained for microscopic study. Valid results can be therefore secured only by the study of a sufficient number of aliquots of tissue of the same tumor for enzyme activity and cellular content. As may be understood, this procedure becomes time-consuming and laborious.

Histochemical Methods

Ideally, histoenzymic technics lend themselves to determinations of the amount of enzyme in tumor cells. Thus, thin sections of tissue may be incubated with specific substrates of the enzyme being studied. The product of the reaction may be insoluble and colored or it may be colorless but capable by suitable reactions of being converted into a colored material. The site of enzyme activity can then be identified by the position of the characteristic stain of the product. The chief drawbacks of this technic are the danger of diffusion of the products of enzyme reaction to a location other than the site of enzyme activity and the additional probability that losses of enzyme activity take place in the course of fixation and embedding of the tissue. The main advantage of the cytochemical method, nevertheless, is the possibility it offers of relating enzyme activity to identifiable cells in tumor and nontumor tissue.

Discussion

How is one to evaluate the validity of data concerning enzyme composition of tumors which have been reported in the literature? It would seem, even though so many different criteria have been employed, that some tentative conclusions may still be drawn. Thus, if any basis of comparison other than cell-counting methods has been used for both the homologous healthy tissue and the tumor, differences of about 100 per cent or more have at least a relative significance. It is justifiable, therefore, to state that a given tumor tissue may be richer or poorer in a given component, but these differences cannot be attributed to the tumor cell without referring the data to the actual number of cells or by the use of more refined methods. Before a statement that the activity of a particular enzyme is depressed or enhanced in all cancer tissue can be accepted as valid, it would seem important to have studied a wide variety of tumors and their tissues of origin. Data of this nature are lacking in the support of many such claims.

If the activity of a given enzyme is changed in a tumor as compared to the adjacent nonhomologous tissue, this difference, if it is consistent, may have some practical significance and enzymatic methods might conceivably be used on tissues as an independent means of confirming the histologic diagnosis yielded by the purely morphologic criteria of the pathologist.

GENERAL DIVISIONS IN THE FIELD OF ENZYMES AND CANCER

In this field, one is concerned with the enzymatic characteristics of the tumor itself and their effects on the tissues and blood of the host. As in the case of enzymes in normal tissues, the pattern of individual enzymes, the respiratory enzyme systems, the enzymes involved in nucleoprotein and protein synthesis, and the mechanisms which regulate enzyme activity are all studied. Alterations of enzyme activity in the blood derived from the tumor are not only of theoretical but also of practical importance. An attempt will therefore be made to review the more important of the known facts and to relate them to each other.

ENZYMIC CHARACTERISTICS OF TUMORS

Extensive studies have been reported by Greenstein[32] in which the activities of a large variety of enzymes have been determined in rat and mouse liver hepatomas. In some of these investigations primary hepatomas were induced in the animals by the feeding of azo dyes, and in other studies hepatomas resulting from the transplantation of tumor were employed. Greenstein has also compared the activity of several enzymes in mouse lymphoma, mammary tumors, rhabdomyosarcoma, and adenocarcinoma of the gastrointestinal tract. Similar systematic studies with human tumor material have not been done, chiefly because of the difficulty of collecting specimens of human cancer. However, in order to arouse interest in this field attention will be given below to the less complete investigations made on human cancer tissue.

Over-all Distribution of Enzymes in Various Animal Tumors

Primary Hepatoma. The enzyme composition of hepatoma induced in animals may show either no change, a reduced, or an increased activity in certain enzymes as compared with healthy liver in the same species. Thus, in the rat, arginase, catalase, cystine desulfurase, dehydropeptidase II, succinic acid oxidase, and cytochrome oxidase, all showed diminished activity, whereas no change in activity was seen with acid phosphatase, ribonucleodesaminase, desoxyribonucleodesaminase, dehydropeptidase I, and benzoylarginineamidase (BAA amidase). Only alkaline phosphatase showed an increased activity.

Comparable data on primary hepatoma in mice have not yet been published. Greenstein states that carbon-tetrachloride–induced hepatomas in Strain A mice do not show the same pattern seen in rat liver tumors. For example, cystine desulfurase, which was lacking completely in rat hepatoma, was always present in mouse hepatoma, although in lower concentration than in the normal liver.

Transplanted Hepatoma. Transplanted hepatoma has been used extensively for studies on the distribution of enzymes. In the mouse and rat, as seen from Greenstein's data in Table 36, the activity of certain of these enzymes is depressed, sometimes completely; other enzymes show no difference from concentrations in healthy liver and a few show increased activity. It should be noted that whereas the alkaline phosphatase was reduced in mouse hepatomas 1, A, 98/75, 7A/77, and 587, marked increase in its activity occurred in second-, fourth-, fifth-, and sixth-generation transplants of hepatoma induced by chloroform.[34]

Greenstein has called attention to the fact that tumors which have gone through generations of transplants may undergo radical changes in their enzyme pattern. Thus, a third-generation transplant of mouse osteogenic sarcoma assayed 1100 units of alkaline phosphatase, whereas a seventeenth generation transplant of the same tumor exhibited practically no alkaline phosphatase activity. However, such instances seem to be the exception, since the enzymic composition of hepatoma induced by use of a many-generation transplant closely resembles that found in primary hepatoma.

Primary versus Transplanted Hepatoma. It is apparent from Greenstein's studies that one may expect to find differing enzyme pictures in hepatomas in the same strain of animal depending on whether or not the tumor originated from azo dye feeding or from a hepatoma transplant. This is an example of still another variable in comparative enzyme studies in experimental tumors.

Mouse Lymphoma. Although few data are given in Table 28, they differ markedly from the pattern of hepatoma enzymes. Thus, arginase is found in increased activity, whereas acid phosphatase and desoxyribonuclease exhibit reduced activity.

Mouse Mammary Tumors. As shown in Table 37, catalase shows no change in activity and arginase activity is increased over that of the activities of these enzymes in healthy hyperplastic breast.

Mouse Adenocarcinomas of the Stomach and Intestine. The most interesting findings in Table 37C are the complete disappearance of pepsin, rennin, and alkaline phosphatase in the tumors. The glands in the adenocarcinoma apparently do not retain the biochemical function of the gastric and intestinal secretory glands.

Discussion

The extensive studies of Greenstein provide the following picture of enzymes in animal tumors: (1) As a rule, the activity of an enzyme rarely exceeds the highest activity found for that particular enzyme in normal tissue. Most frequently a

Table 36. ENZYME CHANGES IN TRANSPLANTED HEPATOMAS
Relative Activity

Complete disappearance	*Markedly reduced*	*Moderately reduced*	*No change*	*Increased*
		MOUSE HEPATOMA		
cystine desulfurase	arginase	esterase	xanthine dehydrogenase (I strain)	acid phosphatase
				alkaline phosphatase (some strains)
	catalase	cytochrome oxidase	BAA amidase	ribonucleodepolymerase
	alkaline phosphatase (some strains)		desoxyribonucleo-depolymerase	desoxyribonucleodesaminase
	transaminase		amidase	ribonucleodesaminase
	xanthine dehydrogenase (strains A, C3H)		dehydropeptidase I	proteinase
			cathepsin	peptidase
		RAT HEPATOMA		
exocystine desulfurase	arginase	esterase	dehydropeptidase I	acid phosphatase
	catalase		desoxyribonucleo-depolymerase	alkaline phosphatase
	dehydropeptidase II			
	cytochrome oxidase		ribonucleodepolymerase	ribonucleodesaminase
	D-amino acid oxidase		amylase	desoxyribonucleodesaminase
	uricase			BAA amidase
	adenosine triphosphatase			xanthine dehydrogenase

From Greenstein[32] (condensed).

TABLE 37. ENZYME CHANGES IN MOUSE TUMORS

RELATIVE ACTIVITY

Complete disappearance	Markedly reduced	Moderately reduced	No change	Increased
		A. LYMPHOMA		
	desoxyribonucleodepolymerase	catalase acid phosphatase		arginase xanthine dehydrogenase alkaline phosphatase
		B. MAMMARY TUMOR (C3H) AND A STRAINS		
			catalase ribonucleodepolymerase	arginase xanthine dehydrogenase acid phosphatase alkaline phosphatase
		C. ADENOCARCINOMA OF THE STOMACH AND INTESTINE		
pepsin (stomach) rennin (stomach) alkaline phosphatase		acid phosphatase	ribonucleodepolymerase	

From Greenstein[32] (condensed).

value for a given enzyme in a tumor is found at some intermediate level between the upper and lower extremes of normal activity. Among tumors the range of enzyme activity is narrower than among normal tissues. (2) With some exceptions, the same enzymes are found in a tumor and in the tissue from which the neoplasm originates. Thus, rennin and pepsin are lacking in gastric adenocarcinoma, alkaline phosphatase in intestinal adenocarcinoma, histidase and exocystine desulfurase in rat hepatoma. (3) The enzymic pattern of a tumor is independent of its growth rate and persists unchanged when the tumor is transplanted into animals of differing genetic strains. (4) The tendency of tumors "to converge, enzymatically, to a common type of tissue"[33] is illustrated by their possession of a typically high rate of glycolysis and by their depletion in the enzyme systems concerned with aerobic respiration (e.g., cytochrome oxidase). However, this tendency does not appear in tumors which contain the same or greater activity of specific enzymes present in the tissue of origin, e.g., acid phosphatase in human prostatic carcinoma and in mouse mammary tumor.

RESPIRATORY ENZYME SYSTEMS

GLYCOLYSIS

The process of the conversion of glycogen or glucose to lactic acid consists of a large number of individual enzyme-catalyzed reactions which, according to our present concepts, are integrated into cycles of metabolites utilizing polycarboxylic acids (citric) and phosphate derivatives of the intermediary products. It is difficult, therefore, to interpret differences in oxygen consumption of tissue slices in the presence of glucose on the basis of alterations in the activity of one member of the glycolytic system. Moreover, it has not yet been established that tumor glycolysis is identical in mechanism and rate with glycolysis in muscle, a supposition which has been accepted by many. Nevertheless, the facts of tumor glycolysis are of real importance and will be described in brief.

The work of Warburg,[67] who showed that tumors possessed a high rate of anaerobic glycolysis, has been confirmed in many contributions to the literature.[6, 15, 20] It has also been found that tumors have a high rate of aerobic glycolysis—in contrast to many normal tissues. In the whole animal, the *p*H of a large tumor mass was observed to drop significantly following the administration of glucose[66] and the lactic acid content of a mouse mammary carcinoma was observed to rise following glucose administration.[14]

These respiratory characteristics of tumors are shared to a certain extent by some nontumor tissues. Thus retinal tissue[68] exhibits both a high rate of anaerobic and aerobic glycolysis; kidney medulla,[16] jejunal mucosa,[17] synovial membrane,[7] and myeloid cells[70] of the rabbit bone marrow, show an accentuated aerobic glycolysis. Accordingly, one cannot state that the property of high aerobic and anaerobic glycolysis is specific to cancer tissue but it is true that these respiratory phenomena are regularly seen in tumor tissue.

Potter *et al.*[53, 54] found that homogenates of rat tumors, unlike homogenates of brain, kidney, liver, and heart muscle, did not show uptake of oxygen when oxalacetate and pyruvate were used as substrates. It may be that tumors lack the enzyme system required for the oxidative condensation between pyruvic and oxalacetic acids which is a prerequisite step in the Krebs tricarboxylic acid cycle, believed to explain the oxidation of lactic and pyruvic acids to carbon dioxide and water. On the other hand, Weinhouse *et al.*[71] concluded that the citric acid cycle does operate in tumors since pure radioactive citric acid was isolated as a product of the oxidation of radioactive palmitic and acetic acids by 3 transplanted mouse tumors and since the three key enzymes of the citric acid cycle, "condensing" enzyme, aconitase, and isocitric dehydrogenase, were found in these 3 tumors.[72] The reader is referred to extensive reviews and discussions of glycolytic phenomena which have appeared elsewhere.[6, 20, 32, 63]

ALDOLASE (ZYMOHEXASE)

This enzyme catalyzes the splitting of hexose diphosphate into triose phosphates and its activity in the serum of rats bearing the transplanted Jensen sarcoma[69] was found to be increased in proportion to the size of the tumor. The distribution of aldolase activity in various tissues has been studied by Sibley and Lehninger,[62] who found that rat sarcoma 39 and Walker carcinosarcoma 256 exhibited enzyme values higher than liver, kidney, spleen, and testis, equal to heart and brain, and less than muscle. Although Warburg and Christian[69] consider it possible that aldolase may be the limiting factor of glycolysis in tumors, Sibley and Lehninger suggest that other enzymes of glycolysis may also be functioning at a low level of activity.

LACTIC DEHYDROGENASE

The most recent systematic study of this enzyme in rodent tumors is that of Meister,[47] who found that a variety of these tumors possessed lactic dehydrogenase activity equal to or higher than the corresponding tissues of origin. The activity of this enzyme was not correlated with the glycolytic rate of the tissue and it was concluded that tumor tissues were not deficient in lactic dehydrogenase.

STRAIN DIFFERENCES AND ENZYMES

Liver Glucuronidase in Inbred Mice. Morrow *et al.*[48] reported that β-glucuronidase activity in the liver of C3H mice was much less than the activities of this enzyme measured in the same organs of mice of many other strains. Later, they reported[49] that low liver β-glucuronidase activity was characteristic of livers of three different C3H strains and in CBA (Andervont). However, CBA (Strong) mice and five other strains showed normal liver β-glucuronidase levels. Low activity in kidney and spleen in the low liver β-glucuronidase strains was demonstrated. A possible relationship between low liver β-glucuronidase and hepatoma formation was suggested. Strain differences have been reported for liver xanthine dehydrogenase[21] and serum and liver esterase[42] and for serum esterase.[61] However, Greenstein, upon examining the collected data for seven different constituents of tissue and serum concluded there was no correlation with tumor incidence.

ENZYME CHANGES DURING CARCINOGENESIS

Glyoxalase and succinoxidase activity are reduced in the livers of rats receiving *para*-dimethylaminoazobenzene reaching a level of 10 per cent of normal in the hepatoma.[13] Both succinic acid dehydrogenase and cytochrome oxidase reached levels in squamous cell carcinomas induced by methylcholanthrene which were higher than values found in the control hyperplastic epidermis.[10] These findings are the opposite of those observed in the tumors studied by Greenstein[32] and by Schneider and Potter.[59] Again, epidermal carcinoma exhibited a much higher level of adenylpyrophosphatase activity than normal skin.[57] Arginase activity was elevated.[56]

Certain enzymes have been observed to disappear during carcinogenesis. No cholineoxidase and very little D-amino acid oxidase was found by Lan[45] in hepatoma 39, while Walker 256 carcinosarcoma contained no histidinase, uricase, choline, and D-amino acid oxidases. Lipase activity of the sebaceous glands of the skin disappears following the cutaneous application of methylcholanthrene.[43]

DISTRIBUTION OF ENZYMES IN HUMAN TUMORS

There is a remarkable paucity of data dealing with the concentration of various enzymes in human tumor tissue. This has been largely due to the physical and mental separation of the clinical disciplines from those of the fundamental sciences. Close collaboration between the biochemist, pathologist, and clinician is now seen more frequently, with a consequent contribution of new and valuable information. This modern teamwork tends to avoid the pitfalls of the earlier isolated worker.

Historically, attention has been centered on proteolytic enzymes and the phosphatases. Present-day literature, however, contains references to studies of a large variety of enzymes. In many of these studies, application of methods developed for tissue analyses has been extended to serum studies in relation to human cancer. These will be discussed in a separate section of this chapter.

PHOSPHATASES

Alkaline Phosphatase

Franseen and McLean[30] in 1935 were the first to report, on the basis of the observation of high levels of this enzyme in the tumor tissue and blood plasma, that an enzyme, alkaline phosphatase, was a product of the neoplastic cell (osteogenic sarcoma). Other types of bone tumors, including osteochondroma, chondrosarcoma, adamantinoma, giant cell tumor, osteolytic type of osteogenic sarcoma, metastatic neuroblastoma, metastatic adenocarcinoma of prostate, all showed alkaline phosphatase activity less than osteoblastic osteogenic sarcoma but greater than that seen in normal bone. High phosphatase activity was observed in ossifying metastases to soft tissue such as lung and lymph node, again suggesting that the neoplastic osteoblast synthesizes phosphatase.

Gutman *et al.*[37] determined both alkaline and acid phosphatase in the lumbar vertebrae and ribs of normal subjects and of subjects with osteoplastic and osteolytic metastases arising from primary cancerous lesions of prostate and breast respectively. Representative data are shown in Table 38. It is clear that osteoplastic lesions of bone characterized by formation of new bone show high levels of alkaline

TABLE 38. PHOSPHATE ACTIVITY OF BONE AND SERUM

Number of subjects		*Serum alk. phosphatase* (Bodansky units)	*Bone phosphatase* Lumbar vertebra *Alk.*	Lumbar vertebra *Acid*	Rib *Alk.*	Rib *Acid*
31 ♀, 74 ♂	Normal subjects	—	1.6–6.8	0.5–1.0	0.5–4.7	0.2
67 ♂	Carcinoma of prostate with osteoplastic bone metastases	44.4	39.4	19.0	53.0	18.6
66 ♀	Carcinoma of breast with osteolytic bone metastases	8.9	0.8	0.2	2.1	0.
52 ♂	Carcinoma of the tail of the pancreas with jaundice due to liver metastases	35.2	3.9	—	2.8	4 —

From Gutman *et al.*[37]

phosphatase but only those which are metastases of prostatic carcinoma exhibit marked acid phosphatase activity.

Bodansky[4] found that human osteogenic sarcoma phosphatase and that of normal rat bone reacted similarly to amino acid inhibitors, in the presence and absence of magnesium and to the shift of the *p*H optimum of the enzyme to 10.5 in the presence of cobalt and amino acid, as well as in other respects.

ACID PHOSPHATASE

Kutscher and Wolbergs[44] were the first to discover that normal prostate tissue was extraordinarily rich in acid phosphatase. This observation was confirmed and extended to carcinoma of the prostate and its metastases to bone by Gutman *et al.*[37] High levels of serum acid phosphatase were observed in patients with skeletal metastases from carcinoma of the prostate. Preparation of acid phosphatase made from normal and cancerous prostate tissues and from blood serum of such patients exhibited similar *p*H optima (5.0–6.5) for the hydrolysis of phenylphosphate. The serum and prostatic acid phosphatases also showed the same activity—substrate concentration curves in the hydrolysis of β-glycerophosphate, a like degree of inhibition by alcohols or sodium fluoride, and a failure to be activated by magnesium salts. The acid phosphatase in the serum of patients with disseminated prostatic cancer was not of erythrocytic origin. It may, therefore, be reasonably concluded that the source of elevated serum acid phosphatase in these subjects is the carcinomatous prostate and its metastases.

This conclusion and the findings of elevated alkaline phosphatase in osteogenic sarcoma of the osteoblastic type are of fundamental importance. They represent the first evidence that a biochemical characteristic of a tissue from which a tumor originates may be transmitted to the neoplasm. The specificity of this phenomenon is also striking, since no other human tumors appear to be as rich in phosphatase as osteogenic sarcoma and disseminated prostatic cancer.

Lemon and Wisseman,[46] in 1949, compared the acid phosphatase activity (towards sodium glycerophosphate) of human neoplasms with their tissue of origin, utilizing both histochemical and quantitative microchemical methods. Carcinoma of the breast, bronchus, skin, bladder, and gastrointestinal tract were richer in acid phosphatase than the tissue of origin. These findings are in agreement with the earlier histochemical studies on human tumors by Gomori.[31] Whereas the enzyme is present in both the nucleus and cytoplasm of normal prostatic epithelium, it is localized exclusively in the nuclei of neoplastic cells examined by Lemon and Wisseman. It is suggested that the increased acid phosphatase of human tumor cells may be related to their rapid uptake and retention of phosphate, observed by others. The failure of the acid phosphatase of tumors other than those of the prostate to escape into the blood stream is ascribed to the nuclear location of the enzyme in nonprostatic cancer cells.

β-GLUCURONIDASE ACTIVITY IN HUMAN TUMORS

In 1947 Fishman and co-workers[24, 26, 27] demonstrated that the majority of specimens of human cancer tissue were rich in β-glucuronidase as compared with the neighboring uninvolved tissue. Primary lesions of the skin, lung, breast, oesophagus, stomach, colon, uterine cervix, and brain were studied. Carcinoma of the endometrium did not show elevated levels of β-glucuronidase activity. Metastases to lymph nodes and other organs were usually rich in β-glucuronidase, as were colonic polyps in a premalignant state.

Campbell[8] and Seligman[60] independently, by two different histochemical technics, demonstrated that animal and human tumors were rich in β-glucuronidase. Inasmuch as the function of β-glucuronidase is apparently related to the action and metabolism of estrogenic[23] and perhaps other steroid hormones, it has been asked whether or not the increased glucuronidase in tumors may be a reflection of the action of steroid hormones in that tissue. So far, direct experimental evidence in favor of this speculation is lacking.

The buffy coat of the blood is relatively rich in β-glucuronidase and studies have been carried out by Anlyan *et al.*[2] on the buffy-coat β-glucuronidase of blood taken from patients with leukemia. A wide range of enzyme activity was found in various types of leukemia, with abnormally high values occurring in myelogenous leukemia.

HYALURONIDASE

This term refers to the enzyme complex which depolymerizes and hydrolyzes the mucopolysaccharide, hyaluronic acid. The possession by certain bacteria of hyaluronidase is thought to account for their ability to invade the tissues of the host. It is readily understood, therefore, why tumors have been studied for hyaluronidase activity, since this system might conceivably explain the invasive property of cancer cells. However, all present data fail to show consistently elevated hyaluronidase activity in tumor tissue.[5, 18, 51] Moreover, no relation between hyaluronidase content and type of tumor was found.[19]

BLOOD ENZYMES AND CANCER

It is in this field that much hope exists for the development of practical methods for the diagnosis of cancer. The clinical usefulness of the determination of serum alkaline phosphatase in osteogenic sarcoma and of serum acid phosphatase in disseminated prostatic carcinoma suggests the possibility that tumors arising in sites other than these may likewise possess enzymatic characteristics of the tissue of origin. For the successful development of serum enzyme diagnosis, it is necessary also that this particular enzyme of tumor tissue enter the blood stream. In this section, therefore, a review will be made of well-known enzymes which undergo changes in the blood in cancer and the significance of these changes will be evaluated. In addition, the mechanism for the control of the concentration of an enzyme in the blood will be discussed.

SERUM ALKALINE PHOSPHATASE

Studies on the serum concentration of this enzyme preceded the tissue analyses previously mentioned. Thus, Kay[41] in 1930 found elevations in serum phosphatase in growing children and in patients with bone disease. On the basis of many considerations the view is widely held that the function of alkaline phosphatase in osteoblasts is the hydrolysis of phosphoric acid esters at the site of ossification. The precipitation of calcium phosphate then follows. Accordingly, elevations in serum alkaline phosphatase, in the absence of hepatic disorders, are usually held to be of osteoblastic origin. Franseen and McLean[30] reported that a marked decline from the high initial level of the serum alkaline phosphatase occurred upon surgical removal of an osteogenic sarcoma. Recurrence of the tumor was accompanied by an increase in the activity of this serum phosphatase. This correlation of serum enzyme levels with surgery and recurrence is of considerable interest and has provided a pattern of investigation for the evaluation of the behavior of other enzymes in human cancer.

SERUM ACID PHOSPHATASE

In 1938 Gutman and Gutman[36] reported significantly increased "acid" phosphatase activity of the serum in 11 of 15 patients with metastasizing prostate cancer, and in only one (Paget's disease) out of 88 patients with other diseases. Similar results were reported by Barringer and Woodard.[3] The comparison of properties of serum and prostatic acid phosphatase has been discussed in a previous section with reference to the acid phosphatase of tissue. They suggested, therefore, that the determination of acid phosphatase in the serum may have a limited value in the diagnosis of disseminated prostatic carcinoma. Clinical experience since then has validated this statement. The use of the serum acid phosphatase in both diagnosis and prognosis is illustrated in Table 39.

Frequently, however, cases of prostatic cancer with extensive bone metastases have been encountered in which the serum acid phosphatase activity has varied within normal limits. Two possible explanations may apply: (1) The level of acid phosphatase in the metastatic tumor may not be sufficiently high in such cases

TABLE 39. PERCENTILE DISTRIBUTION OF SERUM ACID PHOSPHATASE VALUES IN CASES OF PROSTATE CARCINOMA WITH AND WITHOUT METASTASES AND IN OTHER CONDITIONS

			Percentage of Cases with Levels of Serum Acid Phosphatase (Units/100 cc. serum)					
	Diagnosis	*No. of cases studied*	Less than 3	3–4.9	5–9.9	10–100	100–1000	More than 1000
Series of Sullivan and the Gutmans	Prostate carcinoma	200						
	Bone metastases (by X-ray)	130	15	12	25	35	9	4
	No bone metastases (by X-ray)	70	89	11				
	Benign prostatic hypertrophy	75	100					
	Prostatitis	10	100					
	Nonprostatic diseases	570	90	7.5	2.5			
	Normal	30	100					
			Less than 4	4–6	6.1–10	10–100	100–1000	More than 1000
Series of Herger and Sauer	Prostate carcinoma	147						
	Bone metastases demonstrable by X-ray or suspected	47	9	4	30	30	19	2
	No X-ray or clinical evidence of metastases	100	77	22*	1			
	Control patients	283	92.5	7.5				

From Greenstein.[33]

* Only 8 per cent consistently gave serum acid phosphatase values between 4 and 6 units (King-Armstrong).

to enrich the blood enzyme; or (2) the metastases, although possessing high acid phosphatase activity, may not be well enough supplied with lymph channels for the enzyme to leak into the circulation.

Surgical castration or estrogen therapy was followed by a sharp and prompt fall in the serum acid phosphatase to normal levels in patients with metastatic cancer of the prostate who respond to these measures though not in those who are refractory.[35, 39, 64] Administration of androgen or cessation of estrogen therapy resulted in an increase in acid phosphatase activity. The serum level of this enzyme in these patients therefore serves as an indicator of the activity of the tumor and is under hormonal control. The rise in alkaline phosphatase which usually follows castration may be due to ossification of the skeletal metastases.

These observations illustrate the manner in which the activity of a blood component can be employed in diagnosis, prognosis, and for the intelligent management of therapy. The possibility exists that tumors other than those of the prostate may have specific catalytic constituents which may enrich the blood stream in this component and whose measurement will be of practical value. What is required is the will and the effort to discover these important constituents.

Attempts have been made to render the method of determining acid phosphatase more specific for serum acid phosphatase of prostatic origin, since the activity in the serum is undoubtedly due to a mixture of enzymes from various other sources (erythrocytes, kidney). Fischmann *et al.*[22] found that prostatic acid phosphatase hydrolyzed 3-adenylic acid three times as rapidly as β-glycerophosphate and suggested that this difference might be of value in distinguishing prostatic phosphatase from other phosphatases. Abdul-Fadl and King[1] studied the action of a number of inhibitors on various acid phosphatases and found that L-tartrate was a specific inhibitor of prostatic acid phosphatase. Fishman and Lerner[25] have employed L-tartrate inhibition in developing a method for estimating serum acid phosphatase of prostatic origin.

ANTI-ENZYMES

Attempts have been made in the past to employ the antifibrinolytic action of serum as a test for malignancy. Two recent investigations of this sought-for correlation have been reported. Clark *et al.*[12] in 1948 developed an antitryptic activity test based on the greatest dilution of serum in which a clot will still be produced in a system maintained at 36.5° C., and containing trypsin, fibrinogen, and thrombin in suitable concentrations. Sera of patients with malignant neoplasms usually exhibited an elevated titer of antitrypsin, although a significant number of false positives and false negatives were encountered. West and Rapaport[73] studied antichymotrypsin and antirennin in the serum of cancer patients and found that these varied inversely with each other during the course of nitrogen mustard and other therapy. It is stated that the test has limited prognostic value. In both of these studies, the underlying mechanism for the elaboration of antiproteolytic substances in the body is obscure and time will be required to ascertain their clinical usefulness.

ESTERASE

Serum esterase has been observed by Green and Jenkinson[38] to decrease in the blood of rats bearing Jensen sarcoma and in metastatic human cancer. Low values of serum esterase have been observed in infection, vitamin A deficiency, and in many other pathologic conditions. Greenstein[32] suggested that the reduction in serum esterase activity may be due to a defective synthesis of esterase by liver or by other tissues.

ALDOLASE

Sibley and Lehninger[62] found patients with cancer to possess an elevated serum aldolase in approximately 50 per cent of the subjects studied. Occasionally, the increased levels found were six times the normal value. However, 4 out of 45 subjects in a group with nonmalignant pathology (progressive muscle dystrophy, gout, and obstructive jaundice) also exhibited elevated values. While these findings were not considered to be of diagnostic usefulness, they raise the question of the source of the excess enzyme found in blood serum. Warburg and Christian[69] eliminated the tumor as the source of enzyme because the amount of aldolase present in the tumor is sufficient only for the amount of glycolysis taking place in that tissue. They suggested instead that muscle, with its high content of aldolase, might supply aldolase to the blood stream. Sibley and Lehninger's data point not only to muscle but also to liver and kidney as the sources of serum aldolase in animals bearing tumors.

ENZYMES OF BODY FLUIDS AND SECRETIONS

ASCITIC AND PLEURAL FLUIDS

It would appear from the foregoing discussion that the critical consideration in the clinical application of enzyme phenomena is not merely that tumor tissue should be rich in a given chemical constituent but that it is necessary for this substance to leave

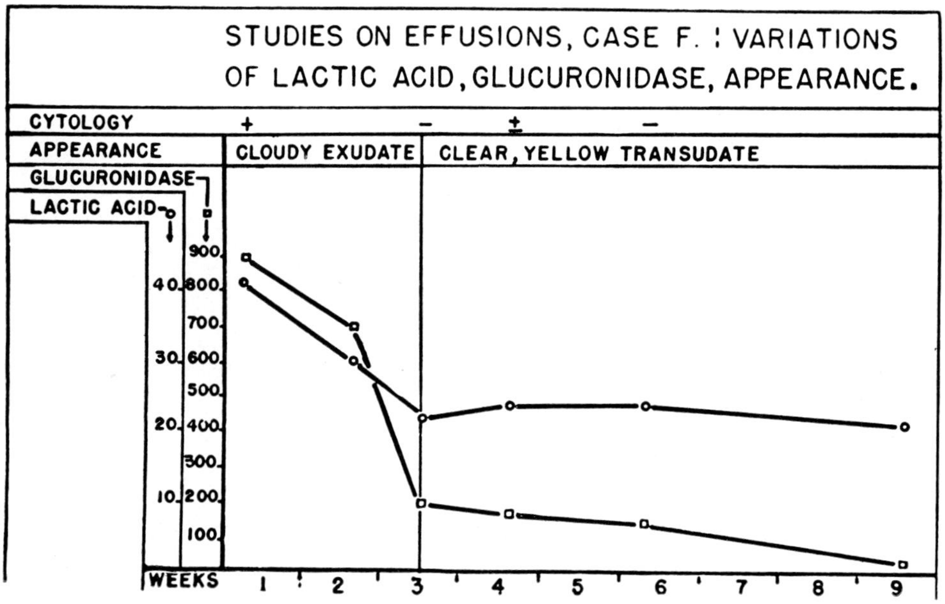

FIG. 119. A spontaneous change in vivo of the chemical and cytologic characteristics of ascitic fluid.

the tissue and to enter the circulation in detectable amounts. Information as to whether it occurs is not forthcoming from the study of enzymatic activity in homogenates of tumor tissue only.

A suitable system for investigation would appear to be fluids accumulated in peritoneal and pleural cavities containing metastatic tumor tissue. In such carcinomatoses, it would be reasonable to expect that the neoplastic effusion would be rich in metabolites and enzymes which normally dissolve or leak out of the tumor. A study of the chemical and enzymatic composition of neoplastic effusions should produce new leads for the development of blood tests in the diagnosis and prognosis of human cancer.

In a preliminary study, Fishman *et al.*[29] found that both β-glucuronidase activity and lactic acid concentration were often elevated in effusions of neoplastic origin as compared with values for these two constituents in benign effusions. Examination of the body fluid with the aid of the Papanicolaou technic was done, and occasionally high lactic acid concentrations and β-glucuronidase activities were observed in fluids obtained from patients with known cancer when the Papanicolaou smear was negative for neoplastic cells. It was possible by following these indications of malignancy in effusions to observe spontaneous changes in the composition of the fluid which showed no clinical correlation. Some of the results are illustrated in Table 40 and Figure 119.

TABLE 40. RELATION OF SITE OF CANCER TO FLUID GLUCURONIDASE AND LACTIC ACID VALUES

		Glucuronidase			*Lactic acid*		
Type of fluid	*Site of cancer*	No. of analyses	Mean	Range	No. of analyses	Mean	Range
Pleural	breast	14	655	230–2725	12	37.5	3– 78
Ascites	uterus	9	435	91– 611	9	61.0	6–109
Pleural	lung	17	1655	160–8000	14	78.9	15–140
Ascites	gastrointestinal tract	35	347	122–2105	29	31.4	11– 62
Ascites	ovary	23	1187	262–3960	15	50.2	15–198
Pleural & ascites	miscellaneous	7	302	164– 495	5	35.0	23– 54
Pleural & ascites	*non-cancer group*	10	206	95– 393	9	24.2	11– 42

VAGINAL FLUID β-GLUCURONIDASE ACTIVITY

On the basis of the elevated β-glucuronidase activity found in tissue taken from cancer of the cervix, Odell *et al.*[50] suggested that the vaginal fluid would become enriched from the β-glucuronidase arising from the cervical tumor. They reported that vaginal fluid β-glucuronidase activity was invariably elevated in women with untreated carcinoma of the cervix. False positives were encountered in 20 per cent of noncancerous healthy women and these were explained by either pregnancy or the presence of *Trichomonas vaginalis* infestation.

A systematic study of factors which influence β-glucuronidase activity in vaginal fluid was made by Fishman *et al.*[28] It was found that high titers of the enzyme occurred most frequently in women in the older postmenopausal group. Moreover, high vaginal fluid β-glucuronidase levels were discovered in vaginal fluid of castrated women, even when the cervix and body of the uterus had been ablated. It was concluded that the concentration of β-glucuronidase in vaginal fluid was not dependent only on the presence of the uterus but appeared to be controlled in part by ovarian function. The fluctuations in vaginal fluid β-glucuronidase with the menstrual cycle indicated ovarian control also. In patients with untreated cancer of the cervix,[40] significant variations from control of β-glucuronidase levels in vaginal fluid were encountered in premenopausal, but not in postmenopausal subjects.

It may be stated that at the present time the uncritical use of β-glucuronidase titers in vaginal fluid as a diagnostic aid in detecting cervical cancer is of no value.

It may be possible to develop a useful diagnostic procedure based on the selection of premenopausal subjects at mid-menstrual cycle for enzyme assay of vaginal fluid.[40]

GENERAL DISCUSSION

It would appear that tumor tissue at times shows an exaggerated behavior of certain specific enzyme systems (e.g. phosphatases, β-glucuronidase, aldolase), while as a rule, most enzymes studied show little change. Tumors uniformly exhibit an enhanced aerobic and anaerobic glycolysis. In view of the difficulties associated with the comparison of tumor enzyme activity discussed in the introduction, it has not been possible to express enzyme data in absolute terms related only to concentrations in cancer cells. However, the comparison of relative values in tumors and in healthy tissues has been of value not only from the viewpoint of fundamental considerations but also with regard to practical applications to human cancer.

While the work of Greenstein suggests the possibility of a cancer pattern of enzymes which is uniform for many types of animal tumors, and in which the enzyme levels are lower and vary within a much smaller range, exceptions can be expected and do occur, as with the majority of biologic phenomena.

Two of the most interesting of these exceptions are the behavior of alkaline phosphatase in osteogenic sarcoma and of acid phosphatase in disseminated prostatic cancer. In both cases, the tumor retains in large measure a biochemical characteristic of the tissue of origin and, in addition, the tumor phosphatase apparently enters the circulation to enrich the blood phosphatases. This last phenomenon has been utilized for clinical purposes.

An interesting line for future work would be to investigate means for shifting at least part of an enzyme from tissue into the blood stream. If this "flushing out" of enzyme from the tumor were effected, then it might be possible to develop clinically useful blood enzyme methods which would have a greater probability of success.

The examination of the chemical constituents of neoplastic ascitic and pleural fluids taken from human cancer patients would seem to offer an approach to the detection of those tumor components which leak out of neoplasms and which might then be expected to appear in the blood stream. This field of study has been opened for investigation by the work on lactic acid content and β-glucuronidase activity in neoplastic effusions.

An important concept relates to the factors which control the level of activity of a given enzyme in the blood stream. Ordinarily, blood enzyme levels in normal healthy subjects remain fairly constant. Animal experiments, in which aldolase[54, 62,] has been injected intravenously, show a rapid disappearance of the enzyme from the blood. Can it be that homeostatic mechanisms for the control of blood enzyme concentration exist? Does an elevated concentration in the blood of a given enzyme represent overproduction, poor utilization, or an enhanced turnover rate? All of these questions await investigation.

In conclusion, it may be said that the field of the relationship of enzymes to cancer has only been superficially tilled up to the present time with the harvesting of a number of fundamentally important and practically significant observations. It may be predicted that this soil will be increasingly productive.

BIBLIOGRAPHY

1. Abdul-Fadl, M. A. M., and King, E. J. Properties of the acid phosphatases of erythrocytes and of the human prostate gland. *Biochem. J. 45:* 51-60, 1949.
2. Anlyan, A. J., Gamble, J., and Hoster, H. A. β-Glucuronidase activity of the white blood cells in human leukemias and Hodgkin's disease. *Cancer 3:* 116-123, 1950.
3. Barringer, B. S., and Woodard, H. Q. Prostatic carcinoma with extensive intraprostatic calcification, with discussion of possible role of prostatic phosphatase. *Tr. Am. A. Genito-Urin. Surgeons 31:* 363-369, 1938.
4. Bodansky, O. The influence of magnesium and cobalt on the inhibition of phosphatases of bone, intestine, and osteogenic sarcoma by amino acids. *J. Biol. Chem. 179:* 81-102, 1949.
5. Boyland, E., and McLean, D. A factor in malignant tissues which increases the permeability of the dermis. *J. Path. & Bact. 41:* 553-565, 1935.
6. Burk, D. A colloquial consideration of the Pasteur and neo-Pasteur effects. *Cold Spring Harbor Symposia on Quant. Biol. 7:* 420-459, 1939; *Symposium on Respiratory Enzymes.* Madison, Wisconsin, University of Wisconsin Press, 1942.
7. Bywaters, E. G. L. The metabolism of joint tissues. *J. Path & Bact. 44:* 247-268, 1937.
8. Campbell, J. G. The intracellular localization of β-glucuronidase. *Brit. J. Exper. Path. 30:* 548-554, 1949.
9. Carruthers, C. The biochemistry of neoplastic tissue. *Ann. Rev. Biochem. 19:* 389-408, 1950.
10. Carruthers, C., and Suntzeff, V. Succinic dehydrogenase and cytochrome oxidase in epidermal carcinogenesis induced by methylcholanthrene in mice. *Cancer Research 7:* 9-14, 1947.
11. Chalkley, H. W. Method for the quantitative morphologic analysis of tissues. *J. Nat. Cancer Inst. 4:* 47-53, 1943; in Greenstein, J. P. *Biochemistry of Cancer.* New York, Academic Press, 1947, p. 182.
12. Clark, G. C. C., Clifton, E. E., and Newton, B. L. Antiproteolytic activity of human serum with particular reference to its changes in the presence of and considerations of its use for detection of malignant neoplasia. *Proc. Soc. Exper. Biol. & Med. 69:* 276-279, 1948.
13. Cohen, P. P. Glyoxalase activity of liver from rats fed *p*-dimethylaminoazobenzene. *Cancer Research 5:* 626-630, 1945.
14. Cori, C. F., and Cori, G. T. The carbohydrate metabolism of tumors: I. The free sugar, lactic acid, and glycogen content of malignant tumors. *J. Biol. Chem. 64:* 11-22, 1925.
15. Dickens, F. Cancer as a problem in tissue metabolism. *Cancer Rev. 6:* 57, 1931.
16. Dickens, F., and Weil-Malherbe, H. Metabolism of normal and tumour tissue: XIV. A note on the metabolism of medulla of kidney. *Biochem. J. 30:* 659, 1936.
17. Dickens, F., and Weil-Malherbe, H. Metabolism of normal and tumour tissue: XIX. The metabolism of intestinal mucous membrane. *Biochem. J. 35:* 7, 1941.
18. Duran-Reynals, F., and Stewart, F. W. The action of tumor extracts on the

spread of experimental vaccinia of the rabbit. *Am. J. Cancer 15:* 2790-2797, 1931.

19. DUX, C., GUÉRIN, M., and LACOUR, F. Investigation of the presence of hyaluronidase in human and experimental tumors by the mucin clot-prevention test. *Compt. rend. Soc. de biol. 142:* 789-790, 1948.
20. ELLIOT, K. A. C. In *Symposium on Respiratory Enzymes.* Madison, Wisconsin, University of Wisconsin Press, 1942.
21. FIGGE, F. H. J., and STRONG, L. C. Xanthine oxidase (dehydrogenase) activity in livers of mice of cancer-susceptible and cancer-resistant strains. *Cancer Research 1:* 779-784, 1941.
22. FISCHMANN, J., CHAMBERLIN, H. A., CUBILES, R., and SCHMIDT, G. Quantitative determinations of acid phosphatase in prostate under various normal and pathological conditions; preliminary report. *J. Urol. 59:* 1194-1197, 1948.
23. FISHMAN, W. H. β-Glucuronidase: Its relation to the action of the estrogenic hormones. *J. Biol. Chem. 169:* 7-15, 1947.
24. FISHMAN, W. H. Some observations on the β-glucuronidase activity of the blood and tissues of obstetrical and surgical patients. *Science 105:* 646, 1947.
25. FISHMAN, W. H., and LERNER, F. A method for estimating serum acid phosphatase of prostatic origin. *J. Biol. Chem. 200:* 89-97, 1953.
26. FISHMAN, W. H., and ANLYAN, A. J. A comparison of the β-glucuronidase activity of normal, tumor, and lymph node tissues of surgical patients. *Science 106:* 66-67, 1947; The presence of high β-glucuronidase activity in cancer tissue. *J. Biol. Chem. 169:* 449-450, 1947; β-Glucuronidase activity in human tissues; some correlations with processes of malignant growth and with the physiology of reproduction. *Fourth Int. Cancer Research Congress 6:* 1034-1041, 1950.
27. FISHMAN, W. H., ANLYAN, A. J., and GORDON, E. β-Glucuronidase activity in human tissues: Some correlations with processes of malignant growth and with the physiology of reproduction. *Cancer Research 7:* 808-818, 1947.
28. FISHMAN, W. H., KASDON, S. C., and HOMBURGER, F. β-Glucuronidase studies in women: I. Observations in 500 nonpregnant, noncancerous subjects. *J.A.M.A. 143:* 350-354, 1950.
29. FISHMAN, W. H., MARKUS, R. L., PAGE, O. C., PFEIFFER, P. H., and HOMBURGER, F. Studies on effusions: I. Glucuronidase and lactic acid in neoplastic effusions of pleura and peritoneum. *Am. J. M. Sc. 220:* 55-59, 1950.
30. FRANSEEN, C. C., and MCLEAN, R. The phosphatase activity of tissues and plasma in tumors of bone. *Am. J. Cancer 24:* 299-317, 1935.
31. GOMORI, G. Distribution of acid phosphatase in the tissues under normal and under pathologic conditions. *Arch. Path. 32:* 189-199, 1941.
32. GREENSTEIN, J. P. The biochemistry of malignant tissues. *Ann. Rev. Biochem. 14:* 643-664, 1945.
33. GREENSTEIN, J. P. *Biochemistry of Cancer.* New York, Academic Press, 1947.
34. GREENSTEIN, J. P., and ESCHENBRENNER, A. B. In GREENSTEIN, J. P. *Biochemistry of Cancer.* New York, Academic Press, 1947, p. 194.
35. GUTMAN, A. B. Serum "acid" phosphatase in patients with carcinoma of the prostate gland: Present status. *J.A.M.A. 120:* 1112-1116, 1942.
36. GUTMAN, A. B., and GUTMAN, E. B. An "acid" phosphatase occurring in the serum of patients with metastasing carcinoma of the prostate gland. *J. Clin. Investigation 17:* 473-478, 1938.
37. GUTMAN, E. B., SPROUL, E. E., and GUTMAN, A. B. Significance of increased

phosphatase activity of bone at the site of osteoplastic metastases secondary to carcinoma of the prostate gland. *Am. J. Cancer 28:* 485-495, 1936.

38. GREEN, H. N., and JENKINSON, C. N. Changes in the esterase and fat content of the serum induced by cancer and cancer-producing agents. *Brit. J. Exper. Path. 15:* 1-14, 1934.
39. HUGGINS, C., and HODGES, C. V. Studies on prostatic cancer: I. The effect of castration, of estrogen and of androgen injection on serum phosphatases in metastatic carcinoma of the prostate. *Cancer Research 1:* 293-297, 1941.
40. KASDON, S. C., FISHMAN, W. H., and HOMBURGER, F. β-Glucuronidase studies in women: II. Cancer of the cervix uteri. *J.A.M.A. 144:* 892-896, 1950.
41. KAY, H. D. Plasma phosphatase: II. The enzyme in disease, particularly in bone disease. *J. Biol. Chem. 89:* 249-266, 1930.
42. KHANOLKAR, V. R., and CHITRE, R. G. Studies in esterase (butyric) activity: III. The effect of foster nursing on the esterase content of blood serum and liver of strains of mice susceptible or insusceptible to mammary cancer. *Cancer Research 4:* 128-133, 1944.
43. KUNG, S. K. Lipase activity during experimental epidermal carcinogenesis. *J. Nat. Cancer Inst. 9:* 435-438, 1948-1949.
44. KUTSCHER, W., and WOLBERGS, H. Prostataphosphatase. *Ztschr. f. physiol. Chem. 236:* 237-240, 1935.
45. LAN, T. H. The *d*-amino acid oxidase, uricase, and choline oxidase in two transplanted rat tumors and in isolated nuclei of tumor cells. *Cancer Research 4:* 42-44, 1944.
46. LEMON, H. M., and WISSEMAN, C. L. Acid phosphomonoesterase activity of human neoplastic tissue. *Science 109:* 233-235, 1949.
47. MEISTER, A. Lactic dehydrogenase activity of certain tumors and normal tissues. *J. Nat. Cancer Inst. 10:* 1263-1271, 1950.
48. MORROW, A. G., GREENSPAN, E. M., and CARROLL, D. M. Liver glucuronidase activity of inbred mouse strains. *J. Nat. Cancer Inst. 10:* 657-662, 1949.
49. MORROW, A. G., GREENSPAN, E. M., and CARROLL, D. M. Comparative studies of liver glucuronidase activity in inbred mice. *J. Nat. Cancer Inst. 10:* 1199-1203, 1950.
50. ODELL, L. D., BURT, J., and BETHEA, R. β-Glucuronidase activity in human female genital cancer. *Cancer Research 9:* 362-365, 1949.
51. PIRIE, A. A hyaluronidase and a polysaccharide from tumours. *Brit. J. Exper. Path. 23:* 277-284, 1942.
52. POTTER, V. R. "Biological energy transformations and the cancer problem." In: *Advances in Enzymology*. New York, Interscience Publishers, Inc., 1946, vol. IV, pp. 201-256.
53. POTTER, V. R., LEPAGE, G. A., and KLUG, H. L. The assay of animal tissues for respiratory enzymes: VII. Oxalacetic acid oxidation and the coupled phosphorylations in isotonic homogenates. *J. Biol. Chem. 175:* 619-634, 1948.
54. POTTER, V. R., and LEPAGE, G. A. Metabolism of oxalacetate in glycolyzing tumor homogenates. *J. Biol. Chem. 177:* 237-245, 1949.
55. POTTER, V. R. *Enzymes, Growth and Cancer.* Springfield, Ill., C. C Thomas, 1950.
56. ROBERTS, E. Determination of arginase activity in tissue homogenates: application to epidermal carcinogenesis in mice. *Federation Proc. 7:* 180-181, 1948.

57. Roberts, E., and Carruthers, C. Adenylpyrophosphatase activity in epidermal carcinogenesis in mice. *Arch. Bioch. 16:* 239-255, 1948.

58. Rosenthal, O., and Drabkin, D. L. The oxidative response of normal and neoplastic tissues to succinate and to *p*-phenylenediamine. *Cancer Research 4:* 487-494, 1944.

59. Schneider, W. C., and Potter, V. R. Biocatalysts in cancer tissue: III. Succinic dehydrogenase and cytochrome oxidase. *Cancer Research 3:* 353-357, 1943.

60. Seligman, A. M., Nachlas, M. M., Manheimer, L. H., Friedman, O. M., and Wolf, G. Development of new methods for the histochemical demonstration of hydrolytic intracellular enzymes in a program of cancer research. *Ann. Surg. 130:* 333-341, 1949.

61. Shimkin, M. B., Greenstein, J. P., and Andervont, H. B. Esterase activity of blood serum of four strains of mice. *J. Nat. Cancer Inst. 5:* 29-34, 1944.

62. Sibley, J. A., and Lehninger, A. L. Aldolase in the serum and tissues of tumor-bearing animals. *J. Nat. Cancer Inst. 9:* 303-309, 1949.

63. Stern, K., and Wilheim, R. *The Biochemistry of Malignant Tumors.* Brooklyn, N. Y., Reference Press, 1943.

64. Sullivan, T. J., Gutman, E. B., and Gutman, A. B. Theory and application of serum "acid" phosphatase determination in metastasizing prostatic carcinoma: Early effects of castration. *J. Urol. 48:* 426-458, 1942.

65. Sumner, J. B., and Myrback, K. *The Enzymes.* New York, Academic Press, 1950, vol. 1, p. 1.

66. Voegtlin, C., Fitch, R. H., Kahler, H., Johnson, J. M., and Thompson, J. W. Experimental studies on cancer: I. The influence of the parenteral administration of certain sugars on the pH of malignant tumors. *Nat. Inst. Health Bull. 164:* 1-14, 1935.

67. Warburg, O. Experiments on surviving carcinoma tissue; methods. *Biochem. Ztsch. 142:* 317-333; 334-350; 1923.

68. Warburg, O. *The Metabolism of Tumors.* London, 1930.

69. Warburg, O., and Christian, W. Gärungsfermente in blutserum von tumorratten. *Biochem. Ztsch. 314:* 399-408, 1943.

70. Warren, C. O. Tissue metabolism studies on bone marrow. Consideration in relation to tumor metabolism. *Cancer Research 3:* 621-625, 1943.

71. Weinhouse, S., Millington, R. H., and Wenner, C. E. Occurrence of the citric acid cycle in tumors. *J. Am. Chem. Soc. 72:* 4332, 1950.

72. Wenner, C. E., Spirtes, M. A., and Weinhouse, S. Enzymes of the citric acid cycle in tumors. *J. Am. Chem. Soc. 72:* 4333, 1950.

73. West, P. M., Rapaport, S. I., and Tempereau, C. E. Enzymatic evaluation of therapeutic agents in cancer. *Cancer 4:* 177-183, 1951.

CHAPTER 21

Cytochemistry and Histochemistry

George Gomori

The main difference between histochemical and biochemical technics lies in their emphasis. Identification of chemical compounds in the tissues is the primary objective of both sciences but histochemistry stresses accuracy of localization, whereas biochemistry stresses quantitation. To some extent, biochemical methods are also capable of localization by selecting the right sample or by first isolating certain morphologic elements such as nuclei or mitochondria by physical means; however, if one may borrow a simile from optics, the resolving power of histochemical methods, as a rule, is far superior to those used in biochemistry.

In essence, histochemistry uses tissue samples, the architecture of which is not grossly disturbed, and utilizes reactions which produce insoluble colored precipitates exactly at the sites occupied by the compound investigated. In this way, localization on a cytologic scale can be accomplished; compounds can be referred to individual cells widely scattered among a vast majority of cells of a somewhat different chemical character.

Unfortunately, the demand for exact localization necessitates a certain manipulation of the tissue which may be incompatible with the preservation of sensitive enzyme systems. This imposes a limitation on the scope of enzymic histochemistry. As a rule, only the hardiest of hydrolytic enzymes can be demonstrated by histochemical methods, while oxidative enzymes are destroyed.

The general principle of localizing enzymes in histochemistry is as follows: The tissue section is incubated with buffered substrate in the presence of a reagent which will form an insoluble precipitate with one of the products of enzymatic hydrolysis. In the case of alkaline phosphatase, for instance, the tissue is incubated with a solution of glycerophosphate buffered at *p*H 9 and containing calcium chloride. As the substrate is hydrolyzed, the liberated phosphate ions are trapped *in statu nascendi* by the calcium ions present to form an insoluble precipitate of calcium phosphate at the sites of enzymatic activity. This precipitate is then transformed, first into cobalt phosphate and then into black cobalt sulfide. In the finished slide, sites of enzymatic activity will be outlined in black. In the case of other enzymes the technic must be modified according to the specific substrate and *p*H requirements of the enzyme investigated.

In contrast to the numerous reports on biochemical differences between normal and malignant tissues, as observed in the test tube, there are few data available on special and demonstrable histochemical features of malignant tissue. In general, the histochemical characteristics of malignant tissue are similar to those of the cell type or of the parent tissue from which they arise, the degree of similarity being roughly proportional to the degree of differentiation. Thus, melanomas contain more or less melanin; carcinoids contain the same phenol as enterochromaffin cells; pheochromocytomas elaborate adrenalin; tumors arising from the lipid-rich Sertoli cells of the dog are rich in lipids;[7] carcinomas of muciparous epithelium continue to produce mucin; osteoblastic tumors of bone[3] and cortical tumors of the adrenal exhibit about the same degree of high alkaline phosphatase activity as osteoblasts and the adrenal cortex, respectively; tumors of adult prostatic epithelium contain large amounts of acid phosphatase;[2] hepatomas are positive for esterase, and the same applies to a certain number of carcinomas arising from esophageal[4] and bronchial epithelium,[12] normally positive for esterase.

In some cases, tumors may exhibit a higher degree of chemical than morphologic differentiation. In such instances histochemical technics may be a valuable adjunct in the diagnosis, especially of metastatic lesions even though the reliability of such methods, owing to the small number of thoroughly investigated cases, is not firmly established. To give some examples: true osteogenic sarcomas, Ewing's tumors, and synoviomas are intensely positive for alkaline phosphatase, whereas lymphoblastomas, neuroblastomas, and reticulum sarcomas are negative;[3] metastases from cancer of the prostate have a high acid phosphatase activity.

Some tumors exhibit special histochemical features, such as the high concentration of glycogen and cholesterol found in hypernephromas, and the intense alkaline phosphatase activity of embryonic carcinomas and of most seminomas of the testis.[6] Since the parent cell types of these neoplasms have not been identified with certainty, it is impossible to tell whether these tumors do or do not follow the histochemical patterns of the parent cell. It should be remarked, however, that none of the parenchymal cells of the testis exhibit any marked degree of alkaline phosphatase activity.

The demonstration of histochemical differences between normal and malignant tissues has been attempted many times. An early and successful attempt has resulted in the Schiller test,[17] based on the disappearance of glycogen from the epithelium of the uterine cervix when it undergoes malignant transformation. Others have shown that in the mouse skin the amount of cytoplasmic protein-bound arginine increases in the course of carcinogenesis,[21] whereas esterase activity of the rat liver declines under analogous conditions.[11] Adenocarcinomas arising from the tubular epithelium of the frog kidney are devoid of alkaline phosphatase,[8] although the parent tissue is highly active. Roskin[13, 14, 15, 22] found that nuclei of malignant cells do not stain with the leukobase of methylene blue (probably because they are poor in dehydrogenases), whereas nuclei of normal tissues and of benign tumors stain in an intense blue shade, and the author proposed the use of this test for diagnostic purposes. On the other hand, newer findings, obtained with the use of triphenyltetrazolium compounds, indicate that cancers tend to retain the high dehydrogenase activity of their parent tissues, and in fact, sometimes considerably exceed it.[11, 20] These findings, however, are in contradiction with results of *in vitro* assays;[16] studies on blood smears also point in the opposite direction[23] by showing that "blast" elements do not reduce tetrazolium salts which the more mature cells do.

A high percentage of malignant epithelial tumors exhibit a phosphamidase activity far in excess of that of the surrounding normal tissues,[5] while only a relatively small number of connective tissue neoplasms shows this differential behavior. The intensity of the reaction roughly parallels the degree of morphologic malignancy, with one curious exception: all polyps of the large intestine examined so far, regardless of whether benign or malignant, had a highly active epithelium.[6]

With a new technic for β-glucuronidase,[18] it was possible to demonstrate this enzyme in the cells of a mammary carcinoma.

Nucleic acids of neoplastic tissue are not demonstrably different from those of normal tissues.[9, 19]

In summary, it may be said that the histochemical differences between normal and neoplastic tissues are only quantitative, and even the quantitative differences are not always significant. Of all available histochemical methods, the phosphamidase reaction seems to be the most promising one for the characterization of malignancy but further observations on a large scale will be required to establish its true value.

BIBLIOGRAPHY

1. Black, M. M., Kleiner, I. S., and Speer, F. D. Tissue respiration and tumor visualization by triphenyl tetrazolium chloride. *Cancer Research 10:* 204-205, 1950.
2. Gomori, G. Distribution of acid phosphatase in the tissues under normal and under pathologic conditions. *Arch. Path. 32:* 189-199, 1941.
3. Gomori, G. The study of enzymes in tissue sections. *Am. J. Clin. Path. 16:* 347-352, 1946.
4. Gomori, G. Distribution of lipase in the tissues under normal and under pathologic conditions. *Arch. Path. 41:* 121-129, 1946.
5. Gomori, G. Histochemical demonstration of sites of phosphamidase activity. *Proc. Soc. Exper. Biol. & Med. 69:* 407-409, 1948.
6. Gomori, G. Unpublished data.
7. Huggins, C., and Moulder, P. V. Estrogen production by Sertoli cell tumors of the testis. *Cancer Research 5:* 510-514, 1945.
8. King, T. J., and Nigrelli, R. F. Glycerophosphatases of the normal and tumorous frog kidney. *Proc. Soc. Exper. Biol. & Med. 72:* 373-376, 1949.
9. Leuchtenberger, C. Cytochemical studies of nucleoproteins in nuclei of a transplanted tumor (sarcoma 180). *Cancer Research 9:* 600-601, 1949.
10. Mackenzie, L. L., and Fuller, D. A new vital stain for malignant cells in vaginal secretions. *J. Lab. & Clin. Med. 35:* 314-316, 1950.
11. Mark, D. D. Distribution of lipase in preneoplastic and neoplastic states induced in the rat liver by *para*dimethylaminoazobenzene. *Arch. Path. 49:* 545-554, 1950.

12. MENK, K. F., and HYER, H. Histochemical demonstration of a lipase in carcinoma of the lung. *Arch. Path. 48:* 305-308, 1949.
13. ROSKIN, G. Histophysiologische Studien an Geschwulstzellen: III. Vergleichende Untersuchung der Oxydoredukase der normalen und der Krebszelle. *Ztschr. Zellforsch. u. mikr. Anat. 14:* 781-805, 1931-32.
14. ROSKIN, G. Expérience sur le diagnostic cytologique différentiel des cellules cancéreuses. *Bull. biol. et méd. expér. URSS 3:* 375-377, 1937.
15. ROSKIN, G. I., and STRUVE, M. E. Differential cytophysiological diagnosis of cancerous and normal tissues. *Stain Technol. 22:* 83-86, 1947.
16. RUTENBURG, A. M., GOFSTEIN, R., and SELIGMAN, A. M. Preparation of a new tetrazolium salt which yields a blue pigment on reduction and its use in the demonstration of enzymes in normal and neoplastic tissues. *Cancer Research 10:* 113-121, 1950.
17. SCHILLER, W. The diagnosis of carcinoma of the cervix in a very early stage. *Lancet 230:* 1228-1232, 1936.
18. SELIGMAN, A. M., NACHLAS, M. M., MANHEIMER, L. M., FRIEDMAN, O. M., and WOLF, G. Development of new methods for the histochemical demonstration of hydrolytic intracellular enzymes in a program of cancer research. *Ann. Surg. 130:* 333-341, 1949.
19. STOWELL, R. E. Histochemical observations on nucleic acids in homologous normal and neoplastic tissues. *Symp. Soc. Exper. Biol. 1:* 190-206, 1947.
20. STRAUS, F. H., CHERONIS, N. D., and STRAUS, E. Demonstration of reducing enzyme systems in neoplasms and living mammalian tissues by triphenyltetrazolium chloride. *Science 108:* 113-115, 1948.
21. THOMAS, L. E., and STEINITZ, L. M. Histochemical study of epidermal carcinogenesis in the mouse. *Cancer Research 10:* 245, 1950.
22. VOINOV, V. A. K tsitodiagnostike rakovoy bolezny (rongalitovaya krasochnaya reaktsiya). *Klinicheskaya Meditsina 18:* 51-53, 1940.
23. WACHSTEIN, M. Histochemical demonstration of reducing activity in normal and leukemic blood and bone marrow cells. *Proc. Soc. Exper. Biol. & Med. 73:* 306-308, 1950.

CHAPTER 22

Experimental Cancer Chemotherapy

David A. Karnofsky

". . . there can be no misunderstanding as to the almost insuperable problem which the chemotherapy of cancer presents, and which, in search of a comparison, we can almost liken to a biological counterpart of the squaring of the circle."—Haddow[60]

"It is almost—not quite, but almost—as hard as finding some agent that will dissolve away the left ear, say, yet leave the right ear unharmed: So slight is the difference between the cancer cell and its normal ancestor."—Woglom[169]

DEFINITION AND HISTORY

Cancer chemotherapy is defined as the use of a systemically administered agent which, while relatively nontoxic to the host, will interfere with, favorably modify, or destroy a neoplastic growth or alleviate its deleterious effects on the host.[73]

Attempts at cancer chemotherapy have been recorded since antiquity. Haddow, in a recent review of the subject,[60] cites a statement by Burrows (*A New Practical Essay on Cancer*, London, 1767) which, unfortunately, remains true today:

> Although the physicians of all nations, from the time of Hippocrates to the present, have, by numberless researches and experiments, made trial of everything in nature, from the most innocent drug to the most virulent poison, both in the mineral and vegetable kingdoms; yet the disease still baffles the power of physic.

Woglom[169] has listed a number of agents that have been tried and discarded for the treatment of cancer. Dyer,[38] in 1949, presented a documented review of the literature on chemotherapeutic studies on cancer, and cited the results of 5031 experiments recorded in 2213 reports. Her report concludes that:

> There is no evidence in the literature to indicate that a specific tumor-destroying agent has been found. While there is little reason to expect the discovery of a single chemical agent which will destroy either all or many different kinds of cancer, there seems to be no chemical known which, when administered systemically, will cause the complete regression of even one kind of cancer and still permit the survival of the host.

In the past decade there has been a great expansion in cancer research on all levels, particularly in the field of cancer chemotherapy.[49, 60, 74, 78, 139, 148] Investigations in cancer chemotherapy were encouraged by the demonstration that radioactive phosphorus had a favorable influence on chronic myelogenous and lymphatic leukemia, and polycythemia vera, and by the successful use of castration or estrogen therapy for the palliation of prostatic cancer. Subsequently, investigations on other radioactive isotopes, the pharmacologic studies on the nitrogen mustards and allied compounds, the elaboration and application of the concept of antimetabolites, and the work on the steroid hormones have all resulted in significant therapeutic contributions to the management of certain types of cancer.

Furthermore, the increased research funds provided by the American Cancer Society, the United States Public Health Service, the Atomic Energy Commission, and many private donors, the decreasing importance of infectious diseases as therapeutic problems in contrast to the increasing prevalence of cancer, and the shift in medical research toward biochemical and physiologic studies have served to stimulate interest in the study of this disease. The intensification of work on the problems presented by cancer in all its manifestations, and the influence of various agents on the growth of normal and neoplastic tissues will no doubt also result in information not only applicable to cancer therapy, but with important implications for many other medical and biologic problems.

BIOLOGIC ASPECTS OF CANCER

A satisfactory definition of cancer would appear to be a prerequisite to a rational chemotherapeutic attack. Cancers show a wide range of growth rates, from a slowly growing tumor which does not produce symptoms for many years after its known onset to a tumor which reaches a size lethal to the host in a few weeks. The growing tumor may remain circumscribed or it may infiltrate and become widely disseminated, occurrences largely independent of its growth rate. Cancer may arise from any tissue, and the cancers stemming from specific tissues do not have uniform biologic properties, but show varying degrees of histologic, functional, and biochemical deviations from their normal analogs; in some cases tumor cells appear to be almost identical with their normal tissue of origin. Within this enormous range of cytologic, organizational, and functional variation it has not been possible, thus far, to define any single characteristic of a cancer cell which distinguishes it from other types of cells, and which can furnish a basic and unified explanation of the disease. The definition of cancer can, therefore, only be a descriptive one: cancer being, from the point of view of the host, an unnecessary, excessive, and progressive proliferation of specific cells which grow and spread until they produce a situation which is incompatible with the continuing survival of the host. No single agent has been found in human cancer which can be shown to be the cause or the continuing stimulus to the growth of the tumor. In fact, if a recognizable, continuous stimulus were found to be the basis for a certain type of cancer, it is likely that the disease no longer would be classified as a cancer but, depending on its demonstrated pathogenesis, would be regarded as a process produced by an infection, metabolic abnormality, or deficiency. Present definitions of cancer, therefore, tell nothing about its cause or the nature of the continuing factor or process responsible for the progression of the disease.

Cancer may result in animals and man from various factors, including: genetic selection—mice have been selectively inbred to produce strains with a high incidence of leukemia, mammary, or lung cancer; exposure to carcinogenic chemicals, roentgen-rays, ultraviolet rays, radioactive isotopes; alterations in hormonal balance; and infection with specific viruses—a high incidence of mammary cancer in some strains of mice is transmitted by a virus present in the mother's milk, and Rous sarcoma in chickens is associated with a filterable agent. These widely divergent stimuli in the proper species or strain of animal result in a comparatively uniform response—the appearance and then the progressive growth of a cancer.

While it is evident that some change has occurred in the cancer cell to endow it with neoplastic properties, the nature of the deviation from normal cells has not been clarified. Tumors, once present, continue to grow independently of any known continuing stimulus; in fact, potent carcinogens, such as roentgen-rays, urethane, arsenic, and nitrogen mustard have been ineffective in inhibiting the growth of certain tumors.[15] Despite the suggestion that cancer cells, irrespective of their etiology, histogenesis, or species wherein found, have a biochemical uniformity,[59] no convincing experimental data have been advanced to support this generalization and no clinically useful agent has resulted from its application. Considering the great variation in the cytologic appearance, structural organization, and growth rate of cancer, and the alterations in the metabolism of the host induced by specific tumors, it seems highly unlikely that a simple or common metabolic or enzymatic defect will be detected easily in cancer tissue. Cancer, therefore, can not be explained at present in terms of an increase or decrease, or qualitative appearance or disappearance of certain metabolic systems.

Furthermore, it has been shown that cancer cells are not necessarily completely autonomous, but may retain metabolic and functional similarities with their tissue of origin. Thus, the growth of some tumors can be accelerated, modified, or depressed by agents altering the activity of the normal analog of the cancer. Certain tumors with specific functional activities may also cause serious alterations in the economy of the host; these effects may be evidenced by hyperfunctioning cancers of the endocrine glands, or by tumors which, in the course of their growth, produce fever, bone marrow depression, destruction of normal tissues, and other systemic alterations.

The experimental cancer chemotherapist should evolve his own concept of the disease, on the basis of which he can plan experiments and interpret their results. This concept should be compatible with the known facts, but not prejudicial to the incorporation of new ones. Cancer may be considered in the nature of a new organ derived from parent cells; the parent cells having developed their neoplastic property from the action of external or internal factors, or controlled somatic mutations. The neoplastic organs arise and continue to grow in a manner predetermined by the parent cells, much as the kidney or lens of the eye arises and develops from a few apparently undifferentiated cells in the embryo. The cancer, depending on its type, presents itself in a variety of forms, which may range from an undifferentiated group of cells to a well-organized tumor practically identical with its tissue of origin. The cancer maintains a more or less close relationship to the tissue of origin, so that it sometimes possesses the functional properties of its normal analog, and is dependent for its growth and function on the same factors as the normal tissue. Tumors, in growing, stimulate the formation of a blood supply, and induce stromal reactions of differing magnitude. The cancer may infiltrate and destroy normal tissue, and spread by local extension or through the lymph channels or blood vessels. Each cancer has its own predetermined natural history, which is modified to some extent by the status of the host. Most cancers grow so rapidly and involve such vital structures that they ultimately kill the host, but it is conceivable that certain tumors, like embryonic organs, have a limited life span and they grow to a certain size and then regress. Willis,[168] in discussing the growth and regression of tumors states:

> A malignant tumor, though anarchic and asocial in its behavior, is nevertheless a part of the organism, and is dependent for its nutritional requirements and the removal of its metabolites on the body politic. Like any other metazoan tissue or group of tissues, a tumor may be conceived to be not immortal but to possess a finite span of life determined on the one hand by the intrinsic proliferative energy with which it is endowed at its inception, and on the other hand, by the adequacy with which its peculiar nutritional requirements are met by the body as a whole. The life-span of a tumor usually outlasts that of the normal tissues with which the tumor is in nutritive competition; but it is conceivable that, under a particular set of circumstances, a tumor endowed at its birth with only moderate proliferative energy, might fail to survive in the individual bearing it and might perish before the termination of the life-span of the organism. In other cases, although the tumor might not perish, it might survive in a condition of nice equilibrium with the other tissues, so that the result will be, not actual retrogression of the tumor, but long survival of the tumorous individual with unimpaired health.

Furthermore, certain tumors conceivably may develop somatic mutations which produce substances antigenic to the host, and this may result in immunologic reactions in the tissue and actual tumor regression.

This broad view of cancer emphasizes the close similarities of the neoplastic and normal tissues of the host, and the variable but characteristic natural course of each tumor. It does not answer any of the questions as to the immediate pathogenesis of cancer, or the nature and possible universality of the cellular abnormality which is primary and basic to the neoplastic process. The chemotherapist, thus, is not provided by the fundamental investigators with a productive approach to the disease, and he can only resort to empirical and often tenuous attacks on the problem.

APPROACHES TO CHEMOTHERAPY

As already noted, the cancer chemotherapist is confronted with the gross manifestations of the disease, with the knowledge of its almost certain progression, but with little or no information on the underlying process, whose interruption or inhibition appears to be the only method of controlling the generalized disease. Three approaches are open to him, each offering some immediate results and the possibility of a major advance.

EMPIRICAL APPROACH

There is ample precedent from experiences with other diseases to lead to the hope that a treatment for cancer can be found before the disease is understood. As Greenstein has stated:

> . . . it must be ruefully admitted that the world might still be waiting for the benefits of digitalis, of morphine, of quinine, and of penicillin, were these therapeutic discoveries to be made on a rational basis.[59]

Consequently, there is a continuing and intensified effort to test all available chemicals and biologic substances for their activity against cancer. These studies are being conducted in tumor-bearing animals and, with selected agents, in patients with various types of cancer. An inhibition of tumor growth by any agent in any of these tests provides the stimulus for a more extensive study of the active material. Thousands of empirical trials have been carried out, and the compilation by Dyer[38] is the most complete record available. Thus far, empiricism has provided little of value for the treatment of cancer in man, but it is the great grab-bag from which some day may be pulled an agent for treating cancer that is the equivalent of sufanilamide or penicillin in infectious diseases. Empiricism should not be minimized as an approach; it is an important area that may yield to the observant and prepared investigator the lead to unravel the fundamental problems of cancer.

INTERFERENCE WITH THE "NEOPLASTIC MECHANISM" IN THE CANCER CELL

It is possible, although not necessarily certain, that cancer cells have a characteristic aberration, which is the continuing stimulus to tumor growth, and which chemically and functionally distinguishes that cancer from the normal cell. If a unique mechanism were to be discovered and defined, it could be used as the basis for attacking the abnormal cellular function in the cancer or the organizational expressions of neoplastic activity. Some theoretical views concerning neoplastic mechanisms and possible points of attack, the significance of which will be determined by fundamental studies, are summarized briefly.

THEORIES OF NEOPLASTIC MECHANISM

Cancer is believed to evolve at the cellular level; that is, permanent alterations occurring in a single or group of normal cells result in continuing neoplastic activity (see Fig. 120). In certain instances the alteration appears to be due to a virus which initiates and, presumably, provides the continuing stimulus to tumor growth, as seen in the Rous sarcoma in chickens. Viruses, however, have not been demonstrated in the great majority of tumors, and somatic mutations, abnormal metabolic pathways, and qualitative or quantitative changes in enzyme patterns have been suggested as basic to the neoplastic transformation.[59, 123]

Once the neoplastic transformation has occurred, it is necessary to inquire into how the altered cell expresses its new properties. It is obvious that repeated cell division is an integral part of the neoplastic process. It seems reasonable to suggest, however, that cancer cells divide in response to an abnormal or neoplastic stimulus, but cell division proceeds by normal mechanisms. Algire's hypothesis[2] that the basic characteristic of a rapidly growing tumor is "its capacity continuously to elicit the production of new capillary endothelium from the host" illustrates this suggestion, since the mitotic activity in the tumor is presumably a normal response of the cells to an excessive blood supply. Further evidence on the similarity of the mitotic mechanisms in normal cells and their neoplastic analogues is derived from the observation that these cells are similarly affected by mitotic poisons, such as colchicine, roentgen-rays, nitrogen mustard, and urethane.

More characteristic of cancer is its invasiveness, metastatic growth, and ability to destroy normal tissue. These processes are very poorly understood; it has been suggested, for example, that the spread of cancer cells is facilitated by their decreased adhesiveness, ameboid movements and an increase in the spreading factor—hyaluronidase—in the tumor.[30] The resistance of the cancer cell to the factors regulating normal tissue growth, or the possession of an aggressive activity permitting it to violate the integrity of normal tissues, may be basic to the process of cancer cell multiplication and invasiveness. Even with the ability to invade normal tissue and metastasize, cancer cells do not necessarily range freely in the host. Certain tumors preferentially metastasize and grow in special sites, and metastases are known to remain dormant for many years after the primary tumor has been removed.

Another property characteristic of many types of cancer is growth on serial transplantation. This has been shown with tumors transplanted in homologous strains of animals, and by heterologous transplants of human and animal tumors in newborn animals, the anterior chamber of the eye of the rabbit and guinea pig, and in the chick embryo.

It would be of the utmost importance to understand the fundamental abnormality resulting in the expressions of neoplastic activity, for cancer then might be viewed as a series of normal responses to a primary aberration. While it is to be hoped that a basic abnormality exists which is uniform for all types of cancer, even if a different primary abnormality were present for each type of cancer, each producing a characteristic neoplastic pattern, the conforming second, third, etc., reactions to the diversified primary stimuli might still converge into a common mechanism.

While the mechanisms of neoplastic activity, per se, are the crux of the cancer problem, it is evident that the cancer cell is carrying out many of the normal functions of cells. These normal processes may be seen in cell growth and division, in the ability of the organized tumor to stimulate a blood supply and a stromal reaction in the host, and in the functional activities, the special properties, dependencies and susceptibilities that the tumor has in common with its tissue of origin.

Direct Destruction of the Neoplastic Mechanism

If cancer, or a certain type of cancer, were found to be caused by a virus, the virus might be inhibited selectively by specific chemicals or interfering viruses; if an abnormal enzyme or enzymatic pattern were involved, it might be poisoned by specific enzyme poisons; if an atypical metabolic pathway were utilized, it might be interrupted selectively by specific antimetabolites. Effective treatment might kill the cancer cell directly, or revert it to normal behavior; the latter would be evidenced by cessation of mitotic activity, differentiation of the cell and then, perhaps, late cellular degeneration in the absence of a useful function for the redundant cells.

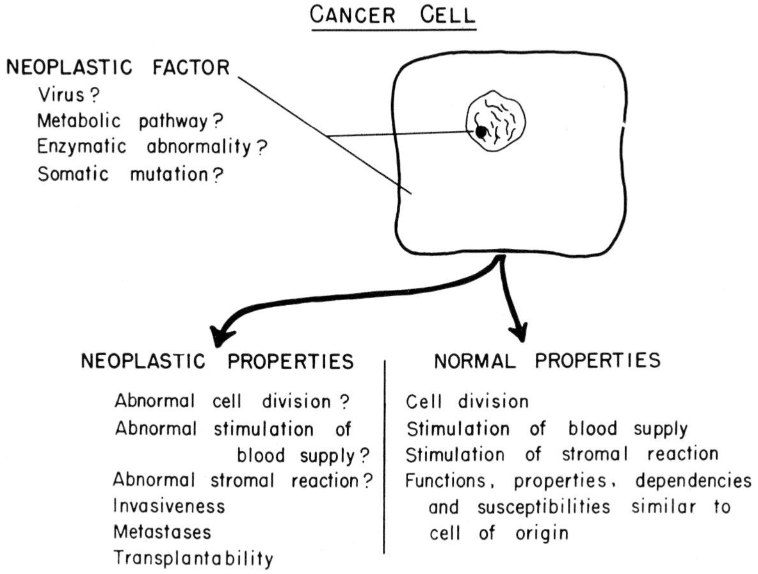

FIG. 120. Schematic representation of the normal and neoplastic properties of the cancer cell.

The curative treatment of cancer would require the destruction or the reversal toward normal of all the cancer cells, since the body, in contrast to its ability to clear up the remnants of infectious processes treated with antibiotics, does not appear to have a satisfactory defense against even a few cancer cells. Thus, an effective but incomplete form of treatment might have to be given repeatedly over an indefinite period of time in order to keep the surviving cancer cells under control.

Specific Interference with Mitotic Activity in Cancer Cells

As noted in Fig. 120, an integral, but not necessarily abnormal, part of the neoplastic process is cell division. If the neoplastic activity were directly related to an abnormality of the mitotic mechanism, and if this pathologic process could be shown to differ qualitatively from that in normal cell division, specific chemicals might be discovered which would inhibit the multiplication of cancer cells.

Interference with the Induction of New Blood Vessels by Cancer

Algire[2] has suggested that the capacity of tumor cells to stimulate the production of new capillaries adjacent to them might be a basic property of neoplastic tissue. From this premise, the search for chemicals which would neutralize the blood-vessel–stimulating property of cancer cells or specifically inhibit the formation of capillary endothelium might possibly yield substances which would interrupt the growth of cancer.

Interference with the Invasive and Metastatic Properties of Cancer

The invasiveness of cancer and its metastatic growth, characteristic manifestations of the disease, may be due to distinctive abnormal mechanisms. Elucidation of these processes may suggest specific measures for confining the neoplastic growth, or preventing the development of metastases. The long latent period after the removal of the primary tumor before metastases develop in some cases and the predilection of certain cancers to metastasize to specific tissues suggest that, in many cases, a favorable environment and a metastatic implant of sufficient size are necessary before the metastasis can develop.[68]

Attacks on the "neoplastic mechanism" and the expressions of the neoplastic trait by the cancer cells offer the best hope for a curative chemotherapeutic agent against cancer. This approach will become important to the chemotherapist if, and when, basic research clearly and reproducibly demonstrates and defines these mechanisms.

INTERFERENCE WITH THE NORMAL ACTIVITIES OF THE CANCER CELL

It is possible that the "neoplastic mechanism" in the cell is not a unique pathologic process, but only a quantitative modification of mechanisms already present in normal tissues. Even aside from the possibility that distinctive biochemical mechanisms in cancer cells may differ only quantitatively from normal cells, cancer cells retain practically all the properties of normal tissues, and sometimes closely resemble their tissue of origin. On the basis of the normal properties of the cancer cell (Fig. 120), therapeutic methods may be considered which have the potentialities of influencing tumor growth and ameliorating the injurious effects of the tumor on the host.

General Cell Poisons

A number of agents has been found to inhibit cell division or seriously damage dividing cells, thus interfering with the growth of certain normal and neoplastic tissues. The type of effects produced by these agents is exemplified by those seen with roentgen irradiation, and the active chemicals include nitrogen mustard and allied derivatives, and urethane. These agents are particularly injurious to normal hematopoiesis and, therapeutically, they can be used only at doses which will not completely or irreversibly inhibit normal bone marrow activity.

Interruption of the Blood Supply to Tumors

If chemicals were known which would specifically or generally interfere with capillary proliferation, it would be possible to limit the growth of some tumors. Another method with therapeutic potentialities would be the production of widespread damage to the vascular bed of a tumor; this is apparently the mechanism whereby several toxic substances, such as colchicine, Coley's toxin, and Shear's purified bacterial polysaccharide, act to produce hemorrhage and transient tumor regression in certain animal and, occasionally, human tumors.

Actions on the Normal Aspects of Cancer Tissue

Considering the remarkable differences in the appearance and function of the normal tissues of the body—the brain cells, bronchial epithelium, prostate, lymphocytes, liver, etc.—it would seem reasonable to expect that eventually various agents would be found which are able to inhibit selectively and separately the growth or cause the destruction of each of these tissues. Since tumors have many similarities with their normal analogs, it might be possible to use these agents to interfere with the growth of tumors arising from these normal tissues. Several mechanisms whereby specific normal tissues can be injured will be discussed briefly.

Specific Antimetabolites. Certain tissues have a high requirement for specific metabolic precursors, such as vitamins, purines, pyrimidines, and amino acids, and an antimetabolite which interferes specifically with the utilization of one of these substances may inhibit the growth of the dependent tissues. Folic acid, for example, is essential for the maintenance of hematopoiesis, and a series of antagonists, the 4-amino derivatives of folic acid, have proven very active in producing bone marrow aplasia.

Concentration of Toxic Substances in the Cell. Certain cells concentrate specific substances as an essential phase of their normal functions. By introducing a toxic analogue of the normal substance, or by labeling the normal precursor with a radioactive isotope, it would be possible to injure these cells selectively. This technic is illustrated by the selective activity of radioactive iodine in destroying the thyroid gland; the radioactive iodine is concentrated, as is normal iodine, by the thyroid, and the gland is then destroyed by the radioactivity.

Alterations in Hormonal Balance. The amount and relative concentrations of the various hormones acting in the body exert a profound effect on the growth and functional activity of certain tissues, and a definite, less marked and, perhaps, secondary effect on many other tissues. For example, the growth and activity of the thyroid gland, the adrenal cortex, and the gonads are regulated by pituitary hormones; the mammary and prostate glands are maintained at a functional level by sex hormones; and an excess of adrenocortical hormone will inhibit somatic growth and characteristically interfere with hair growth and connective tissue formation.[70] Alterations in hormonal concentrations, therefore, can be used to stimulate the growth of one type of tissue, or to inhibit the growth of another.

Tissue-Specific Antibodies. Tissues may contain tissue-specific substances, which are antigenic when injected into another species of animal, so that tissue-specific antibodies can be produced. These tissue-specific antibodies, which can be concentrated and purified to some extent, are injurious to the tissues containing the appropriate antigen. A purified antibody can have a radioactive isotope, such as radioactive iodine, attached, and the isotope is then to some degree specifically localized in the tissue, where it produces further damage by radiation.[124] Neoplastic tissues may retain the tissue-specific antigens of their normal analogues, and they may also contain antigens peculiar to themselves.

Agents Affecting Embryonic Tissues. The tissues of the embryo are undergoing differentiation and rapid growth, whereas many of the tissues of the adult are mature and no longer show a high rate of cell division. In some cases tumors appear to exhibit the embryonic, rather than the mature, pattern of the tissue from which they arise. If an agent is found to be injurious to specific normal tissues in the embryo, it may also cause a selective inhibition in the growth of tumors arising from these adult tissues.

Necrotizing Viruses. Viruses may show an extraordinary species and tissue specificity, and some viruses exert their effects by destroying their host cells.[110] The specificity and virulence of viruses can be enhanced by a process of selection, and it is possible that "trained" viruses may be developed which are capable of specifically damaging any desired normal or neoplastic tissue.

The procedures available for damaging specific normal tissue have been applied, whenever feasible, against tumors arising from these tissues. Some normal organs, such as the thyroid gland, gonads, uterus, cervix, prostate and mammary gland, are not essential to life; if specific agents could be found capable of inhibiting the growth or of destroying each of these tissues, it is possible that the agent would have a similar effect on tumors arising from these tissues. This approach has been effective in treating functioning carcinomas of the thyroid gland with radioactive iodine and carcinoma of the prostate by estrogens or castration, although the tumors are only temporarily affected and the growth of the tumor cells is not permanently inhibited. It is possible, however, that other agents will be found that will attack a more vulnerable and fundamental tissue-specific system, and produce a greater and more protracted injury. Most tissues are essential to life, however, and therapeutic agents used to suppress tumor growth can be given only in doses that do not seriously damage the normal tissues. The folic acid antagonists, the adrenocortical hormones, and the nitrogen mustards, for example, may produce temporary tumor regression and clinical improvement; but these agents can not be given indefinitely at therapeutically active doses because of the increasing resistance of the tumor and the toxic effects which finally intervene in the host.

MISCELLANEOUS ASPECTS OF CANCER CHEMOTHERAPY

Tumor Resistance

Neoplasms, which may originally have been responsive to a chemotherapeutic agent, eventually become resistant to therapy, although host susceptibility to the drug may remain fairly uniform. Resistance may be due to the process of differentiation and maturation in the tumor, perhaps analogous to the increased resistance shown by certain normal tisues to toxic agents as they progress from the embryonic to the adult state. Another possibility is that a specific therapeutic agent destroys all the cells susceptible to it, and the resistant surviving cells gradually become predominant. This situation has been demonstrated in transplantable mouse leukemia.[25, 95] The 4-amino derivatives of folic acid (folic acid antagonists) will inhibit temporarily the growth of transplanted leukemia, but the disease then progresses despite continuing therapy. By isolating and passaging the resistant cells in mice treated with the folic acid antagonists, strains of leukemic cells have been obtained which are resistant to large doses of the folic acid antagonists. The development of tumor resistance is, thus far, an impassable barrier to the production of prolonged remissions in certain neoplastic conditions by effective chemotherapeutic agents.

Combination Therapy

Numerous attempts are being made to enhance the activity of chemotherapeutic agents. Agents, each of which can only incompletely inhibit tumor growth, have been given together or in various sequences in order to bring out an additive or synergic effect.[133, 142] It has been suggested that the effectiveness of an agent may be increased by altering the tumor environment as, for example, by fever, hypoglycemia, or anoxia. Another suggestion is that the tumor-inhibiting effect of an antimetabolite might be enhanced by simultaneously supplying critical doses of the normal metabolite, which would protect or promote the recovery of the normal tissues more readily than that of the tumor.[129] Other procedures have been reported which would increase the sensitivity of tumor tissue to localized radiotherapy.[108]

Regional Chemotherapy

Studies have been undertaken on the effects of chemotherapeutic agents when injected into the arterial blood supply to a tumor.[89] The objective of this approach is to deliver a high concentration of a reactive therapeutic agent to the tumor, and to have most of the agent fixed during its first passage through the capillary bed so that a minimum of systemic toxicity results. Thus, the differences between the susceptibility of the tumor and its normal surrounding tissue can be fully utilized. While only nitrogen mustard has been used for regional chemotherapy with an appreciable selective local effect, it is entirely reasonable to expect that more suitable agents will be found. Regional chemotherapy should be particularly useful in treating localized but inoperable tumors of the head and neck, brain, metastatic and primary tumors of the liver and widespread cancer in the pelvis.

Supportive Therapy

Cancers, in the course of their growth, may invade vital tissues or areas of the body, elaborate toxic or excessive amounts of physiologic substances, undergo spontaneous necrosis, become the site of secondary infection, and produce anemia, anorexia, and weakness in the host. It is of practical importance to understand how the cancer produces its adverse effects in the host, so that appropriate measures can be undertaken to counteract them even though the growth of the tumor itself can not be adequately controlled. Supportive measures, while not regarded as specific treatment against cancer, are of great value in the management of the disease.

LABORATORY PROCEDURES IN CANCER CHEMOTHERAPY

The empirical testing of chemical and biologic substances for therapeutic effects against cancer requires simple technics which will give precise, reproducible, and interpretable results (screening methods). The available experimental materials include several species of animal with a high tumor incidence, and a variety of spontaneous and transplantable tumors. The numerous highly individual methods of testing agents and interpreting results preclude a simple analysis of the screening procedures. These methods have been discussed by Stock,[148] and their rationale analyzed by Lees and Lees.[100] It is possible in this report only to summarize some of the procedures used in experimental cancer chemotherapy (Tables 42 and 43), and to discuss some of the factors involved in screening methods.

IMPORTANT ASPECTS OF THE EXPERIMENTAL MATERIAL USED IN CHEMOTHERAPY STUDIES

Species of Animal. The principal species used are the mouse, rat, rabbit and chicken.

Origin of Tumors. Tumors used in chemotherapy have the following origins: *spontaneous, carcinogen-induced,* and *transplantable* by means of intact *cells,* or by *cell-free extracts.*

Common types of experimental tumors, and their host species.

SPONTANEOUS TUMORS. The best source of spontaneous tumors is the mouse. By selective inbreeding, strains of mice have been developed which show a high incidence of leukemia (AK and C58 strains), lung cancer (A strain), and mammary cancer (related to a viral agent transmitted in the mother's milk as well as to genetic constitution[13]). Lymphomatosis in chickens is a common disease, and is presumably due to a filterable agent.[24] Spontaneous tumors occur less frequently in rats, rabbits, dogs, and guinea pigs. Spontaneous tumors are used infrequently and only for special studies; it is difficult to obtain a large supply of animals bearing spontaneous tumors, there may be widespread variations in the course of the disease in individual animals, and, unless a large series of animals be used, the activity of agents with only a partial or transient effect on tumor growth may be very difficult to interpret. Since spontaneous tumors seem to resemble human cancer in many respects, they provide the most rigorous animal screening test for a chemotherapeutic agent.

TUMORS INDUCED BY CARCINOGENS. In special instances carcinogen-induced tumors have been used for chemotherapy trials. Carcinogens will consistently produce carcinomas of the skin in mice, fibrosarcomas and hepatomas in rats and, less regularly, many other types of tumor.

TRANSPLANTABLE TUMORS, PASSAGED BY INTACT CELLS.* The vast majority of tumors used in chemotherapy are transplantable, since this permits the use of a group of animals carrying a uniform type of tumor with a predictable rate of growth and effect on the host. The tumors originally arise spontaneously, or are produced by carcinogens, and they are then passaged in susceptible animals. Numerous

* See also Chapter 14.

transplantable tumors in mice, rats, rabbits and chickens, are in use (Table 41), and each has its individual characteristics which include: the site of origin of the tumor, the strain or strains of animals in which the tumor will grow on transplantation, its histologic appearance, histochemical properties, rate of growth, the effect on the host, the survival time of the host, the incidence of spontaneous regression and the ability to produce immunity in the host to further challenge by the same tumor, and its transmissibility by cell-free extracts.

The tumor type is classified usually by its site of origin and histologic appearance; thus, transplantable tumors may be called mammary carcinoma, hepatoma, lymphosarcoma, leukemia, neuroblastoma, sarcoma, etc. In many instances tumors are identified further by an eponym (Harding-Passey melanoma) or a laboratory number (Sarcoma 180). One of the important purposes in classifying tumors is to indicate their relationship to a normal tissue for comparative studies, and their similarity to specific human tumors. The specific histologic designations that are attached to transplantable animal tumors should not be taken too literally. Transplantable tumors often lose some of the distinguishing characteristics of the original tumor on progressive passages; this may be due to the predominance of the faster-growing elements of the tumor, or to spontaneous mutations resulting in changes in tumor characteristics. Alveolar mammary carcinomas have become spindle cell tumors, osteogenic sarcomas lose their ability to form bone and to maintain a high alkaline phosphatase activity, and other tumors initially dependent for growth on hormonal influences may become independent after several passages. The genetic compatability of the transplanted tumor with the host is an extremely important consideration in chemotherapeutic trials. A tumor developing in an animal in a highly inbred strain can be transplanted to other animals in the strain without difficulty. The tumor is practically autologous with the host, and is similar in many respects to spontaneous tumors. Even in these optimal circumstances, the tumor, during prolonged transplantation, may undergo mutation, or the inbred line may change so that absolute genetic compatability is no longer attainable. Many tumors show great selectivity as to the strains in which they will grow. If these tumors are inoculated into an incompatible host, they are subjected to host reactions which prevent the tumor from growing or cause it to regress after a short period of growth. By contrast, there are tumors which can grow in, and kill, almost any animal in its species of origin. While these tumors grow actively, they induce immunologic reactions which may cause necrosis in the tumor, and a certain percentage of the tumors will undergo spontaneous regression. Animals can be vaccinated against these tumors by injecting dead or attenuated cells, and in animals in whom the tumors grew and then regressed, an immunity is produced to further inoculation with the same tumor. The response of transplantable tumors (arising in a non-inbred strain or transplanted to a genetically incompatible host) to chemotherapeutic agents may be complicated, and the results obtained with this type of material must be carefully interpreted. The transplantable tumors most frequently used are listed in Table 41, with the strain in which they show their most satisfactory and consistent growth.

TUMORS PASSAGED BY CELL-FREE FILTRATES. There is great interest in the viral origin of cancer,[36] but the viral transmission of cancer has been proved unquestionably in only a few instances. Practically, the Rous sarcoma virus is the only one used regularly to produce tumors in chickens for chemotherapy trials. Although some other tumors are, or have been, associated with a virus, such as fowl leukosis, the Brown-Pearce carcinoma in rabbits, and mammary carcinoma in mice, in chemotherapeutic trials the *intact tumor cells* are transplanted, and these *transplanted cells* continue the growth of the tumor. Where the tumor is transmitted by a cell-free filtrate, the tumor cells arise from, and are presumably autologous with, the host, and only the tumor-stimulating viruses may have antigenic activity. The transplantation of intact cells, even if their neoplastic growth was originated or sustained by a viral agent, presents a different situation, since these growing transplanted cells may not be genetically compatible with the host; these are probably similar to nonviral tumors for chemotherapeutic study.

TABLE 41. TRANSPLANTABLE TUMORS COMMONLY USED IN CHEMOTHERAPEUTIC STUDIES ON CANCER

Tumor Designation	*Suitable Strains*	*References to its use**
	MOUSE	
Crocker sarcoma 180	Almost all strains	11, 12, 48, 111, 134, 147, 148, 154, 155, 163, 173
Sarcoma 37	Almost all strains	34, 62, 85, 101, 130, 165
M.C.D.B.I. sarcoma	Almost all strains	16
Sarcoma L946	C57	117, 130, 147
RC tumor	DBA	48
Ma387	AK	11, 12
T241	C57BL	11, 12, 154
S-13	C3H	46
Ak1394	AK	23
Ak9417	AK	23, 48
Ak4	AK	20, 25
L1210	DBA	58, 93
C1498	C57	20
L825	C58	92
Lymphoma 2	A	85
P1534	DBA	85
Myeloid leukemia lines 15, 686, X, 765	F	86
Lymphoid leukemia lines 876, 926, 974, 100	F	86
$6C_3HED$	C3H	8, 152
Patterson lymphosarcoma	Ak	90, 148, 154
Lymphosarcoma 1	A	58
15091a	A	52
E0771	C57	130, 148, 155
755	C57	48, 85, 133
Adenocarcinoma 63	Almost all strains	91, 126, 147
C_3HBA	C3H	58, 85
Twort	Almost all strains	126, 147
Harding-Passey melanoma	Almost all strains	148, 154, 155, 170
S91 melanoma	DBA	58, 170
S91 amelanotic	DBA	170

TESTING METHODS INVOLVING THE USE OF ANIMALS

Many screening technics, using one or more tumors, are in current use.[49] These methods may be varied regarding the type and origin of tumor, and species and strain of animal used. The compound is usually given to the tumor-bearing animal at a previously determined maximum tolerated dose, as a single dose or by fractionated doses given for arbitrary periods or during the survival of the tumor-bearing animal. The drug may be given orally, subcutaneously, intraperitoneally, intravenously, intra-arterially, or directly into the tumor. Treatment may be started when the tumor first appears, or when it is transplanted, or after it has reached an arbitrary size. Two or more agents may be given in combination, the test agent may be given to animals on a special diet, deprived of certain organs, etc. These diversified methods have different criteria to indicate chemotherapeutic activity.

Histologic Injury to the Tumor. Following the injection of the test substance into tumor-bearing animals, the animals are sacrificed at regular intervals and the tumors are examined for hemorrhage and, microscopically, for evidence of cellular damage. This method reveals agents damaging the capillary bed, such as Shear's polysaccharide, or mitotic poisons, such as roentgen-rays and nitrogen mustard.

TABLE 41. (*Continued*)

Tumor Designation	*Suitable Strains*	*References to its use**
C1300-neuroblastoma	A	39, 52
C198-reticuloendothelioma of liver	C57 Leaden	147
Ridgway osteogenic sarcoma	AK	90
Wagner osteogenic sarcoma	AK	90, 148, 154
Ehrlich ascites tumor	Almost all strains	87
Squamous epithelial carcinoma 119	A	62
Rhabdomyosarcoma (MC-1A)	C3H	107
	RAT	
Murphy lymphosarcoma	Almost all strains	151
Sarcoma R39	Almost all strains	130, 148, 154, 155
Flexner-Jobling carcinoma	Almost all strains	148, 154
Walker carcinoma 256	Almost all strains	56, 63, 130, 148, 154, 161
Rat carcinoma 1643	Almost all strains	58
	RABBIT	
V_2	Almost all strains	31
Brown-Pearce carcinoma	Almost all strains	57, 135
	CHICKEN	
Rous sarcoma virus	Almost all strains	103
Leukosis RPL-12	Almost all strains	136

This list is not complete. It is evident, however, that there are many tumors in use, and the number can easily be increased—and is being increased—by the transplantation and maintenance of spontaneous or carcinogen-induced tumors in susceptible animals. While it is important to have a wide spectrum of tumor types, and there are a number of important gaps to be filled, the development of a new tumor should be based on whether it has distinctive properties not found in the other tumors already in use.

* Numbers in this column refer to items in the bibliography to this chapter.

Cellular changes, characteristically produced by certain chemicals, can be studied by this method.

Tumor Regression. The tumor is allowed to reach a certain size before treatment is begun, and the effect of the treatment is measured by the failure of the tumor to grow, or by its regression and disappearance. The prolongation of the survival time of the host is another index of activity.

Tumor Inhibition. Treatment is initiated almost concurrently with the inoculation of the tumor, and the cessation (failure to "take"), or slowing of the tumor growth, and prolongation of survival of the host are indices of chemotherapeutic activity.

Cytocidal Method. An animal bearing a large tumor is injected with a single dose of the test agent at one or more multiples of the LD_{50} dose. Shortly before the expected death of the animal, or at an arbitrary time after injection, the animal is sacrificed and the tumor tested for viability by transplantation into susceptible animals. The multiples of the LD_{50} dose destroying the viability of the tumor are the index of the direct toxic action of the drug on the tumor cells.

In order to interpret properly the results obtained by these methods, adequate control groups and special studies are necessary to show that death, when survival time is used as a criterion, is due to the tumor growth and not to drug toxicity, that tumor inhibition or regression is not due to inanition or endogenous hormonal alterations, and that histologic changes in the tumor are due to the test agent, and not to stimulation of the adrenal cortex, blood vessel injury, or spontaneous necrosis. In Table 42, a number of chemotherapeutic procedures in current use is summarized.

SPECIAL TESTING METHODS

Special methods have been devised to examine the differential effects of various agents on normal and neoplastic cells.

Tissue Culture. Normal and neoplastic tissues of various types are explanted in tissue culture, and exposed to the maximum concentration of the test agent, previously found to be tolerated by the normal cells. If the growth of the cancer cells is inhibited at concentrations that do not harm the normal cells, a selective chemotherapeutic activity is suggested.

Egg Culture. Tumor cells, usually of mouse origin, are explanted to the chorioallantoic membrane or the yolk sac of the chick embryo, and a few days later the embryo is treated with the maximum dose of the test agent tolerated by the developing embryo. Inhibition of tumor growth, histologic changes in the tumor cells, and loss of viability as determined by transplantation to a susceptible host are indices of a selective chemotherapeutic effect.

In vitro Methods. Neoplastic cells are exposed to various concentrations of the test chemical at a specified temperature and for a certain period of time, and then the cells are assayed in susceptible animals for their viability. An effective com-

TABLE 42. EXAMPLES OF METHODS CURRENTLY USED IN ASSAYING FOR THERAPEUTIC ACTIVITY AGAINST TUMORS IN ANIMALS

MICE

Spontaneous tumors

"As the growth rates of primary tumours vary greatly each tumour must be used as its own control. Induced primary tumours were obtained by injection of 1 mg. methylcholanthrene into stock mice. Induced tumours and spontaneous mammary tumours were measured twice weekly as soon as they were obtained. They were allowed to grow until the sum of two diameters of the tumour had increased by at least 7 mm. and this, the control rate of growth, was expressed in mm. growth per day. . . . The mice were then dosed for 14 days and the rate of growth per day determined. The ratio of these two rates of growth shows the effect of the treatment and from this ratio the inhibition expressed as a percentage of the original growth can readily be obtained. Those cases in which partial retrogression occurred during the treatment are shown by the negative ratio of growth and the inhibition is taken as being over 100%." [16]

Mice with spontaneous mammary carcinomas were biopsied by the slice method before treatment. The tumor-bearing animals were injected intraperitoneally daily for 8 to 26 days, and the rate of growth of the tumor was measured.[155]

C58 and RIL, subline B, inbred leukemic strains of mice show an 80–90 per cent incidence of leukemia, beginning on 6 months of age. Treatment is begun within 3 to 8 days after the disease is diagnosed, and criteria of therapeutic effect are: a fall in the total white-cell count to or below normal limits; a marked reduction in the number of immature cells in the circulating blood; a maintenace of hemoglobin levels; a diminution in the size of enlarged subcutaneous lymph nodes and spleen; and an increase in the survival of the animal as compared with controls. [94]

Carcinogen-induced tumors

Mice were painted with tar twice weekly until the appearance of papillomata. Treatment with the test substance was then started, and the tumors were measured weekly and the mice observed clinically. After death, the mice were autopsied, the lesions were measured and examined microscopically, and a careful search for the presence of metastases was made.[72]

Transplanted tumors

"Injection into mice, bearing a 1-week-old implantation of Sarcoma 37, of a single, maximum tolerated dose. The injection is made into the flank opposite the side bearing the tumor. Sacrifice of the mice at 8, 20, and 48 hours after the injection. Recording of the gross autopsy findings. Fixing of tumor tissue in Zenker-acetic and in acetic-orcein. The wall of the small intestine is taken as control tissue. Evaluation of the cellular changes produced by the treatment." [101, 137]

Small tumor implants of sarcoma 180 (1-2 mm. in any dimension) were made subcutaneously by trocar into the axillary region of CFW or RF mice, 18–22 Gm. in weight. The mice are weighed individually at the beginning and end of the experiment. Beginning 24 hours after, the test drug was injected intraperitoneally twice daily for one week. At the end of the injection period, the tumors were measured with calipers in two diameters. The degree of inhibition of tumor growth was graded as follows:

Marked inhibition (+): no growth of tumors in treated animals to a growth with an average diameter one-quarter that of the untreated controls.

Slight inhibition (±): growth of tumors in treated animals from one to three-quarters the average diameter of the control tumors.

No effect (−): growth of tumors greater than three-quarters the average diameter of the controls.[148, 150]

AKM mice were injected intraperitoneally with 0.1 cc. of a saline suspension of leukemic spleen containing about 1,000,000 cells. Treatment was begun 2 days after the injection of the leukemic cell suspension and consisted of 3 intraperitoneal injections weekly of the candidate drug for a total of 10 injections. The criteria of therapeutic activity was the survival of the treated mice as compared to the controls.[20, 143]

TABLE 42. (*Continued*)

Tumors used were sarcoma 180 in Paris RIII and C57 mice, 755 tumors in C57 mice, RC tumors in DBA mice, E0771 in C57, leukemia 9417 in AK, and lymphosarcoma 6C3HED in C3H mice. After tumor inoculation treatment was begun within 1 to 10 days, and the index of activity was the size and weight of the solid tumors, and survival of the leukemic mice.[48]

Crocker sarcoma 180, Harding-Passey melanoma, mammary adenocarcinoma E0771, and rat sarcoma R39 were used. Treatment was begun 1 to 7 days after tumor transplantation and the injections were continued until there was complete regression of the tumor or until the animal showed evidences of toxicity. The animals were weighed daily, and the tumors measured weekly by calipers. The criteria of effect are the size and histologic appearance of tumor as compared to the controls, and the survival time of the host.[155]

Two lymphosarcomas (1 and 2) and two strains of leukemia (L1210 and L1358) were used. A leukemic cell brei was injected subcutaneously or intramuscularly into susceptible mice—about 800,000 cells were given per mouse. Treatment was begun within 24 to 48 hours and continued daily. The criteria of effect were size of local tumor, study of the blood cells during the course of the disease, survival time of the animals, and histologic appearance of tissues.[96]

Five transplantable mouse tumors (leukemia 1210, lymphosarcoma 1, lymphosarcoma 2, mammary adenocarcinoma C3HBA, melanoma S91) and rat carcinoma 1643 were transplanted by means of a tumor mash injected intramuscularly into the right thigh of a susceptible animal. Injections of the test substance were begun when the tumor became grossly detectable; except for leukemia 1210 which was started on the third to fourth day after implantation. Observations were made on body weight, approximate tumor size and survival, and compared with appropriate controls. Tumor damage was evaluated by the gross and microscopic appearance of treated mice, and control tumor-bearing mice sacrificed at the same time.[58]

The toxicity of the test agent was determined, and the agent was given daily by forced feeding to mice grafted with sarcoma M.C.D.B.I. Dosing was commenced on the day on which the tumor was grafted. Some compounds had a cumulative toxic action and killed mice when one-quarter of the $L.D._{50}$ was administered repeatedly; in these cases a smaller dose was given. The tumors were measured with calipers twice weekly and their sizes compared with those of tumors grafted at the same time in similar but untreated mice. The mean rate of growth of the tumors for all the periods between measurements was calculated and compared with the mean growth rate of the tumors in control mice.[16]

C57 mice were inoculated with fibrosarcoma L946AII, others with E0771. When the tumors were palpable, they were injected directly with the test material, and the survival time of the host and size of tumor were measures of therapeutic activity.[117]

CFW mice were injected intraperitoneally with about 10,000 S-37 cells, and the test substance was injected intraperitoneally 2 to 3 days later. The tumor cells are withdrawn from the peritoneal cavity at 1, 2, 3 or 4, 7, 10 days after treatment, and assayed in susceptible mice for viability, and examined microscopically for evidence of damage.[51]

Cytocidal method: Leukemic cells are injected subcutaneously into mice of the AKm strain. After 7 to 10 days, the mice were found to have developed subcutaneous tumors measuring 1.0 to 2.0 cm. in diameter. They were then injected intraperitoneally with the test drug at various multiples of the LD_{50} (1 to 64), and at least 2 donor mice were used at each dose level. The mice are sacrificed at an appropriate interval after injection (2 hours to 2 days); the tumors are removed and suspended in saline and groups of four AKm mice, 6 to 8 weeks old, are inoculated intraperitoneally with 0.1 cc. of this suspension from each donor mouse at each dose level. The criterion of cytocidal activity is failure of the inoculated cells to produce leukemia, and this indicates the dose level at which the transplantability of the leukemic cells is destroyed.[20]

RATS

Transplanted tumors

"A rat carrying an actively growing implant, 8 to 12 days old, is killed. . . . Fragments cut from the healthy peripheral part and . . . nearly equal in size (200–300 mg.) . . . are implanted by trochar and cannula, subcutaneously, in the right flanks of a number of rats, each 90 to 120 Gm. in weight.

TABLE 42. (*Concluded*)

"Compounds under test are usually given by intraperitoneal injection, started on the day after implantation and continued daily, Sunday excepted, for the first 10 to 12 days of experiment. The treated rats are weighed daily and the doses adjusted for body weight changes. The control animals remain untreated . . . on the fourteenth to fifteenth day of experiment . . . all the animals surviving the experiment are weighed and killed and the tumors dissected out, cut in several planes, blotted on absorbent wool, and weighed." Chemotherapeutic activity is expressed as the percentage inhibition of tumor growth.[58, 69, 164]

RABBITS

Transplanted tumors
Brown-Pearce carcinoma was transplanted bilaterally to the anterior chamber of the eye of rabbits. Treatment was started 3 days after transplantation, when the tumor fragments were vascularized by vessels growing from the iris. Criteria of effect were tumor size, weight, and histologic appearance.[48]

CHICKENS

Transplanted tumors
"We used homogeneous samples of frozen virus, prepared by blending fresh tumor tissue in a Waring mixer and weighing 2 Gm. amounts into sterile Petri plates to be stored in a dry ice chest until used . . . the frozen virus was found to be stable for at least a month. . . . One-day old New Hampshire Red chicks . . . were injected in the right breast with 0.25 ml. of the suspension containing a 1 mg. dose. . . . Approximately 400 chicks (10 to 20 per group) were used in each experiment.

"The chicks were observed daily beginning with the eighth day and continuing through the sixteenth day at which time adequately nourished groups showed 90 to 100 per cent tumors." The tumors were observed and measured to the twentieth day, and their size was used as evidence of chemotherapeutic activity.[103]

RPL-12 tumors were removed in early stage of growth and homogenized with saline solution in a TenBroeck grinder. The infecting dose was usually 0.25 ml. of a 1:1000 suspension of tumor tissue injected into the pectoral muscle of New Hampshire Red chicks. The chicks at inoculation ranged from 1 to 28 days, and treatment was begun 2 to 9 days later. In most cases, chicks up to 2 weeks of age died within 8 days after the tumor became palpable; tumors occasionally failed to develop in untreated chicks, particularly in the chicks inoculated at the older ages. Therapeutic activity was measured by tumor regression or inhibition, and the survival of the chick. Chicks successfully treated were immune to further challenge with RPL-12.[136]

pound will destroy tumor viability at low or at apparently physiologic concentrations.

Metabolic Inhibition. Neoplastic and related normal tissues are placed in an in vitro system, and the respiratory activity or special enzymatic activity measurements are made while the tissues are exposed to various concentrations of the test agent.

In these special technics, tissues frequently are placed under unphysiologic conditions, so that their response to a given agent may differ from their in vivo reaction. Whereas in the animal all the normal tissues serve as controls for the selective effect of an agent on the tumor, it is very difficult, and perhaps theoretically impossible, to obtain a satisfactory tissue to act as an in vitro control for a tumor explant. While these in vitro methods are of interest, the results obtained from their use should be interpreted with circumspection. In Table 43 some of the special methods are summarized.

TABLE 43. SPECIAL TECHNICS USED IN TESTING CHEMICALS FOR SELECTIVE ACTIVITY AGAINST NEOPLASTIC CELLS

TISSUE CULTURE

Roller tubes were explanted with fragments of embryonic mouse skin and tumor L946 from C57 mice or lung tumor Ma387 from AK mice. After 24 hours incubation, the explants were examined, graded, and exposed to the test substance. The cells are then exposed for 24 hours, graded, and the tumor cells are removed and bioassayed by transplantation to susceptible mice. The normal tissue is tested for viability by being transferred to a fresh medium, and grown for 4 more days. The explants are graded by several criteria, and the difference in the scores of the normal and neoplastic cells is termed the "selective index."[115]

Normal kidney tissue, E0771 and L946AII, were explanted in large Carrel flasks, and exposed to the test solution. Activity was measured by comparing the appearance of the exposed tissues.[11, 117]

EGG CULTURE

"Eggs were inoculated with tumor tissue on the fourth day of incubation. By the twelfth day tumor tissue was well established on the inner wall of the yolk sac. The test compound was injected on the twelfth day of incubation through a tiny perforation in the shell in such manner that the material was deposited between the shell and the chorioallantoic membranes. The experimental eggs and their saline-injected controls were harvested 48 hours later on the fourteenth day of incubation and the effect of the test compound evaluated as it affected the weight of the tumor and the chick embryo."[158]

Sarcoma 180 is transplanted to the chorioallantoic membrane of the 8-day chick embryo. Four days later, if the explants are growing well, the egg is exposed to the test substance which, in almost all cases, is introduced into the yolk sac. The maximum tolerated dose for the egg, which has been determined previously, is used. Four to five days later, the embryo is sacrificed, the tissue examined grossly, a portion is taken for microscopic section and study and the remainder is inoculated subcutaneously into mice to determine the viability of the tumor.[81]

EXPOSURE IN VITRO

Tumor fragments were immersed in various concentrations of the test agent in 2 cc. of isotonic saline at pH 7.0., and kept in a refrigerator at 4° to 5° C. for twenty-four hours before transplantation. The percentage of positive assays in the susceptible animals was the measure of *in vitro* tumor inhibition.[155]

The Flexner-Jobling carcinoma was grown in young albino Sprague-Dawley rats. The test solution was made up in 0.8 per cent NaCl solution, and the *p*H adjusted to approximately 7.0. The solutions were tested for isotonicity to red blood cells, and solutions which caused hemolysis or crenation of red cells within 45 minutes were adjusted.

Fresh tumor tissue was minced and suspended in 2 volumes of 0.8 NaCl solution, and 0.5 cc. of this was thoroughly mixed with the same volume of a test solution by drawing it back and forth in a syringe. Appropriate control suspension was also prepared. The mixture is left at room temperature for 30 minutes, and the cells are then tested for viability by injecting 0.2 cc. of the treated and 0.2 cc. of the untreated (control) suspension into the left and right groin of 3 to 5 rats. Tumor growth was followed for 2 to 3 weeks as an index of the viability of the treated cells. Tumor inhibition was classified as complete (no growth) or partial (treated tumor was less than one-half the size of the control).[88]

WARBURG STUDIES

Tissue slices, or minces, in normal horse serum were placed in the Warburg apparatus and the over-all respiration measured. The oxygen consumption of an arbitrary but fixed amount of normal and neoplastic tissue is used, and selective depression of the oxygen utilization of the tumor tissue by the test agent is evidence of chemotherapeutic activity.[141]

THE OBJECTIVES OF SCREENING METHODS

The great goal of all these testing methods is to discover an agent which will specifically eliminate or permanently control the growth of cancer cells without producing serious injury to normal cells or to the tumor-bearing host. Such an agent, if it exists, may be expected to show activity in practically all the procedures listed, just as the potent antibiotic will exhibit its therapeutic effects in vitro and in vivo. If a specific agent, in these screening tests, were found to control or cure mouse cancer, it would represent a great medical advance, even if the agent failed to show this activity against human cancer. The demonstration, in any species, that a chemical exists which will interrupt the growth of cancer in a specific and highly selective manner would be an enormous stimulus in the search for similar substances for human cancer.

A lesser objective of these screening methods is to find chemicals which will specifically affect certain types of cancer. This effort requires the routine use of a variety of tumor types, because of the possibility that only one type may respond to the test agent. The use of a wide spectrum of tumor types is expensive and time-consuming, and it is not feasible to screen all chemicals against a spectrum of tumor types. Also, the experimental tumors available do not adequately cover the range of tumor types seen in man so that, even if an effort were made to use a wide tumor spectrum, an agent, specific against a certain type of human tumor, might be missed. In practice, if an agent has a chemotherapeutic effect in preliminary screening tests, it is usually tested against a tumor spectrum for selective activity.

It may be considered that certain potentially effective agents will not exhibit their selective activity against cancer in vivo, because of difficulties in keeping the chemical in prolonged contact with the cells, or because of its excretion or metabolic destruction, or because of the presence of antagonists of the chemotherapeutic agent in vivo. The use of in vitro methods may circumvent these difficulties and supply useful leads to effective agents. A substance, selectively injurious to tumor cells in an in vitro system, may be modified chemically, or the host metabolism altered, in an effort to obtain a similar activity in vivo.

While the screening methods have not achieved any of these objectives, the discovery of a specific agent for the control of cancer would be of such enormous importance that the widespread use of these methods in empirical testing programs should be encouraged.

Tumor-screening methods are useful for detecting substances which can produce general growth inhibition or interfere with the growth or integrity of a specific normal tissue. The agents which, thus far, have shown some activity in the cancer-screening tests possess biologic activities when studied in the appropriate normal system. Some of the biologic properties of agents active against animal tumors are give in Table 44. It may be noted that if an agent has certain biologic effects, such as carcinogenic, mutagenic, or bone-marrow–depressant activity, it merits testing for chemotherapeutic activity against cancer. In fact, screening procedures for some of the biologic activities listed in Table 44 may be effective in discovering agents which injure neoplastic cells.

TABLE 44. SOME BIOLOGICAL PROPERTIES OF AGENTS WITH CHEMOTHERAPEUTIC ACTIVITY AGAINST CANCER

					Effects on animals			
Agent	*Relative therapeutic activity in human cancer*	*Carcino-genic activity*	*Mutagenic activity*	*Effects on embryonic growth*	Delayed deaths*	Bone marrow depression	Specific lymphatic involution	Intestinal injury
Nitrogen mustard[119]	+146	+64	+5	+50, 83	+54	+54	+80	+54
Triethylene melamine	+79	(+)	(+)	+83	+122	+122	(+)	+122
Urethane	+66, 104	+114		+83, 140	–	+37, 109, 144		+37
Radioactive phosphorus	+125	+	(+)	+116	+	+53, 125	+53	+53
4-Amino derivatives of folic acid[160]	+22, 41			+82	+121	+121	+65	+121
2,6-Diaminopurine	±22			+82	±120	+120	±120	+120
8-Azaguanine	–4			+172	–	–32	–32	–32
Estrogenic hormones[28]	+1, 112	+47		+28	–	±28	+132	–
Androgenic hormones[28]	+112, 113	–		+28	–	–	–	–
Adrenocortical hormones[70]	+118, 159			+84	+83	±6, 118	+70	+70
Radioactive iodine	+162	(+)	(+)	(+)	+162	+162	(+)	(+)
Shear's polysaccharide	±67				–34	–	–	–

Agent	Effects on animals: Growth inhibition	Effects on animals: Hormonal activity	Effects on experimental tumors: Sarcoma 180, 37	Leukemia	Carcinoma E0771, 755	Rat tumors	Rous sarcoma	Miscellaneous tumors	Tissue culture
Nitrogen mustard[75,119]	+	–	± 156	+ 23	± 156	+ 148, 156	– 81	± 156	+ 42
Triethylene melamine	(+)	–	+ 17	+ 21	– 156	+ 156, 164		± 156	(+)
Urethane	(+)	–		+ 23, 92, 94, 143		+ 55			+ 91
Radioactive phosphorus	(+)	–						+ 53	
4-Amino derivatives of folic acid[160]	+ 121	–	+ 111, 155	+ 20, 96	+ 155	+ 155	+ 103	+ 155	– 149
2,6-Diaminopurine	± 120	–	– 150	+ 19					± 11
8-Azaguanine	+ 32	–	– 48, 148	± 48, 93	+ 48, 85, 154	– 85, 154		+ 48	
Estrogenic hormones[28]	+ 28	+				– 164			
Androgenic hormones[28]	–	+	± 43		– 43				
Adrenocortical hormones[70]	+ 70	+	– 157	± 26, 157	– 157	+ 145			
Radioactive iodine	(+)	–	+ 51						
Shear's polysaccharide	–	–	+ 34, 131, 137						– 106

Symbols of activity: + Definite. (+) Presumed. ± Slight or inconstant. – None. * Death occurring two or more days after a single minimum lethal dose.

Numbers throughout the table refer to items in the bibliography at the end of the chapter.

The laboratory tumor-testing methods are used widely in studying the mechanisms of action of cancer- and growth-inhibiting substances, in examining derivatives of known effective compounds for evidence of a greater selective effect on cancer cells, and in determining whether various combinations of two or more effective agents will enhance the destructive effect on the tumor without increased injury to the host. Transplantable tumors with specific properties, such as melanomas, leukemias, osteogenic sarcomas, mammary carcinomas, and virus-induced tumors, are available continuously for special study. Some spontaneous tumors, such as mammary[45] and prostatic carcinomas,[69] may show specific activities or hormonal dependencies, but they usually revert to a more autonomous and rapidly growing tumor after several transplantations. While these tumors, during their period of specialization, are used to determine the effect of chemicals on their specific properties, usually such studies can be carried out more effectively and instructively on the normal tissues whose attributes are retained by the tumor.

The technics and objectives in the search for effective chemotherapeutic agents against cancer are often subjected to criticism.[100, 169] The suggestion may be hazarded that the available methods for testing chemicals for their cancer-destroying or cancer-inhibiting activity are adequate, and the failure to find a satisfactory chemotherapeutic substance lies in the fact that such an agent has not yet been presented for testing. Only when a highly effective agent is found will it be possible to assess the reliability and validity of the various testing methods. The efforts at standardizing the screening technics or quantitating their results, while desirable in principle, will not in themselves solve therapeutic problems, or point the way to a more fruitful approach to the chemotherapy of cancer.

CLINICAL TRIALS OF CHEMOTHERAPEUTIC AGENTS

The final test of a chemotherapeutic agent can be made only in the patient with cancer. The problems presented by clinical trials are difficult and complicated, and they merit careful consideration. Because of the public interest and the financial support given for clinical research, and the trend toward institutional and hospital segregation of patients with cancer, many of the approximately 200,000 patients dying with cancer each year could be made available for clinical trials with chemotherapeutic agents. Many of these patients, with the concurrence of their families, would be willing to submit to any procedure offering even a remote chance for relief of their symptoms or for prolongation of life. However, patients for such trials must be carefully selected to assure a productive and well-planned clinical research program. Factors influencing the suitability of a case are the type and extent of the cancer, the presence of particular features of the disease essential for special studies, objective signs that can serve as indices of therapeutic effect, and a prognosis for survival sufficient to encompass the research program. The investigator must be certain that the study or procedure will not harm the patient, subject him to undue discomfort, or jeopardize by delay the possibility of achieving a favorable effect from a proved form of treatment, and the most searching clinical judgment may be required to balance between the needs of the patient and the aims of the research program. The investigator, consequently, must have an adequate knowledge of the natural course and proper management of the patient's disease, and the hazards and possible benefits which might result from the experimental study. He must, at the same time, have the faith, courage, and perseverance to undertake and complete clinical studies on new agents and procedures, despite the complications, untoward effects, and therapeutic failures that are usually the fruits of his efforts.

SELECTION OF AGENTS FOR CLINICAL TRIAL

Since many patients with cancer are available for clinical trial, it has been suggested that an empirical chemotherapy program be instituted directly in man. There is no evidence to indicate that human cancer differs radically from animal cancer and, since empirical testing against animal tumors, thus far, has failed to produce a generally effective treatment or cure, there is little reason to anticipate an immediate and more successful outcome from a testing program on man, representing a more variable, difficult and costly test subject than the mouse. An empirical screening program against a variety of human tumors, therefore, appears to be untenable. The clinician, however, should not be entirely dependent on the laboratory as a source of agents suitable for clinical trial. From his knowledge of the natural history and special properties of certain types of cancer, or because of a particular clinical experience, he will be able to suggest procedures which merit clinical evaluation or laboratory examination.

It is not possible to give an unbiased and entirely defensible list of the reasons for undertaking the clinical assessment of an agent; some reasons may appear to be extremely rational, whereas others are embarrassingly subjective. In a field where so much remains to be discovered, a strict adherence to the few known facts may be productive of only anticipated and limited results, and it would be unwise to suggest rigid criteria according to which agents are selected for clinical assessment. In present practice, the following types of substances are used for clinical trial against cancer:

1. agents which have been consistently active in tumor-screening programs;
2. potent and selective mitotic inhibitors;
3. consistent bone-marrow depressants;
4. active antimetabolites, including antivitamins;
5. vitamins and essential metabolites;
6. carcinogens;
7. specific inhibitors of embryonic growth;
8. hormones and agents altering hormonal balance;
9. antibiotics;
10. agents with specific therapeutic activity in other conditions: antimalarials, antianemic substances, antithyroid compounds;
11. enzyme preparations and specific enzyme inhibitors;
12. radioactive isotopes, and compounds labeled with radioactive isotopes;
13. necrotizing viruses;
14. biologic extracts with specific pharmacologic activity.

If a compound is found to have a favorable effect on human cancer, further clinical trials are indicated on:

1. Its derivatives and allied compounds, in the hope of finding an agent with greater therapeutic activity in relation to toxicity, or fewer undesirable side-effects;
2. Its combination with other forms of therapy in an effort to enhance its activity;
3. Its local administration—intra-arterially, into an involved cavity or into the tumor—with the possibility that this may concentrate its activity.

Irrespective of the reasons for initiating the clinical trial of an agent or procedure, a precise technic of clinical evaluation must be used which will produce valid, reproducible, and documented results, and from which a decision can be made as to whether an agent has any substantial or useful influence on cancer, or is without effect.

PREREQUISITES FOR CLINICAL ASSESSMENTS

Before undertaking assessment of a chemotherapeutic agent in man, the clinician must be acquainted with the natural course and proper management of the type of cancer under treatment, the pharmacology of the test agent, and the objectives of the study.

Knowledge of the Disease

The natural history and physiopathology of cancer are enormously complex fields, extending over the different clinical and histologic types of cancer, the variations within each category, and the differing relationships of each cancer with its host. Statistical information on each type of cancer is being accumulated in reference to the histologic structure, the averages and variations in the course of the disease, the survival time of the untreated and treated patients, the prognostic significance, and course of specific metastatic lesions and complications, and the spontaneous improvement, regressions and accelerations in the course of the disease.[99, 138] For each patient, the cancer is classified by histologic type, size of the initial tumor and its secondary extensions, the first evidence of onset of the disease and its apparent rate of progression, the reaction of the host and changes in the host produced by the cancer, and the response of the patient to specific therapeutic measures. These observations demonstrate the great range of variation in the natural course of cancer and its response to therapy, and the hazards in drawing conclusions from small numbers of patients. Certain types of cancer present specific objective and measurable findings which facilitate their use for therapeutic studies, or they show an unusual sensitivity to chemotherapeutic procedures which simplify objective evaluation. Some of the clinical findings in the types of neoplastic disease frequently used for chemotherapeutic trials are given in Table 45.

Knowledge of the Test Agent

A considerable knowledge of the properties, the effective dosage and route of administration, the mechanism of action, the tolerated dosage in several species of laboratory animals, and the toxic manifestations of the test agent is desirable. Thus, the dose in patients can be raised to an effective range more rapidly and

TABLE 45. CLINICAL MANIFESTATIONS OF DIFFERENT TYPES OF INOPERABLE OR FAR-ADVANCED NEOPLASTIC DISEASE OFTEN USEFUL IN THE EVALUATION OF CHEMOTHERAPEUTIC AGENTS

Manifestations	*Acute leukemia* 10, 18, 22, 145	*Chronic myelogenous leukemia* 24, 44, 97	*Chronic lymphatic leukemia* 24, 44, 98, 116	*Multiple myeloma* 9, 102, 104, 127, 128	*Hodgkin's disease* 33, 71, 146
Natural course	Rapid	Slow, variable	Slow, variable	Fairly rapid, variable	Slow, variable
Peripheral blood					
Anemia	+ + +*	+ +	+ + +	+ +	+
Abnormal WBC	+ + +	+ + +	+ + +		
Thrombocytopenia	+ + +	+	+ +	+	
Bone marrow	+ + +	+ + +	+ + +	+ + +	
Blood chemistry				+ + + ‡	
Primary site†					
Signs				+	+
Symptoms				+	+
Enlarged nodes	+	+	+ + +		+ + +
Enlarged liver	+	+ + +	+ + +		+ +
Enlarged spleen	+	+ + +	+ + +		+ +
Pulmonary lesions					+ +
Bone lesions	+			+ + +	+
Renal complications				+ +	
Urine				+ §	
Fever	+ + +	+			+ +
Pain	+	+		+ + +	+
Bleeding	+ +	+	+	+	+
Response to known chemotherapeutic agents	Good	Good	Fair	Fair	Good

* + to + + + indicates the relative consistency of occurrence and the usefulness of the particular disease manifestation for chemotherapeutic evaluation.

† The primary tumor usually has been excised or irradiated in an attempt at cure or palliation before the use of a chemotherapeutic agent is considered.

‡ Hyperglobulinemia.

§ Proteinuria, including Bence Jones protein.

‖ Elevated blood acid phosphatase level.

¶ Elevated blood alkaline phophatase level, hypercalcemia.

** Elevated blood alkaline phosphatase level.

†† Increase in chorionic gonadotrophic hormone excretion.

‡‡ Increase in ketosteroid excretion.

safely, the warning signs of toxicity will be sought for, the appropriate types of patients selected for study, and the probable nature of the therapeutic response anticipated. The clinical use of previously untried drugs should be started at a very small dosage and, if no evidence of toxicity appears after a suitable period of observation, the dosage can then be raised until the maximum tolerated level is reached. It is then maintained in this range, if possible, during the indicated period of treatment.

OBJECTIVES OF THE THERAPEUTIC TRIAL

In most instances a therapeutic trial is undertaken with a definite objective, or to answer a particular question. By properly designing the experiment, the clinical trial would be simplified and the results easier to interpret. The initial and limited

TABLE 45. CLINICAL MANIFESTATIONS OF DIFFERENT TYPES OF INOPERABLE OR FAR-ADVANCED NEOPLASTIC DISEASE OFTEN USEFUL IN THE EVALUATION OF CHEMOTHERAPEUTIC AGENTS (*Continued*)

Manifestations	*Lympho-sarcoma* 33, 71, 153	*Prostatic cancer* 49, 113	*Breast cancer* 1, 112	*Lung cancer* 3, 76, 105	*Thyroid cancer* 61, 162	*Osteogenic sarcoma* 29
Natural course	Slow, variable	Fairly rapid, variable	Slow, variable	Fairly rapid, variable	Slow, variable	Fairly rapid, variable
Peripheral blood						
Anemia	+*	+				
Abnormal WBC						
Thrombocytopenia						
Bone marrow	+	+				
Blood chemistry		+++ ‖	+ ¶			+ **
Primary site †						
Signs	++	++	++	+++	++	++
Symptoms	+	++	+	+++	+	++
Enlarged nodes	+++		++	++	+	+
Enlarged liver	++		++	++		
Enlarged spleen	++					
Pulmonary lesions	+		++	+++	++	++
Bone lesions		++	++	+	+++	++
Renal complications		+				
Urine						
Fever	+			+		++
Pain		+++	++	++		++
Bleeding						
Response to known chemotherapeutic agents	Fair	Good	Fair	Fair	Fair	Poor

* + to +++ indicates the relative consistency of occurrence and the usefulness of the particular disease manifestation for chemotherapeutic evaluation.

† The primary tumor usually has been excised or irradiated in an attempt at cure or palliation before the use of a chemotherapeutic agent is considered.

‡ Hyperglobulinemia.

§ Proteinuria, including Bence Jones protein.

‖ Elevated blood acid phosphatase level.

¶ Elevated blood alkaline phosphatase level, hypercalcemia.

** Elevated blood alkaline phosphatase level.

†† Increase in chorionic gonadotrophic hormone excretion.

‡‡ Increase in ketosteroid excretion.

objective of most trials is to demonstrate that a given agent produces some evidence of therapeutic activity, and such results may be seen in the relief of pain, regression in the tumor, change in certain biochemical measurements, etc. This exploratory study has no statistical objective, but merely endeavors to demonstrate that the agent is influencing the disease or the patient's reaction to the disease. The patients selected for this initial study, therefore, should have far-advanced disease; they are thus usually in the terminal stages and unresponsive to other forms of therapy, so that there is ample objective evidence of disease and little likelihood of doing harm if the treatment is ineffective or produces an untoward effect. A group of patients with a specific type of cancer may be used, if such is indicated, or a wide variety of cancers are treated, in looking for a general response to the agent, or in order to survey the field in the hope of finding a type of cancer, stage of the

TABLE 45. CLINICAL MANIFESTATIONS OF DIFFERENT TYPES OF INOPERABLE OR FAR-ADVANCED NEOPLASTIC DISEASE OFTEN USEFUL IN THE EVALUATION OF CHEMOTHERAPEUTIC AGENTS (*Concluded*)

Manifestations	*Wilms' tumor* [35]	*Neuro-blastoma*	*Testicular cancer* [40]	*Adrenal cancer* [14, 40]	*Miscellaneous tumors*
Natural course	Variable, often slow	Fairly rapid, variable	Slow, variable	Slow, variable	Evaluation factors: 1. Regression of primary disease and metastases; 2. Relief of secondary abnormalities due to growth of cancer: uremia; biliary obstruction; neurologic signs; pulmonary effusion
Peripheral blood					
Anemia					
Abnormal WBC					
Thrombocytopenia					
Bone marrow					
Blood chemistry					
Primary site †					
Signs	+ + +*	+ + +	+	+ +	
Symptoms	+ +	+ + +	+	+	
Enlarged nodes		+ +	+ +		
Enlarged liver	+ +	+ +	+ +	+	
Enlarged spleen					
Pulmonary lesions	+ +		+ +	+	
Bone lesions		+			
Renal complications					
Urine			+ ††	+ ‡‡	
Fever	+		+		
Pain					
Bleeding					
Response to known chemotherapeutic agents	Poor	Fair	Poor	Poor	Poor

* + to +++ indicates the relative consistency of occurrence and the usefulness of the particular disease manifestation for chemotherapeutic evaluation.

† The primary tumor usually has been excised or irradiated in an attempt at cure or palliation before the use of a chemotherapeutic agent is considered.

‡ Hyperglobulinemia.

§ Proteinuria, including Bence Jones protein.

‖ Elevated blood acid phosphatase level.

¶ Elevated blood alkaline phosphatase level, hypercalcemia.

** Elevated blood alkaline phosphatase level.

†† Increase in chorionic gonadotrophic hormone excretion.

‡‡ Increase in ketosteroid excretion.

disease, or a particular symptom that is responsive to the treatment. In this phase of the study, the chemotherapist is guided by intuition, experience, enthusiasm, and knowledge of the basis on which the study was begun. The decision to continue or stop a study may be very difficult, and it is in this area that real judgment is required. The skeptic may explain away all his results on the basis of the natural variation in the disease, and he may be discouraged by a few early failures, perhaps due to poor case selection or improper use of the drug, while the enthusiast may magnify and exaggerate effects that are evanescent or coincidental, and attribute to the agent a therapeutic response which may have been due to preceding treatment with an effective agent, to the psychologic improvement in the patient caused by the special attention he receives as a research patient, or to the endeavor of a grateful subject to please the investigator by assuring him of marked symptomatic improvement. In this phase have occurred the extravagant claims which could not be confirmed by others, and the discouraging reports, which were favorably corrected by more enthusiastic, persistent, and intensive investigations.

If an agent shows any evidence of therapeutic activity, more extensive, confirmatory experiments on selected clinical material are indicated. The purpose of this trial may be to show that the agent has a regular and measurable clinical effect in certain types of cancer, or that it will relieve certain signs and symptoms of cancer. This requires the study of a group of patients with potentially responsive findings, in order to determine the frequency and degree of response to treatment, and the hazards incident to the use of the agent. This trial should give relatively rapid results, since it will be measured by the relief of symptoms or the regression of the tumor. If the duration of improvement is brief, and the course of the disease is not appreciably interrupted, it will be apparent that survival time will not be markedly prolonged. An assessment of a temporary and limited palliative agent may be completed within a few months, and it is not necessary to accumulate statistics on its effect on survival time, or on the percentage of five-year survivals.

CRITERIA OF CLINICAL CHEMOTHERAPEUTIC ACTIVITY

As listed in Table 45, the various types of neoplastic disease present symptoms, objective physical findings, radiologic changes, and biochemical abnormalities which are useful in estimating a therapeutic effect. Suitable patients are obtained, and a baseline on their clinical condition established, and then the following criteria are used in evaluating the therapeutic results.

Subjective Improvement

The patient's subjective improvement is measured by his change in mood and attitude, general feeling of well-being, increase in activity and appetite, and alleviation of specific symptoms such as pain, weakness, and dyspnea. While these effects are based on the patient's statements, they are an important part of a therapeutic trial if they are reinforced by concommittant evidence of objective improvement. In the absence of any objective changes, reports of subjective improvement are notoriously misleading as the bases for the evaluation of a new agent. Nursing care, improved diet, a psychologic response to careful and enthusiastic medical attention, and general supportive measures may be entirely responsible for a marked subjective response. Weil,[167] in 1915, stated:

> It is a curious and interesting fact that almost every therapeutic claim made in recent years in connection with cancer has included among its virtues the relief of pain. . . . In view of this it is probably fair to assume that in the great majority of these cases the result is in no small measure psychic. The improvement of function is also largely a subjective phenomenon, and, as such, requires most careful criticism. Osler relates that he has known a patient with gastric cancer to be relieved of digestive disturbances and to gain 18 pounds in weight as the result simply of the visit of a sanguine consultant who denied the presence of a tumor. Improvement in the ability to chew food, to articulate words or to move a limb are phenomena familiar to those who attempt to treat cases of cancer. The victims of this disease seem to be in a very high degree "suggestible" and impressionable and respond nobly to every therapeutic effort.

Objective Improvement

Much more substantial and valuable evidence of therapeutic activity is the occurrence of objective changes in the disease. These changes may be related to the alleviation of specific manifestations of the disease, as fever, enlarged liver and spleen of Hodgkin's disease, or correction of the abnormal bone marrow in leukemia, to regression in the size of the tumor, as seen in lymphosarcoma; to relief of effects secondary to the growth of the tumor, as seen in the improvement of jaundice, uremia, venous obstruction, etc; to changes in radiographic findings, as shrinkage of lung lesions, healing of bone metastases, and improvement in biochemical measurements, as seen in the fall of blood acid phosphatase levels in prostatic cancer; to a rise in serum proteins in carcinoma of the stomach. Objective changes may also be detected by examining repeated biopsies of a lesion for histologic evidence of effect; or finally by the use of special technics such as measuring the uptake of radioactive iodine, as an index of regression of thyroid cancer. The useful measurements, some of which are presented in Table 45, will vary with the type and manifestations of the disease in each patient. The multiplicity of objective effects in some types of cancer makes it very easy to detect any change in its growth; in other cases, a slowly growing mass, perhaps located in the abdomen and difficult to feel, may be the only objective finding and any but the grossest changes will be difficult to detect. While objective measurements are essential for evidence of chemotherapeutic activity, they may present occasional pitfalls, since spontaneous regressions sometimes occur in enlarged masses, and some systemic types of cancer have shown spontaneous remissions.[138] By carefully cataloging the objective evidences of disease in a group of suitable patients, and observing these criteria carefully during the course of treatment, the occurrence of substantial and consistent improvement may be attributed to the treatment.

Performance Status

Another aspect of a therapeutic evaluation is the over-all change in the functional status of the patient, as measured, for example, by his ability to work or care for his personal needs. While subjective and objective changes in the patient are of importance, they may not necessarily be reflected in the patient's activity or function. In order to measure this latter effect, a performance status classification has been developed (Table 46) which roughly indicates the level of the patient's activity, or his dependence on those about him. The patient's performance status (PS) is easily graded at weekly intervals, and it is evident that a rise in PS from 50 per cent (*requires considerable assistance and frequent medical care*) to a PS of 80 per cent (*normal activity with effort, some signs or symptoms of the disease*) under treatment represents a useful degree of rehabilitation. The use of the performance status criterion is recommended by its simplicity and pertinence, although there are obvious deficiencies in it.

Duration of Improvement and Prolongation of Survival Time

If there is definite evidence of improvement from treatment, its duration, from the onset of improvement until evidence of relapse occurs, is measured. If the

TABLE 46. PERFORMANCE STATUS

Condition	*Percentage*	*Comments*
A: Able to carry on normal activity and to work. No special care is needed.	100	Normal, no complaints, no evidence of disease.
	90	Able to carry on normal activity, minor signs or symptoms of disease.
	80	Normal activity with effort, some signs or symptoms of disease.
B: Unable to work. Able to live at home, care for most personal needs. A varying degree of assistance is needed.	70	Cares for self. Unable to carry on normal activity or to do active work.
	60	Requires occasional assistance, but is able to care for most of his needs.
	50	Requires considerable assistance and frequent medical care.
C: Unable to care for self. Requires equivalent of institutional or hospital care.	40	Disabled, requires special care and assistance.
	30	Severely disabled, hospitalization is indicated although death not imminent.
	20	Hospitalization necessary, very sick, active supportive treatment necessary.
	10	Moribund, fatal processes progressing rapidly.
	0	Dead.

From Karnofsky and Burchenal.[77]

duration of improvement is prolonged indefinitely, the disease presumably is arrested or cured, and it will be readily evident that the treatment is prolonging life. In almost all cases, however, chemotherapeutic agents have produced limited periods of improvement. The ability of an agent to produce several distinct remissions in the same patient is, because of this reproducibility, important evidence of therapeutic activity. The correlation of the apparent natural rate of progression of the disease with the nature and duration of improvement induced by a test agent, is an additional criterion for estimating the chemotherapeutic activity.

Consistency of Therapeutic Activity

A major aspect of a therapeutic evaluation is the demonstration that an agent can produce improvement consistently and predictably in specific clinical situations. The report of an isolated and unreproducible favorable response to therapy is rarely convincing—although it should not be ignored—since it may be due to the vagaries of the disease or to a delayed response to a preceding course of treatment. If the agent, however, in a substantial series of patients with a specific type of disease, can be shown to produce, for example, marked improvement in 20 per cent of the cases, moderate improvement in 50 per cent, and no effect in the remainder, a regular and useful type of activity has been demonstrated.

Toxicity of the Test Agent and Hazards Associated with Its Use

Many of the agents studied for chemotherapeutic activity produce disagreeable side-effects or serious toxicity in the host, actions which may outweigh their therapeutic benefits. These toxic effects may be evidenced by nausea and vomiting, anorexia, neurologic and mental changes, fever, bone marrow depression, liver or kidney damage, etc., and they may be sufficiently severe, at least in certain cases, to interdict the use of the agent. There is also the possibility that an agent may accelerate the progress of the disease, or aggravate some of its manifestations. On the other hand, in patients with far-advanced and extensive cancer, the coincidental progression of the disease or alterations in the functions of specific organs with deterioration of the patient has sometimes been attributed erroneously to the therapeutic agent. Also, when an effective agent is deliberately given to the point of tolerance or beyond in the hope of producing or maintaining a therapeutic response in a desperate situation, the death of the patient need not be cited as evidence that the clinical use of the agent is extremely hazardous.

Comparison of the Test Agent with Other Forms of Treatment

The results obtained with an effective new agent should be compared with the response of the disease to other forms of therapy in order to determine whether the new drug answers a previously insoluble therapeutic problem, or merely duplicates the methods of treatment already available. In the latter case, the practical value of the agent will be determined by its expense, availability, method of administration and disagreeable side-effects.

The number of patients and types of cancer necessary adequately to assess a new drug depends on the test agent, and the objectives of the study. If the treatment proves to be extremely effective, the favorable clinical results will be apparent with a small group of patients, and they will be confirmed readily by other clinics. If a large group of patients is necessary to demonstrate and define the activity of an agent, it may be presumed that the agent has a weak and possibly questionable activity.

As long as patients have incurable and progressive cancer, they will turn to physicians demanding treatment, encouragement, and relief. Cancer chemotherapy has a long road to travel before the disease will be brought under control, but by offering the patient palliation, active treatment, and the hope that research may soon solve his problem, it has acquired an essential place in the management of cancer.

SUMMARY

Chemotherapy is the only approach to the treatment of cancer which offers the possibility of curing or controlling the disease, irrespective of the stage at which treatment is initiated. The experimental chemotherapist is working under serious handicaps, since the cancer cell—so far as he is concerned and despite the intensive fundamental research on the problem—appears to be a minor and as yet undefined variant of normal cells. The chemotherapist is applying to his problem the technics and knowledge developed by practically all the scientific disciplines and, as a result, a systematic and fundamental area of study is evolving around methods of modifying the growth of various types of normal and neoplastic tissues.

A large number of technics is being used for the study of the inhibition of tumor growth; the most popular methods require the use of mice and rats bearing transplantable tumors. If cancer be due to a common and continuing abnormality in all types of cancer cells, empirical testing may disclose a universal therapeutic agent. This possibility justifies the empirical testing programs on transplantable tumors.

The less hopeful but more probable view is that a universal cancer treatment is not attainable, and specific therapeutic agents must then be sought for each type of cancer. The search for such substances requires studies on the chemical composition, the special nutritional requirements, the concentration of specific agents and the effect of certain chemicals on each type of embryonic and adult tissue, and on tumors arising from these tissues. These fundamental studies may provide leads or concrete suggestions for the treatment of specific types of cancer in man.

The evaluation of potential chemotherapeutic agents against human cancers presents other difficulties and problems. The clinician should have adequate knowledge of the natural course of each type of cancer, the pharmacologic properties of the test agent and its probable mechanism of action, and a definite plan and objective for the clinical study. The patients must be carefully selected, so that the rate of progress of the disease can be roughly approximated and objective measurements can be made of its response to therapy. Agents are evaluated in suitable patients on the basis of *objective* and *subjective improvement*, change in *performance status*, duration of the *period of improvement*, prolongation of *survival time*, *consistency* of *therapeutic activity* in selected clinical situations, *undesirable side-effects*, *toxicity*, and *practical usefulness* in relation to other methods of therapy.

BIBLIOGRAPHY

1. ADAIR, F. E., MELLORS, R. C., FARROW, J. H., WOODARD, H. Q., ESCHER, G. C., and URBAN, J. A. The use of estrogens and androgens in advanced mammary cancer. *J. A. M. A. 140:* 1193-1200, 1949.
2. ALGIRE, G. H. "Transparent chamber technique as tool in experimental tumor therapy." In *Approaches to Tumor Chemotherapy*. Washington, D. C., A. A. A. S., 1947, pp. 13-26.
3. ARIEL, I. M., AVERY, E. E., KANTER, L., HEAD, J. R., and LANGSTON, H. T. Primary carcinoma of the lung: A clinical study of 1205 cases. *Cancer 3:* 229-239, 1950.
4. ARMISTEAD, G. C., JR., BURCHENAL, J. H., KARNOFSKY, D. A., and SOUTHAM, C. M. Preliminary studies on the clinical toxicity of 5-amino-7-hydroxy-1-*v*-triazolo(*d*)-pyrimidine (guanazolo). *Cancer 2:* 1087-1088, 1949.
5. AUERBACH, C., ROBSON, J. M., and CARR, J. G. The chemical production of mutations. *Science 105:* 243-247, 1947.
6. BAKER, B. L., and INGLE, D. J. Growth inhibition in bone and bone marrow following treatment with adrenocorticotropin (ACTH). *Endocrinology 43:* 422-429, 1948.
7. BALAZO, A., and HOLMGREN, H. J. Effect of sulfomucopolysaccharides on growth of tumor tissue. *Proc. Soc. Exper. Biol. & Med. 72:* 142-145, 1949.
8. BASS, A, D., and FEIGELSON, M. The response of normal and malignant lymphoid tissue to methyl-(β-chloroethyl) amine and ethyl carbamate (urethane) in adrenalectomized and non-adrenalectomized mice. *Cancer Research 8:* 503-509, 1948.
9. BAYRD, E. D., and HECK, F. J. Multiple myeloma; a review of 83 proved cases. *J. Am. Med Assn. 133:* 147-157, 1947.

10. BIERMAN, H. R., COHEN, P., McCLELLAND, J. N., and SHIMKIN, M. B. The effect of transfusions and antibiotics upon the duration of life in children with lymphogenous leukemia. *J. Pediat. 37:* 455-462, 1950.
11. BIESELE, J. J., BERGER, R. E., WILSON, A. Y., HITCHINGS, G. H., and ELION, G. B. Studies on 2-6-diaminopurine and related substances in cultures of embryonic and sarcomatous rodent tissues. *Cancer 4:* 186-197, 1951.
12. BIESELE, J. J., and WILSON, A. Y. Alkaline phosphatase substrate specificities in cultured normal and malignant cells of mouse, rat and fowl. *Cancer Research 11:* 174-179, 1951.
13. BITTNER, J. J. Genetic aspect of cancer research. *Am. J. Med. 8:* 218-228, 1950.
14. BODANSKY, O. Biochemical aids in the diagnosis of cancer. *New York State J. Med. 50:* 2789-2794, 1950.
15. BOYLAND, E. Chemical carcinogenesis and experimental chemotherapy of cancer. *Yale J. Biol. & Med. 20:* 321-341, 1948.
16. BOYLAND, E. Experiments on the chemotherapy of cancer: IV. Further experiments with aldehydes and their derivatives. *Biochem. J. 34:* 1196-1201, 1940.
17. BUCKLEY, S. M., STOCK, C. C., CROSSLEY, M. L., and RHOADS, C. P. Inhibition of the Crocker mouse sarcoma 180 by certain ethylenimine derivatives and related compounds (abstract). *Cancer Research 10:* 207-208, 1950.
18. BURCHENAL, J. H. The newer nitrogen mustards in the treatment of leukemia. *Radiology 50:* 494-499, 1948.
19. BURCHENAL, J. H., BENDICH, A., BROWN, G. B., ELION, G. B., HITCHINGS, G. H., RHOADS, C. P., and STOCK, C. C. Preliminary studies on the effect of 2,6-diaminopurine on transplanted mouse leukemia. *Cancer 2:* 119-120, 1949.
20. BURCHENAL, J. H., BURCHENAL, J. R., KUSHIDA, M. N., JOHNSTON, S. F., and WILLIAMS, B. S. Studies on the chemotherapy of leukemia: II. The effect of 4-amino-pteroylglutamic acid and 4-amino-N^{10}-methyl-pteroylglutamic acid on transplanted mouse leukemia. *Cancer 2:* 113-118, 1949.
21. BURCHENAL, J. H., JOHNSTON, S. F., CREMER, M. A., WEBBER, L. F., and STOCK, C. C. Chemotherapy of leukemia: V. Effects of 2,4,6-triethylenimino-s-triazine and related compounds on transplanted mouse leukemia. *Proc. Soc. Exper. Biol. & Med. 74:* 708-712, 1950.
22. BURCHENAL, J. H., KARNOFSKY, D. A., KINGSLEY-PILLERS, E. M., SOUTHAM, C. M., ESCHER, G. E., MYERS, W. P. L., CRAVER, L. F., DARGEON, H. W., and RHOADS, C. P. The effect of the folic acid antagonists and 2,6-diaminopurine on neoplastic disease. *Cancer 4:* 549-569, 1951.
23. BURCHENAL, J. H., LESTER, R. A., RILEY, J. B., and RHOADS, C. P. Studies on the chemotherapy of leukemia: I. Effect of certain nitrogen mustards and carbamates on transmitted mouse leukemia. *Cancer 1:* 399-412, 1948.
24. BURCHENAL, J. H., MYERS, W. P. L., CRAVER, L. F., and KARNOFSKY, D. A. The nitrogen mustards in the treatment of leukemia. *Cancer 2:* 1-17, 1949.
25. BURCHENAL, J. H., ROBINSON, E., JOHNSTON, S. F., and KUSHIDA, M. N. The induction of resistance to 4-amino-N^{10}-methyl-pteroylglutamic acid in a strain of transmitted mouse leukemia. *Science 111:* 116-117, 1950.
26. BURCHENAL, J. H., STOCK, C. C., and RHOADS, C. P. The effects of cortisone and ACTH on transplanted mouse leukemia (abstract). *Cancer Research 10:* 209, 1950.

27. BURMESTER, B. R., and COTTRAL, D. V. M. The propagation of filtrable agents producing lymphoid tumors and osteopetrosis by serial passage in chickens. *Cancer Research 7:* 669-675, 1947.

28. BURROWS, H. *Biological Actions of Sex Hormones.* Cambridge, England, Cambridge University Press, 1949.

29. COLEY, B. L. *Neoplasms of Bone and Related Conditions.* New York, Paul B. Hoeber, Inc., 1949.

30. COMAN, D. R. Mechanism of the invasiveness of cancer. *Science 105:* 347-348, 1947.

31. COMAN, D. R., EISENBERG, R. B., and MCCUTCHEON, M. Factors affecting the distribution of tumor metastases experiments with V_2 carcinoma of rabbits. *Cancer 9:* 649-651, 1949.

32. COOPERMAN, B., and HOWES, E. L. Influence of triazolopyrimidine on fibroplasia and epithelialization. *Surg. Gynec. & Obst. 92:* 105-109, 1951.

33. CRAVER, L. F. Treatment of chronic forms of malignant lymphomas and leukemias. *Med. Clin. North America,* March, 1949, pp. 527-540.

34. DALTON, A. J.: "Cytopathology," and DILLER, I. C.: "Nuclear changes produced by s. marcescens (B. prodigiosus) polysaccharide." In *Approaches to Tumor Chemotherapy.* Washington, D. C., A. A. A. S., Washington, D. C., 1947, pp. 246-248 and 260-264.

35. DARGEON, H. W. *Cancer in Childhood.* St. Louis, Mo., C. V. Mosby Co., 1940.

36. DURAN-REYNALS, F. Neoplastic infection and cancer. *Am. J. Med. 8:* 490-511, 1950.

37. DUSTIN, P. Cytological action of ethyl carbamate (urethane) and other carbamic esters on normal and leukaemic mice and in rabbits. *Brit. J. Cancer 1:* 48-59, 1947.

38. DYER, H. M. *An Index of Tumor Chemotherapy.* Bethesda, Md., National Cancer Institute, National Institute of Health, 1949.

39. EICHWALD, E. J., EVANS, R. G., and BROWNING, G. B. The significance of the anterior chamber on tumor transplantation: I. Transplantation of mouse neuroblastoma C1300 to homologous hosts. *Cancer Research 10:* 483-485, 1950.

40. TWOMBLY, G. H., and PACK, G. T. eds. *Endocrinology of Neoplastic Disease.* New York, Oxford University Press, 1947.

41. FARBER, S., DIAMOND, L. K., MERCER, R. D., SYLVESTER, R. F., JR., and WOLFF, J. A. Temporary remissions in acute leukemia in children produced by folic acid antagonist, 4-aminopteroyl glutamic acid (aminopterin). *New England J. Med. 238:* 787-793, 1948.

42. FELL, H. B., and ALLSOPP, C. B. Tissue culture experiments on the biological action of methyl *bis* (β-chloroethyl) amine and its hydrolysis products. *Cancer Research 9:* 238-246, 1949.

43. FOLEY, E. J. Retardation of tumor growth in mice by oral administration of methylandrostenediol and methyltestosterone. *Proc. Soc. Exper. Biol. & Med. 75:* 811-813, 1950.

44. FORKNER, C. E. *Leukemia and Allied Disorders.* New York, MacMillan, 1938.

45. FOULDS, L. Mammary tumours in hybrid mice: Hormone-responses of transplanted tumours. *Brit. J. Cancer 3:* 240-246, 1949.

46. FRIEDGOOD, C. E., and GREEN, M. N. The effect of nitrofurazone on growth of fibrosarcoma in mice. *Cancer Research 10:* 613-615, 1950.

47. GARDNER, W. U. Hormonal imbalances in tumorgenesis. *Cancer Research 8:* 397-411, 1948.
48. GELLHORN, A., ENGELMAN, M., SHAPIRO, D., GRAFF, S., and GILLESPIE, H. The effect of 5-amino-7-hydroxy-1*H*-*v*-triazolo(*d*) pyrimidine (guanazolo) on a variety of neoplasms in experimental animals. *Cancer Research 10:* 170-177, 1950.
49. GELLHORN, A., and JONES, L. O. Chemotherapy of malignant disease. *Am. J. Med. 6:* 188-231, 1949.
50. GILLETE, R., and BODENSTEIN, D. Specific developmental inhibitions produced in amphibian embryos by nitrogen mustard compound (β-chloroethylamine). *J Exper. Zool. 103:* 1-32, 1946.
51. GOLDIE, H., and HAHN, P. F. Effects of radioactive iodine on free sarcoma 37 cells in the peritoneal fluid of the mouse. *Proc. Soc. Exper. Biol. & Med. 74:* 634-642, 1950.
52. GORER, P. A. Antibody response to tumor inoculation in mice. *Cancer Research 7:* 634-641, 1947.
53. GRAD, B., and STEVENS, C. E. Histological changes produced by a single large injection of radioactive phosphorus (P^{32}) in albino rats and C3H mice. *Cancer Research 10:* 289-296, 1950.
54. GRAEF, I., KARNOFSKY, D. A., JAGER, V. B., KRICHESKY, B., and SMITH, H. W. The clinical and pathological effects of the nitrogen and sulfur mustards in laboratory animals. *Am. J. Path. 24:* 1-47, 1948.
55. GREEN, J. W., JR., and LUSHBAUGH, C. C. Histopathologic study of the mode of inhibition of cellular proliferation by urethane: Effect of urethane on Walker rat carcinoma 256. *Cancer Research 9:* 199-209, 1949.
56. GREEN, J. W., JR., and LUSHBAUGH, C. C. Histopathologic study of the mode of inhibition of cellular proliferation: Effect of 4-dimethylaminostilbene on the growth of Walker rat carcinoma 256. *Cancer Research 9:* 692-700, 1949.
57. GREENE, H. S. N. Heterologous transplantation of the Brown-Pearce carcinoma. *Cancer 9:* 728-735, 1949.
58. GREENSPAN, E. M., LEITER, J., and SHEAR, M. J. Effect of alphapeltatin, betapeltatin, and podophyllotoxin on lymphomas and other transplanted tumors. *J. Nat. Cancer Inst. 10:* 1295-1333, 1950.
59. GREENSTEIN, J. P. *Biochemistry of Cancer.* New York, Academic Press, Inc., 1947.
60. HADDOW, A. Note on chemotherapy of cancer. *Brit. M. Bull. 4:* 417-426, 1947.
61. HARE, H. F., and SALZMAN, F. A. Cancer of the thyroid: Ten to twenty year follow-up. *Am. J. Roentgenol. 63:* 881-887, 1950.
62. HAUSCHKA, T., SAXE, L. H., JR., and BLAIR, M. Trypanosoma cruzi in the treatment of mouse tumors. *J. Nat. Cancer Inst. 7:* 189-197, 1947.
63. HERBUT, P. A., KRAEMER, W. H., and JACKSEN, J. The effect of hepbisal (heptyl aldehyde-sodium bisulfite addition compound) and thyroxine on Walker rat carcinoma 256. *Am. J. Path. 27:* 59-83, 1951.
64. HESTON, W. E. Induction of pulmonary tumors in strain A mice with methyl-bis (β-chloroethyl) amine hydrochloride. *J. Nat. Cancer Inst. 10:* 125-130, 1949.
65. HIGGINS, G. M., and WOODS, K. H. The influence of the adrenal gland on some of the changes induced in the animal organisms by the folic acid analogue, amino-teropterin. *Proc. Staff Meet., Mayo Clinic 24:* 533-537, 1949.
66. HIRSCHBOECK, J. S., LINDERT, M. C. F., CHASE, J., and CALVY, T. L. Effect of urethane in treatment of leukemia and metastatic malignant tumors. *J. A. M. A. 136:* 90-95, 1948.

67. HOLLOMAN, A. L.: "Reactions of patients and of tumors to injection of S. marcescens polysaccharide in eight cases of malignant disease," and OAKEY, R.: "Reactions of patients to injection of S. Marcescens polysaccharide in nine further cases of malignant disease." In *Approaches to Tumor Chemotherapy*, Washington, D. C., A. A. A. S., 1947, pp. 273-276, 277.
68. HOLLOMAN, J. H., and FISHER, J. C. Nucleation and growth of cell colonies. *Science 111:* 489-491, 1950.
69. HORNING, E. S. The effects of castration and stilbestrol on prostatic tumours in mice. *Brit. J. Cancer 3:* 211-230, 1949.
70. INGLES, D. J. The biologic properties of cortisone: A review. *J. Clin. Endocrinol. 10:* 1312-1354, 1950.
71. JACKSON, H., and PARKER, F. *Hodgkin's Disease and Allied Disorders.* New York, Oxford University Press, 1947.
72. JEDELOO, G. C., LIGNAE, G. O. E., LIGTENBERG, A. J., and VON THIEL, P. H. The biotherapeutic action of trypanosoma cruzi on tar carcinoma in mice. *J. Nat. Cancer Inst. 10:* 809-813, 1950.
73. KARNOFSKY, D. A. Bases for cancer chemotherapy. *Stanford M. Bull. 6:* 257-269, 1948.
74. KARNOFSKY, D. A. Medical progress: Chemotherapy of neoplastic disease. *New England J. Med. 239:* 226-231, 260-270, 299-305, 1948.
75. KARNOFSKY, D. A. "Nitrogen mustards in the treatment of neoplastic disease." In *Advances in Internal Medicine.* Chicago, Year Book Publishers, Inc., 1950, pp. 1-75.
76. KARNOFSKY, D. A., ABELMANN, W. H., CRAVER, L. F., and BURCHENAL, J. H. The use of the nitrogen mustards in the palliative treatment of carcinoma, with special reference to bronchogenic carcinoma. *Cancer 1:* 634-656, 1948.
77. KARNOFSKY, D. A., and BURCHENAL, J. H. "The clinical evaluation of chemotherapeutic agents in cancer." In MACLEOD, C. M. (ed.) In *Evaluation of Chemotherapeutic Agents.* New York, Columbia University Press, 1949, pp. 191-205.
78. KARNOFSKY, D. A., and BURCHENAL, J. H. Present status of clinical cancer chemotherapy. *Am. J. Med. 8:* 767-788, 1950.
79. KARNOFSKY, D. A., BURCHENAL, J. H., ARMISTEAD, G. C., JR., SOUTHAM, C. M., BERNSTEIN, J. L., CRAVER, L. F., and RHOADS, C. P. Triethylene melamine in the treatment of neoplastic disease; a compound with nitrogen mustard-like activity, suitable for oral and intravenous use. *Arch. Int. Med. 87:* 477-516, 1951.
80. KARNOFSKY, D. A., GRAEF, I., and SMITH, H. W. Studies on the mechanism of action of the nitrogen and sulfur mustards *in vivo*. *Am. J. Path. 24:* 275-291, 1948.
81. KARNOFSKY, D. A., PARISETTE, L. M., PATTERSON, P. A., and JACQUEZ, J. A. The behavior and growth of homologous and heterologous normal and neoplastic tissues on the chick embryo: and the influence of various agents on tumor growth. *Unio International Contra Cancrum Acta, 6:* 641-651, 1949.
82. KARNOFSKY, D. A., PATTERSON, P. A., and RIDGWAY, L. P. Effect of folic acid, "4-amino" folic acids and related substances on growth of chick embryo. *Proc. Soc. Exper. Biol. & Med. 71:* 447-452, 1949.
83. KARNOFSKY, D. A., RIDGWAY, L. P., and PATTERSON, P. A. Unpublished data.
84. KARNOFSKY, D. A., RIDGWAY, L. P., and PATTERSON, P. A. Growth-inhibiting effect of cortisone acetate on the chick embryo. *Endocrinology 48:* 596-616, 1951.

85. KIDDER, G. W., DEWEY, V. C., PARKS, R. E. JR., and WOODSIDE, G. L. Further evidence on the mode of action of 8-azaguanine (guanazolo) in tumor inhibition. *Cancer Research 11:* 204-211, 1951.
86. KIRSCHBAUM, A., GEISSE, N. C., JUDD, T., and MEYER, L. Effect of certain folic acid antagonists on transplanted myeloid and lymphoid leukemias of the F strain of mice. *Cancer Research 10:* 762-768, 1950.
87. KLEIN, G. Use of Ehrlich ascites tumor of mice for quantitative studies on the growth and biochemistry of neoplastic cells. *Cancer 3:* 1052-1061, 1950.
88. KLINE, B. E., WASLEY, W. L., and RUSCH, H. P. Tumor inhibitor studies: I. The effect of pure chemical compounds on tumor takes. *Cancer Research 2:* 645-648, 1942.
89. KLOPP, C. T., ALFORD, T. C., BATEMAN, J., BERRY, G. N., and WINSHIP, T. Fractionated intra-arterial cancer chemotherapy with methyl bis amine hydrochloride: A preliminary report. *Ann Surg. 132:* 811-832, 1950.
90. KOPROWSKI, H., and NORTON, T. W. Interference between certain neurotropic viruses and transplantable mouse tumors. *Cancer 3:* 874-883, 1950.
91. LASNITZKI, I. Some effects of urethane on the growth and mitosis of normal and malignant cells in vitro. *Brit. J. Cancer 3:* 501-509, 1949.
92. LAW, L. W. Effect of urethane on a transplantable acute lymphoid leukemia. *Proc. Soc. Exper. Biol. & Med. 66:* 158-161, 1947.
93. LAW, L. W. Studies on the effect of a guanine analog on acute lymphoid leukemias in mice. *Cancer Research 10:* 186-190, 1950.
94. LAW, L. W. Urethane (ethyl carbamate) therapy in spontaneous leukemias in mice. *Proc. Nat. Acad. Sc. 33:* 204-210, 1947.
95. LAW, L. W., and BOYLE, P. J. Development of resistance to folic acid antagonists in a transplantable leukemia. *Proc. Soc. Exper. Biol. & Med. 74:* 599-602, 1950.
96. LAW, L. W., DUNN, T. B., BOYLE, P. J., and MILLER, J. H. Observations on the effect of a folic-acid antagonist on transplantable lymphoid leukemias in mice. *J. Nat. Cancer Inst. 10:* 179-191, 1950.
97. LAWRENCE, J. H., DOBSON, R. L., LOW-BEER, B. V. A., and BROWN, B. R. Chronic myelogenous leukemia: Study of 129 cases in which treatment was with radioactive phosphorus. *J. A. M. A. 136:* 672-677, 1948.
98. LAWRENCE, J. H., LOW-BEER, B. V. A., and CARPENDER, J. W. J. Chronic lymphatic leukemia. A study of 100 patients treated with radioactive phosphorus. *J. A. M. A. 140:* 585-588, 1949.
99. LEES, J. C., and LEES, T. W. Numerical estimation in cancer and cancer treatment. *Cancer 3:* 377-409, 1950.
100. LEES, T. W., and LEES, J. C. The relation between the toxic action and tumor-inhibiting power of some drugs. *Cancer 3:* 580-600, 1950.
101. LEITER, J., DOWNING, V., HARTWELL, J. L., and SHEAR, M. J. Damage induced in sarcoma 37 by podophyllin, podophyllotoxin, alphapeltatin, beta-peltatin and quercetin. *J. Nat. Cancer Inst. 10:* 1273-1293, 1950.
102. LIMARZI, L. R. Diagnostic and therapeutic aspects of multiple myeloma. *Med. Clin. North America*, January, 1951, pp. 189-226.
103. LITTLE, P. A., OLESON, J. J., and SUBBAROW, Y.: The effect of nutrition on the tumor response in Rous chicken sarcoma," and LITTLE, P. A., SAMPATH, A., and SUBBAROW, Y.: "The use of antagonists of pteroylglutamic acid in controlling Rous chicken sarcoma." *J. Lab. & Clin. Med. 33:* 1139-1143, 1144-1149, 1948.

104. Loge, J. P., and Rundles, R. W. Urethane (ethyl carbamate) therapy in multiple myeloma. *Blood 4:* 201-216, 1949.

105. Lynch, J. P., Ware, P. F., and Gaensler, E. A. Nitrogen mustard in the treatment of inoperable bronchogenic carcinoma. *Surgery 27:* 368-385, 1950.

106. McConnell, J. R.: "Preparation of polysaccharide solutions for clinical use and tissue culture experiments." In *Approaches to Tumor Chemotherapy*. Washington, D. C., A. A. A. S., 1947, pp. 271-272.

107. Miller, G. L., Green, E. V., Kolb, J. J., and Miller, E. E. Studies on the proteins of rhabdomyosarcoma and normal muscle of mice: I. Gross composition, extractions with 0.5M KC1, and fractionations by differential centrifugation and dialysis. *Cancer Research 10:* 141-147, 1950.

108. Mitchell, J. S. Clinical trials of tetra-sodium 2-methyl-1:4-naphthohydroquinone diphosphate, in conjunction with x-ray therapy. *Brit. J. Cancer 2:* 351-359, 1948.

109. Moeschlin, S., and Bodmer, A. Urethane-caused blood and bone marrow changes in agranulocytosis and panmyelopathy of the cat. *Blood 6:* 242-260, 1951.

110. Moore, A. E. The destructive effect of the virus of Russian Far East encephalitis on the transplantable mouse sarcoma 180. *Cancer 2:* 525-534, 1949.

111. Moore, A. E., Stock, C. C., Sugiura, K., and Rhoads, C. P. Inhibition of development of sarcoma 180 by 4-amino-N^{10}-methyl pteroylglutamic acid. *Proc. Soc. Exper. Biol. & Med. 70:* 396-398, 1949.

112. Nathanson, I. T. Hormonal treatment in cancer. *Med. Clin. North America,* September, pp. 1409-1417, 1950.

113. Nesbit, R. M., and Baum, W. C. Endocrine control of prostatic carcinoma; clinical and statistical survey of 1818 cases. *J. A. M. A. 143:* 1317-1320, 1950.

114. Nettleship, A., and Henshaw, P. S. Induction of pulmonary tumors in mice with ethyl carbamate (urethane). *J. Nat. Cancer Inst. 4:* 309-319, 1943.

115. Ormsbee, R. A., Cornman, I., and Berger, R. Effect of podophyllin on tumor cells in tissue culture. *Proc. Soc. Exper. Biol. & Med. 66:* 586-590, 1947.

116. Osgood, E. E. Titrated, regularly spaced radioactive phosphorus or spray roentgen therapy of leukemias. *Arch. Int. Med. 87:* 329-348, 1951.

117. Parker, R. C., Plummer, H. C., Siebenmann, C. O., and Chapman, M. G. *Proc. Soc. Exper. Biol. & Med. 66:* 461-467, 1947.

118. Pearson, O. H., and Eliel, L. P. Use of pituitary adrenocorticotropic hormone (ACTH) and cortisone in lymphomas and leukemias. *J. A. M. A. 144:* 1349-1353, 1950.

119. Philips, F. S. Recent contributions to the pharmacology of bis (2-halo-ethyl) amines and sulfides. *J. Pharmacol. & Exper. Therap. 99:* 281-323, 1950.

120. Philips, F. S., and Thiersch, J. B. Actions of 2,6-diaminopurine in mice, rats and dogs. *Proc. Soc. Exper. Biol. & Med. 72:* 401-408, 1949.

121. Philips, F. S., and Thiersch, J. B. Studies on the actions of 4-amino-pteroylglutamic acid in rats and mice. *J. Pharmacol. & Exper. Therap. 95:* 303-311, 1949.

122. Philips, F. S., and Thiersch, J. B. The nitrogen mustard-like actions of 2,4,6-tris (ethylenimino)-s-triazine and other bis (ethylenimines). *J. Pharmacol. & Exper. Therap. 100:* 398-407, 1950.

123. Potter, Van R. *Enzymes, Growth and Cancer.* Springfield, Ill., C. C Thomas, 1950.

124. PRESSMAN, D. Zone of activity of antibodies as determined by the use of radioactive tracers. *Tr. New York Acad. Sc. 11:* 203-206, 1949.

125. REINHARD, E. H., MOORE, C. V., BIERBAUM, O. S., and MOORE, S. Radioactive phosphorus as a therapeutic agent: Review of literature and analysis of results of treatment of 155 patients with various blood dyscrasias, lymphomas and other malignant neoplastic diseases. *J. Lab. & Clin. Med. 31:* 107-215, 1946.

126. Report of a Committee Appointed by the Medical Research Council, (GASK, G. E., Chairman). An inquiry into the effect of H11 in the treatment of malignant disease. *Brit. J. Med. 2:* 701-708, 1948.

127. RUNDLES, R. W., DILLON, M. L., and DILLON, E. S. Multiple myeloma. III. Effect of urethane therapy on plasma cell growth, abnormal serum protein components and Bence-Jones proteinuria. *J. Clin. Investigation 29:* 1243-1260, 1950.

128. RUNDLES, R. W., and REEVES, R. J. Multiple myeloma: II. Variability of roentgen appearance and effect of urethane therapy on skeletal disease. *Am. J. Roentgenol. 64:* 799-809, 1950.

129. SCHOENBACH, E. B., GREENSPAN, E. M., and COLSKY, J. Reversal of aminopterin and amethopterin toxicity by citrovorum factor. *J. A. M. A. 144:* 1558-1560, 1950.

130. SELIGMAN, A. M., MILDEN, M., and FRIEDMAN, O. M. A study of the inhibition of tumor growth in mice and rats with 10-methyl-1,2-benzanthracene and derivatives related to the nitrogen and sulfa beta-chloroethyl vesicants. *Cancer 2:* 701-706, 1949.

131. SELIGMAN, A. M., SHEAR, M. J., LEITER, J., and SWEET, B. Chemical alterations of polysaccharide from serratia marcescens: I. Tumor necrotizing polysaccharide tagged with radioactive iodine. *J. Nat. Cancer Inst. 9:* 13-18, 1948.

132. SELYE, H. Studies on adaptation. *Endocrinology 21:* 169-188, 1937.

133. SHAPIRO, D. M., and GELLHORN, A. Combinations of chemical compounds in experimental cancer therapy. *Cancer Research 11:* 35-41, 1951.

134. SHAPIRO, D. M., GOLDIN, D. M., LANDING, B. H., BERGNER, A. D., FAIMAN, F., and GOLDBERG, B. Cancer chemotherapy: Analysis of results of different screening methods with nitrogen mustard analogues. *Cancer 2:* 100-112, 1949.

135. SHAPIRO, D. M., WEISS, R., and GELLHORN, A. The effect of azaguanine on mitosis in normal and neoplastic tissues. *Cancer 3:* 896-902, 1950.

136. SHARPLESS, G. R., DAVIES, M. C., and COX, H. R. Antagonistic action of certain neurotropic viruses toward a lymphoid tumor in chickens with resulting immunity. *Proc. Soc. Exper. Biol. & Med. 73:* 270-275, 1950.

137. SHEAR, M. J. "Some aspects of joint institutional research program on chemotherapy of cancer: current laboratory and clinical experiments with bacterial polysaccharide and with synthetic organic compounds: I. Scope of program." In *Approaches to Tumor Chemotherapy.* P.-236-247. Washington, D. C., A. A. A. S., 1947, pp. 236-247.

138. SHIMKIN, M. B. Duration of life in untreated cancer. *Cancer 4:* 1-8, 1951.

139. SHIMKIN, M. B., and BIERMAN, H. R. Experimental chemotherapy of neoplastic diseases. *Radiology 53:* 518-529, 1949.

140. SINCLAIR, J. G. A specific transplacental effect of urethane in mice. *Texas Rep. Biol. & Med. 8:* 623-632, 1950.

141. SINGHER, H. O., KENSLER, C. J., and RHOADS, C. P. The effect of various agents on normal and malignant tissues. In *A.A.A.S. Research Conference on Cancer.* Washington, D. C., A. A. A. S., 1945, pp. 310-320.

142. SKIPPER, H. E. Carbamates in the chemotherapy of leukemia: V. Observation on a possible antileukemia synergism between urethane and methyl-*bis* (β-chloroethyl) amine. *Cancer 2:* 475-479, 1949.
143. SKIPPER, H. E., and BRYAN, C. E. Carbamates in the chemotherapy of leukemia: III. The relationship between chemical structure and anti-leukemic action of a series of urethan derivatives. *J. Nat. Cancer Inst. 9:* 391-397, 1949.
144. SKIPPER, H. E., BRYAN, C. E., RISER, W. H., JR., WILTY, M., and STELZENMULLER, A. Carbamates in the chemotherapy of leukemia: II. The relationship between chemical structure, leukopenic action, and acute toxicity of a group of urethane derivatives. *J. Nat. Cancer Inst. 9:* 77-88, 1948.
145. SOUTHAM, C. M., CRAVER, L. F., DARGEON, H. W., and BURCHENAL, J. H. A study of the natural history of acute leukemia with special reference to the duration of the disease and the occurrence of remissions. *Cancer 4:* 39-59, 1951.
146. SPURR, C. L., SMITH, T. R., BLOCK, M., and JACOBSON, L. O. The role of nitrogen mustard therapy in the treatment of lymphomas and leukemias. *Am. J. Med. 8:* 710-723, 1950.
147. Staff of the Roscoe B. Jackson Memorial Laboratory. *Biology of the Laboratory Mouse.* Philadelphia, Blakiston, 1941.
148. STOCK, C. C. Aspects of approaches in experimental cancer chemotherapy. *Am. J. Med. 8:* 658-674, 1950.
149. STOCK, C. C., BIESELE, J. J., BURCHENAL, J. H., KARNOFSKY, D. A., MOORE, A. E., and SUGIURA, K. Folic acid analogues and experimental tumors. *Ann. New York Acad. Sc. 52:* 1360-1378, 1950.
150. STOCK, C. C., CAVALIERI, L. F., HITCHINGS, G. H., and BUCKLEY, S. M. A test of triazolopyrimidines on mouse sarcoma 180. *Proc. Soc. Exper. Biol. & Med. 72:* 565-567, 1949.
151. STOERK, H. C. Growth retardation of lymphosarcoma implants in pyrodoxine-deficient rats by testosterone and cortisone. *Proc. Soc. Exper. Biol. & Med. 74:* 798-800, 1950.
152. STOERK, H. C., and EMERSON, G. A. Complete regression of lymphosarcoma implants following temporary induction of riboflavin deficiency in mice. *Proc. Soc. Exper. Biol. & Med. 70:* 703-704, 1949.
153. SUGARBAKER, E. D., and CRAVER, L. F. Lymphosarcoma: A study of 196 cases with biopsy. *J. A. M. A. 115:* 17-23, 112-117, 1940.
154. SUGIURA, K., HITCHINGS, G. H., CAVALIERI, L. F., and STOCK, C. C. The effect of 8-azaguanine on the growth of carcinoma, sarcoma, osteogenic sarcoma, lymphosarcoma and melanoma in animals. *Cancer Research 10:* 178-185, 1950.
155. SUGIURA, K., MOORE, A. E., and STOCK, C. C. The effects of aminopterin on the growth of carcinoma, sarcoma and melanoma in animals. *Cancer 2:* 491-502, 1949.
156. SUGIURA, K., and STOCK, C. C. Action of 3-bis (β-chloroethyl) aminomethyl-4-methoxy-methyl-5-hydroxy-6-methyl pyridine dihydrochloride, 2,4,6-tris (1-aziridyl)-*s*-triazine and 5-amino-7-hydroxy-1*H*-*v*-triazolo(*d*) pyrimidine on carcinoma, sarcoma, osteogenic sarcoma, lymphosarcoma, and melanoma in animals. *Cancer Research 10:* 244,, 1950.
157. SUGIURA, K., STOCK, C. C., DOBRINER, K., and RHOADS, C. P. The effect of cortisone and other steroids on experimental tumors (abstract). *Cancer Research 10:* 244-245, 1950.

158. TAYLOR, A., and GALINSKY, I. Yolk sac cultivated tumor tissue and experiments in tumor chemotherapy: II. Neutral red, ethyl violet, and janus green (abstract). *Cancer Research 9:* 622, 1949.
159. TAYLOR, S. G., III, AYER, J. P., and MORRIS, R. C. Cortical steroids in treatment of cancer. *J. A. M. A. 144:* 1058-1064, 1950.
160. THIERSCH, J. B., and PHILIPS, F. S. Folic acid antagonists in neoplastic disease. *A. J. M. Sc. 217:* 575-585, 1949.
161. TOURTELLOTTE, W. W., and STORER, J. B. The role of cellular fractions in the transplantation of the Walker rat carcinoma 256. *Cancer Research 10:* 783-785, 1950.
162. TRUNNELL, J. B., MARINELLI, L. D., DUFFY, B. J., JR., HILL, R., PEACOCK, W., and RAWSON, R. W. The treatment of metastatic thyroid cancer with radioactive iodine: credits and debits. *J. Clin. Endocrinol. 9:* 1138-1152, 1949.
163. TURNER, J. C., and MULLIKEN, B. Parasitization of mouse sarcoma 180 by vaccine virus and its effect on tumor growth. *Cancer Research 7:* 774-778, 1947.
164. WALPOLE, A. L. The Walker carcinoma 256 in the screening of tumour inhibitors. *Brit. J. Pharmacol. 6:* 135-143, 1950.
165. WALSH, L. B., GREIFF, D., and BLUMENTHAL, H. T. The effect of low temperature on morphology and transplantability of sarcoma 37. *Cancer Research 10:* 726-736, 1950.
166. WARREN, S., and DIXON, F. J. Effects of continuous radiation on chick embryos and developing chicks: I. Growth rate, gonads and bone; II. Bone marrow, lymphoid tissue and peripheral blood. *Radiology 52:* 714-729, 869-880, 1949.
167. WEIL, R. Chemotherapy and tumors. *J. A. M. A. 64:* 1283-1289, 1915.
168. WILLIS, R. H. *The Spread of Tumors in the Human Body.* London, J. and A. Churchill, 1934, pp. 116-117.
169. WOGLOM, W. H. "General review of cancer chemotherapy." In *Approaches to Tumor Chemotherapy.* Washington, D. C., A. A. A. S., 1947, pp. 1-12.
170. WOODS, M. W., DUBUY, H. G., BURK, D., and HESSELBACH, M. L. Cytological studies on the nature of the cytoplasmic particulates in the Cloudman S91 mouse melanoma, the derived Algire S91A partially amelanotic melanoma, and the Harding-Passey mouse melanoma. *J. Nat. Cancer Inst. 9:* 311-323, 1949.
171. WYATT, G. M., and FARBER, S. Neuroblastoma sympatheticum. *Am. J. Roentgenol. 46:* 485-495, 1941.
172. YOUNGER, J. S., WARD, E. W., and SALK, J. E. Effect of 5-amino-7-hydroxy-1*H*-*v*-triazolo(*d*)-pyrimidine on growth and development of the chick embryo. *Proc. Soc. Exper. Biol. & Med. 75:* 157-161, 1950.
173. ZAHL, P. A., and WATERS, L. L. Localization of colloidal dyes in animal tumors. *Proc. Soc. Exper. Biol. & Med. 48:* 304-310, 1941.

CHAPTER 23

Radiation and Cancer

EXPERIMENTAL STUDIES

Leonidas D. Marinelli
Austin M. Brues

The first observations on the biologic action of ionizing radiations followed closely the discovery of roentgen-rays and radium, at the turn of the century. The information gained in the first three decades of radiobiologic investigations, although empirical and mainly qualitative in nature, was sufficient to provide criteria of practical use in the broad radiotherapeutic attack upon cancer.

For the past twenty years, however, radiation therapy has not benefited to the same extent from experimental radiobiology. Whatever advances are reflected in the statistics of nearly all major radiotherapeutic centers of the world have been due mostly to improved clinical management of the patients and to careful selection of technics evolved from physical and clinical principles and tested by rigorous statistical studies. They cannot be considered to be the result of a deeper understanding of the radiobiologic action of ionizing radiations on experimental tumors.

The latter, for its elucidation, requires a better knowledge of the interaction of radiation with protoplasm. As matters stand today, the nature of the interaction between radiation and matter is fairly well known at the atomic level—when a photon of radiation and an atom interact—but our ability to observe, and hence to describe, the mechanism declines sharply with the complexity of the test object. Fundamental progress, therefore, is likely to be made with observations at the chemical as well as at the biological level as recent developments have clearly shown.[71, 141]

The characteristic property of ionizing radiation in its interaction with matter is the production of ions which, in most biologic experiments related to mammals, need not be more than one in 10^7 atoms of protoplasm on the average to produce profound effects. These ions are highly localized along the tracks of ionizing particles at average distances of the order of 0.1 μ (roentgen-ray) to 0.0002 μ

(alpha-ray) from each other according to the type of radiation, the tracks themselves being produced practically at random in time and space throughout the biologic material.[57] Since the total energy yielded to protoplasm by lethal doses of radiation corresponds to an ultimate increase in temperature no higher than a few thousandths of one degree centigrade, radiobiologic action cannot be accounted for satisfactorily by gross thermal effects.

The view must be held, instead, that these highly localized and relatively infrequent ionizations bring about a set of chemical events which is capable of altering profoundly the complex and relatively massive biochemical processes which govern the future behavior of the biologic system. The physicist describes the passage of an ionizing particle through matter by stating its average loss of energy per unit length, the loss or change of its charge, and its change in direction; the task of the radiochemist and of the radiologist is to describe the alterations occurring in their media as a consequence of that transient event.

Although the study of chemical reactions in gases[93] has contributed significantly to our understanding of the mechanism in the most elementary situations, the information gained could not be applied profitably to radiobiology.

Irradiation in Aqueous Systems

Much more stimulating have been instead the recent investigations on aqueous systems. Indirect as well as direct evidence already gathered points to the fact that the transit of an ionizing particle in water is followed by disruption of the water molecule into radicals and ions of as yet indeterminate lifetime but of very powerful reactive nature.* [84, 138]

The abundance and behavior of each type of ion or radical is not exhaustively known for all conditions of radiation exposure but the extent of their action can be surmised by qualitative and quantitative differences found in many dilute aqueous solutions irradiated by roentgen-rays or alpha-rays in the presence or absence of O_2, of many reducing agents, and of many "protectors" competing for these activating products.[20]

A link between these chemical events and their biologic counterparts is provided by recent evidence that a wide variety of radiobiologic reactions are similarly dependent on the presence of moisture, O_2, etc., at the time of irradiation, and on whether or not the radiation in question produces a densely ionizing track.

Although this parallelism of results points strongly to oxidation of the components of protoplasm through water as one of the first steps in the chain of events released by ionizing radiation, other initial mechanisms cannot be excluded *a priori*. In fact, a good deal of evidence on the radiation effects on crystalline virus and on dry bacteriophage is consistent with the hypothesis of direct effects on the biologic object without the mediation of water.[67, 90]

In attempting to describe the next biochemical step in vivo, however general in

* Although the existence of ionization products resulting from the irradiation of water was postulated some time ago as a result of studies on dilute inorganic aqueous solutions,[38] the importance of their role in irradiated biologic systems has not been realized until recently as a consequence of studies on biochemical solutes (enzymes, viruses, bacteriophages) at low concentration.

scope, one must postulate a mechanism whereby a single ion or radical is capable of affecting the behavior of more than 10^2 to 10^6 molecules, for such is the apparent ionic efficiency of radiation on the cellular metabolic processes observed quantitatively.[103]

Nucleic Acid Metabolism

The most intensively studied of these has been the disturbance of nucleic acid metabolism. Discovered independently by Mitchell[100, 101, 102] on the basis of ultraviolet microphotometric methods on irradiated cells, and by Euler and Hevesy[28] as a result of investigation of P^{32} uptake in the nucleic acid fraction of Jensen rat sarcoma, this phenomenon has been amply confirmed and elucidated further by tracer studies with P^{32} in nucleic acid fractions of irradiated tissues.*

Enzymes

Because of their critical importance in cellular functions, enzymes have been suspected of being the primary seat of oxidation by radiation. In particular, the demonstration of reversible oxidation of the -SH group of enzymes *in vitro* by Barron *et al.*[7] with moderate doses of radiation provides an attractive anologue to the phenomenon of recovery so widely observed in biologic systems. A direct consequence of this hypothesis has been the discovery that cysteine and glutathione act as protective agents in a variety of radiobiologic experiments.[36, 110] It has been argued, however,[39, 96] that the enzymatic theory of radiosensitivity cannot be explained satisfactorily on the basis of results on dilute solutions of pure enzymes, since these conditions are hardly met in protoplasm. An attempt to bridge this gap is being made by studying the effects of small doses of radiation on enzyme-substrate films imitating chromosome architectural structures.[99] In the midst of this controversy, note should be made of Dale's[20] remarks on the importance of cell kinetics: "But this picture" (that of an enzyme in a solution in the presence of a protector) "changes when we turn to a non-homogenous system in which more concentrated regions alternate with more dilute regions. Any solute passing through these dilute regions, which may be likened to a no-man's-land, will be continuously decimated before reaching its objective, by the attack of radicals formed from the water. A cell, especially during mitotic reorientation, constitutes such a non-homogenous system."

Since the issue can hardly be considered closed, some thought should be given to direct experimentation such as the investigation of the biochemical status of irradiated mitochondria and microsomes, which are regarded to be respectively the loci of the enzymes and nucleic acids of the cytoplasm. The work of Claude[17] and others on the separation and biochemical analysis of these particles should facilitate whatever effort is contemplated along these lines.

* It is becoming apparent that the difficulties inherent to quantitative analysis of metabolic effects of radiation ought to be reduced considerably by investigations on turnover rates of intermediary cell metabolism by means of isotopic tracers.[35, 64, 65, 72, 97] There is good reason to believe that, as quantitative metabolic data are accumulated on irradiated organisms, the task of identifying further the responsible "oxidized" entities may become more hopeful. It seems also that these experimental technics will contribute most directly to the evaluation of some theories of action of radiation[29, 119, 133] which postulate unobserved metabolic mechanisms in order to explain some features of histologic or biologic behavior.

GENERAL BEHAVIOR OF IRRADIATED CELLS

Cytologic observations of normal and neoplastic cells have revealed both temporary and permanent effects. The preponderance of either type, and the general sequential behavior of the cell depends greatly on its mitotic stage, the magnitude of the dose, its fractionation, the dose rate, and a fairly large number of other experimental conditions. No radiobiologic response has been discovered in the neoplastic cell itself, which has not been noted also in normal cells (*vide infra*).

Temporary Effects

The temporary effects comprise a delay of mitosis, stickiness and clumping of chromosomes, and various characteristics accompanying abnormal mitosis, the most important of which are thought to be abnormal spindle formation or its complete destruction.[13, 80] The effect most easily observed after small doses is the delay of mitosis; in grasshopper eggs the effect is noticeable with as little as 8 r,[14]* but in tumors and tissue cultures the doses required are distinctly higher (Table 47).

Table 47. DOSES OF ROENTGEN- OR GAMMA-RADIATION REQUIRED TO PRODUCE CERTAIN EFFECTS IN TISSUE CULTURES

Tissue	*Immediate culture death*	*Delayed culture death* *	*Minimal detectable change*	*Reference*†
Avian fibroblast	117.000	22.000 (13 da.)	33 (reduction in mitosis)	125
Chick fibroblast	—	5000	2500 (appreciable inhibition of growth rate)	23, 56
Rat fibroblast	200.000	—	—	61
Rat sarcoma (benzpyrene)	200.000	2000	500 (incapable of prolonged cultivation. No time stated)	23, 56, 61
DBAB mouse tumor	—	80.000 (7–9 da.) 100.000	—	52, 48, 53
C3H mammary adenocarcinomas	—	130.000 (7–9 da.)	—	52, 48, 53
Crocker sarcoma 180	—	>60.000 (2–3 da.)	—	52, 48, 53

* Numbers in parentheses denote the time interval necessary for the occurrence of the effect.
† Numbers refer to items in bibliography at the end of this chapter.

Alteration of nucleic acid metabolism can legitimately be suspected of being intimately associated with these changes because of its radiosensitivity, its transient nature at low doses, and its importance in cell division. The suspicion has been strengthened by the observation that the disturbance seems to precede abnormal mitosis,[70] although the relationship to inhibition of mitosis is not clear (*vide infra*). As to abnormal chromosome behavior, no definite statement can be made at this time since the mechanism of nucleic acid depolymerization advanced by Darlington and LaCour[21] has been demonstrated *in vitro* only at relatively high doses.[124, 130]

* A dose practically identical to that capable of producing measurable inhibition of respiration of these eggs.[129]

Permanent Effects

The permanent effects induced by radiation in cells are seen most conspicuously in chromosome fragmentation and aberration at the metaphase or anaphase of mitosis following irradiation. These abnormalities have been studied quantitatively under different experimental conditions and subjected to detailed scrutiny[90, 91] in order to throw light on the early sites of action. The experiments so far reported are consistent with mediation of O_2 and of H_2O at the time of irradiation in sensitizing the reactions themselves through the production of oxidizing agents capable of diffusing to the structures involved.[131]

The role of the cytoplasm as the site for either transient or permanent effects is dubious.[44] On account of its bulk and its recognized relationship with the nucleus, it is difficult to imagine that it is altogether passive in determining cell behavior. In fact, description of cytoplasmic changes in irradiated normal and tumor cells at moderate doses have not been wanting[31, 32, 33, 34, 95] but the nature of the observations has not lent itself to quantitative analysis capable of assessing the effect of these changes on the subsequent behavior of the cell.

Some important cytochemical observations have been made on irradiated cytoplasm following appropriate ultraviolet microspectrographic analysis of human material. Mitchell[100, 101, 102] attributed the observed increase in density of the irradiated cytoplasm to accumulation of pentose-nucleotides. Partial support for this hypothesis has come from other sources,[126] but later developments[64, 69] have made it apparent that the situation is not a simple one and that further investigation is necessary. It may be stated, however, that inhibition of synthesis of both types of nucleic acid has been noted in irradiated normal and malignant tissues and that to a lesser and more transient extent, it also occurs in nonirradiated tissues of partially irradiated animals.[64, 69, 70, 78] It can be well appreciated that the relevancy of nucleic acid metabolism to cytologic behavior needs to be clarified before this phase of radiobiologic action can be understood, and conversely, how any advance in the latter field may well contribute to elucidation of the former.

Despite this tempting picture, many questions at the cellular level remain to be answered: these include the great variation noted in the radiosensitivity (as measured by the lethal effect) of biologic organisms[125] and the variation of sensitivity of an organism during the different stages of mitosis.[44] The latter could not be correlated with total ribonucleic acid or desoxyribonucleic acid content of *Trillium* cells at mitotic stages for which the lethal dose varies by a factor of 50,[123] neither are quantitative data available for the comparison of the rates of nucleic acid synthesis to the wide radiosensitivity of single-celled organisms.

However, some other reliable observations have been made on this subject. For dry bacteriophage and virus, wholly consisting of nuclear material, the dose required to inactivate a given percentage of a population is an inverse linear function of the size of the organism and this finding has been forwarded to support the "target" hypothesis in radiologic events.[90]

For most organisms investigated (barley seed, yeast, wasp), the survival of the population increases with polyploidy, other experimental conditions being constant.[16]

As to tumor cells, which cannot be analyzed statistically in the same fashion as single-celled populations, sensitivity has been defined in terms of effects on tumor growth rate. (Sensitivity in this sense should be clearly distinguished from the concept of curability in terms of permanent regression or inactivation of tumor mass in mammals.) Almost all basic hypotheses on the biologic action of radiation on neoplasms have linked their radiosensitivity, but not their radiocurability, to the shorter life cycle of the cancer cell.

Genetic arguments, such as those advanced by Muller,[105] attribute a great deal of the damage observed in somatic tissues, including tumors, to the gross chromosome changes induced by radiation. A survey of the factors governing these changes in germ cells, such as the restitution time of broken chromosomes, the decrease in probability of restitution in the presence of many accumulated breaks and the relative sensitivity to breaks in the mitotic stages, leads to the expectation that a given dose of radiation favors the accumulation of lethal genetic damage in the most rapidly dividing tissues.

Hevesy[64] in reviewing the work on nucleic acid metabolism, comes to the same conclusions but on semichemical arguments. Earlier observations[1, 2, 4, 66] on inhibition of nucleic acid synthesis by a given dose of radiation showed that the percentage reduction and the rate of recovery was approximately independent of the growth rate of the tissues investigated. He postulates, therefore, that the more rapidly dividing cell is more easily affected by radiation because it is more apt to divide before complete restoration of nucleic acid metabolism.

Goldfeder[54] (Tables 38 and 39), in comparing the relative radiosensitivity of DBAB and C3H autogenous tumors to their respiratory rate finds that cultures of the dbrB tumor require for inactivation smaller doses than the other, but that this tumor is the more radioresistant when judged by "takes" and "regression" *in vivo*. She attributes the lower radiocurability of the faster growing tumor (dbrB) to its ability to eliminate more rapidly toxic substances produced by radiation.

Closely related to these hypotheses are the quantitative observations made by Gray and Scholes[59] on the roots of *vicia faba* after different doses and dose rates of radiation. These authors have established a very close relationship between chromosome breaks and growth inhibition under widely different conditions of radiation exposure and environment. They have not established whether or not all injury at low doses or dose rates arises from the chromosomal changes seen at metaphase and anaphase, but have shown that at higher doses and higher dose rates another form of injury supervenes and eventually predominates. The latter decreases with increase in duration of exposure and, in contrast to the first, is produced less efficiently by densely ionizing radiations.

On the basis of present knowledge there is a strong inclination to attribute the effects observable at low doses to a close interaction of ionizing particles and cellular structures, whereas the effects supervening at higher doses, could reasonably be attributed to the action of radiation on protoplasm in general, the chemical

TABLE 48. EFFECTS OF ROENTGEN-RAYS ON EXPERIMENTAL TUMORS
(Doses in roentgens)

Species	*Tumor*	*Strain*	*Takes* 50%	*Takes* 0%	*Regressions* 50%	*Regressions* 100%	*Radiation**	*Reference*†
Mice	dbrB	DBA	—	—		1500	L	114
"	Adenocarcinoma	C3H	2000	2800		12.000	L	52, 53, 54
"	DBAB	DBA	3600	5000		24.000	L	
"	Sarcoma 180	Hybrid	1900	2800	1000	1800	L	128
"	" "	—	2700					109
"	" "	—	2800–3000					48
"	Yale Ca	—	4400					89
"	Yale mammary Ca	A			>5000			107
"	" "	AC57–F_2			<2500	5000	L	107
"	Lymphosarcoma	A	2450	4000				5
"	Lymphoma	A	1700	2500				5
"	Mammary Ca	A	3250	4000				5
"	Ca 2146	—	1460		1560		G	58
"	Ca 63	—				2400–2600	L	88
"	Adenocarcinoma 755	C57Y	3600	4500		5500	G. F.	49
"	Woods sarcoma				~1400		L	108
"	Sarcoma 37	DBA		5000		5000	L	63
"	Krebs tumor	Bagg A		3500–7000				83
"	Round cell sarcoma			3500				111
"	Lymphatic leukemia	AK5	<<500	<2000				41
Rat	Galliera sarcoma	—		3500		3500		132
"	Autogenous ret. cell lymphosarcoma	Parent		2000				51
"	Benzpyrene sarcoma	—		7000				60
"	Sarcoma 39	—		—		~10.000	L	43
"	Ca 426	Parent		5000–5500			L	26
"	Jensen sarcoma	—		—		4000–5000	L	122
Rabbit	Brown Pierce tumor	—		6000				117

* Types of Irradiation: *G* = whole body; *L* = local; *F* = fractionated.
† Numbers refer to the items in the bibliography at the end of this chapter.

description of which, undoubtedly complex, may include a disturbance in nucleic acid metabolism brought about by the mechanism of enzyme inactivation.*

Before closing this section it is well to consider briefly that although certain histologic, cytologic, and genetic similarities between the effects of certain drugs (such as nitrogen mustards) and radiation have led to the coining of the word "radiomimetic," the limitations of the observational methods reported hardly justify the assumption of identical primary action. The action of radiation, as

* Although the factors determining recovery in neoplastic and normal tissues are largely unknown, its existence is at present taken for granted, since the bulk of the evidence available shows the incomplete accumulation of radiation effects. A notable exception is the finding that mutations produced by radiations are strictly proportional to the dose administered irrespective of dose rate or fractionation.

Concepts based on the existence of different rates of recovery in tissues, partly supported by indirect evidence[74] have greatly influenced radio therapeutic technics in the last three decades. A review of the subject will be found in R. Paterson's book, *The Treatment of Malignant Disease by Radium and X-rays*, (Baltimore, William and Wilkins, 1949, Chapter 33).

contrasted to that of drugs, maintains its uniqueness because of its simultaneity throughout the cell, independently of cell structure.[86] Observations by Read[113] for instance, have shown that, as far as the growth of *Vicia faba* is concerned, the similarity of drugs and radiation effects must be a partial one, since the presence of O_2 in the medium affects the action of radiation but not that of the nitrogen mustard. This observation is consistent with the postulates of Barron[7] on the role of -SH group in cellular metabolism, since radiation could act on -SH through oxidation (influenced in the case of roentgen-rays by the presence of O_2) whereas the nitrogen mustard could act by alkylation (independent of O_2).

IRRADIATED TUMORS

An extensive literature has accumulated through the years on the histology of irradiated normal tissues in mammals and excellent reviews have been published.[8, 137]

In view of the many factors influencing the behavior of single irradiated cells, it is not surprising that the contribution of histologic studies, based, as they are, on heterogeneous cell populations, have not been decisive to our present understanding of the basic phenomena. They have provided, however, a broad description of the behavior of neoplastic tissues which has proved of great value in the radiotherapy of human and experimental neoplasms. Recently attempts have been made to establish observations on a quantitative basis in order to assess to what extent histologic features of tumors are relevant to their radiotherapeutic behavior. Glucksmann[45, 46] has classified cell populations in terms of four broad categories: resting, mitotic, differentiating, and degenerating cells. By means of serial biopsies in human carcinoma, he has studied changes in these subgroups during radiotherapy, and concludes that this method of study is useful in the evaluation of individual therapeutic results.

Although some investigations on clinical material have shown that a high correlation is obtained between the histologic effects and prognosis in several classes of tumors,[47, 81, 139] the existence of a true differentiation of neoplastic cells as a result of irradiation has been questioned by others.[3, 73] Certain striking effects of irradiation on tumor cytology have received scant attention, presumably because they occur at the time when a tumor begins to regress, and is therefore relatively immune from surgical interference. In this period, gigantic cells with very large nuclei are observed,[12] resembling those seen in normal tissues under certain conditions of prolonged and intense local irradiation.[140] These are often mixed with degenerating or atypical cells of other types, and may be attributed to a dissociation of growth from cell division.

INDIRECT EFFECTS

Both early and recent morphologic and biologic studies have led to the belief that in addition to the direct action of radiation upon cells, neoplastic tissue is subject to an "extracellular" or "indirect" effect, elicited by the radiation. Its importance, however, has been emphasized and questioned with varying degree since the very beginning. It has been observed, for instance, that tumor cultures require for their inactivation, doses of radiation (Table 47) much higher than the doses required to prevent "takes" or cause regression of tumors in animals (Table 48) but the comparisons have not been made on an equitable time basis. More recently, however, an effect of total body irradiation on the growth behavior of an irradiated transplanted mouse lymphosarcoma has been reported;[68] this effect could not be duplicated by irradiation of any single organ.

As a consequence of intensive investigation, four broad categories of indirect effect have come to be recognized, although their intrinsic importance and their mutual interdependence have not been assessed to any serious extent. They are: (1) Histolytic effects; (2) Stroma reaction; (3) Vascular reaction; and (4) Leukocytic reactions.

Histolytic Effect

The histolytic effect of radiation postulates in essence that most sensitive tumor cells are killed by radiation and undergo histolysis, thereby releasing substances noxious to the growth of the remaining tumor cells which have escaped immediate injury. Although some enzymatic alterations have been suspected to be related to this effect[104] biologic experimentation has not supported the theory that such substances influence the fate of intact transplants.[63]

Stroma Effects

The stroma reaction is based on firmer grounds. Cramer,[19] working on autoplasts of spontaneous breast cancer in a stock strain of mice, was one of the first to observe histologically that radiosensitive tumors develop a type of stroma different from that associated with radioresistant tumors. In the radiosensitive group there was an early invasion of macrophages, which later became elongated, assuming the appearance of fibroblasts. In about a week's time this massive stroma reaction split the tumor into small cell groups and was followed by a rapid regression of the neoplasm. In the radioresistant group, the reaction was either entirely absent or only feebly developed, and any regression that followed was slow and incomplete. This observation has been amply confirmed in histologic studies on human and experimental tumors[13, 107, 137] and has led to the quest of radiotherapeutic technics likely to enhance the stroma reaction.[73] Despite their recognized importance, the factors which influence the stroma reaction are unknown, and their exact role in aiding or determining the dissolution of a tumor is not understood. Some evidence based on direct histologic studies on the regression of irradiated Yale mammary mouse adenocarcinoma in the parent A strain and in the AC57 F_2 hybrids, points to a somewhat complex genetic mechanism[106] and similar observations on the effect of dietary factors in the radioresponse of Walker rat carcinoma 256 indicate that the stroma reaction can be influenced favorably by a high protein diet, at least under specific conditions of irradiation.[27] Although highly suggestive, neither critical analysis nor cogent experimentation has been reported on the role which the low cohesiveness of tumor cells[18] plays in this aspect of tumor breakdown.

Vascular Reaction

The vascular reaction, by its very nature, cannot be divorced entirely from either the stroma or the histolytic reactions and intrinsically reflects all that a blood supply impaired by radiation may cause, such as low O_2 supply, osmotic unbalance,[29] further lowering the metabolic rates of already injured cells, etc. Ample indirect evidence is available however, as to its existence.[62, 125] The early work is reviewed by Krebs[82] and further experimentation has been published mainly by Desjardins[22] and Downing *et al.*[25]

Particularly interesting are the quantitative histologic studies that Lasnitzki[87, 88] has made in order to assess the role that impairment of the vascular system plays on the "extracellular effect." Working with mouse adenocarcinoma 63, she has compared the effect on tumors and cultures by observations on mitotic inhibition, and by counts of abnormal mitotic figures and of degenerated cells up to forty-eight hours after irradiation. When the dose used was 200 r (to eliminate the vascular reaction), the responses of mitotic inhibition and cell degeneration were quantitatively of the same order in both instances although abnormal mitosis was more marked and mitotic recovery was more rapid in vivo. When the dose was raised to 2000 r, the effect observed during the first day was mainly a direct one, namely, earlier mitotic recovery in the tumor (evident at three hours as contrasted to forty-eight hours in vitro). This was accompanied by a wave of degenerate cells, as in the case of the intact blood supply. On the second day after exposure, however, a striking relative increase in the number of degenerate cells in vivo and a failure in mitotic recovery supervened, suggesting radiation-induced damage to the circulation. On the basis of these results, the author attributes one-third of the radiation effect to intracellular action and two-thirds to the indirect effect.

Leukocytic Reaction

Leukocytic infiltration of tumors following irradiation has been observed by many investigators.[82] Its contribution to regression is difficult to establish. There are several observations which may have bearing on this phenomenon:

1. A nonirradiated tumor (sarcoma 180) transplanted to an irradiated area of the host is less likely to grow if the inoculation is done within two hours of the irradiation, but the take is not influenced if transplantation is delayed for several days.[128]
2. The transplantability of the same tumor, irradiated in vivo with a given dose, decreases with the length of time spent by the irradiated tumor in the original host, and the growth of cultures from irradiated tumors suffers a similar fate. Concurrently, both in vivo and in tissue cultures, the abundance of polymorphonuclear leukocytes and granulocytes present is in direct proportion to the length of time between irradiation and removal.[15, 127]
3. The evidence reviewed by Krebs[82] indicates that the immunity to tumor transplants is elicited by mechanisms which also induce lymphocytosis. Thus the raising or lowering of this immunity by means of irradiation of the host seems to follow the raising and lowering of the lymphocyte count; but changing the latter by other means, such as pilocarpine or injection of lymphocytes from suitably irradiated animals, does not produce immunity.[120]

Some recent contributions on radiation effects on tumors are pertinent to the issues concerning genetics and immunity of transplantable cancer. Kaplan and Murphy[77] have reported on enhanced frequency of pulmonary metastases in mammary cancer-bearing mice whose tumors were given 400 r locally, after implantation.

Warner *et al.*[114, 134] have reported a change in the transplantability of dbrB and Simpson tumors of the dbr strain. They have noted that small doses of radiation (25–400 r)* administered to the tumor in the shielded DBA animal, confer upon the tumor the property of becoming transplantable in a significant percentage of hosts of strains (A, C57 Black, CBA) which are usually immune to it. The radiated tumors were successfully carried for five transplant generations in these resistant strains and were fully viable when transplanted back into the original host strain. Studies conducted with the Simpson tumor in the C57 black strain[115] show the percentage of "takes" to be influenced to a certain extent by the radiation dose but not by the time elapsed in the DBA host (one to seven days) between irradiation and transplant. The authors suggest that a somatic genetic change has been produced by radiation doses as low as 25 r. If this were so it would have to be demonstrated that the same effect is obtained by irradiating transplants in vitro.

Goldfeder[48, 50] has reported that long-term and practically 100 per cent immunity to sarcoma 180 transplants can be elicited by inoculation of tumor fragments irradiated in vitro with doses of 2000–5000 r, but that no immunity is obtained if the dose is increased to 60,000 r. She points out that whereas the smaller doses are capable of preventing takes and of inducing regression in vivo (Table 48), the larger is necessary for inhibiting proliferation in vitro (Table 47).

Analogous effects have been described by the same author[51] in homozygous rats with a reticulum cell type lymphosarcoma originating in the strain. With 2300–2600 r, the immunity was confined to about three-eighths of the animals tested, but dosages slightly larger (2800 r), which prevented takes completely, failed to confer immunity. In contrast to the results obtained with sarcoma 180, it is difficult in this instance to separate the intrinsic effect on the irradiated implant from the immunizing property which often has been reported to occur whenever a tumor regresses, from whatever the cause. No experimental results have been published on the immunizing properties of irradiated transplants of adenocarcinoma 755 in C57Y mice[49] and of tumors of the C3H and DBA strain, the radiosensitivities of which have been extensively studied by this author.[52] Her recent experiments,[54] however, seem to indicate that implanted, fully grown mammary adenocarcinoma in C3H mice, submitted (while in the host) to radiation in sufficient dosage to cause regression of the tumor, not only confers immunity to further transplantation, but also eliminates the spontaneous tumor incidence expected of the strain.

Many oncologists have inquired into the problem of whether the growth potentiality of a tumor can be changed by radiation; namely whether, once irradiated, the rate of growth of a tumor can be *permanently* changed in *successive* transplantations.

Two investigations will be reviewed. Snellman[122] administered in vivo a total dose greater than that found necessary to cause the regression of Jensen rat sarcoma, by using two equal doses in two successive transplant generations. In transplanting this "irradiated tumor" strain to the third generation he observed that whereas the incidence of takes was decreased temporarily, the progeny of the tumor regained its full potentiality to "take" eight months later. When both types of

* These doses are insufficient to affect "takes" in the parent strain.

tumors were irradiated in the range of 3800–5000 r, the percentage regression of the "irradiated tumor" strain was decidedly less than that of the normal tumor. The rate of growth of unirradiated tumors, as measured on the twentieth day after transplantation in the third generation, was definitely reduced in the irradiated strain of tumor as compared to the control tumor strain, but no further tests were made on successive generations. Histologic examination of the irradiated but viable transplants showed fewer mitoses and a greater proportion of collagen fibers than the normal strain, but no striking differences in cell polymorphism could be established. This evidence, and other of similar nature, cannot decide the fundamental issue because intensive irradiation in vivo in many instances "contaminates" the tumor by favoring the growth of intratumoral fibrotic tissue. Hence growth, transplantability, and radiosensitivity may result on account of changes in the vascular stroma of the tumor instead of being caused by inherent changes in the cancer cells.

More pertinent in this respect are the experiments of Bagg[6] who used a closely inbred strain of albino mice, and observed the rate of growth of sarcoma 180 through 20 transplanted generations while the hosts were being exposed to practically continual whole-body radiation over a period of sixteen months at 2.7 r/hr. for a cumulative dose of 23,000 r. These experiments established that although restraint in growth rate was obtained while the animals were being irradiated, removal from radiation restored the growth of the irradiated progeny to that of the normal strain. Although these tests are subject to some objections because the whole animal was also irradiated, they seem to remain the best evidence that permanent change in growth rate of a transplantable tumor is difficult of attainment.

This conclusion, if considered from the somatic mutation standpoint, is concordant with some deductions of Muller who suggests that since gene mutations are relatively rare and are subject to intercellular selection, they are likely to be a source of minor importance in radiation therapy, except where dominant genes of malignant expression have been engendered in irradiated normal tissue and become the cause of radiation carcinogenesis.

RADIATION CARCINOGENESIS

The induction of malignant disease by external radiation was first observed seven years after Roentgen's discovery of the rays named after him, and this effect received experimental verification in 1908.[116] The carcinogenic effect of absorbed radioactive material was recognized in 1929,[98] although there is reason to suspect that radioactivity has been responsible for occupational lung cancer for several centuries.[118] The subject of radiation carcinogenesis was extensively reviewed by Lacassagne in 1945[85] and a review of more recent development is available.[10]

Such experimental and clinical evidence as is now available suggests that the ionizing radiations are more or less universally carcinogenic to higher species of animals. Not only are several species about equally susceptible to the induction of cancer by radioactive substances, but a large number of tissues show equivalent susceptibility. Thus, bone tumors result from the administration of a variety of bone-seeking radioisotopes,[9] carcinomas of the large intestine result from the feeding of nonabsorbed radioelements;[94] and exposure of the skin to beta rays results in a proportion of skin carcinomas and subcutaneous sarcomas approximately in proportion to the amount of ionizing energy absorbed in the respective tissue layers.[112] One may assume that radioactive carcinogens usually fail to show the species specificity that characterizes chemical carcinogens, which are often metabolized variously by different species, and that they may be controlled as to their site of action with an accuracy not attainable with other agents inducing malignant disease.

It is of considerable interest that the radiations have, in common with certain other carcinogens, both mutagenic and growth-inhibiting properties. This does not serve to prove or disprove hypotheses of the origin of cancer through growth cessation or somatic mutation, but the bulk of the evidence suggests that a number of factors may be active in cancer induction through radiations or otherwise.

If we look at carcinogenesis in the simplest way, we may assume that cancer arises in a single cell which has undergone certain changes conducive to continuous growth. If this is true and if cancer may be attributed to a somatic mutation, then it is clear that it must be a very rare event, because of the large number of cells existing throughout the lifetime of the host without exhibiting this change. It is almost certain that such a "hit" hypothesis of cancer is oversimplified. For one thing, it has been possible to divide the events leading to chemical carcinogenesis into at least two different functional stages, and the latent period of radiation carcinogenesis is, in general, at least as long as that after the chemical insult. Besides, it seems clear that radiation cancer ordinarily arises in tissues that have become deranged as the result of general radiation-induced changes. Radium sarcoma of bone has almost always been seen where aseptic necrosis of bone has occurred.

On the other hand, total-body irradiation, given either as a single sublethal dose or in small continued amounts, is known to increase the normal incidence of various tumors. The most noteworthy instance of this is the rather sharp increase in leukemia and lymphoblastic tumors occurring in various strains of mice after total-body irradiation.[11, 40, 79] Here, a simple mutation hypothesis fails to explain certain circumstances: first, that the leukemogenic activities of methylcholanthrene and roentgen-rays fail to correlate when several strains of mice are studied,[79] and second, that irradiation of either half of the body results in a much lower incidence than would be expected on the basis of total-body exposure.[75]

Other neoplasms which appear to be induced by total-body irradiation are lung adenomas and ovarian tumors in mice. Some experimental evidence[92] suggests that the latter may arise in response to an endocrine imbalance induced by irradiation of the ovaries.

A critical question in relation to radiation carcinogenesis is whether some sort of threshold of dosage exists, below which induction of cancer does not occur, or takes place with a much lower probability than would be expected on a "random hit" hypothesis. It appears that, in the case of genetic mutations, there is no such threshold and that the probability of such mutations may be linear with dosage. A direct empirical approach to the question seems impractical, because of the large numbers of warm-blooded animals necessary to extend significantly our present experimental knowledge.

A few reports have appeared describing attempts to show that the natural cosmic-ray background may be partly responsible for the spontaneous cancer incidence, and are in general inconclusive. Figge[30] noted earlier induction of subcutaneous tumors following optimal doses of methylcholanthrene by the use of lead shields in which cosmic-ray showers are set up, but this observation (dealing as it does with a nearly maximal carcinogenic stimulus) may well be irrelevant to the low-dosage question. Franks and Meek,[37] however, found no significant change in the time of induction and in the incidence of tumors in methylcholanthrene-injected mice kept at "background" radiation intensities of 6 and 0.4 ions/cc./second, respectively, and George *et al.*,[42] conversely, found no increase in chemically-induced tumors where the cosmic ray intensity was increased fivefold.

The extraordinary degree of caution being used at present in the handling of radiations and radioactive substances makes it improbable that any information will come from current industrial experience; in fact, all uncertain factors are being weighed in the other direction, i.e., in the interest of safety.

It may be concluded, in the light of present knowledge, that while radiation cancer is fairly universal among higher species and is statistically reproducible in the laboratory, its genesis is no doubt complex. There is reason to suspect that somatic mutation, in combination with unknown factors, is concerned with the carcinogenic response to radiation. Further investigation is proceeding along diverse lines and forms an important part of research into the nature of cancer.

BIBLIOGRAPHY

1. AHLSTROM, L., EULER, H. v., and HEVESY, G. v. Die Wirkung von Röntgenstrahlen auf den Nukleinsäureumsatz in den Organen der Ratte. *Arkiv. Kemi Mineral Geol. 19A:* 1-16, 1944.
2. AHLSTROM, L., EULER, H. v., and HEVESY, G. v. Über die indirekte Wirkung von Röntgenstrahlen auf das Jensen-Sarkom. *Arkiv. Kemi Mineral. Geol. 19A:* 1-16, 1944.
3. ANDERSON, S. RY. *Treatise for the Doctorate at the University of Copenhagen.* Copenhagen, Einar Munksgaard, 1949.
4. ANDREASEN, E., and OTTESEN, J. Significance of the various lymphoid organs to the lymphocyte production in the albino rat. *Acta. path. et-microbial Scandinav, 54:* 25-32, 1944.
5. AXELROD, D., AEBERSOLD, P. C., and LAWRENCE, J. H. Comparative effects of neutrons and X-rays on 3 tumors irradiated in vitro. *Proc. Soc. Exper. Biol. & Med. 48:* 251-256, 1941.
6. BAGG, H. J. Effect of roentgen rays on tumors in animals treated by prolonged continuous exposure of entire body. *Am. J. Roentgenol. 40:* 418-426, 1938.
7. BARRON, E. S. G. The effect of ionizing radiations on the activity of enzymes. *Brookhaven Conference Report*, BNL-C-4, pp. 10-16, 1948.*

* Information concerning the availability of this document may be obtained by addressing inquiries to the Office of Technical Service, Department of Commerce, Washington 25, D. C.

8. BLOOM, W. (ED.). *Histopathology of Irradiation from External and Internal Sources.* NNES, Div. IV, 221. New York, McGraw-Hill Book Co., 1948.
9. BRUES, A. M. Biological hazards and toxicity of radioactive isotopes. *J. Clin. Investigation 28:* 1286-1296, 1949.
10. BRUES, A. M. "Carcinogenic effects of radiation." In *Advances in Biological and Medical Physics.* J. H. Lawrence and J. G. Hamilton, eds. New York, Academic Press, Inc., 1951, vol. 2, pp. 171-191.
11. BRUES, A. M., FINKEL, M. P., LISCO, H., and SACHER, G. A. Age and lymphoma incidence in CF-1 mice. *Cancer Research 9:* 604, 1949.
12. BRUES, A. M., and RIETZ, L. Effects of external and internal radiation on cell division. *Ann. N. Y. Acad. Sc. 51:* 1497-1507, 1951.
13. BRUES, A. M., and STROUD, A. N. 1951. Unpublished data.
14. CARLSON, J. G. Effects of radiation on mitosis. *J. Cell. & Comp. Physiol. 35:* (Suppl. 1) 89-101, 1950.
15. CHAMBERS, R., and GRAND, C. G. Leucocytic infiltration of irradiated mouse sarcoma 180. *Proc. Soc. Exper. Biol. & Med. 36:* 673-675, 1937.
16. CLARK, A. M., and KELLY, E. M. Differential radiosensitivity of haploid and diploid prepupae and pupae of *Habrobracon. Cancer Research 10:* 348-352, 1950.
17. CLAUDE, A. *Studies on cells: Morphology, Chemical Constitution, and Distribution of Biochemical Functions.* The Harvey Lectures. Springfield, Ill., Charles C Thomas, pp. 121-164, 1947-1948.
18. COMAN, D. R. Invasive character of cancer growth. *Am. J. M. Sc. 211:* 257-260, 1946.
19. CRAMER, W. Experimental observations on the effect of radium on a precancerous skin area. *Tenth Scientific report of the Imperial Cancer Research Fund (London)*, 1932. pp. 81-93.
20. DALE, W. M. Action of radiation on aqueous solutions: Experimental work with enzymes in solution. *Brit. J. Radiol.* Supplement *1:* 46-50, 1947.
21. DARLINGTON, C. D., and LACOUR, L. F. Chromosome breakage and the nucleic acid cycle. *J. Genetics 46:* 180-267, 1944.
22. DESJARDINS, A. V. Causes of cell death in irradiated tissue. *Am. J. Roentgenol. 28:* 398-401, 1932.
23. DOLJANSKI, L., GOLDHABER, G., and HALBERSTAEDTER, L. Comparative studies on radiosensitivity of normal and malignant cells in culture; delayed lethal effect. *Cancer Research 4:* 106-109, 1944.
24. DONALDSON, M. Some new facts concerning prognosis and treatment of carcinoma of cervix by radiation. *Proc. Roy. Soc. Med. 39:* 10-17, 1945.
25. DOWNING, V., BISHOP, F. W., and WARREN, S. L. Effects of roentgen irradiation upon blood vessels of repair tissue and Brown-Pearce rabbit epithelioma. *Am. J. Roentgenol. 43:* 249-261, 1940.
26. EISEN, M. J. Transplantable carcinoma of rat breast. *Am. J. Cancer 39:* 36-44, 1940.
27. ELSON, L. A., and LAMBERTON, L. F. The influence of the protein content of the diet on the response of Walker rat carcinoma 256 to X-radiation. *Brit. J. Cancer 3:* 414-426, 1949.
28. EULER, H. V., and HEVESY, G. Wirkung der Röntgenstrahlen auf den Umsatz der Nukleinsäure im Jensen-Sarkom. *Det Kgl. Danske Videnskabernes Selskab, Biol. Meddelelser 8:* 1-38, 1942.

29. FAILLA, G. Some aspects of biological action of ionizing radiations: Janeway lecture, 1939. *Am. J. Roentgenol. 44:* 649-664, 1940.
30. FIGGE, F. H. J. Cosmic radiation and cancer. *Science 105:* 323-325, 1947.
31. FOGG, L. C., and WARREN, S. Centriole in radiated tumor tissue. *Science 91:* 528-529, 1940.
32. FOGG, L. C., and WARREN, S. Comparison of cytoplasmic changes induced in Walker rat carcinoma 256 by different types and dosages of radiation: Golgi apparatus. *Am. J. Cancer 31:* 567-577, 1937.
33. FOGG, L. C., and WARREN, S. Cytoplasmic changes induced in Walker rat carcinoma 256 by X-radiation of different intensities. *Proc. Soc. Exper. Biol. & Med. 39:* 91-93, 1938.
34. FOGG, L. C., and WARREN, S. Some cytologic effects of repeated doses of radiation on mouse sarcoma 180. *Cancer Research 2:* 517-520, 1942.
35. FORSSBERG, A. The bearing of radiation chemistry on the mode of action of radiation. Abstract 83, *Sixth Internat. Congr. Radiology,* London, 1950.
36. FORSSBERG, A. On the possibility of protecting the living organism against roentgen rays by chemical means. *Acta Radiol. 33:* 296-304, 1950.
37. FRANKS, W. R., and MEEK, G. A. Influence of background radiation on methylcholanthrene carcinogenesis in mice. *Cancer Research 10:* 217, 1950.
38. FRICKE, H. Chemical-physical foundation for biological effects of X-rays. *Cold Spring Harbor Symp., Quant. Biol. 2:* 241-248, 1934.
39. FRIEDEWALD, W. F., and ANDERSON, R. S. Influence of extraneous protein and virus concentration on the inactivation of the rabbit papilloma virus by X rays. *J. Exper. Med. 74:* 463-487, 1941.
40. FURTH, J., and FURTH, O. B. Neoplastic diseases produced in mice by general irradiation with X-rays; incidence and types of neoplasms. *Am. J. Cancer 28:* 54-65, 1936.
41. FURTH, J., TUGGLE, A., and BREEDIS, C. Quantitative studies on effect of X-rays on neoplastic cells. *Proc. Soc. Exper. Biol. & Med. 38:* 490-492, 1938.
42. GEORGE, E. P., GEORGE, M., BOOTH, J., and HORNING, E. S. Influence of cosmic radiation on induced carcinogenesis in mice. *Nature 164:* 1044-1045, 1949.
43. GERSHON-COHEN, J., SHAY, H., and FELS, S. S. Experimental studies with "contact" roentgen rays: Time-intensity factor of "tumor dose" for rat sarcoma 39 in situ. *Am. J. Roentgenol. 46:* 600-604, 1941.
44. GIESE, A. C. Radiations and cell division. *Quart. Rev. Biol. 22:* 253-282, 1947.
45. GLÜCKSMANN, A. Preliminary observations on the quantitative examination of human biopsy material taken from irradiated carcinomata. *Brit. J. Radiol. 14:* 187-198, 1941.
46. GLÜCKSMANN, A. Quantitative histological analysis of radiation effects in human carcinomata. *Brit. M. Bull. 4:* 26-30, 1946.
47. GLÜCKSMANN, A., and SPEAR, F. G. Qualitative and quantitative histological examination of biopsy material from patients treated by radiation for carcinoma of cervix uteri. *Brit. J. Radiol. 18:* 313-322, 1945.
48. GOLDFEDER, A. Relation between radiation effects and cell viability as indicated by induced resistance to transplanted tumors. *Radiology 39:* 426-431, 1942.
49. GOLDFEDER, A. Further studies on the relation between radiation effects, cell viability, and induced resistance to malignant growth: effects of roentgen rays on Bagg-Jacksen mouse carcinoma 755 irradiated in vitro and in situ. *Radiology 44:* 283-292, 1945.

50. Goldfeder, A. Relationship between morphology and X-ray effects in implants of mouse sarcoma 180 irradiated with 5,000 and 60,000 roentgens (in air). *Radiology 45:* 49-55, 1945.
51. Goldfeder, A. Induced resistance in inbred homozygous rats to lymphosarcoma autogenous to the strain. *Proc. Soc. Exper. Biol. & Med. 59:* 104-109, 1945.
52. Goldfeder, A. Further studies on the relation between radiation effects, cell viability, and induced resistance to malignant growth: IV. Comparison of effects of roentgen rays on mammary tumors autogenous to inbred strains of mice (DBA and C3H). *Radiology 49:* 724-732, 1947.
53. Goldfeder, A. Further studies on the radiosensitivity of tumors autogenous to homozygous hosts. *Radiology 52:* 230-238, 1949.
54. Goldfeder, A. Further studies on the relation between radiation effects, cell viability, and induced resistance to malignant growth. VI. Anomolous radiosensitivities of analogous mouse mammary adenocarcinomas. *Radiology 54:* 93-115, 1950.
55. Goldfeder, A. The relative metabolism in vitro of analogous mammary tumors: I. Oxygen uptake and aerobic glycolysis of mammary tumors autogenous to DBA and C3H strains of mice. *Cancer Research 10:* 89-92, 1950.
56. Goldhaber, G., Doljanski, L., and Halberstaedter, L. Comparative studies on radiosensitivity of normal and malignant cells in culture: further studies on inhibitory effect of X-rays on cell outgrowth. *Cancer Research 4:* 110-112, 1944.
57. Gray, L. H. Comparative studies of biological effects of X-rays, neutrons, and other ionizing radiations. *Brit. M. Bull. 4:* 11-18, 1946.
58. Gray, L. H., and Read, J. Comparison of lethal effect of neutrons and gamma rays on mouse tumours; by irradiation of grafted tumors in vivo; by irradiation of tumor fragments in vitro. *Brit. J. Radiol. 21:* 5-10, 1948.
59. Gray, L. H., and Scholes, M. E. The effect of ionizing radiations on the broad bean root: Part VIII (cont.). *Brit. J. Radiol. 24:* 228-236, 1951.
60. Halberstaedter, L., Doljanski, L., and Tannenbaum, E. Experiments on the cancerization of cells in vitro by means of Rous sarcoma agent. *Brit. J. Exper. Path. 22:* 179-187, 1941.
61. Halberstaedter, L., Goldhaber, G., and Doljanski, L. Comparative studies on radiosensitivity of normal and malignant cells in culture: effect of X-rays on cell outgrowth in cultures of normal rat fibroblasts and rat benzpyrene-induced sarcoma. *Cancer Research 2:* 28-31, 1942.
62. Harvey, W. F. Review of irradiation effect on cells and tissues of skin. *Edinburgh M. J. 49:* 529-552, 1942.
63. Henshaw, P. S., and Meyer, L. H. Influence of irradiation-killed cells on tumor growth. *J. Nat. Cancer Inst. 4:* 305-307, 1943.
64. Hevesy, G. On the effect of roentgen rays on cellular division. *Rev. Modern Phys. 17:* 102-111, 1945.
65. Hevesy, G. *Radioactive Indicators.* New York, Interscience Publishers, 1948.
66. Hevesy, G., and Ottesen, J. Rate of formation of nucleic acid in the organs of the rat. *Acta physiol. Scandinav 5:* 237-247, 1943.
67. Hewitt, H. B., and Read, J. Search for an effect of oxygen on the direct X-ray inactivation of bacteriophage. *Brit. J. Radiol. 23:* 416-423, 1950.
68. Hollcroft, J., Lorenz, E., and Hunstiger, A. Effects of ionizing radiations on a transplanted lymphosarcoma. *J. Nat. Cancer Inst. 11:* 1-16, 1950.

69. HOLMES, B. E. The inhibition of ribo- and thymo-nucleic acid synthesis in tumor tissue by irradiation with X-rays. *Brit J. Radiol. 20:* 450-453. 1947.

70. HOLMES, B. E. Indirect effect of X-rays on synthesis of nucleic acid in vivo. *Brit J. Radiol. 22:* 487-491, 1949.

71. HOWARD, A. Report of "Symposium on Mode of Action of Ionizing Radiations." *Nucleonics 7:* 26-30, 1950.

72. HUFF, R. L., BETHARD, W. F., GARCIA, J. F., ROBERTS, B. M., JACOBSON, L. O., and LAWRENCE, J. H. Tracer iron distribution studies in irradiated rats with leadshielded spleens. *J. Lab. & Clin. Med. 36:* 40-51, 1950.

73. JOLLES, B., and KOLLER, P. C. The role of connective tissue in the radiation reaction of tumors. *Brit. J. Cancer 4:* 77-89, 1950.

74. JUUL, J. Experimental studies on roentgen treatment of malignant tumors. *Acta radiol.*, supplement *9:* 1-104, 1929.

75. KAPLAN, H. S. Preliminary studies on effectiveness of local irradiation in induction of lymphoid tumors in mice. *J. Nat. Cancer Inst. 10:* 267-270, 1949.

76. KAPLAN, H. S. Influence of ovarian function on incidence of radiation-induced ovarian tumors in mice. *J. Nat. Cancer Inst. 11:* 125-132, 1950.

77. KAPLAN, H. S., and MURPHY, E. D. The effect of local roentgen irradiation on the biological behavior of a transplantable mouse carcinoma: I. Increased frequency of pulmonary metastasis. *J. Nat. Cancer Inst. 9:* 407-413, 1949.

78. KELLY, L. S., and JONES, H. B. Effects of irradiation on nucleic acid formation. *Proc. Soc. Exper. Biol. & Med. 74:* 493-497, 1950.

79. KIRSCHBAUM, A., and MIXER, H. W. Induction of leukemia in 8 inbred stocks of mice varying in susceptibility to spontaneous disease. *J. Lab. & Clin. Med. 32:* 720-731, 1947.

80. KOLLER, P. C. The effect of radiation on the normal and malignant cell in man. *Brit. J. Radiol.* supplement 1, 84-98, 1947.

81. KOLLER, P. C., and SMITHERS, D. W. Cytological analysis of response of malignant tumours to irradiation as approach to biological basis for dosage in radiotherapy. *Brit. J. Radiol. 19:* 89-100, 1946.

82. KREBS, C. Effect of roentgen irradiation on interrelation between malignant tumors and their hosts. *Acta radiol.*, supplement *8:* 1-133, 1929.

83. KREBS, C. Experiments with mammalian sarcoma extracts in regard to cell-free transmission and induced tumor immunity. *Acta radiol.*, supplement 44, *24:* 190-197, 1942.

84. KRENZ, F. H. Report of "Symposium on Radiation Chemistry." Nucleonics *7:* 67-70, 1950.

85. LACASSAGNE, A. *Les Cancers Produits par les Rayonnements Electro-magnétiques.* Paris, Hermann & Cie., 1945.

86. LACASSAGNE, A. Advances in radiobiology between 1937-1950. Nucleonics *7:* 62-67, 1950.

87. LASNITZKI, I. Quantitative analysis of effect of gamma radiation on malignant cells in vitro and in vivo. *Brit. J. Radiol. 18:* 214-220, 1945.

88. LASNITZKI, I. Quantitative analysis of direct and indirect action of X radiation on malignant cells. *Brit. J. Radiol. 20:* 240-247, 1947.

89. LAWRENCE, J. H., HORN, R., and STRONG, L. C. Radiation studies on mammary carcinoma of mice. *Yale J. Biol. & Med. 10:* 145-154, 1937.

90. LEA, D. E. *Action of Radiations on Living Cells.* New York, Macmillan, 1947.

91. LEA, D. E. The induction of chromosome structural changes by radiation: Detailed quantitative interpretation. *Brit. J. Radiol.* supplement 1, 75-83, 1947.
92. LICK, L., KIRSCHBAUM, A., and MIXER, H. Mechanism of induction of ovarian tumors by X-rays. *Cancer Research 9:* 532-536, 1949.
93. LIND, S. C. The chemical effects of alpha particles and electrons. Am. Chem. Soc. Monograph Series. No. 2, 1928. The Chemical Catalog Company, Inc.
94. LISCO, H., FINKLE, M. P., and BRUES, A. M. Plutonium project: Carcinogenic properties of radioactive fission products and of plutonium. *Radiology 49:* 361-362, 1947.
95. LUDFORD, R. J. Cytological changes after irradiation of malignant growths. *Tenth Scientific Report of the Imperial Cancer Research Fund (London)*, 1932, pp. 125-168.
96. LURIA, S. E., and EXNER, F. M. On the enzymatic hypotheses of radiosensitivity (letter to the Editor). *J.A.M.A. 117:* 2190, 1941.
97. MARINELLI, L. D., and KENNEY, J. M. Absorption of radiophosphorus in irradiated and non-irradiated mice. *Radiology 37:* 691-697, 1941.
98. MARTLAND, H. S., and HUMPHRIES, R. E. Osteogenic sarcoma in dial painters using luminous paint. *Arch. Path. 7:* 406-417, 1929.
99. MAZIA, D., and BLUMENTHAL, G. Inactivation of enzyme-substrate film by small doses of X-rays. *J. Cell. & Comp. Physiol. 35:* (Suppl. 1) 171-186, 1950.
100. MITCHELL, J. S. Disturbance of nucleic acid metabolism produced by therapeutic doses of X and gamma radiations: Accumulation of pentose nucleotides in cytoplasm after irradiation. *Brit. J. Exper. Path. 23:* 296-309, 1942.
101. MITCHELL, J. S. Disturbance of nucleic acid metabolism produced by therapeutic doses of X and gamma radiations: inhibition of synthesis of thymonucleic acid by radiation. *Brit. J. Exper. Path. 23:* 309-313, 1942.
102. MITCHELL, J. S. Disturbance of nucleic acid metabolism produced by therapeutic doses of X and gamma radiations: methods of investigation. *Brit. J. Exper. Path. 23:* 285-295, 1942.
103. MITCHELL, J. S. Experimental radiotherapeutics. *Schweiz. med. Wchnschr. 76:* 883-889, 1946.
104. MIYOSI, H. Effect of X rays upon enzymes in tissue of malignant tumor. *Japan. J. Obst. & Gynec. 23:* 263-283, 1940.
105. MULLER, R. J. Some present problems in the genetic effects of radiation. *J. Cell. & Comp. Physiol 35:* (Suppl. 1) 9-70, 1950.
106. OUGHTERSON, A. W., PLAUT, J., and LAWRENCE, E. A. Tumor response to roentgen irradiation as influenced by host-tumor relation. *Am. J. Roentgenol 47:* 207-209, 1942.
107. OUGHTERSON, A. W., TANNANT, R., and LAWRENCE, E. A. Tumor response and stroma reaction following X-ray of transplantable tumor in inbred strains of mice. *Yale J. Biol. & Med. 12:* 419-425, 1940.
108. OVERGAARD, K., and OKKELS, H. Action of dry heat on Wood's sarcoma. *Acta radiol. 21:* 577-582, 1940.
109. PACKARD, C. Biological effectiveness of high-voltage and low-voltage X-rays. *Am. J. Cancer 16:* 1257-1274, 1932.
110. PATT, H. M., TYREE, E. B., STRAUBE, R. L., and SMITH, D. E. Cysteine protection against X-irradiation. *Science 110:* 213-214, 1949.
111. POULSON, B. R. Investigation into time factor in roentgen irradiation of cancer cells: Protraction experiments with transplantable mouse round-cell sarcoma and transplantable mouse carcinoma. *Acta radiol. 26:* 463-483, 1945.

112. Raper, J. R., Henshaw, P. S., and Snider, R. S. Delayed effects of single exposures to beta rays. MDDC-578. Effects of periodic total surface beta irradiation. MDDC-580, 1946.*

113. Read, J. The effect of nitrogen mustard on the growth of the broad bean root. *Brit. J. Radiol. 23:* 504, 1950.

114. Reinhard, M. C., and Warner, S. G. Preliminary report of effect of X-rays and tumor of known genetic constitution. *Radiology 34:* 438-439, 1940.

115. Reinhard, M. C., Warner, S. G., and Goltz, H. L. Further studies on effect of X-rays on tumor of known genetic constitution. *Cancer Research 1:* 653-655, 1941.

116. Rowntree, L. G. Contribution to the study of X-ray carcinoma and the conditions which precedes its onset (first communication). *Arch. Middlesex Hospital 13:* 182-205, 1908.

117. Sahler, O. de P., and Warren, S. L. Physiological effects of radiation: in vitro lethal single massive roentgen-ray dose (at 200 kv.) for Brown-Pearce rabbit epithelioma. *Am. J. Roentgenol. 41:* 954-961, 1939.

118. Salter, W. T. Chemistry of carcinogens. *Occup. Med. 5:* 441-465, 1948.

119. Sievert, R. M. Zur theoretisch-mathematischen Behandlung des Problems der biologischen Strahlenwirkung. *Acta radiol. 22:* 237-251, 1941.

120. Sittenfield, M. J. Significance of lymphocyte. *J. Cancer Res. 2:* 151, 1917.

121. Sittenfield, M. J. Further studies on the importance of the lymphocyte in cancer immunity. *J. Cancer Res. 4:* 57-59, 1919.

122. Snellman, B. Attempt to develop reduced radio-sensitivity in Jensen rat sarcoma by means of roentgen irradiation. *Acta radiol. 16:* 545-556, 1935.

123. Sparrow, A. H., Moses, M. J., and Steele, R. Sensitivity of chromosomes to breakage by X-rays and its relationship to the nucleic acid cycle in dividing cells. *Cancer Research 10:* 241-242, 1950.

124. Sparrow, A. H., and Rosenfeld, F. M. X-ray-induced depolymerization of thymonucleohistone and of sodium thymonucleate. *Science 105:* 245-246, 1946.

125. Spear, F. G. Biological effects of penetrating radiations. *Brit. M. Bull. 4:* 2-11, 1946.

126. Stowell, R. E. Effects of roentgen radiation on thymonucleic acid content of transplantable mammary carcinomas. *Cancer Research 5:* 169-178, 1945.

127. Sugiura, K. Effect of roentgen rays on growth of mouse sarcoma 180 irradiated in vivo. *Radiology 28:* 162-171, 1937.

128. Sugiura, K. Studies on radiosensitivity of mouse sarcoma 180 irradiated in vivo and in vitro. *Radiology 29:* 352-361, 1937.

129. Tahmisian, T., and Barron, E. S. G. The effect of X irradiation on the oxygen consumption and morphological development of the grasshopper embryo (*Melanoplus differentialis*). Quarterly Report, Biology Division, Argonne National Laboratory, (A. M. Brues, ed.,) ANL-4078, pp. 106-132, 1947.*

130. Taylor, B., Greenstein, J. P., and Hollaender, A. Effects of X-radiation on thymus nucleic acid. *Science 105:* 263-264, 1947.

131. Tobias, C. A. The dependence of some biological effects of radiation on the rate of energy loss. *Symposium on Radiobiology*, June 14-18, 1950, Oberlin, Ohio (in press).

* Information concerning the availability of this document may be obtained by addressing inquiries to the Office of Technical Service, Department of Commerce, Washington 25, D. C.

132. Toniolo, G. Wirkung der Röntgenstrahlen auf das Galliera-Sarkom in vivo und in vitro. *Strahlentherapie 65:* 375-396, 1939.
133. Van der Werff, J. T. *Biological Reactions Caused by Electric Currents and by X-rays.* New York, Elsevier, 1948.
134. Warner, S. G., and Reinhard, M. C. Effect of X-rays on tumor of known genetic constitution. *Proc. Soc. Exper. Biol. & Med. 42:* 673-676, 1939.
135. Warren, S. Effects of radiation on normal tissues. *Arch. Path. 35:* 121-139, 304-353, 1943.
136. Warren, S. Mechanism of radiation effects against malignant tumors. *J.A.M.A. 133:* 462-463, 1947.
137. Warren, S., *et al.* Effects of radiation on normal tissue. *Arch. Path. 34:* 443-450, 562-608, 749-787, 917-931, 1070-1084, 1942.
138. Weiss, J. Some aspects of the chemical and biological action of radiations. *Trans. Faraday Soc. 43:* 314-324, 1947.
139. Wolff, B., and Ellis, F. Quantitative histological analysis of radiation effects in human carcinomata. *Brit. J. Radiol. 20:* 381-386, 1947.
140. Wood, C. A. P. Some factors influencing response of cancer to radiation. *J.A.M.A. 140:* 513-520, 1949.
141. Zirkle, R. E. Relationships between chemical and biological effects of ionizing radiations. *Radiology 52:* 846-855, 1949.

PART III

Clinical Investigation

CHAPTER 24

Steroid Metabolism in Cancer

Lewis L. Engel

The stimuli for the study of possible derangements of steroid metabolism in neoplastic disease are many. The classic studies of Loeb on the relation between estrogenic hormones and mammary carcinogenesis in mice is perhaps the first link between these two areas of investigation, although the structures of the active compounds were not known at that time. When the structures of cholesterol and the bile acids were established in the period 1932–34, their close chemical relationship to the carcinogenic hydrocarbons of the cholanthrene series became apparent and further strengthened the link between steroid biochemistry and the cancer field.

The recognition that the hormones of the gonads and adrenal cortex belong to the steroid class made it necessary to include them in any consideration of the relation between the steroids and carcinogenesis. This concept stimulated the search for abnormal metabolites of the steroid hormones in the urine of patients suffering from benign and malignant tumors of organs which synthesize steroid hormones. In addition, the urine of patients with functioning tumors of the pituitary gland was investigated in the hope of finding steroid compounds elaborated as a result of excessive stimulation of the adrenal glands and gonads by the pituitary tropic hormones. These studies led to the recognition of many metabolites, both normal and abnormal.

More recent work on the palliative effects of castration and estrogenic hormones on cancer of the prostate gland; and of castration, estrogens, and androgens on breast cancer,[104] has directed attention to other aspects of the problem. These investigations have raised the question of whether a fundamental disorder of steroid hormone production or metabolism is associated with the initiation and maintenance of the neoplastic process. These studies also emphasize the important concept that certain tumors are not wholly autonomous, but may be influenced by humoral agents which have a regulatory effect on the growth and development of the normal organism. Thus, it would appear that the problem of steroid metabolism in cancer must be examined in terms of the tumor-host relation and the biologic and biochemical effects of each upon the other. This concept is fortified by the more recent work on adrenal cortical steroids and ACTH which emphasizes the central role of the adrenal gland in many pathologic processes and in stress phenomena.

The increasing interest in this aspect of the cancer problem has produced an intensification of effort to bring order into the body of data which has been amassed. At the present time, no definite answer can be given to the question, "What are the defects in steroid metabolism in cancer?" However, some suggestive and encouraging data have been forthcoming.

It is the intention of this review to outline briefly, first, the methods of attack on the problem of steroid metabolism, second, the excretion of neutral steroids by patients with tumors of steroidogenic organs,* and finally, neutral steroid excretion in patients with tumors of other sites. It is hoped that this discussion will help to organize the known facts, as well as to indicate the many and important gaps in our knowledge of this field. The excretion of estrogens in cancer will not be covered since this phase of the problem is much less developed and the data are insufficient.

STEROID CHEMISTRY AND NOMENCLATURE

For material on the structure and other aspects of steroid chemistry, the reader is referred to the authoritative monograph by Fieser and Fieser.[47] The nomenclature used in this chapter will conform with that used in the monograph. The names and configurations employed here will sometimes differ, therefore, from those used by the original authors. This may appear unnecessarily confusing at present, but ultimately the advantages of a uniform and consistent nomenclature like that of the Fiesers will outweigh the temporary drawbacks.†

Articles on more specialized phases of steroid biochemistry may be found in the two review series, *Vitamins and Hormones*,[54] and *Recent Progress in Hormone Research*.[117] Excellent review articles on the chemistry and metabolism of the steroid hormones may be found in *The Hormones*.[118] Two recent reviews of urinary steroids[44, 94] give important data on excretion studies in various diseases.

URINARY EXCRETION OF NEUTRAL STEROIDS

METHODS FOR THE STUDY OF URINARY STEROIDS

Urinary steroids have been investigated by means of three general approaches: (1) isolation, (2) analysis by more or less specific methods, and (3) bioassay.

The isolation technic has been developed over a period of years into a highly precise tool. Using graded hydrolysis of the conjugates, group reactions for the separation of different classes of steroids, further analysis by systematic fractional chromatography, and finally infrared spectroscopy, Dobriner, Jones, Lieberman and their co-workers[30, 34, 35, 70, 79, 80] have isolated a large number of steroid ketones from the urine of normal and diseased persons. Other investigators, whose work will be

* The term "steroidogenic organs" will be used to designate those organs which synthesize steroid hormones, i.e., adrenal cortex and gonads.

† The author realizes that this is a field involving complex chemistry which cannot be developed here. It is suggested, therefore, that this paper be read in conjunction with references to the Fieser textbook.[47]

referred to more specifically below, have also carried out important studies on the ketonic as well as the nonketonic steroids.

Because of their greater adaptability, especially to the requirements of clinical laboratories, spectrophotometric, fluorometric, and gravimetric methods have found wider application than the costly and time-consuming isolation technics. Many of the methods commonly employed are discussed in the excellent monograph edited by Emmens,[39] and some newer methods are reviewed by Engel.[40]

Bioassay methods which were formerly used very extensively are now being replaced by the less expensive and more rapid chemical and physical methods. Bioassay methods for steroid hormones are also reviewed in the Emmens monograph.[39]

ISOLATION AND DISTRIBUTION OF URINARY STEROIDS

The isolation of steroid compounds from the urine of healthy and diseased persons has occupied the attention of numerous investigations for many years. Such studies are fundamental to an appreciation of the distribution of steroids in urine. To be sure, this type of information can give only partial answers to many questions concerning the pathways traversed by the steroids between the time they leave the sites of their synthesis and their appearance in the urine. Nevertheless, the occurrence in urine of compounds structurally related to the known hormones gives some clue to the reactions involved in the metabolic degradation of these hormones. Further information may also be gained by studying the excretion products in the urine after the administration of steroid and pituitary hormones. The accumulation of data from these different studies has given significant information on the interrelationships between the urinary steroids and their hormonal precursors.

One may draw partial distinctions between the metabolites of the testicular hormones (and under certain conditions, ovarian androgens) and the metabolites derived from the adrenal cortical hormones. Those urinary compounds which bear an oxygen function at C-11 (or artifacts derived therefrom) are on grounds of structural similarity regarded as metabolites of the C-11-oxygenated adrenal cortical compounds. This is also presumably true of neutral steroids of the androstane and pregnane series bearing an oxygen function at C-16, and pregnane derivatives possessing an hydroxyl group at C-17. In contrast, the compounds derived from the testicular hormone do not bear substituents in the 11, 16, or 17 positions. However, many compounds without these labels may also be derived from adrenal cortical precursors.

Steroids either absent under normal circumstances or present only in minute amounts have been isolated from the urine of diseased persons. Although this is significant information, the isolation technic does not lend itself to widespread application. However, before any short-cuts can be taken, we must have information concerning the types of steroid compounds present. Urinary steroid distribution will be discussed under: (1) functioning tumors of steroidogenic endocrine glands, and (2) tumors of other organs and tissues. In the first group it is frequently difficult to distinguish between primary tumors of the adrenal cortex, and hyperactivity due to excessive stimulation by the pituitary tropic hormone. The latter may result from a functioning pituitary tumor.

TABLE 49. NEUTRAL STEROIDS IN HUMAN URINE

Compound	*Diagnosis* N[a]	Ca[b]	ACT[c]	ACH[d]	CS[e]	GT[f]	Preg.[g]	*References**
Δ^{16}-Androstene-3α-ol	+		+					6, 96
$\Delta^{2(or\ 3)}$-Androstene-17-one[j]	+	+		+		+[h] +[i]		30, 41, 59, 80, 113, 139
$\Delta^{3,5}$-Androstadiene-17-one[j]	+		+	+				9, 30, 80, 146
Δ^{5}-3β-chloroandrostene-17-one[j]	+		+	+				15, 42, 56, 64, 80, 95, 146
5-Isoandrostane-3α,17β-diol	+							12
Δ^{5}-Androstene-3β,17β-diol			+					73, 93, 95, 125
Androsterone	+	+	+	+	+	+[h] +[i]	+	11, 13, 16, 17, 20, 21, 22, 23, 38, 41, 43, 57, 58, 60, 72, 73, 80, 87, 93, 95, 139, 146
3-Epiandrosterone	+	+		+			+	18, 19, 60, 80, 112, 113
5-Isoandrosterone	+	+	+	+	+	+[i]	+	18, 19, 20, 21, 41, 43, 57, 58, 59, 60, 72, 73, 80, 93, 95, 146
3-Epi-5-isoandrosterone (variety of diseased individuals)[k]	+						+	82
i-Androstene-6-ol-17-one			+					29
Dehydroepiandrosterone	+	+	+	+	+	+[i]	+	14, 18, 19, 21, 22, 23, 25, 38, 41, 43, 58, 59, 64, 72, 73, 80, 93, 95, 102, 113, 141, 146
Δ^{9}-Androstene-3α,ol-17-one[j]	+							80, 101
$\Delta^{11(?)}$-Androstene-3α-ol-17-one[j]	+		+	+				80, 146
Δ^{9}-5-Isoandrostene-3α-ol-17-one[j]	+	+			+			31, 32, 80
Androstane-3,17-dione	+							80
5-Isoandrostane-3,17-dione	+				+			80
Δ^{1}-Androstene-3,17-dione (variety of healthy and diseased)[k]	+							82
Δ^{4}-Androstene-3,17-dione	+			+				31, 80
Δ^{5}-Androstene-3β,16α-17β-triol	+		+					61, 62, 73, 91, 95
Androstane-3α,11β-diol-17-one	+		+	+	+			72, 73, 80, 92, 93, 95, 101
5-Isoandrostane-3α,11β-diol-17-one	+	+			+			27, 31, 79, 81, 82
5-Isoandrostane-3α,17β-diol-11-one	+							82
Androstane-3α-ol-11,17-dione (many normal and diseased persons)[k]	+							82
5-Isoandrostane-3α-ol-11,17-dione (majority of urines examined)[k]	+	+		+	+			78, 80
Pregnane-3α-ol							+	87
$\Delta^{2(or\ 3)}$-Allopregnene-20-one[j]			+				+	80

TABLE 49. NEUTRAL STEROIDS IN HUMAN URINE (*Continued*)

Compound	*Diagnosis* N[a]	Ca[b]	ACT[c]	ACH[d]	CS[e]	GT[f]	Preg.[g]	*References*
Pregnane-3α,20α-diol	+		+	+		+[i]	+	2, 10, 18, 41, 43, 51, 59, 66, 88, 89, 90, 93, 95, 124, 137, 140
Pregnane-3β,20α-diol				+			+	72, 84, 95
Allopregnane-3α,20α-diol	+						+	55, 75, 88, 89
Allopregnane-3β,20α-diol							+	88, 89
Δ⁵-Pregnene-3β,20α-diol			+					63, 125
Pregnane-3α-ol-20-one				+			+	80, 85, 87, 114
Allopregnane-3α-ol-20-one							+	80, 86
Allopregnane-3β-ol-20-one							+	80, 115
17-Isopregnane-3α-ol-20-one							+	80
Pregnane-3,20-dione				+				80
Allopregnane-3,20-dione							+	80
Pregnane-3α,17α,20α-triol			+	+				18, 19, 72, 93, 95
Δ⁵-Pregnene-3β,16α,20α-triol			+					65
Δ⁵-Pregnene-3β,17α,20α-triol			+					66
Pregnane-3α,6α-diol-20-one							+	80, 82
Allopregnane-3α,6α-diol-20-one							+	80
Pregnane-3α,17α-diol-20-one			+	+				77, 80, 93, 98, 132
Pregnane-3α,20α-diol-11-one	+			+				82
Δ⁵-Pregnene-3β,17α-diol-20-one			+					64
17a-Methyl-Δ⁵-D-homo-androstene-3β,17aβ-diol-17-one[j]			+					64
Pregnane-3α-ol-11,20-dione				+				80, 82
Pregnane-3α,17α,21-triol-11,20-dione	+							126
Δ⁴-Pregnene-11β,17α,21-triol-3,20-dione					+			97
Δ⁴-Pregnene-17α,21-diol-3,11,20-trione	+							126

* Numbers refer to the items in the bibliography at the end of this chapter.
[a] = Normal men and women
[b] = Cancer of sites other than adrenal cortex and gonads
[c] = Adrenal cortical tumors
[d] = Adrenal cortical hyperplasia
[e] = Cushing's syndrome
[f] = Gonadal tumors
[g] = Pregnancy
[h] = Testicular tumors (interstitial cell)
[i] = Masculinizing ovarian tumors
[j] = Compounds regarded as artifacts of dehydration, substitution or rearrangement.
[k] = cf. Ref. 80, 82

FUNCTIONING TUMORS OF STEROIDOGENIC ORGANS

The classification of functioning endocrine tumors published by Nathanson[105] will be employed insofar as it is applicable. Table 49 gives a survey of steroid compounds which have been isolated from human urine. Only those compounds which have been obtained in crystalline form, characterized by standard organic chemical technics, and whose structures are established, are included. Compounds isolated from the urine of normal men and women and from pregnant women are included to provide a basis for comparison. In Table 49 the steroids isolated from human urine are listed in order of increasing substitution of first, the androstane nucleus, and second, the pregnane nucleus. The compounds are classified as saturated monohydroxy-steroids, unsaturated monohydroxy-steroids, saturated monoketones, unsaturated monoketones, saturated monohydroxy-monoketones, unsaturated monohydroxy-monoketones, etc. Those compounds which are generally regarded as artifacts of dehydration, substitution, or rearrangement are designated with asterisks.

It is too early to place any firm interpretation upon the qualitative aspects of the distribution of urinary steroids. A compound may be recorded in the table as absent from the urine of a given type of patient simply because it may occur in minute quantities in a fraction which has not been explored so intensively as the ketonic fraction. Most isolation studies have been concentrated on the neutral steroids, and in particular the ketonic fraction. However, the neutral "nonketonic" fraction contains materials which would undoubtedly repay closer examination.

OVARY

The characterization of steroids in the urine of patients suffering from this rare group of tumors has not been extensive. Only one report may be cited. Engel, Dorfman and Abarbanel[41] studied one such patient. The precise diagnosis of the tumor is still under discussion. The tumor may have been a luteoma, an arrhenoblastoma, or an adrenal cell tumor. The steroids isolated in this instance were $\Delta^{2 (\text{or } 3)}$-androstene-17-one,* androsterone, 5-isoandrosterone, dehydroepiandrosterone, and pregnane-3α,20α-diol. From Table 49 it may be seen that none of these compounds can be regarded as an abnormal urinary metabolite, although in the normal female the androstane derivatives originate in the adrenal cortex.

TESTIS

In the case of functioning tumors of the testis there is again a paucity of information concerning steroid excretion. Venning *et al.*[139] have reported the isolation of both $\Delta^{2 (\text{or } 3)}$-androstene-17-one* and androsterone from the urine of a patient with an interstitial cell tumor of the testis. Such tumors are rare entities and it would be desirable to study more patients to see whether these compounds are characteristic excretion products in this disease. In some instances the patients display no obvious endocrine abnormality,[136] but at least the measurement of urinary ketosteroids is desirable because of the clinical difficulty in detecting "masculinization" of an adult male.

* This compound is considered to be an artifact derived from androsterone. It is probably formed during the processing of the urine.

ADRENAL CORTEX

The urine of patients with functioning tumors of the adrenal cortex has yielded a rich harvest of steroid compounds. This wealth of material is still difficult to interpret since the number of patients examined is relatively small. Many of the compounds listed have been isolated only from the urine of one patient; hence, no generalizations can be made as to the relation between the histologic characterization of the lesion and the steroid compounds isolated from the urine. The need for caution in interpretation is further emphasized by the recognition that many of the

TABLE 50. NEUTRAL STEROIDS IN URINE OF PATIENTS WITH ADRENAL CORTICAL HYPERACTIVITY DUE TO TUMORS AND HYPERPLASIA

I. ADRENAL CORTICAL TUMOR AND CUSHING'S SYNDROME ONLY	
	Δ^5-Androstene-3β,17β-diol
	i-Androstene-6-ol-17-one
	Δ^5-Pregnene-3β,20α-diol
	Δ^5-Pregnene-3β,16α,20α-triol
	Δ^5-Pregnene-3β,17α,20α-triol
	Δ^5-Pregnene-3β,17α-diol-20-one
	17a-Methyl-Δ^5-D-homoandrostene-3β, 17aβ-diol-17-one[a]
II. ADRENAL CORTICAL HYPERPLASIA ONLY	
	Pregnane-3,20-dione
	Pregnane-3α-ol-11,20-dione
III. NORMAL AND ADRENAL CORTICAL TUMOR (INCLUDING CUSHING'S SYNDROME) ONLY	
	5-Isoandrostane-3,17-dione
	Δ^5-Androstene-3β,16α,17β-triol
IV. NORMAL AND ADRENAL CORTICAL HYPERPLASIA ONLY	
	Δ^4-Androstene-3,17-dione
	Pregnane-3α,20α-diol-11-one
	Pregnane-3α-ol-11,20-dione
V. NORMAL, ADRENAL CORTICAL TUMOR AND/OR ADRENAL CORTICAL HYPERPLASIA	
	Δ^{16}-Androstene-3α-ol
	$\Delta^{2(\text{or } 3)}$-Androstene-17-one[a]
	$\Delta^{3,5}$-Androstadiene-17-one[a]
	Δ^5-3β-chloroandrostene-17-one[a]
	Androsterone
	3-Epiandrosterone
	5-Isoandrosterone
	Dehydroepiandrosterone
	$\Delta^{11(?)}$-Androstene-3α-ol-17-one[a]
	Androstane-3α,11β-diol-17-one
	5-Isoandrostane-3α-ol-11,17-dione
	Pregnane-3α,20α-diol
VI. ADRENAL CORTICAL TUMOR AND HYPERPLASIA ONLY	
	Pregnane-3α,17α, 20α-triol
	Pregnane-3α,17α-diol-20-one

[a] Compounds presumed to be artifacts.

isolated compounds have undergone chemical alteration before their excretion in the urine. The ability of the liver, for example, to alter steroids is well known.

Nevertheless, some trends are apparent. In Table 50, the distribution of steroids isolated from normal individuals, patients with adrenal tumors (including Cushing's syndrome), and patients with adrenal hyperplasia are presented in six categories. Six compounds are included in Category I (*Adrenal cortical tumor and Cushing's syndrome only*). The relation between i-androstene-6-ol-17-one and dehydroepiandrosterone is not clear.[94] Dingemanse *et al.*,[29] who isolated the compound from urine of a patient with adrenal cortical tumor, regard it as the primary excretion product and dehydroepiandrosterone as an artifact formed during the processing of the urine. The last compound on this list, Δ^5-17a-methyl-D-homoandrostene-3β,-17aβ-diol-17-one, is considered by Hirschmann[64] to be a rearrangement product of the closely related Δ^5-pregnene-3β,17α-diol-20-one which was isolated from the same urine. The fact that five of the six compounds in this group belong to the Δ^5-3β-stenol series tends to support the view that in adrenal cortical tumors the synthesis or metabolism of steroids is shifted away from the normal 3α-stanols and favors the Δ^5-3β-stenols.

In Category III are listed those steroids which have been isolated from normal and adrenal cortical tumor urine. Only one of these two steroids, Δ^5-androstene-3β,16α,17β-triol, is a Δ^5-3β-stenol and bears an hydroxyl group at carbon 16 which suggests its adrenal origin. However, it is likely that when more refined methods are developed, some of the compounds which now appear to be peculiar to adrenal tumor urine will be found in the urine of normal subjects, although in very much smaller amounts.

The compounds in Category V (*Normal, adrenal cortical tumor and/or adrenal cortical hyperplasia*) include most of the common steroids which are generally regarded as metabolites of the adrenal cortical and testicular hormones. $\Delta^{2(\text{or }3)}$-Androstene-17-one is an artifact probably derived from androsterone. Both $\Delta^{3,5}$-androstadiene-17-one and 3β-chloroandrostene-17-one are presumably derived from dehydroepiandrosterone. $\Delta^{11(?)}$-Androstene-3α-ol-17-one may arise from the dehydration of the corresponding 11β-hydroxyandrostanolone.

There is a difference between those steroids found only in the urine of patients with adrenal tumors (Category I) and the two found only in adrenal hyperplasia (Category II). The latter group consists of one diketone and two pregnane derivatives of the 3α-stanol series. The substitution of these two compounds at C-11 and C-17 suggests that they may arise in the adrenal cortex. Two of the three compounds in Category IV also bear oxygen functions at C-11, thus indicating their adrenal origin. They also belong to the 3α-stanol series.

Category VI contains the two closely related compounds which have been isolated both from urine of patients with adrenal tumor and adrenal hyperplasia. Neither has been found in the urine of normal subjects or of patients with other diseases. Pregnane-3α,17α,20α-triol was at one time considered to be a characteristic excretion product in adrenal hyperplasia, but it has recently been isolated from the urine of an adrenal tumor patient.[93, 95]

The steroids listed in Category V are those which have been found in the three groups under discussion. It must be recalled that all of these compounds are not always present, and that these lists may be subject to considerable alteration as more data are accumulated.

STEROID EXCRETION IN CANCER OF NONSTEROIDOGENIC TISSUES

The search for steroid hormone metabolites which might be generally characteristic of cancer, has occupied the attention of Dobriner and his associates[30, 31, 32, 33, 34, 35, 35a, 77, 78, 79, 80, 81, 82] as well as other investigators for some years. The results which have been amassed at the cost of tremendous expenditure of effort suggest that the abnormality may be a quantitative as well as a qualitative one. While the number of patients examined has necessarily been limited, it is significant that 5-isoandrostane-3α,11β-diol-17-one (or the artifact of dehydration, Δ^9-5-

isoandrostene-3α-ol-17-one), has been found to occur in the urine of cancer patients, patients with adrenal hyperactivity, and patients with hypertension. It occurs only rarely in the urine of normal subjects.[31] The distribution of this important compound is given in Table 51. It is significant that this compound appeared in the urine of 2 patients several years before any obvious tumor was found, and continued to be excreted in the urine of one of these patients for five years after she had presumably been cured of a cancer of the breast by surgery.[35a] The structure of 5-isoandrostane-3α,11β-diol-17-one, its occurrence in the urine of male castrates and of eunuchoids, and its appearance (after orchiectomy) in the urine of 2 male patients with cancer of the breast, all provide evidence that it is of adrenal origin. Further evidence is the fact that the excretion of this steroid is increased after the administration of ACTH.

TABLE 51. DISTRIBUTION OF 5-ISOANDROSTANE-3α,11β-DIOL-17-ONE IN HUMAN URINE

Diagnosis	*Number of patients*	*Isoandrostanediolone present*
Normal males	15	1
Normal females	9	1
Castrates (male)	2	1
Eunuchoids	3	1
Cancer		
Prostate	10	9
Larynx	4	4
Breast (male, after castration)	2	2
Breast (female, alive)	7	4
Breast (female, dead)	7	1
Stomach	4	4
Cervix	1	1
Lymphatic leukemia	4	4
Myeloid leukemia	2	0
Other diseases		
Cushing's syndrome	7	5
Adrenal tumor and hyperplasia	6	0
Hypertension	6	3
Pregnancy		
Normal	3	0
Toxemia	4	0

From Dobriner and Lieberman.[31]

The connection between the excretion of 5-isoandrostanediolone and the carcinogenic process is at present quite obscure. Whether its occurrence in urine indicates a metabolic change related to the appearance of a neoplasm at some later date, or whether it (or its precursor) is produced as a response to the presence of a neoplasm or other endogenous change, are questions which can only be speculated upon at present. Certainly these important observations provide an encouraging starting point for a major attack on the problem of steroid metabolism in cancer.

QUANTITATIVE ASPECTS OF STEROID EXCRETION IN CANCER

STEROID EXCRETION IN TUMORS OF STEROIDOGENIC ORGANS

The availability of a simple colorimetric procedure for the measurement of the neutral 17-ketosteroids in urine has proved of considerable value in surveying the excretion of these compounds in the urine of normal and diseased persons. Considerable effort has been made to study the excretion of ketosteroids in patients, first, with functioning tumors of steroidogenic organs, and finally, with tumors of other organs and tissues. Another approach which is now in the early stages of application is directed toward the elucidation of the patterns of response of cancer patients and suitable control patients to the administration of steroid and pituitary hormones.

TABLE 52. EXCRETION OF KETOSTEROIDS BY PATIENTS WITH OVARIAN TUMORS

Age	*Ketosteroids* (mg./day)	*Diagnosis*	*References**
16	8	Arrhenoblastoma	119
24	4	Typical arrhenoblastoma	116
26	36, 56	Arrhenoblastoma	69
	11	Postoperative	
30	6.9	Arrhenoblastoma	48
	3.2	Postoperative, 5 weeks	
16	54.6	Adrenal-like ovarian tumor	71
	2.6	Postoperative, 6 months	
44	23.8	Diffuse adrenal-like cells	116
50	12–17	Diffuse, nonlipoid containing, adrenal-like tumor	116
	1.8–8.6	Postoperative	
65	43	Adrenal rest tumor	145
8	8	Dysgerminoma	53
19	7.8	Dysgerminoma	48
	2.5	Postoperative value	
12	116	Virilizing ovarian tumor (no clinical or pathologic data)	52
22	40 (per L.)	Ovarian tumor (no histologic data)	1
31	158	"Ovarian tumor"	141
46	16–17	Leydig cell tumor of ovary with virilism	142
	10.5	Postoperative, 1 year	

* Numbers refer to items in the bibliography at the end of this chapter.

Inadequacy of methods and relative inaccessibility of material have impeded studies of the excretion of estrogens and nonketonic steroids in urine. Many phases of the metabolism of these two important classes of steroids can now be more readily attacked with the development of suitable technics for their estimation.

OVARY

In Table 52 are listed ketosteroid estimations in the urine from women with ovarian tumors which were actually or potentially capable of secreting steroid material related to the ketosteroids. The variation in cellular types and the difficulty in assigning the tumors to definite categories make any interpretation of the data difficult. It is clear, however, that under certain circumstances functioning ovarian tumors may secrete precursors of the urinary ketosteroids in substantially increased amounts. In only a few instances, however, do the values approach those recorded for adrenal cortical tumors.

TESTIS

Ketosteroid excretion in patients with testicular and embryonic tumors is listed in Table 53. It will be seen that only in one instance, that of an interstitial cell tumor, is the ketosteroid excretion elevated significantly above the normal level. The rarity of these lesions has precluded examination of more patients in this group.

TABLE 53. EXCRETION OF KETOSTEROIDS BY PATIENTS WITH TESTICULAR AND EMBRYONIC TUMORS

No. of patients	*Age*	*Sex*	*Ketosteroids* (mg./day)	*Diagnosis*	*References*
1	5	M	7.4–10	Interstitial cell tumor	100
1	41	M	1015	Interstitial cell tumor	139
1	54	M	8.9	Interstitial cell tumor	120
2	21, 29	M	22.9	Teratoma testis	37
1		M	28.6	Teratoma testis	141
1	32	M	13.1	Chorionepithelioma	141
1		M	33.0	Chorionepithelioma	141
2	22, 24	F	8.9	Chorionepithelioma	37
1	8	M	10.5, 6.4	Macrogenitosomia (juvenile hercules type)	141
1	14½	M	14.3	Macrogenitosomia	141
1		M	19.4, 16.5	Seminoma	141
1		M	32.2	Seminoma	141
1		M	15.4	Seminoma	141
1		M	20.0	Seminoma	141
1	26	F	7.3	Hydatiform mole	37

It would be worthwhile to examine the urine of all patients with interstitial cell tumors, with or without obvious endocrine abnormalities, to determine the range of values for this type of tumor. The patients with other types of testicular and embryonic tumors do not appear to excrete excessive amounts of ketosteroids. However, with some of these tumors abnormal amounts of gonadotropic hormones are found in the urine.

ADRENAL CORTEX

The urinary excretion of ketosteroids is so frequently elevated in patients with hyperactivity of the adrenal cortex due to adrenal hyperplasia, adenoma, or carcinoma, that this estimation has become a valued diagnostic aid. The classification of the lesions again becomes a difficult point and the diverse terminology employed for describing the histopathologic nature of the lesions does not facilitate correlation of ketosteroid excretion with the histologic character. Moreover, the variations in ketosteroid excretion level and in clinical signs of masculinization in patients whose tumors are histologically similar, is often very striking. It is at present only possible to refer to subtle problems of the tumor-host relation which these observations bring up. Any correlation of these factors must include an evaluation of the relative biosynthetic capacity of the tumor tissue and its relation to the cellular architecture. In addition, the ability of enzymes in other tissues to metabolize the hormones secreted by the tumor must play a role in determining the nature and amount of the excretory product. Finally, the clinical status of the patient must be correlated both with the factors mentioned above and the intrinsic capacity of the end organs to respond to hormonal stimulation.

The fractionation of the neutral ketosteroids into α- and β-fractions has sometimes proved to be useful in distinguishing the hyperplastic adrenal from the adenomatous or carcinomatous gland. Caution must be used in interpreting the results because of the wide variations found in both groups. It is clear that the technic of measuring total ketosteroids can serve as a guide, but thus far no clear-cut correlations have emerged.

To illustrate the complexity of the situation and the problems with which one is confronted in attempting to make any correlation between ketosteroid excretion and the clinical picture, data from the literature have been grouped under four major headings: (1) *Precocious puberty and prepubertal virilism* (Table 54), (2) *Cushing's syndrome without tumor* (Table 55), (3) *Hirsutism without known adrenal cortical hyperactivity* (Table 56), and (4) *Postpubertal adrenal cortical hyperplasia or tumor* (Table 57).

In children before the age of normal puberty, elevated ketosteroids are very frequently associated with disturbances of adrenal function. This is apparent from an examination of Table 54 in which the data for patients up to age 14 are presented. In the few instances in which the ketosteroid excretion is not markedly elevated, the precocity appears to be associated with a premature acceleration of the natural process rather than with the initiation of a pathologic process. The high ketosteroid values recorded in the majority of the patients listed seem to be indicative of abnormal adrenal function rather than simple maturation. The highest values are found in adrenal cancer.

The data in Table 57 indicate that there is no hard and fast rule concerning the ketosteroid excretion level in patients with adrenal cortical hyperplasia or tumors. While it is true that extremely high values are strongly suggestive of these diseases, in many cases normal values or only modest elevations occur. The difficulty of interpreting gross ketosteroid values when the figures lie near the normal range, becomes apparent upon examination of Tables 55 and 56 which list values in diseases which often simulate to a certain extent the borderline cases of adrenal hyperactivity. It is clear that ketosteroid determinations alone cannot be used to make a diagnostic decision. The application of the digitonin precipitation to separate "α-" and "β-" ketosteroids is sometimes useful. Recently devised colorimetric methods for the measurement of dehydroepiandrosterone and its derived artifacts simplify the problem of identifying the tumors in which the preponderant ketosteroids are in the "β-" fraction. Such procedures should ultimately facilitate the classification of adrenal tumors on the basis of their biosynthetic abilities as well as their histologic characteristics. No simple criterion can be used to distinguish

TABLE 54. EXCRETION OF KETOSTEROIDS BY PATIENTS WITH PRECOCIOUS PUBERTY AND PREPUBERTAL VIRILISM

Sex	*Age*	*Ketosteroids* (mg./day)	*Diagnosis*	*References**
F	1	3.0	Adrenal tumor	46
F	1	88.8	Adrenal tumor, primary masculinization	76
M	1½	10	Adrenal hyperplasia with Addison-like symptoms	67a
M	1	3.0	Adrenal tumor	46
M	1	28 (mg./L.)	Adrenal tumor	111
M	1 3/12	2.8	Masculinization and Cushing's syndrome	46
M	2	15	Adrenogenital syndrome, Addison's disease	134
F	2	228	Adrenal cortical adenoma	67
F	2	75	Adrenal cortical adenoma	68
F	3	170	Adrenal tumor	46
F	3	400	Adrenal cancer	36
F	3	13.5	Pseudohermaphroditism with adrenal cortical hyperactivity	46
F	3	160	Adrenal cancer	134
M	3	34	Adrenal cancer	99
F	3½	176	Adrenal tumor	48
F	3½	5.9	Masculinization and Cushing's syndrome or unclassified	52
M	4	18	Adrenal hyperplasia	133
M	4	7.8	Adrenal hyperplasia	133
F	4	8.9	Enlarged breasts and uterus	106
F	4	37	Adrenal hyperplasia or female pseudohermaphroditism	51
F	4	320, 166	Adrenal tumor	52
F	4 1/12	4.0	Enlarged breasts	106
M	4½	3.5	Precocious puberty	106
M	5	5.1	Feminized, enlarged prostate	144
M	5	27	Masculinization and Cushing's disease	111
M	5	20.3	Adrenal hyperplasia	133
M	5	27	Adrenal tumor	134
F	5	37	Pseudohermaphroditism with adrenal cortical hyperactivity	46
F	5	19.2	Adrenal hyperplasia	133
F	5	6	Adrenal hyperplasia or female pseudohermaphroditism	7
F	5½	12.6	Pseudohermaphroditism with adrenal cortical hyperactivity	48
F	5½	19–22	Adrenal tumor, primary masculinization	144
F	6	126–288	Adrenal cortical tumor and Cushing's syndrome	25
F	6	16.7	Adrenal hyperplasia	133
F	6	850	Adrenal cancer	25
F	6	12.4	Adrenal hyperplasia or female pseudohermaphroditism	7
F	6½	9.3	Penis-like clitoris	141
F	6¾	6.8	Menses at 6½ years	106
F	7	37	Adrenal hyperplasia or female pseudohermaphroditism	7

* Numbers refer to items in the bibliography at the end of this chapter.

TABLE 54. EXCRETION OF KETOSTEROIDS BY PATIENTS WITH PRECOCIOUS PUBERTY AND PREPUBERTAL VIRILISM (*Continued*)

Sex	*Age*	*Ketosteroids* (mg./day)	*Diagnosis*	*References**
F	7	34, 37	Adrenal hyperplasia or female pseudohermaphroditism	111
F	7	30	Adrenal hyperplasia	134
F	7	90	Virilism	141
M	7	275–420	Adrenal cancer	62
F	7½	6.0	Menses, enlarged breasts	106
F	8	11.7	Adrenal hyperplasia or female pseudohermaphroditism	133
F	8	23.4	Adrenal hyperplasia or female pseudohermaphroditism	133
F	8	83	Adrenal cancer	146
F	8	17	Adrenal hyperplasia	134
M	8	29.2	Adrenal hyperplasia	48
F	9	30	Precocious puberty	141
F	9	8.4	Menses	141
F	9	25.2	Adrenal hyperplasia	133
F	9	52	Adrenal hyperplasia or female pseudohermaphroditism	111
F	9	50	Adrenal hyperplasia or female pseudohermaphroditism	111
?	9	64	Intersex	67
M	9	33.4	Adrenal hyperplasia	133
M	10	84	Adrenal tumor	52
F	10	325	Adrenal cancer	50
F	10	30	Adrenal hyperplasia or female pseudohermaphroditism	51
F	11	69	Same patient as above, one year later	
F	10	31	Adrenal hyperplasia or female pseudohermaphroditism	72
F	10 5/12	21	Basophilism	141
F	10½	140	Virilism	141
F	11	23.4	Adrenal hyperplasia	133
F	11	29	Adrenal hyperplasia	134
F	11 2/12	10	Menses, 10–11 yr.	106
M	11½	15.7	Precocious puberty	106
F	12	32	Adrenal hyperplasia or female pseudohermaphroditism	7
F	12	93 I.U.	Adrenal hypertrophy	38
F	13	64	Adrenal hyperplasia or female pseudohermaphroditism	111
F	13	13	Virilism	141
F	13	19.8	Precocious puberty	141
F	13	23.4	Adrenal hyperplasia	133
F	13	133	Adrenal cancer	133
F	13	166	Masculinization and Cushing's syndrome	134

* Numbers refer to items in the bibliography at the end of this chapter.

TABLE 55. EXCRETION OF KETOSTEROIDS BY WOMEN WITH CUSHING'S SYNDROME BUT NO TUMOR

No. of patients	*Age*	*Ketosteroids* (mg./day)	*References**
1	12	15	25
1	15	11–20	26
1	16	10.8	141
1	18	12.5	141
1	19	60.0	141
1	20	37.0	141
1	22	23.3	141
1	24	28.6	141
1	25	9.3	141
1	26	29.0	141
1	28	31	110
1	32	20.3	141
1	34	15.1	141
1	36	9.3	141
1	36	28.1	141
2	26, 43	13	134
3	26–49	10.4–19.7	48
1		6.0	141
1		13.5	141
1		19.6	141
1		7.9	141
1		27.4	141

* Numbers refer to items in the bibliography at the end of this chapter.

adrenal tumors from adrenal hyperplasia. Even the determination of the "α-" and "β-" ketosteroids can be misleading in patients with adrenal tumors who have only moderately elevated total ketosteroids and whose "β-" ketosteroids are within normal limits.[72, 74]

TABLE 56. EXCRETION OF KETOSTEROIDS BY HIRSUTE WOMEN WITHOUT KNOWN ADRENAL CORTICAL HYPERACTIVITY

No. of patients	*Age*	*Ketosteroids* (mg./day)	*Diagnosis*	*References**
11	20–36	3.4–33	Hirsutism	141
67		6.4–33.4	Hirsutism	111
5	20–35	20–35	Mild hirsutism, origin unknown	37
7	21–44	10–35 (16.5)	Virilism, without adrenal cortical tumor	24
4	16–54	23.1–37.0	"Simple hirsutism"	138
21		1–29	Hirsutism	49
1	23	9.2	Hirsutism	4
1	20	16.2	Hirsutism	4

* Numbers refer to items in the bibliography at the end of this chapter.

An encouraging approach to this problem has been made by Dingemanse and her associates[28, 67] who have applied a chromatographic-colorimetric technic (see below) to the separation of urinary ketosteroids in patients with adrenal hyper-

TABLE 57. EXCRETION OF KETOSTEROIDS BY POSTPUBERTAL PATIENTS WITH ADRENAL CORTICAL HYPERPLASIA OR TUMOR

Sex	*Age*	*Ketosteroids* (mg./day)	*Diagnosis*	*References**
F	14½	1980	Adrenal cortical carcinoma	8
F	16	30.4	Adrenal cortical carcinoma	67
?F	16	102	Intersex	67
F	16	11.4	Adrenal cancer	48
F	16	54.6	Adrenal tumor	46
F	16	43	Adrenal cortical hyperplasia	7
F	17	160 I.U. androgen	Adrenal cortical adenoma	83
F	17	35	Adrenal cortical hyperplasia	111
F	17	54	Adrenal cortical hyperplasia	7
F	18	56	Adrenal cortical hyperplasia	111
F	18	54	Adrenal cortical hyperplasia	111
F	19	75.2	Pseudohermaphrodite, hyperplasia	46
		123	Two years later	46
F	19	111	Adrenal cortical adenoma	67
F	19	13.3	Adrenal virilism	141
F	19	27.3	Adrenal virilism	141
F	21	240	Adrenal tumor	46
F	21	35–74	Adrenal cortical hyperplasia	52
F	21	45	Adrenal cortical tumor	52
M	22	157	Adrenal cortical tumor	67
F	22	75	Adrenal cortical hyperplasia	7
F	22	143	Adrenal cortical adenocarcinoma	129
F	23	60	Pseudohermaphrodite	134
F	23	72.4	Enlarged adrenals	48
?	24	133	Intersex	67
F	25	367	Adrenal cancer	4
F	25	215	Adrenal tumor	2
F	25	64	Adrenal cancer	25
F	25	131	Adrenal tumor	46
F	25	23.1	Adrenal virilism	141
M	25	23	Sarcomatous dysembryoplasia with functional differentiation	131
M	25	40–64	Adrenal cortical tumor	25
F	26	136	Adrenal cortical carcinoma	73
		2.7	Post-operative	
		110–314	Recurrence (60% "β")	
F	26	107	Adrenal tumor	24
F	27	17.4	Adrenal virilism	141
F	28	61	Adrenal tumor	24
F	28	24–60	Adrenal cortical adenoma	67
F	28	720/L.	Benign blastoma of the adrenal	56, 109
F	28	18.9	Adrenal virilism	141
F	30	2100	Adrenal cancer	37
F	30	28	Adrenal virilism	141
F	31	78.5	Adrenal cortical carcinoma	68
M	32	68	Cushing's syndrome	72
M	34	50–100 I.U. androgen	Adrenal cancer	9
F	34	270	Adrenal tumor	111
F	36	22.8	Adrenal virilism	141
F	36	19.9	Adrenal cortical tumor (urine stored five years)	48

* Numbers refer to items in the bibliography at the end of this chapter.

TABLE 57. EXCRETION OF KETOSTEROIDS BY POSTPUBERTAL PATIENTS WITH ADRENAL CORTICAL HYPERPLASIA OR TUMOR (*Continued*)

Sex	*Age*	*Ketosteroids* (mg./day)	*Diagnosis*	*References**
F	38	53	Adrenal tumor	24
M	39	4.8	Probably non-functioning tumor	72
F	40	30	Adrenal cortical tumor	72
F	40	126	Adrenal cancer	141
M	40	34–108	Adrenal cortical carcinoma	3
F	41	102	Adrenal cortical hyperplasia	45
F	41	77	Adrenal tumor	24
F	42	690	Adrenal cancer	141
M	43	86	Cushing's syndrome	68
F	45	840	Adrenal tumor	46
F	46	516	Adrenal cancer	37
M	46	92.7	Adrenal cortical tumor	143
F	49	269	Adrenal cortical tumor	141
F	52	35.2–445.8	Malignant tumor of adrenal	67
F	53	800	Adrenal cortical tumor	72
F	54	83	Adrenal cortical tumor	141
F	55	1005	Masculinization and Cushing's syndrome	72
F	56	74	Adrenal cancer	48
F	56	74	Adrenal cortical tumor	133
F	61	14.5–20	Cushing's syndrome	24
F	63	48	Granulosa cell tumor of ovary with adrenal hyperplasia	67
F	63	45.6	Adrenal tumor	46
F	Adult	170	Adrenal tumor	111
F	Adult	47	Adrenal tumor	133
F	Adult	74	Adrenal cancer	133
F		325	Masculinization and Cushing's syndrome	49
F		37	Adrenal virilism	141
F		12	Adrenal virilism	141
F		29.8	Adrenal virilism	141
F		37.0	Adrenal virilism	114
F		14.9	Adrenal virilism	141
F		13.5	Adrenal virilism	141
F		5.9	Adrenal virilism	141
F		24	Adrenal virilism	141
F		26.1	Adrenal virilism	141
F		24.0	Adrenal virilism	141
F		20.5	Adrenal virilism	141
F		28.8	Adrenal virilism	141
F		22.7	Adrenal virilism	141

* Numbers refer to items in the bibliography at the end of this chapter.

activity. Distinct differences in patterns have been obtained between the patients studied and normal subjects, but at present the data are too few to determine whether this method will be useful in classifying the various types of adrenal hyperactivity. Zygmuntowicz *et al.*[148] using a modification of the Dingemanse technic, also report abnormal patterns of excretion in adrenal cortical hyperplasia.

STEROID EXCRETION IN CANCER OF NONSTEROIDOGENIC ORGANS

The early hopes that clear-cut quantitative differences in ketosteroid excretion would be found between normal individuals, cancer patients, and patients with other chronic diseases have not been realized. The recognition that the problem is more complex has come about first, as a result of the isolation of a multitude of steroid hormone metabolites from urine, and secondly, from careful studies of ketosteroid excretion in series of cancer patients and normal individuals in the same age group. The latter experiments have demonstrated that while there may be differences in total ketosteroid excretion between cancer patients and normal individuals of the same age group, these differences are small and only apparent when large numbers of patients are studied.[30, 103, 113, 127, 135, 147] The variations within the normal group[121] are such as to make it impossible to assign an individual patient to the cancer or noncancer group on the basis of ketosteroid excretion alone. In fact, some of the workers cited above have found no differences in ketosteroid excretion between the two groups.

The realization that total ketosteroid values alone cannot contribute much more to our understanding of steroid metabolism in cancer has prompted several groups of investigators to devise methods for the further fractionation of the ketosteroid complex.

Dingemanse *et al.*[28] developed a colorimetric-chromatographic method by means of which the 17-ketosteroid complex could be broken down into seven or eight major components. It is probable that each of the major components contains more than one ketosteroid. However, this standardized technic has made possible a finer fractionation of the ketosteroid complex. Utilizing this procedure for a study of normal males and patients with prostatic disease, Robinson and Goulden[122] come to the tentative conclusion that, whereas in normal subjects the amounts of androsterone and 5-isoandrosterone excreted are approximately equal, in patients with prostatic disease there is a somewhat diminished output of androsterone, with the 5-isoandrosterone level remaining relatively constant. These results are in conflict with the earlier findings of Brendler and Scott[5] who found no qualitative differences in ketosteroid chromatogram patterns between normal males and patients with prostatic disease. A suggestion of variations in excretion is also found in the more recent work of Zygmuntowicz *et al.*[148] These investigators reported distinct shifts in pattern in a patient with inflammatory carcinoma of the breast and in a patient with lymphatic leukemia. A second patient with cancer of the breast gave a pattern within the normal range. The patient with inflammatory cancer of the breast appeared to excrete relatively more in the androsterone region than in the 5-isoandrosterone zone. The results of this type of experiment must be accepted with some reserve until more definitive characterizations of the individual components of the fractions have been made.

Another technic which is being employed for the elucidation of the metabolic errors in cancer patients is the study of variations in patterns of response to administered steroid and pituitary hormones. In this procedure a battery of quantitative technics is used to follow the urinary excretion of several groups of steroid compounds from day to day. By this means it is hoped that variations in metabolic pathways not discernible in untreated patients, may become apparent when the organism is put under stress by the administration of the test hormone. Striking variations in the excretion of ketosteroids, nonketonic steroid alcohols, reducing and formaldehydogenic steroids, and estrogens have been observed in patients with malignant and nonmalignant disease following the administration of ACTH.[107] Segaloff *et al.* studied the excretion of steroid hormones in patients with carcinoma of the breast treated with testosterone propionate.[128] They found suggestive differences in hormone excretion between those patients who responded to therapy and those who did not. In a somewhat similar study, Nathanson *et al.*[108] treated 2 patients with cancer of the breast and 1 patient with rheumatoid arthritis each in succession with dehydroepiandrosterone and testosterone. They observed marked differences in the excretion of ketosteroids, nonketonic alcohols, and estrogens in these individuals. It appeared from these experiments that the administered hormones followed different metabolic pathways in the individual patients studied. It is obvious that many more cancer patients and controls will have to be studied before the real significance of these subtle differences in metabolic pathways becomes apparent.

SUMMARY

The author has attempted to review the distribution of steroid hormone metabolites in the urine of normal and diseased persons and to discuss the possible or potential significance of some individual compounds and groups of compounds. This review has been restricted largely to the neutral steroids since this group has been investigated most extensively. Particular emphasis has been placed upon the compounds present in the urine of patients with adrenal disease since the study of this material has been of prime importance in focusing our attention on the manifold synthetic capacity of this gland and its central role in pathologic processes.

Only when the broad outlines of the distribution of urinary steroid hormone metabolites were established did it become possible to study steroid excretion from the quantitative standpoint. These studies, too, were pointed in the direction of adrenal disease for it was in this area that the most rewarding results were obtainable. When attention was turned to neoplasia of nonsteroidogenic organs, the situation became less clear-cut. While evidence has been presented that there is a disorder of steroid metabolism in cancer patients, the precise nature of the disorder has not yet been determined. Only when it has been defined more closely will it be possible to determine whether it is characteristic of cancer alone or is present in other diseases. When this stage has been reached, it will be possible to speculate upon the implications of this metabolic error in cancer.

It is hoped that this review will have helped to organize the widely scattered and sometimes discrepant data in this field. In reviewing some of the problems which have been solved, the author has tried to indicate some of the many gaps and deficiencies in our knowledge as well as some of the current trends of research.

BIBLIOGRAPHY

1. Abarbanel, A. R., and Falk, H. C. Endocrine aspects of a solid ovarian tumor associated with adreno-genital syndrome and polycythemia. *Endocrinology 30:* 1025, 1942.
2. Anderson, A. F., Hain, A. M., and Patterson, J. A case of adrenal carcinoma and its hormone diagnosis. *J. Path. & Bact. 55:* 341-349, 1943.
3. Armstrong, C. N., and Simpson, J. Adrenal feminism due to carcinoma of the adrenal cortex: A case report and review of the literature. *Brit. M. J. 1:* 782-784, 1948.
4. Baumann, E. J., and Metzger, N. Colorimetric estimation and fractionation of urinary androgens. *Endocrinology 27:* 664-669, 1940.
5. Brendler, H., and Scott, W. W. New diagnostic methods in prostatic cancer: I. Investigation of the chromatographic adsorption technique for qualitative analysis of urinary 17-ketosteroids. *J. Urol. 60:* 937-946, 1948.
6. Brooksbank, B. W. L., and Haslewood, G. A. D. Investigation on urinary "pregnanediol-like glucuronide" (PLG): The isolation of Δ^{16}-androstene-3α-ol from normal human male urine. *Biochem. J. 44:* iii-iv, 1949.
7. Broster, L. R. Overactivity of the adrenal cortex. *Proc. Roy. Soc. Med., 40:* 35-39, 1946.
8. Broster, L. R., and Patterson, J. Unusual case of carcinoma (of adrenals) with note on application of new color test (for dehydroisoandrosterone, androgen, in urine). *Brit. M. J. 1:* 781-782, 1948.
9. Burrows, H., Cook, J. W., Roe, E. M. F., and Warren, F. L. Isolation of $\Delta^{3,5}$-androstadiene-17-one from the urine of a man with a malignant tumor of the adrenal cortex. *Biochem. J. 31:* 950-961, 1937.
10. Butenandt, A. Ueber das Pregnandiol, einen neuen Sterin-Abkömmling aus Schwangeren-Harn. *Ber. Chem. Gesellsch. 63:* 659-663, 1930.
11. Butenandt, A. Über die chemische Untersuchung der Sexualhormone. *Ztschr. ang. chem. 44:* 905-908, 1931.
12. Butenandt, A. Über die Chemie der Sexualhormone. *Ztschr. ang. chem. 45:* 655, 1932.
13. Butenandt, A., and Dannenbaum, H. Über Androsteron: Isolierung eines neuen, physiologisch unwirksamen Sterinderivates aus Männerharn, seine Verknüpfung mit Dehydro-androsteron und Androsteron: ein Beitrag zur Konstitution des Androsterons. *Ztschr. f. physiol. Chem. 229:* 192-208, 1934.
14. Butenandt, A., Dannenbaum, H., Hanisch, G., and Kudszus, H. Über Dehydro-androsteron. *Ztschr. f. physiol. Chem. 237:* 57-74, 1935.
15. Butenandt, A., and Grosse, W. Über eine einfache Darstellung des aus Männerharn isolierten Chlorketons $C_{19}H_{27}OCl$ (Dehydro-androsterylchlorid). *Ber. Chem. Gesellsch. 69:* 2776-2778, 1936.
16. Butenandt, A., and Tscherning, K. Über Androsteron, ein krystalliziertes männliches Sexualhormon: I. Isolierung und Reindarstellung aus Männerharn. *Ztschr. f. physiol. Chem. 229:* 167-184, 1934.
17. Butenandt, A., and Tscherning, K. Über Androsteron. II. Seine chemische Charakterisierung. *Ztschr. f. physiol. Chem. 229:* 185-191, 1934.
18. Butler, G. C., and Marrian, G. F. The isolation of pregnane-3,17,20-triol from the urine of a woman showing the adrenogenital syndrome. *J. Biol. Chem. 119:* 565-572, 1937.

19. BUTLER, G. C., and MARRIAN, G. F. Chemical studies on the adrenogenital syndrome: I. The isolation of 3 (β)-hydroxyetioallocholane-17-one (isoandrosterone), and a new triol from the urine of a woman with an adrenal tumor. *J. Biol. Chem. 124:* 237-247, 1938.
20. CALLOW, N. H. The isolation of two transformation products of testosterone from urine. *Biochem. J. 33:* 559-564, 1939.
21. CALLOW, N. H., and CALLOW, R. K. The isolation of 17-ketosteroids from the urine of normal women. *Biochem. J. 33:* 931-934, 1939.
22. CALLOW, N. H., and CALLOW, R. K. The isolation of androsterone and *trans*-dehydroandrosterone from the urine of normal women. *Biochem. J. 32:* 1759-1762, 1938.
23. CALLOW, N. H., and CALLOW, R. K. Excretion of androgens by eunuchs: the isolation of 17-ketosteroids from the urine. *Biochem. J. 34:* 276-279, 1940.
24. CALLOW, N. H., and CROOKE, A. C. Diagnosis of adrenal tumors. Estimation of 17-ketosteroids in urine. *Lancet 246:* 464-465, 1944.
25. CROOKE, A. C., and CALLOW, R. K. The differential diagnosis of forms of basophilism (Cushing's syndrome), particularly by the estimation of urinary androgens. *Quart. J. Med. 32:* 233-249, 1939.
26. DEAKINS, M. L., FRIEDGOOD, H. B., and FERREBEE, J. W. Some effects of testosterone propionate, methyltestosterone, stilbestrol and x-ray therapy in a patient with Cushing's syndrome. *J. Clin. Endocrinol. 4:* 376-384, 1944.
27. DINGEMANSE, E., and HUIS IN'T VELD. Isolation of 11-hydroxyetiocholanol-3 (α)-ol-17 from urine of male patients with adrenal cancer. *Nature 164:* 202-208, 1949.
28. DINGEMANSE, E., HUIS IN'T VELD., L. G., and DE LAAT, B. M. Clinical method for the chromatographic colorimetric determination of urinary 17-ketosteroids: I. *J. Clin. Endocrinol. 6:* 535-548, 1946.
29. DINGEMANSE, E., HUIS IN'T VELD, L. G., and HARTOGH-KATZ, S. L. Isolation of new androstenol-3α-ol-17 from urine of patient (with adrenal cancer). *Nature 161:* 848-849, 1949.
30. DOBRINER, K., GORDON, E., RHOADS, C. P., LIEBERMAN, S., and FIESER, L. F. Steroid hormone excretion by normal and pathological individuals. *Science 95:* 534-536, 1942.
31. DOBRINER, K., and LIEBERMAN, S. "The metabolism of steroid hormones in humans." In *A Symposium on Steroid Hormones* (E. S. Gordon, Ed.). Madison, Wis. University of Wisconsin Press, 1950, pp. 46-88.
32. DOBRINER, K., LIEBERMAN, S., HARITON, L., SARETT, L. H., and RHOADS, C. P. Isolation of Δ^9-etiocholen-3(α)-ol-17-one from human urine. *J. Biol. Chem. 169:* 221-2, 1947.
33. DOBRINER, K., LIEBERMAN, S., and RHOADS, C. P. The excretion in the urine of metabolites of adrenal cortical hormones in health and disease, including neoplastic growth. *Cancer Research 7:* 711, 1947.
34. DOBRINER, K., LIEBERMAN, S., and RHOADS, C. P. Studies in steroid metabolism: I. Methods for the isolation and quantitative estimation of neutral steroids present in human urine. *J. Biol. Chem. 172:* 241-261, 1948.
35. DOBRINER, K., LIEBERMAN, S., RHOADS, C. P., JONES, R. N., WILLIAMS, V. Z., and BARNES, R. B. Studies in steroid metabolism: III. The application of infrared spectrometry to the fractionation of urinary ketosteroids. *J. Biol. Chem. 172:* 297-311, 1948.

35a. DOBRINER, K., LIEBERMAN, S., WILSON, H., EKMAN, B., PEARSON, O., and ELIEL, L. "Adrenal function and steroid excretion in neoplastic disease." In *Proceedings of the First Clinical ACTH Conference* (J. R. Mote, Ed.). Philadelphia, The Blakiston Company, 1950, 158-166.

36. DORFMAN, R. I., and GARGILL, S. P. 513 in Dorfman, R. I.: "Biochemistry of androgens." In Pincus, G., and Thimann, K. V.: *The Hormones.* New York, Academic Press, 1948, vol. I. pp. 467-548.

37. DORFMAN, R. I., and SHIPLEY, R. A. Pp. 510, 512, 515 in Dorfman, R. I.: "Biochemistry of androgens." In Pincus, G., and Thimann, K. V.: *The Hormones.* New York, Academic Press, 1948, vol. I, pp. 467-548.

38. DORFMAN, R. I., WILSON, H. M., and PETERS, J. P. Differential diagnosis of basophilism and allied conditions. *Endocrinology 27:* 1-15, 1940.

39. EMMENS, C. W. (Ed.) *Hormone Assay.* New York, Academic Press, 1950.

40. ENGEL, L. L. The chemical estimation of steroid hormone metabolites. *Recent Progress in Hormone Research 5:* 335-379, 1950.

41. ENGEL, L. L., DORFMAN, R. I., and ABARBANEL, A. R. Neutral Steroids in the urine of a patient with a luteoma. Cited in *Recent Progress in Hormone Research, 5:* 430, 1950.

42. ENGEL, L. L., and OLMSTED, P. C. Unpublished data.

43. ENGEL, L. L., THORN, G. W., and LEWIS, R. A. The urinary excretion of steroid compounds: I. Normal male subjects. *J. Biol. Chem. 137:* 205-215, 1941.

44. ENGSTROM, W. W. Nature and significance of neutral steroids in human urine in normal and abnormal states, with preliminary consideration of adrenal and gonadal steroids and factors which influence their secretion and biologic action. *Yale J. Biol. & Med. 21:* 21-85, 1948.

45. ENGSTROM, W. W. Personal observation in "The 17-ketosteroids: their origin, determination and significance" in H. L. Mason and W. W. Engstrom: *Physiol. Rev. 30:* 321-374, 1950.

46. ENGSTROM, W. W., MASON, H. L., and KEPLER, E. J. Excretion of neutral 17-ketosteroids in adrenal cortical tumor and feminine pseudohermaphroditism with adrenal cortical hyperplasia. *J. Clin. Endocrinol. 4:* 152-155, 1944.

47. FIESER, L. F., and FIESER, M. *Natural Products Related to Phenanthrene.* American Chemical Society Monograph series, New York, Reinhold Publishing Co., 1949.

48. FRASER, R. W., FORBES, A. P., ALBRIGHT, F., SULKOWITCH, H., and REIFENSTEIN, E. C. JR. Colorimetric assay of 17-ketosteroids in urine: A survey of the use of this test in endocrine investigation, diagnosis and therapy. *J. Clin. Endocrinol. 1:* 234-256, 1941.

49. FRIEDGOOD, H. B., and WHIDDEN, H. L. The assay of crystalline and urinary androgens with special reference to their measurement by a colorimetric method. *New England J. Med. 220:* 736-741, 1939.

50. FRIEDGOOD, H. B., and WHIDDEN, H. L. Colorimetric determination of crystalline and urinary ketosteroids: Clinical usefulness of this method. *Endocrinology 27:* 258-267, 1940.

51. GENITIS, V. E., and BRONSTEIN, J. P. Pregnanediol excretion in female pseudohermaphroditism (? congenital adrenal hyperplasia): Studies in two cases. *J.A.M.A. 119:* 704-706, 1942.

52. HAIN, A. M. Adrenal tumours and pseudohermaphroditism: A hormone study of cases. *J. Path & Bact. 59:* 267-292, 1947.

53. HAIN, A. M. An unusual case of precocious puberty associated with ovarian dysgerminoma. *J. Clin. Endocrinol. 9:* 1349-1358, 1949.
54. HARRIS, R. S., and THIMANN, K. V. (Eds.) *Vitamins and Hormones.* New York, Academic Press, 1943-1950, vol. I-VIII.
55. HARTMANN, M., and LOCHER, F. Über Allo-Pregnandiol, einen neuen Alkohol aus dem Schwangernharn. *Helvet. chim. acta. 18:* 160-165, 1935.
56. HENRIQUES, S. B., HENRIQUES, O. B., and WENDEL, L. Isolamento dos esteróides cetonicos da urina da una mujer con tumor da adrenal. *Rev. brasil de biol. 10:* 209-216, 1950.
57. HILL, B. R., and LONGWELL, B. B. Urinary steroids from breast cancer patients. *Endocrinology 32:* 319-326, 1943.
58. HIRSCHMANN, H. Androgens from the urine of ovariectomized women. *J. Biol. Chem. 130:* 421-422, 1939.
59. HIRSCHMANN, H. Steroids of urine of ovariectomized women. *J. Biol. Chem. 136:* 483-502, 1940.
60. HIRSCHMANN, H. Isolation of isoandrosterone from urine in a case of virilism. *Proc. Soc. Exper. Biol. & Med. 46:* 51-53, 1941.
61. HIRSCHMANN, H. Isolation of a new triol from the urine of a patient with an adrenocortical carcinoma. *Federation Proc. 1:* 115, 1942.
62. HIRSCHMANN, H. Steroid excretion in a case of adrenocortical carcinoma: I. The isolation of a Δ^5-androstenetriol-3(β),16,17. *J. Biol. Chem. 150:* 363-379, 1943.
63. HIRSCHMANN, H., and HIRSCHMANN, F. B. Steroid excretion in a case of adrenocortical carcinoma: II. An examination of the non-ketonic fraction precipitable with digitonin. *J. Biol. Chem. 157:* 601-612, 1945.
64. HIRSCHMANN, H., and HIRSCHMANN, F. B. Steroid excretion in a case of adrenocortical carcinoma: III. The isolation of Δ^5-pregnenediol-3(β), 17 (β)-one-20 and of 17a-methyl-Δ^5-D-homoandrostenediol-3(β),17a(α)-one-17. *J. Biol. Chem. 167:* 7-25, 1947.
65. HIRSCHMANN, H., and HIRSCHMANN, F. B. Steroid excretion in a case of adrenocortical carcinoma. IV. Δ^5-pregnenetriol-3β,16α,20α. *J. Biol. Chem. 184:* 259-282, 1950.
66. HIRSCHMANN, H., and HIRSCHMANN, F. B. Steroid excretion in a case of adrenocortical carcinoma: V. Δ^5-pregnenetriol-3β,17α,20α. *J. Biol. Chem. 187:* 137-146, 1950.
67. HUIS IN'T VELD, L. G., and DINGEMANSE, E. Excretion diagrams of 17-ketosteroids in patients with tumors of cortex. *Acta brev. Neerland. 16:* 9-15, 1948.
67a. JAILER, J. Recent studies on adrenal hyperplasia. *Tr. N. Y. Acad. Sci. 13:* 262-263, 1951.
68. JOHNSON, H. T., and NESBIT, R. M. 17-Ketosteroids in the diagnosis of adrenal tumors. *Surgery 21:* 184-193, 1947.
69. JONES, G. S., and EVERETT, H. S. Arrhenoblastoma of the ovary, with a report of two cases. *Am. J. Obst. & Gynec. 52:* 614-622, 1946.
70. JONES, R. N. The characterization of sterol hormones by ultraviolet and infrared spectroscopy. *Recent Progress in Hormone Research 2:* 3-29, 1948.
71. KEPLER, E. J., DOCKERTY, M. B., and PRIESTLY, J. T. Adrenal-like ovarian tumor associated with Cushing's syndrome (so-called masculinovoblastoma, luteoma, hypernephroma, adrenal cortical carcinoma of the ovary). *Am. J. Obst. & Gynec. 47:* 43-62, 1944.

72. Kepler, E. J., and Mason, H. L. Relation of urinary steroids to the diagnosis of adrenal cortical tumors and adrenal cortical hyperplasia: Quantitative and isolation studies. *J. Clin. Endocrinol. 7:* 543-558, 1947.
73. Kepler, E. J., Sprague, R. G., Clagett, O. T., Power, M. H., Mason, H. L., and Rogers, M. H. Cortical tumor associated with Cushing syndrome: case with metabolic studies; pathogenesis of Cushing syndrome. *J. Clin. Endocrinol. 8:* 499-531, 1948.
74. Kepler, E. J., Sprague, R. G., Mason, H. L., and Power, M. H. Pathologic physiology of cortical tumors and Cushing syndrome. *Recent Progress in Hormone Research 2:* 345-389, 1948.
75. Kyle, T. I., and Marrian, G. F. Allopregnane-3α:20α-diol in the urine of pregnant women. *Biochem. J. 49:* 80-83, 1951.
76. Leahy, L. J., and Butsch, W. L. The beta 17-ketosteroids in a case of pseudohermaphroditism due to adrenal cortical tumor. *Ann. Surg. 128:* 1124-1130, 1948.
77. Lieberman, S., and Dobriner, K. The isolation of pregnanediol-3α,17-one-20 from human urine. *J. Biol. Chem. 161:* 269-278, 1945.
78. Lieberman, S., and Dobriner, K. The isolation of etiocholanol-3(α)-dione-11,17 from human urine. *J. Biol. Chem. 166:* 773-774, 1946.
79. Lieberman, S., and Dobriner, K. Steroid excretion in health and disease: I. Chemical aspects. *Recent Progress in Hormone Research 3:* 71-101, 1948.
80. Lieberman, S., Dobriner, K., Hill, B. R., Fieser, L. F., and Rhoads, C. P. Studies in steroid metabolism: II. Identification and characterization of ketosteroids isolated from the urine of healthy and diseased persons. *J. Biol. Chem. 172:* 263-295, 1948.
81. Lieberman, S., Fukushima, D. K., and Dobriner, K. Adrenal cortical metabolites in human urine. *Federation Proc. 7:* 168-169, 1948.
82. Lieberman, S., Fukushima, D., and Dobriner, K. Studies in steroid metabolism: VII. Identification and characterization of additional ketosteroids from the urine of healthy and diseased persons. *J. Biol. Chem. 182:* 299-316, 1950.
83. Lukens, F. D. W., and Palmer, H. P. Adrenal cortical virilism. *Endocrinology 26:* 941-945, 1940.
84. Marker, R. E., Binkley, S. B., Wittle, E. L., and Lawson, E. V. Sterols: XLIII. The 3(β)-hydroxysteriods in human pregnancy urine. *J. Am. Chem. Soc. 60:* 1904-1905, 1938.
85. Marker, R. E., and Kamm, O. Sterols: XVII. Isolation of pregnanolone from human pregnancy urine. *J. Am. Chem. Soc. 59:* 1373-1374, 1937.
86. Marker, R. E., Kamm, O., and McGrew, R. V. Sterols: IX. Isolation of *epi*-pregnanol-3-one-20 from human pregnancy urine. *J. Am. Chem. Soc. 59:* 616-618, 1937.
87. Marker, R. E., and Lawson, E. J. Sterols: XLVIII. Isolation of androsterone and pregnanol-3(α) from human pregnancy urine. *J. Am. Chem. Soc. 60:* 2928-2930, 1938.
88. Marker, R. E., and Rohrmann, E. Sterols: LXX. The steroid content of mare's pregnancy urine. *J. Am. Chem. Soc. 61:* 2537-2540, 1939.
89. Marker, R. E., Wittle, E. L., and Lawson, E. J. Sterols: XLIX. Isolation of pregnanediols from bull's urine. *J. Am. Chem. Soc. 60:* 2931-2933, 1938.
90. Marrian, G. F. Chemistry of oestrin; preparation from urine and separation from unidentified solid alcohol. *Biochem. J. 23:* 1090-1098, 1929.

91. MARRIAN, G. F., and BUTLER, G. C. The isolation of Δ^5-androstene-3(β), 16,17-triol from the urine of normal human males and females. *Biochem. J. 38:* 322-324, 1944.

92. MASON, H. L. Isolation of a urinary steroid with an oxygen atom at carbon 11. *J. Biol. Chem. 158:* 719-720, 1945.

93. MASON, H. L. Urinary steroids in adrenal disease and metabolism of adrenal hormones. *Recent Progress in Hormone Research 3:* 103-123, 1948.

94. MASON, H. L., and ENGSTROM, W. W. The 17-ketosteroids: Their origin, determination and significance. *Physiol. Rev. 30:* 321-374, 1950.

95. MASON, H. L., and KEPLER, E. J. Isolation of steroids from the urine of patients with adrenal cortical tumors and adrenal cortical hyperplasia. A new 17-ketosteroid, androstane-3(α),11-diol-17-one. *J. Biol. Chem. 161:* 235-257, 1945.

96. MASON, H. L., and SCHNEIDER, J. J. Isolation of Δ^{16}-androstene-(α)-ol from the urine of women with adrenal cortical tumors. *J. Biol. Chem. 184:* 593-598, 1950.

97. MASON, H. L., and SPRAGUE, R. G. Isolation of 17-hydroxycorticosterone from the urine in a case of Cushing's syndrome associated with severe diabetes mellitus. *J. Biol. Chem. 175:* 451-456, 1948.

98. MASON, H. L., and STRICKLER, H. S. Identification of pregnane-3(α),17-diol-20-one as the steroid moiety of a new glucuronide isolated from human urine. *J. Biol. Chem. 171:* 543-549, 1947.

99. McCULLAGH, E. P. Cited, p. 513, in R. I. Dorfman: "Biochemistry of androgens." In G. Pincus and K. V. Thimann: *The Hormones, 1:* 467-548, 1948. N. Y., Academic Press.

100. MELICOW, M. M., ROBINSON, J. N., IVERS, W., and RAINSFORD, L. K. Interstitial cell tumors: Review of literature and report of case: Discussion of gynecomastia and testosterone: Incidence in animals and experimental production. *J. Urol. 62:* 672-693, 1949.

101. MILLER, A. M., DORFMAN, R. I., and SEVRINGHAUS, E. L. Metabolism of the steroid hormones: The isolation of an androgen from human urine containing an 11-oxygen substitution in the steroid ring. *Endocrinology 38:* 19-25, 1946.

102. MUNSON, P. L., GALLAGHER, T. F., and KOCH, F. C. Isolation of dehydroisoandrosterone sulfate from normal male urine. *J. Biol. Chem. 152:* 67-77, 1944.

103. NATHANSON, I. T. Studies on the etiology of human breast disease: III. Urinary excretion of estrogens and 17-ketosteroids in premenopausal carcinoma of the breast. *Cancer Research 3:* 132, 1943.

104. NATHANSON, I. T. Endocrine aspects of human cancer. *Recent Progress in Hormone Research 1:* 261-291, 1947.

105. NATHANSON, I. T. "Functioning tumors of the endocrine glands and the hormone therapy of cancer." In *Cancer: A Manual for Practitioners.* American Cancer Society (Mass. Div.), Inc., pp. 239-261, 1950.

106. NATHANSON, I. T., and AUB, J. C. Excretion of sex hormones in abnormalities of puberty. *J. Clin. Endocrinol. 3:* 324-330, 1943.

107. NATHANSON, I. T., ENGEL, L. L., and KELLEY, R. M. The effect of ACTH on the urinary excretion of steroids in neoplastic disease. *Proceedings of the Second Clinical ACTH Conference* (J. R. Mote, Ed.). New York, The Blakiston Co., 1951, vol. I, pp. 54-61.

108. Nathanson, I. T., Engel, L. L., Kennedy, B. J., and Kelley, R. M. "Screening of steroids and allied compounds in neoplastic disease." In *Symposium on Steroids in Experimental and Clinical Practice* (A. White, Ed.). New York, The Blakiston Co., 1951, pp. 379-396.
109. De Paiva, L. M., Lobo, J. I., and Da Silva, A. M. Menarche and pregnancy after removal of an adrenocortical adenoma. *J. Clin. Endocrinol. 11:* 330-337, 1951.
110. Paschkis, K. E., Herbut, P. A., Rakoff, A. E., and Cantarow, A. A case of Cushing's syndrome with adrenal cortical hyperplasia, without pituitary basophilic adenoma or hyperplasia. *J. Clin. Endocrinol. 3:* 212-217, 1943.
111. Patterson, J., McPhee, I. M., and Greenwood, A. W. 17-Ketosteroid excretion in adrenal virilism. *Brit. M. J. 1:* 35-39, 1942.
112. Pearlman, W. H. The isolation of etioallocholanol-3(β),17-one (isoandrosterone) from normal and pathological human urines. *J. Biol. Chem. 136:* 807-808, 1940.
113. Pearlman, W. H. Steroid excretion in cancerous and non-cancerous persons: I. The 17-ketosteroids. *Endocrinology 30:* 270-276, 1942.
114. Pearlman, W. H., and Pincus, G. The ketonic steroids of pregnancy urine. *Federation Proc. 1:* 66, 1942.
115. Pearlman, W. H., Pincus, G., and Werthessen, N. T. The isolation of allopregnanol-3(β)-one-20 from human pregnancy urine. *J. Biol. Chem. 142:* 649-652, 1942.
116. Pederson, J. Virilizing ovarian tumors. *J. Clin. Endocrinol. 7:* 115-129, 1947.
117. Pincus, G. (Ed.). *Recent Progress in Hormone Research.* New York, Academic Press Inc., 1947-1952, vols. I-VII.
118. Pincus, G., and Thimann, K. V. *The Hormones: Physiology, Chemistry and Applications.* New York, Academic Press, 1948, vol. I.
119. Reilly, W. A. Personal communication. Cited in Mason and Engstrom.[94]
120. Reiners, C. R., Jr., and Horn, R. C., Jr. Interstitial cell tumor: Two cases. *Am. J. Clin. Path. 19:* 1039-1047, 1949.
121. Robinson, A. M. The excretion of 17-ketosteroids in men of different age-groups, with special reference to prostatic cancer. *Brit. J. Cancer 2:* 13-16, 1948.
122. Robinson, A. M., and Goulden, F. A qualitative study of urinary 17-ketosteroids in normal males and in men with prostatic disease. *Brit. J. Cancer 3:* 62-71, 1949.
123. Ross, M., and Dorfman, R. I. The urinary excretion of estrogens and androgens by women with carcinoma of the breast. *Cancer Research 1:* 52-54, 1941.
124. Salmon, U. J., Geist, S. H., and Salmon, A. A. Excretion of pregnanediol in women with virilism. *Proc. Soc. Exper. Biol. & Med. 47:* 279-280, 1941.
125. Schiller, S., Miller, A. M., Dorfman, R. I., Sevringhaus, E. L., and McCullagh, E. P. Metabolism of the steroid hormones: The isolation of Δ^5-androstenediol-3(β),17(α) and Δ^5-pregnenediol-3(β),20(α). *Endocrinology 37:* 322-328, 1945.
126. Schneider, J. J. Studies on the excretion of adrenocortical compounds: I. Isolation of 17-hydroxy-11-dehydrocorticosterone and other compounds from the urine of normal males. *J. Biol. Chem. 183:* 365-376, 1950.
127. Scott, W. W., and Vermeulen, C. Studies on prostatic cancer: Excretion of 17-ketosteroids, estrogens and gonadotropins before and after castration. *J. Clin. Endocrinol. 11:* 450-456, 1942.

128. Segaloff, A., Gordon, D., Horwitt, B. N., Schlosser, J. V., and Murison, P. J. Hormonal therapy in cancer of the breast: I. The effect of testosterone propionate therapy on clinical course and hormonal excretion. *Cancer 4:* 319-323, 1951.
129. Simpson, S. L. Discussion: Overactivity of the adrenal cortex. *Proc. Roy. Soc. Med. 40:* 45-46, 1946.
130. Speert, H. Ovarian granulosa cell tumor and acromegaly. *J. Clin. Endocrinol. 9:* 630-635, 1949.
131. Staffieri, J. J., Cames, O., and Cid, J. M. Corticoadrenal tumor with hypoglycemic syndrome, goitre, gynecomastia and hepatosplenomegaly. *J. Clin. Endocrinol. 9:* 255-267, 1949.
132. Strickler, H. S., Schaffer, C. B., Wilson, D. A., and Strickler, E. W. A new steroid glucuronide from human urine. *J. Biol. Chem. 148:* 251-252, 1943.
133. Talbot, N. B., Butler, A. M., and Berman, R. A. Adrenal cortical hyperplasia with virilism: Diagnosis, course and treatment. *J. Clin. Investigation 21:* 559-570, 1942.
134. Talbot, N. B., Butler, A. M., and MacLachlan, E. A. Alpha and beta neutral ketosteroids (androgens): Preliminary observations on their normal urinary excretion and the clinical usefulness of their assay in differential diagnosis. *New England J. Med. 223:* 369-373, 1940.
135. Taylor, H. C. Jr., Mecke, F. E., and Twombley, G. H. Estrogen and 17-ketosteroid excretion in patients with breast carcinoma. *Cancer Research 3:* 180-192, 1943.
136. Tedeschi, C. G., and Burke, F. E. Paratesticular interstitial cell tumor. *Cancer 4:* 312-318, 1951.
137. Venning, E. H., and Browne, J. S. L. Studies on corpus luteum function: I. The urinary excretion of sodium pregnanediol glucuronidate in the human menstrual cycle. *Endocrinology 21:* 711-721, 1937.
138. Venning, E. H., and Browne, J. S. L. Excretion of glycogenic corticoids and of 17-ketosteroids in various endocrine and other disorders. *Endocrinology 7:* 79, 1947.
139. Venning, E. H., Hoffman, M. M., and Browne, J. S. L. Isolation of androsterone sulfate. *J. Biol. Chem. 146:* 369-379, 1942.
140. Venning, E. H., Weil, P. G., and Browne, J. S. L. Excretion of sodium pregnanediol glucuronidates in the adreno-genital syndrome. *J. Biol. Chem. 128:* cvii-cviii, 1939.
141. Warren, F. L. Estimation of urinary 17-ketosteroids in the diagnosis of adrenal cortical tumors. *Cancer Research 5:* 49-54, 1945.
142. Waugh, D., Venning, E. H., and McEachern, D. Sympathicotropic (Leydig) cell tumor of the ovary with virilism: Report of a case. *J. Clin. Endocrinol. 9:* 486-496, 1949.
143. Wilhelm, S. F., and Gross, S. Surgical removal of adrenal adenoma with relief of Cushing syndrome. *Am. J. M. Sc. 207:* 196-204, 1944.
144. Wilkins, L. Feminizing tumor causing gynecomastia in boy of 5 years contrasted with virilizing tumor in 5 year old girl: Classification of 70 cases of adrenal tumor in children according to their hormonal manifestations and review of 11 cases of feminizing tumor (adrenal) in adults. *J. Clin. Endocrinol. 8:* 111-132, 1948.
145. Winsauer, H. J., and Manning, J. C. Jr. A masculinizing tumor of the ovary in a postmenopausal woman. *Endocrinology 9:* 774-781, 1949.
146. Wolfe, J. K., Fieser, L. F., and Friedgood, H. B. Nature of the androgens in female adrenal tumor urine. *J. Am. Chem. Soc. 63:* 582-593, 1941.

147. YOLTON, N., and REA, C. Excretion of androgens and estrogens in males with mammary carcinoma. *Proc. Soc. Exper. Biol. & Med. 45:* 54, 1940.

148. ZYGMUNTOWICZ, A. S., WOOD, M., CRISTO, E., and TALBOT, N. B. Studies of urinary 17-ketosteroids by means of a new micro-chromatographic fractionation procedure. *J. Clin. Endocrinol. 11:* 578-596, 1951.

CHAPTER 25

Clinical Investigation in Cancer Research

Freddy Homburger

At the core of the cancer problem is the patient afflicted with this disease. However, it is of interest to note that a preponderance of cancer research is conducted in the field of the fundamental sciences, remote from the clinical problem. Of 583 grants-in-aid for cancer research awarded by the U. S. Public Health Service in 1951–52, only 173 were directly concerned with patients, and of the 178 papers read at the 1950 meeting of the American Association for Cancer Research, only 33 were the result of clinical investigation. In 1952 at the meeting of this same society 209 papers were read with only 35 dealing with clinical matters.

As basic experimental studies progress, the gap between the results of biologic research and their application to patients widens. This chasm will have to be bridged if progress is to be continuous and directed towards control of the disease in man. Biologists have developed scientific technics for the study of neoplasia in animals and plants but clinicians are only beginning to apply them to studies on patients. The paucity of good studies in man is largely due to the lack of an accurate methodology of clinical investigation. The introduction of scientifically correct methods to clinical studies promises important developments and rapid progress. This has come about whenever exact methods of quantitative science have been brought to bear upon medical problems. It was true of the neo-Hippocratic era of Sydenham and it applies to the chemotherapeutic and antibiotic epochs of modern medicine. It may become true in the field of cancer research, if reliable methodology and scientific thinking are brought to the bedside.

The importance of fundamental research is not minimized. While Max Planck's statement that "scientific discovery and scientific knowledge have been achieved only by those who have gone in pursuit of them without any practical purpose in view," must be kept in mind, nevertheless it is impossible to engage in scientific research on human cancer without "any practical purpose whatsoever in mind," since the problem is characterized by its purpose.

The most important challenge to cancer research should be recognized as that of human cancer. The findings in other species may not be even remotely applicable to man. Certainly they often cannot be directly applied, since it is not possible to transfer into the human equation even such relatively well understood biologic phenomena as the milk factor in mice, chicken viruses, or nutritional influence connected with the hepatic carcinogenesis of azo dyes. It is so far only in the field of chemical and physical carcinogenesis and to some extent in chemotherapy that such direct applications of animal data to human situations are possible.

Great importance may still be attached to animal data from a clinical point of view. Biologic assay methods often aid the clinician in situations where chemical laboratory methods fail. It is possible that some experimental fact may suddenly gain immense practical significance, as did, for example, the originally purely academic classification of mosquitoes when their role in malaria and yellow fever became apparent and it was discovered that only certain types of the insect could transmit the protozoan or the virus.

LIMITATIONS OF THE APPLICATION OF BIOLOGIC METHODS TO HUMAN CANCER

The clinical investigator has still much to learn from the biologic experimentator in the fields of genetics, nutrition, and endocrinology. In recent years experimental biologists have developed reproducible methods and well-controlled experiments. The science of genetics applied to mice has furnished strains of great purity in which susceptibility to cancer is uniform. Nutritional experiments are rendered quantitative by the use of synthetic diets and by close control of environment. The surgical extirpation of gonads, pituitary or other vital glands has become a standardized experimental method in the study of endocrine glands and cancer, and transplantation of organs or tissues, and symbiosis for the study of many cancer phenomena, is now routine in many laboratories. Such methods, applied to experimental biology in mammalians, have greatly advanced our knowledge of neoplastic diseases, but none of them can be used freely with human subjects. With the exception of isolated ethnic groups in some areas of the globe, human genetics are an unresolvable tangle of fortunately uncontrolled cross-breeding. Nutritional experiments of long duration are impossible, excepting where advantage may be taken of tribal alimentary customs still prevailing in large segments of a population.

The classical methods of experimental endocrinology, the removal of endocrine glands, substitution therapy, and so on, are only possible in exceptional circumstances, such as cancer of the breast or prostate, where gonadectomy or adrenalectomy may be of therapeutic value. In such instances, however, control subjects without cancer undergoing similar procedures are but rarely available.

The work of Bierman* and co-workers has shown that the daring application of such intricate experimental methods as symbiosis (or at least cross-transfusion) to human volunteers can yield most interesting data not obtainable in any other way.

Since surgery and radiotherapy are certain to bring at least palliation or even "cure" wherever cancer is operable and since delay of therapy shortens life ex-

* Lanman, J. T., Bierman, H. R., and Byron, R. L. Transfusion of leucemic leucocytes into man: Hematologic and physiologic changes. *Blood 5:* 1099-1113, 1950.

pectancy, there is no opportunity to conduct controlled studies on patients with operable carcinomas. Thus it is that patients with advanced, inoperable cancers, in whom the orthodox therapeutic measures are no longer effective, become the only available subjects for clinical investigation. This situation has a propitious aspect, however, when the proposed experiment is also designed to offer such patients some hope of palliation.

VARIABLE FACTORS TO BE CONSIDERED IN CLINICAL INVESTIGATION OF INOPERABLE CANCER PATIENTS

It must be remembered that proper control of conditions in clinical investigation of inoperable cancer patients is very difficult. There are few patients who have inoperable cancer alone. In most instances, the presence of an inoperable neoplasm is complicated by malnutrition, dehydration, drug addiction, urinary or other chronic infections, and often, to make matters more involved, a number of therapeutic measures have been carried out or are in progress. In addition, since most of these patients belong to a fairly advanced age group, it is seldom that they do not have some other degenerative or chronic disease besides cancer. While these factors are susceptible of proper control with great effort, such an attempt is rarely made. The necessity for such controls may be illustrated by the observation that stimulation of the adrenals with ACTH causes changes that are identical in aged debilitated patients and in those with cancer.[3] A previous study employing healthy controls showed a significant difference between the "cancer group" and the "non-cancer group."[30] Many clinical phenomena which are ascribed to cancer may actually be unspecific and caused by other chronic diseases as well.

Age in itself may be a factor of importance in explaining some abnormal metabolic findings in cancer. Thus it has long been known that the glucose tolerance curve becomes higher (reduced rate of disappearance of glucose from the blood stream) in the elderly patient.[4, 8] It is not surprising therefore, that reports have appeared describing diabetic glucose tolerance curves in cancer patients who usually tend to fall within an elderly age group.

Another confusing variable is the stage of neoplastic disease. Some may talk glibly about degrees of activity of cancer, yet when it comes to the organization of comparative patient groups, these same individuals will not hesitate to speak of a "cancer group" versus a "normal group," without further classification of the components of each group.

In spite of such limitations and particularly when these are properly considered in planning clinical studies valuable information may be collected by clinical cancer research in many fields. Attention will be given in the following to the mechanism of cachexia, protein dynamics in cancer patients, mechanisms of anemia and host-tumor relationships including endocrine dysfunction, predisposition, and organ susceptibility.

THE MECHANISM OF CACHEXIA

One of the most striking phenomena in the natural history of human cancer is the continuous growth of malignant tumors in a host whose tissues are wasting away. It has been shown in animals that tumor growth will proceed at a constant rate even though the host may be in negative nitrogen balance.[43] There is also some evidence that nitrogen is redistributed among various organs in mice bearing transplantable tumors.[18, 27, 34] Little is known, however, of the fat, carbohydrate, and protein metabolism of cancer patients. As in the other types of chronic disease,[5] there is a surprising tendency in cancer patients to store nitrogen if they are force-fed at high caloric levels. This has been quantitatively demonstrated in patients with cancer of the stomach.[23] The mechanism of this derangement of nitrogen metabolism is poorly understood and it cannot be fully explained on the basis of the nutritional depletion of such patients. There is suggestive evidence of an inversely proportional relationship between glucocorticoid excretion in the urine and nitrogen excretion with lowered glucocorticoid levels accompanied by protein anabolism in the chronically ill and in cancer patients, whereas acute stress causing increased glucocorticoid production would promote a catabolic reaction.[5] In cachectic cancer patients coming to autopsy, Sarason[30] has found enlarged adrenals depleted of lipids, while no such anatomic signs of adrenal insufficiency were found in non-cachectic cancer patients.

Dobriner[9] measured the response of cancer patients to administration of ACTH by studying the excretion of various steroid substances in the urine. He found in the urine of cancer patients compounds not previously identified in the urine of normal subjects receiving ACTH. This suggests either adrenal dysfunction or altered metabolism of adrenal secretion products.

While the adrenal thus appears to play a regulating role in the protein-fat-carbohydrate metabolism of cancer patients and so may hold a key position in the causation of cachexia, the site of action of adrenal hormones in man has not been studied intensively. There is some suggestive evidence that adrenal hormones will cause glycogen deposition simultaneously with a loss of nitrogen in patients with panhypopituitarism.[1] This, however, is far from conclusive and similar studies have not been made in cancer patients where hepatic glycogenesis (from ingested glucose) may well be diminished, and may be restored by adrenal extract.[44] The production of obesity by adrenal stimulation in the course of ACTH therapy and in Cushing's syndrome is well known and it is somewhat paradoxical that occasionally cancer patients who show a steroid excretion pattern "approaching that of Cushing's disease" should otherwise give anatomic and functional signs of adrenal insufficiency and clinical cachexia. While previous work by Dobriner has shown abnormal excretion patterns of steroids in urine,[9] there is no conclusive indication that the adrenal gland of cancer patients is deranged in function or is less responsive to ACTH than the adrenal of normal subjects. Reifenstein[30] found a diminished response of the adrenal in patients with gastric cancer as measured by a lack of increase in uric acid in the urine after test doses of ACTH. Bonner, Fishman, and Homburger,[3] conversely, found similar changes in old patients with chronic diseases and could not differentiate between these subjects and patients with cancer by tests of adrenal responsiveness to ACTH.

PROTEIN DYNAMICS IN THE CANCER PATIENT

While the debilitated cancer patient, at least in the case of cancer of the stomach, may show a tendency to store nitrogen when placed on high food intake, this is not used for the synthesis of plasma albumin in which these patients are deficient. There seems to be in cancer patients an equally serious "deficiency of total circulating cell mass and hemoglobin," as well as a "fundamental disturbance in hemoglobin metabolism."[6] There is some evidence to suggest that the replacement of plasma proteins withdrawn from cancer patients by plasmapheresis is slower than protein regeneration in normal subjects.[22] Nothing is known of the sequence of events which leads to an eventual catabolic pattern terminating in cachexia. It has often been loosely stated that cancer causes loss of appetite and that consequently malnutrition and gastrointestinal obstruction caused by the tumor or dysfunction of the digestive glands, achlorhydria, etc., may prevent the normal assimilation

TABLE 58. EFFECT OF PLASMAPHERESIS UPON THE PROTEIN REGENERATION IN MULTIPLE MYELOMA

		Total circulating amounts (Gm.)			
	Plasma volume	T.P.	A.	Gamma plus B.J.	Others
Amounts withdrawn (calculated on basis of average hematocrit and average protein concentration)		1013	160	710	143
Initial values	3260	441	75	300	68.5
Final values (after withdrawal of 12,000 ml.)	2940	347	44.1	257	47.1
Change (loss)	320	94	30.9	43	21.4

of food. In the literature on this subject, the food intake has not as a rule been accurately controlled and much of the information is therefore useless. While there are few quantitative studies available on the metabolic balance of the cachectic patient, the clinical impression is that even an elevated caloric and nutritional intake will not prevent neoplastic tissue from continuing its active anabolism whilst the remainder of the organism is in a catabolic phase. The direct test of this hypothesis in man is extremely difficult. In one type of diffuse malignant tissue, multiple myeloma, where certain proteins (e.g., Bence Jones protein, β- or γ-globulins) are produced by the tumor, it has been found that following plasmapheresis the production (or at least the appearance in the blood stream) of the pathologic "tumor protein" proceeds at a higher rate than the production of the normal plasma proteins. Bellin[2] has shown by studies with N^{15}-labeled glycine that the protein turnover rate in such patients can be considerably increased over the normal rate (Table 58). This phenomenon requires more study and it would be interesting to investigate the effects of known so-called "protein anabolic agents" upon this process.

It is theoretically possible that such agents as testosterone might stimulate somatic growth and arrest cachexia without proportionately increasing the growth rate of the tumor. This type of reaction may be observed clinically in cancer of the breast during administration of testosterone[14] or methylandrostenediol.[20] Some regression of tumor metastases may be seen and there may be weight gain without edema formation. This situation represents the reverse of the metabolic conditions that exist when a tumor progresses rapidly and the host organism undergoes cachexia.

While animal experiments on the subject of cachexia are of interest, mechanisms in man can only be fully elucidated by studies in man, and here there seems to exist a vast field for clinical investigation upon patients with advanced cancer. The methods applicable to such a study might require the use of tracers to determine the turnover rates of various food elements. Another possible approach is through metabolic balance studies. These are laborious and costly and allow only indirect deductions to be made regarding the fate of food constituents. They may succeed in clarifying some of the questions posed, provided they are properly planned and interpreted. Interpretation of metabolic data is very difficult, since the customary assumptions that muscle constitutes the bulk of body protoplasm and that certain body constituents, such as nitrogen, potassium, calcium, phosphorus, or sulfur, occur in relatively fixed proportions in all tissues of the organism of such patients, is *a priori* invalid in subjects in whom the muscle mass has been greatly reduced and in whom the relative contribution of each tissue to the organism is no longer normal.

Recent work[19] has shown that the urine nitrogen:phosphorus ratios may be useful to detect subtle but definite metabolic changes which in the absence of concomitant changes in the calcium excretion may be ascribed to tissues other than bone. If, in addition, the ratio of nitrogen to sulfur is being considered, it may be determined whether observed changes of the nitrogen:phosphorus ratio in the urine should be ascribed to protein metabolism or not.

MERITS OF THE METABOLIC BALANCE METHOD IN HUMAN CANCER

The study of metabolic balances in patients with cancer has already yielded some information regarding the mechanism of action of ACTH and cortisone in lymphomas,[11, 29] and of estrogens and androgens in cancer of the prostate[32] and breast.[13] It is being used as a possible short cut or screening method in the search for new steroid agents for cancer of the breast (*vide infra*).

It has become evident from metabolic studies in subjects with cancer of the stomach that intractable hypoproteinemia persists in spite of a positive nitrogen balance and that therefore the administration of plasma is important in the pre- and postoperative management of patients with such cancer, as it may well be in other types of neoplasia.[23]

Studies on mineral balance and on the distribution of electrolytes in biopsied tissue has led to the concept that intracellular potassium is more readily replaced by extracellular sodium in patients with cancer than in patients with other diseases, so that a conservative attitude towards the use of sodium chloride is indicated in the postoperative treatment of cancer patients[24] and the administration of potassium may improve the postoperative course.[12]

The advances which may result from this type of study are hence twofold: some knowledge may be gained of the mechanisms governing the obscure and complex relationship in man between host and tumor, and observations on the metabolic anomalies of cancer patients may result in considerable improvement in the management of such subjects under the stress of conventional therapy.

Activities in this new but still neglected field of clinical research may go far towards bridging the gap between fundamental cancer research and the problems of the cancer patient.

MECHANISMS OF ANEMIA IN CANCER

The phenomenon of anemia in cancer patients may be interpreted as an instance where there is a defect in the metabolism of another specific protein, hemoglobin, for some reason as yet obscure.

The studies of Shen[33a] have shown that the anemia of cancer patients (60.1 per cent of 193 cases) cannot be explained by mechanical interference of tumor with the bone marrow, since bone metastases were absent in 79.3 per cent of the anemic cases. Hemolysis is not an important pathogenic factor except perhaps in the leukemias and lymphomas. The bone marrow of patients who have widespread tumor metastases in bone is still capable of responding with a good hematopoietic reaction to anoxia induced by cobalt.

Studies on the survival time of normal compatible red cells infused into cancer patients (Shen and Jonsson, unpublished data) show that the life span of the donor's cells as measured by Ashby's technic is normal in patients with cancer other than lymphomas, except when they have complications such as bleeding or infections.

This evidence indicates strongly that, as in the case of albumin in gastric cancer (*vide supra*), there may be some unknown factors interfering with hemoglobin synthesis and red cell formation in the presence of certain neoplasms.

EFFECTS OF HOST UPON TUMOR

The preceding considerations indicate that in the patient harboring a neoplasm, a number of changes are taking place that are more or less direct effects of the tumor upon the host and it is important to direct attention towards these systemic manifestations of the disease in the clinical management of the patient; conversely, there are factors within the patient which can affect the behavior of a neoplasm, and these may profitably be made the subject of clinical research.

AGE AND CANCER

It is well known that the age distribution of cancer favors the more advanced years with only a few exceptions (sarcomas, lymphomas, etc.) and some search for the common denominator in man which is propitious to the development of cancer late in life seems worthwhile. The theory of wear and tear and chronic irritation which takes into account a time factor or a minimal span of exposure to chronic irritants before cancer appears is often plausible but fails to explain why individuals exposed to similar agents for similar lengths of time do not similarly develop cancer. The various degenerative changes of the aging human organism and their possible relationship to cancer should be considered more closely than hitherto. It is a frequent clinical observation that neoplasms grow more rapidly in younger individuals once they appear and that cases of extremely slow progression nearly always occur in aged patients. This is at first sight a paradox; since neoplasms tend to appear in the aged more frequently than in the young, why should they tend to progress more slowly in the aged who are more susceptible to cancer?

SEX AND CANCER

It is commonly observed that a variety of cancers, excluding those of sex organs and accessory sex organs, favor one sex. Cancers of the larynx, stomach, esophagus, and lung definitely predominate in men. The recent increase in cancer of the lung is much more marked in men than in women, yet one of the more favored etiologic factors, cigarette smoking, has increased in the past few decades more strikingly in women than in men. There has also been an increasing consumption of cocktails amongst women, yet cancer of the esophagus and stomach have not become proportionately more common in this sex. All this tends to show that these external etiologic factors which have often been adduced to explain sexual variations of cancer incidence may well be relatively unimportant and that it is the sex factor itself which is responsible for the different incidences.*

ENDOCRINE DYSFUNCTION AND CANCER

There are some types of cancer wherein endocrine dysfunction seems likely to be of pathogenic significance. While it is not definitely known whether women who develop cancer of the breast have an unduly high incidence of menstrual dysfunction, it is well established that changes in the menstrual cycle are often first observed prior to the development of carcinoma of the breast. Taylor[36] noted a close association of cancer of the breast with tumors of the female reproductive organs, an observation which suggests that the entire reproductive system in such patients may be subject to the same stimulus or may be more responsive as a whole to certain stimuli than it is in women who do not have these neoplasms.

Olch[28] found that the onset of the menopause is delayed in women who develop breast cancer, compared with those who do not have this disease, and since the average age of appearance of breast cancer is 52 and that of the menopause is 48 years, it is permissible to speculate on a possible causative relationship between the hormonal imbalance of the menopause and the onset of cancer of the breast. These considerations on the relationship of the endocrines to the etiology of cancer assume added importance in view of the fact that exogenous hormones (estrogens or androgens) have been shown to influence the growth of cancer of some accessory sex organs (breast, prostate), and that likewise the removal of endogenous hormone sources (ovaries, testes, and adrenals) can in turn inhibit the growth of cancer of the breast in either sex and retard the growth of cancer of the prostate. These clinical observations are susceptible of a great many different interpretations. They

* There are, of course, conflicting claims as to the relative importance of such etiologic factors as smoking. These matters are discussed in other chapters (pages 751 and 787).

have in common one factor, that there are naturally occurring endogenous hormonal substances capable of preparing the field for neoplastic growth or stimulating or inhibiting such growth once initiated. They also leave open the problems of why hormonal imbalances similar to those conducive to cancer no doubt occur in many subjects without resulting in that disease and why one and the same hormone given to different patients with apparently the same type of tumor does not always result in the same carcinostatic or carcinolytic effect. There are obviously further factors, many of them still obscure.

"PREDISPOSITION" TO CANCER

One of these other factors is "predisposition" or "susceptibility." In experimental animals, this vague concept has been broken down into its components. Thus it has become quite clear that susceptibility to cancer of the breast in pure inbred strains of mice is due to: (1) the milk factor of Bittner; (2) well-known hormonal factors; and (3) hereditary constitutional elements. Heredity in man is uncontrolled and therefore conclusions are at best tentative. The most famous case of hereditary or at least familial cancer is that of the Bonaparte family. The grandfather and father of Napoleon himself, three sisters and one brother all died of cancer of the stomach.[38]* Certain types of cancer occur notoriously in familial patterns, as in the case, for example, of multiple polyposis of the gastrointestinal tract.[10, 15] Several authors[25, 37] have found a predominance of family history of breast cancer in women with this disease, compared with incidence of such histories in women free from cancer of the breast. There are also to be found in the literature a fair number of cases of familial cancer other than polyposis or cancer of the breast.[16] Warthin[41, 42] described a family in which 41 out of 174 members attaining to the age of 25 years had cancer—the males developed cancer of the large intestine, the females cancer of the uterus.

In clinical practice, the hereditary factor may not appear to be of great significance, but the fact that it has been observed indicates that in man, as in the experimental animal, genetic factors may indeed contribute towards cancer susceptibility.

In some cases, susceptibility may be dependent upon topical factors. Thus Kennaway[26] concludes from the fact that early circumcision in the Jewish male prevents the development of cancer of the glans penis, whereas circumcision as practised by the Moslems, between the ages of 3 and 13 years, does not, that "the train of events leading to the malignant growth is set going early in life and removal of the cause does not avert the development of cancer at a much later date." It seems in this case that a lengthy period of contact between the penis and the "carcinogen" contained in the smegma of the prepuce is necessary to foster the "susceptibility" of the penile tissue to undergo cancerous transformation at a later date.

A case of topical predisposition with practical significance is the tendency of the gastric mucosa in patients with pernicious anemia to undergo malignant changes. Thus pernicious anemia (and perhaps other forms of gastric achlorhydria) become

* The fact that the diagnosis of gastric cancer in Napoleon has often been questioned emphasizes the difficulty of retrospective genetic studies in man.

precursors to gastric cancer, much as intestinal polyposis is a precursor for intestinal cancer. A close watch of individuals bearing these predisposing diseases therefore is likely to pay dividends in terms of early detection of cancers and sometimes in terms of prevention. Zamsheck *et al.* have recently reviewed this subject thoroughly.

ORGAN "SUSCEPTIBILITY" TO CANCER

There is further evidence that "susceptibility" may be defined as a systemic change rendering an organism particularly suitable for the growth of cancer. This is well documented by the observation that a patient having one cancer is much more likely to develop a second primary cancer, often in another organ, than would be predicted by chance alone. This is true not only in the case of bilateral cancer of the breast[7] but also for multiple carcinomas occurring in totally unrelated organs of the same host.[35] The frequency with which such multiple lesions occur in a single individual is about ten times the incidence likely by chance alone.[40, 39]

The foregoing observations suggest quite clearly that there exists in man a "host territory" locally or systemically favorable to the development of cancer. It seems clear that a qualitative and quantitative knowledge of what constitutes this predisposition is necessary. Animal experimentation may indicate the most promising approaches for the elucidation of this problem. The final answers will have to be obtained from the human animal itself.

This approach to clinical investigation in man encounters considerable difficulties, outlined in the introduction to this chapter. Essentially, the experimental methods at present applicable to man may be described as a careful study by all available means of the changes which occur in the host in the presence of a tumor, and of studies on the behavior of tumors in the presence of exogenous factors likely to influence the growth pattern of neoplastic lesions.

DIFFICULTIES IN THE EVALUATION OF CHEMOTHERAPEUTIC EFFECTS

Figure 121 represents schematically the labile equilibrium that exists between the condition of a patient and his tumor, whenever any type of therapy designed to affect tumor growth is applied to the patient.

Assessment of chemotherapy is difficult, because there may be a number of morbid conditions present in the patient besides the cancer, some of which may be alleviated or aggravated by the chemotherapeutic agent. Again, besides the apparent but significant changes that may be brought about by suggestion, change of environment, or an altered threshold to analgesics, there are unspecific factors other than the chemotherapeutic agent which may actually be aggravating the patient's general condition. Some chemotherapeutic agents are known to stimulate appetite (testosterone, ACTH, cortisone), bringing about unspecific changes, or to reduce food intake (nitrogen mustards and other nauseating agents). These difficulties discussed in some details in Chapters 22 and 30 point the way for future research in clinical investigation of cancer patients that must be done as groundwork for this relatively new field of study.

Whenever new chemotherapeutic agents are discovered, it will be necessary not only to ascertain their carcinostatic or carcinolytic properties but also to study their unspecific effects upon patients. This can be done by metabolic balance studies, which show to what extent a substance may cause nitrogen and other food constituents to be retained or lost in patients without cancer, compared with these effects in cancer patients. This method may reveal unspecific effects of chemotherapeutic agents which may be entirely independent of their effects upon tumors. On the other hand, it is possible that such properties of chemotherapeutic agents as their general protein anabolic effect may be necessary in some way for their carcinostatic effects. This seems to be the case with androgenic hormones, such as testosterone, and their action upon cancer of the breast.[33] Methylandrostenediol, whilst having a much less virilizing effect than testosterone, has similar metabolic effects.[20, 21, 25a] Besides sharing the protein anabolic property of testosterone propionate, it also produces creatinuria in some women with cancer of the breast, such as is sometimes seen with testosterone.[33]

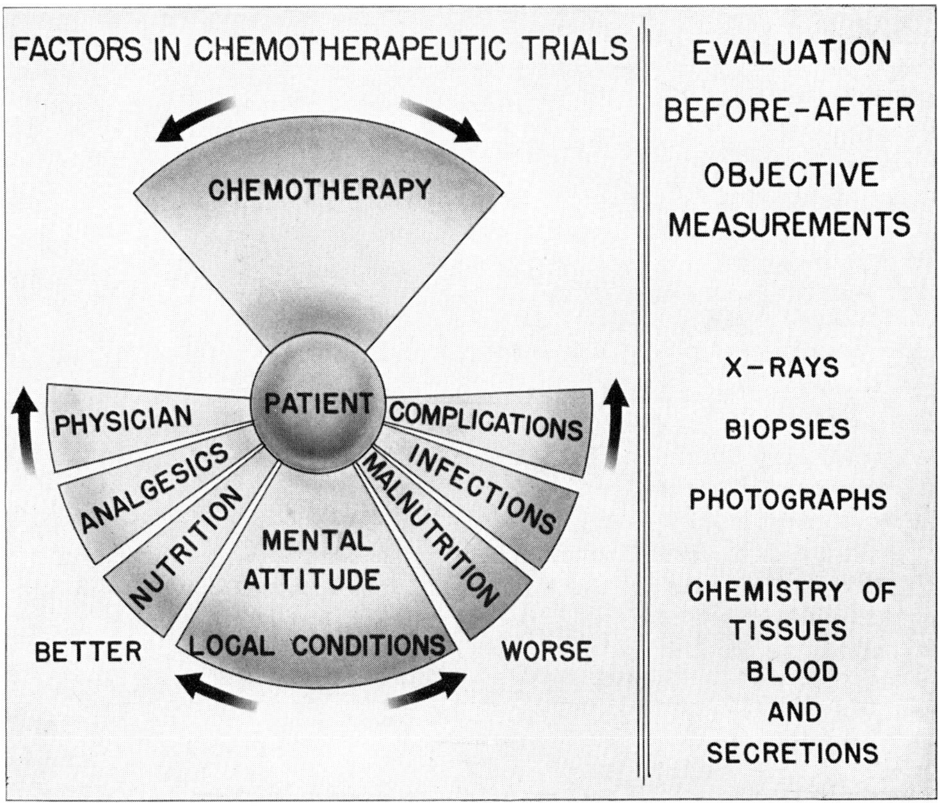

FIG. 121. Factors in chemotherapeutic trials.

The effect of ACTH upon urine steroid patterns in cancer patients may be specifically different from that in patients without cancer. This cannot be established, however, with any degree of certainty, unless experiments are done with control subjects who are equally debilitated and of the same age and sex, etc. These measurements of unspecific effects of chemotherapeutic agents present difficulties ubiquitous in clinical research but all too often ignored.

EVALUATION OF SPECIFIC EFFECTS UPON TUMORS

The evaluation of effects of a specific nature upon tumors, whether mediated through the host or directly acting upon the metabolism of the cancer cell, is even more difficult. Unfortunately, as it is shown in other chapters in this volume, such qualitative and quantitative differences between cancer and homologous tissue are rare and it is therefore seldom possible to measure "tumor activity." Tumors of the thyroid gland may take up radioactive iodine, which may serve as a measure of tumor mass or rate of activity, but this is useful only in a small proportion of such tumors. Only about 70 per cent of all metastasizing cancers of the prostate cause elevations of acid phosphatase and thus have a measurable characteristic which may (or may not) parallel the rate of proliferation of the prostatic tumor tissue. The limitations of other means of objective evaluation shown in Fig. 121 are self-evident.

There are other, more fundamental difficulties in evaluating chemotherapy. In evaluating any therapy, it is necessary to rely on comparisons between the natural course of the untreated disease and the course as modified by the chemotherapeutic agent. Where prognosis of life expectancy is concerned, this method gives good results, permitting comparisons between various therapeutic methods. When dealing with evaluations of more subtle changes, such as "improvement," "slowing of tumor growth," or "length and number of remissions," it is impossible to use or compare the data recorded in patients even one or two decades ago with those obtained today. A series of patients suffering from advanced cancer fifteen years ago certainly did not receive the intensive supportive and antibiotic therapy that is now given routinely to most patients under chemotherapy. The obvious means of objective control—the arbitrary alternation for observation of a treated patient with a similar case left untreated—is difficult, since it would mean withholding presumably effective therapeutic agents from one-half of those with a right to receive them.

SUMMARY

A chapter on clinical investigation in cancer at the present time must consist essentially in a listing of difficulties and problems. There is hope that basic experimental work may yet yield a solution to the cancer problem if its findings are intelligently applied to the human situation. The difficulties enumerated explain the relative rarity of sound clinical investigation of cancer patients. However, at the same time they do indicate promising avenues for clinical cancer research. It will be necessary to forge better tools for the quantitative evaluation of biologic and biochemical phenomena in man. The solution to this problem might well be found at a fundamental level, perhaps in the chemistry of the genes or in the metabolism of amino acids in drosophila. When it comes to the evaluation in patients of the potential therapeutic usefulness of any newly obtained advance, however, we must realize that with our present crude methods of clinical evaluation many unspecific beneficial effects of tested agents may falsely be considered carcinolytic or carcinostatic and that, conversely, even an effective cancer cure might be missed. To learn more about the disease in man and to narrow the gap between the fundamental sciences and the ailing patient, more work in the methodology of clinical investigation is required.

BIBLIOGRAPHY

1. Bartter, F. C., Fourman, P., Albright, F., Forbes, A. P., Jeffries, W. McK., Griswold, G., Dempsey, E., Bryant, D., and Carroll, E. The effect of ACTH in panhypopituitarism. *J. Clin. Investigation 29:* 950-971, 1950.
2. Bellin, J. Nitrogen and mineral metabolism and studies on protein synthesis in multiple myeloma (abstract). *Cancer Research 11:* 235, 1951.
3. Bonner, C. D., Fishman, W. H., and Homburger, F. Response of circulating eosinophiles and uric acid excretion to ACTH in geriatric patients. *Geriatrics 5:* 203-207, 1950.
4. Brandt, W. B. Chemische Körperänderungen beim Altern. *Chem.-Ztg. 67:* 269-273, 1943.
5. Browne, J. S. L., Johnson, L. G., Schenker, V., and Venning, E. H. Protein metabolism in acute and chronic disease and the relation of protein metabolism to the excretion of gluco-steroids. *First Clin. ACTH Conf.*, 1949, Philadelphia, Blakiston, 1950, pp. 108-133.
6. Clark, J. H., Nelson, W., Lyons, C. L., Mayerson, H. S., and De Canys, P. Chronic shock. *Ann. Surg. 125:* 618-646, 1947.
7. Cullen, J. R., and Burns, J. E. Bilateral breast cancer. *Connecticut M. J. 13:* 1041-1044, 1944.
8. Dahmann-Bonn, H., and Kohl, H. Blutzuckerbelastung in verschiedenen Lebensaltern. *Ztschr. f. Altersforsch. 2:* 310-317, 1940.
9. Dobriner, K., Lieberman, S., Wilson, H., Ekman, B., and Rhoads, C. P. "Steroid excretion and adrenal function in neoplastic disease." In *Pituitary Adrenal Function.* American Association for the Advancement of Science, 1950, pp. 158-165.
10. Dukes. Familial intestinal polyps. *J. Clin. Path. 1:* 34-38, 1947.
11. Eliel, L. P., Hellman, L., Pearson, O. H., and Katz, B. The effects of ACTH on the electrolyte content of various tissues. *Second Clin. ACTH Conf.*, 1950, Blakiston.
12. Eliel, L. P., Pearson, O. H., and Rawson, R. W. Post-operative potassium deficit and metabolic alkalosis. *New England J. Med. 243:* 471-478, 1950.
13. Kennedy, B. J. Side effects of large doses of estrogens and androgens in mammary cancer. *Proc. First Conf. Steroid Hormones and Mammary Cancer*, 1949, p. 111; also abstract, *Cancer Research 9:* 551, 1948, with W. Emerson and I. T. Nathanson.
14. Escher, G. Clinical improvement of inoperable breast carcinoma under steroid treatment. *Proc. First Conf. Steroid Hormones and Mammary Cancer*, 1949, pp. 92-99.
15. Halsted, J. A., Harris, E. J., and Marshall, M. K. Involvement of the stomach in familial polyposis of the gastrointestinal tract. Report of a family. *Gastroenterology 15:* 763-770, 1950.

16. HAUSER, I. J., and WELLER, C. Further report on cancer family of Warthin. *Am. J. Cancer 27:* 434-449, 1936.
17. HINSBERG, K. *Das Geschwulstproblem.* Dresden, Theodore Steinkopf, 1942.
18. HOMBURGER, F. Studies on hypoproteinemia: III. Lymphoid hyperplasia and redistribution of nitrogen caused in mice by transplanted tumors (sarcoma 180 and adenocarcinoma of the breast EO 771). *Science 107:* 648-649, 1948.
19. HOMBURGER, F., BONNER, C. D., and FISHMAN, W. H. The questionable significance of the ratios of phosphorus, nitrogen and sulfur with reference to metabolic studies in man. *Metabolism 1:* 435-457, 1952.
20. HOMBURGER, F., KASDON, S. C., and FISHMAN, W. H. Methylandrostenediol: Nonvirilizing derivative of testosterone in metastatic cancer of breast. *Proc. Soc. Exper. Biol. & Med. 74:* 162, 1950.
21. HOMBURGER, F., DART, R. M., BONNER, C. D., BRANCHE G., JR., KASDON, S. C., and FISHMAN, W. H. Some metabolic and biochemical effects of methylandrostenediol. *J. Clin. Endocrinol.* In press.
22. HOMBURGER, F., REIFENSTEIN, E. C., JR., DUFFY, B. J., JR., and PETERMANN, M. L. *Unpublished data.*
23. HOMBURGER, F., and YOUNG, N. H. Studies in hypoproteinemia: I. Hypoproteinemia in patients with gastric cancer; its persistence after operation in the presence of body tissue repletion. *Blood 3:* 1460-1471, 1948.
24. HOMBURGER, F., YOUNG, N. F., POTOR, A., TRUNNELL, J. B., DUFFY, B. J., JR., PETERMANN, M. L., and RHOADS, C. P. Further studies on metabolic changes in patients with gastric cancer. *J. Nat. Cancer Inst. 10:* 489-491, 1949.
25. JACOBSEN, O. Heredity in Breast Cancer. London, H. K. Lewis and Co., Ltd., 1946.
25a. KASDON, S. C., FISHMAN, W. H., DART, R. M., BONNER, C. D., and HOMBURGER, F. Methylandrostenediol in the palliative treatment of breast cancer. *J.A.M.A. 148:* 1212-1216, 1952.
26. KENNAWAY, E. L. Cancer of the penis and circumcision in relation to the incubation period of cancer. *Brit. J. Cancer 1:* 335-344, 1947.
27. NORBERG, E., and GREENBERG, D. M. Incorporation of labeled glycine in the proteins of tissues of normal and tumor-bearing mice. *Cancer 4:* 383-386, 1937.
28. OLCH, I. Y. Menopausal age in women with cancer of the breast. *Am. J. Cancer, 30:* 563-566, 1937.
29. PEARSON, O. H., ELIEL, L. P., RAWSON, R. W., DOBRINER, K., and RHOADS, C. P. ACTH- and cortisone-induced regression of lymphoid tumors in man. *Cancer 2:* 943-945, 1949.
30. REIFENSTEIN, E. C., DUFFY, B. J., and GROSSMAN, M. S. Studies on adrenal cortical functions in cancer: I. Acute effects of ACTH in patients with cancer. *Gastroenterology 13:* 493-500, 1949.
31. SARASON, E. L. Adrenal cortex in systemic disease. *Arch. Int. Med. 71:* 702-712, 1943.
32. SCHILLING, A., and LASZLO, D. The effect of diethylstilbestrol on the calcium, phosphorus and nitrogen metabolism of prostatic carcinoma. *J. Clin. Investigation 29:* 918-924, 1950.
33. SEGALOFF, A., GORDON, D., NORWITT, B. N., SCHLOSSER, J. W., and MURISON, P. J. Hormonal therapy in cancer of the breast: I. The effect of testosterone propionate therapy on clinical course and hormonal excretion. *Cancer 4:* 319-323, 1951.

33a. SHEN, S. C., and HOMBURGER, F. The anemia of cancer patients and its relation to metastases to the bone marrow. *J. Lab. & Clin. Med. 37:* 182-198, 1951.

34. SHERMAN, C. D., JR., MORTON, J. J., and MIDER, G. B. Potential sources of tumor nitrogen. *Cancer Research 10:* 374-378, 1950.

35. SPAIN, D. M. Multiple primary tumors. *New York State J. Med. 49:* 1445-1447, 1949.

36. TAYLOR, H. C., JR. The coincidence of primary breast and uterine cancer. *Am. J. Cancer 15:* 277-279, 1931.

37. VAN RAAMSDONK, WASSINK, C.Ph., and WASSINK, F. L'hérédité du cancer. *Néoplasmes 2:* 145-154, 1923.

38. VINCENT, E. H. The cancer of destiny. *Surg., Gynec. and Obst. 86:* 119-123, 1948.

39. WARREN, S., and EHRENREICH, T. Multiple primary malignant tumors and susceptibility to cancer. *Cancer Research 4:* 554-570, 1944.

40. WARREN, S., and GATES, O. Multiple primary malignant tumors: A survey of the literature and a statistical study. *Am. J. Cancer 16:* 1358-1414, 1932.

41. WARTHIN, A. S. Heredity with reference to carcinoma. *Arch. Int. Med. 12:* 546-555, 1913.

42. WARTHIN, A. S. Further study of a cancer family. *J. Cancer Research 9:* 279-286, 1925.

43. WHITE, FLORENCE R. Source of tumor proteins: II. Nitrogen balance studies of tumor bearing mice fed a low nitrogen diet. *J. Nat. Cancer Inst. 5:* 265-268, 1945.

44. YOUNG, N. F., ABELS, J. C., and HOMBURGER, F. Studies on carbohydrate metabolism in patients with gastric cancer: Defective hepatic glycogenesis; effects of adrenocortical extract. *J. Clin. Investigation 27:* 760-765, 1948.

CHAPTER 26

Environmental Cancer

Wilhelm C. Hueper

DEFINITION AND SIGNIFICANCE OF ENVIRONMENTAL CANCERS

Environmental cancers are malignant tumors which are usually caused by prolonged exposure to exogenous agents of various types. In a few instances, these environmental cancer-producing factors are well-defined physical or chemical agents, in others they are variable and undetermined mixtures of chemicals, while in a third group the carcinogenic exposure is represented by contacts or conditions of a rather vague nature. The different environmental carcinogens which form a part of our natural or artificial environment are practically the only known causes of cancer in man at the present time, and for this reason have considerable general significance. Exposure to these factors is related to occupational activities, medicines, diets, cosmetics, building materials, habits, customs, climate, fauna, contaminants of drinking water, atmospheric air, soil and foodstuffs, and procedures of warfare.

Environmental carcinogens, known or suspected, cover a wide range of inanimate and animate agents. This spectrum, summarized in Table 59, includes a great variety of organic chemicals, both aromatic and aliphatic, several inorganic chemicals, various types of physical radiation, and several parasites.

It is apparent from the above list that the bulk of known environmental carcinogenic agents and the cancers caused by them can be traced to certain occupational agents, most of which have entered the human environment during the past century as the result of modern industrialization.

The various environmental carcinogens differ considerably in their potency not only from each other but also among members of the same type. Within certain limits, for instance, tars and tar oils obtained by the distillation of coal are more carcinogenic than those resulting from the processing of shale oil and definitely more carcinogenic than petroleum tars, although this order may have to be revised with regard to the tar products obtained by the catalytic cracking process of mineral oils, which have displayed in part an unusually high degree of carcinogenic

TABLE 59. ENVIRONMENTAL CARCINOGENIC AGENTS AND SITES OF CANCER

Classification	*Carcinogenic agent*	*Type of contact*	*Site of Cancer*
Organic chemicals, aromatic	Benzol	Cutaneous, respiratory	Leukemia (?) lymphosarcoma (?) myeloma (?)
	Aromatic amines, beta-naphthylamine, benzidine	Cutaneous, respiratory	carcinoma of bladder, ureter renal pelvis
	Coal tar, pitch, asphalt, soot, bitumen, creosote oil, anthracene oil (3,4 benzpyrene)	Cutaneous	Carcinoma of skin
		Respiratory (fumes)	Carcinoma of lung
	Shale oil, lubricating oils, crude paraffin oils	Cutaneous	Carcinoma of skin
	Lignite oils, lubricating oils, crude paraffin oils, tar oils	Cutaneous	Carcinoma of skin
	Petroleums and petroleum products, lubricating oils, crude paraffin oils, fuel oils, commercial soots	Cutaneous	Carcinoma of skin
		Respiratory (mist-dust)	Carcinoma of lung (?)
Organic chemicals, aliphatic	Isopropyl oil (?)	Respiratory	Carcinoma of the nasal sinuses and lung (?)
Inorganic chemicals	Arsenicals, inorganic and organic (?)	Cutaneous, alimentary, respiratory	Carcinoma of the skin
			Carcinoma of the lung (?), carcinoma of the alimentary tract (?), carcinoma of the bladder (?)
	Chromates	Respiratory	Carcinoma of the lung
	Nickel carbonyl,	Respiratory	Carcinoma of the nasal sinuses and lung
	Asbestos (?)	Respiratory	Carcinoma of the lung
Physical agents	Ionizing radiation of electro-magnetic (gamma) and corpuscular types (alpha, beta) from radioactive chemicals	Cutaneous	Carcinoma and sarcoma of the skin,
		Respiratory	Carcinoma of the lung, carcinoma of nasal sinuses,
		Alimentary general body, parenteral	Sarcoma of the bones, leukemia, lymphosarcoma, carcinoma of the liver (?)
	Ionizing radiation from x-ray tubes	Cutaneous	Carcinoma of the skin, sarcoma of connective tissues and bones,
		General body, cutaneous	leukemia, lymphosarcoma
	Ultraviolet radiation—solar radiation	Cutaneous	Carcinoma of the skin

TABLE 59. ENVIRONMENTAL CARCINOGENIC AGENTS AND SITES OF CANCER (*Continued*)

Classification	*Carcinogenic agent*	*Type of contact*	*Site of cancer*
		PRECANCEROUS AND PERICANCEROUS CONDITIONS	
Dietary imbalances	Iodine deficiency	Adenomatous goiter	Carcinoma of thyroid
	Vitamin B complex deficiency (?)	Plummer-Vinson syndrome	Carcinoma of nasopharynx
	Vitamin B complex–protein deficiency (?)	Cirrhosis of liver	Carcinoma of liver
Parasitic infections	*Schistosoma hematobiums*	Chronic cystiti	Carcinoma of bladder
	Schistosoma mansoni (?)	Chronic colitis and proctitis	Carcinoma of colon and rectum (?)
	Clonorchis sinensis (?)	Cirrhosis of liver	Carcinoma of liver
Indeterminate agents	Kangri,kairo,kang (Thermic carbonization of tissue and soot) (?)	Burn ulcers, scars, and thermic dermatitis	Carcinoma of skin
	Khaini quid (tobacco-lime)	Chronic gingivitis	Carcinoma of mucosa of lower lip and gum
	Betel quid (areca nut, tobacco, lime, buyo leaf)	Chronic inflammation of oral mucosa	Carcinoma of oral mucosa, gum, cheek, tongue
	Dhoti (loin cloth) (soot ?)	Chronic dermatitis	Carcinoma of skin
	Tobacco extractives ?	Chronic inflammation of oral mucosa	Carcinoma of oral cavity (?)
	Tobacco combustion products (tar) and thermic burns (chutta)		Carcinoma of oral cavity (?)
			Carcinoma of lung (?)

potency in experimental animals. A similar situation prevails concerning the carcinogenic action of various types of soots, both domestic-industrial and commercial. The source material as well as the type of processing (intensity and duration of heat) apparently play an important role in determining the relative carcinogenic properties of a particular kind of soot. Clinical and experimental evidence attests the carcinogenic potency of various types of domestic-industrial soot. Some isolated observations indicate that commercial soots, such as lamp black and oil black, are carcinogenic. Whether carbon black made by the incomplete combustion of natural gas possesses such qualities for man is still undetermined, while the experimental evidence concerning a possible carcinogenic effect of carbon black produced from petroleum tar oil (residual oil from catalytic cracking operations) or natural gas has been reported. Corresponding differences in carcinogenic potency exist for the different derivatives of petroleum, which vary considerably in their chemical make-up, depending upon the chemical character of the crude oil and the type of processing used in their production.

A further difficulty connected with the interpretation of observations pub-

TABLE 59. ENVIRONMENTAL CARCINOGENIC AGENTS AND SITES OF CANCER (*Concluded*)

Classification	*Carcinogenic Agent*	*Site of Cancer*	*Species*
Potential environmental carcinogenic agents and cancer sites	Aromatic amino-compounds: *o*-aminoazotoluene, *o*-aminoazobenzol, 2,3-azotoluene, *n,n*-diethyl-*p*-amino-1-azobenzol, 4-dimethyl-aminoazobenzene-1-azonaphthalene, 4-oxy-2,3-dimethyl-azobenzol, 2-acetylaminofluorene, 2-aminofluorene, dibenzcarbazole, 4-dimethylamino-azobenzol,	Liver Bladder	Rat, mouse
	Estrogenic compounds, stilbestrol	Breast	Mouse, rat
		Uterus Hematopoietic tissue	Guinea pig, mouse
	Aliphatic compounds, chlorinated hydrocarbons, chloroform, carbon tetrachloride	Liver	Mouse
	Diethylene glycol	Bladder	Rat
	Carbamate derivatives	Lung	Mouse, rat
	Thiourea derivatives	Thyroid (?)	Mouse
	Beryllium	Bone, lung	Rabbit, rat
	Selenium	Liver	Rat

lished on carcinogenic agents such as tar, pitch, asphalt, lubricating oil, and carbon black, is the fact that such terms are applied in different countries to different products. For instance, asphalt in this country is mainly of native type, while in Germany it is usually a product of coal distillation. Lubricating oils used in the United States are, with minor exceptions, of petroleum derivation, while those employed for many years in large parts of the British industry were obtained from shale oil. In Germany, on the other hand, some of the lubricating oils were made by the distillation and cracking of coal or lignite. The term "carbon black" was applied in the United States for many years to certain types of commercial soot made from natural gas exclusively. In more recent years, however, American industry has used the same term for products manufactured from the incomplete combustion of residual oils of petroleum refining. Carbon black in English terminology, on the other hand, designates all kinds of commercial soots, such as bone black, oil black, gas black, acetylene black, lamp black, and other types of "carbons." It is for these reasons that the epidemiologic data on some types of environmental cancer, incomplete and defective as they are, present some complicating factors deserving due consideration.

Although environmental cancers are the end-products of somewhat haphazardly conducted "experiments" on man (since the "experimental" conditions are less rigidly standardized and controlled, because they are not planned, than those usually observed in experiments on animals), whatever evidence they yield is nevertheless of distinctly superior fundamental significance, because it is obtained in the species "man." The information obtained from the study of environmental cancer has thus clearly demonstrated that nonspecific chronic irritation is scarcely a major factor in the production of human cancer. Not only is the cancer incidence rate of certain organs frequently affected by chronic inflammatory processes (chronic sinusitis, chronic salpingitis, chronic urethritis, chronic osteomyelitis, chronic crural ulcers, hemorrhoids) relatively low, but cancer of the skin does not result from most types of chronic industrial dermatitis, nor cancer of the bladder from many types of chronic or repeated chemical irritation of the vesical mucosa sustained by some groups of industrial workers.

Observations made in connection with several forms of occupational cancer, such as those caused by aromatic amines and pitch, indicate that hereditary predisposition does not play a primary role in their genesis because workers sufficiently long and intensely exposed to these agents ultimately developed cancer. Whatever hereditary influences may be active in the development of environmental cancers, and presumably also of most human cancers of unknown etiology, are evidently of an order comparable to that displayed by heredity in determining in part the individual susceptibility to the various infectious diseases.

Likewise, the observations made with environmental, and especially occupational, cancers deflate the long-held theory that prenatal or postnatal tissue misplacements or embryonic anlage furnish an important source of cancers, because the high incidence of multiple cancers, or the development of viscus carcinosis in some instances of occupational carcinogenesis, preclude any reasonable possibility of tissue malformations being involved in such processes.

Environmental carcinogenesis has also refuted the long-held concept that senescent changes are causally involved to a high degree in the development of cancer. This theory is mainly based on the fact that cancers most often occur in elderly persons displaying such alterations in association with malignant growths. The proven long latent period of most environmental cancers, ranging generally from five to thirty years, however, readily places the all-important exposure time to the specific carcinogenic agent, for many cases, in the young or middle adult span of life. While the manifestation age of cancer, therefore, is frequently synchronous with senescing processes, the cancerization reactions usually affect cells of younger age and unimpaired vitality. The relations noted to exist between the age at circumcision, the manifestation age, and the incidence rate of penile cancer provide confirmatory evidence on this point from the field of endogenous carcinogenesis. "Cancer age" and senescence therefore are as a rule merely coincidentally but not causally related.

Thus, the study of environmental cancers has not only thrown much light upon some important aspects of general carcinogenesis, but has opened the door wide for intelligent investigation of the exogenous causes of cancer, the knowledge of which is essential for the institution of rational and effective measures of prevention and control of the disease. The data on hand clearly show that cancer is evidently not a disease with a single cause, but is definitely a disease complex that can be elicited by many agents which may alter their target organ and many of their precancerous and cancerous manifestations with the type of active carcinogen, the route of its introduction, and the intensity of the exposure to it. Many environmental carcinogens produce distinct precancerous and pericancerous reactions as well as benign tumors (papillomas, adenomas). Environmental cancerous diseases appear to be as multifaced and multiphasic as infectious diseases have proven to be after the original miasmatic concept of their genesis had been discarded.

It seems appropriate to point out that almost all known cancer-producing agents are of exogenous, environmental origin. This fact, apparently, is not the result of a mere coincidence, but is of real significance in its broader implications as to the prospective and unknown sources from which cancer in man may arise, and as to the direction for future etiologic research. Indeed, much of the recent experimental investigations on the causation and causative mechanism of cancer are directly derived from observations made in the study of occupational cancers.

EPIDEMIOLOGY

Even a brief and superficial analysis of the various recognized and suspected environmental carcinogens reveals the fact that contact with these agents is widespread and takes on different forms. Paralleling the increasingly rapid pace of industrial development and diversification of industrial processes and products, there were discovered during the last seventy-five years a progressively mounting number and variety of exogenous occupational carcinogens affecting different organs and tissues. In addition, epidemiologic studies on cancer undertaken during recent decades revealed that cancer development is related to environmental factors other than those associated with occupational activity. The environmental carcinogenic spectrum that has evolved during this period contains physical, chemical, and parasitic agents that differ in their properties in many respects as widely as the members composing the pathogenic microbiologic spectrum. There exist, moreover, many other similarities between these two disease complexes in their mode of contact, the development of manifestations, and the type of spread from infectious or carcinogenic foci. It is likely, therefore, that the same epidemiologic methods may be employed in the study of environmental cancers that were so effectively used in broadening the knowledge of infectious disease.

The following considerations seem to be important in conducting environmental cancer surveys: the mere fact that contact of individuals or groups of individuals with any of the listed carcinogenic agents exists does not indicate that all persons becoming exposed to them are destined to develop cancer in some organ. Present evidence demonstrates that the conditions of exposure (intensity, type, and duration) must be proper and adequate for such an outcome. Not only is the information on known environmental carcinogenic agents and their cancerous manifestations at present not standard medical knowledge, but the actual demonstration of the existence of a relationship between a previous specific carcinogenic exposure and a cancer appearing many years later is usually difficult or even impossible to prove (or is not attempted or thought of). Therefore, an undetermined proportion of the environmental cancer cases remains in the so-called "spontaneous" or cryptogenetic group of cancers.

This situation is regrettable, because it is obvious from the nature of the known and suspected carcinogens that they may elicit cancers not only in members of an appreciable number of occupational groups who are both producers and consumers or users of these agents, but also in members of the general public. The general population comes in contact with these agents when they are contained in consumer goods of various types or when they pollute the human environment (air, water, and soil), for instance, by being contained in industrial wastes.

A few citations of actual conditions may help to illustrate this spread of carcinogenic contacts by tracing them from the original producer through the various successive types of consumers to the general public. A carcinogenic arsenic hazard exists for the miners who mine arsenic-containing ores (copper, silver, zinc, lead). The hazard extends from there to the workers in smelters, where the bulk of the white arsenic is obtained as a by-product of metal ore smelting. From there, arsenic reaches the consuming industries which use it in the production of pesticides, weedkillers, glass, lead-base alloys, dyestuffs, cattle and sheep dips, wood preservatives, poison bait, chemical warfare gases, and in the Thylox purification of industrial gases. The list of occupations in which these and other arsenicals are handled is extensive. Since arsenicals at some smelters are freely released into the atmosphere or remain in the slag heaps, there exists the danger of a contamination of drinking water supplies from these sources causing the development of an endemic arsenicism. A similar result may ensue from the liberal spraying and dusting of vineyards, orchards, and cotton fields with arsenical insecticides. Finally arsenicals are administered to man for therapeutic purposes or may be consumed with contaminated foodstuffs, liquor, tobacco, and candies. Cancers of the skin and possibly also of the lung have been traced to most of these various exposures to arsenic.

A similar centrifugal spread of exposure may be noted for the tarry products obtained by the incomplete combustion of coal. Workers employed in gas works and coke ovens where the bulk of the industrially important tar is produced may sustain skin contact with this material or may inhale hot tar fumes and develop cancer of the skin or of the lung, depending on the type of exposure. The tar is then fractionated into tar oils, creosote, pitch, and anthracene oil, in addition to lighter and more volatile products, which, with the exception of benzol, are usually noncarcinogenic. These fractionation products are either used as they are for a great number of purposes or are processed and transformed into well-defined chemical compounds, forming, together with petroleum derivatives, the main source of material for the modern organic chemical and pharmaceutic industry. Since the entire list of products into which tar, pitch, asphalt, creosote oil, anthracene oil, mineral waxes, and related materials enter is very long, only a selection of the most common uses can be given. These are enamels, paints, inks, varnishes, roof-coating material, cement, mortar, putty, shingles, tiles, roofing paper, water-proofed paper, felt, textile, nets, cords and panels, acoustic blocks, compositions and felts, calking material, wood preservative, road construction material, electric appliance and wire insulation material, casting molds, battery boxes, cork composition, ditch, dike and jetty protectives, leather composition, linoleum, foundry cores, friction tape, pipe-coating, tree-surgery paste, lubricants, cable-splicing compounds, clay pigeons, fuel, floor treads, optical polishing base, knobs, mirror backing, phonograph records, frothing oils, flotation oils, depilatories, pesticides, cattle sprays, and medicinal and cosmetic ointments and lotions. It is quite obvious even from the limited enumeration of uses of tar, pitch and related substances, that contact with these agents is not only widespread in industry, but extends to a definite degree to the general public for reasons of consumption and general environment. It may suffice to mention that petroleum derivatives enjoy a similar range of distribution as those cited for tar, although it seems that most of them fortunately are of a lower degree of carcinogenic potency.

Although we have become accustomed recently to connect occupational radioactive hazards with the production of atomic energy, there are considerable additional radioactive cancer hazards in professional and industrial fields. Perhaps the most well known are those encountered by the personnel of radiologic laboratories in research establishments, hospitals, and industries, such as foundries and shipyards. The manufacture, application, and removal of radioactive luminous dial paint occupied many hundreds of persons during the second World War and is an operation in which a considerable number of workers are still engaged. Radioactive hazards have been introduced lately into the pharmaceutic and other industries through the use of radioactive isotopes employed in the production and application of tracer substances. Radioactive substances are handled, moreover, in the production of radio tubes, electrostatic eliminators, gas mantles, radium type vacuum gauges, and nickel polonium alloy spark plugs. In this connection, it is interesting to note that a considerable amount of the tremendous quantities of radium used in luminous paint is unaccounted for, since markers, dials and rope carrying the radioactive material have occasionally found their way into the hands of persons not qualified to dispose of them properly. While thus, on the one hand, a certain degree of environmental radioactive hazards may have come to elements of the population not generally expected to sustain such exposures, there remains the probability that the cancer hazard from contact with radioactive dust and gases starts with the mining and milling of the ore, if the experiences made with lung cancers in miners of such ores in Czechoslovakia and Germany should prove to be of general application.

The available evidence justifies the statement, that given a carcinogenic environmental agent and the proper type of exposure, the development of cancer in exposed individuals is mainly a matter of time or the latent period. Although the wisdom of this lesson of modern occupational cancer research may as yet not always be appreciated properly, the inexorable facts are bound in the long run to provide convincing proof of its validity through adequate epidemiologic surveys.

There are a few more dogmas that have developed from the studies of occupational cancers which appear to merit consideration from an epidemiologic viewpoint.

1. Occupational cancers appear at sites where the contact with the carcinogenic agent is most intense and prolonged.

2. The type of contact in turn depends on the type of exposure, i.e., skin exposure, inhalation, ingestion or parenteral introduction, the physical status of the agent, and the chemical properties, metabolism, excretion, or deposition of the carcinogenic agent.

For instance, skin contact with tar, pitch, mineral oil and similar agents causes cancer of the skin, as does ingestion of arsenicals which in part are stored in the skin and its appendages. Inhalation of hot tar fumes or of arsenical dust may elicit cancer of the lung. The same result may ensue after the inhalation of asbestos and chromate dust, and nickel carbonyl and isopropyl oil vapors, whereby the vapor hazards in addition give rise to cancers of the nasal sinuses. Cancer of the skin follows direct contact of this tissue with radioactive material; upon ingestion of radioactive matter osteogenic sarcomas develop; prolonged intermittent, mild, general body irradiation seems to cause leukemia; and inhalation of radioactive gases and dust results in cancer of the lung.

3. Exposure conditions appear to control to a large extent the sex ratio of environmental cancers. Whenever both sexes are equally exposed to a particular carcinogenic agent there is a tendency towards equalization of the sex incidence of cancer involving a certain site. For instance, bladder cancer due to aromatic amines so far has been observed in males only, while osteogenic sarcoma caused by ingestion of radioactive material has appeared so far in females only. Cancer of the skin in mulespinners was restricted for many years to males. With the introduction of female workers into this trade during recent decades, cancer of the vulva has been noted in several female mulespinners. Whereas the usual male to female sex ratio of lung cancer is 5 to 1, it is about 2.5 to 1 for asbestosis cancer of the lung.

4. No conclusions, moreover, can be drawn from its toxic properties as to the degree of carcinogenic potency of a particular chemical agent. Indeed, some of the most potent carcinogenic chemicals have a very low toxicity. For instance among the carcinogenic aromatic amines, β-naphthylamine is highly carcinogenic to man but is of very low toxicity under the conditions existing in industry. Benzidine, on the other hand, is more toxic but less carcinogenic than β-naphthylamine. It is moreover well established that the carcinogenic potency of a particular agent is not uniform for all tissues, but may vary considerably. These differences are in part due to local variations in the intensity and duration of exposure related to the solubility or retention of the agent and to the speed of its removal or metabolism.

5. Since environmental cancers and those caused by carcinogenic agents do not possess any properties by which they can be distinguished from the so-called spontaneous cancer, the recognition of the environmental nature of a cancer is based on circumstantial evidence. The bulk of this evidence is of statistical and epidemiologic nature. An increased total cancer morbidity and mortality, with a shift in the distribution of cancers as to sites as well as an excessive incidence of cancer of a certain organ or organs within a restricted population group, should arouse the

suspicion of an environmental cause of these cancers. This interpretation receives support if there is a demonstrable shift of the number of cancers from older to younger age groups and of the male—female sex ratio of cancer. Finally, the demonstration of a comon type of exposure aids in establishing the environmental character of the cancers observed. However, with this type of reasoning, cancers of a "spontaneous" nature are unavoidably included among the environmental cancers occurring in the surveyed population group. Some of these spontaneous cancers can be eliminated from the occupational group by evaluating properly the length of the exposure period and the intensity and type of contact to the carcinogenic agent in relation to the site and latent period of the cancer scrutinized. For others it may be possible, on the other hand, to demonstrate manifestations preceding or accompanying the cancerous process and characterizing the etiologic agent. Some such manifestations are of a precancerous nature and form a part of the cancerization process, such as hyperkeratosis, warts, papillomas, adenomas, leukemoid reactions, chronic periostitis, and other hyperplastic lesions, while others provide merely symptomatic telltale footprints of the carcinogenic agents and may be called pericancerous in character. Such lesions are melanoderma and leukoderma, chronic dermatitis, telangiectases, hemorrhages, comedones, boils, and atrophies and other phenomena of a degenerative nature.

It is not unusual that some members of the surveyed population group who are not affected by cancer may display some or all of these precancerous and pericancerous reactions which compose the environmental cancer pattern and which thereby furnish confirmatory evidence as to the environmental nature of the cancerous reactions observed in this group. The discovery and recognition of environmental cancers is thus based on a complex type of evidence which in some instances forms a mosaic of a definite design, the environmental cancer pattern. Familiarity of the medical profession with these symptomatic characteristics and peculiarities of environmental cancers is important for the discovery of environmental cancer hazards. However, such warning signals of the impending advent of environmental cancer are not present in many environmental cancers. Often, there may be scarcely any preliminary symptoms of toxic nature preceding the development of cancer. In fact, in many instances the general health may remain good for a long time even in the presence of an environmental or occupational cancer.

At the present time, environmental cancer appears primarily as an industrial problem, although it extends into many nonindustrial occupations. Fully 90 per cent of the known environmental carcinogens never existed in dangerous concentrations until the development of industrial processes which brought workers into frequent and close contact with them. As the injurious agents have made their appearance with the growth of various industries, cancers have developed among exposed workers. Perhaps one of the most striking examples of this pattern is the appearance of bladder cancers among dye workers subsequent to the establishment of aniline dye factories in various countries. Observations in many industries indicate that the appearance of the specific occupational cancers, whenever the exposure is sufficiently intense, depends upon the proper latent period elapsing since the start of the operation.

Industrial carcinogens not only provide a serious hazard to the exposed workers but may possibly also affect the health of the general population through various routes of contact, as pointed out above. A rarely considered route of spread of occupational cancer hazards is created when contaminated clothing worn by workers in carcinogenic operations is laundered without proper precautions in the factory, home, or commercial laundry. However, the same or similar exogenous carcinogens which appear as industrial hazards may also be part of the general or artificial environment quite independently of any industrial operations. These possible nonoccupational contacts with environmental carcinogens deserve serious consideration in conducting epidemiologic studies. Recognized and suspected sources of nonoccupational environmental cancer are listed in Table 60.

TABLE 60. RECOGNIZED AND SUSPECTED SOURCES OF NON-OCCUPATIONAL ENVIRONMENTAL CANCER

Method of exposure and carcinogen	*Potential site of cancer*
HABITS	
Smoking (tar, burns) or chewing of tobacco (khaini)	Lip, tongue, oral cavity, larynx, lung
Betel nut-lime-tobacco quid chewing	Lip, tongue, oral cavity, cheek
Chewing of tar, paraffin (?)	Oral cavity
CUSTOMS	
Carrying of special heating devices beneath clothing near abdominal skin (kairo, kangri), or sleeping on hot stoves (kang) causing burns and exposure to tar and soot	Skin
Smoking cigars with lighted end in mouth (chutta) (tar and burn injury)	Oral cavity
Wearing of loin cloth (dhoti) with exposure to soot, friction, and decomposed sebum	Skin (loin, groin)
HOBBIES AND HOME ACTIVITIES	
Gardening with exposure to solar rays, and arsenicals and other chemical pesticides and weedkillers (soot, etc.)	Skin, internal organs
Sailing, fishing, golfing, and other forms of outdoor sports with exposure to solar radiation	Skin
Home-engineering with contact with derivatives of petroleum (lubricants, metal dust, solvents, etc.) (?)	Skin, internal organs
Use of paints and paint removers, containing benzol, chlorinated hydrocarbons, chrome pigments, asphalts, tars, carbon blacks (?)	Skin, lung, hematopoietic tissue
Use of chlorinated hydrocarbons in cleaning fluids, floor waxes, etc., with hepatotoxic properties modifying metabolism of endogenous and exogenous carcinogens (?)	Liver, internal organs
MEDICINES AND MEDICAL DEVICES	
Arsenicals	Skin, internal organs
Tar, impure petrolatum, and mineral oil	Skin, internal organs
Hepatotoxic chemicals (chlorinated aliphatic hydrocarbons, cinchophen, etc.) (?)	Liver
Hematotoxic chemicals (benzol, sulfonamides) (?), aromatic chemicals causing agranulocytosis (?)	Hematopoietic tissue

TABLE 60. RECOGNIZED AND SUSPECTED SOURCES OF NON-OCCUPATIONAL ENVIRONMENTAL CANCER (*Continued*)

Method of exposure and carcinogen	*Potential site of cancer*
Ultraviolet radiation	Skin
X-radiation	Skin, bone, hematopoietic tissue, uterus (?), breast (?)
Radioative chemicals (ionizing radiations)	Skin, bone, lung (?), liver (?), hematopoietic tissue (?), uterus (?)
DIETARY FACTORS	
Dietary iodine deficiency	Thyroid
Dietary protein and vitamin B complex deficiency	Liver
Dietary vitamin B complex deficiency	Laryngo-naso-pharynx
Arsenical contaminants in food, drinking water, air	Skin, lung (?), internal organs
Heated mineral oil as fat substitute in baked goods and mineral oil in salad dressings, mayonnaises, etc. (?)	Internal organs
Impure coal tar dyes in foodstuffs (?)	Internal organs
Heated animal and vegetable fats (?)	Alimentary organs
COSMETIC FACTORS	
X-radiation for depilation	Skin
Ultraviolet lamp exposure for tanning (?)	Skin
Arsenicals in hair lotions and tonics (?)	Skin, internal organs
Lamp black in eyebrow pencils (tar) (?)	Skin
Impure petrolatum and mineral oils in ointments, creams, etc. (?)	Skin
Impure coal tar dyes in lipsticks, etc. containing dye intermediates (?)	Bladder
Estrogens in skin creams (?)	Breast, Uterus (?)
OTHER ENVIRONMENTAL FACTORS	
Tar, soot and petroleum derivatives in atmospheric air (?)	Lung, skin (?)
Arsenicals in dust of ore smelters and orchards, cotton fields, etc. sprayed with arsenical pesticides or weedkillers (?)	Skin, lung, internal organs
Dry and sunny climate or high altitude with excessive solar irradiation	Skin
Ionizing radiation in water, air, foodstuffs in regions with radioactive ores (?)	Lung, bone, hematopoietic tissue

The action of these and other still unknown environmental carcinogenic factors is suggested by the existence of marked differences in the incidence rates of cancers of various sites according to regions, countries, nations, races, sexes, socio-economic status, customs, etc. While the percentage figures of cancer incidence given in tables (Table 61) in support of this contention have no absolute value, since the reporting is so uneven from one part of the world to another, they nevertheless indicate relative and significant trends which support a more general causation of human cancer by environmental agents than that indicated by the evidence available for specific environmental cancers.

Several approaches are available for obtaining the objectives of environmental cancer surveys. The first method suggested, analysis of death certificates, provides

TABLE 61. EVIDENCE SUPPORTING AN ENVIRONMENTAL CAUSATION OF HUMAN CANCER

1. Differences in rates of recorded cancer mortality in various geographic areas of the United States and Europe, the rates being in general highest in the northern regions and lowest in the southern parts of the two geographical units cited.

In 1930:	Rhode Island	127 cancer deaths per	100,000 inhabitants
	Arkansas	56	100,000

2. Differences in the incidence of certain types of cancers (skin, lung, etc.) in various parts of the United States and Europe.

In 1938:	Cancer of the skin: Morbidity rates, white population	Atlanta, Georgia	157 per 100,000 inhabitants
		New Orleans, La.	129
		Detroit, Mich	37
		Pittsburgh, Pa	25
		Chicago, Ill.	24
In 1942:	Cancer of the stomach:	England and Wales	22.2% of total cancer mortality
		United States	42.8
		Holland	55.5
		Sweden	60.5
		Czechoslovakia	66.0

Primary cancer of the liver: percentage of all cancer deaths

United States (whites and Negroes)	1–5 (also American Chinese and Japanese)
Europeans	1–5
Javanese	57
Chinese	30.8
African Negroes	29

3. Differences in cancer incidence related to certain customs:
   Penile cancer: Occurrence and age period of circumcision:
   Jews: circumcision performed during first eight days of life
   Incidence rate: 0%
   Mohammedans: Circumcision performed between 3 and 14 years of age
   Incidence rate: 2.1% to 1.5%
   Chinese: Non-circumcised. Incidence rate: 15% of all cancers
4. Socio-economic distribution of cancer: (England and Wales)
   Cancer of scrotum highest in lowest economic group having the lowest standard of cleanliness
   Cancer of skin: Incidence increases with lowering of socio-economic group in males, but not in females

Cancer of stomach:	Highest group:	38.8% of total cancer of males only
	Group 2	40.1
	3	48.5
	4	56.8
	5	63.4
	6	68.5

5. Differences in sex distribution of certain cancers:
   Male-female ratio, not sex conditioned but exposure conditioned: Cancer of

skin in whites	4:1
lung	4:1–7:1
larynx	10:1
bladder	5:1
esophagus	10:1

6. Differences in incidence due to endemic infections:

Cancer of the bladder:	United States and Europe:	2–4% of total cancer rate
	Egypt (schistosomiasis of bladder)	23.3%

a preliminary or exploratory approach which may give valuable clues and points to fruitful fields of further investigation. The second approach, occupational history studies of cancer deaths, involves tracking down possible occupational factors in the etiology of individual cancer cases. The third approach, the plant survey, is essential for determining precisely which workers come into dangerous contact with carcinogens, how many may be affected, through which route the exposure takes place, what organ or organs develop cancerous responses, and other important aspects of occupational or environmental carcinogenesis.

ANALYSIS OF DEATH CERTIFICATES

Working on the premise that certain occupational activities or contact with various occupational or environmental agents result in an abnormally high incidence of total cancer deaths, as well as in an abnormal distribution of cancers as to sites, the effects of such factors on cancer mortality might be demonstrated through a critical analysis of data recorded in death certificates. If such environmental carcinogenic influences are sufficiently pronounced and specific in a certain area, and the worker population is relatively stable, it might be profitable to plot the local distribution of cancer deaths as to total number and as to sites. Comparison of these data with data from an area having a different environmental and, particularly, occupational carcinogenic spectrum should reveal suggestive relations between these factors and cancer incidence. By comparing the relative frequency of cancer cases for various sites in the region under study with the normally expected frequency, it may be possible to locate regional foci of carcinogenic exposure—plants, industries or occupations which deserve further investigation and in which protective and preventive measures are needed. These would prove most successful in areas in which the industrial conditions are relatively uncomplicated—that is, dominated by one particular type of industry. A recent analysis of lung cancer deaths among the population of several counties in Montana, where mining and smelting of arsenic-containing copper ores represent the major industrial activity, provides a good illustration of the possibility of this approach (Lull, Wallach) (Table 62).

The estimated crude death rate for lung cancer among white males in the entire United States in 1947 was 10.9 per 100,000 population.

OCCUPATIONAL HISTORY STUDIES

When studying the environmental and occupational histories of selected cancer cases in order to discover possible causal factors, it is advisable to use for this purpose living cancer patients. Such investigations are indicated for confirming and elaborating upon previously made observations, and for determining the scope of the known and suspected environmental cancer hazards as to regional distribution, industrial operations, consumer aspects, general environmental extensions, sex distribution, and other pertinent relations. In planning such a study, proper consideration must be given to the fact that these tumors usually result from extended exposure and appear only after long latent periods, the latter ranging ordinarily from five to twenty-five years. It is necessary, therefore, to ascertain the occupational and nonoccupational exposures for as long a period as possible preceding the appearance of the particular cancer.

Through this approach it is possible to uncover, also, new industrial and environmental carcinogenic agents and foci. Such a procedure appears to have special value for cancers of certain organ systems (gastrointestinal, nervous), as exogenous carcinogenic agents have so far not been demonstrated for some of them, although geographical, topographical, age, and sex distribution implicate such factors.

PLANT SURVEYS

In individual plant surveys, two different types of conditions may be met. In certain kinds of industries (such as those concerned with the manufacture of chromates or tars) it appears that all, or almost all, workers employed have some degree of exposure to a carcinogenic agent. In other industries, carcinogenic hazards exist for limited groups of only those individuals either engaged in a specific opera-

TABLE 62. LUNG CANCER MORTALITY IN SEVERAL COUNTIES OF MONTANA, 1947–1948

County and total population, 1940	*Major industry*	*No. lung cancer*			*Total cancer deaths*	*Lung cancer (%)*		*Annual lung cancer death rate/100,000*	
		Male	*Female*	*Total*		*Male*	*Female*	*Male*	*Female*
Deer Lodge 13,627	Copper smelting	21	0	21	98	30.8	0.0	145.7	
Silver Bow 53,207	Copper mining	27	2	29	259	22.6	1.5	48.6	3.9
Cascade 41,999	Copper mining smelting	20	5	25	299	12.7	3.5	46.3	12.3
Gallatin 18,269	Farming	1	0	1	81	3.0	0.0	5.2	

tion or coming in contact with some particular agent present in, and common to, different operations. In either case, the investigations should be extended not only to individuals regularly employed in such operations or constantly in contact with carcinogenic agents, but also to those entering the hazardous area or coming into contact with carcinogens at irregular intervals. Intermittent, irregular, or rhythmic exposures of varying intensity may be sustained by such workers as watchmen, maintenance and repair men, packers, shippers, truckers, supervisors, control chemists, guards, and yardmen. Consideration should also be given to workers engaged in the disposal of wastes and emptied containers of carcinogenic materials, as well as to those workers who are employed in noncarcinogenic operations located near hazardous ones, and who possibly become exposed to carcinogenic gases, vapors, fumes, mists, dusts, etc., originating from the latter.

Since several years of contact with the carcinogenic agent are usually required for effective exposure and since the latent period is seldom shorter than five years and sometimes more than twenty-five years, cancer records of industrial operations should be obtained for as long a period as possible. Occupational cancer surveys of plants and industries are never spot surveys but always time surveys. Where possible, pertinent data should be collected as to the final fate of former workers sufficiently long employed in hazardous operations to make the subsequent development of occupational cancers a distinct probability. It is essential, for this reason, to consider the degree of labor turnover, since a rapid labor turnover can effectively obliterate any evidence as to the existence of a carcinogenic hazard that may be obtained from an analysis of employment and medical records of a plant surveyed.

Any reliable occupational cancer survey requires an adequate knowledge of the technical aspects of the industry studied and of the epidemiologic and biologic peculiarities of the carcinogenic hazards and cancers that may be encountered, as well as the strict observance of the basic epidemiologic and statistical rules. It is for these reasons that recent attempts to determine the presence of occupational cancer hazards by correlating cancer incidence with the total work-man-hours of workers employed without giving any consideration to the length of employment of individual workers and to the existence of an adequate latent period, has led to misleading and fallacious conclusions.

ENVIRONMENTAL CARCINOGENS AND CANCERS

The following summaries present the salient facts available concerning the known and suspected environmental human carcinogens and their cancerous reaction products.

ORGANIC CHEMICALS

1. Anthracene Oil

Crude anthracene oil is a product of the distillation of coal tar and is used in the manufacture of anthracene and grease, while anthracene oil residue is occasionally employed as a fuel. The active carcinogenic ingredient is not anthracene but an undetermined constituent of the oily portion. Cancers affecting the skin of the forearms, hands, face, and scrotum following direct contact with the material were reported from Germany and England. The total number of anthracene oil cancers from all sources is about a dozen. The exposure time of the skin cancers ranged from seventeen to forty-two years. The manifestation age of the patients with skin cancer ranged from 33 to 72 years. Chronic dermatitis, melanotic spots, atrophic areas, and keratotic warts constitute the environmental cancer pattern that preceeds and accompanies the development of the papillary and ulcerative carcinomatous lesions. So far only males have been involved.

The hazard is entirely occupational. The incidence rate of skin cancer of the exposed worker population corresponds to 3 affected out of 25 to 30 workers. The experimental reproduction of this occupational cancer was successfully achieved in mice through skin applications of anthracene oil.

2. Aromatic Amines

Aromatic amino- and azo-compounds are obtained by the fractionation and processing of tar and are used extensively for the production of dyes, pharmaceuticals, photographic chemicals, antioxidants of rubber, and flotation agents of ores.

Of the great number and variety of these chemicals a few have exhibited carcinogenic properties in man, while others have elicited such reactions in experimental animals. Of the human carcinogens of this nature, those with a β-naphthylamine and benzidine base have an established carcinogenicity to the urogenous organs, especially the bladder; it is questionable whether this is true of aniline, which in American experience has not displayed any carcinogenic properties. The highly carcinogenic β-naphthylamine, on the other hand, is active even when present as an impurity in presumably noncarcinogenic chemicals, such as α-naphthylamine.

Among the aromatic amino- and azo-compounds, *o-m*-dimethylazobenzol, benzidine, 2-amino-5-azotoluol, 2-acetylaminofluorene, *n*-ethyl-3,4,5,6-dibenzcarbazole, 4-dimethylaminoazobenzene-1-azonaphthalene, diazoaminobenzol, *m*-methyl *p*-dimethylaminoazobenzene, and several compounds closely related chemically, have induced cancers in internal organs, particularly the liver and bladder in experimental animals.

The total number of occupational bladder cancers caused by beta-naphthylamine, benzidine, and possibly aniline and recorded among dye workers of Germany, Switzerland, Great Britain, Austria, Russia, Italy, Japan and France stands at present close to 1500. A few of these cancers involved the ureter or kidney. The route of exposure to these chemicals is by skin contact, inhalation, and ingestion. The exposure time ranged from six months to forty years. The latent period, which in most instances was equal to the exposure period, was as short as two years and averaged from twelve to fifteen years. The manifestation age for the majority of the cancer cases was below 50 years and the rate of multiplicity was high. In several instances individuals in their third decade of life were involved.

Telangiectases and hemorrhages of the bladder mucosa, leukoplakias, polyps, and papillomas usually preceded the appearance of papillary or infiltrative and often multiple carcinomas. Because of the employment conditions existing in the dye industry, so far only male workers have exhibited bladder cancers due to exposure to the aromatic amines mentioned. The hazard is, according to existing knowledge, entirely an occupational one. In the past when the exposure was severe, a condition no longer encountered in modern plants, 100 per cent of the exposed workers developed bladder cancers. The experimental reproduction of bladder cancer by feeding β-napthylamine to dogs was successfully accomplished, while similar results were rare when benzidine was given; this substance, however, elicited hepatomas, cancer of the large intestine, cancers of the eustachian tube, and leukemia in rats.

3. Benzol

Benzol is a distillation product of tar and is employed for many purposes in a great number of industrial operations and products (rubber processing, printing, lithography, leather enameling, artificial leather making, rotogravure, rubber gasket can production, shoe manufacture, explosive production, paint remover, airplane dope, degreaser, bronzing pigment, vehicle, rubber cement, dry cleaning fluid, impregnation of textiles with plastic, electroplating, buna rubber production, aromatic industrial chemicals, and pharmaceuticals). While from an industrial hygiene aspect benzol is best known for its pronounced degenerative action on the hematopoietic system, an appreciable number of more recent observations suggest that a prolonged and mild exposure to benzol may cause leukemia. The development of both myeloid and lymphoid leukemias as well as of lymphosarcomas has been attributed to previous exposure to benzol. Reports on this subject have come from the United States, Italy, Germany, France, England, and Belgium. The total number of cases recorded, however, is small (about 15). The route of exposure was by skin contact and inhalation. The exposure time ranged from three to ten years. The age of the individuals affected was from 20 to 60 years.

The environmental cancer pattern found in these patients, as well as among other workers simultaneously exposed to benzol, showed the following manifestations: aplastic anemia, leukopenia, purpura, degeneration of the bone marrow (aplasiogenic effects), as well as erythrocytosis, leukocytosis, leukemoid reactions, hyperplasia of bone marrow, heterotopic myeloid foci, and leukemoid proliferations in bone marrow and internal organs. The male-female ratio is 4:1. The type of exposure encountered was occupational. Attempts at experimental reproduction of benzol leukemia in mice yielded contradictory results.

4. Chlorinated Hydrocarbons

While occupational exposure to chlorinated hydrocarbons, especially those of aliphatic nature, have caused acute and chronic liver injury (acute yellow atrophy, cirrhosis) in man, no information exists as to a direct or indirect carcinogenic effect of these chemicals. Experiments on mice, on the other hand, demonstrated that prolonged administration of chloroform and carbon tetrachloride resulted in the development of hepatomas and carcinomas.

5. Creosote Oil

Creosote oil is a fractionation product of wood and coal tar and is used as a wood preservative, as a mold-covering in brick and tile manufacture, and as a disinfectant. Skin contact with creosote oil, especially when hot, has been followed by the development of cancer of the skin (hands, forearms, scrotum) in some 55 cases reported from England, Germany, and France. The exposure time ranged from fifteen to forty years and the manifestation age was from 51 to 70 years. The appearance of cancerous lesions was preceded and accompanied by chronic dermatitis, hyperkeratoses, warts, and papillomas. Multiple cancers were present in about 12 per cent of the cases. The hazard was entirely an occupational one. Skin cancers were produced in mice painted with creosote oil.

6. Estrogens

It has been possible to produce breast cancers with both synthetic and natural estrogenic substances in mice and rats, papillomas of the bladder in mice and rabbits, and leukemias and testicular tumors in mice. Medicinal and occupational exposure of humans of both sexes has resulted in gynecomastia. There are some 15 cases in which male patients treated for cancer of the prostate with large amounts of estrogens over prolonged periods of time developed unilateral or bilateral cancer of the breast. A causal relationship between the estrogenic medication and subsequent appearance of breast cancers in these patients appears likely

7. Petroleum and Petroleum Derivatives (Lubricating Oils, Fuel Oils, Tar, Pitch, Oil Black, Coke, Crude Paraffin Oil, Asphalt)

The chemical composition of crude petroleums varies in different fields and even in different areas within the same field. Some crude petroleums contain considerable amounts of benzolic compounds, while in others aliphatic-paraffinic constituents predominate. The chemical nature of crude petroleum derivatives obtained by fractionation and cracking (thermodistillation, catalytic cracking under high pressure and temperature) depends in part on the chemical character of the crude product and in part on the cracking procedures used. Products obtained by the application of high temperature and pressure have a relatively high content of aromatic compounds because under such conditions aliphatic compounds are converted into aromatic compounds. Observations made on mice have shown that fractions obtained by the catalytic process that have a boiling point lower than 700° F. were apparently noncarcinogenic, while some products boiling above this temperature and known as bunker fuels displayed definite carcinogenic properties when painted on the skin of mice. Other experimental investigations demonstrated that some oils obtained by thermodistillation and having a boiling point around 700° F. were carcinogenic. Human experience has shown that prolonged contact with crude paraffin oil, such as that encountered by paraffin pressmen, may cause cancer of the skin, particularly of the scrotum. Other observations indicate that exposure to other heavy petroleum derivatives, such as fuel oils and lubricants, may be followed by cancer of the skin (hands, forearms).

The total number of recorded petroleum oil cancers is relatively small (about 100). Contact with petroleum products is by skin contact, inhalation, ingestion, and parenteral introduction (diesel jet injuries, lubricating gun injuries). The exposure time ranged from ten to sixty years and was, for the majority of cases, from twenty to forty years. The latent period after cessation of exposure was up to twenty years in some cases. The manifestation age was over 50 years in the majority of cases. Chronic dermatitis, comedones, boils, hyperkeratoses, warts, and papillomas preceded and accompanied the appearance of these oil cancers which showed a multiplicity in 10 to 20 per cent of the cases. Males were mainly involved. The majority of the reported cases was of occupational origin, a few being of medicinal derivation. Skin cancers have been successfully reproduced in mice by the repeated application of various petroleum oils. Whether or not exposure to oil mists or ingestion of impure petroleum oils for various reasons (occupational, medicinal, dietary) can result in cancer of the lung or of the gastrointestinal tract is an open question.

8. Shale Oil and Lignite Oils

Shale oil is obtained by the retorting of oil shale, which is found in many parts of the world. Shale oil production has been carried out for over seventy-five years in Scotland, where the processed oils have been used extensively as lubricants in the textile plants for some time, and to a limited extent in Australia, and for a few years in the United States. Crude shale oil stands chemically between crude petroleum oils and coal tar. In its carcinogenicity it also occupies an intermediate position, being, generally speaking, less carcinogenic than gas-house tar and more carcinogenic than petroleum oils. Oil directly extracted by benzol from oil shale is not carcinogenic and does not contain any benzpyrene. This chemical is found in the carcinogenic processed oils obtained by heating oil shale in retorts to temperatures of 1200–1400° F.

Oils of similar nature and industrial use are generated by the retorting of lignite (Germany). Both shale oils and lignite oils are used for the production of paraffin. Contact with the crude paraffin oil also has given rise to the development of skin cancer. In the paraffin workers, as also in the mulespinners, of Great Britain the most frequent site of cancer was the scrotum.

There are about 1900 cases of shale oil and lignite oil cancer on record, the majority of which occurred among workers of the British textile industry; a few cases were observed in the United States following the use of imported shale oil. Exposure to the oils is by skin contact, inhalation, and ingestion. The exposure time for most cases ranged from thirty to fifty years for shale oil and from ten to thirty years for crude paraffin oil. The latent period was up to thirty years after cessation of exposure. The manifestation age during recent years was about 60 years. Hyperkeratoses, warts, comedones, boils, chronic dermatitis, and papillomas usually preceded and accompanied the development of skin cancers which were multiple in about 15 per cent of the cases. While for a long time shale oil cancers affected males exclusively, the later employment of female mulespinners was followed by the appearance of skin cancers involving, in part, the vulva, a site corresponding to the scrotum which is the predominant localization of the male mulespinners' cancer. Shale oil cancer was reproduced successfully in mice but failed to develop when rabbits, guinea pigs and rats were used.

9. Coal Tar, Pitch, Asphalt, Soot

Tar, pitch, asphalt and soot are generated during the incomplete combustion of carbonaceous matter, such as coal, lignite, oil shale, petroleum, native asphalt, wood, vegetable matter (tobacco), and natural gas. The tarry matter present in all these materials and extractable from them by various organic solvents apparently contains carcinogenic substances responsible for cancers observed in man and experimental animals after prolonged exposure. The carcinogenic potency of the various products mentioned varies a great deal, depending on the character of the source material and the methods of processing (temperature, oxygen supply) used, which in turn determine the relative amounts of tarry matter present and its chemical character. Thus different types of coal tars, for instance, display a remarkable variation in carcinogenic potency, gas-house and coke-oven tars usually being considered as most carcinogenic. Similar variations may exist in regard to the great number of domestic, industrial and commercial soots. While some of the soots contain appreciable amounts of tarry matter (chimney soot of fire places, lamp black), others have extremely small amounts (some of the carbon blacks). Products containing tars of various origin are produced and used extensively throughout industry (gas works, coke ovens, blast furnaces, steel plants, patent and packaged fuel manufacture, tar distilleries, chemical and paint manufacture, foundries, road construction, manufacture of tiles, linoleum, shingles, cables, insulation of electric appliances, corkstone, inks, rubber, roofing paper, water proofing of textiles, paper and masonry, cables, composition for optical glass grinding, and many others).

The occurrence of occupational and medicinal tar cancers mainly due to contact with coal tar, pitch or soot has been reported from many countries (Great Britain, United States, Germany, France, Italy, Belgium, Japan, Spain, Hungary, Switzerland, Russia, Austria, India, Holland). In fact, scrotal cancer in chimney sweeps was the first occupational cancer recognized (1775). Approximately 1700 cases of tar and pitch cancer have been placed on record, the majority (1500) of them being observed in Great Britain. This number, however, does not include the soot cancers found in sweeps. Exposure was by direct contact with the skin (dust, liquid) or by inhalation (dust, fumes) or by ingestion or by parenteral introduction (tar burns). Almost all of the recognized tar cancers in man were located in the skin and affected the exposed parts (face, neck, hands, forearms) in addition to the scrotum. More recent evidence suggests that the inhalation of hot tar fumes, such as those encountered by stokers of coke retorts, may cause cancer of the lung. Whether or not exposure to abnormally high amounts of atmospheric soot and to tar from excessive smoking of tobacco, especially cigarettes, carries a similar liability is still controversial but deserves serious consideration. Claims, moreover, have been advanced that occupational exposure to tar was responsible for cancer of the oral cavity and bladder as well as for leukemia.

The average exposure time ranged from ten to twenty years, although a few cases seemed to have developed after a contact of one to two years, especially in connection with tar burns. The latent period after cessation of exposure was as long as thirty years. The manifestation age varied a great deal and depended on the age at first contact as well as on the intensity of exposure and on the potency of the tar. Thus, scrotal cancer in chimney sweeps was found about one hundred years ago even in boys in their teens who had entered this occupation when five to six years old. The majority of tar cancers of the skin in more recent times is found in persons between 50 and 60 years of age. Chronic dermatitis, melanosis, atrophic patches in the skin, warts, hyperkeratoses, and papillomas compose the environmental cancer pattern of tar and pitch cancers. Multiplicity of cancers was observed in 20 per cent of the cases. The majority of cancers was found in males. The incidence rate among effectively exposed workers has run as high as 100 per cent after prolonged exposure to a potent tar (pitch workers with forty years of exposure or more). Tar cancers of the skin have been successfully reproduced in various species (mice, rabbits, rats, dogs) although other species have been refractory (monkeys). Cancers of various other internal organs (lungs, bladder, brain, connective tissues, stomach, bone marrow, uterus) have been elicited either by tar or by 3,4-benzpyrene, the carcinogen isolated from coal tar and soot.

It is reasonable to assume that contact with soot and other tarry matter generated in certain heating devices (kangri, kairo) carried beneath the cloaks in Kashmere and Japan plays a definite role in the production of cancers of the abdominal skin. A similar causative mechanism apparently is active in the production of cancers of the skin due to exposure to soot and the development of burns in Chinese who sleep on overheated brick stoves (kang). The dhoti cancer of the loin and groin seen in East Indians also probably has a causal relation to exposure to domestic soot.

Since cancers in old burn scars and ulcers follow upon the production of third degree burns only, but never after first or second degree burns, it is likely that the carbonization of the tissue and the possible generation of tarry combustion products from carbonaceous tissues occurring with third degree burns has a significant part in the development of these cancers. This mechanism also may contribute to the appearance of cancer of the oral cavity among the natives of India who smoke cigars with the lighted end placed in the mouth (chutta) and thereby expose their oral mucosa not only to an intense action of tar fumes given off from the tobacco smoked, but also to the frequent intraoral burns.

An excessive smoking of tobacco (pipe, cigar, cigarette) has been related for quite some time to the development of cancer in the organs of the smoke tract (lip, tongue, cheek, oral cavity, larynx, bronchi and lung). However, the epidemiologic evidence advanced in support of such claims, although somewhat suggestive, has not been convincing, while the experimental evidence has remained contradictory. The possibility of such connections, however, remains an important problem deserving serious study (see pages 722 and 787).

A causal relation between tobacco smoking and the recent increase in lung cancer incidence would be made much more probable if the surveys at present conducted on this question would show that heavy smokers (two or more packs of cigarettes a day) have a considerably higher lung cancer incidence than nonsmokers of the same age and sex; that this reaction is most pronounced in persons who inhale the smoke and smoke their cigarettes until only a small stump is left; that there is a shift of the manifestation age of lung cancer in smokers toward a younger age group than that found in previous decades as typical for lung cancers, and seen among nonsmokers; that the present male:female ratio of lung cancers (about 5:1) is shifted in favor of the female sex because of the increasing participation of women in the group of heavy smokers; and that the histologic type of cancers of the lung in women is shifted from a predominantly adenocarcinoma type to the squamous cell or anaplastic variety that prevails among males. Since the carcinogenicity of a tar tends to increase with the temperature at which the tar is produced and may also rise if the fumes are hot, it may be well to inquire into other details of the smoking habit, such as whether an individual is a fast or a slow smoker. Obviously, surveys of this type are complex and may not readily yield unequivocal answers.

The epidemiologic studies so far published on the subject, which place the main blame for the recent remarkable increase of lung cancers on the rapid rise of the tobacco smoking habit, reveal several serious defects. The most fundamental of these is the complete neglect of any consideration of other recognized or suspected respiratory carcinogens of relatively wide distribution which made their first general appearance at about the same time as the adoption of the habit of cigarette smoking. Some of these carcinogens are without doubt much more powerful cancer-producing agents (coal, tar and petroleum tars and oils used in the construction and maintenance of roads, industrial soots, arsenical insecticides, etc.) than tobacco tars have proved to be from experimental evidence. In a recent study of Huguenin, Fauvet, and Bourdin, it was suggested that the occurrence of cancer of the lung among French turners, millers, planers, mechanics and fitters, at first thought to be due to tabagism, was most probably caused by the inhalation of oil mist from cutting oils.

The only aliphatic chemical that may be involved in the development of cancer of the nasal sinuses and of the lung when inhaled as a vapor is apparently isopropyl oil, a waste product of the manufacture of isopropyl alcohol. Although neither the actual existence of these occupational respiratory cancers nor the nature of the causal agent are as yet entirely established, the observations made in two plants are of sufficient significance to deserve further study. If confirmed, these findings would open a large new field of environmental chemical agents (straight chain and cyclic aliphatic hydrocarbons) that would require intensive scientific and epidemiologic investigations for evidence of potential carcinogenic properties to man. The likelihood of the actual existence of such relations is suggested by the fact that cancers have been produced in experimental animals by the introduction of several aliphatic chemicals (cancer of the liver in mice by carbon tetrachloride and chloroform; benign and malignant tumors of the bladder in rats given diethylene glycol; cancer of the lung in mice and rats treated with urethane [diethyl carbamate] and several urethane derivatives.)

INORGANIC CHEMICALS

1. Arsenic and Arsenicals

Arsenic compounds are found in several metal ores (copper, zinc, silver, cobalt, lead) and are obtained as a by-product of the smelting of these ores. Arsenicals are used as pesticides, weed killers, wood preservatives, and in the manufacture of pharmaceuticals, glass, lead base alloys, dyestuffs, chemical warfare gases, sulfuric acid, and many other products. Arsenicals may enter the general environment (air, water) from arsenicals released with smelter fumes, and from slag heaps of smelters or sprayed or dusted as pesticides on orchards, vineyards, and cotton fields.

It is generally agreed that inorganic arsenicals may cause cancers of the skin when ingested, especially following prolonged medicinal administration. Occupational cutaneous exposure to arsenical dust is recognized by most but not all investigators as a carcinogenic hazard. Inhalation of arsenical fumes or dust, on the other hand, has been blamed for causing cancer of the lung in smelter workers and manufacturers of arsenical sheep dip. Claims have been made as to the causation of cancers of the upper alimentary tract following contact with arsenicals. Multiple epitheliomatosis of the skin was attributed to preceding parenteral administration of organic arsenicals (arsphenamines).

The great majority of arsenic cancers were of medicinal origin (145 of 175) and affected the skin where they were situated on exposed and unexposed parts. Multiplicity of arsenic cancers was found in over 50 per cent of the cases. The exposure time of the medicinal cancers ranged from six weeks to many years, while that of the occupational cancers ranged from four to forty-six years, with an average of about twenty-five years. The latent period of the medicinal cancers was from three to forty years (average eighteen years) while the exposure-free interval was up to eighteen years. The manifestation age of medicinal arsenic cancers was from 25 to 75 years and that of the occupational ones from 35 to 60 years.

The environmental cancer pattern preceding and accompanying the cancerous manifestations was characterized by chronic dermatosis, melanoderma, leukoderma, hyperkeratoses, (palmar and plantar) warts, and papillomas. Squamous cell carcinomas and basal cell cancers were found. The sex distribution for the medicinal cancers were three males to one female, while only males were involved in the occupational cases. The carcinogenic arsenic hazard was of occupational, medicinal, and dietary-environmental nature. So far, no reliable experimental reproduction of arsenic cancers in animals has been accomplished.

2. Asbestos

Asbestos is a silicate containing calcium, magnesium, iron, nickel, and/or copper. The chemical composition and physical characteristics vary with the different types of asbestos mined in Canada, United States, South Africa, Russia, Chile, and Cuba. Asbestos is extensively used in industry for the manufacture of insulation material, filters, brake lining, fireproof material (sheets, blankets, ropes, textiles, clinkers, mortar, paper, tiles, shingles), and gaskets.

Carcinogenicity of asbestos is not as yet definitely established. In view of the statistically excessive incidence of lung cancer among individuals affected by pulmonary asbestosis a causal connection between these two processes appears to be probable. A total of 60 cases of lung cancer co-existing with asbestosis has been reported from the United States, England, Canada, and Germany. The incidence rate of lung cancer in persons with asbestosis that came to autopsy was between 13 and 15 per cent. The average manifestation age was around 50 years (range 35 to 75 years). The exposure time ranged from three to twenty-seven years (average fifteen years. The latent period after cessation of exposure was from ten to twelve years. Multiple lung cancers were found in several cases. The experimental reproduction of asbestos lung cancer in mice has been reported.

3. Beryllium and Beryllium Compounds

Beryllium and its compounds are relative newcomers in the industrial field in which they have found widespread application (alloys, phosphors in fluorescent tubes, gas mantles, electric heating elements, atomic energy operations). Acute and chronic pulmonary reactions of inflammatory or granulomatous nature have been reported from the United States, England, and Germany, and have occurred not only among workers in beryllium operations but also among persons residing in the immediate neighborhood of such plants. Since osteogenic sarcomas were produced in rabbits by the intravenous injection of several beryllium compounds and bronchiogenic carcinomas have developed in rats after prolonged inhalation of beryllium compounds, the possibility of future cancerous reactions due to beryllium in man deserves consideration.

4. Chromium and Chromium Compounds

Chromium and chromium compounds are obtained from chromite ores mined mainly in South Africa, New Caledonia, Philippine Islands, and Turkey. Metallic chromium is used in various alloys (stainless steel, ferrochrome) for armor plates, high speed tools, gas turbines, jet motors, and stainless steel sheeting. Chromite is employed in the manufacture of plastic cement and refractory brick, while chromic acid, chromates, and other chromium compounds are used for electroplating pigments in paints, inks, ceramic glazes, rubber, linoleum, shingles, enamel, artificial marble, candles, crayons, and for glass frosting.

An excessive incidence of lung cancer was observed among workers employed in German and American chromate plants where they were exposed to the inhalation of chromate dust. Recent German observations relate the occurrence of lung cancers to workers of chromium pigment factories (zinc chromate, lead chromate). There are at present more than 100 cases of lung cancer in chromium workers on record. The exposure time ranged from less than five years to forty-seven years with an average of fifteen years. The manifestation age was from 29 to 69 years. The latent period after cessation of exposure was more than five years. The environmental cancer pattern included chrome holes of the skin, eczema, and perforated nasal septums. Nasal sinusitis is frequently present. Gastrointestinal disturbances, especially gastric ulcer, may have some significance. All individuals affected were males. The lung cancer death rate among exposed chromate workers is more than fifteen times that of the general population. Experimental production in animals of lung cancers following exposure to chromates has not yet been accomplished.

5. Nickel and Nickel Compounds (Nickel Carbonyl)

Nickel-copper ores are mined mainly in Ontario, Canada, and Finland, where they are in part processed, or sent to refineries in South Wales, Great Britain, and in Norway. The Mond process involving the production of nickel carbonyl is used in most refineries. Nickel is employed for electroplating and in the manufacture of nickel steel, monel metal, German silver, nickel chrome alloys, nickel catalysts, coins, ceramics, pigments, storage batteries, and enamels.

Cancers of the nasal cavity and sinuses and of the lungs have been reported among the workers employed in the British and Norwegian refineries. No similar observations have been made in Canada, the United States, and Germany. The causation of the cancers of the respiratory tract among nickel refinery workers is still unsettled. While the bulk of the evidence incriminates nickel matte dust and nickel carbonyl vapors, it is held by some investigators that the inhalation of arsenic dust and fumes generated from impure sulfuric acid used in the refining process is the etiologic agent.

Up to 1939 there were a total of 34 cancers of the nasal sinuses and twenty-four cancers of the lung on record from the British refineries. These figures have risen to 47 cases of cancer of the nares and nasal sinuses and 82 cases of cancer of the lung for the period 1923–1948 (Merewether). The average employment period was 19.4 years for nasal cancers, and 21.4 years for lung cancers. The average death age was 51 years for nasal cancers and 53 years for lung cancers (Amor).

The hazard is one of inhalation and the involvement of the nasal sinuses in addition to the lung makes it likely that this is due to the inhalation of vapors and not of dust or fumes. The average latent period of the cancers was twenty-two years. Nasal polyps and papillomas often precede the development of nasal cancers. The hazard is entirely occupational, affecting males exclusively. An experimental reproduction of these cancers in animals has not yet been undertaken.

6. Saltpeter-Sodium Nitrate

Cancer of the skin of the hands and feet was recorded among the workers employed in the nitrate fields of Northern Chile. Since the climate of these parts is very dry and sunny, it appears probable that not the chemical contact but excessive exposure to solar radiation represents the actual causative factor. A total of 17 cases of cancer of the skin were placed on record. The exposure time was from twenty-eight to fifty years. The latent period after cessation of exposure was up to twenty-five years. The manifestation age ranged from 37 to 78 years. The environmental cancer pattern consisted of chronic dermatitis, dyskeratosis, and papillomas. The hazard is an occupational one involving males exclusively. An experimental reproduction of these cancers in animals has not yet been attempted.

7. Selenium and Selenium Compounds

Selenium and selenium compounds have found widespread use in modern industry and are the cause of endemic selenosis among cattle in certain parts of the United States where the soil contains excessive amounts of this element. The evidence as to carcinogenic properties of selenium and its compounds is at present entirely of an experimental nature. Rats fed selenium develop cirrhosis of the liver and hepatomas.

PHYSICAL AGENTS

1. Radioactive Substances

The number of radioactive chemicals originally belonging to the elements composing the uranium, actinium, and thorium series has been increased considerably in recent years through the production of chemicals with synthetic radioactivity obtained by their exposure to ionizing radiation from a cyclotron or in a radioactive pile. Exposure to radioactive dust and gases may be sustained by working with radioactive ores such as pitchblende, carnotite, and monazite sand or by consuming or bathing in the water of radioactive springs. Radioactive ores are mined in Czechoslovakia, Germany, Canada, the Belgian Congo, and the United States. Radioactive substances are used for diagnostic and therapeutic medicinal purposes, and industrially in luminous paints, electrostatic eliminators, certain radio tubes, gas mantles, tracer substances, and in the testing of welds and casts, in addition to the development of atomic energy and atomic weapons. Radioactive substances emit ionizing radiation of particulate (alpha and beta rays) and/or electromagnetic (gamma) type rays. These radiations, which vary greatly in type, intensity and duration, may elicit cancerous reactions in human tissues after excessive and usually prolonged exposure. The site of resulting cancers depends upon the type of exposure. Direct skin contact with the rays may cause carcinoma or sarcoma of the skin; ingestion of radioactive matter has been followed by the development of osteogenic sarcomas because certain radioactive metals are stored in the bones; sarcoma of the liver was reported many years after the intravenous injection of colloidal thorium dioxide (thorotrast), which is stored by the reticulo-endothelial cells. It is likely that inhalation of radioactive dust and gases by the miners of the cobalt mines in Schneeberg and of the uranium mines in Joachimsthal is the cause of the highly excessive incidence of lung cancers among members of this occupational group. Suggestive evidence indicates that prolonged general exposure to radioactive radiation or a single massive exposure to ionizing radiation may be causally related to leukemia and lymphosarcoma.

The total number of the various types of radium cancers of occupational and medicinal origin is not large if one excludes the several hundred cases of lung cancers that have been seen in the miners of radioactive ores and the leukemias among survivors of the atom bomb explosions in Japan, as well as all those cases in which a combined exposure to roentgen-rays was present. There are not more than half a dozen radium cancers of the skin on record, some 7 or 8 osteogenic sarcomas in luminous dial painters, and perhaps a few leukemias among workers employed in radium concentration plants. The exposure time of osteogenic sarcomas was up to nine years, while that of cancers of the lung ranged from thirteen to twenty-seven years, with an average of seventeen years. The manifestation age of bone sarcomas was between twenty and thirty-four years, of lung cancers between forty and seventy-five years, and only exceptionally as early as the middle twenties.

The environmental cancer pattern of radium cancers of the skin consists of chronic radiodermatitis with atrophies, telangiectases, melanotic spots, hyperkeratoses, loss of hair, loss of sweat and sebum secretion, papillomas, and indolent ulcers. Osteogenic sarcomas are preceded by a chronic radio-osteitis, while leukemic reactions may be preceded by and/or associated with transitory anemia, leukopenia, lymphocytosis, degeneration of bone marrow, erythrocytosis, hyperleukocytosis, monocytosis, leukemoid reactions, and hyperplasia of the bone marrow with maturation arrest. Multiplicity of cancers is most frequently observed with osteogenic sarcomas.

The sex distribution of radium cancers followed closely the occupational conditions of employment. Osteogenic sarcomas occurred exclusively in females; cancers of the lungs, on the other hand, were observed in males only. Approximately reliable incidence figures of radium cancers among the total exposed worker-population are available only from the still somewhat controversial lung cancer group at Schneeberg, where since 1876, between 70 and 80 per cent of all deceased miners have shown cancer of the lung. The rate is said to be between 40 and 50 per cent for the Joachimsthal group. For comparison, it may be mentioned that the incidence rate of lung cancers among the general population stands at present at about 1 per cent of all deaths, but was less than $\frac{1}{10}$ of 1 per cent before the turn of the last century.

There were approximately 400 cases of lung cancer among the Schneeberg miners between 1876 and 1939, while 42 cases of this disease came to observation among the Joachimsthal miners during 1929 to 1938 (Peller). The exposure time for the majority of the Schneeberg miners was from twenty to fifty years, but was occasionally as short as seven years. The exposure time of the Joachimsthal miners was from thirteen to twenty-three years. There was a distinct shift toward a younger age group, since the majority of the lung cancers occurred in individuals less than fifty years of age (66 per cent of 112 cases).

Statistical studies of recent years yielded an excessive death rate from leukemia among radiologists and roentgenologists. Successful experimental reproduction of radium cancers in experimental animals has been accomplished for cancers of the skin, bone, lung, and hematopoietic tissue.

2. Roentgen Radiation

Roentgen radiation, which is generated by roentgen tubes, is used in industry for testing casts and welds, golf balls, molecular structures and crystalline forms of chemicals. It is employed for fitting shoes in retail stores, and for the removal of superfluous hair in cosmetic establishments. Its most widespread use is in medical and dental laboratories for diagnostic and therapeutic purposes. Roentgen radiation, which is similar to gamma radiation, is carcinogenic. Roentgen cancers, especially those of medicinal origin, have been reported from many countries. The total number of recorded occupational roentgen cancers of the skin seen among radiologists, roentgen technicians and nurses, manufacturers and mechanics of roentgen apparatus, and physicists, is about 150.

Medicinal roentgen cancers of the skin, joint tissues, and bones have been recorded in appreciable numbers. The apparently excessive evidence of leukemia among roentgenologists has been attributed to prolonged exposure to weak penetrating radiation. Excessive exposure of the lungs for occupational or medicinal reasons, on the other hand, has not been followed by cancerous developments but by more or less severe and sometimes fatal fibrotic changes.

The exposure time varied greatly. Usually repeated exposures to roentgen-radiation, which sometimes extended over a period up to twenty-five years, were recorded. The latent period ranged from one to twelve years for skin cancers and from five to seventeen years for bone cancers after cessation of exposure. The manifestation age was between 10 and 80 years. The environmental cancer pattern was identical with that described for the various cancerous manifestations caused by radioactive radiation. Multiplicity of skin cancers was reported in 30 per cent of the cases. Both males and females have been affected, the males predominating in the occupational group. Cancers of the skin, bone, and hematopoietic tissue were produced in experimental animals by the administration of x-radiation.

3. Solar Radiation and Ultraviolet Radiation

Ultraviolet radiation, which is contained in the solar spectrum generated by various types of ultraviolet lamps and which occurs in the welding arc, possesses carcinogenic properties for the skin of man, mice, and rats. It seems that this effect is limited to the mid-ultraviolet range covering 2700–3400 Å. Ultraviolet ray cancer of the human skin so far has resulted only from excessive and prolonged solar irradiation and mainly in individuals constitutionally predisposed, i.e., mainly blonde or red-haired, blue or grey-eyed and fair-complexioned, and often freckled individuals who show little or no tendency to tan when exposed to excessive amounts of solar radiation. Solar or ultraviolet-ray cancer of the skin is therefore unknown in Negroes and in members of other dark-pigmented races.

Since the relative amounts of ultraviolet rays which inhabitants of dry and sunny climates or of regions of high altitude receive are especially high, solar cancer of the skin is particularly frequent among the outdoor workers of the midwestern and southwestern States and of the Rocky Mountain area (Colorado). Similar climatic conditions account for the high skin cancer incidence among the inhabitants of Australia and the Argentine. Intense ultraviolet irradiation is sustained by seafaring people (deck-hands, mainly). Cancer of the skin, especially the eyelids, has been observed also among the light-coated cattle in Texas, Australia and the highlands of Columbia.

Solar cancer affects the exposed parts of the skin, the face, nose, eyelids, lower lip, neck, hands, forearms, and feet. The exposure time is, as a rule, several decades unless a constitutional predisposition is present (xeroderma pigmentosum). The latent period is from ten to forty years and the manifestation age is from 30 to 80 years, the majority of cases being observed after 50 years. The environmental cancer pattern is characterized by the changes found in farmers' or sailors' skin, i.e., atrophies, dryness, scaliness, melanodermic spots, hyperkeratoses, and papillomas. Multiplicity of cancers is frequent. Due to the predominance of males in outdoor activities, and because of the better protective care that women as a rule give their skin, solar cancer is much less frequent in females than in males. Cancers (carcinomas and sarcomas) of the skin (ears, eyelids) have been produced in rats and mice exposed to the radiation emitted from ultraviolet lamps.

4. Thermic Radiation

The claim has been made that workers such as railroad engineers and steelmill workers, who are exposed to intense radiating heat, have an abnormal liability to develop cancers in the exposed skin which becomes chronically congested and inflamed. Apart from the fact that only a few cases of such an apparent origin have been reported, proper cognizance should be taken of the associated contact with tar fumes and soot usually present in occupations having the thermic hazard.

Such chronic thermic injuries must be distinguished, moreover, from those produced by acute burns which, when extensive and of third degree, may be followed after a prolonged latent period by the development of cancer in the scar. It is important to note that cancerous sequelae have not been observed after first or second degree burns but have appeared only when carbonization of the tissue was present. Cancers of the abdominal skin, not infrequently present among the shepherds of Cashmere and among Japanese who carry a metal or earthenware container filled with embers under their cloaks (kangri, kairo), exemplify this causative mechanism.

MISCELLANEOUS AGENTS

1. Parasites

Of the many parasitic infections for which causal relations to subsequent cancerous reactions have been claimed, only infections with *Schistosoma hematobium* provide evidence of more or less definite nature. Recent investigators, however, have doubted the actuality of such a relationship connecting schistosomiasis of the bladder with subsequent development of cancer of this organ. While the bulk of the observations stem from Egypt where schistosomiasis is prevalent among the fellahs, similar evidence may appear in the future among American soldiers who contracted schistosomiasis during their war service in countries where this disease is endemic. Claims have been made, moreover, that schistosomiasis of the intestine and liver has been the cause of cancers in these organs. Schistosomiasis cancers of the bladder have a manifestation age of 30 to 40 years and are present mainly in males.

2. Tobacco

In considering the question of potential carcinogenic properties of tobacco, a sharp distinction must be made between the action that may be exerted by extractives when cured and processed tobacco is chewed and that claimed for the various combustion and volatilization products when tobacco is smoked.

Numerous observations indicate that the habitual chewing of the betel nut quids consisting of a betel nut, powdered lime, tobacco, and a buyo leaf is related to the high incidence of cancer of the oral cavity among East Indians and Filipinos of both sexes. The causal agent in the quid is still controversial. Aromatic extractives of the buyo leaf, nonspecific chemical irritation by the lime or by the tobacco extractives have been blamed for the cancerous effects. Since cancers of the lower lip and of the gum are prevalent among East Indians indulging in the khaini habit, where a quid of tobacco and lime is placed into the groove behind the lower lip, it is unlikely that the betel nut and the buyo leaf are responsible for the cancers of the mouth associated with the chewing of betel nut quids. It seems, therefore, that the number of potential carcinogens in the betel nut quid is narrowed to two substances, lime and tobacco. Recent observations made during World War II showed that the natives of New Guinea, who chew a betel nut quid which does not contain tobacco, do not suffer from cancer of the mouth. This holds true, also, for the Indians in the American Andes who chew quids of coca leaves without the addition of tobacco and who apparently do not have an excessive incidence of oral cancer. From this circumstantial evidence it appears that extractives of cured and processed tobacco may be involved in the production of cancer of the mouth.

Because it is not likely that the tobacco of the orient is contaminated with arsenical insecticides, as American-made tobacco frequently is, there is little probability that this chemical has any role in the production of betel nut cancer. Since the habit of chewing tobacco is not widespread in the United States, the question of the causation of oral cancer by tobacco extractives is of lesser importance here than that raised by the smoking habit.

The question of a direct carcinogenic action of tobacco extractives receives additional importance because of the claim that the inhalation of tobacco dust creates an increased liability to cancer of the lung. This contention is based on rather questionable statistical data on lung cancer incidence among tobacco farmers, tobacco workers, cigar makers, and tobacco dealers.

3. Viruses

Although the causative role of virus infections in the production of cancer in various animal species is a well-established fact, there is no similar evidence available from the field of human carcinogenesis. The occasional development of penile cancer on the basis of virus-induced condylomata acuminata, however, may represent a hint that perhaps some of the cancers observed in man are causally related in some way to environmental virus infections.

CARCINOGENESIS

The process of carcinogenesis is influenced not only by the potency of the carcinogen but also by various other factors which are responsible in part for the variations and fluctuations observed in the sex ratio, incidence rate, localization of cancer, length of latent period, manifestation age, and primary multiplicity.

SEX

While a great deal of speculation has been expended in the search for plausible explanations for the often striking differences in the incidence rate of certain cancers in the two sexes (respiratory cancers, bladder cancers, skin cancers), for obvious reasons environmental cancers do not always follow these standards. Most of the occupational cancers are found in males only, because only male workers are employed in the hazardous operations (aromatic amine cancer of the bladder; chromate cancer of the lung; lung cancer in uranium ore miners, etc.). Whenever female workers enter the same operations, the respective cancers occur also among them. For instance, shale oil cancer among textile workers was found originally in male mulespinners only, until female spinners entered the trade, when cancer of the skin, including the vulva, appeared among them. Cancer of the lung in workers with asbestosis was found not only in both male and female workers but there was also a shift of the sex ratio in favor of the females. Instead of a male-female ratio of 5:1, asbestosis cancer displays a ratio of about 2:1.

Thus with equalization of the degree and duration of exposure to a carcinogenic agent there may follow an equalization of the sex ratio. A similar observation has been made in regard to the male : female sex ratio of oral cancer among East Indians chewing betel nut quids. While, as a rule, oral cancer is definitely more common in males than females, in certain parts of India this ratio is reversed. Likewise, factors that influence the degree of susceptibility to a carcinogen, such as skin pigmentation, may exert a similar influence on the sex ratio. While cancer of the skin in whites is highly predominant in males, the sex difference in the incidence rate of skin cancers is much less marked in Negroes.

INCIDENCE RATE

Intensity of Exposure

Variations in incidence rates of environmental cancers depend on factors that are not always readily apparent and that have given rise to various misinterpretations. Incidence rates of environmental and especially occupational cancer exhibit a direct dependence on the intensity and duration of exposure to the carcinogenic agent. The intensity of exposure, in turn, is influenced by the relative potency of the particular carcinogenic agent. Without any doubt, marked differences exist in carcinogenic potency of various carcinogens, as well as of the same carcinogen when present in different physicochemical states and concentrations.

For instance, compared with β-naphthylamine, gas-house tar appears to be a relatively weak carcinogen. This potency of tar is lessened when it occurs in a dilute form, such as soot, in which only a rather small portion is actually tar, while the bulk is apparently noncarcinogenic carbon. A respiratory carcinogen, when present in the form of vapors and fumes, appears to be more active than the same agent when existing in the form of dust. If it is present in the form of dust the degree of exposure is, in turn, greater if the particles are below one micron in size than if they are much larger, since the finer particles remain suspended in the air longer, and penetrate more deeply into the respiratory tract than do the larger particles. Likewise, cancers appear to be caused more readily by contact with hot rather than with cold tar.

Working Habits: Continuous or Intermittent Exposure

The type of work done and working habits determine to a definite extent the intensity of exposure. Even when employed in the same operation, some workers, because of the particular type of work they do, are bound to have a more intense and prolonged contact with the carcinogenic agents present than others, and for this reason exhibit a greater tendency for developing the specific occupational cancer. For instance, workers engaged in strenuous physical labor requiring deep and frequent respiratory movements sustain a more severe inhalation hazard than do their fellow workers employed in light labor. Moreover, some persons are by habit dirty and careless, and thereby enhance their contact with hazardous material.

To sustain an effective exposure to a carcinogenic agent it is not essential, on the other hand, that the contact be a continuous one. It may well be intermittent and, in fact, severe intermittent exposures may prove to be more effective in eliciting a cancerous response than may continued mild exposure. This relationship between type and interval of exposure and incidence rate of cancer is further evidenced by the fact that in some carcinogenic operations the maintenance and repair workers who have intense periodic contacts are particularly susceptible to the development of occupational cancers.

Heredity

From the information available on the influence of individual heredity upon the susceptibility of exogenous carcinogens, it appears that heredity plays no significant role in this respect. Since exposures to occupational carcinogens are often relatively intense, the carcinogenic effect appears to be sufficiently severe to overcome any minor hereditary differences in reactivity that might be present. Experiences in occupational carcinogenesis demonstrated that, given a potent carcinogenic agent and an exposure of sufficient intensity and duration, there are no appreciable differences in susceptibility noticeable among the exposed workers, if due consideration is given the various factors mentioned that modify the degree of individual exposure.

Race

Racial characteristics, on the other hand, definitely control the susceptibility to certain types of carcinogens, such as ultraviolet radiation and carcinogenic oils and tars. It is common experience that Negroes display a remarkable, while not absolute, degree of resistance to carcinogenic oils and tars. Whether the same holds true as to the action of solar rays remains to be determined, since Negroes in the tropics are apt to develop cancers in ulcers of the lower leg where the normal protective epidermal covering has become defective and solar rays can act on unprotected proliferating epithelium.

Age, Intensity and Length of Exposure

In determining incidence rates of environmental cancers, the age at onset of exposure and the intensity of exposure is important. Clinical and experimental evidence has shown that the length of the latent period depends in part on the intensity of exposure, i.e., the more intense the exposure, the shorter the latent period. However, the reduction of the length of the latent period is subject to definite limitations, since it apparently cannot be decreased below a certain minimum. On the other hand, if the intensity of exposure is very mild or the carcinogenic agent is weak, it is likely that the latent period will be correspondingly very long, and cancers from such exposures are apt to appear at a late period of life. A similar effect is produced if the age at onset of exposure is shifted into the more advanced periods of life. Cancers under such conditions are likely to occur during the senescence period, or the average manifestation age may lie even beyond the average life span.

The various considerations mentioned that determine incidence rates of environmental and especially occupational cancers are of definite importance in epidemiologic and statistical studies. While it is permissible and justifiable to calculate incidence figures on lung cancers for the entire present and former worker population of chromate plants, since all workers of such plants are exposed to the inhalation of chromate dust, the same procedure applied to dye workers for determining the incidence rate of bladder cancers due to aromatic amines is highly misleading, because only that relatively small group employed in the manufacture of the dye intermediates, α- and β-naphthylamine and benzidine, have appreciable contact with these carcinogens, unless production of these chemicals is carried out under improper technical and sanitary conditions.

It appears, moreover, that the younger the average manifestation age of a certain occupational cancer, the better are the chances of determining the actual scope of a hazard and the more complete the incidence figures tend to be. On the other hand, the older the average manifestation age of an occupational tumor, the greater is the probability and possibility that effectively exposed individuals may die from other causes than occupational cancer.

SITE OF CANCER

The site of environmental cancers is dependent, in part, on the type of exposure and in part on the physicochemical properties of the carcinogenic agent. Direct skin contact, for example, results in most instances in the development of cancer of the skin (tar, soot, pitch, petroleum products, solar rays, roentgen-radiation, etc.). The same location, however, may result if the carcinogenic agents, such as arsenicals, are stored in the skin after having entered the body through other routes (ingestion, inhalation). Direct primary contact, also, accounts for the cancers of the respiratory system (lung, nasal sinuses) due to the inhalation of carcinogenic vapors, gases, fumes, or dust (tar, chromates, arsenic, nickel, asbestos, and radioactive minerals). The cancer of the bladder of dye workers is caused by an excretory mechanism, since the aromatic carcinogens are excreted with the urine and reach the bladder where they come in contact with the bladder mucosa over a longer period of time than with any other part of the urinary tract. A depository mechanism again is active in the production of osteogenic sarcomas after the ingestion of radioactive material and in the development of leukemia after exposure to benzol, since radium is deposited in the bony substance, while benzol is retained in the fat cells of the bone marrow. The osteogenic sarcomas following repeated medicinal irradiation with roentgen rays, on the other hand, are reactions to direct primary contact with the carcinogenic agent.

MULTIPLICITY

An excessive multiplicity of primary cancers is characteristic of many occupational reactions, such as bladder cancers in dye workers; arsenic cancer of the skin (both occupational and medicinal); roentgen cancers of the skin; tar, pitch, and oil cancers of the skin; and radium sarcomas of the bone. Occasionally, multiple synchronous or heterochronous cancers may affect different organ systems such as skin, stomach, and lung in paraffin oil workers; skin and lung or upper digestive tract in arsenic workers; and skin and bladder in tar workers. It is likely that such multicentric responses to carcinogenic agents reflect, to some degree, the intensity of exposure. In part, they may be the result of simultaneous contact through various routes, which occurs not infrequently under various occupational conditions.

ENVIRONMENTAL CANCER AND PREVENTIVE MEDICINE

Since the prevention of cancer depends fundamentally on adequate information as to its etiology, the study of environmental cancers, which may bring vastly increased knowledge as to the causes of all types of cancers, is one of the most important approaches to a future control of the disease. The prevention of cancer by the elimination of carcinogenic hazards is by all accounts superior to the best type of present-day cancer cure. There can be little doubt that, with serious efforts, most of the presently recognized environmental cancers either can be prevented entirely by sufficiently removing the causative agents from the human environment, or their incidence rate can be greatly decreased by reducing effectively the intensity and frequency of human exposure to these agents.

SELECTED BIBLIOGRAPHY

GENERAL

BAUER, K. H. *Das Krebsproblem.* Berlin, Springer-Verlag, 1949.

CAROZZI, L. Le cancer professionel. *Méd. du trav. 6:* 31-38, 1934; Arch. d'éléctr. Méd. *42:* 85-93, 118-142, and 155-160, 1934.

HELLER, J. Occupational Cancers. *J. Indust. Hyg. 12:* 169-197, 1930.

HUEPER, W. C., *Occupational Tumors and Allied Diseases.* Springfield, Ill., Charles C Thomas, 1942.

HUEPER, W. C. Environmental and occupational cancer. *Pub. Health Rep. Supp. 209:* 1-69, 1948.

HUEPER, W. C. A methodology for environmental and occupational cancer surveys. *Pub. Health Technical Monograph* No. 1, 1950, p. 37.

HUEPER, W. C. Carcinogens and carcinogenesis. *Am. J. Med. 8:* 355-371, 1950.

HUEPER, W. C. Present and potential occupational cancer hazards and carcinogenic operations in modern industry. *South M. J. 43:* 118-124, 1950.

HUEPER, W. C. Environmental lung cancer. *Indust. Med. & Surg. 20:* 49-62, 1951.

ORGANIC CHEMICALS

Anthracene Oil (Environmental)

LEYMANN Steinkohlenteer-Pechkrätze und Krebs. *Zentralbl. f. Gewerbehyg. 5:* 2-7, 35-40, 51-55, 170-174, 1917.

O'DONOVAN, W. J. Epitheliomatous ulceration among tar workers. *Brit. J. Dermat. & Syph. 32:* 215-245, 1920; Carcinoma cutis in an anthracene factory. *33:* 291, 1921; Cancer of the skin due to occupation. *Arch. Dermat. 19:* 595-606, 1929.

Aromatic Amines (Environmental, Bladder)

ABOULKER, P., and GAULTIER, M. Quatre cas nouvenaux d'amino-tumeurs de la vessie. *Arch. d. mal. profess. 10:* 370, 1949.

BARSOTTI, M., and VIGLIANI, E. C. Bladder lesions from aromatic amines: Statistical considerations and prevention. *Med. d. lavoro 40:* 129-137, 1949.

BILLIARD-DUCHESNE, J. L. Les amino-tumeurs de la vessie. *Arch. d. mal. profess. 9:* 109-116, 1948.

DESOILLE, H., HOCHFELD, N., and ABOULKER, P. Le depistage des tumeurs vésicales chez les travailleurs des produits colorants. *Arch. d. mal. profess. 9:* 149-152, 1948.

EVANS, E. E. Causative agents and protective measures in the aniline tumor of the bladder. *J. Urology 38:* 212-250, 1937.

FERGUSON, R. S. Clinical significance of the aniline tumor of the bladder. *J. Urol. 38:* 243-250, 1937.

FERGUSON, R. S. Symposium on aniline tumors of the bladder. *J. Urol. 31:* 121-171, 1934.

GAY, D. M. Pathology of aniline tumor of the bladder. *J. Urol. 38:* 221-249, 1937.

GAY, D. M. Pathology of bladder tumors. *J. Urol. 7:* 48-51, 1935.

GEHRMANN, G. H. *Industrial Medicine and Industrial Toxicology 31:* 1-12, 1935.

GEHRMANN, G. H., FOULGER, J. H., and FLEMING, A. J. Occupational tumors of the bladder. *Proc. Ninth International Congress on Indust. Med.* 1948, p. 472-475.

GOLDBLATT, M. W. Vesical tumors induced by chemical compounds. *Brit. J. Indust. Med. 6:* 65-81, 1949.

GOLDBLATT, M. W. The problem of vesical neoplasms. *Technical Report of Imperial Chemical Industries, Ltd.*, Dyestuffs Group, March 3, 1937, p. 483.

HUEPER, W. C. Allergy and neoplasia with special reference to occupational tumor formation. *J. Indust. Hyg. & Toxicol. 18:* 140-157, 1936.

HUEPER, W. C. Aniline tumors of bladder in dogs by administration of betanaphthylamine. *J. Indust. Hyg. & Toxicol. 20:* 46-84, 1938.

HUEPER, W. C., BRIGGS, F. A., and WOLFE, H. D. Experimental investigation of the etiology of aniline tumors. *J. Indust. Hyg. & Toxicol. 20:* 85-91, 1938.

MARTINEK *Arbeit und Gesundheit,* "Dritte Verordnung über Ausdehnung der Unfallversicherung auf Berufskrankheiten vom 16, Dezember 1936." Leipzig, Georg Thieme, 1937, Heft 29.

MÜLLER, A. Bemerkungen zur Pathogenese der Anilintumoren: Mitteilung eines Falles von Ureterpapillom nach Benzidinschädigung. *Schweiz. med. Wchnschr. 70:* 232-233, 1940.

MÜLLER, A. Rückblick auf die gewerblichen Blasen- und Nierenschädigungen in der Baseler Farbstoffindustrie. *Schweiz. med. Wchnschr. 79:* 445-450, 1949.

MÜLLER, A. Ueber Anilintumoren der Blase. *Schweiz. med. Wchnschr. 64:* 241-244, 1934.

MÜLLER, A. Ueber Anilintumoren im Industriegebiet Basel. *Schweiz. med. Wchnschr. 63:* 951-952, 1933.

MÜLLER, A. Zweimalige Entstehung eines primären Karzinoms bei einem Anilinarbeiter. *Schweiz. med. Wchnschr. 66:* 1031-1034, 1936.

MÜLLER, A. Die Prophylaxe der Blasenschädigungen in der Farbstoffindustrie. *Schweiz. med Wchnschr. 75:* 42, 1945.

MÜLLER, A. Blasenschädigungen durch Amine, Erfahrungen aus dem Industriegebiet Basel. *Ztschr. f. Urol. Chir. 36:* 139, 1933.

MÜLLER, A. Erfahrungen über die Behandlung von Anilintumoren der Blase. *Ztschr. f. Urol. 25:* 411-413, 1931.

MÜLLER, A. Erfahrungen über die Behandlung der Anilinkarzinome der Blase. *München. med. Wchnschr. 77:* 1387, 1933.

MÜLLER, A. Zweimalige Entstehung eines primären Karzinoms bei einem chemischen Arbeiter. *Arztl. Sachverst. Ztg. 42:* 255, 1936.

REHN, L. Blasengeschwülste bei Fuchsin-Arbeitern. *Arch. f. klin. Chir. 50:* 588-600, 1895.

REHN, L. Ueber Blasenerkrankungen bei Anilinarbeitern. *Verhandl. d. deutsch Gesellsch. f. Chir. 35:* 313-314, 1908.

REHN, L. Ueber Harnblasengeschwülste bei Anilin-Arbeitern. *Verhandl. d. deutsch Gesellsch. f. Chir. 34:* 220-223, 1905.

REHN, L. Weitere Erfahrungen über Blasengeschwülste bei Farbarbeitern. *Verhandl. d. Deutsch. Gesellsch. f. Chir. 33:* 231-240, 1904.

SPITZ, S., MAGUIGAN, W. H., and DOBRINER, K. The carcinogenic action of benzidine. *Cancer 3:* 789-804, 1950.

WASHBURN, V. D. The treatement of aniline tumors of the urinary bladder. *J. Urol. 38:* 232-242, 1937.

WASHBURN, V. D. Tumors of the urinary bladder: Diagnosis and treatment. *J. Am. Inst. Homoeopathy. 29:* 527-531, 1936.

WOLFE, H. D. Routine cystoscopic examination as a control measure in aniline tumor of the bladder. *J. Urol. 38:* 216-220, 1937.

Aromatic Amines (Experimental, Bladder)

HUEPER, W. C., BRIGGS, F. A., and WOLFE, H. D. Experimental investigation of the etiology of aniline tumors. *J. Indust. Hyg. & Toxicol. 20:* 85-91, 1938.

MAYER, R. L. Antihistaminic substances and experimental sensitizations. *Ann. Allergy. 5:* 113-125, 1947.

MAYER, R. L. Aromatic amines and azo-dyes in allergy and cancer. *J. Invest. Dermat. 10:* 389-396, 1948.

SPITZ, S., MAGUIGAN, W. H., and DOBRINER, K. The carcinogenic action of benzidine. *Cancer 3:* 789-804, 1950.

WILEY, F. H. The effect of beta-naphthylamine on tissue respiration. *J. Indust. Hyg. & Toxicol. 20:* 92-93, 1938.

WILEY, F. H. The metabolism of beta-naphthylamine. *J. Biol. Chem. 124:* 627-630, 1938.

Benzol (Environmental: Leukemia)

ANDERSON, D. H. Benzol poisoning with hyperplasia of the bone marrow. *Am. J. Path. 10:* 101-111, 1934.

ANDERSON, D. H. Editorial: "Preventable Cancer." *New England J. Med. 236:* 451, 1947.

ERF, L. A., and RHOADS, C. P. Hematological effects of benzene (benzol poisoning). *J. Indust. Hyg. & Toxicol. 21:* 421, 1939.

FALCONER, E. H. Instance of lymphatic leukemia following benzol poisoning. *Am. J. M. Sc. 186:* 353-361, 1933.

GALL, E. A. Benzene poisoning with bizarre extra-medullary hematopoiesis. *Arch. Path. 25:*315-326, 1938.

GREENBURG, L., MAYERS, M. R., GOLDWATER, L. J., and SMITH, A. R. Benzene (benzol) poisoning in rotogravure printing industry in New York City. *J. Indust. Hyg. & Toxicol. 21:* 395-420, 1939.

MALLORY, F. B., GALL, E. A., and BRICKLEY, W. Chronic exposure to benzene (benzol) pathologic results. *J. Indust. Hyg. & Toxicol. 21:* 355-393, 1932.

KIRCHBAUM, A. Recent studies on experimental mammalian leukemia. *Yale J. Biol. & Med. 17:* 163-185, 1944.

LIGNAC, G. O. E. Die Benzolleukämie bei Menschen und weissen Mäusen. *Klin. Wchnschr. 12:* 109-112, 1933; *Krankheitsforsch. 9:* 403-453, 1932.

Chlorinated Hydrocarbons (Experimental)

EDWARDS, J. E., and DALTON, A. J. Induction of cirrhosis of the liver and of hepatomas in mice with carbon tetrachloride. *J. Nat. Cancer Inst. 3:* 19-41, 1942.

ESCHENBRENNER, A. B., Induction of hepatomas in mice by repeated oral administration of chloroform, with observations on sex differences. *J. Nat. Cancer Inst. 5:* 251-255, 1945.

Creosote Oil (Environmental)

BRIDGE, J. C., and HENRY, S. A. "Industrial Cancers." *Report of the International Conference on Cancer*, Bristol, John Wright & Sons, Ltd., 1928, pp. 258-268.

HELLER, J., and HENRY, S. A. Occupational cancers. *J. Indust. Hyg. & Toxicol. 12:* 169-197, 1930.

O'DONOVAN, W. J. Cancer of skin due to occupation: Tar carcinoma. *Arch. Dermat. & Syph. 19:* 595-606, 1929.

Creosote (Experimental)

CABOT, S., SHEAR, N., and SHEAR, M. J. Development of skin tumors in mice painted with 3,4 benzpyrene and creosote oil fractions. *Am. J. Path. 16:* 301-312, 1940.

Estrogens (Environmental)

ABRAMSON, W., and WARSHAWSKY, H. Cancer of the breast in male, secondary to estrogenic administration: Report of a case. *J. Urol. 59:* 75-82, 1948.

ENTZ, E. H. Probable metastatic carcinoma of the male breast following stilbestrol therapy. *J. Urol. 59:* 1203-1207, 1948.

CAMPBELL, J. H., and CUMMINS, S. D. Metastases, simulating mammary cancer, in prostatic carcinoma under estrogenic therapy. *Cancer 4:* 303-311, 1951.

Petroleum and Petroleum Derivatives (Environmental, Skin)

DAVIS, B. F. Paraffinoma and wax cancer. *J.A.M.A. 75:* 1709-1711, 1920.

DAVIS, B. F. Paraffin cancer: Coal and petroleum products as causes of chronic irritation and cancer. *J.A.M.A. 62:* 1716-1720, 1914.

GAFAFER, W. M. Disabling morbidity and mortality from cancer among the male employees of an oil refining company with reference to age, site and duration, 1933-1938. *Pub. Health Rep. 55:* 1517-1526, 1940.

HAAGENSEN, C. D. Occupational neoplastic disease. *Am. J. Cancer 15:* 641-703, 1931.

HAYHURST, E. R. A survey of industrial health hazards and occupational diseases in Columbus, Ohio, 1915.

HENRY, S. A. Occupational cutaneous cancer attributable to certain chemicals in industry. *Brit. M. J. 4:* 389-401, 1947.

SCHAMBERG, J. F. *J. Cut. Dis. 28:* 680-686, 1910.

WISE, F. Paraffin keratosis and epithelioma. *Arch. Dermat. & Syph. 22:* 546, 1930.

TWORT, C. C., and LYTH, R. Selection of non-carcinogenic from carcinogenic oil. *J. Hyg. 33:* 464-473, 1933.

TWORT, C. C., and LYTH, R. Comparative activity of some carcinogenic hydrocarbons. *J. Hyg. 39:* 161-169, 1939.

SUGIURA, K., SMITH, W. E., and SUNDERLAND, D. Carcinogenic action of certain catalytically cracked oils with high boiling points. *Cancer Research 9:* 631, 1949.

Shale Oil (Environmental, Skin)

BROCKBANK, E. M. Mulespinners' cancer: Epithelioma of the skin in Cotton Spinners. London, H. K. Lewis & Co. 1941, p. 36; *Brit. M. J. 1:* 622-624, 1941; *Clin. J. 71:* 180-188, 1942.

CRUICKSHANK, C. N. D., and SQUIRE, J. R. Skin cancer in the engineering industry from the use of mineral oil. *Brit. J. Indust. Med. 7:* 1-11, 1950.

HENRY, S. A. Occupational cutaneous cancer attributable to certain chemicals in industry. *Brit. M. J. 4:* 389-401, 1947.

HENRY, S. A. Study of fatal case of cancer of scrotum from 1911 to 1935 in relation to occupation, with special reference to chimney sweeping and cotton mule spinning. *Am. J. Cancer 31:* 28-57, 1937.

HENRY, S. A. *Cancer of the Scrotum in relation to occupation.* London, Oxford University Press, 1946, p. 120.

KENNAWAY, N. W., and KENNAWAY, E. A study of the incidence of cancer of the lung and larynx. *J. Hyg. 36:* 236-267, 1936.

Shale Oil (Experimental)

BERENBLUM, T., and SCHOENTAL, R. The apparent anticarcinogenic action of lanolin. *Cancer Research 7:* 390-392, 1947.

BERENBLUM, T., and SCHOENTAL, R. Carcinogenic constituents of shale oil. *Brit. J. Exper. Path. 24:* 232-239, 1943.

BERENBLUM, T., and SCHOENTAL, R. The difference in carcinogenicity between shale oil and shale. *Brit. J. Exper. Path. 25:* 95-96, 1944.

Coal Tar, Pitch, Asphalt, Oil Grease, Soot (Environmental, Skin)

CHASE, P. P. Cancer scroti. *Rhode Island, M. J. 25:* 104-106, 1942.

HAAGENSEN, C. D. Occupational neoplastic disease. *Am. J. Cancer 15:* 641-703, 1931.

HELLER, I. Occupational cancers. *J. Indust. Hyg. & Toxicol. 12:* 169-197, 1930.

HENRY, S. A. Occupational cutaneous cancer attributable to certain chemicals in industry. *Brit. M. J. 4:* 389-401, 1947.

HENRY, S. A. The study of fatal cases of cancer of the scrotum from 1911 to 1935 in relation to occupation, with special reference to chimney sweeping and cotton mule spinning. *Am. J. Cancer 31:* 28-57, 1937.

HIEGER, I. Symposium-industrial skin cancer with special reference to pitch and tar cancer: chemical aspect of industrial skin cancer caused by pitch and tar. *Brit. J. Radiol. 20:* 145-149, 1947.

SCHÜRCH, O. Das Karzinom der Korksteinarbeiter. *Deutsch. Med. Wchnschr. 57:* 139-141, 1931.

SOMERFORD, A. R. Aetiology of cancer of skin, with special reference to occupation. *Brit. M. J. 1:* 1305-1310, 1935.

TEUTSCHLAENDER, O. Ueber den Pechkrebs der Brikettarbeiter, auf Grund von Fabrikbesuchen in Baden und Südwales. *Ztschr. f. Krebsforsch. 28:* 283-300, 1929.

TEUTSCHLAENDER, O. Neue Untersuchungen über die Wirkungsweise von Teer und Pech bei der Entstehung beruflicher Hautkrebse. *Ztschr. f. Krebsforsch. 30:* 573-580, 1930.

TEUTSCHLAENDER, O. Das Johr-Kleinschmidtsche Pechzerstäubungsverfahren als Verfahren zur Verhütung des Pechkrebses in Brikettfabriken (Ergebnisse eines Besuches auf Zeche Engelsburg bei Bochum). *Ztschr. f. Krebsforsch. 30:* 231-240, 1929-30.

TEUTSCHLAENDER, O. Die Berufskrebse mit besonderer Berücksichtigung ihrer Verhütung und die Unfallgesetzgebung. *Acta, union internat. contre cancer. 2:* 67-84, 1937.

TEUTSCHLAENDER, O. Occupational cancer in two briquette factories in Baden, Germany. *Report of the International Conference on Cancer,* pp. 289-300, Bristol, John Wright & Sons, Ltd., 1928.

Tar (Medicinal, Skin)

BERENBLUM, I. Liquor picis carbonis, a carcinogenic agent. *Brit. M. J. 2:* 601-603, 1948.

Environmental (Skin Soot, Kangri-Kairo-Kang)

LAYCOCK, H. T. The "kang cancer" of North-West China. *Brit. M. J. 1:* 982, 1948.

NEVE, E. F. Causation of cancer. *Indian Med. Gaz. 65:* 665-687, 1930.

NEVE, E. F. Kangri-burn cancer. *Indian Med. Gaz. 76:* 133-140, 1941.

TREVES, N., and PACK, G. T. Development of cancer in burn scars: Analysis and report of 34 cases. *Surg., Gyn. & Obst. 51:* 749-782, 1930.

KENNAWAY, E. L., and KENNAWAY, N. M. Some factors affecting carcinogenesis. *Acta, Union Internat. Contre. Cancer 2:* 101-134, 1937.

Tar Fumes and Dust, Soot (Lung, Environmental)

CAMPBELL, J. A. Lung tumors in mice and man. *Brit. M. J. 1:* 179-183, 1943.

LEITER, J., SHIMKIN, M. B., and SHEAR, M. J. Production of subcutaneous sarcomas in mice with tars extracted from atmospheric dusts. *J. Nat. Cancer Inst. 3:* 155-165, 1942.

SCHNURER, L. Further studies on relation of pneumoconiosis to respiratory diseases in Pittsburgh district. *J. Indust. Hyg. & Toxicol. 20:* 14, 1938.

KURODA, S., and KAWAHATA, K. Ueber die gewerbliche Entstehung des Lungenkrebses bei Generatorgasarbeitern. *Ztschr. f. Krebsforsch. 45:* 36-39, 1936.

Tar (Experimental)

COOK, J. W., and KENNAWAY, E. L. Chemical compounds as carcinogenic agents: Second supplementary report: Literature of 1938 and 1939. *Am. J. Cancer 39:* 381-521, 1940.

SEELIG, M. G., and COOPER, Z. K. Review of recent literature of tar cancer (1927–1931 inclusive). *Am. J. Cancer. 17:* 589-667, 1933.

WEIGERT, F. The biochemistry of benzpyrene. *Cancer Research 8:* 169-171, 1948.

WOGLOM, W. H. Experimental tar cancer. *Arch. Path. 2:* 533-576; 709-752, 1926.

Tobacco Tar (Environmental, Lung)

BOGEN, E., and LOOMIS, R. N. Tobacco tar: Experimental investigation of its alleged carcinogenic action. *Am. J. Cancer 16:* 1515-1521, 1932.

DOLL, R., and HILL, A. B. Smoking and carcinoma of the lung. *Brit. M. J. 1:* 739-748, 1950.

LEVIN, M. L., GOLDSTEIN, H., and GERHARDT, P. R. Cancer and tobacco smoking. *J.A.M.A. 143:* 336-337, 1950.

SCHREK, R., BAKER, L. A., BALLARD, G. P., and DOLGOFF, S. Tobacco smoking as an etiologic factor in disease: I. Cancer. *Cancer Research 10:* 49-58, 1950.

WYNDER, E. L., and GRAHAM, E. A. Tobacco smoking as a possible etiologic factor in bronchiogenic carcinoma. *J.A.M.A. 143:* 329-335, 1950.

Tobacco Tar (Environmental, Mouth)

KINI, M. G. Epitheliomas of palate caused by smoking of cigars with lighted end inside mouth. *Indian Med. Gaz. 79:* 572-574, 1944.

INORGANIC CHEMICALS

Arsenic (Environmental, Skin)

ANDERSON, N. P. Arsenic as the cause of cancer of mucous membrane. *Arch. Dermat. & Syph. 42:* 647, 1940.

ANDERSON, N. P. Arsenical keratoses of the palms and soles: Pickle-cell epithelioma of a finger: Multiple benign superficial epitheliomas. *Arch. Dermat. & Syph. 35:* 1062-1073, 1937.

ANDERSON, N. P. Bowen's precancerous dermatoses and multiple benign superficial epitheliomas: Evidence of arsenic as an etiologic agent. *Arch. Dermat. & Syph. 26:* 1052-1064, 1932.

ANDERSON, N. P. Multiple benign superficial epitheliomatosis. *Arch. Dermat. & Syph. 47:* 136, 1943.

ANDERSON, N. P., and BURPEAU, C. Superficial benign basal cell epithelioma. *Arch. Dermat. & Syph. 52:* 46, 1945.

FRANSEEN, C., and TAYLOR. G. W. Arsenical keratoses and carcinomas. *Am. J. Cancer 22:* 287-307, 1934.

HENRY, S. A. *Cancer of the Scrotum in Relation to Occupation.* London, Oxford Univ. Press, 1946, p. 120.

HILL, A. B., and FANING, E. L. Studies on the incidence of cancer in a factory handling inorganic compounds of arsenic: I. Mortality experience in the factory. *Brit. J. Indust. Med. 5:* 2-15, 1948.

MONTGOMERY, H. M. Arsenical keratoses: Bowen's precancerous dermatosis? *Arch. Dermat. & Syph. 45:* 407, 1942.

MONTGOMERY, H., and WAISMAN, M. Epithelioma attributable to arsenic. *J. Invest. Dermat. 4:* 365-383, 1941.

PACK, G. T. Treatment of cutaneous epithelioma. *Arch. Dermat. & Syph. 53:* 576-585, 1946.

NEUBAUER, O. Arsenical cancer: A review. *Brit. J. Cancer 1:* 193-251, 1947.

PERRY, K., BOWLER, R. G., BUCKELL, H. M., DRUETT, H. A., and SCHILLING, R. S. F. Studies on the incidence of cancer in a factory handling inorganic compounds of arsenic: II. Clinical and environmental investigations. *Brit. J. Indust. Med. 5:* 6, 1948.

SCHWARTZ, L., and TULIPAN, L. *A Text Book of Occupational Diseases of the Skin.* Philadelphia, Lea & Febiger, 1939, p. 515.

WILHELM, L. F. X., and GOECKERMANN, W. H. Arsenical poisoning with superficial epitheliomatosis. *Arch. Dermat. & Syph. 48:* 342, 1943.

Arsenic (Environmental, Lung)

FRANSEEN, C. C., and TAYLOR, G. W. Arsenical keratoses and carcinomas. *Am. J. Cancer 22:* 287-307, 1934.

GOECKERMANN, W. H., and WILHELM, L. F. Arsenic as cause of cancer of mucous membrane. *Arch. Dermat. & Syph. 42:* 641-648, 1940.

PERRY, K., BOWLER, R. G., BUCKELL, H. M., DRUETT, H. M., and SCHILLING, R. S. Studies in the incidence of cancer in a factory handling inorganic compounds of arsenic: II. Clinical and environmental investigations. *Brit. M. J. 5:* 1-15, 1948.

Asbestos (Environmental, Lung)

EGBERT, D. S., and GEIGER, A. Pulmonary asbestosis and carcinoma: Report of a case with necropsy findings. *Am. Rev. Tuberc. 34:* 143-150, 1936.

HOLLEB, H. B., and ANGRIST, A. Bronchiogenic carcinoma in association with pulmonary asbestosis: Report of two cases. *Am. J. Path. 18:* 123-135, 1941.

HOMBURGER, F. The co-incidence of primary carcinoma of the lungs and pulmonary asbestosis. *Am. J. Path. 19:* 797-807, 1943.

LYNCH, K. M., and SMITH, W. A. Pulmonary asbestosis: A report of bronchial carcinoma and epithelial metaplasia. *Am. J. Cancer 36:* 567-573, 1939.

MEREWETHER, E. R. A. Asbestosis and carcinoma of lung: Annual report of Chief Inspector of Factories for the year 1947. London, H. M. Stat. Office, p. 15.

Beryllium (Environmental, Lung)

GARDNER, L. U. Generalized pulmonary granulomatosis occurring among workers believed to be exposed to beryllium or its compounds. *Indust. Hyg. Foundation Tr. 11:* 89, 1946.

VAN ORDSTRAND, H. S., HUGHES, R., DENARDI, J. M., and CARMODY, M. G. Beryllium poisoning. *J.A.M.A. 129:* 1084-1094, 1945.

GRIER, R. S., NASH, P., and FREIMAN, D. G. Skin lesions in persons exposed to beryllium compounds. *J. Indust. Hyg. & Toxicol. 30:* 228-239, 1948.

Beryllium (Experimental, Bone)

DUTRA, F. R., and LARGENT, E. J. Osteosarcoma induced by beryllium oxide. *Am. J. Path. 26:* 197-209, 1950.

DUTRA, F. R., LARGENT, E. J., and ROTH, J. L. Osteogenic sarcoma after inhalation of beryllium oxide. *Arch. Path. 51:* 473-479, 1951.

GARDNER, L. U. Osteo-sarcoma from intravenous beryllium compounds in rabbit. *Federation Proc. 5:* 221, 1946.

Chromates (Environmental: Lung)

ALWENS, W., BAUKE, E. E., and JONAS, W. Auffallende Häufung von Bronchialkrebs bei Arbeitern der chemischen Industrie. *München. med. Wchnschr. 83:* 485-487, 1936; *Arch. f. Gewerbepath. u. Gewerbehyg. 7:* 69-84, 1936.

BAETJER, A. M. Pulmonary carcinoma in chromate workers: I. A review of the literature and report of cases. *Arch. Indust. Hyg. and Occup. Med. 2:* 487-504, 1950.

MACHLE, W., and GREGORIUS, F. Cancer of the respiratory system in the United States chromate-producing industry. *Pub. Health Rep. 63:* 1114-1127, 1948.

SCHINZ, H. R. Metal as new carcinogenic principle. *Schweiz. med. Wchnschr. 72:* 1067-1070, 1942.

Nickel (Environmental, Lung, Nasal Cavity and Sinuses)

AMOR, A. J. Growths of the respiratory tract. *Ber. u. d. 8. Intern. Kong. F. Unfallmed. u. Berufsk. 2:* 941-958, 1938.

STEPHENS, G. A. An important factor in the causation of industrial cancer. M. Press. 187-194, 216, 1933.

MEREWETHER, E. R. *Annual Report of the Chief Inspector of Factories and Workshops for the Year 1948.* London, H. M. Stationery Office, 1949.

Nitrate (Environment, Skin)

GUZMAN, L. Epitheliomas de la peau chez les travailleurs du salpètre. *Acta, union internat. contre cancer 1:* 340, 1936.

Selenium (Experimental, Liver)

NELSON, A. A., FITZHUGH, O. G., and CALVERY, H. O. Liver tumors following cirrhosis caused by selenium in rats. *Cancer Research 3:* 230-236, 1943.

PHYSICAL AGENTS

Radioactive Substances and Roentgen-Radiation (Environmental, Bone)

CAHAN, W. G., WOODARD, H. Q., HIGINBOTHAM, N. L., STEWART, F. W., and COLEY, B. L. Sarcoma arising in irradiated bone. *Cancer 1:* 3-29, 1948.

FLINN, F. B. Controlled radium hazards. *Indust. Med. 2:* 57-60, 1941.

FLINN, F. B. Radioactive material and industrial hazard. *J.A.M.A. 87:* 2078-2081, 1926.

FLINN, F. B. Some precautions to be taken when making tests for radioactivity in living body. *Am. J. Roentgenol. 22:* 554-556, 1929.

FLINN, F. B. Stimulating action of radioactive deposits in the body. *Radiology 23:* 331-338, 1934.

MARTLAND, H. S. Occupational poisoning in manufacture of luminous watch dials: General review of hazard caused by ingestion of luminous paint with special reference to the New Jersey cases. *J.A.M.A. 92:* 466-552, 1929.

MARTLAND, H. S. Occurrence of malignancy in radioactive persons: General review of data gathered in study of radium dial painters, with special reference to occurrence of osteogenic sarcoma and inter-relationship of certain blood diseases. *Am. J. Cancer 15:* 2435-2516, 1931.

MARTLAND, H. S. Radium poisoning. *Monthly Labor Rev.*, U. S. Dept. of Labor Bull. *28:* 62, 1929.

MARTLAND, H. S. Malignant conditions in radioactive persons. *J.A.M.A. 97:* 1737, 1931.

MARTLAND, H. S., and HUMPHRIES, R. E. Osteogenic sarcoma in dial painters using luminous paint. *Arch. Path. 7:* 406-417, 1929.

SCHWARTZ, L., KNOWLES, F. L., BRITTEN, R. H., and THOMPSON, L. R. Health aspects of radium dial painting. *J. Indust. Hyg. & Toxicol. 15:* 362-367, 1933.

Radioactive Substances and Roentgen-Radiation (Environmental, Hematopoietic Tissues)

CARMAN, R. D., and MILLER, A. Occupational hazards of the radiologists in the special reference to changes of the blood. *Mayo Clinic Reports 16:* 1112, 1924.

DUBLIN, L. I., and SPIEGELMAN, M. Mortality of medical specialists, 1938-1942. *J.A.M.A. 137:* 1519-1524, 1948.

HENSHAW, P. S., SNIDER, R. S., and RILEY, E. F. Aberrant tissue developments in rats exposed to beta rays: The late effects of P^{32} beta rays. *Radiology 52:* 401, 1949. 1949.

HENSHAW, P. S., HAWKINS, J. W., MEYER, H. L., WOODRUFF, J., and MARSHALL, J. F. Incidence of leukemia in physicians. *J. Nat. Cancer Inst. 4:* 339-346, 1944.

LAWRENCE, J. S., DOWDY, A. H., and VALENTINE, W. M. Effects of radiation on hemopoiesis. *Radiology 51:* 400-413, 1948.

MARCH, N. C. Leukemia in radiologists. *Radiology 43:* 275-278, 1944.

OSGOOD, E. E. Action of benzol, roentgen rays and radium on blood and blood-forming organs. *Ann. Int. Med. 6:* 771-774, 1932.

ULRICH, H. The incidence of leukemia in radiologists. *New England J. Med. 234:* 45-46, 1946.

UEHLINGER, E., and SCHÜRCH, O. Experimental production of sarcoma with radium and mesothorium. *Deutsch. Ztschr. f. Chir. 251:* 12-33, 1938.

Radioactive Substances and X-Radiation (Environmental, Lung)

HARTUNG, F. H., and HEESE, W. Der Lungenkrebs, die Bergkrankheit in den Schneeberger Gruben. *Ztschr. f. gerichtl. Med. 30:* 296-313, 1879.

LORENZ, E. Radioactivity and lung cancer: A critical review of lung cancer in the miners of Schneeberg and Joachimsthal. *Cancer Inst. 5:* 1-15, 1944.

LOWY, J. Der Bronchialkrebs als Berufskrankheit. *Acta, union interna. contre cancer 3:* 182-187, 1938.

LOWY, J. Die Wirkungen der Joachimsthaler Pechblende im Tierversuch. *Med. Klin. 18:* 619, 1936.

LOWY, J. Ueber die Joachimsthaler Bergkrankheit. *Med. Klin. 25:* 141, 1929.

MACKLIN, M. T., and MACKLIN, C. C. Does chronic irritation cause primary tumor of the human lung? *Arch. Path. 30:* 924-955, 1940.

PIRCHAN, H., and SIKL, H. Cancer of the lung in miners of Joachimsthal. *Am. J. Cancer 16:* 681-722, 1932.

Radioactive Substances and Roentgen-Radiation (Environmental, Skin)

ADAIR, F. E. Epithelioma of the hand secondary to irradiation. *Ann. Surg. 100:* 373, 1934.

BROWN, P. *American Martyrs to Science Through the Roentgen Rays.* Springfield, Illinois, C. C Thomas, 1936.

CANNON, A. B. Extensive roentgen-ray dermatitis: Epitheliomas; results of treatment. *Arch. Dermat. & Syph. 47:* 737-738, 1943.

COLE, H. N. Chronic roentgen-ray dermatosis as seen in the professional man. *J.A.M.A. 84:* 865-874, 1925.

COLE, H. N., and DRIVER, J. R. Radiodermatitis of the hands with malignant degeneration. *Arch. Dermat. & Syph. 41:* 149, 1940.

DALAND, E. M. Radiation damage to tissue and its repair. *Surg., Gynec. & Obst. 72:* 372-383, 1941.

MULSOW, F. W. Roentgen carcinoma and sarcoma of man with report of a case. *J.A.M.A. 96:* 2030-2031, 1931.

PORTER, C. A., and WHITE, C. J. Multiple carcinomata following chronic x-ray dermatitis. *Ann. Surg. 46:* 649-671, 1907.

SAUNDERS, T. S., and MONTGOMERY, H. Chronic roentgen and radium dermatitis: An analysis of 259 cases. *J.A.M.A. 110:* 23-28, 1938.

WOLBACH, S. B. A summary of the effects of repeated roentgen-ray exposures upon the human skin. *Am. J. Roentgenol. 13:* 139-143, 1925.

WOLBACH, S. B. The pathological histology of chronic x-ray dermatitis and early x-ray carcinoma. *J. Med. Research 21:* 415-449, 1909.

Radioactive Substances and Roentgen-Radiation (Experimental, Bone)

BRUES, A. M., LISCO, H., and FINKEL, M. Carcinogenic action of some substances which may be a problem in certain future industries. Oak Ridge, Tenn., U.S. Atomic Energy Commission, MDCC *145:* 4, 1946.

SCHÜRCH, O., and UEHLINGER, E. Experimentelles Ewing-Sarkom nach Mesothorium-bestrahlung beim Kaninchen. *Ztschr. f. Krebsforsch. 45:* 240-251, 1937.

SCHÜRCH, O., and UEHLINGER, E. Experimentelles Knochensarkom nach Radium-bestrahlung bei einem Kaninchen. *Ztschr. f. Krebsforsch. 33:* 476-484, 1930-1931.

SCHÜRCH, O., and UEHLINGER, E. Über experimentelle Knochentumoren. *Arch. f. Klin. Chir. 183:* 704, 1935.

SCHÜRCH, O., and UEHLINGER, E. Bestrahlungsversuche an experimentellen malignen Knochengeschwuelsten. *Schweiz. med. Wchnschr. 77:* 1163-1165, 1947.

Radioactive Substances and Roentgen-Radiation (Hematopoietic Tissues)

FURTH, J., and FURTH, O. B. Neoplastic diseases produced in mice by general irradiation with x-rays: Incidence and types of neoplasms. *Am. J. Cancer 28:* 54, 1936.

HENSHAW, P. S., RILEY, E. F., and STAPLETON, G. E. The carcinogenic effect of pile-radiation. *Cancer Research 7:* 48, 1947.

HENSHAW, P. S. Leukemia in mice following exposure to x-rays. *Radiology 43:* 279-285, 1944.

HUEPER, W. C. Leukemoid and leukemic conditions in white mice with spontaneous mammary carcinoma. *Folia Haemat. 52:* 167-178, 1934.

Radioactive Substances and X-Radiation (Experimental, Lung)

LISCO, H., and FINKEL, M. P. Observations on lung pathology following inhalation of radioactive cerium. *Federation Proc. 8:* 360-361, 1949.

LORENZ, E., HESTON, W. E., DERINGER, M. K., and ESCHENBRENNER, A. B. Increase in incidence of lung tumors in Strain-A mice following long-continued irradiation with gamma rays. *J. Nat. Cancer Inst. 6:* 349-353, 1946.

RAJEWSKY, B., SCHRAUB, A., and KAHLAU, G. Experimentelle Geschwulsterzeugung durch Einatmung von Radiumemanation. *Naturwissenschaften 31:* 170-171, 1943.

Radioactive Substances and Roentgen-Radiation (Experimental, Skin)

BLOCH, B. Experimental roentgen-ray cancer. *Schweiz. med. Wchnschr. 54:* 857-865, 1924.

MOTTRAM, J. C. Production of epithelial tumors by irradiation of precancerous skin lesions. *Am. J. Cancer 30:* 746-748, 1937.

Ultraviolet and Solar Radiation (Environmental, Skin)

APPERLY, R. L. The relation of solar radiation to cancer mortality in North America. *Cancer Research 1:* 191-195, 1941.

APPERLY, R. L. Relation of pernicious anemia to solar radiation and skin cancer. *Am. J. M. Sc. 203:* 854-856, 1942.

APPERLY, R. L. Sunlight, skin cancer and cancer immunity. *Am. J. Path. 16:* 650-651, 1940.

BLUM, H. F. Sunlight and cancer of the skin. *J. Nat. Cancer Inst. 1:* 397-421, 1940.

BLUM, H. F. Sunlight as a causal factor in cancer of the skin. *Cancer Research 5:* 592, 1945; *9:* 247-258, 1948.

Blum, H. F. Physiological effects of sunlight on man. *Physiol. Rev. 25:* 483-530, 1945.

Hyde, J. N. The influence of light in the production of cancer of the skin. *Am. J. M. Sc. 131:* 1-22, 1906.

Kirby-Smith, J. S., Blum, H. F., and Grady, H. G. Penetration of ultraviolet radiation into skin as a factor in carcinogenesis. *J. Nat. Cancer Inst. 2:* 403-412, 1942.

McDowell, A. Incidence of cancer in Dallas and Fort Worth, Texas and surrounding counties, 1938. *Pub. Health Rep. 57:* 125-139, 1942.

Mason, M. L. Carcinoma of the hands and feet. *Surgery 5:* 27-46, 1939.

Peller, S. Cancer and climatic conditions. *Am. J. Hyg. 32:* 39-43, 1940.

Peller, S. Malignant melanoma cutis. *Cancer Research 1:* 538-542, 1941.

Peller, S. Further studies in role of irritation in cancer. *Human Biology 9:* 57-64, 1937.

Peller, S. Carcinogenesis as means of reducing cancer mortality. *Lancet 2:* 552-556, 1936.

Peller, S., and Stephenson, C. S. Cancer in United States Navy. *Am. J. Hyg. 29:* 34-59, 1939.

Peller, S., and Stephenson, C. S. Cancer in the mentally ill. *Pub. Health Rep. 56:* 132-149, 1941.

Peller, S., and Stephenson, C. S. Skin irritation and cancer in U.S. Navy. *Am. J. M. Sc. 194:* 326-333, 1937.

Phillips, C. Relationship between skin cancer and occupation in Texas. *Texas State J. Med. 36:* 613-616, 1941.

Sharp, G. S. The treatment of cancer of the eyelids. *J.A.M.A. 111:* 1617-1622, 1938.

Sharp, H. C. Lentigo maligna: Report of one case treated with radium. *Am. J. Cancer 15:* 1557-1569, 1931.

Smith, L. M. Chronic actinic dermatitis: Hazard of the Southwest. *Texas State J. Med. 33:* 644-647, 1938.

Sutton, R. L., Jr. Carcinoma of the skin: Statistical analysis of 560 basal cell carcinomas. *J. Missouri M. A. 39:* 203-207, 1942.

Ultraviolet and Solar Radiation (Experimental)

Bain, J. A., and Rusch, H. P. Carcinogenesis with ultraviolet radiation of wave length 2800-3400 Å. *Cancer Research 3:* 425-430, 1943.

Baumann, C. A., Rusch, H. P., Kline, B. E., and Jacobi, H. P. Does cholesterol stimulate tumor development? *Am. J. Cancer 38:* 76-80, 1940.

Beard, H. H., Boggess, T. S., and von Haam, E. Experimental production of malignant tumors in albino rat by means of ultraviolet rays. *Am. J. Cancer 27:* 257-266, 1936.

Blum, H. F. Wavelength dependence of tumor induction by ultra-violet radiation. *J. Nat. Cancer Inst. 3:* 533-537, 1943.

Blum, H. F. Relationships between spontaneous tumors of the lung and cutaneous tumors induced with ultraviolet radiation in strain A mice. *J. Nat. Cancer Inst. 5:* 89-97, 1944.

Blum, H. F. The effect of intensity on tumor induction by ultraviolet radiation. *J. Nat. Cancer Inst. 3:* 539-543, 1943.

Blum, H. F. Some fundamental aspects of tumor development illustrated by studies with ultraviolet radiation. *J. Nat. Cancer Inst. 3:* 569, 1943.

BLUM, H. F., GRADY, H. G., and KIRBY-SMITH, J. S. Relationships between dosage and rate of tumor induction by ultraviolet radiation. *J. Nat. Cancer Inst. 3:* 91-97, 1942.

BLUM, H. F., GRADY, H. G., and KIRBY-SMITH, J. S. Quantitative induction of tumors in mice with ultraviolet radiation. *J. Nat. Cancer Inst. 2:* 259-268, 1941.

VON HAAM, E., ALEXANDER, H., and BEARD, H. Cytological studies on experimental rat tumors. *Proc. Soc. Exper. Biol. & Med. 34:* 758-760, 1936.

HUEPER, W. C. Cutaneous neoplastic responses elicited by ultraviolet rays in hairless rats and in their haired litter mates. *Cancer Research 1:* 402-406, 1941.

HUEPER, W. C. Morphological aspects of experimental actinic and arsenic carcinoma in skin of rats. *Cancer Research 2:* 551-559, 1942.

PUTSCHAR, W., and HOLTZ, F. Erzeugung von Hautkrebsen bei Ratten durch langdauernde Ultraviolettbestrahlung. *Ztschr. f. Krebsforsch. 33:* 219-260, 1930.

RUSCH, H. P., KLINE, B. E., and BAUMANN, C. A. Carcinogenesis by ultraviolet rays with reference to wavelength and energy. *Arch. Path. 31:* 135-146, 1941.

RUSCH, H. P., KLINE, B. E., and BAUMANN, C. A. The nonadditive effect of ultraviolet light and other carcinogenic procedures. *Cancer Research 2:* 183-188, 1942.

Infrared and Thermic Radiation (Environmental)

STAHR, H. Schlosserkrebs durch strahlende Wärme. *Ztschr. f. Krebsforsch. 22:* 379-383, 1925.

WANIEK, H. Injuries caused by radiant heat in rolling mills: Development of skin cancer. *Arch. f. Gewerbepath. u. Gewerbehyg. 10:* 486-490, 1941.

PARASITES

Schistosomiasis (Bladder)

ARCADI, J. A. Bladder carcinoma and vesical schistosomiasis. *Urol. & Cutan. Rev. 53:* 472-474, 1949.

DIAMANTIS, A. Le Cancer bilharzien vésical; à propos de onze cas personnels dont deux cas de cancer bilharzien vésical non-infecté. *J. d'Urol. 40:* 408-432, 1935.

HUTCHINSON, H. S. Pathology of bilharziasis. *Am. J. Path. 4:* 1-16, 1928.

MAKAR BEY, N. Two interesting cases of bilharzial papilloma and epithelioma. *J. Egypt. M. A. 31:* 217-221, 1948.

MAKAR BEY, N. A case of bilharziel epithelioma of the groin. *Urol. & Cutan. Rev. 52:* 481-483, 1948.

FISCHER, W. "Tierische Parasiten der Leber und der Gallenblase." In HENKE, F., and LUBARSCH, O.: *Handbuch der Speziellen Pathologischen Anatomie und Histologie.* Berlin, J. Springer, 1930, Vol. V., Pt. 1, p. 713.

HARTZ, P. H. Role of schistosomiasis in the etiology of cancer of the liver in the Chinese. *Arch. Path. 39:* 1-2, 1945.

USAGES AND HABITS

Betel Nut Quid Chewing (Mouth)

EISEN, M. J. Betel chewing among natives of the Southwest Pacific islands. *Cancer Research 6:* 139-141, 1946.

KHANOLKAR, V. R. Oral cancer in Bombay, India: A review of 1,000 consecutive cases. *Cancer Research 4:* 313-319, 1944.

KHANOLKAR, V. R., and SURYABAI, B. Cancer in relation to usages. *Arch. Path. 40:* 351-361, 1945.
SNIJDERS, E. P. The cancer problem in the tropics. *China M. J. 38:* 303-304, 1924.
VEDDER, E. R. The incidence of cancer in Filipinos. *J.A.M.A. 88:* 1627-1629, 1929.
WOELFEL, W. C., SPIES, J. W., and CLINE, J. K. Cancer of the mouth and some chemical aspects of buyo-cheek cancer. *Cancer Research 1:* 748, 1941.

DIETARY FACTORS

Vitamin B Complex Deficiencies (Liver and Oropharynx)

ABELS, J. C., REKERS, P. E., MARTIN, H., and RHOADS, C. P. The relationship between dietary deficiency and the occurrence of papillary atrophy of the tongue and oral leukoplakia. *Cancer Research 2:* 381-392, 1942.
AHLBOM, H. E. Praedisponierende Faktoren fuer Plattenepithelkrebs im Mund, Hals und Speiseroehre. *Acta Radiol. 18:* 163-185, 1937.
AHLBOM, H. E. Simple achlorhydric anemia, Plummer-Vinson syndrome, and carcinoma of mouth, pharynx and oesophagus in women. *Brit. M. J. 2:* 331-333, 1936.
BERMAN, C. Primary carcinoma of the liver in the Bantu races of South Africa. *South African J. M. Soc. 5:* 54-72, 1940.
BERMAN, C. The clinical features of primary carcinoma of the liver in the Bantu races of South Africa. *South African J. M. Soc. 5:* 92-109, 1940.
BERMAN, C. The etiology of primary carcinoma of the liver with special reference to the Bantu races of South Africa. *South African J. M. Soc. 6:* 145-156, 1941.
BERMAN, C. The pathology of primary carcinoma of the liver in the Bantu races of South Africa. *South African J. M. Soc. 6:* 11-26, 1941.
BERMAN, C. Malignant disease in Bantu of Johannesburg and Witwatersrand gold mines. *South African J. M. Soc. 1:* 12-30, 1935.
COPELAND, D. H., and SALMON, W. D. The occurrence of neoplasms in the liver, lungs and other tissues of rats as a result of prolonged cholin deficiency. *Am. J. Path. 22:* 1059-1079, 1946.
GILLMAN, J., GILLMAN, T., MANDELSTAM, J., and GILBERT, C. The production of severe hepatic injury in rats by the prolonged feeding of maize-meal porridge (mealie-pap) and sour milk. *Brit. J. Exper. Path. 26:* 67-81, 1945.
KENNAWAY, L. L. Cancer of the liver in the negro in Africa and in America. *Cancer Research 4:* 313-319, 1944.
SUGIURA, K. The relation of diet to the development of gastric lesions in the rat. *Cancer Research 2:* 770-775, 1942.
MARTIN, H., and KOOP, C. E. Precancerous mouth lesions of avitaminosis B: Their etiology, response to therapy and relationship to intra-oral cancer. *Am. J. Surg. 57:* 195-225, 1942.

CHAPTER 27

Statistical Studies in Cancer

Herbert L. Lombard

The disease, cancer, presents to the epidemiologist one of the most difficult problems in medicine. Unlike acute conditions, cancer is usually a disease of long duration. Its predisposing factors may cover years rather than days or weeks. Moreover, there is every reason to believe that the entity which we know as cancer is, in reality, a combination of many diseases, all of them having in common the characteristic of a disorderly cell growth.

It is the problem of the epidemiologist to determine, to the best of his ability, answers to questions regarding this group of diseases. Are there factors which are common in the excitation of several of these diseases, or does each cancer have an etiology of its own? Is the incidence of cancer increasing? Is the increase limited to some types of cancer, or is the apparent increase due wholly to such factors as age distribution and better diagnosis? Are any of the types of cancer subject to Mendel's laws of heredity? Is cancer a constitutional disease? To what extent do the various agents that have been found to be carcinogenic in laboratory animals affect, in like manner, human beings? How important is chronic irritation? Is cancer related to normal physiologic processes, such as child birth and nursing? Do derangements of the endocrine system favor the occurrence of some forms of cancer?

Problems such as these are constantly before the epidemiologist who studies cancer. In front of him are the available records and data. His background postulates at least a mediocre knowledge of the sum total of information that has been accumulated over the years regarding both the disease and the application of the calculus of probability to medical problems.

STATISTICAL APPROACH

Frederick L. Hoffman, one of the leading American statisticians in the early part of this century, stated: "Statistics is chiefly an auxiliary method in connection with scientific inquiries; but it is none the less necessary to caution the inexperienced against the use of a method or science which on its own account requires as much study and consideration, and as much practical experience, as medicine or surgery or both combined. The liability to error in the interpretation of collective phenomena subjected to critical analysis is fully as great as the chances of mistakes in medical or surgical diagnosis."

Statistics may be divided into two classes, descriptive and inductive. Descriptive statistics deal with the facts concerning large groups of events that have happened, and with the diagrammatic ways of presenting these facts. They are necessary to measure such factors as hospitalization, the volume of clinic attendance, and the cancer death rate. Inductive statistics seek to extend to events as yet unobserved, and perhaps to ones that have not yet occurred, the characteristics of those observed. Such statistics are used to appraise types of treatment and to study such subjects as future needs in cancer control, the etiology of cancer, and other related problems.

Studies have been based on diverse types of data, the more common being death records, hospital records, morbidity reports, records from special surveys, as well as industrial, military, and insurance records. Obstacles to good statistics occur in the collection of the data because of errors or inadequacies in diagnosis, classification, nomenclature, sampling, and reporting. Any intelligent individual can collect data, but it requires some degree of mathematical ability to perform computations on the material and it demands an individual with sound judgment and mature thought to analyze it correctly. The analysis of data has been varied and often inadequate. While the use of biometric methods to determine significance has been a common practice among some investigators, in the majority of statistical papers on cancer such methodology has been ignored.

Probability

Probability is fundamental in statistical theory. It is fundamental even in life, as knowledge and beliefs represent degrees of probability. The analysis of data by biometric methods consists primarily in making use of the theory of probability to determine whether or not the observed findings are chance phenomena. The real problem of statistics is so to treat the fluctuations of a series of figures as to determine how much of the fluctuation is lawful and how much is due to chance.

Samples

The data require analysis with attention to hidden fallacies. All possible causes should be noted and an attempt made to determine whether all of the significant ones are of importance, or some only apparently so, due to interrelationship with other variables. In statistical work it is often necessary to form conclusions from samples which are selected in some way from a large mass of material. For example, in studying a disease it is impossible to use all of the known cases of the disease. A few must be selected as representative of the entire group and it is necessary to pass judgment on whether or not a fair sample has been chosen. A good sample is representative, qualitatively, of the universe from which it is drawn, and large enough to satisfy the requirements of the theory of probability. When drawing conclusions from samples the fairness of the samples are postulated.

Types of Variability

It should be borne in mind always that three things must be considered in studying variability. There is the sampling error, which is a pure coin-tossing chance; there is actual variability, which is a physical chance coming from unknown causes; and there are systematic errors. The statistician is attempting to discover the actual variability and the causes thereof, but he must always keep in mind the sampling errors and the possibility of other errors. The statistician should work slowly, collect and digest a large amount of material, bring every available point of view to the subject, and study the data carefully.

The relationship between two variables can be determined by either association or correlation. Correlation depicts the simultaneous occurrence of events but does not indicate causation. If there is a good biologic reason for a relationship between two variables, the correlation coefficient is corroborative evidence. In the last analysis the value of the conclusion drawn depends on the statistician himself. If the conclusions are wrong, the trouble may lie in the way the statistics were used. Fallacious reasoning should not be charged against statistics. No statistical procedure, however elaborate or refined, is a substitute for careful choice in accurate collection of original material, or for the thoughtful, correct interpretation of the results of its analysis. Common sense is the chief requisite for the study of statistics, and experience is the best teacher.

Statistical studies may be classified according to the purpose for which they are made: to determine the etiology of the disease; to evaluate programs and various methods of therapy; and to ascertain the incidence, prevalence, and related facts. The literature of cancer statistics is voluminous, contradictory, superficial, and often misleading, this being due, in part, to the selection of data and their analysis.

ETIOLOGIC STUDIES

The collection of data intended to prove or disprove hypotheses regarding etiology offers many difficulties. Ideally, the methodology consists of recording environmental factors for a large number of individuals from birth to death, and then securing an autopsy on each individual at death. The life history of those in whom cancer developed would be compared with the life history of those who did not have the disease. This method would make possible the recording of environmental information as it occurred, rather than necessitate an attempt to elicit a history of events long after their occurrence, but it has the possible disadvantage that certain factors would not be discussed as freely at the time as in retrospect. The data would be accurate regarding the occurrence of cancer, with the exception that an occasional individual might die from a noncancerous condition, although cancer might have developed had he lived longer. However, such a study would take the lifetime of several investigators to cover the span of years necessary, and the difficulties inherent in obtaining such life histories of individuals is evident.

A long-term study could be done by one investigator if continuous information were obtained from every individual in the selected population for a period of twenty-five or thirty years. This would be less complete than the lifetime study, but would be a valuable means of collecting data. However, it would be very expensive and it is doubtful whether sufficient funds could be obtained for such a study.

An approach that has been used to a limited extent consists of the collection of data, from individuals both with and without cancer, regarding their hereditary and environmental history. The percentage incidence of the various environmental factors is compared, tested for significance, and also tested to determine whether the relationship persists when the effect of interrelated variables is removed. A review of the literature on cancer reveals that only a few studies of this nature have been made. In some studies the methodology has been to compute the percentage of individuals with cancer who had been exposed to certain environmental factors and, if this percentage was high, to draw the conclusion that there was a relationship between cancer and the given factor. Other investigators have added control series and have compared the percentages found in the cancer group with those for the control group. Many of these investigators have made no mention of computing sampling errors when drawing their conclusions; and only a few of them have discussed the interrelationship of multiple variables.

A mere association between two variables without other confirmatory evidence cannot be considered as even suggestive of etiologic significance. With many variables under investigation, it would be expected that a few would show association by chance alone, others would show association because of the interrelationship of the variables, while some might show association because of real etiologic significance.

At one time or another nearly every factor connected with living has been suggested as a cause of cancer. This chapter does not attempt to include all factors, and is limited to a discussion of some of the better statistical studies of cancer among humans.

There are a number of statistical papers dealing with occupational factors as causative agents in cancer. The majority of these studies are not included in this chapter since they are discussed in Chapter 26.

TUMOR SUSCEPTIBILITY

In recent years a number of articles have been published on the subject of multiple primary cancers. The studies of Warren and his associates indicated that the incidence of multiple primary cancers was sufficiently high to presuppose increased individual susceptibility. On the other hand, Peller suggested that a cured cancer protects against the development of other malignant neoplasms, and even advocated the experimental induction of a skin cancer to prevent subsequent occurrence of cancers of other organs. Lombard, Levin, and Warren studied this problem and compared expected and observed values for secondary cancers. They obtained expected values by multiplying person-years by the age-sex-site-specific incidence rates.* They showed that persons with skin cancers are predisposed to

* The term *rate* as ordinarily employed means the crude death rate; that is the total number of deaths from a given disease in a one-year interval, divided by the total population at the middle of the year in which the deaths occurred, and expressed as a rate per 100,000. The term morbidity rate substitutes cases for deaths (continued on p. 782).

other skin cancers. There was also an indication that males with lip cancers have some predisposition to multiple skin cancers, but there was no evidence that immunity to the formation of a second primary cancer was elicited by the presence of a skin cancer.

FAMILIAL INCIDENCE

While many geneticists are convinced that there is an hereditary component in the causation of cancer, there appears to be no universal acceptance of this hypothesis.

There is even less agreement regarding the problem of whether dominant or recessive, autosomal or sex-linked alleles, single or multiple factor combinations, or one or many different genotypes are responsible for the appearance of a trait. Some believe heredity is the causal factor in all cancers, others believe it is a factor in selected sites only.

Macklin believes that both hereditary and extrinsic factors produce cancer, and that as one of these variables becomes large the other may be permitted to become correspondingly small. If both factors are potent, malignant changes would be expected early; when both factors are minimal one would expect the individual to be relatively cancer resistant. She cited retinoblastoma as a type of cancer in which there was little ground for believing that external factors were operating and gave skin cancers of workers with x-ray as an example of the other extreme. However, Jacobsen, in studying breast cancer, stated that case histories gave no grounds for supposing that exogenous factors play any important role in its development.

The statistical study of this problem is full of pitfalls, and the difficulties of confirming hypotheses from available data are great. Death records are faulty in respect to diagnosis and this error increases with the antiquity of the data. The recollections of individuals interviewed regarding the cause of death of their relatives are even less accurate. Over three-quarters of them have some idea of the cause of death of their parents, but the percentage knowing about grandparents, uncles, and aunts is small.

Several methods of studying data on humans have been used. The pedigree method consists of studying family trees, and Warthin's family study would be this type. In 1913 and again in 1925, Warthin reported on a family with

---

A specific rate is obtained by dividing the cases or the deaths in a specific category by the population in that category; as for example, an age-sex-site specific rate might be:

$$\frac{\text{females, age 40–50, with cancer of the breast}}{\text{total female population, age 40–50}}$$

Person-years have been substituted for the general population in some computations. A person under observation for one year furnishes one person-year; a person under observation for five years would give a total of five person-years. The total person-years for the individuals under observation furnish the denominator upon which the rate is based.

Significance is determined by obtaining a difference between rates and comparing this to its standard error.

If $\frac{(p_1-p_2)}{\sigma(p_1-p_2)} > 2.6$, significance is assumed. p_1 and p_2 are the rates per capita. $q=1-p$; n=number of cases $\sigma(p_1-p_2)=\sqrt{\frac{(p_1 q_1)^2}{(n_1)^2}+\frac{(p_2 q_2)^2}{(n_2)^2}}$

numerous deaths from cancer. In 1936 Hauser and Welles brought this data up to date. At that time there were 43 primary carcinomas among 41 individuals, in a total population of 305, and comprising 174 persons over the age of 25. There was a cancer incidence of 23.6 per cent in this latter group. Anatomic location was of great importance, as 26 of the cancers occurred in the gastrointestinal tract and 15 in the endometrium.

Another method is a tabulation of cancers among the ancestors of individuals both with and without cancer. Several studies of this type have been completed, but the results are contradictory. Deelman compared two series of data received from physicians: one series consisted of data on the cancer incidence among brothers and sisters and father and mother of individuals with cancer, the other consisted of similar figures for relatives of patients without cancer. Both series were the same in respect to age, the number of members of the families, the number of brothers and sisters and the number with unknown causes of death. Deelman drew the following conclusions:

1. In a series of families of cancer patients cancer is more frequent than in any other series of families.
2. The surplus of cancer in the family of cancer patients always accumulates in certain distinct families.
3. There is a large group of cancer patients in whose family cancer is absolutely not more frequent than with the expected "normal" chance of dying of cancer.
4. Hereditary influences are only evident in a small category of cancer cases.

So far as can be judged from this material, there is no difference between the groups alluded to in 3 and 4 so far as the localization of the primary tumor is concerned.

Hunter found a greater cancer incidence among the ancestors of the controls than among the ancestors of the cancer group. Wainwright found the reverse situation; while Massachusetts figures showed little difference between the two groups.

Still another method consists in comparing the cancer incidence among non-blood relatives of a cancer patient; for example, in the case of females, maternal aunts with paternal aunts.

A method used occasionally when several members of the same family have cancer is to compute the mathematical probability of occurrence, and if this is found to be very small to assume that familial incidence exists. Macklin stated: "When one computes the probability of finding a family of three children, with all three living to the age of 30, with all three developing rectal cancer, it becomes apparent that on the basis of a chance distribution of rectal cancer such an event is highly improbable. On the basis that all three developed rectal cancer because they inherited the factors for it, the event is highly probable."

Some investigators compute an expected number of cases or deaths from cancer which they compare with the observed data. Crabtree, using this method, discussed familial cancer in respect to several sites.* He found the incidence of fatal

* Expected or theoretical data may be obtained in several different ways. In the Crabtree studies it was done by computing "the number of deaths which would be expected to have occurred had these parents experienced mortality normal for the country as a whole."

cancer in parents and siblings of white females with cancer of the skin to be nearly twice as great as would be expected on the basis of normal experience; and breast and cervix cancer deaths more than one and a half times as great. For males with cancer of the skin, excessive familial incidence was noted only for those whose cancers developed at an early age. Lip cancer was only slightly in excess of normal, and cancer of the lung below normal. Where an excessive familial incidence was noted it was almost invariably limited to the parents and siblings of those patients whose cancer developed early in life. Penrose, MacKenzie, and Karn, also utilizing this method of analysis, showed that in 510 cases of mammary cancer the same disease occurred more frequently than would be expected. Among the mothers of 408 women with mammary cancer, 25 had mammary cancer, compared with an expected incidence of 11. Among 307 sisters of patients with mammary cancer, 23 had mammary cancer, compared with 7 expected cases. Neither the mothers nor sisters had types of cancer significantly different from the class expected.

Perhaps the best method for studying the heredity of cancer among humans is to obtain data on twins. Differences in the cancer incidence between identical and fraternal twins furnish strong evidence. Macklin's data show that identical twins differ from fraternal twins in respect to tumor incidence, and that genetically identical individuals are very likely to develop the same type of tumor in the same organ. Macklin found that 22 of 23 identical twins had cancer of similar sites, while only 6 of 13 pairs of like-sexed fraternal twins had cancer of similar sites.

CONTAGION

During the past four hundred years the question of contagion has been brought forward but at present nearly all investigators oppose this theory. There have been few statistical papers on the subject, and most of the statements concerning contagion have reiterated the fact that physicians and nurses have no more cancer than other people. Ciocco reported a greater incidence of cancer among the spouses of cancer patients,* but the data of Potter and Tully failed to confirm this. Perhaps one of the best statistical arguments is the statement that the coefficient of disturbancy of cancer is much less than that of the common communicable diseases. Charlier's coefficient of disturbancy attempts to measure in percentage the variation after the removal of chance variation.† If a series is normal and only chance operating, the coefficient is zero; if more than chance is operating, the coefficient is a positive quantity. The following coefficients have been computed from the death rates for the respective diseases in the 48 states.

* The method of analysis was to compute an expected number of couples dying of cancer by dividing the number of cancer deaths of the wives by the total population and multiplying this rate by the number of cancer deaths of the husbands and then testing for significance by means of the chi square from fourfold tabulation.

$$X^2 = \sum \frac{(observed - expected)^2}{expected}$$

† $$P = \frac{100\sqrt{\sigma^2\ universe - \sigma^2 B}}{mean}$$

TABLE 63. COEFFICIENTS OF DISTURBANCY

	Percentage
Measles	320
Diphtheria	74
Scarlet fever	67
Whooping cough	56
Diabetes	36
Cancer	30
Nephritis	27
Cerebral hemorrhage	21

ECONOMICS

There appears to be a rather definite relationship between cancer of certain sites and factors connected with economic circumstances. The Registrar General's *Decennial Supplement* for England and Wales, 1921 and 1931, showed forty sites of cancer analyzed according to social classes.

Mortality from cancer of the sites most exposed to external irritation, such as skin, larynx, upper alimentary tract, uterus, penis, and vulva increased from Class I, the highest economic level, to Class V, the lowest. Other cancers were more prevalent among the higher economic groups than among the lower. These included cancer of the breast, ovary, testes, and mediastinum. There was no change in the incidence of other cancers in relation to social class. These cancers included the intestines, rectum, lung, pancreas, kidney, bladder, and prostate.

OBESITY

Studies from the actuaries suggest a greater incidence of cancer among the overweight, but the weights recorded were those at the issuance of the life insurance policies and in some cases these may vary considerably from the weight maintained throughout life. Dublin and Marks showed the standardized death rates for specific causes of death by weight classes.*

* Rates are frequently compared, which in reality are not comparable. The cancer rates of a city with a preponderance of young adults is not comparable to another city with a preponderance of old adults. Adjustments are necessary, the most common being that for age and sex. Adjustments may be made also for other factors, such as nationality, color, economic position, etc.

The age adjustment is computed as follows: First, obtain rates for each age group by dividing the deaths in each age group by the populations of the same groups. For example, the 45–50 age-specific cancer rate $= \frac{\textit{cancer deaths among individuals 45–50}}{\textit{population between 45–50}}$. If additional factors need adjustment, this can be done. For example, we might obtain

$$\frac{\textit{Cancer deaths 45–50 among females of Irish extraction in poor economic group}}{\textit{population 45–50 among females of Irish extraction in poor economic group}}$$

The age-specific rates are applied to a standard population, to furnish a theoretical number of deaths for that age group. These theoretical deaths in the various age groups are summed and divided by the total standard population. This gives a theoretical rate, based on the hypothesis that all factors remain the same except the population structure, which is that of

The figures in Table 64 are taken from their table:

TABLE 64. DEATHS FROM CANCER AND DIABETES BY WEIGHT CLASSES

	Cancer	*Diabetes*
15–34% underweight	54	9
5–14% underweight	64	9
Normal weight	61	14
5–14% overweight	64	22
15–24% overweight	73	45
25%+ overweight	86	117

While the incidence of cancer showed an increase in the overweight group, it was far less marked than that for diabetes.

None of the Massachusetts studies in which the maximum weight during life has been recorded have shown any significant relationship between obesity and cancer. Hoffman found no significant difference in the percentage of stout individuals among the cancer and control groups.

DIET

There is no statistical evidence that diet is of importance as a causative factor of cancer. Several studies have been made regarding this subject. After a very careful study of certain religious orders, Greenwood and Copeman found no evidence for the hypothesis that abstinence from meat-eating prevented the occurrence of cancer. Hoffman studied not only meat-eating but the consumption of other items of food and found no statistical differences between his cancerous and noncancerous groups.

ALCOHOL

The excessive use of alcohol appears to be correlated with cancer of the esophagus and cancer of the tongue but there is no correlation with cancer of the

the standard population. In this way communities with different age structures can be compared, and the same community can be compared with itself at different times. A brief example is

Age Group	*Deaths*	*Population*	*Age-specific death rate per 100,000*	*Standard Population*	*Theoretical Deaths*
Under 20	10	100,000	10	500,000	50
20–50	40	200,000	20	300,000	60
Over 50	60	100,000	60	200,000	120
	110	400,000		1,000,000	230

$$\text{Crude rate} = \frac{110}{400{,}000} = 27.5 \text{ per } 100{,}000 \text{ population}$$

$$\text{Age-adjusted rate} = \frac{230}{1{,}000{,}000} = 23.0 \text{ per } 100{,}000 \text{ population}$$

stomach. Stevenson compared the cancer death rate among individuals in the ten occupation groups having the greatest alcohol consumption ("measured by cirrhosis of the liver as the best available criterion") with that in the ten groups with the lowest consumption. The rate for cancer of the esophagus was 18.7 in the group with the highest alcohol consumption and 7.8 in the lowest. He found that the correlation coefficient of these two variables was $.358 \pm .046$ and for cirrhosis and cancer of the tongue, $.278 \pm .049$.*

Several other writers have suggested a relationship between cancer and alcohol but Stevenson's paper gives the best statistical presentation.

TOBACCO

The data regarding the use of tobacco are unreliable for the most part, but a few studies appear to be of value. Potter and Tully reported on 2927 male patients at the Massachusetts cancer clinics who were over the age of 40. They were classified according to their use of tobacco as those who did not use it at all, those who reported slight use, moderate use, and excessive use. Attack rates were computed for cancer of the buccal cavity, digestive tract, respiratory tract, skin, and for cancer of all other sites. There was a definite association between cancer of the buccal cavity and the use of tobacco. There also appeared to be some association between tobacco and cancer of the respiratory tract. None of the other sites showed any relationship. Data were not available for eliminating the effects of other possible etiologic factors.

Levin, Goldstein, and Gerhardt have presented data from the Roswell Park Memorial Institute which suggested a causal relationship between cigarette smoking and cancer of the lung, and pipe smoking and cancer of the lip. The prevalence rates were age-standardized, and the significant differences were confined to those who had smoked either cigarettes or a pipe for twenty-five years or longer. While their data showed a strong significance, the authors admitted that it might be due to some other unidentified common factor between these types of smoking and lung and lip cancer. They stated, "It is somewhat surprising to find that the type of smoking, i.e., cigarettes for lung cancer, pipe for lip cancer, is the associated factor, rather than the actual use of tobacco."

Wynder and Graham reported that excessive and prolonged use of tobacco, especially cigarettes, seemed to be a strong factor in bronchiogenic carcinoma. They reported a higher percentage of smokers among the lung cancer group than did

* Two methods used to study relationship between different variables are *association* and *correlation*. One shows that relationship exists; the other gives a mathematical measurement as to the degree of relationship. Whether or not association is of importance must be determined by the significance of the association. Here the calculus of probability is used and one tries to determine what the probability is that the occurrence which has been observed could happen as a chance phenomenon. If this probability is small, one is justified in feeling that a real association exists.

Correlation measures the relationship between two variables. The degree of correlation ranges from $+1$ to -1. Complete independence or absence of relationship is measured by a coefficient of zero. Here, again, significance is measured by the relationship of the coefficient to its standard error. Significance can be assumed if the correlation coefficient is more than 2.6 times its standard error. The results of both association and correlation must be tested, however, by the criterion of common sense, and effort made to determine if other variables may not be the determining factor for the relationship.

Levin, Goldstein, and Gerhardt, and also a greater percentage of cigarette smoking. They found that most of their patients with lung cancer had a history of smoking for over twenty years. "Tobacco seems at this time to play a similar but somewhat less evident role in the induction of epidermoid and undifferentiated carcinoma in women. Among this group a greater percentage of non-smokers will be found than among the men, with 10 of 25 being non-smokers." They stated that they intended to learn the relative importance of previous diseases of the lungs, rural-urban distribution of patients, various occupations, and hereditary background as well as smoking habits, and they hoped to determine whether any of these factors, either singly or in combination, have had an effect in increasing the incidence of bronchiogenic carcinoma. In this paper the emphasis was on smoking and the effect of the other variables was not discussed.

ASSOCIATION WITH OTHER DISEASES

The presence of certain pre-existing diseases has been suggested as a cause of cancer, and the methodology of attempting to confirm such an hypothesis has been varied. Correlation coefficients have been computed on time and space series. In some studies association tables have been constructed, and the expected probability for the occurrence of the two diseases together has been compared with the observed probability. Death rates, morbidity rates, and proportionate mortality have been used as measurements of the occurrence of cancer and the other disease. Different results have been obtained depending upon the type of rate which was used. Association, utilizing the morbidity rate, would appear to be the method of choice if accurate morbidity rates were available.

Cancer morbidity has been obtained by surveys, reporting, and by use of the formula $\frac{\textit{deaths} \times \textit{duration}}{\textit{case fatality}}$. Inasmuch as morbidity estimates utilizing all three methods have been similar for Massachusetts, it is believed that morbidity rates obtained by any one of these methods can be utilized. With some other diseases the situation is different. For example, in diabetes, morbidity is not reportable, and the number of cases computed from the formula differs greatly from that found by Wilkerson in the Oxford, Massachusetts survey.

DIABETES

A possible relationship between cancer and diabetes has been suggested by several investigators over a period of years. One of the earliest reports was by Maynard in 1910. One of the most recent was a monograph of Jacobsen in 1948. In the interim a number of reports have been prepared, only a few of which will be mentioned. Doering showed a positive correlation between the two diseases using data for the Registration Area* of 1920. Potter in 1937 (unpublished data) con-

* The United States Bureau of the Census established a registration area for deaths. The criteria for admission has been satisfactory state registration laws and 90 per cent completeness in reporting. Since 1933 all states have met these standards. Massachusetts, New Jersey and the District of Columbia were admitted in 1880. Connecticut, New Hampshire, New York, Rhode Island and Vermont in 1890, and Maine, Michigan, and Indiana in 1900.

firmed this using data for the 48 states, $r = .841 \pm .045$, and showed that the relationship persisted when by means of partial correlation with the variables latitude, nativity, age, medical attention, density, and economic status held constant, the correlation coefficient was $.409 \pm .129$.* On the other hand, Stevenson in 1921 showed no relationship between diabetes and cancer, the correlation coefficient being $-.010 \pm .052$. Wilson and Maher, using association, found a very strong correlation between the two diseases. However, their paper was written before Joslin and Lombard had shown that 25 per cent of individuals dying with diabetes did not have the disease mentioned on the death certificate, and before Wilkerson had demonstrated that morbidity far exceeded previous estimates. The results of Wilson and Maher, corrected for these facts, would be different.

It is obvious that a true appraisal of an association between these two diseases has not yet been determined.

Goiter

Several investigators have reported a high cancer death rate in communities where the incidence of goiter was also high. Stocks reviewed the data for Switzerland, Norway, and the United States and found the correlation coefficient between deaths from cancer and estimated goiter cases to be $.6459 \pm .0302$. He also correlated the deaths from cancer of the esophagus, stomach, intestines, and rectum with goiter cases and obtained a correlation coefficient of $.7130 \pm .0596$. Stocks and Karn found that the correlation coefficient between the rate for goiter in 12-year-old girls and the standardized cancer death rate for females was $.1928 \pm .076$; and between boys and the standardized cancer death rate for men was $.1490 \pm .0772$. They concluded that a positive correlation existed between thyroid enlargement in children and cancer mortality in the large towns of England and Wales. McClendon compared the recorded incidence of cancer in World War I draftees according to whether they lived in one of the more goitrous states or one of the less goitrous states. There was a significant difference between the mean of the rates in the two groups of states. This type of evidence is suggestive but not conclusive proof of etiologic relationship.

Syphilis

Syphilis is of importance in the etiology of cancer of the tongue, the cervix, and the esophagus. Both Stevenson, and Young and Russell showed a strong correlation between cancer of the esophagus and syphilis in the zero order, and in the partial order, holding cirrhosis of the liver constant (Table 65). Stevenson found a partial correlation between cancer of the esophagus and syphilis, holding cancer of the tongue constant. Young and Russell were not in agreement with these latter findings.

Table 66, prepared by Stevenson, shows cancer mortality in occupations, grouped by mortality from syphilitic diseases.

* The methodology used in computing partial correlation coefficients consisted of first obtaining zero order coefficients and applying these coefficients to the formula for partial correlation developed by Pearson and described by Yule and Kendall.

TABLE 65. SYPHILIS AND CANCER OF THE TONGUE AND ESOPHAGUS

	Correlation coefficient
Syphilis and cancer of the esophagus	
(Stevenson)	.480 ± .041
(Young and Russell)	.369 ± .062
Syphilis and cancer of the tongue	
(Stevenson)	.359 ± .046
(Young and Russell)	.467 ± .057
Cancer of the esophagus and syphilis holding cancer of the tongue constant	
(Stevenson)	.387 ± .045
(Young and Russell)	.116 ± .071
Cancer of the esophagus and syphilis holding cirrhosis of the liver constant	
(Stevenson)	.393 ± .044
(Young and Russell)	.279 ± .067

TABLE 66. CANCER MORTALITY (C.M.F) IN OCCUPATIONS GROUPED BY MORTALITY FROM SYPHILITIC DISEASES

		Occupations graded by mortality from syphilis	
Site of cancer	*All occupations*	*10 of highest mortality*	*10 of lowest mortality*
Skin	3.0	4.1	2.7
Lip	1.0	2.0	0.5
Tongue	7.5	13.8	2.8
Esophagus	9.7	16.4	4.2
Stomach	29.5	40.2	18.7
Other Sites	77.7	94.8	64.4
All Sites	128.4	171.9	93.6

TUBERCULOSIS

Cancer and tuberculosis have been considered by some investigators to be antagonistic, by others to be associated, and by a few to be independent. Cherry has compiled extensive data on the death records of individuals with cancer and tuberculosis. He found that there was almost a uniform percentage when he added together the deaths from tuberculosis and cancer, and divided the sum by the number of deaths from all causes for the same time interval. He stated that: "Hence I conclude that the two diseases are closely related. Analysis of the records of the occupations confirms this correlation and makes it probable that the incidence of cancer depends on the facility with which adults come into contact with the tubercle bacillus." While data of this type are interesting, they do not establish relationship.

Pearl, from a study of over 6000 postmortem records, concluded that there was an incompatibility between cancer and tuberculosis, and made the suggestion that some product of the tubercle bacillus might have a curative influence on cancer.

Carlson and Bell, also reporting on postmortem data, found active tuberculosis much less frequent in cancerous than in noncancerous subjects, but it was even less frequently associated with heart disease than with cancer. They concluded that they did not find any statistical evidence to support the view that there was an antagonism between cancer and tuberculosis.

Wilson and Maher, reporting on Massachusetts death records, concluded that there seemed to be little or no evidence in favor of an antagonism or dissociation between cancer and tuberculosis, and a considerable variety of evidence in favor of a slight degree of positive association between the two.

CANCER OF SELECTED SITES

Breast

Heredity. The epidemiology of cancer of the breast has been studied by a number of investigators. Among these is Jacobsen, who concluded that the sole cause was of an hereditary nature and that the study of case histories gave no ground for supposing that exogenous factors play an important role in the development of breast cancer. On the other hand, Macklin believes that both hereditary and extrinsic factors produce cancer; as one of these variables becomes large the other may become correspondingly small.

Trauma. The relationship between trauma and cancer of the breast has been shown by several epidemiologists to be statistically significant. This relationship, however, must be regarded with caution. It is believed that a woman with breast cancer is more apt to attempt to recall past injuries than a woman who does not have the disease, since many think that breast cancer follows trauma. Lane-Claypon considered a history of injury with and without bruising, as well as repeated slight injuries, and found all to be significantly related to cancer.

Busk and Clemmensen found a greater frequency of cancer in the left breast than in the right. They quoted from Lane-Claypon's data and stated that "injury seemed to occur more frequently to the left than to the right breast. . . . But whether the differences in injuries sustained by the breast has any connection with the difference in cancer incidence, or is a mere coincidence, nobody can tell at present."

Fertility. Low fertility was shown to be related to cancer of the breast in the British Ministry of Health Report No. 32. Unmarried women have a greater incidence of cancer of the breast than married women; and married women without children have a greater incidence than married women with children.

Nursing. The Cancer Commission of the League of Nations reported that there was a larger number of women among cancer patients who for one reason or another had never suckled their children. The findings of both Lane-Claypon and Wainwright agreed with this observation.

Adair found only 8.5 per cent of his cases of mammary cancer had a normal history of nursing, compared with 80 per cent for his control cases.

Chronic Mastitis. Warren found that the development of chronic cystic mastitis and chronic mastitis predisposes to the development of breast cancer, but he did not believe the risk to be sufficiently great to warrant bilateral mastectomy. The attack rate for women in the age group 20–49 was 11.7 times the rate for the normal female population of comparable age. In the age group over 50 it was 2.5 times as great.

Skin

Many cases of cancer of the skin are the result of occupational hazards. As these are discussed elsewhere only brief mention is made here. Atkin, Fenning, Heady, Kennaway, and Kennaway reported that the mortality from cancer of the skin or lip is highest among agricultural workers, intermediate in miners, and lowest in the professional group. Cancer caused by arsenic can be both an occupational disease and the result of long-continued medication with certain arsenical products.

There appears to be some susceptibility to multiple skin cancer. Lombard, Levin and Warren showed a far greater number of secondary skin cancers than would be expected by the laws of probability if no susceptibility existed.

Several investigators have reported on the high incidence of skin cancer in the southern states, which they believe to be due to exposure to the actinic rays of the sun. The relation of chronic irritation, sunlight, dermatitis from roentgen-ray irradiation, and other irritations to skin cancer needs more statistical investigation.

Buccal Cavity

The use of tobacco, syphilis, poor oral hygiene, irritation by the teeth or dentures, vitamin deficiency, betel-nut chewing, and leukoplakia have been suggested as etiologic factors in cancer of the buccal cavity. There are no statistical studies to support some of these hypotheses. A strong association between cancer of the tongue and syphilis has been found. Stevenson compared the cancer rates for individuals in the ten occupations having the highest syphilitic rates with the ten having the lowest (see Table 57). While the rate for cancer of all sites was about twice as great in the occupations having high syphilitic rates as in those having the lowest rates, the rate for cancer of the tongue was nearly five times greater. Good data regarding the relationship between cancer of the mouth and tobacco are limited (see pages 722, 751, 787).

Cancer of the mouth, probably attributable to the chewing of the "betel," is common in Java, the Philippines, India, and Ceylon. The statistical evidence is the relatively large percentage of cases with cancer of the mouth in these areas, rather than different incidences of oral cancer in chewers and non-chewers. Fells reported from Southern India that out of 377 cases of malignancy 346 were of the buccal cavity, most of them being of the mucous membrane of the cheek. In Ceylon and India 94 per cent of individuals with malignant disease of the oral cavity chewed betel nut, but it is estimated that about 90 per cent of all inhabitants do so.

Lung

The relationship of cancer of the lung to certain occupational hazards is discussed in Chapter 26 and it is sufficient to state that there is good statistical data to substantiate the hypotheses implicating some phases of industrial work.

Another factor that appears to be of importance is tobacco, which has been mentioned elsewhere in this chapter. The Kennaways discussed air pollution and stated that "higher mortality from cancer of the lung in town (Stocks), low mortality in agricultural occupations, and the absence of a social gradient (Stevenson) are compatible with an etiological factor in the air such as coal smoke. But in any comparison of urban and rural areas, the question of facilities for diagnosis must be considered."

There has been considerable conjecture as to whether the tar from streets might be a causative factor in cancer of the lung. The Kennaways could find no data suggestive of such a relationship, but Scheele stated at the United States Technical Conference on Air Pollution at Washington, D. C., May 4, 1950: "Studies conducted at the Public Health Service's National Cancer Institute have at least raised serious questions as to the role of community air pollution in the causation of cancer. Analyses of dusts collected from the ordinary air in several large cities showed that 10 per cent of the dust consisted of particles of tar. A single subcutaneous injection of these soluble particles produced malignant tumors in mice. And these carcinogenic substances were collected from the air in streets, homes, offices, and schools."

CERVIX

Statistical papers indicate that cancer of the cervix is positively associated with low economic status, chronic infections and irritations, and factors related to the marital status, but negatively associated with either racial or environmental factors pertaining to Jewish women.

Low Economic Status. The report of the Registrar General of England and Wales showed that the incidence of cancer of the uterus increased inversely with the economic condition. The standardized mortality in the highest economic group was 65, contrasted with 130 in the lowest. This study did not separate rates for cancer of the cervix from those for cancer of the body of the uterus, but data from other sources suggested that the incidence of cancer of the fundus did not follow the same economic pattern as cancer of the cervix. If the rates for the two diseases had been treated separately, it seems probable that the poor would have shown an even greater incidence of cancer of the cervix.

Infections and Irritations. Syphilis appears to be related to cancer of the cervix. In 1931 Belote discussed the association of cancer and syphilis. Harding reported on it in 1942, and in the same year Levin, Kress, and Goldstein confirmed this hypothesis using data from the reporting system of New York State. Lombard and Potter confirmed this finding and reported it at the Fourth International Cancer Congress. The repeated occurrence of this association with different types of data obtained from different geographical locations greatly strengthens the belief that syphilis is sometimes a precursor of cancer of this site.

Unrepaired lacerations of the cervix have been considered a precancerous condition. Ewing stated "Lacerations, cervical erosions in all their phases, and chronic catarrhal inflammation precede and lead directly to the great majority of cervical cancers." There is considerable difficulty in proving this relationship by statistical methods, because the incidence of unrepaired lacerations cannot be ascertained accurately. In a Massachusetts study, 26 per cent of the 523 individuals in the cancer of the cervix series stated that they had an unrepaired laceration, while individuals in the six control series had rates for lacerations varying from 10.1 to 15.0. It was felt that the element of error was about equal in all of the series studied and that the difference in the rates in the cancer and control series could be considered valid.

Factors Related to Married Life. The Cancer Commission of the League of Nations reported in 1927 "Although cancer of the cervix is mainly a disease of women who have borne children, the work of the Commission has confirmed the conclusions of Peller and Deelman that it is the fact of a pregnancy and not the number of pregnancies which is the predisposing factor in the production of cancer of the uterus."

Lombard and Potter, using partial association and partial correlation, showed that early marriage, early termination of pregnancies, and divorce or separation, remained significant; while the number of children, duration of marriage, the fact of pregnancy, contraception, abortions, rapidity of pregnancies, and instrumental deliveries were eliminated in either the zero or partial orders.* In the group with cancer of the cervix 44.6 per cent of the individuals married before the age of 20, while in the control groups the rates varied from 16.3 to 23.7. In the cervix group 20.7 per cent had been divorced or separated contrasted with 5.4 to 10.4 in the control groups. The completion of pregnancies before age 25 occurred in 24.3 per cent of the cervix cases, while it ranged from 4.8 to 12.8 in the control series. Hormonal imbalance was suggested as a possible explanation for these associations.

Incidence among Jewish Women. The work of Sorsby clearly demonstrated that the incidence of cancer of the cervix was low among Jewish women. Kennaway made an exhaustive study of this subject and reported in part: "All of the twenty collections of data which have been found in the literature show an incidence of uterine cancer which is greater in non-Jewish than in Jewish women."

EVALUATIVE STUDIES

Many studies and reports of an evaluative nature have been made. These include measurements of, improvement in the cancer situation, motivating knowledge of the individual, exposure to and assimilation of cancer information, teaching effort, and public interest.

CHANGES IN THE DEATH RATES

The best measurement of the efficacy of a cancer program is derived from a study of death certificates over a period of time. Age-sex adjusted death rates rather than the crude rates should be used in such comparisons.

* The method of partial association which was used consisted of breaking the data into partial universes and in each universe obtaining the difference in the rates between the cervix and breast groups for the respective variables. These differences were divided by their standard errors to obtain unit deviates. These deviates were averaged and compared for significance with the standard error of the mean. A detailed account of this method, with application, was published in *Biometrics*, Sept., 1947.

The partial correlation coefficient was obtained by using zero order coefficients from the formula for a 2 × 2 table described by Yule and Kendall, and applying these coefficients to the formula for partial correlation.

SURVIVAL AND CURE RATES

A comparison of the percentages of cures is a good method of measuring results, provided the material is adequate and is analyzed properly. Great care should be exercised to make certain that all factors entering into the data are considered. These are often multiple, covering such items as differences in the stages of the disease, in diagnosis, in treatment, in degree of malignancy, and perhaps even in the type of after-care. Whatever differences occur in the basic data must be considered as affecting, in some respect, the results. An increased percentage of cures would represent such factors as improved diagnosis and surgery, improved knowledge of cancer on the part of the lay public, and probably others.

The different methods employed make it extremely difficult to compare the results of treatment reported by different individuals. Some investigators report all their cases with cancer of a given site; others use selected cases, such as those operated upon or those favorable for a cure. The completeness of follow-up varies from only a few untraced cases to many. The cases with unknown disposition are classified as dead, omitted entirely, or omitted in part, depending on the investigator. The individuals who died of intercurrent disease and without recurrence are considered by some as cures and by others as indeterminate, hence omitted from the calculations. Greenwood discussed the following method:

> Assuming the normal expectation of life of a woman aged 55 to be 18.87 years, and the expectation of life for a woman with untreated cancer of the breast to be 3.25 years, the duration of life for a woman with untreated breast cancer would be 17.22 per cent of the normal duration of life, or $\frac{3.25}{18.87}$.* If the average woman lived 12.93 years following operation she would have 68.52 per cent of the normal duration of life, or $\frac{12.93}{18.87}$ The advantage secured by these individuals operated on under the most favorable conditions would be the difference between 68.52 and 17.22, or 51.30 per cent.

In order to make computations by this method it is necessary that all patients be followed until death. This is rarely done.

Macdonald omitted the untraced cases and computed the percentage of individuals alive at the end of each year. The omission of untraced cases is made on the assumption that they would be distributed as the known cases, and this may not be so. On the other hand, some of those who died of intercurrent disease might well have been cured of cancer.

Nathanson and Welch plotted survival curves and compared these with similar curves from the total population.

Martin computed the results of treatment by using only the determinate group. In the indeterminate group he included those "dead as the result of other causes and without recurrence," and those "lost track of without recurrence." In the determinate group he included "dead as the result of cancer," "lost track of with

* In untreated cancer of the breast Lazarus-Barlow found a mean duration of 39.8 months, Wyard 39.6, Lane-Claypon 39.3, and Daland 40.5, an average of 3.3 years.

disease (probably dead)," "living with recurrence," and "successful results (free of disease after 5 years or more)."

One of the most complete survival tables has been prepared by Wells, using Hartford Hospital data (Table 67). The subdivision of the data into all possible classifications enables a comparison of the Hartford data with those of others.

Two methods have been suggested which are not mentioned in the literature as far as is known.

TABLE 67. SURVIVAL TABLE (WELLS)

Treatment	*No. of cases*	*Five year survival with cancer*	*Five year survival without cancer*	*Died under five years with cancer*	*Died under five years without cancer*	*Still living with cancer*	*Still living without cancer*	*Died after five years without cancer*
Radical mastectomy	350	15	146	175	14	15	109	12
Simple mastectomy	35	9	10	16	0	4	0	1
Simple mastectomy plus axillary dissection	12	1	3	6	2	0	3	0
Excision of tumor	9	1	1	6	1	1	0	1
No treatment	13	0	0	13	0	0	0	0
Radiation only	56	6	0	50	0	1	0	0
Secondary to Hartford	95	11	10	60	3	11	10	0
TOTAL	570	43	170	326	20	32	131	14

From Wells, D. B.: *Connecticut State M.J. 14:*3–15, 1950

In a report of the Second Conference on Cancer Teaching held in Minneapolis in October 1949, the discussion by Newell, Nathanson, and Haagensen incorporated the suggestion that the yearly rate of incidence of cancer recurrence be tabulated. Hammond of the American Cancer Society suggested the following methodology.

An expected number of deaths for a five-year period, in an unselected population with the same age and sex distribution as the cancer patients under consideration, should be computed, and this expected number of deaths subtracted from the original number of cases, in order to obtain the number who would normally be expected to live five years. This figure would be used as the denominator in computing survival and cure rates. The five-year minimum survival rate would be the number that actually survived five years divided by the number who would normally be expected to survive five years. The maximum survival rate would be the number of cases known to be alive at the end of five years plus the number of untraced cases, divided by the number normally expected to be alive at the end of five years. The minimum cure rate would be computed from the formula:

$$\frac{\textit{Number of cases alive and free from cancer at the end of five years.}}{\textit{Number of cases that would normally be expected to be alive at end of five years.}}$$

The maximum cure rate would be computed from the formula:

$$\frac{\textit{Number of cases alive and free from cancer at the end of five years plus the untraced cases.}}{\textit{Number of cases that would normally be expected to be alive at end of five years.}}$$

If follow-up were complete the minimum and maximum survival rates would be identical. If there was much spread between the two figures it would suggest that too great dependence could not be put on the rate, due to the large number of untraced cases.

MEASUREMENTS OF MOTIVATING KNOWLEDGE

Measurements of motivating knowledge are of importance. Data for this purpose may be obtained from hospital and cancer clinic records and from the physician's office, and may include such facts as the attendance at hospital and clinic, reasons for seeking advice, and the period of delay between first recognizable symptoms and treatment. The period of delay between the first recognizable symptom and the first visit to a physician is one of the earliest indications of improvement that can be ascertained. This measures the delay on the part of the patient, while the interval between the first visit to a doctor and treatment measures, jointly, the efforts of the physician and the patient. A number of studies have been made featuring these delays. In the Massachusetts cancer clinics in 1927 there was a 6.5 months' delay between first recognizable symptoms and first consultation with a physician. In 1949 this had been reduced to 3.2 months. In 1927 there was a 5.4 months' delay between visit to first physician and admission to a cancer clinic. In 1949 this had been reduced to 2.1 months.

The Philadelphia Committee for the Study of Pelvic Cancer has attempted to apportion delay among physicians and patients for the total pelvic group, and to discuss physicians' delay for the four important sites of pelvic cancer. They found that in 29.0 per cent there was no delay; in 41.5 per cent the delay was due to the patient; in 14.8 to physician and patient; and in 14.6 to the physician alone. The average length of physicians' delay was shortest for cervix cases and longest for cancer of the vulva. Fifty per cent of physicians' delay was due to failure to examine patients.

Data for the years 1923–1948 at the Memorial Hospital in New York have been studied to determine the culpability for delay and to measure improvement. The latest paper of this series divided the cancer cases into four groups: superficial, breast, thorough, and special. The thorough group included those cancers that could be detected or suspected by a careful history and a complete physical examination. The special group required in addition to history and physical examination, roentgenographic or endoscopic studies, or both. The series indicated that during the earlier years the improvement which occurred was due to the patient, but since 1946 it has been due to the physician.

Another study of a somewhat different type has emanated from the Memorial Hospital. This dealt with factors contributing to delay by patients seeking medical care. The data indicated that delay or non-delay resulted from the interrelationship of numerous factors and attitudes associated with the patient's past experience and background. The patient's reaction to this disease was similar to that toward other diseases. The tendency to delay was great among certain types of patients: those who interpreted the disease as being a common condition or recurrence of some prior illness; those who feared either examination, knowledge, surgery, or disfigurement; those who believed that financial sources were inadequate for medical care; those who did not have a family doctor; and those who were not in the habit of consulting physicians except in the case of acute discomfort or under pressure by relatives or friends.

MEASUREMENTS OF MEDICAL INFORMATION

The percentage of the population with sufficient knowledge of cancer to act if occasion demands may be ascertained by means of questionnaires and public opinion polls. A repetition of such a study at a later period will determine whether there has been improvement in cancer knowledge in the community. At the same time that medical information is being measured, measures of the exposure of the individual to knowledge derived from lectures, from listening to radio programs on cancer, and from reading published articles can be ascertained.

Several surveys have been conducted in Massachusetts cities to determine the individual's background knowledge of cancer and the source of the information. Nearly three-quarters of the surveyed population believed that cancer could be cured. Over four-fifths of the population believed that cancer is not contagious. The most discouraging part of the study was the lack of knowledge of the danger signals, which have been published so frequently as a phase of cancer education. Nearly one-half named none of these signals, about one-third named one, and about one-fourth named two or more. The most valuable source of knowledge was the lecture, with reading material next in importance.

MEASUREMENTS OF TEACHING EFFORT

Another type of measurement, but less factual, is the tabulation of facilities available for acquiring cancer knowledge. The number of lectures given, the amount of space used by the newspapers, the number of pamphlets and other material distributed, all measure the control activities. Such listings do not furnish a measure of how much of the information disseminated was actually assimilated.

Recently Bierman has reported his findings obtained during four years of study of the knowledge on cancer among medical students in many medical schools. (Bierman, H. R.; Towner, L. W., Jr.; Galloway, D. W., and McClelland, Y. M. *Cancer Learning in the Medical School.* Berkeley, California, The University of California Press, 1952.)

MEASUREMENTS OF PUBLIC INTEREST

The least valuable type of measurement is that relating to public interest. Examples of this type of measurement include: the extent of cooperation of individuals in carrying out the cancer control program; the fact that Legislatures appropriate money for programs; and the fact that facilities are being provided for the care and treatment of patients.

STUDIES OF INCIDENCE, PREVALENCE, AND RELATED FACTS

INCIDENCE AND PREVALENCE FROM MORTALITY DATA

Cancer is worldwide in occurrence, but neither the exact incidence or prevalence in any country is known. In those countries with death registration and some estimate of population, death rates can be computed, but, as Dorn has shown, death records may vary greatly from morbidity.

Incidence may be defined as new cases under treatment during the year; and prevalence as all cases under treatment during the year.

Table 68 shows the death rates for cancer and other malignant tumors for 46 countries in 1940.

TABLE 68. CANCER DEATH RATES IN 46 COUNTRIES: 1940
Rates per 100,000

1. Switzerland	176.0	24. Uruguay	98.8
2. England and Wales	172.3	25. Italy	86.2
3. Austria	164.2	26. Argentina	85.4
4. Scotland	162.7	27. Bulgaria (towns)	83.8
5. Germany (1940 terr.)	149.2	28. Japan (proper)	70.9
6. Denmark	147.4	29. Chile	69.7
7. Netherlands	138.2	30. Spain	65.3
8. Norway	136.2	31. Brazil (cities)	63.9
9. Northern Ireland	136.1	32. Costa Rica	62.8
10. Sweden	135.7	33. Greece	52.3
11. France	133.3	34. Portugal	45.8
12. Ireland	127.6	35. Rumania	43.8
13. Iceland	126.3	36. Lithuania	43.6
14. Czechoslovakia	124.2	37. Panama	39.6
15. New Zealand (ex. Maoris)	120.2	38. Paraguay (districts)	36.4
16. United States	120.0	39. Columbia	25.9
17. Belgium	119.9	40. Venezuela	25.8
18. Canada	117.2	41. Egypt (towns)	23.2
19. Estonia	117.2	42. Mexico	23.2
20. Australia	116.8	43. Ecuador	19.2
21. Union of South Africa (Eur.)	102.8	44. Peru	14.0
22. Finland	101.6	45. El Salvador	12.9
23. Hungary (1940 terr.)	101.3	46. Ceylon	11.3

Age adjustments would decrease the range in these rates, as all of the countries with low rates have a smaller percentage of individuals in the older age groups.

Some countries report high rates for cancer of certain sites. For example: Cancer of the breast is practically unknown among Japanese women, except among those members of the race who live in a European manner; in China, carcinoma of the penis is reported to be frequent; cancer of the cheek is reported to be extremely prevalent in India; an area with a high incidence of cancer of the liver extends from the west coast of Africa over to and across Southern and Southeastern Asia, including Sumatra, Java, and the Philippines. Many dark-skinned races show a high incidence of the disease, probably associated with parasitic infestations and cirrhosis of the liver; kangri cancer is practically unknown outside a comparatively circumscribed area in Asia.

The distribution of cancer deaths varies in the United States. Gover studied the recorded mortality in five geographic sections, the Northeast, East North Central, South, West Central, and Pacific. In each section the rate for females was higher than for males. Cancer mortality for all sites combined was highest in the Northeast, and lowest in the South. Among males, the rates for cancer of internal sites formed the major part of the mortality, while among females the rates for cancer of internal sites represented a little more than one-half of the mortality. Among females, cancers of the buccal cavity, skin, and female genital organs were higher in the South than in other sections of the country. Among males, cancer of the skin was higher in the South.

Differences in death rates between countries are extremely important if they are real, as a great deal may be learned by comparing the customs and environment of one country with those of another in the search for the etiology of cancer. However, many factors tend to lessen credence in incidence rates. Among the factors are: adequacy of diagnosis and of medical care, longevity, and classification of causes of death. The inaccurate population enumeration and incomplete recording of deaths in some parts of the world prohibit reliable statistics.

Both Dorn and Macdonald have shown that the recording of cancer deaths by sites is not as accurate as the recording of cancer deaths of all sites combined. Dorn found that 4.8 per cent of cancer cases were classified as dying of nonmalignant causes; while Macdonald found 5 per cent. When they subdivided the cancers by broad sites, agreement between reported diagnosis and actual diagnosis occurred in 84.5 per cent in Dorn's series, and in 78.2 per cent in Macdonald's. When the exact site was used, rather than the broad groupings, the percentage agreement was not quite as high.

MORBIDITY ESTIMATES

Estimates of morbidity have been made in several different ways. In New York State, exclusive of New York City, cancer reporting has been used more extensively to estimate morbidity than in other parts of the country. Reports from physicians and hospitals are supplemented by death record reports, so that the composite is believed to be a reasonable estimate of both prevalence and incidence. Some other states have inaugurated reporting systems, but at the present time the data from New York appears to be the best. New York is also utilizing these data for epidemiologic investigation, for evaluation of progress in cancer control, for education, and for certain services.

Connecticut has a system for estimation based on hospitalized cases. The medical profession in that state is greatly interested in this system and is attempting to make it as complete as possible.

Dorn has utilized the survey method to estimate morbidity. He contacted all physicians, either by letter or by interview, in ten areas; Atlanta, Pittsburgh, Detroit, Chicago, New Orleans, Dallas, Forth Worth, San Francisco and Alameda County, Birmingham, Philadelphia, and Denver. This study did not include individuals who had never consulted a physician, or those treated by physicians outside of the surveyed area. While for the most part it represented conditions in urban areas, it furnished the best information available on morbidity on a nation-wide scale, and showed that morbidity data varied greatly from mortality data. In the South, the death rate from cancer was low, while the morbidity was higher than in other parts of the country. Dorn stated: "Since the lower death rate in the South cannot be explained by a lower illness rate, it must be due either to better medical care or to a more favorable prognosis of the disease which may result from a large proportion of cases with forms of cancer which are most readily cured or from the initiation of treatment at an early stage in the development of the tumor. There is no reason to believe that physicians in the North are less competent than those in the South, so that a more favorable prognosis would seem to be the primary explanation of the lower death rate in the South."

On the basis of his surveys, Dorn suggests a prevalence estimation of 475,000–500,000 and an incidence figure of 300,000.

PROBABILITY OF DEVELOPING CANCER

Levin and Goldstein have estimated the probability of developing cancer from birth onwards, based on the cancer morbidity reports of New York State (Table 69).

TABLE 69. PROBABILITY OF DEVELOPING CANCER FROM BIRTH ON BY SEX AND SITE

Male		*Female*	
Site	*Probability (%)*	*Site*	*Probability (%)*
Skin	2.459	Breast	4.974
Stomach	2.277	Cervix	2.196
Prostate	2.224	Intestine	2.167
Intestine	1.619	Skin	1.786
Lung and bronchus	1.095	Stomach	1.736
Rectum	1.081	Fundus Uteri	1.366
Bladder	0.966	Ovary	0.916
Lip	0.567	Rectum	0.897
Pancreas	0.473	Liver	0.550
Leukemia	0.473	Bladder	0.493
Esophagus	0.403	Leukemia	0.425
Liver	0.394	Pancreas	0.419
Larynx	0.302	Biliary passages	0.336
Brain	0.290	Lung and bronchus	0.276
Kidney	0.255	Brain	0.216
Tongue	0.207	Kidney	0.195
Hodgkin's disease	0.173	Bones and joints	0.140
Mouth	0.170	Esophagus	0.139
Pharynx	0.170	Hodgkin's disease	0.114
Bones and joints	0.143	Mouth	0.061
Biliary passages	0.126	Tongue	0.053
Testes	0.125	Pharynx	0.048
Breast	0.058	Lip	0.041
		Larynx	0.039
All others	2.237	All others	2.636
All sites	18.287	All sites	22.219
Sexual sites	2.534	Sexual sites	9.761

Based on Cancer Morbidity Reports New York State, Exclusive of New York City, 1942–44.

Tables 70-73 are examples of descriptive statistics which furnish pertinent information regarding cancer.

TABLE 70. RATIO OF CANCER DEATHS TO TOTAL DEATHS
United States Registration Area, 1947

Age groups	*Male*	*Female*	*Total*
Under 30	1.7	2.1	1.9
30–39	6.6	17.7	11.4
40–49	10.4	27.2	17.1
50–59	14.4	26.8	19.0
60–69	15.9	20.9	17.9
70–79	14.0	14.5	14.2
80+	9.4	8.5	8.9
TOTALS	11.4	15.3	13.1

INCREASE OF CANCER

Many statistical papers have been written on the increase of cancer. Some have claimed the increase was real; others have contended that it was only apparent. Schereschewsky, using data from the ten original registration states* between 1900 and 1920, apportioned a part of the increase to change in age distribution, and a part to better diagnosis, but found above these an increase which he believed to be

TABLE 71. CANCER DEATHS IN THE UNITED STATES: 1948

Site	*Number of deaths*	*Sex ratio male/female*
Buccal cavity and pharynx	5,712	3.9
Esophagus	3,681	3.4
Stomach	26,215	1.7
Rectum and anus	10,834	1.3
Intestines	22,860	0.8
Liver and biliary	10,598	0.8
Pancreas	8,234	1.4
Lung	10,493	3.0
Other respiratory	8,477	5.6
Uterus	17,120	—
Other female genitals	6,142	—
Breast	19,162	—
Prostate	11,758	—
Bladder	6,278	2.1
Skin	3,568	1.5
All others	25,910	1.3
TOTALS	197,042	0.97

* Prior to 1933 comparable data from year to year were not available inasmuch as the addition of new states to the Registration Area increased the number of recorded deaths. In order to exclude these increments, the Registration Area of 1900 has been used in this study. (See footnote, page 788.)

TABLE 72. MEDIAN AGE AT TIME OF DEATH OF INDIVIDUALS WITH CANCER*

Site	*1948 Mass. deaths*	*1947 U.S. deaths*
Buccal cavity	69.9	66.8
Stomach	68.8	68.0
Other digestive	68.5	66.9
Respiratory	62.9	61.2
Uterus	61.7	58.1
Other female genitals	61.4	58.3
Breast	64.3	60.7
Male genitals	74.4	72.9
Urinary organs	69.8	66.6
Skin	76.7	73.0
Other and unspecified	60.8	58.9
TOTALS	66.9	65.0

* The median is the mid-point in a series when the items are arranged in the order of magnitude.

real. In 1940 Wilcox reaffirmed the conclusions of an earlier study that most of the increase was in inaccessible sites and was the result of better diagnosis.

Table 74 shows that the crude death rate between 1920-1944 has increased in all countries mentioned except Japan, and that there are great differences between countries.

In 1900, cancer was in eighth position as a cause of death in the United States. In 1920 it had risen to fourth position, and at the present time it is in second

TABLE 73. CRUDE AND ADJUSTED CANCER DEATH RATES
Registration Area of the United States, 1933–1947

	Crude cancer death rates		*Age-adjusted cancer death rates**	
Year	Male	Female	Male	Female
1933	92.3	112.3	102.3	126.5
1934	96.6	116.2	105.3	128.5
1935	98.0	118.4	105.2	128.9
1936	101.5	121.3	107.2	129.9
1937	103.8	121.0	107.8	127.5
1938	106.9	123.0	109.4	127.5
1939	110.0	125.1	110.7	127.7
1940	114.1	126.3	112.9	126.5
1941	114.5	125.8	112.0	124.3
1942	115.7	127.2	111.9	124.1
1943	116.7	128.8	111.7	124.1
1944	119.8	129.6	113.5	123.4
1945	124.0	131.9	116.2	124.2
1946	127.1	132.7	117.9	123.7
1947	132.8	135.5	122.0	125.1

* Adjusted to the age distribution of the total population of the United States for 1940. Ten-year age groupings were used between the ages of 35–84, with under 35 as one group and 85 and over as another.

TABLE 74. PERCENTAGE INCREASE IN THE CANCER DEATH RATE: 23 COUNTRIES, 1920–1944

Rank order	*Country*	*Percentage increase*
1	Estonia	89.0
2	France	80.1
3	Union of South Africa (Europeans)	78.5
4	Chile	74.3
5	Germany	68.9
6	Belgium	62.0
7	Ireland	59.4
8	Canada	55.7
9	England and Wales	47.8
10	Hungary (Trianon territory)	47.4
11	United States	44.2
12	Northern Ireland	43.1
13	Switzerland	39.7
14	New Zealand (ex. Maoris)	39.3
15	Scotland	36.7
16	Norway	30.5
17	Italy	25.1
18	Australia (ex. aboriginals)	22.4
19	Netherlands	22.3
20	Ceylon	18.9
21	Sweden	12.1
22	Denmark	8.4
23	Japan (proper)	0

position, being exceeded only by heart disease. In the middle thirties a downward trend was noticed among women and a few years later several papers appeared discussing this occurrence.

The percentage change in the female rate in Massachusettes between 1932-1948 is shown in Table 75.

TABLE 75. PERCENTAGE CHANGE OF CANCER INCIDENCE AMONG FEMALES IN MASSACHUSETTS; BY AGE GROUPS, 1932–1948

Under 30	+ .70
30–39	− .78
40–49	− .76
50–59	− .48
60–69	− 1.10
70–79	− .30
80+	+ 1.10

Stocks and MacKay, using age-specific rates for England and Wales; and Potter (Table 76), using adjusted rates from the Registration Area of the United States, reported mortality trends for various sites of cancer. In 1947 the Metropolitan Life Insurance Company reported similar results, using data on their insurance policy holders.

TABLE 76. AVERAGE ANNUAL PERCENTAGE CHANGES IN MORTALITY RATES FROM CANCER; CONTINENTAL UNITED STATES, 1933–1944

White males	*Annual percentage change*	*White females*	*Annual percentage change*
	WITH SIGNIFICANT DOWNWARD TREND		
Buccal cavity	−3.8	Stomach	−3.8
Skin	−2.4	Buccal cavity	−3.4
Stomach	−2.1	Liver	−3.3
Liver	−2.1	Skin	−2.5
		Uterus	−1.4
	WITHOUT SIGNIFICANT TREND		
Bladder	—	Bladder	—
Breast	—	Breast	—
Esophagus	—	Esophagus	—
Scrotum	—	Kidney	—
		Larynx	—
		Rectum	—
		Vulva-vagina	—
	WITH SIGNIFICANT UPWARD TREND		
*Other respiratory	+20.1	*Other respiratory	+15.5
Lung	+ 5.8	Pharynx	+ 5.6
Pharynx	+ 4.9	Ovary	+ 3.3
Pancreas	+ 2.8	Lung	+ 2.1
Intestines	+ 2.1	Pancreas	+ 1.6
Kidney	+ 1.8	Intestines	+ 1.0
Larynx	+ 1.6	All others	+ 4.0
Prostate	+ 1.6		
Rectum	+ 1.6		
Testes	+ 1.6		
All others	+ 3.6		

*Includes 80% Bronchus, 15% Mediastinum and unspecified parts, and remainder Trachea and Pleura.

THE FUTURE OF CANCER STATISTICS

An increasing number of statisticians are being trained in the Public Health Schools, and several medical schools are including statistical courses in their curricula. The Public Health Service, several state health departments, the Public Health Cancer Association of America, and the American Cancer Society are developing strong statistical units, and several of these offer statistical aid to physicians. Concurrent with this expanding interest in the field of cancer statistics is an increase in the number of sound statistical studies; these in turn will augment knowledge of the disease and strengthen world-wide cancer control.

REFERENCES

1. ADAIR, F. E. Etiological factors of mammary cancer in 200 women. *New York State J. Med. 34:* 1-8, 1934.
2. ARKIN, H., and COLTON, R. *An Outline of Statistical Methods* (ed. 4). New York, Barnes & Noble, Inc., 1939.
3. ATKIN, M., FENNING, J., HEADY, J. A., KENNAWAY, E. L., and KENNAWAY, N. M. The mortality from cancer of the skin and lip in certain occupations. *Brit. J. Cancer 3:* 1-15, 1949.
4. BALENDRA, W. Betel chewing in relation to oral sepsis and carcinoma. *Antiseptic 32:* 570-573, 1935.
5. BELOTE, G. H. The association of cancer and syphilis as determined by positive serology. *Am. J. Syph., Gon. & Ven. Dis. 15:* 372-375, 1931.
6. BERKSON, J., and GAGE, R. P. Calculation of survival rates for cancer. *Proc. Staff Meet., Mayo Clin. 25:* 270-286, 1950.
7. BIGELOW, G. H., and LOMBARD, H. L. *Cancer and other Chronic Diseases in Massachusetts.* Boston, 1933. Houghton Mifflin Co.
8. BLOTNER, H. Studies in glycosuria and diabetes mellitus in selectees. *J.A.M.A. 131:* 1109-1114, 1946.
9. BUSK, T., and CLEMMENSEN, J. The frequencies of left- and right-sided breast cancer. *Brit. J. Cancer 1:* 345-351, 1947.
10. CARLSON, H. A., and BELL, E. T. A statistical study of the ocurrence of cancer and tuberculosis in 11,195 postmortem examinations. *J. Cancer Research 13:* 126-135, 1929.
11. CHERRY, T. Cancer and tuberculosis: VIII; A survey of recent work on the causation of cancer. *M. J. Australia 2:* 197-212, 1933.
12. CIOCCO, A. Studies on the biological factors in public health: III. On the mortality in husbands and wives. *Human Biol. 12:* 508-531, 1940.
13. CLEMMESEN, J., and BUSK, T. On the apparent increase in the incidence of lung cancer in Denmark, 1931-1945. *Brit. J. Cancer. 1:* 253-259, 1947.
14. CLEMMESEN, J., and BUSK, T. Cancer mortality among males and females in Denmark, England and Switzerland: IV and V. Mortality of accessible and inaccessible cancer in Danish towns and rural areas. *Cancer Research 9:* 411-414, 1949.
15. CRABTREE, J. A. Observations on the familial incidence of cancer. *Am. J. Pub. Health 31:* 49-56, 1941.
16. DALAND, E. M. Untreated cancer of the breast. *Surg., Gynec. & Obst. 44:* 264-268, 1927.
17. DEELMAN, H. T. Heredity and cancer. *Ann. Surg. 93:* 30-34, 1931.
18. DOERING, C. R. "Statistical methods." In *Preventive Medicine and Hygiene* (ed. 6). New York, D. Appleton-Century, 1935.
19. DORN, H. F. Illness from cancer in the United States. *Pub. Health Rep. 59:* 33-48, 1944.
20. DORN, H. F. Illness from cancer in the United States. *Pub. Health Rep. 59:* 65-77, 1944.
21. DORN, H. F. Illness from cancer in the United States. *Pub. Health Rep.* Reprint No. 2537, 1944.

22. DORN, H. F. Illness from cancer in the United States concluded. *Pub. Health Rep. 59:* 97-115, 1944.
23. DORN, H. F. Morbidity from cancer. *J. Washington Acad. Sc. 39:* 117-119, 1949.
24. DORN, H. F., and HORN, J. I. The reliability of certificates of deaths from cancer. *Am. J. Hyg. 34:* 12-23, 1941.
25. DUBLIN, L. I. The relation between overweight and cancer: A preliminary examination of evidence from insurance statistics. *Proc. Assoc. Life Insurance, Medical Directors of America 15:* 3-6, 1929.
26. DUBLIN, L. I., and MARKS, H. H. The influence of weight on certain causes of death. *Human Biol. 2:* 159-184, 1930.
27. EWING, J. *Neoplastic Diseases.* Philadelphia, W. B. Saunders Co., 1940.
28. Federal Security Agency. Summary of the International Vital Statistics; 1937-1944, 1947.
29. FELLS. Cancer of the mouth in Southern India, with an analysis of 209 operations. *Brit. M. J. 1:* 1357, 1908.
30. FISHER, R. A. *Statistical Methods for Research Workers* (ed. 10). London, Oliver and Boyd, 1946.
31. FROST, W. H. Risk of persons in familial contact with pulmonary tuberculosis. *Am. J. Pub. Health 23:* 426-432, 1933.
32. GARRISON, F. H. *An Introduction to the History of Medicine.* Philadelphia. W. B. Saunders Co., 1929.
33. GARRISON, F. H. The history of cancer. *Bull. N. York Acad. Med. 2:* 179-185, 1926.
34. GOVER, M. Cancer mortality in the United States: I. Trend of recorded cancer mortality in the death registration states of 1900, from 1900 to 1935. *Pub. Health Bull.* No. 248, 1939.
35. GOVER, M. Cancer mortality in the United States: II. Recorded cancer mortality in geographic sections of the death registration states of 1920, from 1920–1935. *Pub. Health Bull.* No. 252, 1940.
36. GOVER, M. Cancer mortality in the United States: III. Geographic variation in recorded cancer mortality for detailed sites, for an average of the years 1930-32. *Pub. Health Bull.* No. 257, 1940.
37. GOVER, M. Cancer mortality in the United States: IV. Age variation in mortality from cancer of specific sites, 1930-32. *Pub. Health Bull.* No. 275, 1941.
38. GREENWOOD, M. *Epidemiology: Historical and Experimental.* The Herter Lectures for 1931, Baltimore, Lord Baltimore Press, 1932.
39. GREENWOOD, M. A report on the natural duration of cancer. *Reports on Public Health and Medical Subjects,* No. 33. London Ministry of Health, 1926.
40. GREENWOOD, M. *Epidemics and Crowd-Diseases.* New York, Macmillan, 1935.
41. GREENWOOD, M., and COPEMAN, S. *Public Health and Medical Subjects: No. 36, Diet and Cancer.* London, Ministry of Health, 1926.
42. HALL, M. F. *Public Health Statistics* (ed. 2). New York, Paul B. Hoeber, Inc., 1950.
43. HAMER, SIR W. *Epidemiology Old and New.* New York, Macmillan, 1929.
44. HARDING, W. G. The influence of syphilis in cancer of the cervix uteri. *Cancer Research 2:* 59-61, 1942.
45. HARNETT, W. L. A statistical report on 2529 cases of cancer of the breast. *Brit. J. Cancer 2:* 212-239, 1948.

46. HAUSER, I. J., and WELLER, C. V. A further report on the cancer family of Warthin. *Am. J. Cancer 27:* 434-449, 1936.
47. HAWKINS, J. W. Evaluation of breast cancer therapy as a guide to control programs. *J. Nat. Cancer Inst. 4:* 445-460, 1944.
48. HOFFMAN, F. *The mortality from cancer throughout the world.* Newark, N. J., The Prudential Press, 1915.
49. HOFFMAN, F. *Cancer and Diet.* Baltimore, Md., The Williams & Wilkins Co., 1937.
50. HOWSON, J. Y. The procedures and results of the Philadelphia Committee for the Study of Pelvic Cancer. *Wisconsin M. J. 49:* 215-219, 1950.
51. HUEPER, W. C. Environmental and occupational cancer. Supplement 209, *Pub. Health Rep.*, 1948.
52. HUNTER, A. The inheritance of cancer in mankind. *Am. J. Cancer. 19:* 79-82, 1933.
53. JACOBSEN, O. *Heredity in Breast Cancer.* London, H. K. Lewis, 1946.
54. JACOBSON, P. H. A statistical study of cancer among diabetics. *Milbank Mem. Fund Quart. 26:* 90-118, 1948.
55. JOSLIN, E. P., and LOMBARD, H. L. Diabetes epidemiology from death records. *New England J. Med. 214:* 7-9, 1936.
56. KENNAWAY, E. L. The racial and social incidence of cancer of the uterus. *Brit. J. Cancer. 2:* 177-212, 1948.
57. KENNAWAY, E. L., and KENNAWAY, N. M. A further study of the incidence of cancer of the lung and larynx. *Brit. J. Cancer 1:* 260-298, 1947.
58. KING, R. A., and LEACH, J. E. Factors contributing to delay by patients in seeking medical care. *Cancer* 3: 567-579, 1950.
59. KWAN, K. W. Carcinoma of the esophagus: A statistical study. *Chinese M. J. 52:* 237-254, 1937.
60. LANE-CLAYPON, J. E. Cancer of the breast, and its surgical treatment. *Reports on Public Health and Medical Subjects,* No. 28, London, Ministry of Health, 1924.
61. LANE-CLAYPON, J. E. A further report on cancer of the breast. *Reports on Public Health and Medical Subjects,* No. 32, London, Ministry of Health, 1926.
62. LANE-CLAYPON, J. E. Cancer of the uterus. *Reports on Public Health and Medical Subjects,* No. 40, London, Ministry of Health, 1927.
63. LANE-CLAYPON, J. E. Report on the late results of operation for cancer of the breast. *Reports on Public Health and Medical Subjects,* No. 51, London, Ministry of Health, 1928.
64. LANE-CLAYPON, J. E. Report on cancer of the lip, tongue, and skin. *Reports on Public Health and Medical Subjects,* No. 59, London, Ministry of Health, 1930.
65. LANE-CLAYPON, J. E. Incurable cancer. *Reports on Public Health and Medical Subjects,* No. 66, London, Ministry of Health, 1931.
66. LAZARUS-BARLOW, W. S., and LEEMING, J. H. Natural duration of cancer. *Brit. M. J. 2:* 266-267, 1924.
67. LEACH, J. E., and ROBBINS, G. F. Delay in the diagnosis of cancer. *J.A.M.A. 135:* 5-8, 1947.
68. League of Nations. Presented to the Health Committee on Behalf of the Commission by Sir George Buchanan (President). Report on the Work of the Cancer Commission for the Years 1923 to 1927. November 1927, III. *Health,* 1927, III. 17.
69. LEES, J. C., and LEES, T. W. Numerical estimation in cancer and cancer treatment. *Cancer 3:* 377-409, 1950.

70. LEVIN, M. L. The epidemiology of cancer: From the viewpoint of the Health Officer. *Am. J. Pub. Health 34:* 611-620, 1944.
71. LEVIN, M. L. Cancer reporting in New York State. *New York State J. Med. 44:* 880-883, 1944.
72. LEVIN, M. L., GOLDSTEIN, H., and GERHARDT, P. Cancer and tobacco smoking; A preliminary report. *J.A.M.A. 143:* 336-338, 1950.
73. LEVIN, M. L., and GOLDSTEIN, H. Cancer incidence, mortality, and expectancy in upstate New York. *Cancer Control Booklet,* Office of Public Health Education, New York State Department of Health, 1949.
74. LEVIN, M. L., KRESS, L. C., and GOLDSTEIN, H. Syphilis and cancer. Reported syphilis prevalence among 7,761 cancer patients. *New York State J. Med. 42:* 1737-1745, 1942.
75. LOMBARD, H. L., and POTTER, E. A. Environmental factors in the etiology of cancer. *De L'union Internationale Contre Le Cancer 6:* 1325-1333, 1950.
76. LOMBARD, H. L. Studies on the familial aspects of cancer. *New England J. Med. 218:* 711-713, 1938.
77. LOMBARD, H. L., and POTTER, E. A. Epidemiological aspects of cancer of the cervix. *Cancer 3:* 960-967, 1950.
78. LOMBARD, H. L. Study of educational techniques used in a cancer program. *Massachusetts Health J. 31:* 12-13, 1950.
79. LOMBARD, H. L., and JOSLIN, E. P. Certification of death of 1,000 diabetic patients. *Am. J. Digest. Dis. 14:* 275-278, 1947.
80. LOMBARD, H. L., LEVIN, M. L., and WARREN, S. Multiple malignant growths. *Cancer Research 6:* 436-440, 1946.
81. LOMBARD, H. L., and DOERING, C. R. Treatment of the fourfold table by partial association and partial correlation as it relates to public health problems. *Biometrics 3:* 123-128, 1947.
82. LOMBARD, H. L., TULLY, M. R., and POTTER, E. A. Evaluation of the cancer educational program in Massachusetts. *Human Biol. 16:* 115-125, 1944.
83. LUND, C. C. Pathology of carcinoma of the buccal mucosa in relation to results of treatment. *New England J. Med. 209:* 126-131, 1933.
84. LUND, C. C., and HOFFMAN, V. The accuracy of death certificate diagnoses in cases of buccal carcinoma. *New England J. Med. 209:* 719-722, 1933.
85. MACDONALD, E. J. Accuracy of the cancer death records. *Am. J. Pub. Health 28:* 818-824, 1938.
86. MACDONALD, E. J. The present incidence and survival picture in cancer among females in Connecticut, 1935-1946. *J. Am. M. Women's A. 3:* 152-162, 1948.
87. MACDONALD, E. J. The present incidence and survival picture in cancer and the promise of improved prognosis. *Bull. Am. Coll. Surgeons 33:* 75-93, 1948.
88. MACDONALD, E. J. The common health, cancer. *Massachusetts Dept. Pub. Health 21:* No. 4, 1934.
89. MACHLE, W., and GREGORIUS, F. Cancer of the respiratory system in the United States chromate-producing industry. *Pub. Health Rep. 63:* No. 35, USPHS, 1948.
90. MACKLIN, M. T. Pitfalls in dealing with cancer statistics, especially as related to cancer of the lung. *Dis. of Chest 14:* 525-533, 1948.
91. MACKLIN, M. T. Inheritance and human cancer. *Ohio State M. J. 43:* 836-840, 1947.
92. MARBLE, A. Diabetes and cancer. *New England J. Med. 211:* 339-349, 1934.
93. MARTIN, H. E. Five year end-results in the treatment of cancer of the tongue, lip, and cheek. *Surg., Gynec. & Obst. 65:* 793-797, 1937.

94. Martin, H. E. Five year end-results in the treatment of cancer: Cancer Control in Public Health. Presented at the Cancer Symposium, New York City, 1943, Public Health Cancer Association of America.
95. Martynova, R. P. Studies in the genetics of human neoplasms: 1. Genetics of cancer of the breast based upon 201 family histories. *Am. J. Cancer 29:* 530-540, 1937.
96. Maynard, G. D. A statistical study in cancer death rates. *Biometrika 7:* 276-304, 1910.
97. McClendon, J. F. The statistical relation between goiter and cancer. *Am. J. Cancer 35:* 554-558, 1939.
98. McKinnon, N. E. Breast cancer mortality, Ontario, 1909-1947. *Canad. J. Pub. Health 40:* 257-269, 1949.
99. McKinnon, N. E. Cancer mortality trends under different control programs. *Canad. J. Pub. Health 41:* 7-14, 1950.
100. Metropolitan Life Insurance Co. Recent gains in cancer control. *Stat. Bull. 28:* 1-4, 1947.
101. Metropolitan Life Insurance Co. International variation in longevity. *Stat. Bull. 31:* 1-3, 1950.
102. Nathanson, I. T., and Welch, C. E. Life expectancy and incidence of malignant disease: I. Carcinoma of the breast. *Am. J. Cancer 28:* 40-53, 1936.
103. Nathanson, I. T., and Welch, C. E. Life expectancy and incidence of malignant disease: III. Carcinoma of the gastro-intestinal tract. *Am. J. Cancer 31:* 457-466, 1937.
104. Nathanson, I. T., and Welch, C. E. Life expectancy and incidence of malignant disease: V. Malignant lymphoma, fibrosarcoma, malignant melanoma and osteogenic sarcoma. *Am. J. Cancer 31:* 598-608, 1937.
105. Pack, G. T., and Gallo, J. S. Culpability for delay in the treatment of cancer. *Am. J. Cancer 33:* 443-462, 1938.
106. Pack, G. T., and Livingston, E. M. *Treatment of Cancer and Allied Diseases.* (Vol. I). New York, Paul B. Hoeber, Inc., 1940.
107. Pearl, R. Cancer and tuberculosis. *Am. J. Hyg. 9:* 97, 1929.
108. Pearl, R. *Introduction to Medical Biometry and Statistics* (ed. 3). Philadelphia, W. B. Saunders Co., 1940.
109. Peller, S. Metachronous multiple malignancies in 5,876 cancer patients. *Am. J. Hyg. 34:* 1-11, 1941.
110. Peller, S. Race, stock and environment in human cancer. *J. Hered. 35:* 175-181, 1944.
111. Penrose, L. S., MacKenzie, H. J., and Karn, M. N. A genetical study of human mammary cancer. *Brit. J. Cancer 2:* 168, 1948.
112. Potter, E. A. The changing cancer death rate. *Cancer Research 7:* 351-355, 1947.
113. Potter, E. A. Small sample surveys as adapted to a cancer program. *Am. J. Pub. Health 36:* 1124-1128, 1946.
114. Potter, E. A. The New Bedford survey. *Bull. Am. Cancer Soc. 27:* No. 7, 1945.
115. Potter, E. A., and Tully, M. R. The statistical approach to the cancer problem in Massachusetts. *Am. J. Pub. Health 35:* 485-490, 1945.
116. Registrar-General's Decennial Supplement. *England and Wales, Part II. Occupational Mortality, Fertility, and Infant Mortality, 1921.* London, His Majesty's Stationery Office, 1927.

117. Registrar-General's Decennial Supplement. *England and Wales, Part IIa. Occupational Mortality, 1931.* London, His Majesty's Stationery Office, 1938.
118. ROBBINS, G. F., CONTE, A. J., LEACH, J. E., and MACDONALD, M. Delay in diagnosis and treatment of cancer. *J.A.M.A. 143:* 346, 1950.
119. SCHEELE, L. A. Tar in air may cause cancer. *Science News Letter*, May 13, 1950.
120. SCHEELE, L. A. Air pollution as a health problem. Delivered at the United States Technical Conference on Air Pollution, Wardman Park Hotel, Washington, D. C., May 4, 1950.
121. SCHERESCHEWSKY, J. W. The course of cancer mortality in the ten original registration states for the 21-year period, 1900-1920. *Pub. Health Bull.*, No. 155, 1925.
122. SORSBY, M. *Cancer and Race: The Incidence of Cancer Among Jews.* New York, William Wood & Co., 1931.
123. STERN, C. *Principles of Human Genetics.* San Francisco, Calif., W. H. Freeman & Co., 1949.
124. STEVENSON, T. H. C. "The relation of cancer to syphilis and alcoholism." In *Report of the International Conference on Cancer, London, 17th-20th July, 1928.* New York, William Wood & Co., 1928.
125. STOCKS, P. Cancer and goitre. *Biometrika 16:* 364-401, 1924.
126. STOCKS, P. Some further notes on cancer and goitre distributions. *Biometrika 17:* 159-164, 1925.
127. STOCKS, P., and KARN, M. N. On the relation between the prevalence of thyroid enlargement in children and mortality from cancer and other diseases. *Ann. Eugen. 2:* 395-404, 1927.
128. STOCKS, P., and MACKAY, R. Cancer mortality in England and Wales. *Month. Bull. Min. Health & Emerg. Pub. Health Lab. Serv. 5:* 172-180, 1946.
129. TANNENBAUM, A. Relationship of body weight to cancer incidence. *Arch. Path. 30:* 509-517, 1940.
130. THOMAS, G. M. A report on cancer of the skin. *Reports on Pub. Health & Med. Subjects*, No. 70, London, Ministry of Health, 1933.
131. VIDEBAEK, A. Familial leukemia. *Acta med. Scandinav. 127:* 26-52, 1947.
132. WAINWRIGHT, J. M. A comparison of conditions associated with breast cancer in Great Britain and America. *Am. J. Cancer 15:* 2610-2645, 1931.
133. WARREN, S. The relation of chronic mastitis to carcinoma of the breast. *Surg., Gynec. & Obst. 71:* 257-273, 1940.
134. WARREN, S., and EHRENREICH, T. Multiple primary malignant tumors and susceptibility to cancer. *Cancer Research 4:* 554-570, 1944.
135. WARREN, S., and GATES, O. Multiple primary malignant tumors: A survey of the literature and a statistical study. *Am. J. Cancer 16:* 1358-1414, 1932.
136. WARREN, S., and GATES, O. Cancer of the skin in relation to multiple malignant growths. *J.A.M.A. 115:* 1705-1707, 1940.
137. WELCH, C. E., and NATHANSON, I. T. Life expectancy and incidence of malignant disease: II. Carcinoma of lip, oral cavity, larynx and antrum. *Am. J. Cancer 31:* 238-252, 1937.
138. WELCH, C. E., and NATHANSON, I. T. Life expectancy and incidence of malignant disease: IV. Carcinoma of the genitourinary tract. *Am. J. Cancer 31:* 586-597, 1937.
139. WELLS, D. B. An audit of the treatment of breast cancer at the Hartford Hospital, 1932-1939. *Connecticut State M. J. 14:* 3-15, 1950.

140. WELLS, H. G. *The nature and etiology of cancer.* *Am. J. Cancer 15:* 1919-1968, 1931.

141. WHIPPLE, G. C. *Vital Statistics* (Ed. 2). New York, Wiley, 1923.

142. WILCOX, W. F. *Studies in American Demography.* Ithaca, New York, Cornell University Press, 1940.

143. WILCOX, W. F. On the alleged increase of cancer. *Pub. Am. Statist. Ass. 15:* 701-782, 1917.

144. WILKERSON, H. L. C., and KRALL, L. P. Diabetes in a New England Town: A study of 3,516 persons in Oxford, Massachusetts. *J.A.M.A. 135:* 209-216, 1947.

145. WILSON, E. B. Morbidity and the association of morbid conditions. *J. Preventive Med. 4:* 27-38, 1930.

146. WILSON, E. B., and MAHER, H. C. Cancer and tuberculosis with some comments on cancer and other diseases. *Am. J. Cancer 16:* 227-250, 1932.

147. WYARD, S. Natural duration of cancer. *Brit. M. J. 1:* 206-207, 1925.

148. WYNDER, E. L., and GRAHAM, E. A. Tobacco smoking and bronchiogenic carcinoma. *J.A.M.A. 143:* 329-336, 1950.

149. YOUNG and RUSSELL. *Medical Research Council Special Report* No. 99, 1910-1912. London, His Majesty's Stationery Office, 1926.

150. YULE, G. U., and KENDALL, M. G. *An Introduction to the Theory of Statistics* (Ed. 14). London, Charles Griffin & Company, 1950.

PART IV

Practical Applications

CHAPTER 28

Evaluation of Diagnostic Tests

Freddy Homburger

The past decade has seen considerable improvement in cure rates for cancer obtained by conventional methods of surgery and radiation. It is doubtful how much these results can be improved by a further perfecting of these technics. Next to a successful search for new curative methods, the greatest enhancement of results obtainable with conventional cancer therapy may be expected from public health activities. One of these is still more intensive education of the public, aimed at shortening the interval between the appearance of the first symptoms and the day the patient first consults a physician. Another promising approach would be the development of new means to enable the medical profession to arrive more rapidly at cancer diagnosis. The therapeutic methods for dealing with cancer as they are known and available to-day, even without further improvements, could yield a much greater proportion of cures if only it were possible to reduce the lapse of time between the onset of a carcinoma and its diagnosis, with the subsequent application of appropriate therapy. It is evident that the ideal way of achieving this would be a diagnostic test so specific and sensitive that it could be used to screen entire populations periodically for cancer, with rapidity and reliability. An essential of such a test would be its ability to detect the lesions at the earliest possible stage.

This evident necessity and the relatively poor yield of the existing diagnostic methods have inspired in the past decade or so numerous attempts aimed at discovering the diagnostic test for cancer that would answer all these requirements.

*METHODOLOGY OF EVALUATION OF DIAGNOSTIC TESTS**

One of the most fundamental problems in this field is the methodology required to determine whether any given procedure advocated as a diagnostic test fulfills the criteria necessary for it to be accepted as reliable.

STATISTICAL CRITERIA

The statistical requirements that must be met by such a procedure have been competently defined by Dunn and Greenhouse.[53] They demonstrated that, in order

* This chapter is based in part on a review by this author: "Evaluation of diagnostic tests for cancer." *Cancer 3:* 143-172, 1950.

to be acceptable as a screening test for cancer, a procedure must detect at least 90 per cent true positives, against 5 per cent false positives at the most. Consideration of a population survey demonstrates why such high standards of performance are indispensable. If a community of 100,000 is to be screened for cancer, the number of individuals to be actually tested may be reduced to about 40,000, by taking into account only those over the age of 35, after which age cancer occurs more frequently than in younger individuals. On the basis of morbidity data, about 250 cancer cases per year might be expected. In the application of a test giving 10 per cent false positive reactions in healthy subjects, there would be 4225 positive test results, amongst which 250 actual cancer cases would still have to be identified.

Since the population so tested would probably be largely symptom-free and in apparent good health, extensive diagnostic precedures would have to be applied to individuate the cancer subjects amongst the group screened out by positive test results. The technical and economic difficulties of this situation make it obvious that a test with such a poor performance would be of no practical value.

The statistical methods used to determine the actual performance of a procedure are beyond the scope of this discussion and may be found in the monograph published by Dunn and Greenhouse. It may be mentioned here however, that the size of the sample groups necessary for judgement on a given procedure is an important element. It is apparent that a smaller group of samples is necessary to reject a procedure as poor than is required to prove an acceptable performance. Thus the tables of Dunn and Greenhouse show that if a test gives 27 per cent or more false negatives and 5 per cent false positives, a sample group of 25 normal individuals and 25 cancer cases will be sufficient to demonstrate its poor performance. The risk of accepting a poor test as an apparently acceptable one is considerable if samples of less than 100 patients are used, whereas it becomes considerably smaller with larger groups. It is also important to consider the natural frequency of various types of cancer and their sex incidence in the average population when collecting a group of patients to serve as the "cancer group" in the evaluation of a proposed test.

CLINICAL REQUIREMENTS

Although it is relatively simple to state the requirements for a procedure in terms of the percentage of false positive and false negative results that may be tolerated for it still to remain useful for early diagnosis of cancer, difficulties arise in the definition of "false positive" and "false negative" tests. This is a fundamental prerequisite in any methodology for the assessment of the clinical utility of a procedure advocated as a diagnostic test.

Evidently, a positive test result is the only acceptable answer in a patient in whom carcinoma has been diagnosed by conventional pathologic means or by the now (admittedly) reliable method of exfoliative cytology, and a negative result in such a patient would be a false negative test. Certain conditions might render a test result negative even in proven cancer. This might occur in advanced stages of the disease when chemotherapy or radiation were being given and perhaps inhibiting the tumor, or in the presence of concurrent disease or other complicating factors. Such a false negative result would not necessarily invalidate a procedure as a diagnostic tool and should be considered separately. A false negative test is thus not very difficult to define.

It is in the evaluation of the false positive result that obstacles arise which appear to be to some extent insurmountable. This may be illustrated as follows: If a diagnostic procedure were to give a number of positive results coinciding with the figure of statistical expectancy for a given group but none of the conventional clinical methods gave evidence of cancer in these subjects, should they be condemned as "false positive"? Might not some of these "false positives" indicate the existence of early and otherwise as yet undetectable cancer? This is a problem which only time will resolve, and it emphasizes the importance of programs for the long-term evaluation of diagnostic tests, with repeated checks on as many as possible of the "false positives" in the control group.

A related problem might arise. A patient with cancer may have undergone surgery and a previous positive test may have given place to a negative one after the operation. Since certain types of cancer are liable to recurrence after a variable period of time, would fresh positive tests in such an individual be indicative of a possibly still latent recurrence not detectable by other methods or would they be simply false positives?

"Activity" of Cancer

Varying degrees of neoplastic activity are mentioned by some investigators and sharp distinctions are made as to the moment in the development of a neoplastic lesion when it ceases to be latent, demonstrable perhaps by roentgen-ray examination but not yet indicating activity by other tests, and becomes active and detectable by a given procedure. Such situations raise questions which are extremely difficult, if not impossible, to answer, but an unfortunate aspect of their practical significance is that they may be used to gloss over poor results obtained by uncritical or biased researchers who are trying to demonstrate the efficacy of a particular diagnostic procedure for cancer.

SELECTION OF "CONTROL" SUBJECTS

It is extremently difficult to collect a matching control or "normal" group for comparison with a corresponding cancer group. A group of "normals" does not necessarily mean that there is the same degree of normalcy in all individuals in the group, and a group of cancer patients may offer a range from early cancer to far advanced lesions. In both groups there are basic factors, such as age, state of nutrition and activity, sex, and the presence of miscellaneous minor diseases which account for individual differences. It is thus manifestly unfair to compare a group of laboratory workers, medical students, and nurses as "controls" with a group of cancer patients representing all stages of the disease. It is often impossible to obtain relevant information from publications on cancer diagnostic tests on these important data. Even those who talk of varying degrees of "activity" of neoplastic lesions will unhesitatingly proceed to classify their own results in terms of those dealing with "cancer patients" versus those referring to "normals."

These brief considerations emphasize the need for a standardized methodology for the evaluation of diagnostic tests at the time of their publication. Such a methodology may not be perfect, and compromises may be necessary in situations presenting particular difficulty, such as those outlined above, but it must set minimum standards of acceptability for the specific purposes in view.

VARIOUS PURPOSES OF DIAGNOSTIC TESTS

It may be of interest to discuss briefly the various purposes for which diagnostic tests, such as those to be reviewed below, are designed, and also to list some of the principles underlying diagnostic tests as we know them today.

The early diagnosis of cancer in the screening of a population is not the only situation in which a diagnostic test would be advantageous. It is extremely desirable to have a procedure for the early detection of recurring cancer following a "cure" by surgery or radiation, in order to facilitate a second curative attempt at an early stage of the recurrence. It is also important to be able to measure indications of the changes of growth rate that neoplasms may undergo when subjected to chemotherapy. Thus it is possible, for example, to follow reasonably closely the response of leukemia to chemotherapy, since it is easy to take biopsies of blood and bone marrow and study the changes as they occur. The general response of carcinoma of the prostate to such therapeutic measures as castration or hormonal therapy may also be observed to some extent, by measurement of the acid phosphatase activity of the blood, which increases with the acceleration of tumor growth and decreases as the tumor becomes quiescent.

It is almost impossible, however, to gauge the response to chemotherapy of such tumors as gastrointestinal carcinomas and indeed of the majority of neoplastic diseases. It is probably significant that the greatest progress in chemotherapy has been made in those neoplastic diseases where there are measurable characteristics of the disease, and observation of any alteration in biochemical or biologic factors paralleling changes in the rate of neoplastic growth can be of great value. Some procedures, for example, the antienzyme test of West,[203] therefore, are proposed for the specific aim of following changes as they occur in neoplasms during therapy, rather than as diagnostic tests. The evaluation of such behavior of biochemical phenomena paralleling presumable neoplastic growth activity is very difficult, since it is possible that the chemotherapeutic agent itself has unspecific effects on the organism which provoke changes simulating those of the regressing neoplasm.

Cancer diagnostic tests would also be invaluable in complex problems of differential diagnosis.

PRINCIPLES UNDERLYING DIAGNOSTIC TESTS

Diagnostic tests as they have been proposed up to the present are based upon two essential principles: the detection of substances produced by a tumor and the detection of changes occurring within the host owing to indirect effects of the tumor upon the host. Typical procedures falling within the first category are those for measuring the appearance of increased amounts of acid phosphatase in the blood of a certain percentage of patients with carcinoma of the prostate in certain stages of that disease, for the detection of atypical proteins in the blood stream or the urine in cases of multiple myeloma, and for recording the appearance in the urine of hormones produced by neoplasms of the adrenal gland.

Into the second category fall such procedures as those for the observation of changes of the gonadotropins in men with testicular tumors, of changes in the coagulation of the blood in cancer patients, of changes in the plasma protein patterns as measured by a variety of precipitation methods, of changes in urinary excretion patterns of steroid hormones, and of the appearance of a variety of biologically active substances in the urine.

The limitation of the procedures based on the first type of substance, that produced by the tumor, is that the tumor has to reach a considerable size before any such secretion products appear in measurable quantities in the body fluids of the host. With regard to the second type of substances, those which occur in the host owing to the indirect effect of the tumor upon it, it is usually an extremely sensitive group of substances which is susceptible to such changes, and the difficulty here is that a great many other entirely unspecific stresses, unrelated to cancer, will also readily produce the same kinds of changes in the host.

PROCESS OF EVALUATION OF DIAGNOSTIC TESTS FOR CANCER

According to the specific purpose for which a diagnostic procedure is destined (screening test, differential diagnostic test, a test to detect early recurrence or to follow the course of the tumor under chemotherapy or radiation), the minimal criteria for its acceptability and the mechanisms of its evaluation will vary.

REPRODUCIBILITY OF PROPOSED METHOD

Before the actual evaluation is made, the technical aspects of a laboratory procedure have to be carefully studied and its reproducibility by different operators using aliquots from the same specimen must be ascertained. It is essential that the end point of a procedure be objectively measurable and reproducible. The wide fluctuations in results obtained with some procedures are explainable on the basis of the subjective nature of the end point determination. This is true for Bolen's drying blood drop test[30] and for methods for the determination of whether or not serum protein has completely coagulated,[109, 110] as they are carried out in heat and other coagulation procedures, and for a number of other proposed diagnostic tests.

Before a true assessment of their intrinsic value can be made, procedures often have to be revised to make it feasible for observers in different laboratories to reproduce the same end results. If a procedure requires a variable substrate, as is the case for many tests based upon proteolysis and in certain immunologic tests where many steps are required to prepare an antigen from a biologic source, conclusive evaluation may be impossible unless there is a sufficient amount of a stable and readily available preparation on hand for the entire evaluation study. Even so, there is no guarantee that the production methods for such substrates or antigens are in turn exactly reproducible.

PHYSICAL STATE OF SPECIMEN

If a procedure proves to be reproducible by various observers in different laboratories, then it is advisable to determine whether it must be carried out on fresh sera or secreta or whether results are identical when done on frozen samples. If freezing does not alter the results of the test it will be possible to draw upon serum banks holding specimens taken from many patients—and sometimes repeatedly from the same subject—under varying conditions and stored together with clinical records for the purpose of test evaluations. Such serum banks exist as part of the U. S. Public Health Service testing program for cancer diagnostic tests. They enable the observer to ascertain in a short period of time how closely test results follow the course of the disease in patients from whom aliquots have been taken repeatedly over a period of months or years.

DIFFERENTIAL DIAGNOSIS

In the study of the performance of a differential diagnostic test, those cancer cases which present differential diagnostic problems are concentrated upon. For example, it was soon established that acid phosphatase is pathognomonic of cancer of the prostate if found elevated in the blood stream, but it was also found that this does not apply in all cases and that in about 20 per cent of subjects with metastases and in most cases without metastases no increase is found.

For the evaluation of a procedure designed to follow the course of the activity of neoplasia, cases of advanced cancer may be chosen and test results followed whilst the patients' responses are simultaneously recorded by roentgenographic and clinical observation. This may be done also throughout the pre- and postoperative courses of subjects undergoing surgery for cancer. This type of study must be controlled by investigation of the effects of operations performed for benign conditions.

SCREENING TESTS FOR CANCER

In the evaluation of screening tests, data may first be assembled on a group of healthy young adults. If these results are all negative, a group of patients with early but proven cancer may next be investigated. This group must be controlled by a series of healthy subjects of comparable age and sex distributions. As mentioned above, a relatively small sample of about 25 healthy individuals versus 25 cancer patients will be sufficient to demonstrate the tentative value of a procedure when the criteria of Dunn and Greenhouse are applied.

It is only after these preliminary studies have been successful that full-scale testing on larger groups is indicated. This type of rigid standardization has been applied to few procedures, and until now all so-called cancer tests thus evaluated have failed to perform satisfactorily and have been abandoned in some cases even by their originators.

The difficulty of fulfilling the above criteria does not mean that an effective screening test for cancer is impossible but it does show that the impressive work already done has not brought an acceptable solution, and that perhaps such a solution should be sought in new approaches that have not been well tested hitherto. It is with this thought in mind that the following critical survey of some of the more interesting biochemical procedures (Table 77) brought forward as diagnostic tests for cancer is presented.

TABLE 77. CLASSIFICATION OF PROCEDURES TO BE DISCUSSED*

Procedure
MORPHOLOGIC TECHNICS
Cytology†
Blood morphology†
Patterns of blood drop
TESTS BASED ON URINARY CONSTITUENTS
Decoloration of redox dyes
Lactic acid
Sulfur
Reduced riboflavin excretion
Changes in ascorbic acid excretion
Clotting effects on blood
Gonadotropic assay† (for testicular tumors and chorionic tumors)
Roffo's "gonadotropin"
Beard's "gonadotropin"
Aron's "adrenotropin"
Abortive factor
Lethal factor
"Oxyproteid acid"
Aromatic substances
Bence-Jones protein†
CHEMICAL CHANGES IN BLOOD
K, Mg, and Hb liberated by blood clot
Fats and lipids, saponification values
Sedimentation rate of R.B.C.'s
Hydrophile albumin
Protein precipitation tests in plasma and serum, using:
Copper acetate
Tannic acid and carbol fuchsin
Sodium vanadate
Sodium vanadate and heat (56° C.)
Magnesium chloride
Citric acid and potassium iodide
Nitric acid
Distilled water
Ricinoleic acid
Hydrochloric, acetic, and sulfosalicylic acid
Nitrochloraldehyde
Heat
Heat coagulation prevented by iodoacetic acid
Gelification of blood by lactic acid
Lecithin precipitation
Electrophoretic changes of blood proteins
Mucoprotein
Proteoses
Congo red absorption
Neutral red changes
Surface tension of serum
Decoloration of redox dyes
CHEMICAL CHANGES IN BODY SECRETIONS
Stomach juice:
Decoloration of methylene blue
Physical chemical study
Achlorhydria
Lactic acid
Effusions:
Glycolysis (lactic acid)
IMMUNOLOGIC CHANGES
"Defense proteases"
Urinary antigen against Aron's "adrenotropin"
Cytotoxins
Hemolysins
Cytolysins
Antibody fixation by guinea-pig serum
Fixation of complement
Skin test with "cancer fatty acid"
Inhibition of growth of tissue cultures
Antibody-antigen reactions
ENZYMOLOGIC CHANGES
Acid phosphatase†
Alkaline phosphatase†
Effect of zinc ions on alkaline phosphatase
Enzyme inhibitors
Peptidases
Hemolysins
Proteolytic enzymes
Antifibrinolysins
Lipase
"Pentolysine"

* This Table is taken in part from a previous review by the author. (See footnote, p. 815).
† Indicates procedures of some established diagnostic value.

REVIEW OF PROPOSED "DIAGNOSTIC TESTS"

It is felt that a useful purpose will be served in reviewing the various procedures that have appeared in cancer research literature with claims to diagnostic value. Some of these tests have been proved to be of no value, some have not been fully evaluated, and others would not stand up to the minimal technical criteria outlined above. A certain number of these procedures will have to be reinvestigated, and some old ideas may prove to be of merit if modern methods can be applied to them. Some procedures have been included that may possibly lend themselves to adaptation for diagnostic purposes, although originally they were not claimed to have diagnostic significance but were described for their biologic interest.

This presentation is obviously incomplete and at the risk of omitting some findings that might unexpectedly gain significance later on, attention has been given only to those procedures that have a reasonable experimental basis.* There may also be procedures based upon sound methods that have escaped the author's attention.

Procedures that are specific for certain types of tumors, such as the uptake of radioactive iodine by functional thyroid neoplasms or the excretion of certain hormones by subjects with testicular, adrenal, or other functional endocrine tumors, will not be included here. Purely morphologic technics, such as the various modifications of the Papanicolaou method or the visualization of tumors by contrast media and roentgen-ray technics and other accepted diagnostic methods, will also be omitted. Some of these are discussed in other chapters of the book.

A classification of the "diagnostic" methods that have been proposed is desirable, and the following scheme has been adopted:

1. Tests based on chemical changes in urine, blood, and body secretions.
2. Tests based on immunologic principles, in urine, blood, and secretions.
3. Tests based on enzymologic principles, in urine, blood, tissues and secretions.

TESTS BASED ON CHEMICAL CHANGES

CHEMICAL CHANGES IN URINE

Lactic Acid

Gleassner[84] described the appearance of lactic acid in the urine of patients with cancer following intravenous injection of dextrose. This finding has a sound basis in the voluminous literature on lactic acid as a metabolite of cancerous tissues, which begins as early as 1910 with the observations of Fulci,[80] who demonstrated high levels of lactic acid in tumor tissue. This finding has been confirmed by many workers and was quantitated by Warburg, Wind, and Nagelin,[199] who found 40 to 50 mg. of lactic acid per ml. blood drawn from malignant tumors. It has been calculated that human carcinoma produces lactic acid to the extent of approximately 10 per cent of its dry weight in one hour.[41, 187] These large amounts of lactic acid are partly neutralized in the tissues and by the buffer activity of the blood, and reach the liver as sodium lactate, where they are metabolized. It is only in the presence of liver dysfunctions that the blood lactic acid level may be significantly elevated.[79]

From these data, it would appear that lactic acid excretion in the urine would be likely to reach significant levels in the presence of large tumor masses, and perhaps more readily in the presence of associated liver disease, but that it would be

* The following reviews were consulted and are considered to contain reliable and valuable information: Bing and Marangos,[22] Furuhjelm,[82] Hinsburg,[105] and Woodhouse.[210]

unlikely to be of any value for early diagnosis anywhere excepting possibly in an enclosed cavity surrounding a tumor, where the metabolic process would not readily destroy lactic acid as it accumulated.

Sulfhydryl Groups

In 1923, Fuhs and Lintz[79] described the decoloration of methylene blue by urine as occurring only in cancer patients and not in normal subjects. They made the reservation that there were "a few other" conditions, such as acute rheumatism and nephritis, in which their test was positive. The reduction of methylene blue in blood has more recently been used as a diagnostic test for cancer (see later) and has been shown to depend largely on the number of sulfhydryl ions.[187] A great many conditions are known which will promote tissue catabolism and will result in an increase of sulfur in the urine, producing reduction of methylene blue. Salomon and Saxl[175, 176] based one of their urine tests on the presence of sulfur in the urine but Romani, in evaluating this procedure, found it positive in only 40 per cent of the cancer cases and concluded that this test is not specific for cancer.

Amino Acids

Preliminary work on amino acid excretion in patients with cancer, chiefly leukemia, has been done by Young[212] and showed variable amounts of amino acid and peptiduria, subject to changes with the degree of the disease and with chemotherapy, but in no way specific for cancer. More recently, Roberts, Ronzoni and Frankel[168] found that increases in free urinary glycine such as they found in some cancer patients also occurred when ACTH was administered.

Steroid Hormones

The work of Dobriner *et al.* on the excretion of steroid hormones in health and disease, conducted continuously since 1942, has resulted in basic findings of considerable interest and indisputable value, but so far has not been conclusive in terms of components that would characterize the cancer patient. Thirty-five α-ketosteroids and seven β-ketosteroids were isolated from human urines. One compound, Δ^9-etiocholenolone, has been found to be predominantly associated with neoplasia, but it was also found in essential hypertension and in Cushing's syndrome, as well as on rare occasions in patients in whom no evidence for cancer could be discovered during a prolonged period of observation. These studies, although productive of a large body of interesting data, are still far from any practical diagnostic application. They represent one avenue of approach that rests on a sound clinical and experimental basis and that may yet yield practical results in a diagnostic sense. They have produced evidence to show that in cancer and other diseases, changes in the urinary steroid excretory patterns exist and are detectable by sound and reproducible methods, (see page 687).

Vitamins

The interrelationships of vitamins and cancer have been the subject of numerous studies. Few papers are concerned with changes in urinary vitamin excretion, and although a decreased excretion of riboflavin has been claimed by Leeman,[128] this author has also found that the riboflavin tolerance test results were not abnormal.

Spellberg and Keeton[183] noted that the excretion of ascorbic acid in relation to saturation and utilization had some diagnostic implications in diseases with increased metabolic activity, including neoplasms.

Clotting Factor

Robertson[169] and also Hardesty and Love,[99] attributed to the urine of cancer patients the property of causing the blood of cancer patients to clot, whereas normal blood will not clot in the urine of cancer patients.

Bioassay Method

Bioassay methods represent a simple and often more sensitive tool than chemical methods for the detection of minimal amounts of biologically active substances whose structure may be as yet unknown. They have often been applied with varying degrees of technical acumen to the urine of cancer patients. The expansion of bioassays to include the microbiologic methods deserves further study by competent technicians in this field. The possibility that some micro-organism might require a factor that would exist only in secretions or urine of cancer subjects cannot be dismissed without proper investigation. It is certainly not impossible a priori that some material occurring in patients with cancer might be capable of producing measurable and reproducible changes in a test animal, such as the mouse or rat. Actually, the diagnosis of testicular tumors is possible by the measurement of urinary gonadotropins by bioassay.[193] These gonadotropins will be chorionic in nature, if chorionic elements are contained in the testicular tumor, or of pituitary origin, if testicular function is sufficiently destroyed. This method has proved to be a reliable diagnostic tool. However, other bioassay results so far reported have been disappointing.

Roffo[173] has claimed the demonstration of gonadotropins in the blood and urine of patients with cancer by a single injection of blood or urine (0.5 cc.) into immature rats. In the females, considerable hypertrophy of the genital tract occurred with the blood or urine from pregnant women or cancer patients. In males, hypertrophy of the testicles, seminal vesicles, and prostate ensued. The active principle, claimed to be a steroid named E, had been extracted by methods eliminating the proteins and was found to be fat-soluble. The active material also caused splenic hypertrophy.

These findings, if true, would constitute not only a diagnostic method for cancer but also the discovery of a new gonadotropin of steroid nature. This revolutionary finding was published in 1944 but has not been reliably confirmed anywhere outside Roffo's Institute.

In 1947, Beard[18] published no less sensational findings. He injected urine extracts from cancer subjects and obtained hypertrophy of the genital tract of rats, as well as splenomegaly in those animals that had received urine extracts from cancer patients.

The rationale of this procedure was the alleged existence of trophoblasts in cancer,[122] which would account for the active substance in the urine. It is again surprising that no confirmation has been forthcoming from any established laboratories on such a simple procedure, which would have the utmost practical importance if it were as accurate as is claimed. In the Report of the Council on Pharmacy and Chemistry,[46] it is observed of Beard's findings that "this work is considered to be in a highly experimental stage by the Council."

Recently, Wilt and Nicholson[204] found that "this biological test was of no value (in their hands) for the diagnosis of malignant tumors."

Klar[116] has found that a protein in the urine of cancer patients invariably caused abortion in pregnant mice, whereas control injections with material from noncancer urines caused abortion in seven of 23 cases in which this was tested. This study has not been verified.

Carcinogens have been sought in the urine of cancer patients, but these attempts met with failure.[32] Aron[8] has found that extracts of urine from patients with cancer cause specific changes in the adrenal cortex of rabbits when injected intraperitoneally. In a later paper which will be discussed in the section on immunology, Aron himself stated that this reaction was often difficult to interpret because of the variability of the adrenal cortex from animal to animal, and that this had resulted in many well-founded objections to and criticisms of his test. He discarded the test as impractical, but was able to evolve from it the immunologic procedure recently published.[68] Purjesz claimed that guinea pigs were killed within twenty-four hours after peritoneal injection of protein-free urine of patients with cancer.

Thus, with few exceptions, the results of bioassay procedures have been disappointing, but the failures of the past should not discourage efforts in these directions, especially since poor results may be traced largely to the imperfections in the methods used. The sum of the data obtained by bioassay is far from being in a state from which final conclusions could be drawn. This approach has not been followed systematically and much remains to be done.

Miscellaneous Urinary Constituents

Salomon and Saxl[175, 176] observed a polypeptide in urine of cancer patients, "oxyproteid acid," but this likewise was found not to be specific, and the methodology employed would hardly be adequate by modern standards. The same applied to findings on urinary cholesterol.[39]

The dilution factor for any substance derived from a tumor and excreted in the urine would be very great, in spite of its possible concentration by renal reabsorption. Probably such substances would be excreted in measurable amounts only in the presence of large amounts of tumor tissue, as in the instance of melanin in cases of melanoma. Urinary studies of anomalous components that might appear as end products of a metabolism disturbed by systemic effects of a tumor would merely express the end results of involved metabolic processes and stand a very small chance indeed of being specific.

However, the possibility that trace elements, antibodies, enzymes, or complex but well-defined chemical compounds, might appear in the urine of cancer patients at fairly early stages should not be dismissed before modern methodology has been applied to this problem. It is possible that there might be altered metabolic pathways of such compounds as amino acids or steroids that might be found to be reasonably specific in cancer patients. Work done in these directions has not resulted in conclusive findings so far and may serve to ilustrate the immense technical difficulties still to be surmounted in this field of study.

A long list of chemicals, which were thought at one time to appear in the urine only in the case of cancer, might be added. In 1911, J. Wolff[209] painstakingly reviewed the literature on the entire cancer problem, including diagnostic methods Most of the facts then gathered are now of only historical interest. Some of this old information, particularly that regarding an increase of aromatic substances in urine (skatol, indoxyl, and phenol), has been studied again more recently[2] and may deserve further attention.

CHEMICAL CHANGES IN BLOOD

The multitude of factors that assure homeostasis—the maintenance of normal quantitative relationships of the components normally occurring in the blood—render it extremely unlikely that metabolic changes caused by tumors at an early stage would be reflected in the circulating blood. Most of these components, if their normal concentration is exceeded, will be excreted, neutralized, or metabolized. Studies on such changes have been conducted chiefly on subjects with fairly advanced cancer, and even then results have rarely been conclusive. Owing to the imperfections of the methods, a study of the older literature is confusing and largely of historical interest.

Miscellaneous Substances

A review on this subject is found in Behan's[19] book. Some "specific" tests have been based on the determination of chemical components of blood, such as Link's test and that of Dannmeyer, both reviewed by Woodhouse.[210] In the former procedure, potassium, hemoglobin, and magnesium are measured in three successive samples of serum as they extrude from the blood clot. Calculation based on these data results in an arbitrary value that is "diagnostic." It is possible that this represents an indirect and complicated way of measuring hemolysis, which may be accelerated in patients with cancer.[48, 123] The second procedure rests upon the measurement of fats and lipids, together with determination of their acidity and saponification values. Some mathematics applied to the values yielded a "cancer number" of less than 100 in the normal subject, higher than 100 in cancer. Several Russian authors recently described a factor in serum from cancer patients that is toxic for the *Paramecium caudatum*, whereas normal serum does not have such toxicity. Egan[55] has lately reviewed the literature pertaining to this test and in experiments of his own came to the conclusion that such a toxic factor is indeed found in cancer serum. He feels, however, that both the specificity of the reaction and its adaptability to the clinical laboratory will have to be further investigated.

A number of miscellaneous substances in the blood, including vitamins, have, of course, been studied in this connection, but no evidence is available to raise our hopes of findings of diagnostic significance.

Lactic Acid

A difficult situation exists as regards lactic acid in the blood of cancer patients. Owing to its rapid metabolic utilization, there is no hope that it will be found elevated in the blood of patients with early cancer. Even in the presence of large tumors, blood lactic acid levels have been found abnormally and conclusively elevated only when there was simultaneous liver damage.[41, 209] No studies are recorded on the behavior of lactic acid in the blood of cancer patients following administration of large amounts of dextrose. Bueding and Goldfarb[40] report a slight rise in blood lactic acid and pyruvic acid in normal subjects, which returned to normal levels within two hours.

Proteins

It had been suggested first that plasma-protein substances might possibly be of indirect diagnostic value, because of their effect on the sedimentation rate of erythrocytes.[143] The literature on this subject is voluminous and contradictory. Thus, Moeschlin[149] found that the same method as that used by Mendel[143] was of no diagnostic value in his hands. There is no evidence to show that the sedimentation rate is accelerated in early cancer, and its value is strictly in the nature of a rough clinical screening test for various conditions, including carcinomatosis at fairly advanced states.

A great many reactions have been devised that are based on the precipitation of proteins, lipids, or lipoproteins from the blood serum by a variety of agents. These "tests" have been tabulated by Bing and Marangos[22] and some of them have been listed by Woodhouse.[210]

In Kahn's albumin test, the hydrophile portion of serum albumin is extracted and measured. Kahn believed this fraction was much reduced in cancer. In Vernes's test, plasma proteins are precipitated by increasing amounts of copper acetate, and a turbidimetric curve is derived. This is much the same principle as that of Weltmann's coagulation band. Wigand's test adopts the same principle, employing tannic acid and carbol fuchsin as precipitants. Bendien's test uses sodium vanadate as a precipitant. It has been complicated by Cronin Lowe by the repetition of the test several times after heating the serum to 56° C. Bruer's test determines the albumin-globulin ratio by precipitation with magnesium chloride. Botelho observed that citric acid enables iodine in potassium iodide to precipitate proteins more readily in the serum of cancer patients than in that of normal subjects. Itchikawa studied and modified Botelho's reaction. Another modification of Botelho's reaction was that of Mondain, Douris, and Beck, using nitric acid as a precipitant. Douris and Giquel employed distilled water as a precipitant. Izar employed ricinoleic acid. Lange and Heuer used silver nitrate, and Surányi, hydrochloric acid as well as acetic acid and sulfosalicylic acid. In the case of a positive test, no precipitate was obtained. The same principle, probably due to a protective colloidal effect of the larger globulin molecules, was observed by Vercelotti and Pavesi, who used nitrochloraldehyde, which caused no precipitate in cancer serum. Vernes used copper acetate, Kopaczewski lactic acid.

The accuracy of these various tests, tabulated by Bing and Marangos,[22] may be summarized as follows: For Bendien's test: 440 cancer cases, 72.2 to 96.3 per cent positive; 319 controls, 5.3 to 54.3 per cent false positive. For Botelho's test: 2932 cases, correctly positive from 52.4 to 91.5 per cent, correctly negative from 20 to 88.2 per cent. Izar's procedure: 75 to 92 per cent correctly positive, as high as 80 per cent false positive. Kahn's soluble albumin reaction: 739 control cases, 61.3 to 80.6 per cent correctly negative; 506 cancer cases, 67 to 96.6 per cent correctly positive. Lange and Heuer's procedure: 130 cancer cases gave 13 per cent strongly and 66.1 per cent weakly positive and 68 control cases only yielded 41.4 per cent negative findings. Surányi's test was 57 per cent positive in cancer cases and 47.8 per cent negative in controls. Wigand's test had approximately 85 per cent correctly positive and as high as 76 per cent false-negative results.

Heat Coagulation of Serum Proteins

More recently, heat coagulation, alone or combined with chemical precipitants, has been reviewed and studied by Huggins, Miller, and Jensen.[108] They found that neither the heat-coagulation defect nor the iodoacetic index as related to total protein was specific for cancer. At first they found their method "rather useful" as a diagnostic instrument, but since then they have abandoned the iodoacetate index to concentrate upon heat coagulation *per se* as related to the "least coagulable protein."

Interest in heat coagulation has thus been revived. Glass[85,86] had earlier found considerable overlapping of results of heat coagulation in patients with and without cancer, and following the wide publicity given the announcement of the iodoacetic acid test of Huggins *et al.*, Glass, in a letter to the Editor of *Cancer Research*, cautioned that the limitations of such tests should be thoroughly understood to avoid grave misunderstandings and great confusion. He emphasized the fact that there is no evidence that the test described by Huggins's group could be employed as a "cancer test" for screening patients.

Evaluation of the procedure was carried out in our laboratories on 536 cases. The results[107] indicate that the iodocetate-index test does not fulfill our criteria for a satisfactory diagnostic procedure. Since that time, others have also come to the same conclusion (Dvoskin and LaDue,[54] Pollak and Leonard[165]).

Studies by Bodansky[28] show that the factors upon which the iodoacetic reaction is based may be part of the unspecific syndrome of adaptation to stress.

Since it is well known that unspecific stresses may produce changes in the protein components of the blood, a number of the procedures already described may actually find their explanation in such unspecific changes produced by the stress of chronic disease.[28, 31]

These new developments will make it necessary, in the evaluation of many procedures, to investigate the possibility of their being subject to unspecific influences by the pituitary-adrenal system.

Some of these protein precipitation procedures are the predecessors of tests that were later found to be useful in obtaining rough estimates of the globulin content of serum, such as is done currently by use of the formol-gel method. Properly evaluated, the "lecithin" precipitation test, proposed in 1908 by Weil and Braun,[200] might perhaps have become the equivalent of Hanger's cephalin-flocculation test.

Electrophoresis of Plasma Proteins

With the advent of new and reproducible methods (e.g., electrophoresis) for the determination of plasma proteins, the large molecular substances of the plasma such as proteins and polysaccharides have received increased attention. Since there is no well-studied series of patients with chronic disease in whom electrophoresis has been done, all findings in cancer patients may be simply the result of chronic debilitation and not of cancer. Mider, Alling and Morton[148] published analyses of the electrophoretic findings in the plasma of 258 individuals with cancer, comparing them with "normal adults." Their findings in the cancer patients were similar to those of Seibert,[180] who earlier described an increase in α_2-globulin and polysaccharide content together with a decrease of total protein in cases of carcinoma. This paper suffers from the fault so common to many of these studies, that no distinction is made as to the stage or type of tumor. The "carcinomas" include "lesions of the lungs, colon, rectum, stomach, pancreas, liver, brain, temple, tongue, heart, uterus and cervix." There is no statement regarding the nutritional condition of these patients or the extent of carcinomatosis.

The first attempts at a careful correlation of electrophoretic findings in blood plasma of cancer patients with the clinical situation was made by Petermann.[162, 163] She studied electrophoretic patterns of patients with various types of lymphomas, and found no specific changes beyond those of chronic disease in general. In the case of cancer of the lungs and of the stomach, a mucoprotein was found that is probably identical with the mucoprotein described by Winzler.[205, 206, 207] This mucoprotein, at least in gastric cancer, did occur at fairly early stages of the disease. It may well be that some day a suitable chemical method will be developed for the measurement of these protein polysaccharides in the blood of patients with certain types of neoplastic disease. Evaluation of such a test by the methods already outlined might then become possible. The work of Shetler *et al.*[182] along this line has shown that this hope may not be justified, since they found that the serum polysaccharide level was not specific for cancer but in some cases was associated with cell proliferation.

In multiple myeloma, electrophoretic patterns are sometimes of help in arriving at the diagnosis, and prevent errors in treatment although unfortunately at present an early diagnosis in these cases is of little value to the patient, since we do not yet possess any effective therapeutic means against this disease.

Proteoses

Proteoses are substances of roughly 10,000 to 30,000 molecular weight, non-dialyzable through cellophane, and not precipitable by salt or acids at the concentration necessary to precipitate proteins. Winzler and Burk[205,] have studied extensively the proteoses in the serum of patients with cancer and in other conditions. They are not increased in early cancer nor do they have a high degree of specificity for cancer.

Physicochemical Methods

Some of the absorption tests, such as the retention of Congo red,[45] may be based on an increase of large molecular substances, as suggested by the in vitro findings of Munro.[152] A similar hypothesis was proposed by Brossa (quoted by Woodhouse[210]). However, even the original investigators quoted here[210] doubt the significance of the test, at least in vivo.

In this section on substances occurring in normal blood that may be changed in cancer patients, attention must again be called to the controversy regarding -SH groups, which are the basis for the decoloration of methylene blue by serum and have been discussed already.

The Roffo reaction deserves mention here. This is based on the appearance of a red tint when 0.26 cc. of 1:10,000 solution of Grübler's neutral red is added to 1 cc. of serum collected under paraffin. This method, which depends largely upon the *p*H of the mixture, has been the subject of considerable controversy, since most authors who did not belong to Roffo's Institute obtained inconclusive results, although Roffo's pupils accumulated thousands of correctly positive tests.[144, 150, 189] An evaluation of the reaction published in 1927[192] showed results from six sources, with an average accuracy of approximately 60 per cent in the positive cases and 40 per cent in the negative ones.

Ascoli and Izar[44] thought that in cancer the surface tension of serum was lowered when the serum was incubated with an antigen derived from tumor cells. This calls to mind possible effects of hyaluronidase described as being present in tumors.

Morphologic Elements of Blood

Mention should be made, in passing, of the many studies directed toward finding a characteristic for cancer in the appearance of the morphologic elements of the blood. These investigations have been reviewed by O. C. Gruner.[94] The situation is best summarized in the author's statement that "there is no specific blood picture in cancer, but attention is drawn to a pattern of changes which constitutes the guide to a diagnosis."

Bolen[30] has described a diagnostic test of high accuracy based on simple observation of the patterns of a drying blood drop. Evaluation of his procedure in our hands gave 58 per cent correct positive and 85 per cent correct negative findings. When Bolen himself repeated his procedure in our laboratory on 315 patients, his accuracy was close to that previously obtained by us in contrast to the high accuracy he had obtained in his own group. Hawk and his co-workers[101] recently found a considerably higher accuracy. The wide divergence of results obtained with this procedure, even by its originator, suggest that a more objective means of reading the end point must be found before objective evaluation becomes possible.

CHEMICAL CHANGES IN BODY SECRETIONS

Gastric Juice

Among all the body secretions that have been studied in the hope of discovering diagnostic characteristics for cancer, gastric juice probably ranks first. Ever since the use of gastric-juice aspiration by Boerhaave,[29] Monro Secundus (1767), and Philip Syng Physick (1768-1805), gastric juice has been readily available for study. It is surprising that although the diagnosis of gastric cancer has always been a serious problem and has become truly vital since curative resection has become possible, no diagnostic means of real value, other than roentgen-ray study, gastroscopy, and, lately, cytology has been discovered. All these methods, with the exception of cytology, rely upon the existence of a tumor large enough to be seen. Barrett concludes the chapter on "Diagnosis" in his scholarly review[13] on gastric cancer by the pessimistic statement that "there is much to emphasize the gravity of the situation but little to suggest a possible solution of the difficulties." The same reviewer cites seven innovations in diagnosis of gastric cancer since 1940: (1) the decoloration of methylene blue; (2) an electrogram;[121] (3) a dietoquimogram;[175] (4) a physicochemical method of study of gastric juice; (5) a method involving the determination of vitamin C in gastric tissue; (6) an electrocardiogastrograph;[60] (7) the pattern formed by a drying blood drop on a glass slide.[30]

These methods are recorded here to illustrate the complexity of the situation. No true improvement in early diagnosis of gastric cancer has been developed from any one of them so far.

Barrett gives the reasons why the finding of achlorhydria gastrica is in no way diagnostic of gastric cancer. The somewhat indirect relationship between achlorhydria and gastric cancer has, however, enabled Rigler materially to increase the proportion of gastric cancer detectable in roentgen-ray population surveys, if these are limited to subjects with achlorhydria.[167, 188]

A vast body of information was accumulated in the 1920's and 1930's on the possible diagnostic value of high concentrations of lactic acid in gastric juice. Much of this discussion, however, is based on poorly established facts, for the Uffelman reaction, which had been used by many of these investigators, was shown by Norpoth and Kaden[156] in 1933 to be all too insensitive and often negative in the presence of lactic acid. Similar findings have been obtained in our laboratory, in comparing the results of the ferric chloride tests with those obtained by quantitative methods.

The first critical and well-controlled work on the subject of gastric cancer and lactic acid was done by Robertson and his co-workers in the late 1920's, and the historical development of the problem is reviewed in Robertson's monograph.[171] They concluded that "lactic acid frequently occurs in the stomach when there is no reason whatsoever to suspect carcinoma. The theory that its production is due to specific action of the cancer cells therefore appears untenable."

The work of Rigler[167] has conclusively demonstrated the value of gastric analysis in its streamlined form as a screening test, using histamine as a stimulant. The recent technical improvements in exfoliative cytology have made reliable and early diagnosis of gastric cancer by this means quite likely in the foreseeable future but this does not obviate the need for continued biochemical research on the gastric secretions as a possible means for the early diagnosis of cancer by biochemical procedures.

Effusions

Exudates and transudates are another type of body fluid in which chemical substances produced by tumors may be expected to accumulate. Such fluid collections, although occurring late in neoplastic disease, often offer difficulties for differential diagnosis. In addition, because the exudates and transudates are not readily in equilibrium with the circulating blood, they offer an excellent medium for research and for exploration of the potentialities of methods which might be diagnostic for cancer.

A recent paper from the Mayo Clinic[164] deals only with the morphology of cells found in such fluids and with the determination of specific gravity. This demonstrates the lack of any biochemical method of diagnostic value in the study of such fluids. The results of the specific-gravity determination showed that there was an overlap between the characteristics of exudates and transudates in effusions shown to be caused by neoplastic disease. This fact is to be expected, since neoplasms can cause mechanical obstruction as well as inflammatory reactions, and it further confuses a situation that is already complicated. In addition to the classical means of differentiating an exudate from a transudate, such as cytology (including white-cell counts), measurements of protein content or specific gravity, there are some findings in the literature that deserve further investigation and might turn out to be helpful in cancer diagnosis. Once more, lactic acid is high among possible substances of value. In enclosed fluid collections, ideal conditions for study prevail for the reasons just outlined. It is possible to study the end product of glycolysis (lactic acid) simultaneously with the substrate (glucose) and at the same time to study the concentrations of these compounds existing in the blood.[61, 82, 137, 179] This has been done by several authors and the sum of their findings can be stated thus: In bacterial exudates, the lactic acid content is very high, often four times that of the blood, and the sugar concentration is low, often lower than blood sugar. In the simple transudate caused by mechanical obstruction, both lactic acid and sugar are present in the concentrations in which they are found in blood. In the "neoplastic exudate," lactic acid is high, but not quite so high as in infectious effusions, and the sugar levels are not below those of the blood. These data are based on good experimental evidence and are worthy of further investigation.

Fishman and co-workers have recently studied the level of activity of β-glucuronidase as well as the lactic acid content in exudates surrounding tumors (see p. 610). This seemed logical, since high concentrations of this enzyme usually occur in tumor biopsies. Indeed, it was found that high levels of β-glucuronidase activity prevailed in some exudates containing tumor cells but that this was not constant. Autopsy studies of the patients in this series showed that mechanical factors such as compression of large vessels leading to transudation and detection of tumor exudates probably account for the marked differences of enzyme concentrations observed in exudates. Thus β-glucuronidase levels in exudates are not in themselves diagnostic except when high values are found but they may be used to detect those peritumoral exudates which are most likely to contain other tumor metabolites.

TESTS BASED ON IMMUNOLOGIC PRINCIPLES

In Urine

Abderhalden's "defense" reaction may be placed somewhere between the immunologic and the enzymologic procedures that have been suggested for the diagnosis of cancer. This reaction is based on the formation of "defensive" proteases in the blood, which allegedly have the property of breaking down specifically those proteins in response to which they were formed by the organism. These proteases were first measured in the blood, by the methods described hereafter, and later in the urine. The latter procedure may be considerably simpler and of more practical significance, if proved specific, than the serum determinations would be. Abderhalden[1] briefly reviewed the work on this reaction in 1946, in a note to the *Swiss Medical Journal*, and concluded that "we have in this reaction without doubt the best means for the diagnosis of cancer known so far." This paper also contains a table showing the percentage of accuracy obtained with the reaction on various types of cancer. These percentages vary from 70.59 to 100 per cent. The total number of cases was 196, about one half being cancers of the stomach, the remainder distributed among cancer of the intestines, liver, bile duct, pancreas, lung, and miscellaneous organs. No comment was made concerning the stage of the disease, the nutritional condition of the patients, or the absence or presence of complications. No data were reported on cases known not to have cancer. Brief mention was made of the fact that the test was negative for sarcoma. The reaction was also negative in advanced stages of the disease.

The technic of this reaction is relatively simple. The proteinase can be precipitated from the urine by the use of alcohol or acetone at *p*H 7. The precipitate is taken up in isotonic solution of sodium chloride, and an aliquot of this suspension is incubated together with a protein substrate (tumor extracts, in the case of cancer diagnosis) for sixteen hours at 37° C. A control serum minus substrate is likewise incubated. The mixture is then deproteinized and the amino nitrogen (ninhydrin) and total nonprotein nitrogen are determined. This is done by a number of methods, chemical, colorimetric, or optical.

A voluminous literature has accumulated on this reaction, dealing chiefly with technical modifications. Some of the studies made in an attempt to evaluate this method have indicated results somewhat less impressive than those of the originator. In a series of 170 cancer patients, Tetzner[189] found that 129 gave negative reactions, 30 were positive, and 11 doubtful. On the other hand, Tuno[192] reported that of 116 patients with gastric cancer, 103 were positive, and of 28 with gastric ulcers, 27 were negative, while the lone positive one later proved to have an ulcer-cancer. In 12 healthy individuals, no false positives were obtained. After the removal of tumors, the proteases disappeared from the urine.

There has been much discussion as to the soundness of the assumptions behind this test as applied to the diagnosis of pregnancy as well as in connection with the cancer problem. This academic question cannot be answered easily. On the other hand, the reaction could be standardized by the preparation of uniform tumor substrates, and the methods used in its chemistry are reproducible. It is one of the "tests" that could be conclusively evaluated by the application of the principles outlined in the first part of this chapter. So far, such principles have not been applied in any of the studies designed for the evaluation of the procedure.

Fontaine, Aron, and Buck[68] have published a procedure that stands halfway between immunologic tests in urine and blood. They use a urine extract as an "antigen," which is precipitated by an antibody contained in the serum of patients with cancer. The history of this test is interesting. In 1933, Aron observed characteristic changes in the adrenal cortex of rabbits that were given intraperitoneal injections of urine extracts obtained from cancer patients. He also found that the injection of serum from a rabbit thus treated into another rabbit protected the latter's adrenal cortex from the effects of cancer urine. It thus appeared that the urine extracts from cancer patients behaved like an "antigen," causing the appearance of neutralizing antibodies in the blood. Aron was cautious in explaining that the term "antigen" should not be used in its strict immunologic sense and had merely been adopted to render the discussion more convenient. He argued, though, that perhaps the blood of cancer patients, like that of rabbits injected with urine extracts, might contain an "antibody" capable of precipitating such urine extracts from aqueous solutions. The technic of the test is described in detail in the paper quoted.

According to its originator, the following results have been obtained: Of 34 cases of cancer, each given with histologic diagnosis and duration of disease, 39 reactions were done; 34 were positive, 2 were negative, and 3 doubtful. Of 66 cases with various noncancerous diseases, 61 were negative, 3 were doubtful, and 1 was positive.

Verification of these results will have to be awaited. It seems possible that this test does not actually represent an immunologic procedure, but another "salting out" method, in this case by a complex copper salt formed by heating copper sulfate with an amorphous urinary extract. If this were so, its specificity would probably be reduced in the course of verification to the percentages found by the many precipitation procedures discussed earlier in this review.

Recently considerable newspaper publicity has been given to a test involving a precipitin reaction applied to serum of patients and using an antigen prepared from human cancerous livers. An extremely high degree of accuracy has been claimed by the originators. So far as we know, this accuracy has not been achieved by others using this test. Gottlieb and Kangas,[88] in 119 malignant cases, using an antigen prepared by Penn, achieved an accuracy of 73 per cent. In miscellaneous nonmalignant diseases, false positive results were obtained in 49 per cent. In the healthy group 95.4 per cent had a negative test.*

A great many difficulties are inherent in the preparation of an antigen from

* After this chapter had gone to press the following original articles by Penn and his group appeared: PENN, H. S. Tumor lipoids: I. Preparation of a serologically active nonsaponifiable fraction of liver of cancer-bearing patients. *J. Nat. Cancer Inst. 12*:1389-1399, 1952. HALL G. C., DOWDY, A. H., PENN, H. S., and BELLAMY, A. W. Tumor lipoids: II. Clinical Evaluation of a serologically active nonsaponifiable fraction of liver of cancer-bearing patients. *J. Nat. Cancer Inst. 12*:1399-1416, 1952.

human cancerous material. More recently, the same Penn group claimed excellent test results using a "synthetic" antigen. The results of an impartial investigation must be awaited to verify this claim.

In Blood and Tissues

The statement made by Greenstein,[89] that "for the most part the results of immunological studies have been controversial and inconclusive," applies to most of the work that will be discussed in this section. Nevertheless, the points of view of various researchers in this field are briefly presented in order to take an inventory of trends.

The modern methods of quantitative immunochemistry are attractive because of their accuracy and the possibility of detecting and measuring minute quantities of antigens and antibodies. The use of radioactive tracers attached to immune bodies offers new and practically unlimited approaches to the problem of immune response of the tumor host.

There is little doubt that true immunization to tumors exists in animals. This has been demonstrated in the case of transplantable tumors by Oswald and Kuttelwascher,[160] and by Gross.[90] Harris[100] demonstrated the formation of antibodies and cytotoxins in heterotransplantation, and a vast literature exists on this subject which is not directly pertinent to the situation prevailing in spontaneous tumors in man (see p. 357).

In the case of the Brown-Pearce tumor in the rabbit, the immunologic factors have received particularly close attention in the studies of Kidd and Friedenwald.[115] The findings of these authors are paralleled in part only by those of Jacobs and Houghton[111] and of Cheever.[42] The antibodies that have been described in animals with tumors as being formed against the provoking antigen are mostly precipitins. Cytotoxins,[32] hemolysins,[48] and proteases[78] have also been described. The last named have been mentioned already, and the hemolysins will be considered later with the enzymes, for they have been obtained from tumor extracts and are probably not immune bodies in the strict sense of that term.

Little methodologically sound work has been done on immune phenomena caused by neoplasms in man.

The studies of Mann and Welker[136] made use of the deposition in rabbits of small amounts of antigen prepared from carefully dissected and washed human tumor tissue suspended in aluminum cream.

The unspecific antibodies formed in response to blood and normal-tissue protein disappear at the end of a suitable interval, when the tissue stores of these antigens have presumably been exhausted, leaving tumor-specific precipitins in the rabbits' serums. This approach, which at first seemed promising, failed, however, when further study showed that the precipitins were actually less specific than had appeared at the outset.

In spite of the paucity of data on the question of whether or not malignant tumors in man are antigenic, and, if so, whether or not antibodies produced might be reasonably specific, there are a number of suggested "diagnostic" procedures based on "immunologic" mechanisms.

Lehmann-Facius' test (quoted in Woodhouse[210]) postulates a fixation of serum albumin by an antibody present in guinea-pig serum. The "antigen" is destroyed in normal blood by heating to 63° C. but is heat-stable in the serum of patients with cancer. Hirzfeld's test (quoted in Woodhouse[210]) is based on the fixation or derivation of the complement. The antigen employed is a cholesterinized tumor extract. Fry[73] employed alcoholic tumor extracts, serum, and a cholesterol emulsion, and measured the density of precipitation caused by cancer serum. Freund and Kaminer[69] postulate the existence in normal blood of a cytolysin capable of destroying cancer cells and base their "tests" on the demonstration of the survival of cancer cells in serum from cancer patients. Similar lines were followed by Kavetskiy. Freund and Kaminer also devised an in vivo test, whereby the injection of a tumor extract, presumably rich in a "cancer fatty acid," causes a firm nodule in the skin of the cancer patient but is inactive when injected into normal subjects. Of 261 cases of histologically proved cancer, 252 showed a positive reaction. Of 176 cases without cancer, 26 had a "false positive" reaction.

Bing and Marangos[22] are doubtful of the value of this cytolysin reaction. Their tabulation of the literature shows correctly positive findings in from 63 to 95.6 per cent of the cases and false-negative results in from 4.3 to 9.5 per cent. There are close to 20 per cent questionable results in some series and up to 21 per cent false-positive findings. In 1940, Maier and Christiani[132] finally concluded, after a close study of its mechanisms, that this reaction was totally unsuited to the diagnosis of cancer.

The procedure of Gruskin (quoted in Woodhouse[210]) is a modification of such a skin test and is based on the claim that the injection of an embryonic extract into the skin provokes an allergic response in subjects with cancer, who presumably have antibodies against embryonic tissues.

Moppett (quoted in Woodhouse[210]) claimed that the antibodies present in cancer serums inhibit the growth, in vitro, of tissue cultures of tumor cells.

A review of these procedures leaves the impression that much wishful thinking has blinded the objectivity of a great many investigators and contributed to the discredit of methods that have been shown to be accurate and reliable in other fields of biology, if properly used and controlled. It is highly desirable that an attempt be made to elucidate the important immunologic problems in neoplastic disease from the point of view of basic investigation, rather than with the hope of obtaining a handy tool for diagnosis. It is from such unprejudiced study that great practical advances may naturally develop in the long run.

TESTS BASED ON ENZYMOLOGIC PRINCIPLES

In Urine

Abderhalden's work[1] on defensive proteases in urine has already been discussed with the immunologic procedures.

There are, to our knowledge, no other enzyme systems which have been studied in urine that can lay claims to any diagnostic utility.

In Blood

Abnormal enzymes circulating in the blood plasma of patients with cancer may either be produced by the cancer or may have been activated by products of tumor metabolism. Conversely, tumors may produce enzyme inhibitors or may indirectly stimulate the production of inhibitors.

Phosphatases. The one serum enzyme system that is of the greatest practical importance in cancer diagnosis today is that of serum acid phosphatase. First described in urine by Dmochowski,[50] and then found to be predominantly localized in the prostate,[125] it became of practical significance through the work of the Gutmans[96, 97] and Barringer and Woodard.[14] The situation regarding acid phosphatase and cancer of the prostate was carefully evaluated by Gutman in 1942.[96] A number of papers on this subject have appeared since then and have been reviewed in Herbert's article.[103] Of 259 cases of prostatic cancer with bone metastases collected in that paper, 224 had elevated serum acid phosphatase, as did 28 of 145 cases of prostatic cancer without bone metastases. In Trafton and Perkin's series[191] from the Lahey Clinic, 81 per cent of the cases with bone metastases and 48 per cent of an unselected group of 50 with and without bone metastases had elevated serum acid-phosphatase levels.

These figures convey an idea of the percentage of accuracy one may expect under ideal conditions from diagnostic methods based on sound and sensitive methodology for the measurement of an enzyme produced by a tumor. It is possible that ultimately modifications of the method, such as the inactivation of prostatic phosphatase by alcohol as suggested by Herbert,[103] for example, may still further increase the diagnostic yield of this method. It is also possible that additional enzyme systems associated with prostatic cancer may be found. Thus the work of Meister[141] suggests a relationship between adenosinetriphosphate dephosphorylation with liver disease and with bony metastases of prostatic cancer (see also p. 607).

It has been suggested by Roche *et al.*[171] that alkaline phosphatase is activated in normal subjects by the addition of a 10^{-5} molar solution of zinc sulfate to the serum. In cases with cancer, however, the phosphatase activity was allegedly decreased. These studies were reinvestigated in our laboratory[67] and elsewhere.[27] Inhibition was observed[26] with varying zinc concentrations in blood from cancer subjects, but a similarly marked inhibition also took place in all control cases.

The diagnostic usefulness of alkaline phosphatase is discussed in another chapter (see p. 607).

Plasma Zymohexase. This enzyme splits hexose diphosphate into triose phosphates and is found to be increased in the serum of tumor-bearing animals. The source of this elevation of enzyme activity is not clear. From a practical point of view, the use of this enzyme for diagnostic purposes is unlikely. No increase in human plasma was found by Warburg and Christian,[198] who expected this negative result, since the tumors have to reach about 2 per cent of the weight of the host animal before the enzyme is found to be increased.

β-Glucuronidase. The problem of the relationship of tumor size to the level of enzyme activity is well illustrated by the case of the enzyme β-glucuronidase (see also later). This enzyme, which is believed to function in the metabolic conjugation of estrogenic hormones, has been demonstrated in malignant tumors at levels of activity often many times those of the surrounding tissue.[75] Yet "there seemed to be no correlation of the blood glucuronidase with the incidence of cancer."[62] There is evidence of an inhibitor of β-glucuronidase activity in plasma,[65] which in this case may play a role in the regulation of enzyme activity in tissues and blood.

The approach to inhibition of enzymes contained in sera is an important one and has been but partially explored. The results of Duboff and Hirschfield[106] on the effect of sera on the tyrosinase activity of an isolated potato prepartion point to an interesting path that merits further study.

Weis[202] found that carotine inhibited the glycolysis of erythrocytes in patients with neoplasms, whereas it caused its activation in normal subjects. She stated that there is an apparent correlation between neoplasms and anaerobic glycolysis in erythrocytes and the effect of carotine upon this system. Analysis of the data reveals that the differences found between the different groups of patients are within the technical error of the methods employed, and that therefore interpretation of the data is inconclusive from the limited number of studies presented in the paper quoted above.

An inhibitor of hyaluronidase has been found in cancer patients by Fulton, Marcus, and Robinson.[81]

West[203] studied inhibitors of the enzymes chymotrypsin and rennin and related the ratio of the serum concentrations of these anti-enzymes to "clinical signs of tumor activity." This procedure was never claimed to be of diagnostic value but rather it appeared to its originators to have "limited diagnostic value." It is, of course, highly desirable to obtain objective means for the measurement of "tumor activity" but there are numerous difficulties inherent in this endeavor, outlined above and elsewhere in this book.

Peptidases. Another group of serum enzymes which have been linked with cancer is that of the *d*-peptidases. The enzymes, capable of selectively splitting *d*-peptides from racemic mixtures of peptides, were first claimed by Waldschmidt-Leitz and his co-workers[194, 195, 196] to exist in cancer patients only. Such *d*-peptidases could be produced in normal subjects by the injection of *d*-peptides. It was also claimed that *d*-peptides, when injected into cancer patients, would cause the *d*-peptidases to diminish and would bring slight clinical improvement. Protection of mice against chemical carcinogens following treatment with *d*-peptides was also claimed. These findings were immediately challenged by Bayerle and Podloucky,[15] as well as by Herken and Erxleben.[104] A controversy followed,[15, 196] in which the originator of the method argued that the faulty methodology of the later investigators was responsible for their failure to duplicate his findings. Euler *et al.*[57] found *d*-peptidase activity in only 3 of 7 bloods tested, and Maver, Johnson, and Thompson[138] found it in 1 serum of 19 tested. Berger, Johnson, and Baumann,[20] as well as Ahlström, Euler, and Högberg[4] later on, concluded that the *d*-peptidase reaction was of no specific value in the diagnosis of cancer.

Hemolysins. The remaining enzyme systems, which are altered in the blood of cancerous subjects, are pertinent to the clotting mechanism of blood and to hemolysis. As early as 1901, Ascoli,[9] followed in 1906 by Bard (quoted in Bing and Marangos[22]), reported autolysis of red cells in cancer serum, and hemolysins were shown by Kullman[123] in extracts from gastric cancers.

Crile[48] applied the phenomenon diagnostically and found that cancer serum would hemolyse red cells in 80 percent of 80 cancer cases, whereas no hemolysis occurred in 125 control cases. Those cancer cases in whose serum no hemolysin was found were usually far advanced. Crile cautioned that the test was not specific, since hemolysis occurred in tuberculosis, for example, as well. Without referring to this old literature, Gross brought up the subject in connection with experimental animals[92] and an editorial of the Journal of the American Medical Association[7] stressed the importance of these findings. In a later paper, Gross[93] claims the presence of hemolysins in extracts of human tumor tissue. The subject is worthy of reinvestigation, although Crile's early figures are not too encouraging from the diagnostic point of view.

In 1910, Elsberg, Neuhof, and Geist[56] reviewed the literature on hemolysis in cancer patients and suggested a diagnostic procedure based on the fact that the subcutaneous injection of washed red blood cells produced a marked red discoloration at the site of the injection in 90 per cent of patients with carcinoma, with the exception of the advanced cases. There were only 4.6 per cent false-positive reactions in healthy individuals.

Proteolytic Enzymes. The last group of enzymes and enzyme inhibitors in blood that have been suggested as being of possible diagnostic value are the proteolytic enzymes and their antagonists and, more specifically, fibrinolysins and antifibrinolysins. Brieger and Trebing,[38] in 1908, described the inhibition by cancer serum of the proteolytic activity of trypsin solutions. Of 100 cancer cases, only 4 failed to show the antitryptic effect. It was further observed that pancreatin by mouth depressed the antifibrinolysin of cancer serum but increased it in the case of healthy individuals. A controversy ensued, with von Bergman[21] and Braunstein[34] challenging the specificity of the reaction.

Weil[201] reviewed the situation in 1910 and stated that "all observers are agreed that the great majority of cases of cancer give evidence of increased antitryptic value in the serum. In some series the percentage of positive results in cases of cancer range as high as 90 per cent, in others as low as 70 per cent. It is, however, very frequently found in the acute infections, such as pneumonia, typhoid fever, sepsis and polyarticular rheumatism and in chronic infections, notably tuberculosis, as well as in diabetes and severe anemias, and in Graves's disease almost constantly.

These data amply demonstrate that the change in the serum is not to be regarded as a characteristic biologic response to the presence of new growths. As a general diagnostic method, the increase in the antitryptic index occurs in too many conditions to have the value of a specific symptom. On the other hand, the absence of the antitryptic reaction in the blood may be taken generally as arguing against the existence of cancer. In the presence of a neoplasm of doubtful character, a positive reaction (in the absence of complicating conditions, notably tuberculosis) argues with a strong degree of probability in favor of the diagnosis of malignancy.

The improved methodology of Clark, Cliffton, and Newton[43] succeeded in placing sera from patients with diseases "which gave false positive reactions with previous fibrinolysin tests" into the "doubtful range." The authors feel that the method is of value as a screening mechanism with a degree of correlation warranting extremely careful observation in all patients with a consistently elevated titer. In principle, the statements of Weil just quoted still apply to the results obtained in this modern work. The percentage (75) of positive findings in cancer patients has not been increased, and merely an increase in the number of "doubtful" results was obtained, with only 60 per cent clearly negative reactions in patients with diseases other than neoplasia. Recently the work of Guest[95] and his co-workers has shown "a tendency for the fibrinolysin activity to be increased in a number of different diseases," such as "pneumonia, coronary thrombosis, pernicious anemia, secondary anemia, cirrhosis of the liver, intestinal obstructions and acute bacterial endocarditis." The continued study of the basic factors involved in this reaction should be pursued in the hope that one might deal with a number of more or less specific antiproteolysins in various conditions which sooner or later might be eliminated by suitable methods.

The field of proteolysins cannot be dismissed without discussing the "cancer reaction" of Fuchs.[76] This investigator applied careful micro-Kjeldahl studies to the measurement of the nonprotein nitrogen liberated during the incubation, in the presence of chloroform, of serums with fibrin as substrate. The history of this reaction is peculiar and exemplifies the confusion in this field of diagnostic tests.

Fuchs published a series of papers[74, 75, 76, 77, 78] dealing primarily with the fact that serum of a given species would never break down the fibrin of the same species, excepting when the donor of the serum had been immunized or was the carrier of a neoplasm. This latter fact was discovered by accident, when horse serum was found to digest horse blood fibrin and investigations revealed the presence of a malignant tumor in the serum-donor horse. Fuchs was hopeful that this meant a diagnostic test for cancer but stated[74] rather cautiously in 1926 that, because of the fact that fibrinolysis occurred in patients with infections, it became impossible "to conclude from the mere fact of fibrinolysis of normal human fibrin substrate by serum of a patient that a malignant tumor exists in this patient." He continued that "this was particularly regrettable, since the particular infections present difficulties for the diagnosis and may cause erroneous conclusions." The author noted that "a series of further observations strongly suggested that fibrin from patients with cancer may not be subject to attack by normal serum, as is the case for normal fibrin."

It is quite possible that antifibrinolysin was present in the fibrin substrate of the cancer patient and that this reaction is closely related to those previously described. In a long series of papers, Fuchs extended his work to various situations relating to infectious disease and to species and strain differences, as well as to various stages of the development of frogs. Then, in 1936, in a paper which is a masterpiece of methodological description,[76] he suddenly departed from the basic approach and claimed that his method was "a cancer reaction," which had clearly demonstrated that in patients with malignant tumors there is present an antigen specific for *all* malignant cells (the italics are Fuchs's).

Again he stated the principle of this reaction as follows: "Serum substrate of cancer patients was not attacked or degradated by either its own serum or the serum from other patients with cancer. Conversely, it was attacked by the serum of normal subjects, as well as by those of patients with any other infectious disease." (Translated from the German; this reviewer feels that, from the context, the words "serum substrate" should correctly read "fibrin.") It is again tempting to conclude that this represents merely a different way of measuring antifibrinolysis.

Fuchs's reaction has been discussed at some length because it has held the attention of many investigators for a long time. Bing and Marangos[22] call it "the most reliable of those reactions which are based upon enzymatic degradation." They quote the results of confirmatory studies, including their own, and arrive at 92 to 94 per cent correct diagnoses from among approximately five thousand determinations. Hinsberg[105] arrived at exactly the opposite conclusion, namely, that Fuchs's reaction was of no value.

While many of his conclusions remain to be reinvestigated, Fuchs deserves the credit for having been the first to apply exact micromethods to the analytic part of his reaction.

Miscellaneous Enzymes. A number of other enzyme systems have been claimed to be of diagnostic value in cancer. Thus Waldschmidt-Leitz[196] claimed that there was an enzyme in cancer serum capable of hydrolysing glutathione. This reaction, for which polarographic analysis was employed, was found to be unspecific by Albers[5] and Schmidt[179] and was later investigated by Woodward.[211] A small amount of an enzyme was demonstrated in serum capable of hydrolysing oxidized glutathione with liberation of cystine. There was no difference in activity between serum from cancer patients and that from other subjects.

Serum lipases have been found reduced in patients with cancer and these enzymes are lowered in the blood of tumor-bearing animals at an early stage. However, the diagnostic possibilities are extremely limited, in view of the fact that a great many pathologic conditions other than cancer produce similar effects upon these enzymes.

Menkés has described the phenomenon of pentolysis which occurs in cancer serums but not in normal serums,[146, 147] observing that pentoses added to serums are recovered readily from normal serums but seem to be split in cancer serums.

Polarography. The polarographic study of serum has lately been revived by Kuske and Riva,[124] who were able to correlate certain types of polarographic patterns with typical changes in the distribution of proteins in the serum. While they succeeded in distinguishing thus between patterns of "nephrotic" and "cirrhotic" type, these patterns lacked the specificity necessary to make the method a diagnostic tool for cancer.

Boyland[33] has recently employed the method in conjunction with other procedures, such as electrophoresis and the iodoacetic acid-coagulation test, and has found it to be of use in correlating the severity and extent of neoplasms with the results of polarographic analyses. There was no correlation between the latter and the iodoacetate procedure.

In Tissues and Body Secretions

The cytologic methods developed to demonstrate the site of tissue-enzyme activity form one of the most promising approaches to the diagnostic problem, but as they belong to the realm of tissue diagnosis, they are outside the scope of this review.

We are not aware of any enzyme studies that have been used on body fluids with the aim of developing diagnostic procedures for cancer. Again, the study of walled-off fluid collections is most attractive for the reasons mentioned above. It should be possible to detect enzyme activity in such fluids as ascites and pleural effusions in cases in which tumors are in contact with the exudate or transudate. Most enzymes are diminished in tumor tissue as compared with normal tissue, with few possible exceptions, e.g. β-glucuronidase.[63] Study of this last-named enzyme in body fluids suggests that β-glucuronidase may sometimes be of assistance in determining the etiologic nature of such exudates or transudates.

Recently, Odell *et al.*[157, 158] have reported the presence of higher than normal levels of glucuronidase in cervical tissues and vaginal secretions of women with cancer of the lower genital tract. They have proposed making use of this difference in the diagnosis of female genital carcinoma.

Further study of this procedure in our laboratory by Fishman and associates[66] in more than 400 patients has shown a high incidence of false negatives and false positives. Other data suggest that the vaginal fluid glucuronidase is affected by many factors and is not specifically high in uterine cancer (see also Chapter 20).

DISCUSSION

In reviewing the history of the search for diagnostic tests for cancer, a trend becomes apparent that is common to most of the procedures. The sights have been set too high, and emotion, coupled with ambitious eagerness, has caused failure in most cases. In an endeavor to develop a diagnostic test that would reveal all types of cancer, the most unspecific characteristics have been investigated, and those are the ones most susceptible to modification by innumerable factors other than neoplasia. Only those procedures that are based on specific changes, narrowly confined to one type of neoplasia, have had some measure of enduring success. Such procedures are steroid determinations in functional tumors of the adrenals, study of gonadotropic hormones in tumors of the testes, discovery of Bence Jones protein in multiple myeloma and the acid phosphatase determination in metastasizing tumors of the prostate.

The lesson to be learned seems clear, namely, to search for some characteristic that may be specific for given types of neoplasms and to apply to these the best weapons available in our methodologic armory. Thus it seems reasonable to hope that further improvements may be made in the sensitivity of methods of measuring acid phosphatase in order to arrive perhaps at an earlier diagnosis of prostatic cancer. It is not impossible that investigation along immunologic lines may reveal measurable specificity of some tumor components not detectable by the methods that have been applied to date.

The production of lactic acid by tumor tissue is well established and a skilful use and combination of various tools may render it measurable in sites in which this has not been done successfully so far. It is possible that methods may be developed in the near future for a chemical determination of those proteins that have been shown to appear in the blood stream in certain types of cancer.[162]

Above all, however, standard methods for the clinical evaluation of such procedures should be developed and rendered available for the rapid and decisive evaluation of new "tests." Recent experience with the application of such standardized methods of evaluation of diagnostic tests for cancer indicates already that much time and effort can be saved and clear-cut and conclusive answers can be obtained. At the same time, hasty and incautious dismissal of any new developments must be avoided. The diagnostic solution for any given type of tumor may come from unexpected quarters. We do not know, for instance, what the physical methods, such as tracer studies[130] or measurements of changes in electrical potentials,[127] may offer (see also Chapter 32). The field of labeled metabolites and immune bodies has likewise barely been touched.

The history of medicine and of mankind is full of instances in which opportunities were lost because of prejudice and rash, ill-considered judgment leading to the dismissal of measures that later, in the light of new facts, proved invaluable. So, here again, we must maintain a vivid sense of our ignorance and keep an open mind, while judiciously avoiding all loss of time in ill-directed efforts, so sadly illustrated in some of the work reviewed in this chapter. With our present lack of more precise knowledge, it appears impossible today to foresee a general test for cancer, and concentration on specific tests for individual types of tumors may be the safer and more promising path. Yet it should not be forgotten that the impossible of today frequently comes to pass on the morrow and that we need the methods to be able to recognize the precious fact if and when it presents itself. One must remain true at all times to Goethe's maxim "to investigate what is, not what suits us."

BIBLIOGRAPHY

1. Abderhalden, E. Studien über die Verwendbarkeit der Abwehrproteinasereaktion (A.R.) zur Diagnose des Karzinoms. *Schweiz. med. Wchnschr. 76:* 47, 1946.
2. Abels, J. C., Pack, G. T., and Rhoads, C. P. Metabolic studies in patients with cancer of the gastrointestinal tract: XVII. The conjugation of phenols. *Cancer Research 3:* 177-179, 1943.
3. Adams, W. S., Alling, E. L., and Lawrence, J. S. Multiple myeloma: Its clinical and laboratory diagnosis with emphasis on electrophoretic abnormalities. *Am. J. Med. 6:* 141-161, 1949.
4. Ahlström, L., Euler, H. v., and Högberg, B. Ueber die Spaltung von d-Leucyl-glycyl-glycin und d-Leucyl-glycin. *Ztschr. f. physiol. Chem. 273:* 129-157, 1942.
5. Albers, D. Nachprüfung der polarographischen Prager Krebs-Reaktion. *Biochem. Ztschr. 306:* 236-244, 1940.
6. Albertini, A. v. Vergleichende histologische Geschwulstuntersuchungen mit dem Phasenkontrastverfahren. *Schweiz. Ztschr. f. Path. u. Bakt. 10:* 4-29, 1947.
7. Anon. Cancer hemolysins. (Editorial.) *J.A.M.A. 137:* 647, 1948.
8. Aron, M. Présence, dans l'urine des sujets atteints de tumeur maligne, d'un principe doué d'une action sur la cortico-surrénale. *Compt. rend. Acad. d. sc. 197:* 1702-1704, 1933.
9. Ascoli, M. Isoagglutinine und Isolysine menschlicher Blutsera. *München. med. Wchnschr. 48:* 1239-1241, 1901.

10. Ascoli, M., and Izar, G. La sierodiagnosi dei tumori maligni con la reazione meiostagmica. *Biochim. e terap. sper. 2:* 322-331, 1910.
11. Barker, S. B., and Summerson, W. H. Colorimetric determination of lactic acid in biological material. *J. Biol. Chem. 138:* 535-554, 1941.
12. Barnett, G. D., and McKenney, A. C., Jr. Lactic acid in exudates and transudates. *Proc. Soc. Exper. Biol. & Med. 23:* 505-506, 1926.
13. Barrett, M. K. Avenues of approach to the gastric-cancer problem. *J. Nat. Cancer Inst. 7:* 127-157, 1946.
14. Barringer, B. S., and Woodard, H. Q. Prostatic carcinoma with extensive intraprostatic calcification with a discussion of the possible role of prostatic phosphatase. *Tr. Am. A. Genito-Urin. Surgeons 31:* 363-369, 1938.
15. Bayerle, H., and Podloucky, F. H. Ueber sterische Auslese durch Peptidasen in normalen und carcinomatösen Seren. (Experimentelle Feststellungen zu einer Arbeit von E. Waldschmidt-Leitz and K. Mayer.) *Ztschr. f. Krebsforsch. 50:* 220-229, 1940.
16. Bayerle, H., and Podloucky, F. H. Zur Frage des Vorkommens von sterisch auslesenden Enzymen im carcinomatösen Organismus: Feststellungen zu zwei vorläufigen Mitteilungen von E. Waldschmidt-Leitz und Mitarbeitern. *Ztschr. f. physiol. Chem. 264:* 189-195, 1940.
17. Beard, H. H. Correlation of the results of the biological test with clinical diagnosis of human malignancy. *Acta, Union internat. contre cancer 6:* 576-594, 1949.
18. Beard, H. H., Halperin, B., and Libert, S. A. Effect of intraperitoneal injection of malignant urine extracts in normal and hypophysectomized rats. *Science 105:* 475-476, 1947.
19. Behan, R. J. *Cancer, with Special Reference to Cancer of the Breast.* St. Louis, Mo., C. V. Mosby, 1938.
20. Berger, J., Johnson, M. J., and Baumann, C. A. Enzymatic hydrolysis of *d*-peptides. *J. Biol. Chem. 137:* 389-395, 1941.
21. Bergmann, v. Zur Brieger'schen Serumreaktion. *Verhandl. d. berl. med. Gesellsch. 39* (Pt. 1): 227-243, 1908.
22. Bing, M., and Marangos, G. Die diagnostischen Krebsreaktionen: Eine kritische Uebersicht. *Beitr. z. klin. Chir. 160:* 417-444, 1934.
23. Black, M. M. Changes in the reducing power of serum or plasma of patients with malignant neoplastic disease. *Cancer Research 7:* 321-325, 1947.
24. Black, M. M. Sulfhydryl reduction of methylene blue with reference to alterations in malignant neoplastic disease. *Cancer Research 7:* 592-594, 1947.
25. Boas, I. Bermerkungen zur diagnostischen Bedeutung und zum Nachweis der Gährungsmilchsäure im Mageninhalt. *Berl. klin. Wchnschr. 32:* 189-192, 1895.
26. Boas, I. Der Nachweis der Milchsäure im Magensaft nach Fletcher und Hopkins. *Arch f. Verdauungskr. 33:* 146-148, 1924.
27. Bodansky, O., and Blumenfeld, O. Effect of zinc on serum alkaline phosphatase activity in patients with and without cancer. *Proc. Soc. Exper. Biol. & Med. 70:* 546-547, 1949.
28. Bodansky, O., and McInnes, G. F. Thermal coagulation of serum proteins in cancer, in the post-operative phase of surgery, and in the administration of adrenocorticotropic hormone. *Cancer 3:* 1-14, 1950.
29. Boerhaave, H. *Praelectiones Academicae in proprias Institutiones Rei Medicae.* Amsterdam, J. Wetstenium, 1744; Vol. 6, pp. 387-388, para. 1138.
30. Bolen, H. L. Diagnostic value of blood studies in malignancy of the gastrointestinal tract. *Am. J. Surg. 63:* 316-323, 1944.

31. BONNER, C. D., FISHMAN, W. H., and HOMBURGER, F. Response of circulating eosinophiles and uric acid excretion to ACTH in geriatric patients. *Geriatrics 5:* 203-207, 1950.
32. BOWMAN, R. O., and MOTTSHAW, H. R. Failure to find carcinogens in urine from patients with cancer. *Cancer Research 1:* 308-309, 1941.
33. BOYLAND, E. Personal communication.
34. BRAUNSTEIN, A. Ueber die Entstehung und die klinische Bedeutung des Antitrypsins, insbesondere bei Krebskranken. *Deutsche med. Wchnschr. 35:* 573-575, 1909.
35. BRIEGER, L. Diskussion über die Demonstration des Herrn. G. v. Bergmann: Zur Brieger'schen Carcinomreaktion, über die Vorträge der Herren Sticker, Hofbauer und Falk: Ueber Beeinflussung und Behandlung der bösartigen Geschwülste etc. *Verhandl. d. berl. med. Gesellsch. 39* (Pt. 1): 231-233, 1908.
36. BRIEGER, L., and TREBING, J. Ueber die antitryptische Kraft des menschlichen Blutserums, insbesondere bei Krebskranken. *Berl. klin. Wchnschr. 45:* 1041-1044, 1908.
37. BRIEGER, L., and TREBING, J. Ueber die Kachexiereaktion, insbesondere bei Krebskranken. *Berl. klin. Wchnschr. 45:* 2260-2261, 1908.
38. BRIEGER, L., and TREBING, J. Weitere Untersuchungen über die antitryptische Kraft des menschlichen Blutserums, insbesondere bei Krebskranken. *Berl. klin. Wchnschr. 45:* 1349-1351, 1908.
39. BRUGER, M., and EHRLICH, S. B. Cholesterol content of the urine in patients with cancer. *Arch. Int. Med. 72:* 108-114, 1943.
40. BUEDING, E., and GOLDFARB, W. Blood changes following glucose, lactate, and pyruvate injections in man. *J. Biol. Chem. 147:* 33-40, 1943.
41. BÜTTER, H. E. Blutmilchsäure und Carcinom. *Klin. Wchnschr. 5:* 1507-1508, 1926.
42. CHEEVER, F. S. A complement-fixing antibody in sera of rabbits bearing Brown-Pearce carcinoma. *Proc. Soc. Exper. Biol. & Med. 45:* 517-522, 1940.
43. CLARK, D. G. C., CLIFFTON, E. E., and NEWTON, B. L. Antiproteolytic activity of human serum with particular reference to its changes in the presence and considerations of its use for detection of malignant neoplasia. *Proc. Soc. Exper. Biol. & Med. 69:* 276-279, 1948.
44. COMAN, D. R. Mechanism of the invasiveness of cancer. *Science 105:* 347-348, 1947.
45. CONNELL, H. C., MUNROE, L. A., and MEDLEY, A. Restropin factor in cancer in relation to the reticulo-endothelial system. *Canad. M.A.J. 54:* 161-164, 1946.
46. COUNCIL ON PHARMACY AND CHEMISTRY. Report of the Council: "Cancer and the need for facts." *J.A.M.A. 139:* 93-98, 1949.
47. CRANDALL, L. A. Thiocyanate as source of error in ferric chloride test for lactic acid, with method for elimination of thiocyanate. *J. Lab. & Clin. Med. 13:* 1046-1047, 1928.
48. CRILE, G. W. The cancer problem. *J.A.M.A. 1:* 1883-1887, 1908; *M. Rec. 73:* 929-933, 1908.
49. DAVIDSON, L. S. P., and CALDER, A. Diagnosis of carcinoma of the stomach, with special reference to lactic acid. *Practitioner 129:* 584-606, 1932.
50. DMOCHOWSKI, A. Sur les phosphatases de l'urine. *Compt. rend. Soc. de biol. 113:* 956-957, 1933.
51. DODDS, E. C., and ROBERTSON, J. D. Lactic acid and carcinoma of the stomach. *Lancet 1:* 171-174, 1930.

52. Dodds, E. C., and Robertson, J. D. Origin and occurrence of lactic acid in human gastric contents, with special reference to malignant and non-malignant conditions. *Quart. J. Med. 23:* 175-193, 1930.
53. Dunn, J. E., and Greenhouse, S. W. National Cancer Institute program for the evaluation of cancer diagnostic tests. New York, Public Health Cancer Association Meeting, October, 1949.
54. Dvoskin, S., and LaDue, J. S. Experiences with the Huggins Test. *New York State J. Med. 50:* 1488, 1950.
55. Egan, R. W. Investigation of the paramecium toxicity test for the detection of human malignant tumors. *Cancer 3:* 26-31, 1950.
56. Elsberg, C. A., Neuhof, H., and Geist, S. H. A skin reaction in carcinoma from the subcutaneous injection of human red blood cells. *Am. J. M. Sc. 139:* 264-271, 1910.
57. Euler, H. v., Ahlström, L., Skarzynski, B., and Högberg, B. Spaltung von d-Leucylglycin durch Seren. *Ztschr. f. Krebsforsch. 50:* 552-564, 1940.
58. Falkenhausen, M. v., and Fuchs, H. J. Ueber proteolytische Fermente im Serum: VI. Mitteilung: Ueber die Spezifität des proteolytischen Fermentes im Serum verschiedener Kaninchenrassen. *Biochem. Ztschr. 181:* 438-443, 1927.
59. Falkenhausen, M. v., Fuchs, H. J., and Schubert, M.: Ueber proteolytische Fermente im Serum. IX. Mitteilung: Ueber das verschiedene Verhalten der Sera in den einzelnen Metamorphosestudien der Anuren. *Biochem. Ztschr. 193:* 269-275, 1928.
60. Feros, J. M. Study on the electro-cardiogastrographic test. *Rev. Gastroenterol. 12:* 99-110, 1945.
61. Ferrari, S. Ricerche sul contenuto di glucosio e acido lattico nelle raccolte purulente acute e tubercolari. *Boll. Soc. Med.-chir. Modena. 42:* 467-475, 1941-42.
62. Fishman, W. H. β-Glucuronidase activity of the blood and tissues of obstetrical and surgical patients. *Science 105:* 646-647, 1947.
63. Fishman, W. H., and Anlyan, A. J. The presence of high β-glucuronidase activity in cancer tissue. *J. Biol. Chem. 169:* 449-450, 1947.
64. Fishman, W. H., Kasdon, S. C., and Homburger, F. Proposed cancer test. *J.A.M.A. 142:* 125, 1950.
65. Fishman, W. H., Altman, K. I., and Springer, B. Blood plasma anti-glucuronidase activity. *Federation Proc. 7:* 154, 1948.
66. Fishman, W. H., Kasdon, S. C., and Homburger, F. Factors in the evaluation of β-glucuronidase activity in cancer of the uterine cervix. *Cancer Research 10:* 216, 1950.
67. Fishman, W. H., Wayne, A., and Homburger, F. The evaluation of diagnostic tests for cancer: II. Inhibition of serum alkaline phosphatase by zinc ion (the Roche test). *Cancer Research 9:* 681-683, 1949.
68. Fontaine, R., Aron, M., and Buck, P. Réaction sérologique de diagnostic du cancer; ses résultats statistiques. *Schweiz. med. Wchnschr. 79:* 227-230, 1949.
69. Freund, E., and Kaminer, G. Ueber die Beziehungen Zwischen Tumorzellen und Blutserum. *Wien. klin. Wchnschr. 23:* 1221-1223, 1910.
70. Friedemann, T. E., and Graeser, J. B. Determination of lactic acid. *J. Biol. Chem. 100:* 291-308, 1933.
71. Friedewald, W. F., and Kidd, J. G. Distinct types of antibodies in the blood

of rabbits carrying the transplanted V2 carcinoma. *Proc. Soc. Exper. Biol. & Med. 47:* 130-132, 1941.

72. Friesz, J., and Mohos, E. Milchsäureuntersuchungen in Exsudaten und Transsudaten. *Deutsches Arch. f. klin. Med. 173:* 545-549, 1932.
73. Fry, H. J. B. Further observations on a flocculation reaction for the serum diagnosis of malignant disease. *J. Path. & Bact. 29:* 353-364, 1926.
74. Fuchs, H. J. Ueber proteolytische Fermente im Serum: I, II, IV. *Biochem. Ztschr. 170:* 76-101; *175:* 185-201; *178:* 152-154, 1926.
75. Fuchs, H. J. Beitrag zur colorimetrischen Milchsäurebestimmung, nach Mendel-Goldscheider. *Klin. Wchnschr. 8:* 1500, 1929.
76. Fuchs, H. J. Die "CaR" (Krebsreaktion) nach Fuchs. *Ztschr. f. d. ges. exper. Med. 98:* 70-132, 1936.
77. Fuchs, H. J., and Falkenhausen, M. v. Ueber proteolytische Fermente im Serum. III. Mitteilung: Ueber eine chemisch messbare Toxin-Anti-toxin-Bindung in vitro. *Biochem. Ztschr. 176:* 92:100, 1926.
78. Fuchs, H. J., and Falkenhausen, M. v. Ueber proteolytische Fermente im Serum. V. Mitteilung: Ueber das Verhalten von Immunserum and Immunfibrin. *Biochem. Ztschr. 178:* 154-160, 1926.
79. Fuhs, J., and Lintz, W. La signification diagnostique de la réaction du bleu de méthylène dans l'urine, spécialement envisagée au point de vue de la malignité: Rapport préliminaire. *Néoplasmes 2:* 62-64, 1923.
80. Fulci, F. Contributo alla conoscenza dei costituenti chimici dei neoplasmi. *Gazz. internaz. di med. 12:* 509-513, 1910.
81. Fulton, Marcus, and Robinson. "On an inhibitor for the enzyme found in cancer patients." In: Duran-Reynals, F., and Goldsmith, E. D. Ground substance of the mesenchyme and hyaluronidase: A symposium. *Science 110:* 74-75, 1949.
82. Furuhjelm, L. Erfarenheter av tre karcinomreaktioner. *Nord. med. 3:* 2082-2086, 1939.
83. Gates, O., and Warren, S. *A Handbook for the Diagnosis of Cancer of the Uterus by the Use of Vaginal Smears.* Cambridge, Harvard University Press, 1947.
84. Glaessner, K. Milschsäureausscheidung bei Carcinose. *Klin. Wchnschr. 4:* 1868-1869, 1925.
85. Glass, J. Sur l'application de la recherche du point de coagulation thermique du sérum sanguin pour l'évaluation clinique de divers états morbides ainsi que pour le diagnostic de certains néoplasmes malignes. *Bull. internat. Acad. polon. d sc. et d. lett., Cl. med.* (1936): 935-953, 1936.
86. Glass, J. Znaczenie badanego punktu krzepnięcia surowicy krwi pod wpływem gorąca dla oceny klinicznej róznych stanów chorobowych i rozpoznania niektórych nowotworów złosliwych. *Polskie arch. med. wewnetrz.* 15: 136-196, 1937.
87. Gordon, J. J., and Quastel, J. H. Estimation of lactic acid in biological material by oxidation with ceric sulfate. *Biochem. J. 33:* 1332-1337, 1939.
88. Gottlieb, J., and Kangas, V. L. The cancer serum flocculation test employing the Penn antigen. *Maine M. J. 41:* 391-395, 1950.
89. Greenstein, J. P. *The Biochemistry of Cancer.* New York, Academic Press, Inc., 1947, p. 137.
90. Gross, L. A propos de la nature de l'immunité antinéoplastique chez le lapin. *Bull. internat. Acad. polon. d. sc. et d. lett., Cl. méd.* (1938): 581-584, 1938.

91. GROSS, L. Experimental immunization against the implantation of cancer. *Quart. Bull. Polish Inst. Arts & Sc. America 1:* 418-430, 1943.
92. GROSS, L. Hemolytic action of mouse mammary carcinoma filtrate on mouse erythrocytes in vitro. *Proc. Soc. Exper. Biol. & Med. 65:* 292-293, 1947.
93. GROSS, L. Destructive action of human cancer extracts on red blood cells in vitro. *Proc. Soc. Exper. Biol. & Med. 70:* 656-662, 1949.
94. GRUNER, O. C. *A Study of the Blood in Cancer: with Special Reference to the Needs of the Tumour Clinic.* Montreal, Renouf Publishing Company, 1942.
95. GUEST, M. M., DALY, B. M., WARE, A. G., and SEEGERS, W. H. A study of the antifibrinolysin activity in human plasmas during pathological states. *J. Clin. Investigation 27:* 793-794, 1948.
96. GUTMAN, A. B. Serum "acid" phosphatase in patients with carcinoma of the prostate gland: Present status. *J.A.M.A. 120:* 1112-1116, 1942.
97. GUTMAN, A. B., and GUTMAN, E. B. An "acid" phosphatase occurring in the serum of patients with metastasizing carcinoma of the prostate gland. *J. Clin. Investigation 17:* 473-478, 1938.
98. GUTMAN, A. B., MOORE, D. H., GUTMAN, E. B., MCCLELLAN, V., and KABAT, E. A. Fractionation of serum proteins in hyperproteinemia, with special reference to multiple myeloma. *J. Clin. Investigation 20:* 765-783, 1941.
99. HARDESTY, W. L., and LOVE, B. The Robertson test for carcinoma: A preliminary report. *West Virginia M. J. 39:* 151-153, 1943.
100. HARRIS, M. The role of humoral antagonism in heteroplastic transplantation in mammals. *J. Exper. Zool. 93:* 131-143, 1943.
101. HAWK, B. O., THOMA, G. E., and INKLEY, J. J. An evaluation of the Bolen Test as a screening test for malignancy. *Cancer Research 11:* 157-160, 1951.
102. HENRIQUES, S. B., HENRIQUES, O. B., and SELYE, H. Influence of cold on blood fibrinogen concentration. *Proc. Soc. Exper. Biol. & Med. 71:* 82-84, 1949.
103. HERBERT, F. K. The estimation of prostatic phosphatase in serum and its use in the diagnosis of prostatic carcinoma. *Quart. J. Med. 15:* 221-241, 1946.
104. HERKEN, H., and ERXLEBEN, H. Ueber Nachweis von d-Peptidasen mit Hilfe von d-Aminosäureoxydase: Vorläufige Mitteilung. *Ztschr. f. physiol. Chem. 264:* 251-263, 1940.
105. HINSBERG, K. Ueber die chemischen Krebsreaktionen beim Menschen und ihre biochemischen Zusammenhange. *Angew. Chemie 53:* 356-362, 1940.
106. HIRSHFIELD, S., DUBOFF, G., and WEST, P. M. Demonstration of an enzyme-inhibiting factor in the serum of cancer patients: Preliminary study. *Cancer Research 6:* 57-60, 1946; (correction, *6:* 224, 1946).
107. HOMBURGER, F., PFEIFFER, P. H., PAGE, O., RIZZONE, G. P., and BENOTTI, J. Evaluation of diagnostic tests for cancer: III. Inhibition of thermal coagulation of serum by iodoacetic acid (the Huggins-Miller-Jensen test). *Cancer 3:* 15-25, 1950.
108. HUGGINS, C., CLEVELAND, A. S., and JENSEN, E. V. Thermal coagulation of serum in diagnosis. *J.A.M.A. 143:* 11-15, 1950.
109. HUGGINS, C., MILLER, G. M., and JENSEN, E. V. Simplified procedure for serum coagulation test. Privately circulated, 1949.
110. HUGGINS, C., MILLER, G. M., and JENSEN, E. V. Thermal coagulation of serum proteins: II. Deficient coagulation in cancer and the iodoacetate index. *Cancer Research 9:* 177-182, 1949.

111. JACOBS, J. L., and HOUGHTON, J. D. Complement-fixation tests on rabbits with Brown-Pearce carcinoma. *Proc. Soc. Exper. Biol. & Med. 47:* 88-90, 1941.

112. KAHN, H. Ueber eine einfache Flockungs-Trübunreaktion bei malignen Tumoren. *Strahlentherapie 15:* 808-811, 1923.

113. KAMINER, G. Die diagnostische Verwendbarkeit der Freund-Kaminerschen Impfreaktion zur Erkennung von Karzinomen. *Wien. klin. Wchnschr. 4:6* 1576-1578, 1933.

114. KIDD, J. G. Suppression of growth of the Brown-Pearce tumor by a specific antibody. *Science 99:* 348-350, 1944.

115. KIDD, J. G., and FRIEDEWALD, W. F. A natural antibody that reacts in vitro with a sedimentable constituent of normal tissue cells: I. Demonstration of the phenomenon; II. Specificity of the phenomenon: General discussion. *J. Exper. Med. 76:* 543-556; 557-578, 1942.

116. KLAR, E. Über den Nachweis des frühgeburtauslösenden Eiweisskörpers bei Kranken mit bösartigen Tumoren. *Ztschr. f. Krebsforsch. 50:* 155-162, 1940.

117. KOENEMANN, R. H. Modification of the Miller-Muntz method for colorimetric determination of lactic acid. *J. Biol. Chem. 135:* 105-109, 1940.

118. KOPACZEWSKI, W. La réaction de lactogélification sérique dans les affections hépatiques. *Compt. rend. Soc. de biol. 118:* 846-848, 1935.

119. KOPACZEWSKI, W. La réaction de lactogélification sérique dans le cancer; bases expérimentales; techniques d'exécution. *Bull. d. sc. pharmacol. 42:* 135-145, 1935.

120. KOPACZEWSKI, W. Les protides et la lactogélification sérique dans divers états pathologiques. *J. de physiol. et de path. gén. 35:* 50-70, 1937.

121. KOZAWA, S., FUKUSHIMA, K., OKADA, I., and FURUKAWA, G. Electrogastrogram, a method for the early diagnosis of cancer. *Collect. Papers* (1938), *Fac. Med. Imperial University Osaka* (1939): 47-51, 1939.

122. KREBS, E. T., JR., and GURCHOT, C. Trophoblast elements in cancer. *Science 104:* 302, 1946.

123. KULLMAN. Ueber Hämolyse durch Carcinomextracte. *Ztschr. f. klin. Med. 53:* 293-307, 1904.

124. KUSKE, H., and RIVA, G. L'analyse du serum sanguin par la methode polarographique. *27ième Congrès franç. méd., Genève,* September 29-30; October 1, 1949.

125. KUTSCHER, W., and WOLBERGS, H. Prostataphosphatase. *Ztschr. f. physiol. Chem. 236:* 237-240, 1935.

126. LAND, E. H., BLOUT, E. R., GREY, D. S., FLOWER, M. S., HUSEK, H., JONES, R. C., MATZ, C. H., and MERRILL, D. P. A color translating ultra-violet microscope. *Science 109:* 371-374, 1949.

127. LANGMAN, L., and BURR, H. S. Electrometric studies in women with malignancy of the cervix uteri. *Science 105:* 209-210, 1947.

128. LEEMANN, H. Ueber den Lactoflavingehalt der Carcinome und die Lactoflavinausscheidung bei Tumorkranken. *Klin. Wchnschr. 21:* 60-62, 1942.

129. LIEBERMAN, S., DOBRINER, K., HILL, B. R., FIESER, L. F., and RHOADS, C. P. Studies in steroid metabolism: II. Identification and characterization of ketosteroids isolated from urine of healthy and diseased persons. *J. Biol. Chem. 172:* 263-295, 1948.

130. LOW-BEER, B. V. A. Surface measurements of radioactive phosphorus in breast tumors as a possible diagnostic method. *Science 104:* 399, 1946.

131. McChesney, E. W. Determination of lactic acid in presence of certain interfering substances. *Proc. Soc. Exper. Biol. & Med. 32:* 94-95, 1934.

132. Maier, E., and Christiani, A. v. Methodik und Ergebnisse von Stoffwechseluntersuchungen beim Krebs. *Ztschr. f. Krebsforsch. 49:* 679-719, 1940.

133. Mann, L. S., and Welker, W. H. A specific precipitin antiserum for carcinoma protein. *Am. J. Cancer 39:* 360-364, 1940.

134. Mann, L. S., and Welker, W. H. Further studies of specific precipitin antiserums for the protein of cancer tissue. *Cancer Research 3:* 193-195, 1943.

135. Mann, L. S., and Welker, W. H. Further studies of specific precipitin antiserums for the protein of cancer tissue: II. The application of in vivo absorption. *Cancer Research 3:* 196-197, 1943.

136. Mann, L. S., and Welker, W. H. Further studies of specific precipitin antiserums for the protein of cancer tissue: III. Relation of the proteins of different malignant tissues to each other. *Cancer Research 6:* 625-626, 1946.

137. Margreth, G. Sul contenuto in acido lattico degli essudati e dei trasudati. *Policlinico (sez. med.) 36:* 314-320, 1929.

138. Maver, M. E., Johnson, J. M., and Thompson, J. W. The *d*-peptidase activity of serum as an alleged diagnostic test for cancer. *J. Nat. Cancer Inst. 1:* 835-843, 1941.

139. Mehl, J. W., Humphrey, J., and Winzler, R. J. Studies on the mucoproteins of human plasma: III. Electrophoretic studies of mucoproteins isolated from perchloric acid filtrates of plasma. *Proc. Soc. Exper. Biol. & Med. 72:* 106-109, 1949.

140. Mehl, J. W., Humphrey, J., and Winzler, R. J. Studies on the mucoproteins of human plasma: V. Isolation and characterization of a homogeneous mucoprotein. *Proc. Soc. Exper. Biol. & Med. 72:* 110-114, 1949.

141. Meister, A. Dephosphorylation of adenosinetriphosphate by normal and pathological human sera. *J. Clin. Investigation 27:* 263-271, 1948.

142. Mendel, B., and Engel, W. Ueber die Milchsäurebildner beim Magenkarzinom. *Arch. f. Verdauungskr. 34:* 370-380, 1924-25; Abstr. in *Klin. Wchnschr. 4:* 119-120, 1925.

143. Mendel, D. L., and Korenberg, M. Maintenance of the sedimentation rate of erythrocytes in cases of cancer. Hodgkin's disease and leukemia. *Canad. M.A.J. 51:* 353-355, 1944.

144. Mendez Huergo, L. M. Reacción de Roffo en el cáncer de estómago. *Bol. Inst. de med. exper. para el estud. y trat. d. cáncer 20:* 641-649, 1943.

145. Menkès, G. Pentolyse et glycolyse. *Arch. d. sc. 2:* 386-393, 1949.

146. Menkès, G. Recherches sur la propriété pentolytique du sérum sanguin. *Bull. schweiz. Akad. d. med. Wissensch. 5:* 280-287, 1949.

147. Menkès, G. Recherches sur la propriété pentolytique du sérum sanguin; étude du ferment et du processu de dégradation. *Arch. d. sc. 2:* 337-339, 1949.

148. Mider, G. B., Alling, E. L., and Morton, J. J. The effect of neoplastic disease and allied diseases on the concentrations of the plasma proteins. *Cancer 3:* 56-65, 1950.

149. Moeschlin, S. Die klinische Verwertbarkeit der fraktionierten Senkungsreaktion (Koster-Feldman) für die Malignomdiagnose. *Helvet. med. acta 11:* 209-224, 1944.

150. Moguilevsky, L. La reacción Roffo: Su importancia como medio de diagnóstico precoz de las neoplasias: Sus modificaciones en el curso de los tratamientos

aplicados en cancerologia: Su valor pronóstico. *Bol. Inst. de med. exper. para el estud. y trat. d. cáncer 21:* 621-625, 1944.

151. MOORE, C., and ROBERTS, W. M. The diagnostic significance of HCl and of lactic acid in the stomach-contents in cancer of the stomach. *Quart. J. Med. 22:* Proceedings of the Association of Physicians of Great Britain and Ireland (appended), 1928.
152. MUNRO, L. A. Protective colloids in cancer. *J. Phys. Chem. 48:* 187-195, 1944.
153. MURRAY, I., and ROBERTSON, A. B. The significance and origin of lactic acid in the gastric contents. *Brit. M. J. 1:* 607-609, 1932.
154. NEUWIRTH, I., and KLOSTERMAN, J. A. Demonstration of rapid production of lactic acid in the oral cavity. *Proc. Soc. Exper. Biol. & Med. 45:* 464-467, 1940.
155. NEVER, H. E., and VINCKE, E. Euber einen einfachen Nachweis von Milchsäure im Mageninhalt. *Klin. Wchnschr. 15:* 1910-1912, 1936.
156. NORPOTH, L., and KADEN, E. Untersuchungen über die Milchsäure des Magensaftes. *Arch. f. exper. Path. u. Pharmakol. 169:* 414-428, 1933.
157. ODELL, L. D., and BURT, J. C. β-Glucuronidase activity in human female genital cancer. *Cancer Research 9:* 362-365, 1949.
158. ODELL, L. D., BURT, J., and BETHEA, R. β-Glucuronidase activity. *Science 109:* 564-565, 1949.
159. ORNSTEIN, I. La réaction de Kopaczewski dans la pellagre. *Compt. rend. Soc. d. biol. 121:* 574-576, 1936.
160. OSWALD, W., and KUTTELWASCHER, H. Zur serologischen Antigen-Analyse der Impftumoren. *Ztschr. f. Immunitätsforsch. u. exper. Therap. 98:* 427-430, 1940.
161. PAPANICOLAOU, G. N., and TRAUT, H. F. *Diagnosis of Uterine Cancer by the Vaginal Smear.* New York, The Commonwealth Fund, 1943.
162. PETERMANN, M. L., and HOGNESS, K. R. Electrophoretic studies on the plasma proteins of patients with neoplastic disease: I. Gastric cancer; II. An acid protein present in the plasma. *Cancer 1:* 100-103, 104-108, 1948.
163. PETERMANN, M. L., KARNOFSKY, D. A., and HOGNESS, K. R. Electrophoretic studies on the plasma proteins of patients with neoplastic disease: III. Lymphomas and leukemia. *Cancer 1:* 109-119, 1948.
164. PHILLIPS, S. K., and MCDONALD, J. R. An evaluation of various examinations performed on serous fluids. *Am. J. M. Sc. 216:* 121-128, 1948.
165. POLLACK, O. J., and LEONARD, A. Diagnostic value of the iodoacetate index. *J.A.M.A. 142:* 872-875, 1950.
166. PRESSMAN, D., HILL, R. F., and FOOTE, F. W. The zone of localization of anti-mouse-kidney serums as determined by radioautographs. *Science 109:* 65-66, 1949.
167. RIGLER, L. G. X-ray aspects of gastric cancer. Abstract, *Proc. Fourth Conf. Gastric Cancer*, San Francisco, 1948.
168. ROBERTS, E., RONZONI, E., and FRANKELS, S. Influence of ACTH on the urinary secretion of amino acids. *Cancer Research 1:* 275, 1951.
169. ROBERTSON, F. N. Further work on test for cancer. *Bull. Vancouver M. A. 17:* 155-158, 1941.
170. ROBERTSON, J. D. *Gastric Acidity: An Historical and Experimental study.* London, John Murray, Middlesex Hospital Press, 1931.
171. ROCHE, J. THOAI, N.-VAN, MARCELET, J., DESRUISSEAUX, G., and DURAND, S. Sur l'inversion de l'activation de la phosphatase alcaline du sérum par l'ion zinc chez de nombreux cancéreux. *Bull. Acad. de méd., Paris 130:* 294-298, 1946.

172. Roffo, A. H. Existencia en la sangre y en la orina de cancerosos y embarazadas de un principio activo de crecimiento esplénico. *Bol. Inst. de med. exper. para el estud. y trat. d. cáncer 17:* 415-458, 1940.

173. Roffo, A. H. Hormona tumoral gonadotrópica en los cancerosos. *Bol. Inst. de med. exper. para el estud. y trat. d. cáncer 21:* 419-586, 1944.

174. Sainz, P. A., and Rodriguez, A. El dietetoquimograma. *Rev. méd. cubana 53:* 1033-1040, 1942.

175. Salomon, H., and Saxl, P. Ueber einen Harnbefund bei Karzinomatösen. *Wien. klin. Wchnschr. 22:* 1768-1769, 1909.

176. Salomon, H., and Saxl, P. Eine Schwefelreaktion im Harne Krebskranker. *Wien. klin. Wchnschr. 24:* 449-451, 1911.

177. Savignac, R. J., Grant, J. C., and Sizer, I. W. Reducing properties of serum from malignant and nonmalignant patients and from normal individuals. *A.A.A.S. Research Conference on Cancer*, Washington, D. C., American Association for the Advancement of Science, 1945, pp. 241-253.

178. Scheller, R. Ueber den Milchsäuregehalt pathologischer Ergüsse. *München. med. Wchnschr. 73:* 1879-1881, 1926.

179. Schmidt, H. W. Erfahrungen zur polarographischen Krebsdiagnose im enteiweissten Serum. *Ztschr. f. Krebsforsch. 50:* 390-406, 1940.

180. Seibert, F. B., Seibert, M. V., Atno, A. J., and Campbell, H. W. Variation in protein and polysaccharide content of sera in chronic diseases, tuberculosis, sarcoidosis and carcinoma. *J. Clin. Investigation 26:* 90-102, 1947.

181. Shen, S. C., and Homburger, F. Studies on effusions: II. A simple technique for the discovery of cancer cells in neoplastic exudates. *Cancer 3:* 36-42, 1950.

182. Shetlar, M. R., Foster, J. V., Kelly, K. H., and Everett, M. R. The serum polysaccharide level in malignancy and in other pathological conditions. *Cancer Research 9:* 515-519, 1949.

183. Spellberg, M. A., and Keeton, R. W. Excretion of ascorbic acid in relation to saturation and utilization, with some diagnostic implications. *Arch. Int. Med. 63:* 1095-1116, 1939.

184. Stadie, W. C. The reducing properties of serum from subjects with malignant disease. *Science 108:* 211, 1948.

185. Stahl, O., and Warburg, O. Ueber Milchsäuregärung eines menschlichen Blasencarcinoms. *Klin. Wchnschr. 5:* 1218, 1926.

186. State, D., Gaviser, D., Hubbard, T. B., Jr., and Wangensteen, O. H. An attempt to determine likely precursor groups of gastric cancer. *J. Nat. Cancer Inst. 10:* 443-453, Disc. 491-496, 1949.

187. Stuckert, B. G. La reacción de Roffo: Su importancia diagnóstica en la clínica del cáncer: Resultados obtenidos en 9005 reacciones. *Bol. Inst. de med. exper. para el estud. y trat. d. cancer 18:* 1141-1181, 1941.

188. Tantini, E. Ricerche di controllo alla reazione di lattogelificazione dei sieri secondo Kopaczewski. *Tumori 10:* 56-76, 1936.

189. Tetzner, E. Ueber den Nachweis von Abbaufermenten im Harn bei Tumoren mittels der Abderhaldenschen Reaktion. *Ztschr. f. Krebsforsch. 50:* 465-471, 1940.

190. Thomas, J. De la serologie du cancer. *Bol. Inst. de med. exper. para el estud. y trat. d. cancer 4:* 611-631, 1927.

191. Trafton, H., and Perkin, H. J. The clinical significance of serum acid phosphatase with especial reference to carcinoma of the prostate gland. *Lahey Clin. Bull. 4:* 59-63, 1944.

192. TUNO, S. Studien über die Harn-Protease: III. Mitteilung. Ueber die Krebsdiagnose mittels der Harnprotease. *J. Biochem. 32:* 371-388, 1940; Abstr. in *Hukuoka acta med. 33:* (Abstr. Sect.) 93-94, 1940.

193. TWOMBLY, G. H., TEMPLE, H. M., and DEAN, A. L. Clinical value of the Aschheim-Zondek test in the diagnosis of testicular tumors. *J.A.M.A. 118:* 106-111, 1942.

194. WALDSCHMIDT-LEITZ, E. Über diagnostisch verwertbare Veränderungen im Serum bei Krebs. *Angew. Chemie 51:* 324-327, 1938.

195. WALDSCHMIDT-LEITZ, E., and HATSCHEK, R. Zur Frage des Vorkommens von sterisch auslesenden Enzymen im Carcinomatösen Organismus. Bemerkungen zur Arbeit von H. Bayerle und F. H. Podloucky. *Ztschr. f. physiol. Chem. 264:* 196-197, 1940.

196. WALDSCHMIDT-LEITZ, E., HATSCHEK, R., and HAUSMANN, R. Ueber d-Peptidase im Serum. *Ztschr. f. physiol. Chem. 267:* 79-90, 1940.

197. WARBURG, O. Ueber Carcinomversuche. *Klin. Wchnschr. 5:* 2119, 1926.

198. WARBURG, O., and CHRISTIAN, W. Gärungsfermente im Blutserum von Tumor Ratten. *Biochem. Ztschr. 314:* 399-408, 1943.

199. WARBURG, O., WIND, F., and NEGELEIN, E. Ueber den Stoffwechsel von Tumoren im Körper. *Klin. Wchnschr. 5:* 829-832, 1926.

200. WEIL, E., and BRAUN, H. Ueber Antikörper bei Tumoren. *Wien klin. Wchnschr. 18:* 650-652, 1908.

201. WEIL, R. The antitryptic activity of human blood serum: Its significance and its diagnostic value. *Am. J. M. Sc. 139:* 714-725, 1910.

202. WEIS, I. Beitrag zur Frage einer biochemischen Krebsdiagnostik: Ueber Beeinflussung des Erythrozytenstoffwechsels durch Carotin bei Gesunden und Karzinomkranken. *Krebsarzt 4:* 63-74, 1949.

203. WEST, P. M., RAPAPORT, S. I., and TEMPEREAU, C. E. Enzymatic evaluation of therapeutic agents in cancer. *Cancer 4:* 177-183, 1951.

204. WILT, J., and NICHOLSON, D. Effects of urine extracts from cancer patients on rat gonads and spleen. *Cancer 3:* 290-298, 1950.

205. WINZLER, R. J., and BURK, D. Blood proteose and cancer. *J. Nat. Cancer Inst. 4:* 417-428, 1944.

206. WINZLER, R. J., and SMITH, I. M. Studies on the mucoproteins of human plasma: II. Plasma mucoprotein levels in cancer patients. *J. Clin. Investigation 27:* 617-619, 1948.

207. WINZLER, R. J., DEVOR, A. W., MEHL, J. W., and SMYTH, I. M. Studies on the mucoproteins of human plasma: I. Determination and isolation. *J. Clin. Investigation 27:* 609-616, 1948.

208. WOGLOM, W. H. The reaction of the cancer cell. *J. Cancer Research 8:* 34-44, 1924.

209. WOLFF, J. *Die Lehre von der Krebskrankheit von den ältesten Zeiten bis zur Gegenwart.* Jena, Gustav Fisher, 1911, Vol. II, pp. 450-458.

210. WOODHOUSE, D. L. The chemodiagnosis of malignancy. *Am. J. Cancer 40:* 359-374, 1940.

211. WOODWARD, G. E. Hydrolysis of glutathione by blood serum. *Biochem. J. 33:* 1171-1174, 1939.

212. YOUNG, N. F., and HOMBURGER, F. (introduced by GALLAGHER, T. F.) The application of paper chromatography to the study of amino aciduria in patients with liver disease. *Federation Proc. 7:* 201, 1948 (and unpublished data).

CHAPTER 29

Chemotherapy

Alfred Gellhorn

PRESENT STATUS OF RESEARCH

The accomplishments of chemotherapy in malignant disease of man are not comparable with the dramatic successes achieved by antibacterial chemotherapy. The tremendous advances achieved in this latter field of medical therapy, however, have had a powerful influence on cancer chemotherapy because the demonstration that a chemical compound can selectively destroy an invading micro-organism has spurred the hope that a similar effect on the neoplastic cell may be achieved. Sober reflection of the comparative difficulties posed by the therapy of infection and of cancer leads to the realization that there are a number of fundamental differences in the two problems. In microbial infections the offending invader is foreign to the host and efficient defense mechanisms provide strong support to supplement and complement the effects of chemotherapeutic drugs. The malignant cell, on the other hand, is qualitatively indistinguishable from the normal cells of the body and no innate restrictive defenses are mobilized against it.

In spite of the recognized basic difficulties which theoretically raise the odds impressively against successful chemotherapy of malignant disease, the practical problem of the therapeutic management of disseminated cancer is so great that enormous efforts have been made and will continue to be directed toward its solution. When it is appreciated that after the diagnosis has been made only about 25 per cent of patients with malignant disease are salvaged for five years by currently available therapeutic measures, the emphasis on research in the field of cancer chemotherapy is more readily understood.

At the present time the cancer problem is being investigated from every angle. It is possible that fundamental studies of normal and abnormal growth will illuminate the intimate mechanisms of the neoplastic cell so that a completely rational chemotherapeutic approach can be developed. It is also conceivable, however, that empiric trials of chemical compounds against neoplastic disease may lead to the discovery of an agent which can be used both as a therapeutic agent and as a tool for the investigation of basic cellular biology. The problem of malignant disease is so urgent that both approaches merit effort and support.

In the past ten years a number of drugs have been introduced for the treatment of disseminated neoplastic disease. Although the scientific and medical literature has emphasized that these chemical compounds do not cure cancer in any form, the lay press has often been unduly enthusiastic. In order to prevent painful disillusionment of the public it is important for physicians and surgeons to know the facts so that proper interpretations can be made to their nonprofessional associates. In this regard it is just as fallacious to indicate that no advances have been made in cancer chemotherapy as it is to paint an overoptimistic picture of the present status of the problem.

In this chapter four types of drugs will be described in detail, nitrogen mustards, urethane, the folic acid antagonists, and hormones, because their judicious use is of practical value in selected cases of malignant disease. A number of other chemical compounds which have been carefully investigated in the laboratory and the clinic but have failed to make a useful contribution in the therapeutic management of malignancy will be briefly discussed in order to illustrate the difficulties of transferring observations on the experimental animal to man. Finally, a number of therapeutic procedures which have been inadequately evaluated but for which extravagant claims may be made will be reviewed in order to provide the medical practitioner with the available facts.

NITROGEN MUSTARDS

The nitrogen mustards have been intensively and extensively investigated for their clinical value in the therapy of neoplastic disease. Until recently these drugs have been available for investigational purposes only but now, as a result of experience in thousands of cases over a period of eight years, one of the nitrogen mustards is commercially available. For the safe and proper use of this toxic drug it is imperative to have knowledge of its clinical pharmacology and to recognize clearly the indications, contraindications, and limitations of its use. With this information in hand, the nitrogen mustards can contribute significantly to the medical management of the malignant lymphomas, certain blood dyscrasias, and bronchiogenic carcinoma.

HISTORY

The introduction of nitrogen mustards into the therapeutic management of malignant disease was made independently in 1942–1943 by Gilman, Goodman, Lindskog, and Dougherty at Yale, and Jacobson, Spurr, and their associates at the University of Chicago. The developments, however, which led to the clinical study of this agent are closely linked to the history of dichloroethyl sulfide, the dreaded "mustard gas" of the first World War. This latter chemical compound was synthesized by Richie in 1854, rediscovered by Gutherie and Niemann in 1860, and further characterized both chemically and biologically by Victor Meyer in 1886. These chemists appreciated the highly toxic local actions of the haloalkyl sulfide inasmuch as they and their associates in the laboratory sustained severe skin burns from contact with the compound. Meyer conducted experiments on laboratory animals which confirmed the local vesicant action and further noted that when given parenterally in small doses, the dichloroethyl sulfide was lethal. The knowledge of the toxicologic properties of this compound was disregarded until the first World War.

During the spring of 1917 the Germans carried out secret field tests with such satisfactory results that they adopted dichloroethyl sulfide as an artillery shell filling and accumulated a large quantity of these (yellow cross) shells without the knowledge or at least understanding of Allied intelligence. On the night of July 12, 1917, the Germans bombarded the British positions near Ypres in Flanders with these shells. The devastating effect produced by this unexpected chemical offensive warfare is indicated by the statistic of 14,276 casualties processed through British casualty stations in the first weeks of mustard gas use.

Descriptions of sulfur mustard intoxication soon appeared in the medical literature with initial attention focused on the local actions as manifested by skin vesication progressing to deep ulceration, conjunctivitis, photophobia, and lacrimation; irritative laryngitis, bronchitis with intractable cough and aphonia; secondary bronchopneumonia associated with severe damage to alveolar epithelium, massive pulmonary edema and death. Somewhat later, however, serious systemic toxicity was recognized as a major complication of mustard intoxication and descriptions of profound hematopoietic depression, dissolution of lymphoid tissues, and gastrointestinal ulceration were recorded. Laboratory studies designed to define the mechanism of cytotoxic action were undertaken but the termination of the first World War led to the discontinuation of these investigations before a careful evaluation of the problem had been completed.

In the interim between the first and second World Wars only scattered studies on the biologic effects of sulfur mustard were reported; however, there was continued activity in the chemical warfare laboratories of the French and Germans directed toward the discovery of more toxic agents. With the advent of the second World War new compounds were proposed as potential offensive agents. Sulfur mustard shared interest with a series of nitrogen analogs, bis- and tris-(β-chloroethyl) amines. It was soon demonstrated that the nitrogen mustards were also contact vesicants and careful pathologic studies revealed the cytotoxicity of these compounds on a number of tissues following their absorption. As had been noted in the studies with sulfur mustard, lymphoid structures were especially susceptible to damage by the nitrogen mustards. These observations, coupled with the fact that the hydrochloride salts of the nitrogen mustards were crystalline compounds, thereby facilitating their handling, led the groups at Yale and Chicago to explore the therapeutic possibilities of these agents in the malignant lymphomas.

CHEMISTRY

An understanding of the mechanism of action and the clinical pharmacology of the nitrogen mustards must rest on some basic knowledge of the chemistry of these compounds. The structural formulas for sulfur mustard and for the nitrogen mustards used clinically are shown in Fig. 122.

A large series of aliphatic and aromatic nitrogen mustards have been synthesized and studied in the laboratory. Although a number of these compounds have appeared to offer some advantages in experimental chemotherapy of animal tumors or to have been less toxic than HN_2, clinical trials have failed to substantiate the laboratory experience.

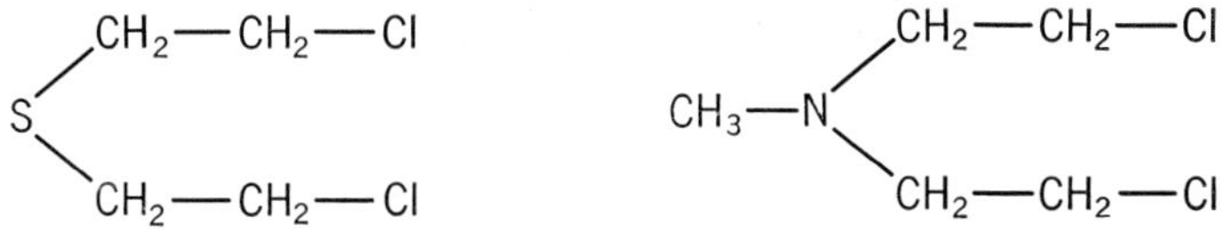

FIG. 122. *Left,* Dichloroethyl sulfide (sulfur mustard, mustard gas, yperite) and (*right*) methyl bis-(β-chloroethyl) amine hydrochloride (nitrogen mustard, HN_2, mechlorethamine, mustargen).

When methyl bis-(β-chloroethyl) (Mechlorethamine hydrochloride)* amine is placed in neutral or alkaline solutions at 37° C. it is rapidly transformed into a cyclic onium cation and Cl^- as shown in Fig. 123.

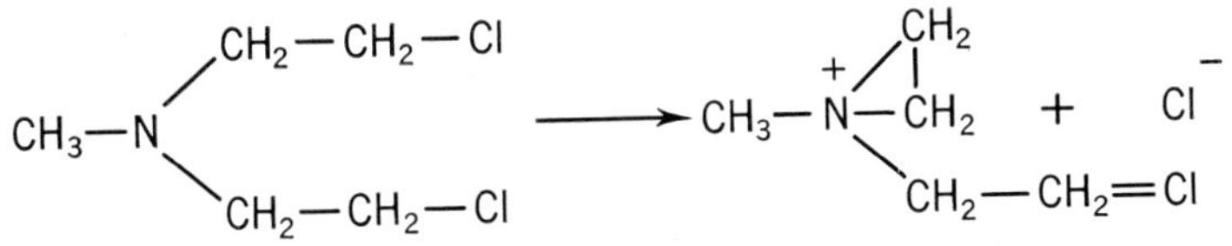

FIG. 123. Intramolecular cyclization of methyl bis-(β-chloroethyl) amine.

This interesting phenomenon of intramolecular cyclization takes on additional importance from the fact that the immonium cation is very reactive chemically. Figure 124 shows how the reaction shown in Fig. 123 would proceed in an aqueous solution.

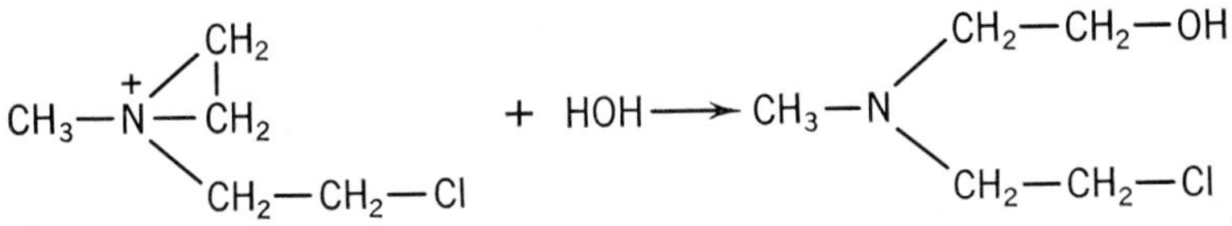

FIG. 124. Second step of reaction of Fig. 123 in aqueous solution.

Under such circumstances, after the first ring had formed and reacted, the second chloroethyl group would undergo cyclization and react in turn (Fig. 125).

It has been clearly established that the biologic activity of nitrogen mustard is related to the formation of the chemically reactive ethyleneonium cation which then is capable of reacting with a variety of chemical radicals. This chemical condensation, which is known as alkylation, has been studied in a large number of chemical

* Trade name of Merck & Co. Inc., Rahway, N. J., under which this compound is commercially available.

compounds of biologic interest which include amino acids, peptides, nicotinic acid and amide, pyridoxine, thiamine, adenine, adenosine, adenylic acid, adenosine triphosphate, guanine, cytidine diphosphate, hexose and triose phosphates, and succinate. The fact that the mustards show such high reactivity with the above relatively simple molecules accounts for the susceptibility of proteins in general to

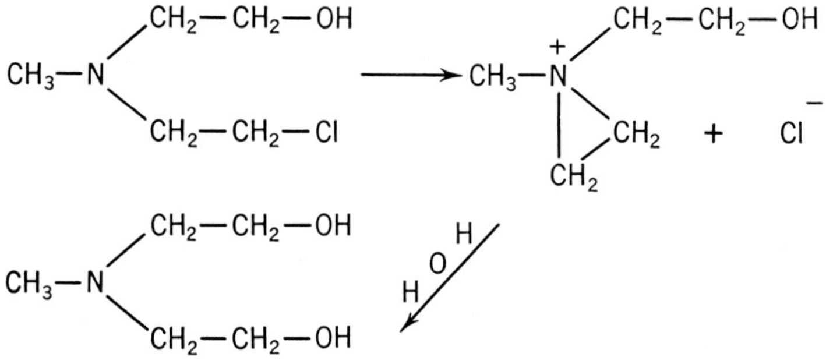

FIG. 125. Third step of reaction of Fig. 123.

alkylation by these compounds. Nucleoproteins, serum proteins, hemoglobin, collagen, and others have been proven to react with the mustards. Considerable attention has also been directed toward the study of enzyme inactivation by chemical reaction with the alkylamines. Surprisingly it has been found that the function of the majority of enzymes is not interfered with when they are incubated in vitro with these compounds in low concentrations. However, a small group of enzymes, including hexokinase and adenosinetriphosphatase which are concerned with phosphate transfer, and cholineoxidase, cholinesterase, and cholineacetylase, are readily inactivated in vitro by the mustards.

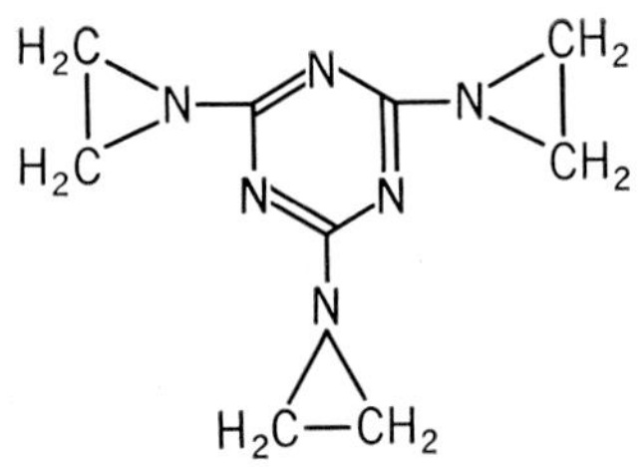

FIG. 126. 2,4,6-Triethylene-imino-*s*-triazine (triethylenemelamine, TEM).

More recently a new type of nitrogen mustard has received experimental and clinical attention. From the experience to date, it appears likely that this drug will be useful in clinical cancer therapy and therefore it will be discussed in this section and subsequently (Fig. 126).

It is to be noted that this drug is a heterocyclic compound with three ethylene imine side groups whereas the other nitrogen mustard pictured is a chlorinated ethylamine. It will be recalled that when HN_2 is placed in alkaline solution a reactive quarternary ethyleneonium cation is formed. In the case of TEM on the other hand, the ethylene imine configuration occurs with the nitrogen in the trivalent state. One important consequence of this is that triethylene melamine is relatively stable in alkaline solution but in acid solutions the immonium cation is formed which is chemically reactive. The reaction of 2,4,6-triethylene-imino-*s*-triazine in an acid solution with an amino acid might be visualized as in Fig. 127.

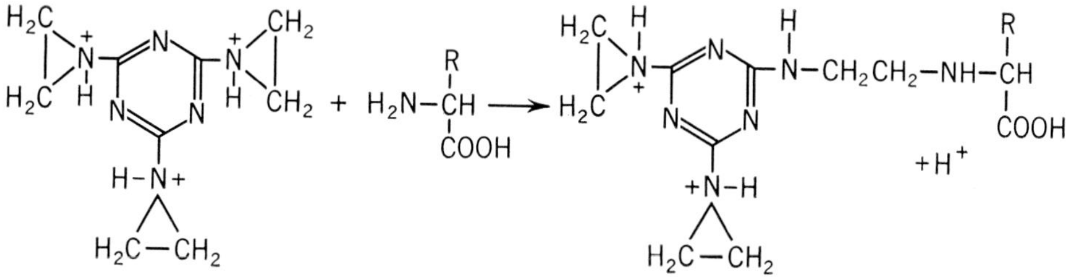

FIG. 127. Reaction of 2,4,6-triethylene-imino-*s*-triazine with amino acid in acid solution.

Although at the present time far less study of the chemical reactions of TEM has been conducted than of HN_2, the pharmacologic investigations suggest that this compound will duplicate the properties noted for the sulfur and the alkyl nitrogen mustards.

MECHANISM OF ACTION

The pharmacology of the nitrogen mustards is complex because, depending on the dosage administered, a variety of actions on different organ and tissue systems can be elicited. Thus at acutely lethal doses there is marked stimulation of the central nervous system resulting in tonic and clonic convulsions and death due to respiratory arrest. At these high doses parasympathomimetic effects are demonstrable, manifested by miosis, salivation, bronchorrhea, bronchospasm, intestinal spasm, and so on. This is followed by a parasympatholytic action. Careful study of these latter pharmacologic phenomena has shown that the mustards are not acting directly on the autonomic nervous system but are stimulating or depressing postganglionic cholinergic effector cells.

With subconvulsive doses of HN_2 a delayed neurologic disturbance occurs, resulting in progressive paralysis of all striated muscles. The paralytic syndrome appears to be due to disruption of the motor function of the central nervous system rather than to peripheral effects of the chemical compound, because transmission of electrical impulses by motor nerves and function of the myoneural junction and of muscles is unimpaired.

Further consideration of these fascinating pharmacologic actions of HN_2 is not justified here, for they have no counterpart in the human subject. Of real pertinence to the clinician using nitrogen mustard, however, is the delayed lethal syndrome observed in mammalian species, particularly dogs, following the administration of a minimum lethal dose of the drug. The events which characterize this syndrome take three to seven days and result either in death of the experimental animal or in recovery. Anorexia is evident in the first day following the injection of the drug and persists throughout the period. Associated with this there is loss of weight which, however, exceeds the effect of starvation alone. Usually profuse vomiting occurs within several hours after intoxication and continues for two or three days. On the third day there is the onset of diarrhea, which progresses to ulceration of the gastrointestinal tract with large losses of fluid, electrolytes, and blood. The syndrome is complicated by marked depression of hematopoiesis manifested by progressive lymphopenia, granulocytopenia, and thrombopenia. Complex disturbances of electrolyte and water metabolism also occurs, with loss of intracellular potassium and cellular dehydration. Terminally, there is hypothermia and shock, followed in several hours by coma and respiratory failure.

The precise cause of death in nitrogen-mustard intoxicated animals is understandably obscure. The disruptions of physiologic function produced by the hemorrhagic necrosis of the gastrointestinal tract, by aplasia of the bone marrow, and by alterations of electrolyte and water distribution due to toxic effects on cells, as well as possibly on renal transport systems, are extensive and interrelated. The problem is further complicated by the fact that correction of the obvious abnormalities by appropriate substitution therapy in the form of transfusions, electrolyte solutions and so on, fails to prevent the lethal outcome. This suggests that subtle toxic effects on the cells are produced which irreparably damage their function.

The toxic manifestations and pathologic changes produced by HN_2 resemble in many details the effects of total body roentgen irradiation. The radiomimetic action of the chemical compound accounts, in part, for the great efforts that have been put forth to discover its intimate mechanism of action, because it has been hoped that the understanding thus gained would shed light on cellular effects produced by ionizing radiation.

It must be admitted that the precise mechanism of mustard action is still not known. As was mentioned before, the nitrogen mustards can inactivate enzymes; however, the theory that this accounts for the observed changes produced by HN_2 in the animal body does not appear tenable. Most of the "sensitive" enzymes cited were not appreciably inactivated by concentrations of mustard below 10^{-4} M. Since even in minimum lethal doses of HN_2 the concentration would not be greater than 10^{-5} M, it appears unlikely that a direct inhibitory effect on enzymes is of major importance.

There is increasing evidence from biochemical, histochemical, and morphologic studies which points to the nucleic acids as the cellular site of action of these chemical compounds. Cytologic experiments have demonstrated mitotic inhibition of cells exposed to extremely low concentrations of mustard, and specific alterations of chromosomal structure are characteristic in these cells. Since it has been established that the chromosome is a complex nucleoprotein which is qualitatively different—by virtue of the desoxypentose nucleic acids present—from the cytoplasmic nucleoprotein, the morphologic evidence suggests that the mustards react with these chemical entities. The induction of heritable mutations in Drosophila and in certain fungi by the mustards also provides convincing proof that these chemical agents alter chromosomal function.

The inactivation of viruses, particularly those rich in desoxypentose nucleic acids, the changes in viscosity of thymonucleate, and the evidence which indicates suppression of desoxypentose nucleic acid synthesis, all produced by the mustards, suggest that disturbances in anabolism of nucleic acids and/or interference with the cyclic polymerization and depolymerization of these important molecules account for the cellular effects observed.

In summarizing the basic science of the nitrogen mustards which is pertinent to their clinical application, the following points should be noted:

1. The biologic effects of the nitrogen mustards are related to the chemical reactivity of the ethylene immonium cation formed when the drugs are in solution under proper *p*H conditions.
2. The toxicity of nitrogen mustard closely parallels that produced by total body roentgen irradiation. The chemical compound and the physical agent both have the greatest effect on rapidly proliferating cells such as those of the hematopoietic system, the intestinal tract, and the gonads.
3. The intimate mechanism of action of nitrogen mustard is probably related to alterations of the metabolism of nucleoprotein, particularly of the desoxypentose nucleic acids of the nucleus.

CLINICAL TOXICITY

The toxicity of nitrogen mustard in therapeutic doses is appreciable and the safe use of this drug requires a knowledge of the toxic manifestations. These may be conveniently divided into local and systemic categories.

Local Toxicity

Local toxicity should rarely be observed if the nitrogen mustards are administered as described in the following section. If, however, there is leakage of the nitrogen mustard solution into the subcutaneous tissues, the cytotoxic action of the chemical compound will be evidenced by a painful inflammatory reaction which may proceed to sloughing of the involved area. Usually the end result of such a leakage is a brawny indurated area which persists and is tender for a prolonged period. If there is infiltration of the subcutaneous tissue through faulty intravenous administration and this is recognized early, prompt injection into the involved area of one-sixth molar sodium thiosulfate or even isotonic saline together with the application of an ice compress for a period of six to twelve hours will minimize the local damage. The rationale for these procedures is that nitrogen mustard will react with thiosulfate more rapidly than other substances and saline will at least dilute the mustard present. The cold environment will slow the rate of chemical reaction of the mustard, thus providing time for dissipation of the mustard by absorption or dilution.

Phlebothrombosis or thrombophlebitis is another local toxic effect of the mustards which should rarely occur if the drug is injected into the tubing of a saline infusion. Since the mustards will damage the endothelium of veins with resulting thrombophlebitis if the contact is prolonged and the concentration adequate, attention should be given to avoid these conditions in patients with elevated venous pressure in the antebrachial veins, such as those with mediastinal tumor and partial obstruction of the great veins in the superior mediastinum.

Systemic Toxicity

The systemic toxicity of the nitrogen mustards is evidenced by gastrointestinal symptoms, depression of the circulating formed elements of the blood, disturbances in blood coagulation, and skin eruptions. The latter two manifestations are uncommon, whereas the first two are characteristic.

The nausea and vomiting that occurs following the intravenous injection of the mustards is central in origin and usually starts one to three hours after the administration of the drug. Nausea and anorexia may persist for twenty-four hours after a single injection, but emesis usually stops in the first eight hours. Although some observers believe that a measure of tolerance develops to the emetic actions of nitrogen mustards, this is not very great at best and unless measures are adopted to minimize this unpleasant effect, the patient will usually have a miserable experience. With therapeutic dosages, ulceration of the gastrointestinal epithelium does not occur and the bloody diarrhea characteristic of lethal doses in experimental animals has not been reported in the literature.

Hematologic Effects. Hematologic effects of the nitrogen mustards constitute the limiting factor in determining the dosage. The changes which occur in the peripheral blood have been described repeatedly and are now recognized to follow a characteristic pattern. The first change is a lymphocytopenia which usually is apparent within twenty-four hours of the first dose of the drug and progresses for six to eight days. The total leukocyte count declines due to neutropenia for ten days to three weeks. It is significant that although a granulocytopenia exists, agranulocytosis is a rarity. This probably accounts for the fact that severe infections are not a major complication of HN_2 therapy. The duration of the leukopenia is relatively short and recovery is complete within two weeks of the maximum reduction.

It is difficult to give representative figures for the leukocyte counts at the various stages, because the type and stage of the disease and the previous treatments are important factors in determining both the initial levels and the effect of mustard therapy. For example, in disseminated Hodgkin's disease the total white count may be low owing to the generalized disease or to recent radio- or chemotherapy. Treatment with nitrogen mustard might well result in a rise in the white cell count in the former situation, whereas in the latter a profound depression might reasonably be expected.

A variable degree of thrombocytopenia is usually present in the second or third week after completion of the course of treatment. This occasionally leads to hemorrhagic manifestations including bleeding from the gums and gastrointestinal tract, or petechiae and small subcutaneous hematomas. Fortunately in the majority of instances the purpura is transient and fatalities have not been reported except in patients in whom the underlying disease was far advanced.

Erythrocyte and hemoglobin levels decline during the first two weeks after a course of nitrogen mustard but rarely by more than 300,000 cells per cubic millimeter or 1.0 Gm. of hemoglobin per 100 milliliters. Studies of total urobilinogen excretion indicate an increase in intravascular hemolysis.

Morphologic studies of the bone marrow in patients receiving nitrogen mustard have consistently revealed depression of hematopoietic activity with all degrees of hypoplasia up to aplasia. The changes are manifest by the fourth day after treatment and are maximal by the tenth day. Incipient regeneration—shown by nucleated red cells, leukocyte precursors, premyelocytes, myelocytes, young polymorphs, and megakaryocytes—becomes evident in two to three weeks and general hyperplasia is present between the fifth and seventh weeks. It is to be recalled that the sensitivity of cells to the toxic action of HN_2 is related to their rate of proliferation. For this reason it is advisable to space courses of nitrogen mustard at intervals of greater than six weeks in order to avoid damage to bone marrow function when the hematopoietic cells are maximally susceptible.

Following lethal doses of roentgen irradiation or nitrogen mustard a hemorrhagic syndrome has been observed in experimental animals, which is due to an excessive amount of an anticoagulant in the circulation, presumably heparin. Hyperheparinemia rarely occurs following a therapeutic course of nitrogen mustard. Although bleeding complications of nitrogen mustard therapy are certainly more frequently due to thrombopenia than to an excessive concentration of heparin or a heparin-like substance, this latter possibility should be borne in mind, since the intravenous administration of protamine or the basic dye, toluidine blue, will specifically correct the condition.

Skin Reactions. A generalized maculopapular skin eruption following HN_2 therapy has been occasionally observed. This is probably an idiosyncratic manifestation rather than a true hypersensitivity due to the reaction of antigen and antibodies, because the skin reaction does not necessarily recur in subsequent courses of therapy. In any event, this type of skin reaction is rare and constitutes no contraindication to future therapy. As has been mentioned earlier, petechiae and purpuric skin lesions may occur associated with thrombopenia. Another skin lesion which may develop is herpes zoster. It would appear that a latent herpes infection is not uncommonly present in patients, particularly those with malignant lymphomas, and nitrogen mustard or radiotherapy may be followed by overt manifestations of the virus disease. In such cases it is not unusual to observe a flare-up of herpes zoster with each course of mustard therapy.

Menstrual Disturbances. A minor complication of HN_2 therapy but one which may cause emotional distress to female patients is a temporary disturbance of the menstrual cycle. The next catamenia following a course of nitrogen mustard is usually delayed or occasionally may be skipped. In some instances several consecutive menstrual periods may be missed. This effect is presumably due to arrest of maturation of the graafian follicles but no permanent damage to ovarian function has been observed.

ADMINISTRATION AND DOSAGE

Methyl bis-(β-chloroethyl) amine hydrochloride, "mechlorethamine," must be freshly dissolved and administered intravenously. In order to avoid the potential hazard of thrombophlebitis and/or infiltration of the subcutaneous tissues with the drug, it is strongly recommended that the nitrogen mustard be injected into the rubber tubing of an intravenous infusion set. This gives assurance that the needle is properly within the lumen of the vein and the rapid dilution of the drug by the infusing fluid prevents a high concentration of the compound, which otherwise may locally damage the vascular endothelium. The nitrogen mustard is injected into the rubber tubing rather than added to the entire volume of the infusion in order to minimize a chemical reaction between the drug and the solution. It is for this same reason that the drug is dissolved immediately before use.

Nausea and Vomiting

Nausea and vomiting are characteristic sequelae of nitrogen mustard injections if nothing is done to ameliorate the symptoms. The usual drugs for relieving the symptoms of radiation sickness or the nausea and vomiting of pregnancy such as pyridoxine and dramamine have been tried with little success. Since these unpleasant symptoms are due to stimulation of the medullary emetic center, the most satisfactory procedure has been to depress the central nervous system by means of barbiturates. This is usually done by giving 0.3–0.4 Gm. of a short-acting hypnotic such as pentobarbital ("nembutal") or "seconal" in divided doses one or two hours before the administration of the nitrogen mustard and, if the patient is in the hospital, by administering 0.06 Gm. of sodium luminal subcutaneously if nausea or vomiting occurs later.

If the patient is adequately sedated so that he sleeps soundly, vomiting can be prevented or appreciably decreased.

A more heroic and also more effective procedure is the administration of scopolamine by hypodermic injection and pentobarbital intravenously. Following this, patients will sleep for twelve hours and after this time the effect of the mustard on the emetic center is past. Obviously this requires hospitalization of the patient and preferably supervision by the anesthesiologist; for these reasons it probably will not be used in the great majority of treatments. It is preferable to give the nitrogen mustard injections at night whenever possible, because the normal habits of sleep and the decrease of disturbing stimuli, such as noise, facilitate the action of the sedative regimen.

Intra-arterial Injection

Another method of administration of the nitrogen mustards still in the experimental stage is by the intra-arterial route. A polyethylene catheter is inserted into an artery which principally supplies blood to a tumor-bearing area of the body and then multiple doses of nitrogen mustard are injected over intervals of several days. The rationale for this procedure rests on the fact that nitrogen mustard is rapidly fixed to tissues after injection, and by injecting the compound intra-arterially the major fraction of the dose is removed by the tissues supplied by the artery. This permits the administration of far larger doses than could be tolerated following intravenous injection, because only a small part of the drug gets into the systemic circulation to depress hematopoietic function. This method of administration would be ideally suited for a discrete carcinoma which received its blood supply from a single accessible artery. This is rarely met, however, and in practical experience there is considerable damage to surrounding normal tissues which also receive their blood supply from the same artery that serves the neoplasm.

Dosage

Many dosage regimens have been explored for intravenous nitrogen mustard. Although an apodictic statement is not possible, the consensus of investigators is that 0.4 mg. per Kg. body weight represents the total dose for a course of HN_2 in the majority of cases. This is best given in divided doses. According to the majority of reports, 0.1 mg. per Kg. body weight has been given on four successive days; no greater toxicity is noted, however, if the course is compressed into two injections of 0.2 mg. per Kg. at twenty-four-hour intervals. Since the nausea and vomiting is no greater with the larger dose, it is more satisfactory and more economical to shorten the treatment period. In certain patients with normal hematopoietic function—in cases of bronchiogenic carcinoma, for example—larger doses of nitrogen mustard may be given. Thus in many clinics, total doses of 0.6 or even 0.8 mg. per Kg. body weight are administered. If this is done, however, the incidence of serious depression of bone marrow function rises and it must be recognized that a greater risk is associated with these larger doses.

At the present time the commercially available preparation of HN_2, "mechlorethamine," is packaged in sterile, rubber-topped vials containing 10 mg. of the drug together with 90 mg. of sodium chloride.

At the time of administration, 10 cc. of sterile water is injected into the vial and the contents dissolved by brisk agitation; the required dose is then withdrawn into the syringe and the injection made into the tubing of an intravenous infusion as previously described.

CLINICAL APPLICATION

Hodgkin's Disease

The results of HN_2 therapy in over 400 cases of Hodgkin's disease have been reported in the literature and there is impressive agreement among clinical observers on the value of nitrogen mustard in the management of this malignant disease. This does not imply that chemotherapy has supplanted conventional radiotherapy, but rather that the drug, if judiciously used, can supplement and complement roentgen-ray therapy.

A primary criterion which should be met before even considering HN_2 therapy of Hodgkin's disease is evidence of disseminated disease. It is appreciated that it is not yet known whether this disease has a primary focus from which generalized metastases stem or whether it originates in multiple foci. From a practical standpoint, however, this is academic, because experience has demonstrated that vigorous therapy of the apparent primary manifestation of the disease may be followed by protracted remissions measurable in terms of years. Since it is now definitely known that nitrogen mustard is incapable of curing Hodgkin's disease or any other neoplastic process, it is not logical to employ a systemic agent for the control of a localized area of disease. For this reason aggressive radiotherapy with the delivery of cancericidal doses of roentgen-rays is indicated when careful physical and roentgen examinations indicate that only a single site is involved by the malignant process. In some clinics radical surgery with or without postoperative irradiation is employed under such circumstances, but insufficient evidence is available at this time to advocate this procedure as a routine.

When Hodgkin's disease is obviously generalized, as evidenced by lymphadenopathy in several superficial regions of the body, hepatosplenomegaly, fever and other constitutional symptoms, intrathoracic disease, or osseous involvement, then a choice between radiotherapy and chemotherapy can be considered.

One of the most constant effects of nitrogen mustard in Hodgkin's disease is the reduction of fever to normal temperatures within a few days. Associated with this response there is a rapid subjective improvement, with greatly improved appetite and dramatic increase in general strength. Prior to the availability of nitrogen mustard, roentgen-ray therapy to the retroperitoneal region accomplished the same end results, but the response was relatively slow. For this reason many clinics routinely administer nitrogen mustard under these circumstances and, after the patient has been afebrile for a week or two, radiotherapy is initiated to any areas of evident residual disease. This offers a rapid and effective method for controlling both constitutional symptoms and localized accumulations of disease.

In many patients extensive lymphadenopathy and hepatosplenomegaly are present together with such symptoms as malaise or anorexia. In this situation, irradiation of multiple areas of involvement is impractical because of the time required and the deleterious effects on hematopoiesis. Nitrogen mustard is helpful and advantageous because it attacks the disease in all areas at once. Again, after an interval of two weeks, radiotherapy of sites in which regression has been incomplete can be carried out.

When Hodgkin's disease compresses vital structures, such as those in the mediastinum due to hilar adenopathy or the spinal cord due to an extramedullary mass, nitrogen mustard often offers dramatic relief. The advantages of chemotherapy in these situations are the rapidity of the effect and the absence of an associated inflammatory reaction. The vascular engorgement and edema, a characteristic tissue reaction to irradiation, may lead to greater compression of important structures before there is shrinkage of the tumor. In order to avoid such a complication, radiotherapy must be given in small doses until there has been a sufficient decrease in tumor size so that the radiation reaction can be disregarded. The drug counterpart of this tissue response is only seen following intra-arterial nitrogen mustard.

Pruritus and bone pain may be strikingly ameliorated by HN_2 therapy, although the results are not as consistently good as in the control of fever.

As might be expected, the stage of the disease and the number and types of treatments previously employed are important factors influencing the response to nitrogen mustard therapy. In the advanced stages of disease or after many courses of roentgen-ray treatment, the responses to nitrogen mustard may be brief, incomplete, or nil. However, before the terminal phase of the disease has been reached, an appreciable beneficial response can be expected in about 80 per cent of patients to whom nitrogen mustard courses have been administered. The duration of the remissions induced by the chemical compound is subject to many variables of interpretation, so that a quantitative expression is grossly inaccurate. A median duration of six weeks probably is a fair and reasonable characterization of the remission interval.

In spite of the large number of reports describing the early responses of Hodgkin's disease to chemotherapy, there are only a few quantitative evaluations of the contribution of this therapy over a protracted time interval. In one such report, a comparison of the life expectancy in patients treated with nitrogen mustard and radiotherapy in alternating courses with that of patients treated by radiotherapy alone demonstrated no significant effect of the combined therapeutic regimen. Even though nitrogen mustard fails to alter the duration of the disease, evidence has been accumulated showing that the amount of roentgen-ray therapy required can be materially reduced by the use of chemotherapy, that patients can be made asymptomatic for a greater proportion of the course of the disease and that the economic burden can be significantly reduced through shorter hospitalizations and fewer x-ray treatments.

Lymphosarcoma

The immediate response of patients with lymphosarcomas to nitrogen mustard therapy is qualitatively similar to that noted in Hodgkin's disease. Constitutional symptoms, bulky lymphadenopathy, and visceral infiltrations may regress dramatically and the general condition of the patient may strikingly improve. However, the experience from reporting clinics indicates that the satisfactory remissions induced by chemotherapy are less predictable and less complete than in Hodgkin's disease. As in the latter disease, the duration of the illness, the extent of involvement, and the amount and type of previous treatments are important factors which influence the response to chemotherapy. When the disease is in its final stages and multiple courses of radiotherapy have produced extensive fibrosis in diseased areas, nitrogen mustard therapy produces only a partial and temporary regression of tumor masses and of constitutional manifestations.

The lymphosarcomas embrace a number of morphologically separable neoplasms. Although pathologists are not in complete accord on what should be included in the general category of lymphosarcoma, three types will be arbitrarily classified under this heading in the present discussion. These are the giant follicular lymphosarcoma, the small cell or lymphocytic cell lymphosarcoma, and the reticulum cell lymphosarcoma. In the consideration of the indications for nitrogen mustard therapy in a patient with disseminated lymphosarcoma, the histologic characterization is an important factor.

Giant Follicular Lymphosarcoma

The giant follicular lymphosarcoma is a relatively benign neoplasm and remissions following nitrogen mustard therapy are measurable in terms of many months or even years. The response of this tumor is so striking that it is a serious prognostic sign when a satisfactory remission is not produced by chemotherapy. In our clinic it has been found that when a patient with giant follicular lymphosarcoma no longer responds to nitrogen mustard, a repeat biopsy very frequently shows a conversion of the initial histologic picture to a reticulum cell lymphosarcoma. Since this alteration of the morphologic and biologic characteristics of the neoplasm may occur spontaneously without any form of treatment, it is not considered likely that the nitrogen mustard is implicated in the transformation of a less malignant tumor to one of a more malignant type.

Small Cell or Lymphocytic Lymphosarcoma

The response of the small cell or lymphocytic lymphosarcoma to chemotherapy is variable, although a partial remission at least can be anticipated. A practical therapeutic regimen for the management of patients with generalized lymphosarcoma of this type is the administration of nitrogen mustard followed after two weeks by radiotherapy of the residual manifestations of disease. The combined use of chemo- and radiotherapy which has been recommended here as well as in the management of selected cases of Hodgkin's disease requires caution in order to avoid complications. It has been stressed that nitrogen mustard characteristically depresses hematapoietic function temporarily. If roentgen-ray therapy is indicated shortly after a course of HN_2, it must be appreciated that irradiation of major red bone marrow areas, such as the sternum, ribs, and vetebral bodies, may lead to an additive toxicity on bone marrow function with consequent hematologic complications.

Reticulum Cell Lymphosarcoma

Significant remissions following nitrogen mustard therapy of reticulum cell lymphosarcoma occur rarely. It is not unusual to observe regression of superficial lymphadenopathy or visceral infiltrations, but the depression of the neoplastic cells is dishearteningly transient. In a number of clinics, the results of chemotherapy of this highly malignant neoplasm have been so unsatisfactory that it has not been considered justifiable to subject the patient to the discomforts of the treatments. This conclusion has been reached in our clinic after it was demonstrated that of 15 patients with disseminated reticulum cell lymphosarcoma who received nitrogen mustard therapy none were alive after nine months.

Prognosis. The available evidence on nitrogen mustard therapy of the lymphosarcomas indicates that the life expectancy is not increased by the use of this agent. Nevertheless, in the management of generalized involvement by the giant follicular and small cell types of lymphosarcoma or for the relief of tumor masses compressing vital structures, nitrogen mustard is a helpful addition to the therapeutic armamentarium.

Bronchiogenic Carcinoma

Nitrogen mustard has been given therapeutic trial in a wide variety of inoperable carcinomas. Although instances of temporary regression of a number of epithelial tumors have been recorded, only bronchiogenic carcinomas have responded with sufficient regularity to merit consideration of the chemical compound for routine treatment when surgery is impossible. It must be recognized that although subjective and/or objective improvement follows the administration of nitrogen mustard in approximately 75 per cent of inoperable cases of bronchiogenic carcinoma, the remissions so induced are usually brief (two weeks to two months) and subsequent courses of therapy are less effective.

The histologic characteristics of the tumor influence the immediate response to chemotherapy. Thus the rapidly progressing anaplastic bronchiogenic carcinomas, including the oat cell type, are temporarily inhibited more frequently than the relatively well differentiated epidermoid or mucous gland bronchiogenic carcinomas.

In patients with this malignant neoplasm who have a satisfactory response to nitrogen mustard, there is alleviation of symptoms such as cough, dyspnea, hemoptysis, pain, weakness, and the syndrome produced by obstruction of the superior vena cava. Objective changes consisting of roentgen evidence of regression of pulmonary and metastatic lesions, as well as resorption of pleural effusions, also occur, particularly in the anaplastic tumors. There is general agreement among observers that the superior mediastinal compression syndrome caused by bronchiogenic carcinoma should be attacked initially by nitrogen mustard, in order to avoid additional embarrassment of circulatory function by the radiation reaction. In this connection it should be remembered that the venous pressure in the upper extremities is markedly elevated and appropriate measures to prevent stagnation of the injected nitrogen mustard should be taken in order to avoid thrombophlebitis.

Studies have been undertaken to determine whether the combination of nitrogen mustard and roentgen-ray therapy improves the immediate or long term results; there is no evidence yet which indicates that this therapeutic approach significantly improves the results.

Although temporary remissions are seen in the majority of patients with bronchiogenic carcinoma following nitrogen mustard therapy, it must be appreciated that qualitatively and quantitatively they are not comparable to those seen in Hodgkin's disease. In fact, so fleeting is the improvement in most patients that some clinics reserve nitrogen mustard therapy for patients who have superior mediastinal obstruction, because in this situation symptomatic relief is of major importance to the individual.

Blood Dyscrasias

The striking action of nitrogen mustard on hematopoiesis would suggest that the drug would be effective in the blood dyscrasias, particularly the leukemias. In fact, the responses observed have not indicated any significant advantage of this agent over other available drugs or roentgen-ray therapy for the treatment of disorders of the blood-forming organs.

Burchenal and his associates have established certain criteria for the clinical evaluation of chemotherapeutic agents in leukemia. An ideal drug would return the formed elements of the blood and the hemoglobin concentration to normal levels; following its use, all abnormal cells would disappear from the peripheral blood and smears of the bone marrow would show normal cell distribution. Tissue infiltrations as manifested by lymphadenopathy and hepatosplenomegaly would be destroyed; the bleeding tendency would decrease and the basal metabolic rate would fall to normal. Subjective improvement and increased appetite would be associated with effective therapy.

Acute Leukemia

In acute leukemia, nitrogen mustard fails completely to produce even a partial remission. The trial of mustard therapy in this disease has been sufficiently extensive and the results sufficiently uniform for further consideration to be unwarranted.

Chronic Myelocytic Leukemia

The responses to nitrogen mustard, noted in chronic myelocytic leukemia have been far more encouraging, but the immediate response is importantly influenced by the stage of the disease at the time of therapy. Thus in the early course of this blood dyscrasia it can be anticipated that the total white cell count will be reduced, the differential count will be partially returned toward normal, visceral and lymph node enlargement will be reduced, and subjective improvement will follow. Rise of the hemoglobin concentration and erythrocyte count is more variable. The remissions induced at this stage of the disease may be protracted and are usually measured in terms of three to twelve months.

As the disease progresses and approaches the end of its natural course the remissions are far less complete and of brief duration. At this time success in reducing the total white cell count may be the only effect noted. In the absence of other objective or subjective improvements this result is of no value to the patient.

Although precise quantitative data are not yet available, the impression of those treating chronic myelocytic leukemia is that nitrogen mustard does not alter the progress of the disease. Although the duration of life may not be prolonged, the palliative value of the drug is definite in that the patient is usually able to live a comfortable, fairly normal life for most of the course of the disease. Comparison of the relative efficacy of urethane, arsenic, roentgen-ray irradiation, radiophosphorus, and nitrogen mustard fails to reveal any outstanding value of any one therapeutic approach over the others. Nitrogen mustard does offer the pragmatic advantages of ease of administration, rapidity of effect, and inexpensiveness.

Chronic Lymphocytic Leukemia

The indications for nitrogen mustards in the treatment of chronic lymphocytic leukemia are less easily defined. This blood dycrasia responds less predictably and less regularly to irradiation and the same may be said for the response to nitrogen mustards. Patients who are in poor condition as a result of the disease respond unsatisfactorily to the drug. The satisfactory responses are observed in persons with an apparently relatively benign form of the blood dyscrasia. In these individuals, hematologic improvement and regression of visceral infiltrates may be very gratifying. The consensus of observers indicates that radiotherapy is preferred to chemotherapy with nitrogen mustard in the management of this disease. It has been further noted that if HN_2 is tried in the later stages of the disease, the drug should be administered more cautiously than usual, because profound depression of the already compromised normal hematopoietic function may be produced.

Polycythemia Vera

Polycythemia vera has been treated with alkylamines in a relatively small series of patients. Satisfactory and prolonged remissions up to two years have been reported, as well as complete therapeutic failures. From the available evidence it would appear that conventional management by phlebotomies or the administration of radiophosphorus produces hematologic and subjective improvement with greater regularity than does nitrogen mustard.

Cutaneous Blastomatous Diseases

A wide variety of neoplastic and non-neoplastic skin diseases have been treated with nitrogen mustard. Of the former, the most impressive immediate responses have been noted in mycosis fungoides and lymphoblastomas involving the skin and subcutaneous tissues. Kaposi sarcoma, a rare disease, has also been controlled temporarily by HN_2. In mycosis fungoides, nitrogen mustard should be reserved for patients with extensive skin involvement. In approximately half of these patients, rapid relief of pruritus and shrinkage of skin lesions may occur with improvement for from one to five months. In the bulky and rapidly progressing disease the response is usually disappointingly evanescent.

When the lymphoblastomas involve the skin and subcutaneous tissues in multiple body areas, HN_2 is indicated and satisfactory remissions can be anticipated.

Miscellaneous Diseases

Temporary therapeutic results following nitrogen mustard have been reported for a number of disseminated malignant tumors in adults, including gastric, mammary, ovarian, and uterine carcinomas, seminomas and chorioepitheliomas. The number of cases studied has been too limited and the results too unpredictable to warrant the use of HN_2 in all patients with inoperable carcinoma.

A small series of cases with sarcoidosis has been reported to respond favorably but very slowly to nitrogen mustard. The difficulties of assessing a therapeutic agent in this disease which so frequently goes into spontaneous remissions are recognized and further experience with HN_2 will be necessary for precise evaluation.

Triethylenemelamine

As has been mentioned in an earlier section, many derivatives of HN_2 have been synthesized and studied in the laboratory and clinic. None of the alkyl or aromatic chloroethyl amines have demonstrated any advantages over methyl bis-(β-chloroethyl)amine. Recently, however, triethylenemelamine, which was described earlier, has received clinical trial and, although the drug is not as yet generally available, it is possible that it will merit inclusion in the physician's therapeutic armamentarium when additional experience has been obtained.

This nitrogen mustard possesses the advantage over HN_2 of ease of administration, because it can be given by mouth. In addition, the incidence of nausea and vomiting is appreciably less, occurring in about 50 per cent of patients. The drug is available in 5 mg. tablets and should be given after six or seven hours of fasting. In our clinic the patient is given triethylenemelamine (or TEM) on awakening in the morning, together with 2 Gm. of sodium bicarbonate. The alkali is administered in order to curtail the gastric acidity and thereby minimize the chemical reactivity of the drug in the gastrointestinal tract. In other clinics this adjuvant is not given and at the present time the only apparent difference in the two technics is that the dosage of TEM required is smaller when sodium bicarbonate is added.

The dosage schedules with this new nitrogen mustard have not been established precisely. It has been found advisable to give 5 mg. on two successive mornings and then observe the patient for a week to assess the therapeutic and toxic effects. The systemic toxicity is qualitatively similar to that noted for HN_2; however, there is a greater depressant effect on the red cell count and hemoglobin. If after one week there has been no significant depression of hematopoiesis as judged by examination of the peripheral blood and if a therapeutic response has not been obtained, then another 10 mg. of TEM can be given as before. As experience with an individual patient's response to the chemical compound is obtained, the dosage may be increased or decreased as the situation demands. In many instances, 10 mg. will be sufficient to induce a remission in Hodgkin's disease, lymphosarcoma, chronic myelogenous leukemia, and bronchiogenic carcinoma.

The evidence indicates that TEM is effective in the same neoplastic diseases which respond to HN_2. The drug may be valuable in these diseases because ambulatory therapy is facilitated. It is also possible, though not yet conclusively demonstrated, that TEM may be given in maintenance doses and thereby prolong remissions.

URETHANE

HISTORY

Ethyl carbamate or urethane was first synthesized in 1834 with the hope that it would be a useful hypnotic drug for man. Although it was found to be insufficiently potent for this purpose, it became a popular drug for anesthetizing laboratory animals since it had minimal side actions on the cardiorespiratory system.

The use of urethane as a chemotherapeutic agent in malignant disease stems from the experimental observations of Haddow and Sexton on the effect of the drug on animal tumors. These investigators, in a systematic screening of "mitotic inhibitors" for carcinoclastic activity, examined a series of carbamates because botanists had repeatedly noticed the striking arrest of mitosis produced by these chemical compounds in the cells of cereal roots and other plant species. The experimental neoplasms utilized in these studies were a spontaneous mammary adenocarcinoma in mice and the Walker rat carcinoma. Several of the carbamic acid esters were found to retard growth of these tumors, urethane being the most active. In the mammary carcinoma, tumor inhibition occurred only during administration of the drug, whereas a profound modification of the morphology of the Walker carcinoma was produced, characterized by an apparent maturation of the undifferentiated cells. Although the experimental studies indicated that urethane had a carcinostatic rather than a carcinolytic action, its easy availability and low toxicity prompted clinical trial in advanced and therapeutically intractable cancer in man.

MECHANISM OF ACTION

Before urethane found application in the field of cancer chemotherapy, its mechanism of action was carefully studied in order to shed light on the physiology of anesthesia. Significant cytologic, histopathologic, and biochemical responses have been observed in experiments with urethane and it is difficult to determine which may be of primary importance to the anticancer activity of the drug and which are secondary manifestations related or unrelated to its chemotherapeutic activity. In spite of renewed interest in this chemical compound, the mechanism of carcinostatic action remains unknown.

$$O = C \begin{matrix} OC_2H_5 \\ \\ NH_2 \end{matrix} \quad + \quad HOH \quad \frac{\text{Enzymatically}}{\text{catalyzed}} \quad {}^*CO_2 + C_2H_5OH + NH_3 \atop \text{hydrolysis}$$

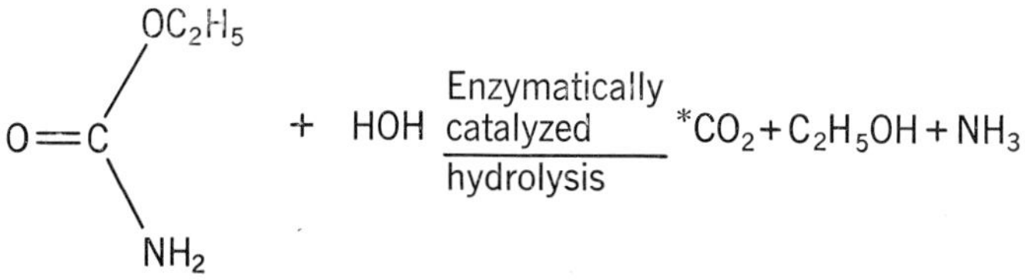

Urethane

FIG. 128. Degradation of urethane in vivo.

Morphologic descriptions of cell division in the presence of urethane demonstrate that the drug affects nuclear division. "Stickiness" of chromosomes with the formation of chromosome bridges have been reported. That these fundamental disturbances in nuclear function are produced by minute quantities of the drug is indicated by Skipper's studies on the metabolism of isotopically labelled urethane. In experimental animals he has demonstrated a rapid breakdown of the molecule, with about 90 per cent of the carbonyl carbon appearing in the expired carbon dioxide within the first twenty-four hours. Of the remainder of the carbonyl carbon, 5 to 10 per cent was found in the urine and about 1 per cent was retained in a fixed form widely distributed in normal and neoplastic tissues at twenty-four hours after injection. Skipper has suggested that the general mode of degradation of urethane in vivo is as shown in Fig. 128.

Haddow and Sexton have suggested that urethane may act by competing with a natural amine in the biosynthesis of nucleotides. This concept is based on the well established evidence that the synthesis of nucleoproteins is accomplished from smaller molecules rather than by the utilization of purines and pyrimidines. Skipper has investigated this attractive hypothesis of competition between urethane and a naturally occurring amino acid, but he finds no significant localization of the drug in the nucleic acid fractions of nucleoproteins.

CLINICAL APPLICATION

The clinical investigation of urethane in man was initiated in 1943 by Paterson and her associates. The first patients treated had far advanced malignant disease.

The clinical results were uniformly disappointing, but it was noted that in some instances there was a striking fall in the leukocyte count. This suggested the trial of urethane in patients with leukemia.

Acute Leukemia

The initial report on 32 cases of leukemia led to conclusions which have been substantiated by independent investigations elsewhere. In acute leukemia, urethane may lower the peripheral white count but there is no associated clinical improvement and the course of the disease is not altered. For these reasons there is no indication for the drug in acute leukemia.

Chronic Myelocytic Leukemia

The best results with urethane have been in the treatment of chronic myelocytic leukemia. The effects produced—represented in the most favorable cases by a fall in total white cell count to normal limits, a tendency for the differential count to approach a more normal pattern, diminution in size of the spleen and enlarged lymph nodes, and a rise in hemoglobin, as well as subjective improvement—are remarkably similar to those obtained by standard methods of deep roentgen-ray therapy. Although evidence of improvement in some of the criteria just mentioned occurs in about 80 per cent of the cases, complete response is far less frequent. It has also been established that urethane has no permanent effect on the leukemic process and after a remission interval of variable duration, additional treatment is required.

Chronic Lymphocytic Leukemia

In chronic lymphocytic leukemia the response to urethane is less consistent. This re-emphasizes the interesting biologic differences in the two chronic leukocytic blood dyscrasias, because nitrogen mustard and radiotherapy also fail to improve lymphocytic leukemia regularly. In this disorder of leukopoiesis a reduction of the circulating white cells associated with urethane therapy can usually be anticipated but spontaneous increase of the hemoglobin concentration, decrease of visceral and lymph node infiltrations and subjective improvement are infrequent.

Serial studies of the bone marrow in patients showing a favorable response to urethane reveal a progressive decrease in the mitotic activity of the immature cells in the leukocyte series and an increased number of erythroblasts. At later stages there is an increased number of more mature leukocytic forms, although it is impossible to state that these arise from neoplastic precursors.

From the experience gained during the past nine years, it would appear that urethane is a satisfactory therapeutic agent in producing temporary remissions in the chronic leukemias. No obvious advantage for the drug over conventional radiotherapy can be claimed and many observers prefer the latter. In spite of the fact that this chemotherapeutic agent probably does not prolong life, its ready availability, ease of administration, and inexpensiveness recommend its use if radiotherapy is contraindicated for any reason.

Multiple Myeloma

A more recent application of urethane has been in the management of multiple myeloma. In the initial series of patients treated with this drug by Paterson, there were 2 cases of advanced myelomatosis. Neither patient showed any improvement. In 1947 Alwall reported a beneficial effect in one case and Aas in 1949 observed symptomatic improvement in another case. The most intensive work in this field has been done by Rundles and his associates. In over 25 cases now treated, favorable responses have been observed in about 35 per cent. With a daily dose of 3–5 Gm. urethane continued to a total dosage of 120–240 Gm., clinical improvement is usually manifest within three to six weeks. The improvement includes subsidence of skeletal pain and fever, return of red cell and hemoglobin levels toward normal, decrease in the number and size of the myeloma cells found in bone marrow smears, marked reduction of serum globulins, some improvement in renal function, and roentgenographic evidence of apparent cessation of progression of skeletal lesions. Recalcification can be demonstrated only rarely but a fall in high serum calcium levels and a rise in the alkaline phosphatase may be indicative of a measure of bone repair.

The stage of the natural course of the disease appears to be an important factor in predicting the effects of urethane therapy. In the majority of patients who have failed to respond, the disease has been advanced and clinically the patient's general condition has been precarious. It must also be appreciated that the beneficial effects of urethane do not appear for a matter of weeks and sufficient time must be available for therapy to be effective.

Although the effects of urethane in this disease have been confirmed in other clinics, the period of observation is limited to only two and a half years and the number of cases treated is relatively small. The optimal procedure to follow if a remission is induced has not been established. Discontinuation of therapy and readministration of the drug when symptoms reappear has been successful; maintenance doses to prolong remission intervals are being investigated. In spite of the fact that a final evaluation of the effectiveness of the drug in prolonging life in multiple myeloma can not be made at this time, it would nevertheless appear to be the therapeutic agent of choice in this disease.

Depression of hematopoietic function has been noted in the series of patients treated and appropriate precautions must be taken.

Miscellaneous Diseases

A great variety of neoplastic diseases have been treated with urethane since its clinical introduction and scattered reports of temporary remissions of disseminated epithelial tumors have been made. So variable and so infrequent have the responses been that the drug cannot be recommended for trial in widespread cancer.

An initial report of successful palliation of prostatic carcinoma resistant to androgen-control therapy has not been confirmed in a larger series of carefully observed patients.

ADMINISTRATION AND DOSAGE

Urethane may be most conveniently administered by mouth. Since the drug may produce gastrointestinal symptoms from local irritation, it is usually given in enteric coated capsules and tablets containing 0.3 Gm. or 0.5 Gm. of the drug. If diarrhea is present, so that the enteric coated medication is expelled before it can be absorbed, urethane may be prescribed in a liquid vehicle:

	Gm. or cc.
Urethane	30
Syrup of orange	50
Chloroform water, to make	300

The dosage of urethane is in part determined by the tolerance of the patient. Most patients are given 3 Gm. per day in divided doses of 1 Gm. after each meal, but from 1–5 Gm. may be given each twenty-four hours. The amount of urethane necessary to produce a fall in the leukocyte count to about 20,000 per cu. mm. varies within wide limits (19–134 Gm.). In the treatment of the chronic leukemias, therapy is arbitrarily discontinued at this leukocyte count, because there is a lag in the white cell response and a further decrease can be anticipated. The dosage of urethane cannot be correlated either with body weight or with the initial leukocyte count. The time taken for the leukocyte count to fall to the arbitrary end point is also variable (eleven to thirty-six days, average thirty days).

CLINICAL TOXICITY

There are three general types of toxic manifestations due to urethane. Gastrointestinal disturbances evidenced by anorexia, nausea, and vomiting are presumably due to local irritation and can usually be controlled by decreasing the dosage. It must be remembered, however, that malnutrition may further depress erythropoiesis in patients with chronic leukemia and therefore urethane therapy should not be continued if benefit is not evidenced within a reasonable time.

Mild sedation may occur during urethane therapy, but this is rarely sufficiently prominent to require dosage modification. The usual precautions to avoid accidents should be taken; driving an automobile or pursuing hazardous occupations requiring quick reflex actions are contraindicated while on urethane.

The most serious toxicity that may be encountered is bone marrow depression. This may occur gradually and may be associated with hypoplasia of the bone marrow or it may develop with explosive rapidity and lead to complete aplasia of the marrow. The latter form of toxicity, which is undoubtedly an idosyncratic reaction, such as may be seen with a variety of drugs (sulfonamides, antiepileptics, antithyroid agents, and so on), is particularly dangerous, because it is difficult to anticipate. Although it may occur either early or late after the initiation of urethane therapy, it is fortunately uncommon. The only premonitory sign of this form of toxic reaction that has been noted is a rapidly developing anemia. When this occurs, irrespective of the leukocyte count, urethane should be stopped and the patient carefully followed for evidences of developing pancytopenia.

It is advisable to determine the peripheral blood count at weekly intervals during treatment of chronic leukemia and as the end point is approached more frequent observations are indicated.

FOLIC ACID ANTAGONISTS

The folic acid antagonists merit inclusion in the group of useful cancer chemotherapeutic agents because of their ability to modify the course of acute leukemia. Although it is evident that these drugs have a limited effectiveness in this disease, they nevertheless have provided important insights into the biology of this hitherto intractable blood dyscrasia.

HISTORY

The introduction of folic acid antagonists into cancer chemotherapy followed clinical observations with the ineffective folic acid conjugates, teropterin and diopterin. Since a full discussion of these latter chemical compounds is not warranted, a brief summary of their rise and fall will be included here.

The concept that certain organs and tissues have a natural resistance to the growth of metastatic cancer cells has long been popular, although the supporting objective evidence is weak. Through the years, however, therapeutic investigations using various organ extracts have been undertaken periodically with little regard to the mass of past negative results. In 1938 Lewisohn and his associates reported than an extract of beef spleen caused significant regression of sarcoma 180 in mice. An extract of mouse spleen was found to cure spontaneous mammary carcinomas in mice. Due to the impracticality of large-scale extraction of mouse spleens, extracts obtained from a number of other sources were screened for their antitumor activity. Extracts of barley and yeast seemed to have carcinolytic activity and this focused attention on the vitamin B complex. In 1945 the Leuchtenbergers, Lazlo, and Lewisohn reported that *L. casei* fermentation factor caused complete regression of 30 per cent of spontaneous breast cancers in mice. At the time of their report *L. casei* fermentation factor was considered to be folic acid. Subsequent chemical characterization, however, revealed the material to be a folic acid conjugate, pteroyltriglutamic acid or teropterin. Folic acid, pteroylglutamic acid, was ineffective against the experimental tumors.

Although the laboratory investigations above described could not be confirmed, and it was further shown that the folic acid conjugate was rapidly split in the human body with the release of folic acid, teropterin and diopterin (pteroyldiglutamic acid) were studied clinically for their effect against human malignant disease.

Among the great variety of neoplastic diseases for which teropterin and diopterin were used as therapeutic agents, none showed convincing objective evidence of improvement, but Farber and his associates observed that the course of acute leukemia was apparently accelerated. This finding constituted the basis for their trial of antifolic drugs, the folic acid antagonists, in acute leukemia.

Teropterin and diopterin, which received notoriety through over-enthusiastic reporting in the lay press, have now been discarded. Even the claims that these agents improved the sense of well-being and decreased pain in cancer patients are now regarded with skepticism.

CHEMISTRY

The structural relationships of the several analogs to folic acid in clinical use can be most conveniently visualized from the formulae (Figs. 129-132):

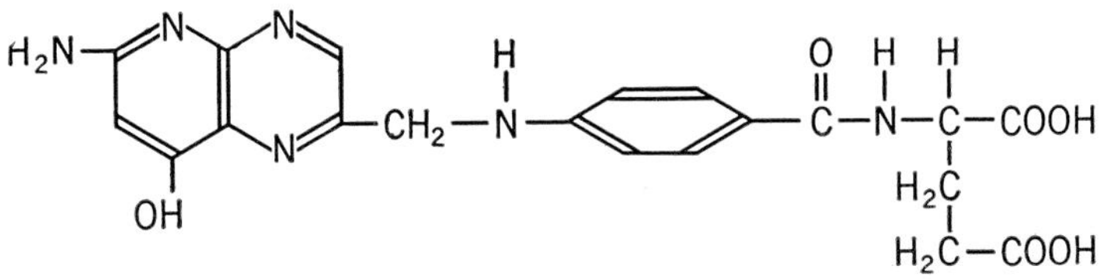

FIG. 129. Pteroylglutamic acid (folic acid).

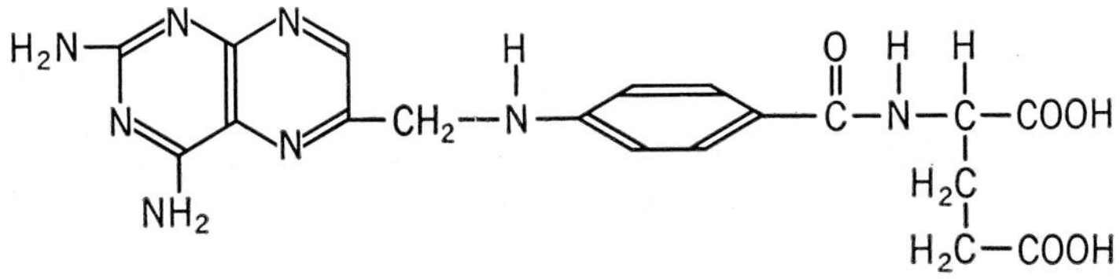

FIG. 130. 4-Amino-pteroylglutamic acid (aminopterin).

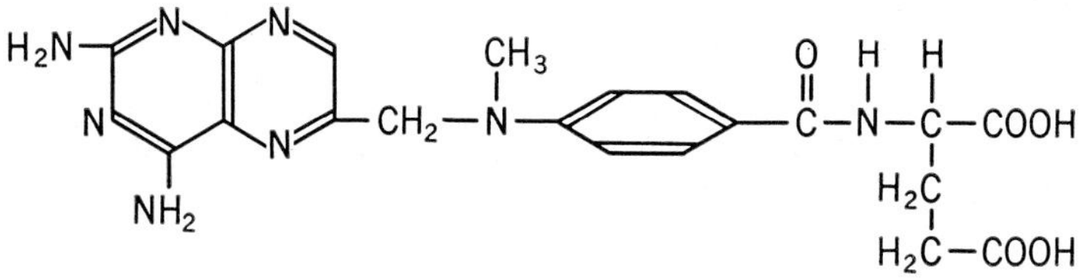

FIG. 131. 4-Amino-N^{10}-methyl-pteroylglutamic acid (a-methopterin).

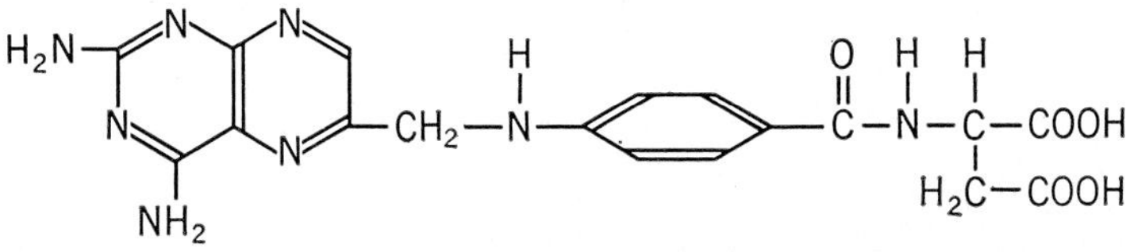

FIG. 132. 4-Amino-pteroylaspartic acid (amino-an-fol).

Many more biologically active folic acid analogs have been synthesized but the ones depicted are the most important because of their high potency and their use in clinical medicine.

The substitution of an amino group for the hydroxyl radical in the fourth position of the pteridine ring, as in aminopterin, creates the most powerful antagonist of pteroylglutamic acid. The evidence which allows the conclusion that aminopterin and the other analogs of folic acid are antagonists of this vitamin is as follows:

1. The structural similarities between the analogs and pteroylglutamic acid are so great that it seems eminently reasonable that the physiologic activity of the analog is due to an interference with the functioning of the naturally occurring substance.

2. The toxicity of the analogs in mice, rats, monkeys, and guinea pigs is similar to that seen when these animals are placed on a folic-acid–deficient diet.

3. The growth of micro-organisms which require folic acid can be inhibited by the folic acid analogs in low concentrations and the inhibitory effect can be reversed by the addition of folic acid.

It is of interest that further modifications of the folic acid molecule beyond the 4-amino substitution decrease the toxicity of the analog thus formed. A-methopterin, which has the substitution of an amino group in the 4 position and a methyl group on the N^{10} atom, is less toxic than aminopterin and the replacement of the glutamic acid moiety of aminopterin with aspartic acid ("amino-an-fol") leads to an even less toxic agent.

TOXICITY

The toxicity of the folic acid analogs in experimental animals has been carefully studied in order to throw light on the mechanism of action of the drugs and in order to anticipate the hazards in their clinical application. Animals receiving single, fatal doses of the analogs survived for at least forty-eight hours and usually succumbed between the third and fifth day. The characteristic syndrome of toxicity is manifested by progressive weight loss, anorexia, bloody diarrhea, leukopenia, depression, terminal collapse, and coma.

As could be anticipated from the clinical course of fatal intoxication with the folic acid analogs, the chief pathologic changes were found in the intestinal tract and the bone marrow. Microscopic examination of the small and large intestine revealed swelling and cytoplasmic vacuolization of the epithelium as early as six hours after the parenteral administration of the drugs. The initial changes were followed by desquamation of the epithelial cells, extravasation of plasma into the intestinal lumen, and intensive leukocytic infiltration of the submucosa. Within three days after acute poisoning or somewhat later after chronic intoxication, the whole mucous membrane from the duodenum to the anus was edematous, swollen, and in part, hemorrhagic.

On the third day of acute intoxication, the bone marrow of the experimental animals was found to be grossly abnormal. At this time the peripheral blood showed marked granulocytopenia, reticulocytopenia, and moderate lymphopenia. Serial examination of the bone marrow revealed progressive depletion of all cells in the erythroid and myeloid series.

Apart from the lesions of the bone marrow and the intestines, no outstanding pathologic changes have been noted. Decrease in the size of lymph nodes and spleen have been described but histologic studies have not revealed striking cytotoxicity to lymphoid cells.

A most significant observation that has been made in toxicity studies with the folic acid analogs is the limited success of preventing the action of these drugs by the administration of folic acid itself. Thus it has been found necessary to inject large doses of pteroylglutamic acid before administering the analogs, in order to observe any success in inhibiting the inhibitor. If both folic acid and one of the potent antagonists are given in chronic doses, the onset of the toxic manifestations may be delayed, but eventually the animal dies with the typical findings described above. So striking has been this comparative ineffectiveness of folic acid to overcome the biologic action of its analogs that the hypothesis was entertained that the analogs were antagonists of folic acid and in addition had a direct cytotoxic effect through some unrelated mechanism. More recent advances in the knowledge of the biochemical function of folic acid and of its metabolism indicate that the earlier observations can now be adequately explained on a single basis.

MECHANISM OF ACTION

Microbiologic technics and tracer studies with radiocarbon and stable isotopic nitrogen have provided insights into the biochemical function of folic acid. The description of the role of pteroylglutamic acid in intermediary metabolism is far from complete but sufficient evidence is available to demonstrate its importance in the synthesis of nucleoproteins. With the increasing recognition of the key position of these complex protein structures in the normal functioning of cells, the importance of chemical compounds which can interfere with their synthesis is readily understandable.

A complete review of the available evidence on the mechanism of action of folic acid and of its antagonists is beyond the scope of this presentation. In order, however, to appreciate how the folic acid analogs can produce the striking toxic changes in experimental animals and in man, certain observations merit discussion.

Evidence has accumulated which strongly indicates that folic acid is converted in the animal organism to a related form which is biologically active. In studies of the nutritional requirements of micro-organisms, a bacterial species, *Leuconostoc citrovorum*, was found which required an accessory growth factor present in liver or yeast extracts which was neither folic acid nor vitamin B_{12}. Interest in this citrovorum factor was quickened when it was demonstrated that the administration of folic acid to experimental animals and man resulted in the excretion in the urine of a substance which supported the growth of *L. citrovorum*. The concentration of the citrovorum factor in the urine was found to be proportional to the folic acid intake.

It was further shown in other studies that rat liver slices incubated in a medium containing folic acid produced the citrovorum factor. Although the citrovorum factor has not as yet been completely characterized chemically, evidence has been obtained which indicates that it is closely related to pteroylglutamic acid. The citrovorum factor, also known as folinic acid or leucovorin, can remedy folic acid deficiency states in experimental animals and can substitute for pteroylglutamic acid in supporting the growth of bacterial species which require this latter vitamin.

An impressive demonstration of the biologic activity of the citrovorum factor has been its ability to counter and/or prevent the toxicity of aminopterin or other less powerful folic acid analogs. When it was further shown that the folic acid analogs could block the conversion of folic acid to the citrovorum factor, the explanation for the inability of folic acid effectively to counter the action of its powerful analogs was apparent. Thus, to summarize the evidence presented to this point, folic acid is converted by the liver and possibly other tissues into some related form which is active in biochemical processes. This new substance, called the citrovorum factor, is able to counteract the toxic actions of the folic acid analogs. The analogs are, in part, active because they are able to prevent the conversion of folic acid to the active form of the vitamin. In addition, the folic acid antagonists, presumably by substituting for folinic acid, block those reactions in which the latter functions as a part of catalytic systems.

It is unquestionably a great oversimplification to diagram the synthesis of desoxypentose nucleic acids and yet, in order to indicate the fundamental mechanisms which are distorted by the antifolic compounds, this liberty will be taken.

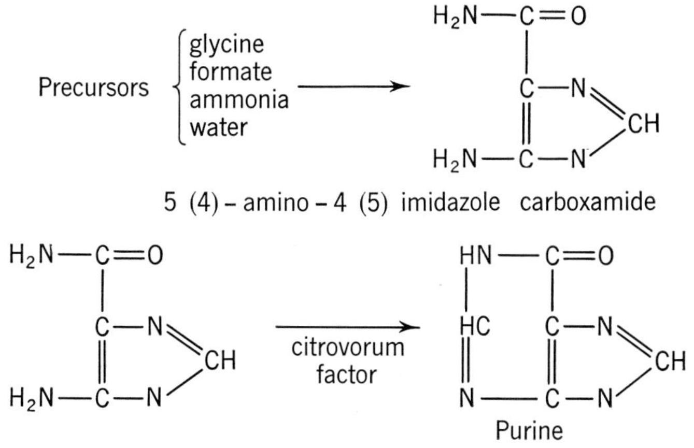

FIG. 133. Synthesis of desoxypentose nucleic acid, Step 1.

From evidence obtained with radioactive tracers it is known that the purines and pyrimidines, which are the basic structural units of nucleotides, are built up from simple molecules. This is schematically represented in Fig. 133.

In reaction (1) the enzymes which catalyze the synthesis of the intermediate have not been characterized. The aminoimidazole carboxamide has been isolated in bacterial culture media in which microbial growth has been inhibited either by a sulfonamide or by aminopterin. The incorporation of a carbon atom into this intermediate amine, thus completing the purine nucleus, is catalyzed by the biologically active form of folic acid which at the time of writing appears to be the so-called citrovorum factor. The folic acid analogs, by blocking this step, interfere with a fundamental process in nucleic acid synthesis.

The next process in the synthesis of the desoxypentose nucleic acids is the addition of a sugar moiety to the purine and pyrimidine bases (Fig. 134).

As indicated in the diagram, evidence has been obtained which demonstrates that vitamin B_{12} is a part of the coenzyme system catalyzing this reaction. To date there is no indication that the folic acid analogs interfere with this process directly. From microbiologic studies it would appear that the desoxyribosides formed in reaction

(3) are reversibly converted to thymidine and once again the citrovorum factor is an important part of the catalyzing system in the reaction (Fig. 135).

The full implications of this reaction in nucleoprotein synthesis are still in the realm of speculation, but the folic acid analogs inhibit the process and thereby interfere with normal synthetic mechanisms.

$$
\begin{array}{cc}
\text{Purines} & \text{Purine desoxyribosides}
\end{array}
$$

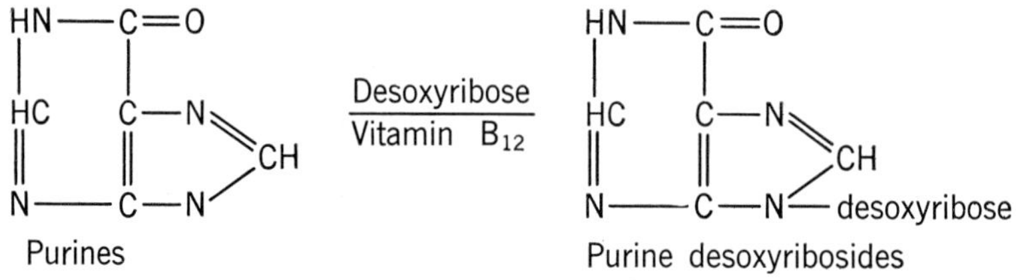

FIG. 134.　Synthesis of desoxypentose nucleic acid, Step 2.

As yet the mechanisms for the phosphorylation of the desoxyribosides, the polymerization of these complex units, and the integration of the phosphoric acid esters with a protein moiety to form the far more complex nucleoproteins, are still unknown. Whether the folic acid analogs interfere with these additional synthetic mechanisms is not known but sufficient evidence has been presented to provide some understanding of the biologic activity which they display.

$$
\text{Purine desoxyribosides} \xrightleftharpoons[\substack{\text{citrovorum}\\\text{factor}}]{} \text{thymidine}
$$

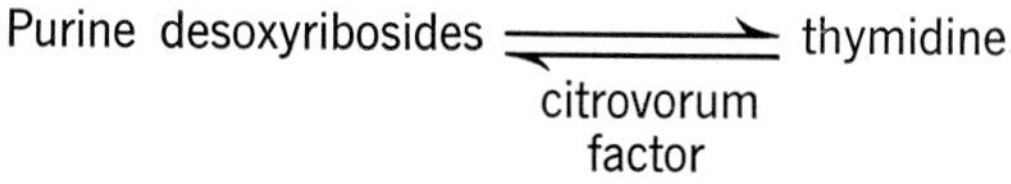

FIG. 135.　Conversion of desoxyribosides to thymidine.

In the preceding discussion a scheme of nucleoprotein synthesis has been described which presumably occurs, with modifications, in all cells. It is justifiable to ask, therefore, why leukemic cells, normal hematopoietic elements, and intestinal epithelium are so susceptible to the action of the folic acid analogs. In large measure it would appear that this is not due to any qualitative selectivity of these drugs for the particular tissues, but rather is explained by the rapid rate of turnover of these cells. It is understandable that cells which are undergoing division at a fast rate would be injured more readily than cells which are proliferating at a more leisurely pace. In addition, leukemic cells may have a special susceptibility because it has been shown that the concentration of pteroylglutamic acid in these abnormal leukocytes is unusually high.

CLINICAL APPLICATION

The folic acid analogs are noteworthy because associated with their administration the incidence of remissions in acute leukemia is significantly greater than could made unequivocally now, although when these drugs were first introduced the be accounted for on the basis of spontaneous improvement. This point can be question was raised whether the intensification of nonspecific supportive measures such as antibiotics and transfusions could account for the favorable results.

With the acceptance of the fact that antifolic drugs can produce hematologic and clinical remissions in acute leukemia, it is important at the outset to recognize the major limitations and qualifications of this therapeutic regimen. These can be listed as follows:

1. The folic acid analogs are significantly more effective in the chemotherapy of acute leukemia in childhood than in adult acute leukemia. So striking is this difference in the relative therapeutic susceptibility of the disease depending upon the age of the victim that it is justifiable to suspect that the fundamental biology of the dyscrasia differs in the two age groups.

2. Precise statistical data on the incidence of induced remissions of acute leukemia in childhood are still not available. In many instances the reported series of treated cases are too small to permit interpretation on this issue, since favorable results varying between 10 and 90 per cent have been recorded. Taking into account all the published results, however, it would appear that only slightly more than 50 per cent of children with this disease will experience significant improvement. No criteria have been found which will permit a prediction of the favorable or unsatisfactory outcome of therapy with the exception that acute monocytic leukemia has not been observed to respond.

3. Acute leukemia cannot be cured by folic acid antagonist therapy. Asymptomatic remission periods varying from two weeks to nine months can be induced by the treatment, but exacerbations of the disease occur which are increasingly difficult to control and eventually a fatal outcome results, due to either the fundamental disease process or complications of therapy. It is still too early to state with exactness how long life can be prolonged by these agents. A conservative estimate is that, in those cases in which a remission is induced, the average duration of life after onset of therapy is twelve months. This is approximately twice the expected duration of life in untreated cases.

4. Treatment with the folic acid analogs cannot be undertaken lightly, because in the vast majority of patients toxic manifestations from the drugs employed must be anticipated. For this reason, the initial course of therapy must be given in a hospital, so that the patient can receive all of the safeguards provided by the institutional facilities.

Selection of the Drug. Only two of the folic acid analogs have been extensively employed, 4-amino-pteroylglutamic acid (Aminopterin) and 4-amino-N^{10} methyl-pteroylglutamic acid (A-methopterin). Although the latter drug is less toxic than aminopterin, larger doses must be employed and the toxic manifestations are qualitatively the same. The dosage for aminopterin is 0.5–2.0 mg. per day given either intramuscularly or by mouth. A-methopterin is given orally in doses ranging between 2.0 and 5.0 mg. per day. It is customary to start treatment at the lower dosage and gradually increase it, depending on the changes observed in the peripheral blood and bone marrow. Treatment is continued until a marked depression of the normal and abnormal formed elements of the peripheral blood and/or bone marrow has been induced or until one of several toxic manifestations unrelated to hematopoiesis appear.

It is impossible to state arbitrary blood counts at which therapy should be temporarily terminated. When the initial leukocyte count is high, treatment may be stopped when the white blood cells have dropped to 2000; when leukopenia is present before the onset of treatment, the antifolic drugs may be continued until the leukocyte count is 500 or less. The objective of therapy is a normal differential leukocyte count rather than the number of cells. Rarely the bone marrow and peripheral blood picture may be converted to normal without drastic effects on the leukocyte level; more frequently, however, a marked hypoplasia of the bone marrow must be produced, which is followed by regeneration by normal hematopoietic elements rather than leukemic cells.

While administering the drugs to obtain the objective of a normal leukocytic series, frequent transfusions must be given to correct the severe anemia which may develop. Since the erythropenia associated with bone marrow depression and the direct toxic effect of the drugs on the red cells can be controlled by substitution therapy, this is not a limiting factor of the treatment. Other toxic manifestations, however, must be carefully watched for and with their appearance treatment must be stopped.

Thrombocytopenia with bleeding is difficult to counter and may necessitate the termination of drug administration. In many instances purpura is difficult to evaluate, because of its presence before the onset of therapy. Ulcerative stomatitis is a frequent complication of aminopterin or a-methopterin therapy and should be looked for each day. With the first appearance of changes in the buccal mucous membrane, treatment should be discontinued in order to avoid serious gangrenous infections of the soft parts of the face and neck. Diarrhea is another warning symptom of severe folic acid deficiency and with its appearance treatment should be stopped. Disregard of this sign may be followed by a hemorrhagic enteritis and death due to intestinal perforation. A less common and not serious toxic reaction is alopecia. This may be distressing to the patient or his parents but it is not permanent nor is it obligatory to withhold treatment because of it.

It would be completely unfair to continue the discussion of folic acid analogs in acute leukemia without presenting the picture of successful therapy. The dramatic change which can be produced in a moribund child is exciting and gratifying. In those patients who respond, the peripheral blood and bone marrow picture of the leukocytic series may be entirely normal. Associated with this change the red cell count and platelets may rise to normal levels. Hemorrhagic manifestations cease, the temperature curve returns to normal, the child begins to eat with relish and to react to his surroundings and associates with renewed vigor and pleasure, and bone pain and objective signs of the leukemic process, such as peripheral lymphadenopathy and hepatosplenomegaly, disappear. A critically ill child may be returned to normal health within a period of two weeks.

The response presented above is observed in approximately one-third of the cases. Another group comprising about 20 per cent of the total show only a moderate hematologic response but nevertheless show marked symptomatic improvement. In this group the abnormal cells do not fall below 10 per cent of the total. The third group, about one-half of the total cases, suffer a severe initial bone marrow depression and hemorrhagic phenomena, which along with the depradations of the disease contribute to their death early in the course of treatment.

Following the induction of a remission, experience indicates that maintenance doses of the drug should be given. Doses of 0.5–1 mg. of aminopterin or 1–2 mg. of a-methopterin every other day may be tried with careful attention to the avoidance of toxic complications. In spite of this regimen, however, abnormal cells in the peripheral blood and bone marrow inevitably make their appearance, heralding the onset of an exacerbation.

Reinstitution of therapy with the same or another folic acid analog is indicated when the acute leukemic signs and symptoms return. At this time, the incidence of success in producing a remission is unfortunately considerably less than before. Again, precise figures on the probabilities involved are not available and, in any event, they are of academic interest. It is not possible to predict in which cases another successful outcome will be observed and the attempt is therefore indicated.

The ever-decreasing effectiveness of the folic acid analogs in subsequent exacerbations of the disease is no longer a mystery. Burchenal and Law have independently demonstrated that aminopterin is very effective in controlling certain acute leukemias in mice. If, when there is an exacerbation of the leukemic process, the disease is passed on to other recipient mice by transplantation of a splenic suspension, aminopterin therapy is less effective. Eventually it is possible to demonstrate that the once susceptible cells are completely resistant to the folic acid analogs. This refractoriness is analogous to drug resistance in micro-organisms. Evidence has been produced which indicates that the folic acid antagonist, by destruction of susceptible leukemic cells, permits mutant resistant cells to become predominant.

The introduction of cortisone and ACTH into the therapy of acute leukemia offers another approach. The alternation of the adrenal steroids with the folic analogs or a combination of the drugs will forestall the inevitable outcome for a still longer period.

Aminopterin and a-methopterin have been used in many neoplastic diseases other than acute leukemia of children. As was mentioned earlier, these drugs produce remissions of acute leukemia in adults with far less regularity than in children. Although Dameshek observed significant improvement in 9 out of 27 adults treated, the general experience has been less satisfactory. Chronic leukemias have not been observed to be favorably influenced by the antifolic compounds.

An occasional case of lymphosarcoma, reticulum cell sarcoma, melanosarcoma, and sympathicoblastoma will go into temporary remission following the administration of these drugs. However, because of the irregularity of the response and the very significant toxic hazards, therapeutic trial of these agents in all far advanced malignant diseases is not recommended.

HORMONES

One of the most vigorously exploited fields of cancer research at the present time is the relationship of steroid hormones to abnormal growth. In large part this may be ascribed to the increasing body of knowledge which has demonstrated the significance of hormones as modifiers of cellular enzymatic reactions and therefore, by implication, as regulators of growth processes. A more direct relationship of hormones to cancer is apparent in the effects of administration or deprivation of certain steroids on a number of malignant neoplasms in man.

Currently the sex hormones are widely used in the treatment of carcinoma of the prostate and breast. Adrenocorticotropic hormone (ACTH) and cortisone have also been tried against a variety of tumors and their indications and limitations are now well defined. In this section the contribution of these steroids and their synthetic substitutes will be evaluated together with a preliminary assessment of bilateral adrenalectomy in a variety of neoplastic diseases.

ANDROGEN-CONTROL THERAPY OF PROSTATIC CARCINOMA

Bilateral orchiectomy together with the administration of an estrogen, usually stilbestrol, is an accepted and generally employed regimen for the management of disseminated prostatic cancer. The rationale for this type of treatment rests upon biologic observations which demonstrated that malignant prostatic epithelial cells are in part dependent on androgen for multiplication and survival.

The development of androgen-deprivation therapy of prostatic carcinoma was made by Huggins, who correlated a number of clinical and experimental findings. The essential observations which permitted his deductive reasoning were: (1) normal, adult prostatic epithelium is dependent upon androgen for growth and function; (2) normal prostatic epithelium is rich in an acid phosphatase; (3) malignant prostatic epithelium is also rich in acid phosphatase and when the tumor has extended beyond the confines of the gland the serum acid phosphatase is elevated. On the basis of these facts Huggins and his associates suggested that prostatic carcinoma retained some of the characteristics of normal prostate epithelium and should, therefore, atrophy when the androgen supply was decreased.

In putting the hypothesis to clinical test Huggins utilized not only the subjective response of the patient but also the serum acid phosphatase concentration as a measure of the efficacy of treatment. He showed that following castration and/or the administration of estrogen, the serum acid phosphatase fell abruptly and there was clinical improvement. These observations were rapidly confirmed and accumulated experience has shown that in the majority of patients with widespread prostatic carcinoma, the immediate effects which can be anticipated include dramatic relief of bone pain and an improved sense of well-being. Associated with improved appetite, there is weight gain and correction of anemia.

Objectively, in addition to a fall in serum acid phosphatase, there may be a gradual drop in elevated serum alkaline phosphatase concentration, diminution in the size of the primary tumor and of soft tissue metastases. Serial biopsy studies have revealed morphologic changes in the malignant epithelial cells characterized by progressive pyknosis of the nuclei, vacuolization in the cytoplasm, and eventually rupture of the cell membrane. Scar tissue replaces the tumor. A significant observation, however, has been that complete destruction of all tumor cells does not occur.

When androgen-control therapy was first introduced and employed widely, it was found that the clinical improvements described above could be accomplished either by castration or by the administration of estrogens. This raised the question of the proper method of management—should patients be castrated initially and estrogens administered only when exacerbation of the disease occurred or should the order be reversed? Sufficient experience has now been obtained to advise that castration and the administration of estrogens be instituted simultaneously. On this combined therapeutic regimen, the statistics indicate that the percentage of survivals for three years after the diagnosis of disseminated prostatic cancer is about 55 per cent. This is significantly greater than in untreated cases.

A major problem in the treatment of prostatic cancer is the explanation for the ultimate failure of androgen-control therapy. Two hypotheses have been advanced. One suggests that there is progressive dedifferentiation of surviving prostatic cells which no longer are dependent upon androgenic substance for their growth. This implies that an entirely different tumor exists whose biologic characteristics must be defined in order to attack it therapeutically. The second possibility is that androgenic hormone is being produced from another source thereby nullifying the program of androgen-control therapy. It is known that the adrenal cortex can elaborate androgenic steroids. Adrenalectomy in patients with prostatic cancer was attempted some years ago but the maintenance of life was so unsatisfactory with the available adrenal steroids and extracts that it was impossible to evaluate the effects of the procedure on the prostatic tumor. The availability of cortisone has now made it possible to reexamine this question. In February, 1951, Huggins began a new series of cases in which the prerequisite for bilateral adrenalectomy was failure of the androgen-control regimen. Although the immediate effects in terms of subjective improvement were dramatic, sufficient time has now passed to evaluate the longer term results better. Although the number of patients in the series is relatively small, experience indicates that remissions following adrenalectomy for disseminated prostatic cancer last for three to nine months. It is interesting that in a number of instances, when exacerbation has occurred, the reinstitution of stilbestrol therapy has been followed by clinical remissions. If these observations can be duplicated with regularity, and if the susceptibility of the tumor to estrogen is sufficiently lasting, adrenalectomy may prove to be of greater value than is now apparent.

There is one other neoplasm which regresses dramatically following the institution of androgen control. This is carcinoma of the breast in men. This rare tumor is seldom recognized sufficiently early to permit definitive surgical intervention and therefore castration is usually indicated because of dissemination. Sufficient cases for statistical analysis are not available but remissions of the disease for periods of three years and frequently much longer are common. It has also not been established whether estrogenic therapy should be started coincident with orchiectomy. The common practice is to withhold estrogens until there is evidence of exacerbation of the disease.

The hazards of androgen-control therapy by orchiectomy and estrogen administration are minimal. Because of the age group, castration in these patients does not pose an important psychologic problem. The estrogens may produce gastrointestinal symptoms and water and electrolyte imbalances due to increasing the renal tubular absorption of sodium, gynecomastia, and, extremely rarely, carcinoma of the breast. With reasonable care, none of these toxic manifestations need be of serious consequence.

ANDROGENS IN CANCER OF THE BREAST

The existence of a relationship of the ovarian hormones to cancer of the breast was first clearly demonstrated by Leo Loeb and his associates. They found that the incidence of spontaneous carcinoma of the breast in mice was significantly decreased by castration. The importance of the stimulative action of estrogen on the development of carcinoma of the breast was emphasized by Lacassagne who showed that the tumor could be regularly induced in strains of mice with a low incidence of spontaneous breast cancer by the prolonged administration of estrogens. These observations led to the suggestion that antagonism of estrogen by androgen might provide a significant therapeutic advance in the treatment of inoperable human mammary cancer.

Experimental trial of the hypothesis in mice showed that it was necessary to administer testosterone continuously from early life in order to prevent the appearance of breast cancer. If androgen therapy was delayed until shortly before the expected onset of the tumor or until after the appearance of the cancer no prophylactic or curative effects were demonstrable. In spite of the disappointing results in the laboratory, androgen therapy was tried in disseminated carcinoma of the human breast. Sufficient time has elapsed since Adair and his associates popularized this method of treatment to define its indications and limitations with considerable assurance.

A cardinal principle in androgen therapy of breast cancer is that it should not be considered in a patient who has an operable lesion or even when the lesion is inoperable but still apparently localized to the breast and regional lymph nodes. In the latter situation irradiation is indicated. It is also not justifiable to employ androgenic substances for the management of breast cancer if, in addition to the primary lesion there are only several distant soft tissue or bony metastases. It may be fairly stated that the administration of androgens is indicated only when metastases are sufficiently numerous and widespread that irradiation is not practical.

Experience has further shown that the most satisfactory clinical response is observed in patients with symptomatic osseous metastases. Under these circumstances, although roentgenographic evidence of repair is rare, relief of pain and improvement in sense of well-being is the rule. Regression of soft tissue metastases is far less regular than the relief of symptoms from osseous lesions although subjective improvement still occurs. Androgen therapy of disseminated breast cancer may be employed in women of all ages without appreciable danger of accelerating the progress of the neoplasm.

In a recent summary of the current status of hormone therapy of advanced mammary cancer, subjective improvement was observed in about 80 per cent of over 450 patients when optimal doses of testosterone propionate were administered. Objective evidence of regression of soft tissue or bone lesions was noted in about 20 per cent of the cases. In this regard it is interesting and significant that only rarely was it possible to demonstrate morphologic changes in metastatic disease even when there was regression of the lesions. In the large series summarized in this report, the mean survival time in those patients showing improvement was about one year from the institution of androgen therapy, whereas those who were unimproved lived about eight months. It is probable that the difference in survival time is not significant and therefore it may be concluded that androgen therapy does not prolong life but permits the patient to live in far greater comfort with her disease.

At the present time there are two androgenic substances which have been widely employed. These are testosterone propionate, which is administered intramuscularly at a dosage of 50 to 100 mg. three times weekly, and methyl testosterone. The optimal dosage for the latter drug has not been conclusively established; it is active following oral administration and the dosage range is from 50 to 200 mg. daily. It appears likely that the higher doses will be required more frequently than the lower. An important feature of androgen therapy is that the onset of a favorable response is delayed and therefore it is necessary to continue treatment for six to ten weeks before it is permissible to conclude that therapy will be ineffective. When a favorable response is obtained experience indicates that medication should be continued until there is an exacerbation of symptoms. Drug withdrawal at this time may occasionally be followed by another remission.

Androgen therapy is not without its disadvantages. The undesirable side effects include virilism with hirsutism, deepening of voice, acne, and increased libido. Occasionally these changes are sufficiently distressing to the patient that therapy must be abandoned. More serious toxic manifestations which must be guarded against are edema and hypercalcemia. The edema is largely due to the effect of the steroids on renal tubular function leading to greater reabsorption of sodium. In individuals with normal cardiovascular and renal function, edema is transient and appropriate homeostatic readjustments occur naturally. In patients with cardiac disease or impaired renal function, hypervolemia, peripheral and pulmonary edema may occur necessitating sodium restriction, digitalization, and diuretics. Hypercalcemia secondary to the mobilization of calcium from bone may produce renal damage, central nervous system symptoms, and sudden death. The best treatment of this potentially serious complication is early recognition and discontinuation of therapy.

ESTROGENS IN CANCER OF THE BREAST

Estrogenic substances were initially proposed for the treatment of advanced breast cancer on the basis of a highly speculative theory of hormone imbalances. Since no convincing evidence has been advanced to support the hypothesis and since there is a reasonable explanation for the efficacy of the sex hormones in breast carcinoma, further historical discussion is not warranted.

Estrogen therapy of breast cancer is more strictly limited in its indications than in the case of androgens for not only should it be reserved for disseminated, symptomatic disease but also it should be given to women who are *at least* five years postmenopausal. This latter condition should be assiduously met in order to avoid fulminating progression of the neoplastic process.

When the cases are properly selected, estrogenic therapy may be followed by marked subjective improvement, relief of bone pain, and regression of soft tissue metastases particularly in lymph nodes and pulmonary parenchyma. Abdominal visceral infiltrations respond rarely.

A number of synthetic and natural hormone preparations have been used, including stilbestrol, ethinyl estradiol, and estradiol dipropionate. There is no evidence of greater efficacy of one over the others and therefore stilbestrol has been employed most frequently because it is active after oral administration and is inexpensive. The usual dose is 15 mg. daily in divided doses. There is a lag in the onset of evident beneficial effects so that a trial period of six weeks to two months is necessary before it is justifiable to conclude that therapy will be ineffective.

In a series of 300 cases of widespread breast cancer treated by estrogens approximately 40 per cent showed some evidence of improvement. The survival time of those who had a beneficial effect was approximately twice that of those who failed to respond. The mean survival time from the initiation of hormone treatment for the latter group was about eight months whereas the comparable figure for the successfully treated patients was fifteen months. It is to be noted that patients with breast cancer who are past 60 have a more favorable prognosis than younger women probably because the biologic characteristics of malignancy in the aged are less virulent.

The toxic manifestations of estrogen therapy include gastrointestinal symptoms, edema, hypercalcemia, and uterine bleeding. All of these reactions are potentially hazardous so that the patients must be observed frequently while on this regimen.

As was mentioned earlier, Huggins has recently performed bilateral adrenalectomy in a variety of neoplastic diseases. In addition to the beneficial effects observed in prostatic cancer, the only other disease process which, in Huggins' opinion, has been modified, is disseminated breast cancer. The salutary responses observed have not been uniform and the selection of patients who may be expected to benefit from the operation has not been defined. In premenopausal patients, surgical castration as well as adrenalectomy has often been performed. This confuses the interpretation of the results of adrenal extirpation since ovariectomy alone may be followed by remissions in breast cancer. At the present time insufficient evidence is available to assess critically adrenal surgery in breast cancer. Since a number of other clinics in this country are evaluating the procedure it can be anticipated that the issue will be clarified in the near future.

Mechanism of Action

The evidence for a fundamental action of hormone therapy on the neoplastic breast cells is minimal. As has been mentioned, only rarely is it possible to observe in serial biopsies morphologic alterations of the tumor even when there has been clinical evidence of some regression. Godwin and Escher treated primary operable cases of breast cancer for as long as one month preoperatively with the sex hormones. They concluded that there were ". . . no pathognomonic histological changes demonstrable . . ." Another bit of circumstantial evidence suggesting a nonspecific effect of the hormones in breast cancer is the report of clinical improvement following androgen therapy in thyroid cancer metastatic to bone.

The fact remains that a certain proportion of women treated with androgens or estrogens are definitely improved. A reasonable explanation for the observed clinical effects lies in the metabolic actions of the sex hormones. It has been shown in laboratory animals and in man that the gonadal steroids stimulate protein anabolism. The cellular mechanisms by which this is accomplished are unknown. Since it is known that extensive neoplastic disease leads to disturbances of protein metabolism it is possible that androgens and estrogens effectively counter this deleterious effect of the tumor on its host thereby producing clinical improvement. The relief of bone pain may also in part be ascribed to the hormone-accelerated deposition of osteoid. This explanation for the action of the hormones in breast cancer is conjectural and certainly an oversimplification. The fact that there is extensive fibrosis in a small proportion of breast cancers under hormone therapy indicates perhaps that at times there may also be a direct effect of these chemical compounds on neoplastic cells.

ADRENOCORTICOTROPIC HORMONE (ACTH) AND CORTISONE IN MALIGNANT DISEASE

These tremendously active hormones at one time appeared to be panaceas for all human ills and they were tried in most disease syndromes including neoplastic disease.

Results in a variety of cancers have failed to demonstrate significant benefit and at the present time they are indicated therapeutically only in the lymphoma-leukemia group of malignant tumors. Even within this area, the hormones have very significant limitations.

In the lymphomas—which include, for the purpose of this discussion, Hodgkin's disease and the lymphosarcomas—ACTH and cortisone are not indicated for definitive therapy because there is little evidence to suggest that they destroy malignant cells. There are, however, certain situations in which the drugs can be helpful. In these diseases after multiple courses of roentgen-ray therapy and/or nitrogen mustard it is common for the patient to develop systemic signs of disease activity and symptoms such as weakness, anorexia, and fever together with pancytopenia due in part to the fundamental pathologic process and probably in larger part due to therapy with bone marrow depressants. Under these conditions further treatment with cytotoxic drugs or irradiation is contraindicated and in the past this was considered the preterminal phase of the disease. The availability of ACTH and cortisone has modified the situation somewhat because associated with their administration the temperature falls, appetite improves, and a rise of the formed elements of the blood may occur. It is to be noted that the effects of the disease on the patient are modified rather than the disease process itself. When the drugs are discontinued all of the symptoms recur within a few days. The value of ACTH or cortisone then is merely to temporize and provide the patient a period during which he may have sufficient recovery to withstand further definitive therapy. The mechanism of the antipyretic action of adrenal steroid therapy is not known.

In adults with acute leukemia who in addition to having the systemic symptomatology above described also exhibit purpura, a course of ACTH or cortisone may control all symptoms without significantly altering the leukemic blood or bone marrow status. During this period of subjective improvement, the anemia can be corrected by transfusions and occasionally the patient will then experience a spontaneous remission which will justify the institution of the temporizing regimen with ACTH or cortisone. Again the mechanism of the antipurpuric action of adrenal cortical steroids is not clear.

In acute leukemia of childhood, on the other hand, significant effects on the course of the disease follow the administration of the hormones. In this disease clinical remissions are induced in about 70 per cent of the cases and hematologic remissions in more than half of these patients. The duration of the remission varies from two weeks to nine months and there are no signs which permit a prediction of the degree of success to be anticipated.

There are several noteworthy features about hyperadrenal therapy of acute leukemia. The hazards of immediate toxicity are minimal as compared to the folic acid antagonists. There is usually prompt evidence of stimulation of erythropoiesis and, in fact, all elements of the bone marrow may show increased activity. The frequency of remissions following exacerbation of the disease is progressively smaller with each successive course of treatment and inevitably the disease becomes refractory to ACTH or cortisone. There is no relationship between refractoriness of acute leukemia to the folic acid antagonists and ACTH or cortisone. It has been repeatedly observed that a remission can be induced by these latter compounds after the disease has failed to respond to aminopterin or a-methopterin. The reverse situation also pertains. Although the evidence is not conclusive, it appears that once refractoriness to either form of therapy has developed, only rarely does the neoplasm become sensitive again to this method of treatment.

The toxic manifestations of ACTH or cortisone are those of hyperadrenalcorticism. There may be the accumulation of edema fluid due to sodium and water retention, development of moonface, elevation of blood pressure, diabetes, and psychic aberrations. Some or all of these signs and symptoms occur in the majority of patients because the dosage of the drugs required to control the disease is high. Thromboembolic complications which may occur associated with ACTH or cortisone therapy of other disorders has not been observed in patients with acute leukemia.

At the present time there is no basis for preferential selection of ACTH or cortisone for cancer therapy. It is possible that ACTH may induce a more rapid response, but the delay in onset of action of cortisone is measurable in days. More important factors in selection are the availability of the two drugs and their relative costs.

INEFFECTIVE CHEMOTHERAPEUTIC AGENTS

In this section will be presented a number of compounds which have offered sufficient promise to merit clinical trial but which have failed to find a place in therapy because of excessive toxicity or ineffectiveness against human disease.

PRODUCTS OF MICRO-ORGANISMS

Before the days of effective antibacterial chemotherapeutic agents, an occasional observation was recorded of regression of a malignant tumor coincident with a severe bacterial infection. The presence of a tumor-necrotizing substance in the metabolic products of a variety of micro-organisms was clearly demonstrated in a number of independent laboratory investigations, particularly by Gratia and Linz, Schwartzman, and Shear. The latter worker is chiefly responsible for the continued interest in this potential approach to cancer chemotherapy, for in his laboratory careful fractionation of culture filtrates of a gram negative rod, *Serratia marcescens*, led to the isolation of a polysaccharide which when injected in minute quantities produced necrosis of tumors in laboratory animals. The dramatic changes induced in experimental neoplasms are characterized by extensive hemmorrhage into the tumor within hours after parenteral administration of the polysaccharide, followed by necrosis of the malignant cells during the next forty-eight hours.

In experimental cancer chemotherapy, three major drawbacks became apparent: (1) The tumors were never completely destroyed so that a rim of viable cells persisted which rapidly proliferated as a new blood supply developed by capillary invasion; (2) the polysaccharide proved to be a potent antigen so that immunity to its carcinolytic action developed quickly; and (3) the systemic toxicity of the polysaccharide paralleled its tumor-necrotizing activity.

Persistent laboratory investigations, both chemical and biologic, have sought to separate the immunologic, toxic, and tumor-necrotizing properties of Shear's polysaccharide from *Serratia marcescens*. Although some evidence has been advanced which indicates that the antigenic property is separable from the others, it still remains to be proved that the systemic toxicity and the tumor effect are not due to the same component. It is recognized that bacteria are potent sources of powerful pharmacodynamic substances, as demonstrated, for example, by the hemolytic streptococci, which produce eight separable endo- and exo-toxins. However, neither the polysaccharide from *S. marcescens* nor the more highly publicized endotoxin from *Schizotrypanum cruzi* developed by the Russian investigators, Roskin and Klyueva (and called K-R serum), has made any practical contribution to cancer therapy.

In the earlier part of this century, before the potent bacterial polysaccharide had been isolated, Coley enthusiastically advocated the administration of a mixture of bacterial culture filtrates. The material, known as "Coley's toxin," never had widespread use in clinical medicine, because results were not impressive and toxic reactions were frequent and serious. More recently clinical experiments with Shear's polysaccharide have been conducted but toxicity rather than therapeutic efficacy has characterized the results. Following the administration of small amounts of the polysaccharide intravenously, a rapidly developing constitutional reaction occurs, manifested by hyperpyrexia to as high as 107° F., peripheral vascular collapse, and shock. The tumor-necrotizing action of the compound, so dramatically evident in experimental tumors, has been negligible in human malignant disease.

Work continues on products of micro-organisms, in part stimulated by the miraculous successes achieved in the field of antibacterial chemotherapy with antibiotics. The background of information supplied by the investigations discussed in the preceding paragraphs indicates the potential value of such an approach but also demonstrates the difficulties that may be encountered. A more complete survey of the work in this field can be gained from study of the references listed in the bibliography.

PODOPHYLLIN

In 1942 Kaplan, a New Orleans dermatologist, reported that the local application of podophyllin (a mixture of substances from the roots and rhizomes of the mandrake plant) to condylomata accuminata was followed by rapid involution of the tumors. In 1947 Sullivan repeated the observations on clinical material and noted striking effects on mitosis which were very similar to those produced by colchicine.

Considerable chemical and biologic work has been done with this substance in the past few years. The inhibition of mitotic division in metaphase has been confirmed and chemotherapy of experimental tumors produced significant retardation of growth. However, as had previously been found in studies with colchicine, there was no selectivity of the drug for neoplastic tissue, so that significant host toxicity and tumor effect were inseparable. Chemical characterization of podophyllin yielded four components: podophyllotoxin, picropodophyllin, podophylloresin, and quercetin. The colchicine-like effect appears to be due to podophyllotoxin.

Limited clinical trial of podophyllotoxin in cancer chemotherapy has merely demonstrated that man reacts to the chemical compound in the same way as laboratory animals. Following parenteral administration, gastrointestinal disturbances, manifested particularly by severe diarrhea, occur long before any demonstrable tumor effect is evident. This obviously rules out the possibility of using the drug systemically. Scattered reports on the topical application of podophyllin or podophyllotoxin for skin carcinomas have appeared, with apparent successful eradication of the disease. In general, chemotherapy of localized and accessible cancer is contraindicated, because such lesions can be successfully cured by surgery or irradiation. Further, it has been demonstrated by the sad follow-up experiences in patients treated by escharotic pastes that malignant cells usually extend beyond the circumference of the grossly evident lesion so that recurrences occur with great frequency when only the macroscopic tumor is treated.

THE RETICULOENDOTHELIAL SYSTEM IN CANCER CHEMOTHERAPY

The reticuloendothelial system has well established physiologic functions in cellular and humoral immunity, erythrocyte phagocytosis and pigment metabolism, repair and regeneration of tissues, and lipoid storage. In addition to these recognized functions it has been popular at intervals to assign to it more general and less precisely defined abilities. Thus, on the basis of circumstantial and incomplete objective evidence, the reticuloendothelial system has been considered to provide the natural defense mechanisms of the body against neoplastic disease. In order to understand the rationale behind the development of "antireticular cytotoxic serum" (ACS), "reticuloendothelial inhibiting serum" (REIS) and spleen extracts, it is necessary to review briefly the evidence which implicates the reticuloendothelial system as a limiting factor to neoplastic cells.

Morphologic examination of this widespread system in experimental tumor-bearing animals has revealed a marked hypertrophy, particularly of the elements in the spleen and liver. This is manifested by proliferation of histiocytes and Kupffer cells in the liver and by reticular hyperplasia in the spleen. It has been alleged that a correlation exists between the reaction of the follicular elements of the spleen in animals treated with chemical carcinogens and the incidence of tumor production in these animals. In refractory animals there is marked hyperplasia of follicles and of reticuloendothelial elements, whereas in those animals in which a malignancy is produced follicular aplasia of the spleen is noted. Splenic hypertrophy has also been observed in animals bearing various types of neoplasms. This latter finding is interpreted as an expression of a physiologic defense mechanism. Another piece of circumstantial evidence which is supposed to indicate a carcinolytic ability of the spleen is the low incidence of metastatic malignancy in this organ. Admittedly the reported occurrence of 3.2 per cent splenic metastases in one autopsy series is surprising, in view of the rich blood and lymphatic supply of this organ, as well as its proximity to gastrointestinal organs which are so frequently the site of carcinomas.

When the function of the reticuloendothelial system is depressed either by splenectomy or by overloading of the cells with certain colloids, there appears to be stimulation of tumor development and growth.

At the present time the importance of mesenchymal tissues in health and disease has been highlighted by the striking therapeutic applications of adrenal corticotropic hormone and adrenal cortical steroids. Recognizing, therefore, that the physiologic contributions of the reticuloendothelial system may be significant in the biologic behavior of neoplastic growth, it nevertheless must be pointed out that the available evidence on this issue is not impressive. Thus, the hypertrophy of reticuloendothelial elements in tumor-bearing animals can be also reasonably explained on the basis of bacterial infection, for it is known that transplants are, more frequently than not, contaminated. The characteristic infiltration of the lymph nodes, liver, and spleen by the malignant lymphomas and the frequent metastases of carcinoma to the liver are difficult facts to reconcile with the alleged carcinoclastic activity of the reticuloendothelial system. The concept that the reticuloendothelial system elaborates some carcinolytic principle (e.g. "splendothelan") fails to be substantiated by tissue culture studies, in which no effect on tumor growth can be demonstrated when tumor and splenic explants are grown side by side.

In spite of the lack of convincing evidence, many attempts have been made during the years to "stimulate" the reticuloendothelial system or to extract a therapeutic substance from it. Perhaps the most notorious example of this approach has been antireticular cytotoxic serum (ACS) developed by the Russian biologist Bogomoletz and his associates. This serum was prepared by immunizing horses to human spleen and bone marrow. The antiserum thus obtained was administered in small amounts on the hypothesis that homeopathic doses of a noxious agent would "stimulate" the reticuloendothelial system, while large doses would "depress" it. Suffice it to say that in spite of enthusiastic claims for this therapeutic regimen in a variety of human diseases including malignant tumors, adequate confirmation has not been forthcoming and the Russian reports provide insufficient evidence for an objective evaluation.

The American counterpart of ACS is REIS (reticuloendothelial immune serum). Pomerat and his associates in Texas have demonstrated that a potent antiserum to spleen and bone marrow can be developed by appropriate heterologous immunization with antigen prepared from spleen and bone marrow. As yet no clinical applications or claims have been made for REIS.

The clinical use of splenic extracts in cancer chemotherapy has been introduced and reintroduced on many separate occasions. The enthusiastic heralding of dramatic responses in preliminary reports followed by silence would appear to be an indication of the variability in the natural course of malignant diseases under ineffective therapy.

STILBAMIDINE IN MULTIPLE MYELOMA

At the present time urethane is the chemotherapeutic agent of choice in the management of widespread, symptomatic plasma cell myelomatosis. Before the demonstration of the efficacy of ethyl carbamate in multiple myeloma, stilbamidine was introduced by Snapper as a drug for the treatment of this disease.

The rationale for the selection of stilbamidine rests on very tenuous reasoning. The diamidines, of which stilbamidine is one, were found to be effective in the treatment of leishmaniasis, or kala-azar, through their destructive action on the pathogenic protozoa, *Leishmania donovani.* One of the characteristics of kala-azar is a hyperglobulinemia which returns to normal levels following effective chemotherapy with either the diamidines or organic antimonials. In multiple myeloma the plasma globulin is frequently increased; it was on the basis of this single apparent similarity between the microbial disease, leishmaniasis, and the neoplastic disorder, multiple myeloma, that stilbamidine was selected for trial in the latter condition.

Several important fallacies are apparent in the rationalization just described but a discussion of these is not relevant to this presentation. Therefore, it will be accepted that stilbamidine was tried empirically and our attention will be directed toward an evaluation of the clinical results.

From Snapper's results with stilbamidine treatment of multiple myeloma two effects on the disease process are noteworthy. In 80 per cent of patients with bone pain there was subjective relief of this symptom for variable time periods. The only objective evidence for a direct action of the drug on the malignant cells was the development of cytoplasmic granules in the plasma cells. Histochemical studies have demonstrated that these granules consisted of ribonucleic acid and stilbamidine. The significance of the finding in terms of cellular physiology is unknown. In spite of symptomatic improvement in the majority of cases treated, the myeloma cells or myeloma cells with cytoplasmic granules persisted in undiminished number in the bone marrow. In addition, Bence Jones proteinuria continued and the hyperglobulinemia was unaffected. Serial roentgen-ray examinations of the skeleton failed to disclose recalcification but progression of the lesions appeared to be slowed.

This summary of the subjective and objective effects produced by stilbamidine indicates that the drug might be a useful palliative agent which would not be expected to alter the course of the disease significantly. This conclusion, however, fails to take into account the significant toxic side-actions of the diamidine. Of these, the central nervous system toxicity manifested by subjective disturbances and dissociated anesthesia of areas supplied by the sensory branches of the trigeminal nerve is the most important. This reaction, which may develop two and one-half to five months after the completion of stilbamidine therapy, is characterized by subjective symptoms of numbness, formication, heaviness, and itching of the affected areas. The sensation of light touch is lost but pain, temperature, and pressure modalities are intact. From experimental studies in dogs it appears probable that neuronal and myelin disintegration of the principal sensory nucleus of the fifth nerve accounts for the observed signs and symptoms. Inasmuch as the incidence of this toxicity in man is greater than 50 per cent, no satisfactory therapy is available, and the symptoms persist for many months, the use of stilbamidine is contraindicated.

More recently Snapper has reported that a stilbamidine derivative, 2-hydroxystilbamidine, has the same effect on multiple myeloma as stilbamidine without producing the toxic neuropathy. The experience with this new drug is limited and because it is evident that, at best, the diamidines can only produce symptomatic relief, whereas urethane apparently affects the neoplastic cells directly, the latter drug is the agent of choice for this malignant disease.

MISCELLANY

In this short section, mention will be made of several chemical compounds which have been given limited clinical trial in cancer chemotherapy. The purpose is not to correct misrepresentations of published reports, because in almost every instance the authors have been adequately critical of the results obtained. The material is included merely for the general information of the interested reader.

VITAMIN DEFICIENCIES

Avidin

The role of biotin as a part of normal catalytic systems essential to growth has been well established. The finding that avidin, a protein present in egg-white, antagonized the function of biotin suggested a possible cancer chemotherapeutic agent. Although experimental neoplasms in mice failed to regress when the animals were placed on a biotin-deficient diet and fed large amounts of avidin, a comparable experiment was conducted in man. Twelve patients with cancer have received large amounts of egg-white without demonstrable effect on the tumors and without any evidence of biotin deficiency.

Pyridoxine

The dependence of lymphoid tissue for growth and development upon pyridoxine is recognized. Regression of transplantable lymphosarcomas in mice and rats was evident if the animals were placed on a vitamin-B_6–deficient diet. A small series of humans with lymphosarcoma and leukemia have been placed on a pyridoxine-deficient diet and at the same time given the anti-vitamin, desoxypyridoxine. No significant therapeutic effects were noted.

Although the vitamin antagonists mentioned have been ineffective, this approach to cancer chemotherapy may still be fruitful. For example, it is known that there are significant quantitative differences in the concentrations of vitamins of the B complex between normal and neoplastic tissues. If this indicates significant differences in the metabolic functions of the two types of cells, and when more powerful antagonists become available, it is possible that new cancer chemotherapeutic agents will emerge.

Synthetic Vitamin K

The search for drugs which would potentiate the effects of roentgen irradiation or synergise with it has been the objective of many investigations. Recently Mitchell has suggested that tetrasodium-2-methyl-1,4-naphthohydroquinone diphosphate, a synthetic vitamin K substitute ("synkayvite"), was a synergistic drug which significantly improved radiotherapy of malignant tumors.

Quinones, but not this particular one, have been demonstrated to alter nucleoprotein metabolism, and "synkayvite" in high concentrations was noted to interfere with the growth of embryonic chick fibroblasts in tissue culture. In a small series of inadequately controlled cases of inoperable bronchiogenic carcinomas, Mitchell claimed that the combination of "synkayvite" and radiation increased the survival time over that of patients receiving roentgen-ray therapy alone. Critical examination of Mitchell's data fails to substantiate his conclusions and confirmation of his results from other sources has not appeared.

Although combination therapy as here reported has not proved useful, nevertheless this approach to cancer chemotherapy certainly merits thorough exploration. At the experimental level, it has been possible to demonstrate synergistic action of cancer chemotherapeutic agents.

MYELOKENTRIC AND LYMPHOKENTRIC ACIDS

Extraction of the urine of patients with chronic myelogenous and chronic lymphatic leukemia has led to the isolation of two crude substances which have been named myelokentric and lymphokentric acid respectively. The former, obtained from patients with chronic myelogenous leukemia, when injected into rodents produces myeloid metaplasia; the lymphokentric acid from chronic lymphatic leukemia patients produces lymphoid metaplasia when administered to test animals. Neither of these crude substances has been chemically characterized.

On the hypothesis that the chronic leukemias represent an imbalance of normal regulatory substances for lymphoid and myeloid cytopoiesis, Miller, Herbert, and Jones have treated 8 patients with lymphatic leukemia with crude myelokentric acid. Although they observed partial remissions and autopsy evidence suggestive of a specific effect on the abnormal cells, this method of treatment is far from extensive clinical trial. The preparation of the extracts is difficult, the product crude, and the dosage unstandardized.

CANCER CHEMOTHERAPEUTIC AGENTS IN SHADOWLAND

Although the majority of "therapeutic" regimens to be discussed may be properly classed as nostrums, some may have been introduced by sincere people who honestly think that their remedy does modify the course of neoplastic disease.

A few general remarks on the evaluation of cancericidal drugs are relevant at this point. Contrary to lay and professional opinion, the critical evaluation of cancer chemotherapy in man is extraordinarily difficult. A thorough knowledge of the natural course of the malignant diseases being treated is essential, for in many of these illnesses spontaneous and protracted remissions may occur. Such episodes coincident with therapy may lead the unwary to entirely erroneous and unwarranted conclusions on the efficacy of the treatment being given. It also must be appreciated that most cancers produce a chronic rather than an acute disease. Survival for many months after the clinical appearance of the terminal phase of the disease is the rule rather than the exception. For this reason, the mere persistence of life in the face of a hopelessly advanced malignancy cannot be considered as positive evidence that the therapy being given at the time is of significance.

The fact that cancer is a chronic disease which kills slowly also means that eventually the patient realizes the diagnosis. This leads to depression, emotional instability, and psychosomatic symptoms which complicate the clinical picture directly produced by the disease. In such an environment, psychotherapy finds receptive and responsive material. It can be confidently anticipated that subjective improvement will follow the institution of any new form of treatment in a patient with advanced cancer, particularly if enthusiasm and optimism are part of the regimen. Thus alleviation of pain is a singularly poor criterion on which to base a claim of efficacy for a cancer chemotherapeutic agent.

The practitioner may find it necessary to evaluate some unheard-of cancer cure. In his honesty he may feel that an important contribution has been made which he has missed in his hasty coverage of the medical literature. For him it is well to recognize some of the earmarks of the fraudulent. In the first place, it is certain that when an important and significant advance in cancer chemotherapy is made every medical person in the world will know about it, even if he never turns the page of a single medical journal. Therefore if a patient asks him about a "cancer cure" with which he is unfamiliar, *a priori* he can be confident that it is not of major import.

The allegation of the cancer quack that the medical profession will not recognize his cure because of vested interests is unmitigated nonsense. Only the most ignorant or small of mind could ever be taken in by this paranoid cry. A secret remedy is another clear mark of the fake. No proprietary drug need ever be given serious consideration in cancer therapy. It is self-evident that, if any one person ever does discover a chemical compound or combination of chemical compounds which will cure any malignant disease, his fame and fortune is assured without the necessity of keeping his discovery a secret.

If it is necessary to look into an alleged cancer cure with more care, attention should be focused on the documentation of the disease that has been cured. A favorite trick of the quack is to diagnose as malignant a lesion which is inflammatory or otherwise self-limited. Under these circumstances his remedy cures "cancer" with dramatic success. At the present time, it is essential for cancer to be diagnosed unequivocally by histologic sections before accepting the results of any therapeutic regimen.

The centuries-old history of cancer chemotherapy is replete with completely inert substances or toxic agents without effect on neoplastic cells which have been heralded as cancer cures. Vile galenical concoctions, snake venoms, "electric waters," biologic extracts of every conceivable variety, and many others have been given by sincere but inexperienced physicians or by charlatans. For each and every ineffective therapy no paucity of dramatic patient testimonials exist, but cancer still kills in spite of the magical cures. Because of the tremendous lay interest in cancer, the charlatans are finding easy prey. In order to keep the medical profession informed on the nostrums that crop up here, there and everywhere, a special committee has been established by the National Research Council called the Committee on Cancer Diagnosis and Therapy.

In the following paragraphs a few of the ineffective and/or fraudulent cancer treatments which are currently in evidence will be briefly summarized.

COLLODAURUM

Advertisements to physicians from the Kahlenberg Laboratories, Sarasota, Florida, suggest that "Collodaurum" produces palliative effects in advanced cancer comparable to radiotherapy. In addition, "A small number of so-called hopeless cases are cured and remained cured." Collodaurum is an 0.02 per cent preparation of colloidal gold. Chrysotherapy has been carefully evaluated because of its application in the management of rheumatoid arthritis. It has been demonstrated that colloidal gold is taken up by the reticuloendothelial system and remains in the body for prolonged periods of time as inert particulate material; soluble gold salts, on the other hand, do have biologic actions but none which affect neoplastic cells. Since the purveyors of Collodaurum emphasize that their product is completely free of soluble gold salts it can be concluded that the preparation is pharmacologically inert and worthless.

CAUSTIC PASTES

Preparations containing arsenic, copper, di- or tri-chloracetic acid and other escharotics for topical application to tumors are legion. The fallacy of this treatment has been pointed out in the earlier discussion of podophyllin in this chapter. Thus the eradication of a skin cancer by an escharotic is unsafe because the malignant cells extend beyond the limits of the grossly evident lesion. The quacks, however, do not limit their treatment to skin cancer but include metastases or even primary tumors which can be palpated through the skin, such as breast tumors. This form of treatment is reprehensible, because not only is it ineffective but also it may be used on patients who have tumors which can be cured by conventional therapeutic means.

For years the name of Hoxsey has been associated with cancer "treatments" which employ this particular fallacious approach.

KOCH'S SERUM

The medical profession has heard about William F. Koch since 1920 in connection with cancer cures, most recently through a broadside in the Congressional Record. Koch has a secret "synthetic antitoxin" which sometimes is called "glyoxylide." Koch represents "glyoxylide" in a masterpiece of double talk, pseudoscientific balderdash, and unsubstantiated hypotheses as an unsaturated diketone which catalyzes the destruction of "toxins" that are supposed to be responsible for the growth of cancer. Like many other frauds, Koch's serum not only "cures" cancer but also is stated to be useful in the therapy of tuberculosis, psoriasis, leprosy, poliomyelitis, and syphilis. More recently Koch has invaded veterinary medicine with his compound, claiming value for it in the treatment of mastitis and other diseases in cattle.

AF-2

It must not be thought that America has a corner on the development of "cancer cures." Italy has the dubious distinction of having a "Professor" Francesco Guarnieri who has produced AF-2, a "serum" derived from the livers of "cancer-resisting" animals such as goats, sheep and pigs. Although extravagant claims for the therapeutic value of AF-2 in human malignant disease have been made, the Professor is loth to submit his evidence to the Italian medical profession for examination.

It is probably unwarranted to accord AF-2 the dignity of pointing out certain glaring fallacies in its promotion; however, it should be mentioned that the dietary habits of man are such that goats, sheep and pigs are rarely permitted to attain that ripe old age when cancer might be expected to make its appearance in them. Thus the basic hypothesis that these animals are "cancer-resistant" does not rest on a firm foundation. Needless to say there is no evidence that liver extracts from these alleged cancer-resistant species modify human neoplastic disease.

H-11

A preparation which has for many years been the favorite "cancer cure" in Great Britain is H-11. At the present time H-11 is obtained by extracting normal human urine. Before the war the "laboratory" supplying this material made extracts of cattle parathyroid glands on the unsubstantiated hypothesis that this endocrine organ controlled normal and abnormal cellular growth. With the shortage of animal glands occasioned by the war, the assumption was made that this unidentified parathyroid principle would be excreted in the urine and therefore this has become the source of H-11. Claims of efficacy of H-11 in both experimental and clinical neoplastic disease have been made, but a careful evaluation of the available evidence together with an independent laboratory investigation led a committee appointed by the Medical Research Council (comparable to the American National Research Council) to the conclusion that H-11 had no effect on tumors in experimental animals or man.

MISCELLANEOUS

Many more remedies could be mentioned which follow the pattern of being based on elaborate but unsubstantiated theories on the cause of cancer. A therapeutic regimen is then devised on these fanciful hypotheses and clinical results are reported on inadequately diagnosed patients who are not properly followed. Thus "tumolyse," an extract of the bark of certain trees that have "recovered from cancers," "chymotrypsin," a pancreatic enzyme which is alleged to destroy cancer, Gerson's diet, which consists of the juice of raw vegetables and fruit and little else, a secret mixture of herbs prepared by one Rees Evans, and so on, all fall into this category. This approach to the cancer problem is not only to be considered ludicrous because of the depths of ignorance displayed by its advocates; it is cruel and mean because it preys on human beings, distorting the known facts about cancer, and using the fear of the disease to obtain money from the patient and his family.

The medical profession must assume the responsibility of preventing, in so far as possible, the laity from being hoodwinked. This can best be done by examining with a critical eye all reports on therapeutic procedures for malignant disease, irrespective of the source.

REFERENCES

GENERAL REVIEWS

CADE, S. Chemotherapy in the treatment of malignant disease. *Brit. M.J. 2:* 1193-1196, 1949.

CLARK, R. L. JR. The present status of cancer therapy. *Postgrad. Med. 6:* 89-95, 1949.

DODDS, E. C. Chemotherapy in the treatment of malignant disease. *Brit. M.J. 2:* 1191-1193, 1949.

GELLHORN, A., and JONES, L. O. Chemotherapy of malignant disease. *Am. J. Med. 6:* 188-231, 1949.

HADDOW, A. Note on the chemotherapy of cancer. *Brit. M. Bull. 4:* 417-426, 1947.

KARNOFSKY, D. A. The nitrogen mustards and their application in neoplastic disease. *New York State J. Med. 47:* 992-993, 1947.

KARNOFSKY, D. A. Chemotherapy of neoplastic disease. *New England J. Med. 239:* 226-231, 260-270, 299-305, 1948.

KARNOFSKY, D. A., and BURCHENAL, J. H. Present status of clinical cancer chemotherapy. *Am. J. Med. 8:* 767-788, 1950.

KARNOFSKY, D. A., BURCHENAL, J. H., and ESCHER, G. C. Chemotherapy of neoplastic disease. *M. Clin. North America 34:* 439-458, 1950.

MITCHELL, J. S. Current therapeutics: VI. Chemotherapy of cancer. *Practitioner 160:* 476-487, 1948.

REINHARD, E. H., GOOD, J. T., and MARTIN, E. Chemotherapy of malignant neoplastic diseases. *J.A.M.A. 142:* 383-390, 1950.

RHOADS, C. P. Advances in treatment of malignant disease. *Bull. New York Acad. Med. 25:* 271-284, 1949.

SHIMKIN, M. B., and BIERMAN, H. R. Experimental chemotherapy of neoplastic diseases. *Radiology 53:* 518-529, 1949.

NITROGEN MUSTARDS:

Laboratory

American Association for the Advancement of Science. *Approaches to Tumor Chemotherapy.* Washington, 1947.

ANSLOW, W. P. JR., KARNOFSKY, D. A., JAGER, B. V., and SMITH, H. W. The toxicity and pharmacological action of the nitrogen mustards and certain related compounds. *J. Pharmacol. & Exper. Therap. 91:* 224-235, 1947.

AUERBACH, C., ROBSON, J. M., and CARR, J. G. The chemical production of mutations. *Science 105:* 243-247, 1947.

BARRON, E. S. G., BARTLETT, G. R., and MILLER, Z. B. The effect of nitrogen mustards on enzymes and tissue metabolism: I. The effect on enzymes. *J. Exper. Med. 87:* 489-501, 1948.

BARRON, E. S. G., BARTLETT, G. R., MILLER, Z. B., MEYER, J., and SEEGMILLER, J. E. The effect of nitrogen mustards on enzymes and tissue metabolism: II. The effect on tissue metabolism. *J. Exper. Med. 87:* 503-519, 1948.

BERENBLUM, I., and SCHOENTAL, R. Action of mustard gas (β^1-dichloro-diethylsulfide on nucleoproteins. *Nature 159:* 727-729, 1947.

BODENSTEIN, D. The effects of nitrogen mustard on embryonic amphibian development. I. Ectodermal effects. *J. Exper. Zool. 104:* 311-341, 1947.

BODENSTEIN, D., and KONDRITZER, A. A. The effect of nitrogen mustard on nucleic acids during embryonic amphibian development. *J. Exper. Zool. 107:* 109-121, 1948.

BOYLAND, E. The pharmacology of chloroethylamines. *Biochem. Soc. Symp. 2:* 61-70, 1948.

CHANUTIN, A., and GJESSING, E. C. The effect of nitrogen mustards upon the ultraviolet absorption spectrum of thymonucleate, uracil and purines. *Cancer Research 6:* 599-601, 1946.

CHANUTIN, A., and LUDEWIG, S. Biochemical studies on the whole and fractionated thymus of rats injected with β-chloroethyl vesicants. *J. Biol. Chem. 176:* 999-1008, 1948.

ELMORE, D. T., GULLAND, J. M., JORDAN, D. O., and TAYLOR, H. F. W. The reaction of nucleic acids with mustard gas. *Biochem. J. 42:* 308-316, 1948.

GILLETTE, R., and BODENSTEIN, D. Specific developmental inhibitions produced in amphibian embryos by a nitrogen mustard compound. *J. Exper. Zool. 103:* 1-32, 1946.

GILMAN, A., and PHILIPS, F. S. The biological actions and therapeutic applications of the β-chloroethyl amines and sulfides. *Science 103:* 409-415, 1946.

GJESSING, E. C., and CHANUTIN, A. The effect of nitrogen mustards on the viscosity of thymonucleate. *Cancer Research 6:* 593-598, 1946.

GOLDACRE, R. J., LOVELESS, A., and ROSS, W. C. J. Mode of production of chromosome abnormalities by the nitrogen mustards: The possible role of cross-linking. *Nature 163:* 667-669, 1949.

GOLUMBIC, C., FRUTON, J. S., and BERGMANN, M. Chemical reactions of the nitrogen mustard gases: I. The transformations of methyl-bis (β-chloroethyl) amine in water. *J. Org. Chem. 11:* 518-535, 1946.

GRAEF, I., KARNOFSKY, D. A., JAGER, V. B., KRICHESKY, B., and SMITH, H. W. The clinical and pathologic effects of the nitrogen and sulfur mustards in laboratory animals. *Am. J. Path. 24:* 1-47, 1948.

HERRIOTT, R. M. Inactivation of viruses and cells by mustard gas. *J. Gen. Physiol. 32:* 221-239, 1948.

HOUCK, C. R., CRAWFORD, B., BANNON, J. H., and SMITH, H. W. Studies on the mechanism of death in dogs after systemic intoxication by the intravenous injection of methyl-bis (β-chloroethyl) amine or tris (β-chloroethyl) amine. *J. Pharmacol. & Exper. Therap. 90:* 277-292, 1947.

HUNT, C. C., and PHILIPS, F. S. The acute pharmacology of methyl-bis (2-chloroethyl) amine (HN_2). *J. Pharmacol & Exper. Therap. 95:* 131-144, 1949.

KARNOFSKY, D. A., GRAEF, I., and SMITH, H. W. Studies on the mechanism of action of the nitrogen and sulfur mustards in vivo. *Am. J. Path. 24:* 275-291, 1948.

KINDRED, J. E. Histologic changes occurring in the hemopoietic organs of albino rats after single injections of 2-chloroethyl vesicants: A quantitative study: *Arch. Path. 43:* 253-295, 1947.

KOLLER, P. C. Experimental modification of nucleic acid systems in the cell. *Symposia Soc. Exper. Biol. 1:* 270-290, 1947.

LANDING, B. H., GOLDIN, A., and NOE, H. A. Testicular lesions in mice following parenteral administration of nitrogen mustards. *Cancer 2:* 1075-1082, 1949.

LANDING, B. H., GOLDIN, A., NOE, H. A., GOLDBERG, B., and SHAPIRO, D. M. Systemic pathological effects of nitrogen mustards, and a comparison of toxicity, chemical structure and cytotoxic effect, with reference to the chemotherapy of tumors. *Cancer 2:* 1055-1066, 1949.

MCKINNEY, G. R. The effect of a nitrogen mustard on certain synthetic reactions in vitro. *J. Pharmacol. & Exper. Therap. 96:* 188-192, 1949.

ROSE, H. M., and GELLHORN, A. Inactivation of influenza virus with sulfur and nitrogen mustards. *Proc. Soc. Exper. Biol. & Med. 65:* 83-85, 1947.

SPURR, C. L. Influence of nitrogen mustards on the antibody response. *Proc. Soc. Exper. Biol. & Med. 64:* 259-261, 1947.

SPURR, C. L. Physiological effects of beta-chloroethyl amines of interest in the chemotherapy of neoplasms. *Texas Rep. Biol. & Med. 8:* 215-226, 1950.

STAHMANN, M. A., and STAUFFER, J. F. Induction of mutants in Penicillium notatum by methyl bis(β-chloroethyl) amine. *Science 106:* 35-36, 1947.

Wilmer Institute Staff. Studies on the physiology, biochemistry, and cytopathology of the cornea in relation to injury by mustard gas and allied toxic agents. *Bull. Johns Hopkins Hosp. 82:* 81-352, 1948.

Clinical Toxicity

BIERMAN, H. R., STRAIT, L. A., and HRENOFF, M. K. Excretion of urinary coproporphyrins in patients with neoplastic diseases treated with methyl bis(β-chloroethyl) amine hydrochloride (HN_2). *J. Nat. Cancer Inst. 10:* 93-103, 1949.

BLOCK, M., SPURR, C. L., JACOBSON, L. O., and SMITH, T. R. Histopathologic effects of nitrogen mustard therapy upon normal and neoplastic hematopoietic tissues. *Am. J. Clin. Path. 18:* 671-689, 1948.

BROWN, A., and DAVIS, L. J. The hematological effects of nitrogen mustard therapy with special reference to the cytology of the sternal bone marrow. *Glasgow M.J. 31:* 93-113, 1950.

CAMERON, G. R., COURTICE, F. C., and JONES, R. P. The effects of β, β[1]-dichlorodiethyl methylamine hydrochloride on the blood-forming tissues. *J. Path. & Bact. 59:* 425-435, 1947.

DANOWSKI, T. S., GREENMAN, L., GOW, R. C., WEIGAND, F. W., MATTER, F. M., PETERS, J. H., COSGROVE, E. F., SEIFERTH, W., and DAVIS, N. Electrolyte and nitrogen balance studies in patients receiving a nitrogen mustard. *J. Pharmacol. & Exper. Therap. 98:* 147-152, 1950.

JACOBSON, L. O., MARKS, E. K., GASTON, E., ALLEN, J. G., and BLOCK, M. H. The effect of nitrogen mustard and x-irradiation on blood coagulation. *J. Lab. & Clin. Med. 33:* 1566-1578, 1948.

OSGOOD, E. E., and CHU, I. T. The effect of nitrogen mustard on granulocytic cells as observed by the marrow culture technic. *Cancer Research 10:* 98-102, 1950.

SMITH, T. R., JACOBSON, L. O., SPURR, C. L., ALLEN, J. G., and BLOCK, M. H. A coagulation defect produced by nitrogen mustard. *Science 107:* 474, 1948.

SPURR, C. L. Physiological effects of beta chloroethyl amines of interest in the chemotherapy of neoplasms. *Texas Rep. Biol. & Med. 6:* 215-226, 1950.

Clinical Application

General

ALPERT, L. K., GREENSPAN, E. M., and PETERSON, S. S. The treatment of the lymphomas and other neoplastic diseases with nitrogen mustard. *Ann. Int. Med. 32:* 393-432, 1950.

ARIEL, I. M., and KANTER, L. Nitrogen mustard therapy: Clinical studies on the effects of methyl-bis(β-chloroethyl) amine hydrochloride upon various types of neoplastic disease. *Am. J. Surg. 77:* 509-521, 1949.

BRUES, A. M., and JACOBSON, L. O. Comparative therapeutic effects of radioactive and chemical agents in neoplastic diseases of the hematopoietic system. *Am. J. Roentgenol. 58:* 774-782, 1947.

BAUER, R. D., and ERF, L. A. The clinical effect of nitrogen mustard on neoplastic diseases. *Am. J. M. Sc. 219:* 16-26, 1950.

BEN-ASHER, S. Nitrogen mustard therapy: The use of methyl bis(β-chloroethyl) amine hydrochloride in Hodgkin's disease, leukemia, lymphosarcoma and cancer of the lung. *Am. J. M. Sc. 217:* 162-168, 1948.

BICHEL, J. Chemotherapy in leukemia, Hodgkin's disease, and allied disorders. *Acta Radiol. 30:* 49-63, 1948.

BIERMAN, H. R., SHIMKIN, M. B., METTIER, S. R., WEAVER, J., BARRY, W. C., and WISE, S. P. Methyl-bis(β-chloroethyl) amine in large doses in the treatment of neoplastic diseases. *California Med. 71:* 117-125, 1949.

CRAVER, L. F. Recent advances in treatment of lymphomas, leukemias and allied disorders. *Bull. New York Acad. Med. 24:* 3-25, 1948.

CRAVER, L. F. The nitrogen mustards: Clinical use. *Radiology 50:* 486-493, 1948.

DAMESHEK, W. Chemotherapy of "lymphoma" and leukemia. *Bull. New England M. Center 11:* 49-62, 1949.

FALOON, W. W., and GORHAM, L. W. Clinical experience with nitrogen mustard. *New York State J. Med. 48:* 612-616, 1948.

GOLDMAN, R., EGEBERG, R. O., WARE, E. R., EVANS, E. R., and FISHKIN, B. G. Clinical experience with nitrogen mustard therapy. *Arch. Int. Med. 82:* 125-139, 1948.

GOODMAN, L. S., WINTROBE, M. M., DAMESHEK, W., GOODMAN, M. J., GILMAN, A., and McLENNAN, M. T. Nitrogen mustard therapy: Use of methyl-bis (β-chloroethyl) amine hydrochloride and tris(β-chloroethyl) amine hydrochloride for Hodgkin's disease, lymphosarcoma, leukemia and certain allied and miscellaneous disorders. *J.A.M.A. 132:* 126-132, 1946.

HOFMEYR, H. O. Clinical experiences with nitrogen mustards in Hodgkin's disease. *South African M. J. 21:* 195-198, 1947.

JACOBSON, L. O., SPURR, C. L., BARRON, E. S. G., SMITH, T., LUSHBAUGH, C., and DICK, G. F. Nitrogen mustard therapy: Studies on the effect of methyl-bis(β-chloroethyl) amine hydrochloride on neoplastic diseases and allied disorders of the hemopoietic system. *J.A.M.A. 132:* 263-271, 1946.

JACOBSON, L. O., SPURR, C. L., SMITH, T. R., and DICK, G. F. Radioactive phosphorus P^{32} and alkylamines (nitrogen mustards) in the treatment of neoplastic and allied diseases of the hemopoietic system. *M. Clin. North America 31:* 3-18, 1947.

KENNEDY, B. J., and AUB, J. C. The therapeutic indications for nitrogen mustards in lymphoma. *M. Clin. North America* 1301-1311, 1949.

KURNICK, N. B., PALEY, K. R., FIEBER, M. H., and ADLER, D. K. Treatment of malignant disease with nitrogen mustard. *Ann. Int. Med. 30:* 974-1003, 1949.

LEUCUTIA, T. Nitrogen mustard therapy. *Am. J. Roentgenol. 61:* 104-107, 1949.

RHOADS, C. P. Report on a cooperative study of nitrogen mustard (HN_2) therapy of neoplastic disease. *Tr. A. Am. Physicians 60:* 110-117, 1947.

ROSWIT, B., and KAPLAN, G. The role of nitrogen mustard (HN_2) as a systemic adjunct to the radiation therapy of certain malignant diseases. *Am. J. Roentgenol. 61:* 626-636, 1949.

SHULLENBERGER, C. C., WATKINS, C. H., and KIERLAND, R. R. Experiences with nitrogen mustard therapy. *J.A.M.A. 139:* 773-777, 1949.

SPITZ, S. The histological effects of nitrogen mustards on human tumors and tissues. *Cancer 1:* 383-398, 1948.

SPURR, C. L., SMITH, T. R., BLOCK, M., and JACOBSON, L. O. The role of nitrogen mustard therapy in the treatment of lymphomas and leukemias. *Am. J. Med. 8:* 710-723, 1950.

SPURR, C. L., SMITH, T. R., and JACOBSON, L. O. Chemotherapy in human lymphomas, leukemias and allied disorders of the hemopoietic system. *Radiology 50:* 387-394, 1948.

Hodgkin's Disease

AP THOMAS, M. I. R., and CULLUMBINE, H. Nitrogen mustards in Hodgkin's disease: Report on 21 cases and 4 of other reticuloses. *Lancet 1:* 899-901, 1947.

CORNELL, V. H., and BLAUW, A. S. Histopathologic observations in cases of Hodgkin's disease treated with nitrogen mustard. *Am. J. Path. 25:* 233-237, 1949.

DAMESHEK, W., WEISFUSE, L., and STEIN, T. Nitrogen mustard therapy in Hodgkin's disease. *Blood 4:* 338-379, 1949.

ERF, L. A., and BAUER, R. D. The clinical effect of nitrogen mustard on Hodgkin's disease. *Am. J. Clin. Path. 19:* 372-380, 1949.

GELLHORN, A., and COLLINS, V. P. Quantitative evaluation of nitrogen mustard therapy in Hodgkin's disease. *Ann. Int. Med. 35:* 1250-1259, 1951.

NABARRO, J. D. N. Nitrogen mustard therapy with special reference to Hodgkin's disease. *Brit. M. J. 2:* 622-625, 1949.

WILKINSON, J. F., and FLETCHER, F. Effect of β-chloroethylamine hydrochlorides in leukemia, Hodgkin's disease, and polycythemia vera. *Lancet 2:* 540-545, 1947.

WINTROBE, M. M., and HUGULEY, C. M., JR. Nitrogen-mustard therapy for Hodgkin's disease, lymphosarcoma, the leukemias and other disorders. *Cancer 1:* 357-382, 1948.

WINTROBE, M. M., HUGULEY, C. M., JR., MCLENNAN, M. T., and LIMA, L. P. Nitrogen mustard as a therapeutic agent for Hodgkin's disease, lymphosarcoma and leukemia. *Ann. Int. Med. 27:* 529-540, 1947.

ZANES, R. P., JR., DOAN, C. A., and HOSTER, H. A. Studies in Hodgkin's syndrome. VII. Nitrogen mustard therapy. *J. Lab. & Clin. Med. 33:* 1002-1018, 1948.

Bronchiogenic Carcinoma

BOYLAND, E., CLEGG, J. W., KOLLER, P. C., RHODEN, E., and WARWICK, O. H. The effects of chloroethylamines on tumors, with special reference to bronchogenic carcinoma. *Brit. J. Cancer 2:* 17-29, 1948.

GAENSLER, E. A., MCKAY, D. G., WARE, P. F., and LYNCH, J. P. Cytologic changes in bronchogenic carcinoma following treatment with nitrogen mustard (methyl-bis[β-chloroethyl] amine). *Arch. Path. 46:* 503-518, 1948.

KARNOFSKY, D. A., ABELMANN, W., CRAVER, L. F., and BURCHENAL, J. H. The use of the nitrogen mustards in the palliative treatment with particular reference to bronchogenic carcinoma. *Cancer 1:* 634-656, 1948.

KENT, L., and REH, E. P. Treatment of bronchogenic carcinoma with nitrogen mustard. *Dis. of Chest 17:* 190-201, 1950.

LYNCH, J. P., WARE, P. F., and GAENSLER, E. A. Nitrogen mustard in the treatment of inoperable bronchiogenic carcinoma. *Surgery 27:* 368-385, 1950.

SKINNER, E. F., CARR, D., and DENMAN, W. E. The treatment of inoperable bronchiogenic carcinoma with methyl bis. *J. Thoracic Surg. 17:* 428-438, 1948.

Miscellaneous

BLAIR, A., III, and NURNBERGER, C. E. Nitrogen mustard therapy for malignant tumors, with particular reference to tumors of epithelial origin. *Alexander Blain Hosp. Bull. 7:* 43-51, 1948.

BRIXEY, A. M., and LAMB, J. H. Lymphoblastoma cutis: Report of a case treated with nitrogen mustard. *Arch. Dermat. & Syph. 61:* 800-812, 1950.

BURCHENAL, J. H. The newer nitrogen mustards in the treatment of leukemia. *Radiology 50:* 494-499, 1948.

BURCHENAL, J. H., MYERS, W. P. L., CRAVER, L. F., and KARNOFSKY, D. A. The nitrogen mustards in the treatment of leukemia. *Cancer 2:* 1-17, 1949.

GOLDBERG, L. C., and MASON, L. M. Treatment of cutaneous blastomas and other diseases with nitrogen mustard. *Arch. Dermat. & Syph. 60:* 181-189, 1949.

HENSTELL, H. H., TOBER, J. N., and NEWMAN, B. A. The influence of nitrogen mustard on mycosis fungoides: Observations relating its effect to the reticulo-endothelial system. *Blood 2:* 564-577, 1947.

KIERLAND, R. R., WATKINS, C. H., and SHULLENBERGER, C. C. The use of nitrogen mustard in the treatment of mycosis fungoides. *J. Invest. Dermat. 9:* 195-201, 1947.

OSBORNE, E. D., JORDON, J. W., HOAK, F. C., and PSCHIERER, F. J. Nitrogen mustard therapy in cutaneous blastomatous disease. *J.A.M.A. 135:* 1123-1128, 1947.

PHILPOTT, O. S., WOODBURNE, A. R., and WALDRIFF, G. A. Nitrogen mustard in the treatment of mycosis fungoides. *J.A.M.A. 135:* 631-633, 1947.

SNIDER, G. E. The treatment of Boeck's sarcoid with nitrogen mustard; preliminary report. *South M. J. 41:* 11-14, 1948.

SPURR, C. L., SMITH, T. R., BLOCK, M., and JACOBSON, L. O. A clinical study of the use of nitrogen mustard therapy in polycythemia vera. *J. Lab. & Clin. Med. 35:* 252-264, 1950.

SWEITZER, S. E., CUMMING, H. A., and MCAFEE, G. D. Lymphosarcoma treated with nitrogen mustard. *Arch. Dermat. & Syph. 61:* 12-19, 1950.

WOODRUFF, A. W. Nitrogen mustard in polycythemia vera. *Brit. M. J. 2:* 299, 1948.

URETHANE

Laboratory

BODINE, J. H., and FITZGERALD, L. R. Effect of diethyldithiocarbamate on the respiration of active and blocked embryonic cells. *Proc. Soc. Exper. Biol. & Med. 69:* 442-445, 1948.

BRYAN, C. E., SKIPPER, H. E., and WHITE, L., JR. Carbamates in the chemotherapy of leukemia: IV. The distribution of radioactivity in tissues of mice following injection of carbonyl-labeled urethane. *J. Biol. Chem. 177:* 941-950, 1949.

CLARK, A. J. *Mode of Action of Drugs on Cells.* London, Arnold, 1933.

COWEN, P. N. Some studies on the action of urethane on mice. *Brit. J. Cancer 1:* 401-405, 1947.

FISHER, K. C., and STERN, J. R. The separation of "activity" metabolism from the total respiration of yeast by the effects of ethyl carbamate. *J. Cell. & Comp. Physiol. 19:* 109-122, 1942.

FLORIJN, E., and SMITS, G. Mechanism of the action of urethane in the treatment of malignant growth. *Nature 164:* 699, 1949.

GREEN, J. W., JR., and LUSHBAUGH, C. C. Histopathologic study of the mode of inhibition of cellular proliferation by urethane: Effect of urethane on Walker rat carcinoma 256. *Cancer Research 9:* 199-209, 1949.

HADDOW, A., and SEXTON, W. A. Influence of carbamic esters (urethanes) on experimental animal tumors. *Nature 157:* 500-503, 1946.

KIRSCHBAUM, A., and LU, C. S. Effect of urethane on maturation of leukocytes of mouse myelogenous leukemia. *Proc. Soc. Exper. Biol. & Med. 65:* 62-63, 1947.

LASNITZKI, I. Some effects of urethane on the growth and mitosis of normal and malignant cells in vitro. *Brit. J. Cancer 3:* 501-509, 1949.

LUSHBAUGH, C. C., GREEN, J. W., JR., and STORER, J. B. Histopathologic study of mode of inhibition of cellular proliferation by urethane; effect of urethane on wound healing. *J. Nat. Cancer Inst. 8:* 201-207, 1948.

MITCHELL, J. H., JR., HUTCHISON, O. S., SKIPPER, H. E., and BRYAN, C. E. Carbamates in the chemotherapy of leukemia: VII. The rate of catabolism of urethane in normal and neoplastic mice. *J. Biol. Chem. 180:* 675-680, 1949.

ORMSBEE, R. A., and FISHER, K. C. The effect of urethane on the consumption of oxygen and the rate of cell division in the ciliate Tetrahymena geleii. *J. Gen. Physiol. 27:* 461-468, 1944.

OSGOOD, E. E., and CHU, I. T. The effect of urethane on the nuclear morphology of cells of the granulocyte series as observed in marrow cultures and leukemic blood. *Blood 3:* 911-917, 1948.

QUASTEL, J. H. Effects of narcotics and benzedrine on metabolic processes in the central nervous system. *Tr. Faraday Soc. 39:* 348-359, 1943.

SKIPPER, H. E., BRYAN, C. E., RISER, W. H., JR., WELTY, M., and STELZENMULLER, A. Carbamates in the chemotherapy of leukemia: The relationship between chemical structure, leukopenic action, and acute toxicity of a group of urethane derivatives. *J. Nat. Cancer Inst. 9:* 77-88, 1948.

SKIPPER, H. E., RISER, W. H., JR., STELZENMULLER, A., and HOLT, H. Carbamate in the chemotherapy of leukemia: I. A procedure for screening compounds for leukotoxic action. *Blood 3:* 774-779, 1948.

CLINICAL APPLICATION

AAS, K. Myelomatosis with normal serum protein values, treated with urethane. *Acta med. scandinav. 135:* 426-438, 1949.

BARNARD, R. D. Urethane in anaplastic carcinoma. *J.A.M.A. 135:* 450-451, 1947.

BEDINGER, P. L. Further studies on the effect of urethane on leukemia. *J. Lab. & Clin. Med. 33:* 1647-1648, 1948.

BEDINGER, P. L., PONCHER, H. G., and LIMARZI, L. R. Effect of urethane on leukemia. *J. Lab. & Clin. Med. 32:* 1394-1395, 1947.

BERMAN, L., and AXELROD, A. R. Effect of urethane on malignant diseases. *Am. J. Clin. Path. 18:* 104-129, 1948.

CRESKOFF, A. J., and FITZ-HUGH, T., JR. Urethane therapy in leukemia. *Rev. Gastroenterol. 16:* 243-249, 1949.

DILLON, E. S., DILLON, M. L., and RUNDLES, R. W. Changes in electrophoretic patterns of sera in patients with multiple myeloma treated with urethane. *Am. J. Med. 7:* 242, 1949.

GOODMAN, M. J., and LEWIS, H. P. Urethane in leukemia. *J.A.M.A. 132:* 1105, 1946.

HARRINGTON, W. J., and MOLONEY, W. C. The treatment of multiple myeloma with urethane. *Cancer 3:* 253-271, 1950.

HIRSCHBOECK, J. S., LINDERT, M. C. F., CHASE, J., and CALVY, T. L. Effects of urethane in the treatment of leukemia and metastatic malignant tumors. *J.A.M.A. 136:* 90-95, 1948.

KENNEDY, B. J., NATHANSON, I. T., and AUB, J. C. Ethyl carbamate (urethane) in the treatment of mycosis fungoides. *Cancer 3:* 66-73, 1950.

LAPIDES, J. Clinical value of urethane therapy in prostatic cancer. *Cancer 2:* 469-474, 1949.

LEUCUTIA, T. Urethane therapy. *Am. J. Roentgenol. 59:* 421-424, 1948.

LOGE, J. P., and RUNDLES, R. W. Urethane (ethyl carbamate) therapy in multiple myeloma. *Blood 4:* 201-216, 1949.

MOESCHLIN, S. Zum Wirkungsmechanismus des Urethans bei Leukämien. *Helvet. med. acta 14:* 279-294, 1947.

PATERSON, E., HADDOW, A., AP THOMAS, I., and WATKINSON, J. M. Leukemia treated with urethane, compared with deep x-ray therapy. *Lancet 1:* 677-682, 1946.

RUNDLES, R. W., DILLON, M. L., and DILLON, E. S. Multiple myeloma: III. Effect of urethane therapy on plasma cell growth, abnormal serum protein components and Bence-Jones proteinuria. *J. Clin. Investigation 29:* 1243-1260, 1950.

RUNDLES, R. W., DILLON, M. L., DILLON, E. S., and ARMSTRONG, J. Effect of urethane (ethyl carbamate) in multiple myeloma. *J. Clin. Investigation 28:* 807-808, 1949.

RUNDLES, R. W., and REENES, R. J. Multiple myeloma: II. Variability of roentgen appearance and effect of urethane on skeletal disease. *Am. J. Roentgenol. 64:* 799-809, 1950.

SHERWOOD, F. The use of urethane in the treatment of leukemia. *Acta haemat. 1:* 253-266, 1948.

WATKINS, C. H., COOPER, T., and GRIFFIN, H. Z. The use of urethane (ethyl carbamate) in the treatment of leukemia. *Blood 3:* 892-895, 1948.

WEBSTER, J. J. Urethane in leukemia. *J.A.M.A. 135:* 901-903, 1947.

WEDER, C. Urethane in the treatment of multiple myeloma. *Canad. M. A. J. 62:* 589-590, 1950.

FOLIC ACID ANALOGS

LABORATORY

Toxicity

FERGUSON, F. C., JR., THIERSCH, J. B., and PHILIPS, F. S. Action of 4-amino, N 10-methyl pteroylglutamic acid in mice, rats and dogs. *Federation Proc. 8:* 291, 1949.

HIGGINS, G. M. The effect of folic acid on the toxicity of its analogue 4-aminopteroylglutamic acid (aminopterin). *Blood 4:* 1142-1155, 1949.

PHILIPS, F. S., and THIERSCH, J. B. Studies of the actions of 4-aminopteroylglutamic acid in rats and mice. *J. Pharmacol. & Exper. Therap. 95:* 303-311, 1949.

PHILIPS, F. S., THIERSCH, J. B., and FERGUSON, F. C. Studies of the action of 4-aminopteroylglutamic acid and its congeners in mammals. *Ann. New York Acad. Sc. 52:* 1349-1359, 1950.

Experimental Chemotherapy

BURCHENAL, J. H., BABCOCK, G. M., BROQUIST, H. P., and JUKES, T. H. Prevention of chemotherapeutic effects of 4-amino-N10-methylpteroylglutamic acid on mouse leukemia by citrovorum factor. *Proc. Soc. Exper. Biol. & Med. 74:* 735-737, 1950.

BURCHENAL, J. H., BURCHENAL, J. R., KUSHIDA, M. W., JOHNSTON, S. F., and WILLIAMS, B. S. Studies on the chemotherapy of leukemia: II. The effect of 4-amino-pteroylglutamic acid and 4-amino-N^{10}-methyl-pteroylglutamic acid on transplanted mouse leukemia. *Cancer 2:* 113-118, 1949.

GOLDIN, A., GOLDBERG, B., ORTEGA, L. G., and SCHOENBACH, E. B. Reversal of aminopterin-induced inhibition of sarcoma 180 by folic acid. *Cancer 2:* 857-862, 1949.

HIGGINS, G. M., and WOODS, K. A. The effect of the folic acid antagonist, 4-amino-pteroylglutamic acid on the growth of transplanted mammary tumors in C_3H mice. *Proc. Staff Meet., Mayo Clin. 24:* 238-243, 1949.

LAW, L. W., and BOYLE, P. J. Development of resistance to folic acid antagonists in a transplantable lymphoid leukemia. *Proc. Soc. Exper. Biol. & Med. 74:* 599-602, 1950.

MOORE, A. E., STOCK, C. C., SUGIURA, K., and RHOADS, C. P. Inhibition of development of sarcoma 180 by 4-amino-N^{10}-methyl-pteroylglutamic acid. *Proc. Soc. Exper. Biol. & Med. 70:* 396-398, 1949.

SCHOENBACH, E. B., GOLDIN, A., GOLDBERG, B., and ORTEGA, L. G. The effect of folic acid derivatives on sarcoma 180. *Cancer 2:* 57-64, 1949.

SKIPPER, H. E., EDWARDS, P. C., BRYAN, C. E., CHAPMAN, J. B., BELL, M. and HUTCHISON, O. S. Studies on the antileukemic action of certain compounds related to moieties of the 4-aminopteroylglutamic acid (aminopterin) molecule. *Cancer 3:* 348-353, 1950.

SUGIURA, K., MOORE, A. E., and STOCK, C. C. The effect of aminopterin on the growth of carcinoma, sarcoma and melanoma in animals. *Cancer 2:* 491-502, 1949.

Mechanism of Action

BARDOS, T. J., BOND, T. J., HUMPHREYS, J., and SHIVE, W. Relationship of the folinic acid group and the Leuconostoc citrovorum factors. *J. Am. Chem. Soc. 71:* 3852, 1949.

BETHELL, F. H., and SWENDSEID, M. E. The folic acid content of leukocytes: Observations on normal subjects and persons with leukemia. *J. Clin. Investigation 25:* 917-918, 1946.

BOND, T. J., BARDOS, T. J., SIBLEY, M., and SHIVE, W. The folinic acid group, a series of new vitamins related to folic acid. *J. Am. Chem. Soc. 71:* 3852-3853, 1949.

BROQUIST, H. P., STOKSTAD, E. L. R., and JUKES, T. H. Some biological and chemical properties of the citrovorum factor. *J. Biol. Chem. 185:* 399-409, 1950.

FRANKLIN, A. L., BELT, M., STOKSTAD, E. L. R., and JUKES, T. H. Biological studies with 4-amino-10-methylpteroylglutamic acid. *J. Biol. Chem. 177:* 621-629, 1949.

FRANKLIN, A. L., STOKSTAD, E. L. R., HOFFMANN, C. E., BELT, M., and JUKES, T. H. Inhibition of growth of Escherichia coli by 4-aminopteroylglutamic acid and its reversal. *J. Am. Chem. Soc. 71:* 3549-3550, 1949.

FRANKLIN, A. L., STOKSTAD, E. L. R., and JUKES, T. H. Observations on the effect of 4-aminopteroylglutamic acid on mice. *Proc. Soc. Exper. Biol. & Med. 67:* 398-400, 1948.

KERESZTESY, J. C., and SILVERMAN, M. Partial purification of a factor essential for growth of Leuconostoc citrovorum. *J. Biol. Chem. 183:* 473-479, 1950.

NICHOL, C. A., and WELCH, A. D. Synthesis of citrovorum factor from folic acid by liver slices: Augmentation by ascorbic acid *Proc. Soc. Exper. Biol. & Med. 74:* 52-55, 1950.

NICHOL, C. A., and WELCH, A. D. On the mechanism of action of aminopterin. *Proc. Soc. Exper. Biol. & Med. 74:* 403-411, 1950.

OLESON, T. T., HUTCHINGS, B. L., and SUBBAROW, Y. Studies on the inhibitory nature of 4-aminopteroylglutamic acid. *J. Biol. Chem. 175:* 359-365, 1948.

PLAUT, G. W. E., BETHEIL, J. J., and LARDY, H. A. The relationship of folic acid to formate metabolism in the rat. *J. Biol. Chem. 184:* 795-805, 1950.

PRUSOFF, W. H., TEPLY, L. J., and KING, C. G. The influence of pteroylglutamic acid on nucleic acid synthesis in Lactobacillus casei. *J. Biol. Chem. 176:* 1309-1317, 1948.

SAUBERLICH, H. E. Relationship of purines, folic acid, and other principles in the nutrition of Leuconostoc citrovorum 8081. *Federation Proc. 8:* 247, 1949.

SAUBERLICH, H. E. The relationship of folic acid, vitamin B_{12}, and thymidine in the nutrition of Leuconostoc citrovorum 8081. *Arch. Biochem. 24:* 224-232, 1949.

SAUBERLICH, H. E. The effect of folic acid upon the urinary excretion of the growth factor required by Leuconostoc citrovorum. *J. Biol. Chem. 181:* 467-473, 1949.

SAUBERLICH, H. E., and BAUMANN, C. A. A factor required for the growth of Leuconostoc citrovorum. *J. Biol. Chem. 176:* 165-173, 1948.

SAUBERLICH, H. E., and BAUMANN, C. A. Further studies on the factor required by Leuconostoc citrovorum 8081. *J. Biol. Chem. 181:* 871-877, 1949.

SHIVE, W., EAKIN, R. E., HARDING, W. M., RAVEL, J. M., and SUTHERLAND, J. E. A crystalline factor functionally related to folic acid. *J. Am. Chem. Soc. 70:* 2299, 1948.

SHIVE, W., ACKERMANN, W. W., GORDON, M., GEBENDAUR, M. E., and EAKIN, R. E. 5(4)-Amino 4(5)-imidazolecarboxamide, a precursor of purines. *J. Am. Chem. Soc. 69:* 725-726, 1947.

SNELL, E. E., and CRAVENS, W. W. Reversal of aminopterin inhibition in the chick embryo with desoxyribosides. *Proc. Soc. Exper. Biol. & Med. 74:* 87-91, 1950.

STETTEN, M. R., and FOX, C. L., JR. An amine formed by bacteria during sulfonamide bacteriostasis. *J. Biol. Chem. 161:* 333-349, 1945.

Clinical Application

BERMAN, L., AXELROD, A. R., VONDERHEIDE, E. C., and SHARP, E. A. Use of a folic acid antagonist in chronic leukemia. *Am. J. Clin. Path. 19:* 127-133, 1949.

DAMESHEK, W. The use of folic acid antagonists in the treatment of acute and subacute leukemia. *Blood 4:* 168-171, 1949.

FARBER, S. Some observations on the effect of folic acid antagonists on acute leukemia and other forms of incurable cancer. *Blood 4:* 160-167, 1949.

FARBER, S., DIAMOND, L. K., MERCER, R. D., SYLVESTER, R. F., and WOLFF, J. A. Temporary remissions in acute leukemia in children produced by the folic acid antagonist, 4-amino-pteroyl-glutamic acid (aminopterin). *New England J. Med. 238:* 787-793, 1948.

GUNZ, F. W. The effect of 4-amino-pteroylglutamic acid (aminopterin) on human leukemic leukocytes in vitro. *Blood 5:* 161-166, 1950.

JACOBSON, W., LEVIN, W. C., and HOLT, G. Observations on the treatment of acute leukemias with analogues of folic acid. *J. Lab. & Clin. Med. 23:* 1641-1642, 1948.

MEYER, L. M., FINK, H., SAWITSKY, A., ROWEN, M., and RITZ, N. D. Aminopterin (a folic acid antagonist) in the treatment of leukemia. *Am. J. Clin. Path. 19:* 119-126, 1949.

PIERCE, M., and ALT, H. Treatment of acute leukemia with aminopterin. *J. Lab. & Clin. Med. 23:* 1642-1643, 1948.

SACKS, M. S., BRADFORD, G. T., and SCHOENBACH, E. B. The response of acute leukemia to the administration of the folic acid antagonists, aminopterin and amethopterin: Report of 14 cases. *Ann. Int. Med. 32:* 80-115, 1950.

SILVERMAN, F. N. Treatment of leukemia and allied disorders with folic acid antagonists: Effect of aminopterin on skeletal lesions. *Radiology 54:* 665-678, 1950.

STICKNEY, J. M., HAGEDORN, A. B., MILLS, S. D., and COOPER, T. Changes in blood and bone marrow in acute leukemia induced by aminopterin. *J. Lab. & Clin. Med. 33:* 1481, 1948.

STICKNEY, J. M., MILLS, S. D., HAGEDORN, A. B., and COOPER, T. The treatment of acute leukemia with folic acid antagonists. *Proc. Staff Meet., Mayo Clin. 24:* 525-533, 1949.

TAYLOR, S. G., III, HASS, G. M., CRUMRINE, J. L., and SLAUGHTER, D. P. Toxic reactions of 4-aminopteroylglutamic acid (aminopterin) in patients with far-advanced neoplastic disease. *Cancer 3:* 493-503, 1950.

THIERSCH, J. B. Bone-marrow changes in man after treatment with aminopterin, amethopterin, and aminoanfol. *Cancer 2:* 877-883, 1949.

WEBER, E. J., KARPINSKI, F. E., and HEINLE, R. W. The treatment of acute leukemias of childhood with folic acid antagonists. *J. Pediat. 36:* 69-78, 1950.

WILSON, S. J. Platelet regeneration during therapy of acute leukemia with folic acid antagonists. *Proc. Soc. Exper. Biol. & Med. 73:* 620-622, 1950.

HORMONES

ADAIR, F. E., and HERRMANN, J. B. The use of testosterone propionate in the treatment of advanced carcinoma of the breast. *Ann. Surg. 123:* 1023-1035, 1946.

GODWIN, J. T., and ESCHER, G. C. Hormone-treated primary operable breast carcinoma: A pathological study of 33 cases. *Cancer 4:* 136-140, 1951.

GOMORI, G. Distribution of acid phosphatase in the tissues under normal and under pathological conditions. *Arch. Path. 32:* 189-199, 1941.

GUTMAN, A. B., and GUTMAN, E. B. An "acid" phosphatase occurring in the serum of patients with metastasizing carcinoma of the prostate gland. *J. Clin. Investigation 17:* 473-478, 1938.

HUGGINS, C., and HODGES, C. V. Studies on prostatic cancer: I. The effect of castration, of estrogen and of androgen injection on serum phosphatases in metastatic carcinoma of the prostate. *Cancer Research 1:* 293-297, 1941.

HUGGINS, C., MASINA, M. H., EICHELBERGER, L., and WHARTON, J. D. Quantitative studies of prostatic secretion: I. Characteristics of the normal secretion; the influence of thyroid, suprarenal and testis extirpation and androgen substitution on the prostatic output. *J. Exper. Med. 70:* 543-556, 1939.

HUGGINS, C., STEVENS, R. E., and HODGES, C. V. Studies on prostatic cancer: II. The effects of castration on advanced carcinoma of the prostate gland. *Arch. Surg. 43:* 209-223, 1941.

KUTSCHER, W., and WOLBERGS, H. Prostataphosphatase. *Ztschr. f. physiol. Chem. 236:* 237-240, 1935.

LEMON, H. M., RAVIN, I. S., ROSS, J. F., SISSON, J. H., ANGLEM, T. J., and BRANCA, A. W. Testosterone therapy of metastatic adenocarcinoma of the thyroid, with remission. *Cancer 4:* 1176-1192, 1951.

NESBIT, R. M., and BAUM, W. C. Endocrine control of prostatic carcinoma. *J.A.M.A. 143:* 1317-1320, 1950.

Subcommittee on Steroids and Cancer of the Committee on Research, Council of Pharmacy and Chemistry, American Medical Association. Current status of hormone therapy of advanced mammary cancer. *J.A.M.A. 146:* 471-477, 1951.

INEFFECTIVE CHEMOTHERAPEUTIC AGENTS

Products of Micro-organisms

ANDERVONT, H. B. The reaction of mice and of various mouse tumors to the injection of bacterial products. *Am. J. Cancer 27:* 77-83, 1936.

Annual Report of the Surgeon General of the Public Health Service of the U.S. for the Fiscal Year 1932. Washington, D. C., Government Printing Office, 1932, pp. 25-26.

BEEBE, S. P., and TRACY, M. The treatment of experimental tumors with bacterial toxins. *J.A.M.A. 49:* 1493-1498, 1907.

BRUES, A. M., and SHEAR, M. J. Chemical treatment of tumors: Reactions of four patients with advanced malignant tumors to injection of a polysaccharide from Serratia marcescens culture filtrate. *J. Nat. Cancer Inst. 5:* 195-208, 1944.

COLEY, W. B. Contribution to the knowledge of sarcoma. *Ann. Surg. 14:* 199-220, 1891.

COLEY, W. B. The diagnosis and treatment of bone sarcoma. *Glasgow M. J. 126:* 49, 128, 1936.

CREECH, H. J., HAMILTON, M. A., and DILLER, I. C. Comparative studies of the immunological, toxic and tumor-necrotizing properties of polysaccharides from Serratia marcescens (Bacillus prodigiosus). *Cancer Research 8:* 318-329, 1948.

CREECH, H. J., HAMILTON, M. A., NISHIMURA, E. T., and HANKWITZ, R. F., JR. The influence of anti-body containing fractions on the lethal and tumor-necrotizing actions of polysaccharides from Serratia marcescens (Bacillus prodigiosus). *Cancer Research 8:* 330-336, 1948.

CREECH, H. J., and HANKWITZ, R. F., JR. Further studies of the immunological properties of polysaccharides from Serratia marcescens (Bacillus prodigiosus): III. Passive immunization against the lethal activity of the polysaccharides with fractions of mouse antiserum elicited by a single injection of polysaccharide. *Cancer Research 9:* 589-591, 1949.

CREECH, H. J., HANKWITZ, R. F., JR., and WHARTON, D. R. A. Further studies of the immunological properties of polysaccharides from Serratia marcescens (Bacillus prodigiosus): I. The effects of passive and active immunization on the lethal activity of the polysaccharides. *Cancer Research 9:* 150-157, 1949.

DILLER, I. C. Degenerative changes induced in tumor cells by Serratia marcescens polysaccharide. *Cancer Research 7:* 605-626, 1947.

DILLER, I. C., BLAUCH, B., and BECK, L. V. Histological changes in adrenal glands of tumor-bearing mice injected with Serratia marcescens polysaccharide alone and in combination with adrenal cortical extract. *Cancer Research 8:* 591-605, 1948.

DURAN-REYNALS, F. Reaction of transplantable and spontaneous tumors to blood-carried bacterial toxins in animals unsusceptible to the Shwartzman phenomenon. *Proc. Soc. Exper. Biol. & Med. 31:* 341-344, 1933.

DURAN-REYNALS, F. Reaction of spontaneous mouse carcinomas to blood-carried bacterial toxins. *Proc. Soc. Exper. Biol. & Med. 32:* 1517-1521, 1935.

FOWLER, G. R. The use of animal toxins in the treatment of inoperable malignant tumors. *Am. J. M. Sc. 116:* 161-190, 1898.

GRATIA, A., and LINZ, R. Le phenomene de Shwartzman dans le sarcome du cobaye. *Compt. rend. Soc. de biol. 108:* 427-428, 1931.

HANGER, F. M., JR. Effect of intravenous bacterial filtrates on skin tests and local infections. *Proc. Soc. Exper. Biol. & Med. 25:* 775-777, 1928.

HARTWELL, J. L., SHEAR, M. J., and ADAMS, J. R., JR. Chemical treatment of tumors. Nature of the hemorrhage-producing fraction from Serratia marcescens (Bacillus prodigiosus) culture filtrate. *J. Nat. Cancer Inst. 4:* 107-122, 1943.

HAUSCHKA, T. S. Trypanosoma cruzi "endotoxin" in the treatment of mouse tumors. *Fourth Internat. Cancer Research Congress,* September 1947, pp. 89-90.

HAUSCHKA, T. S., and GOODWIN, M. B. Trypanosoma cruzi endotoxin (KR) in the treatment of malignant mouse tumors. *Science 107:* 600-602, 1948.

HAUSCHKA, T. S., SAXE, L. H., JR., and BLAIR, M. Trypanosoma cruzi in the treatment of mouse tumors. *J. Nat. Cancer Inst. 7:* 189-197, 1947.

HOLLOMAN, A. L. "Reactions of patients and of tumors to injection of S. marcescens polysaccharide in eight cases of malignant disease." In AMERICAN ASSOCIATION FOR THE ADVANCEMENT OF SCIENCE: *Approaches to Tumor Chemotherapy.* Washington, D. C., 1947, pp. 273-276.

KELLY, SISTER THOMAS AQUINA, and McDOWELL, SISTER MARGARET ANN. Studies in vitro and in vivo on the effects of a *Staphylococcus aureus* extract on mouse carcinoma. *Cancer Research 8:* 495-499, 1948.

NAUTS, H. C., SWIFT, W. E., and COLEY, B. L. The treatment of malignant tumors by bacterial toxins as developed by the late William B. Coley, M.D., reviewed in the light of modern research. *Cancer Research 6:* 205-216, 1946.

OAKEY, R. "Reactions of patients to injection of S. marcescens polysaccharide in nine further cases of malignant disease." In AMERICAN ASSOCIATION FOR THE ADVANCEMENT OF SCIENCE: *Approaches to Tumor Chemotherapy.* Washington, D. C., 1947, pp. 277-278.

ROSKIN, G. Toxin therapy of experimental cancer: The influence of protozoan infections upon transplanted cancer. *Cancer Research 6:* 363-365, 1946.

ROSKIN, G. Toxin therapy of experimental cancer: Influence of protozoan infections upon transplanted cancer. *Am. Rev. Soviet Med. 4:* 111-115, 1946.

SACK, T., and SELIGMAN, A. M. Chemical alteration of polysaccharide from Serratia marcescens: II. Effects of iodopolysaccharide in patients with malignant tumors. *J. Nat. Cancer Inst. 9:* 19-34, 1948.

SELIGMAN, A. M., and SACK, T. Chemical alteration of polysaccharide from Serratia marcescens: III. Reaction of polysaccharide with radioactive P-iodobenzene diazonium chloride and the use of the product in an experimental and clinical study. *J. Nat. Cancer Inst. 10:* 105-118, 1949.

SELIGMAN, A. M., SHEAR, M. J., LEITER, J., and SWEET, B. Chemical alteration of polysaccharide from Serratia marcescens: I. Tumor necrotizing polysaccharide tagged with radioactive iodine. *J. Nat. Cancer Inst. 9:* 13-18, 1948.

SHEAR, M. J. Studies on the chemical treatment of tumors: II. The effect of disturbances in fluid exchange on transplanted mouse tumors. *Am. J. Cancer 25:* 66-88, 1935.

SHEAR, M. J. Chemical treatment of tumors: IX. Reactions of mice with primary subcutaneous tumors to injection of hemorrhage-producing bacterial polysaccharide. *J. Nat. Cancer Inst. 4:* 461-476, 1944.

SHEAR, M. J., PERRAULT, A., and ADAMS, J. R., JR. Chemical treatment of tumors: VI. Method employed in determining the potency of hemorrhage-producing bacterial preparations. *J. Nat. Cancer Inst. 4:* 99-105, 1943.

SHEAR, M. J., and TURNER, F. C. Studies on the chemical treatment of tumors: V. Separation of the hemorrhage-producing fraction from Bacillus prodigiosus filtrates. *J. Biol. Chem. 133:* lxxxvii-lxxxviii, 1940.

SHEAR, M. J., and TURNER, F. C. Chemical treatment of tumors: V. Isolation of the hemorrhage-producing fraction from Serratia marcescens (Bacillus prodigiosus) culture filtrate. *J. Nat. Cancer Inst. 4:* 81-97, 1943.

SHWARTZMAN, G. A new phenomenon of local skin reactivity to B. typhosus culture filtrate. *Proc. Soc. Exper. Biol. & Med. 25:* 560-561, 1928.

SHWARTZMAN, G. *Phenomenon of Local Tissue Reactivity.* New York, Paul B. Hoeber, Inc., 1937.

SHWARTZMAN, G., and MICHAILOVSKY, N. Phenomenon of local skin reactivity to bacterial filtrates in treatment of mouse sarcoma 180. *Proc. Soc. Exper. Biol. & Med. 29:* 737-741, 1932.

TRACY, M. Study of the toxins of Bacillus prodigiosus. *J. Med. Research 16:* 307-327, 1907-1908.

WHARTON, D. R. A., and CREECH, H. J. Further studies of the immunological properties of polysaccharides from Serratia marcescens (Bacillus prodigiosus): II. Nature of the antigenic action and the antibody response in mice. *J. Immunol. 62:* 135-153, 1949.

Zahl, P. A., Hutner, S. H., Spitz, S., Sugiura, K., and Cooper, F. S. The action of bacterial toxins on tumors: I. Relationship of the tumor-hemorrhagic agent to the endotoxin antigens of gram-negative bacteria. *Am. J. Hyg. 36:* 224-242, 1942.

Podophyllin

Belkin, M. Effect of podophyllin on transplanted mouse tumors. *J. Pharmacol. & Exper. Therap. 93:* 18-25, 1948.

Kaplan, I. W. Condylomata acuminata. *New Orleans M. & S. J. 94:* 388, 1942.

King, L. S. Effects of podophyllin on mouse skin: I. Histological sequence after a single dose. *J. Nat. Cancer Inst. 8:* 215-225, 1948.

King, L. S., and Cauldwell, E. W. Effects of podophyllin on mouse skin: II. Consideration of some functional aspects. *J. Nat. Cancer Inst. 10:* 131-146, 1949.

King, L. S., and Sullivan, M. The similarity of the effect of podophyllin and colchicine and their use in the treatment of condylomata acuminata. *Science 104:* 244-245, 1946.

King, L. S., and Sullivan, M. Effects of podophyllin and of colchicine on normal skin, on condyloma acuminatum and on verucca vulgaris. *Arch. Path. 43:* 374-386, 1947.

Ormsbee, R. A., Cornman, I., and Berger, R. E. Effect of podophyllin on tumor cells in tissue culture. *Proc. Soc. Exper. Biol. & Med. 66:* 586-590, 1947.

Sullivan, M., and Blanchard, K. Podophyllotoxin. *Bull. Johns Hopkins Hosp. 81:* 65-67, 1947.

The Reticuloendothelial System in Cancer Chemotherapy

Abernethy, J. W., Morris, L. M., Harrell, G. T., Valk, H. L., and Cheek, K. M. The effect of anti-reticular cytotoxic serum on cases of Hodgkin's disease. *North Carolina M. J. 9:* 341-350, 1948.

Andervont, H. B. The influence of trypan blue upon the resistance of mice to transplantable and induced tumors. *Pub. Health Rep. 51:* 591-600, 1936.

Anigstein, L., Whitney, D. M., Pomerat, C. M., and Orr, M. F. Reticuloendothelial immune serum (REIS): VI. Production of potent serum by anamnestic reaction. *Proc. Soc. Exper. Biol. & Med. 64:* 279-280, 1947.

Bogomolets, A. A. Anti-reticular cytotoxic serum as a means of pathogenetic therapy. *Am. Rev. Soviet Med. 1:* 101-112, 1943.

Dulaney, A. D., and Arnesen, K. Cytotoxic action of antisera to cell components of normal and leukemic mouse spleens. *Proc. Soc. Exper. Biol. & Med. 72:* 665-668, 1949.

Flantchik, L. I. Morphological and biological characteristics of cancer metastasis in the spleen. *Vopr. Onkologie,* Moscow, *10:* 38-50, 1936. (Abstract in *Am. J. Cancer 31:* 152, 1937.)

Frieden, E. H., Pomerat, C. M., and Anigstein, L. Identification of the inhibitory factor of a reticulo-endothelial immune serum (REIS) in a globulin fraction. *Science 102:* 354, 1945.

Friedman, R., and Stritzler, C. Mycosis fungoides resisting treatment with both nitrogen mustard and anti-reticular cytotoxic serum. *J. Invest. Dermat. 10:* 227-228, 1948.

Jones, L. O. *In vitro* studies on the effect of spleen, striated muscle, and kidney upon the growth of sarcoma 180 and mammary carcinoma of mice. *Cancer Research 9:* 27-34, 1949.

KHALETZKAYA, F. M. Influence of splenectomy upon the development of tumors induced by chemical agents. *Var. patol. anat.*, Moscow, *5:* 31-37, 1939. (Abstract in *Am. J. Cancer 40:* 262, 1940.)

KLING, D. H. Failure of antireticular cytotoxic serum in arthritis. *J. Lab. & Clin. Med. 33:* 1289-1296, 1948.

LATTA, J. S., and JOHNSON, H. N. Studies of lymphatic tissue grown in vitro with splenic extract as culture medium. *Arch. f. exper. Zellforsch. 16:* 221-229, 1934.

LEWISOHN, R. Effect of subcutaneous injections of concentrated spleen extract on mouse sarcoma 180. *Surg., Gynec. & Obst. 66:* 563-576, 1938.

LEWISOHN, R. "Chemotherapeutic regressions of transplanted and spontaneous cancers in mice: 1. Review of the work of the laboratory 1937-1945." In AMERICAN ASSOCIATION FOR THE ADVANCEMENT OF SCIENCE: *Approaches to Tumor Chemotherapy*. Washington, D. C., 1947, pp. 139-147.

MALTZ, M. Studies in cellular growth: III. Effect of antigranulation-tissue-serum on wound healing in mice. *J. Immunol. 60:* 411-417, 1948.

MALTZ, M., SPAIN, D. M., and MOLOMUT, N. Studies in cellular growth: I. Effect of antisplenic-tissue-serum on experimentally induced wounds in mice. *J. Immunol. 60:* 303-311, 1948.

MALTZ, M., SPAIN, D. M., and MOLOMUT, N. Studies in cellular growth: II. Effect of antisplenic-tissue-serum (ASTS) on large experimentally-induced wounds in guinea pigs. *J. Immunol. 60:* 313-316, 1948.

MARCHUK, P. D. A method of preparing and preserving anti-reticular cytotoxic serum. *Am. Rev. Soviet Med. 1:* 113, 1943.

MOVITZ, D., SAPHIR, O., and STRAUSS, A. A. Effects of an antireticular cytotoxic serum on the Brown-Pearce carcinoma of the rabbit. *Cancer Research 9:* 17-26, 1949.

NOWINSKI, W. W. Influence of anti-organ sera upon metabolic processes: I. Reticulo-endothelial immune serum (REIS) and the oxygen uptake of rat spleen. *Texas Rep. Biol. & Med. 6:* 493-503, 1948.

POMERAT, C. M. A review of recent developments on reticulo-endothelial immune serum (REIS). *Quarterly of Phi Beta Pi 42:* 203-208, 1946.

POMERAT, C. M., FRIEDEN, E. H., and YEAGER, E. Reticulo-endothelial immune serum (REIS): V. An experimental anemia in Bartonella-infected rats produced by anti-blood immune serum. *J. Infect. Dis. 80:* 154-163, 1947.

ROGOFF, B., FREYBERG, R. H., POWELL, H. M., and RICE, R. M. Experiences with antireticular cytotoxic serum (ACS) in arthritis. *Am. J. M. Sc. 214:* 395, 1947.

SKAPIER, J. Therapeutic use of antireticular cytotoxic serum (ACS) in Hodgkin's disease. *Cancer Research 7:* 369-371, 1947.

STRAUS, R. Studies on anti-reticular cytotoxic serum: I. Introduction and review of the literature. *J. Immunol. 54:* 151-154, 1946.

STRAUS, R., HORWITZ, M., LEVINTHAL, D. H., COHEN, A. L., and RUNJAVAC, M. Studies on antireticular cytotoxic serum: III. Effect of ACS on the healing of experimentally produced fractures in rabbits. *J. Immunol. 54:* 163-177, 1946.

WATSON, G. F., DILLER, I. C., and LUDWICK, N. V. Spleen extract and tumor growth. *Science 106:* 348, 1947.

Stilbamidine

AIWALL, N. Urethane and stilbamidine in multiple myeloma: Report on two cases. *Lancet 2:* 388-389, 1947.

BIERMAN, H. R., and SOKOLOW, M. Cardiovascular effects produced by stilbamidine in patients with multiple myeloma. *J. Nat. Cancer Inst. 10:* 279-289, 1949.

KIRK, R., and HENRY, A. J. Observations on the toxicity of stilbamidine. *Ann. Trop. Med. 38:* 99-118, 1944.

Medical Division, Merck & Co. Inc. *Stilbamidine in the Treatment of Multiple Myeloma: A Summary of 194 Cases.* Rahway, N. J., 1948.

NAPIER, L. E. Urethane and stilbamidine in multiple myeloma. *Lancet 2:* 489, 1947.

PROPP, S., GORHAM, L. W., and KANTOR, S. Recent studies of multiple myeloma: Sternal and rib puncture and the results of treatment with stilbamidine. *Blood 4:* 36-53, 1949.

SEN GUPTA, P. C. Observations on neuropathic sequel of diamidino-stilbene therapy in kala-azar. *Indian M. Gaz. 78:* 537-543, 1943.

SNAPPER, I. On the influence of stilbamidine upon multiple myeloma. *J. Mt. Sinai Hosp. 13:* 119-127, 1946.

SNAPPER, I. Treatment of multiple myeloma with "stilbamidine": Clinical results and morphologic changes. *J.A.M.A. 137:* 513-516, 1948.

SNAPPER, I. Influence of 2-hydroxystilbamidine on the course of multiple myeloma. *J. Mt. Sinai Hosp. 15:* 156-163, 1948.

SNAPPER, I., MIRSKY, A. E., RIS, H., SCHNEID, B., and ROSENTHAL, M. Development of inclusion bodies containing ribose nucleic acid in myeloma cells after injections of stilbamidine: Determination of stilbamidine in myeloma tissue. *Blood 2:* 311-322, 1947.

SNAPPER, I., SCHNEID, B., and KURNICK, N. The presence of diamidines in myeloma cells after treatment with stilbamidine and 2-hydroxystilbamidine. *Acta haemat. 3:* 129-134, 1950.

MISCELLANEOUS CHEMOTHERAPEUTIC APPROACHES

Vitamin Deficiencies

Biotin

KAPLAN, I. I. One year observations of treatment of cancer with avidin (egg white). *Am. J. M. Sc. 207:* 733-743, 1944.

KENSLER, C. J., WADSWORTH, C., SUGIURA, K., RHOADS, C. P., DITTMER, K., and DU VIGNEAUD, V. The influence of egg white and avidin feeding on tumor growth. *Cancer Research 3:* 823-824, 1943.

LAURENCE, W. L. Induced biotin deficiency as possible explanation of observed spontaneous recessions in malignancy. *Science 94:* 88-89, 1941.

RHOADS, C. P., and ABELS, J. C. Administration of egg white and avidin concentrates to patients with cancer. *J.A.M.A. 121:* 1261-1263, 1943.

WEST, P. M., and WOGLOM, W. H. Abnormalities in the distribution of biotin in certain tumors and embryo tissues. *Cancer Research 2:* 324-331, 1942.

Pyridoxine

GELLHORN, A., and JONES, L. O. Pyridoxine deficient diet and desoxypyridoxine in the therapy of lymphosarcoma and acute leukemia in man. *Blood 4:* 60-65, 1949.

MUSHETT, C. W., STEBBINS, R. B., and BARTON, M. N. Histologic changes produced by 2,4-dimethyl-3-hydroxy-5-hydroxymethyl pyridine, an analogue of pyridoxine. *Am. J. M. Sc. 213:* 509, 1947.

PORTER, C. C., CLARK, I., and SILBER, R. H. The effect of pyridoxine analogues on tryptophane metabolism in the rat. *J. Biol. Chem. 167:* 573-579, 1947.

STOERK, H. C. Effects of calcium deficiency and pyridoxine deficiency on thymic atrophy (accidental involution). *Proc. Soc. Exper. Biol. & Med. 62:* 90-96, 1946.

STOERK, H. C. The regression of lymphosarcoma implants in pyridoxine deficient mice. *J. Biol. Chem. 171:* 437-438, 1947.

STOERK, H. C., EISEN, H. N., and JOHN, H. M. Impairment of antibody response in pyridoxine deficient rats. *J. Exper. Med. 85:* 365-371, 1947.

STOERK, H. C., and ZUCKER, T. F. Nutritional effects on the development and atrophy of the thymus. *Proc. Soc. Exper. Biol. & Med. 56:* 151-153, 1944.

Synthetic Vitamin K

GELLHORN, A., and GAGLIANO, T. The effect of tetra-sodium 2-methyl-1:4-naphthohydroquinone diphosphate (Synkayvite) on a variety of malignant tumors in experimental animals. *Brit. J. Cancer 4:* 103-107, 1950.

MITCHELL, J. S. Clinical trials of tetra-sodium 2-methyl-1:4-naphthohydroquinone diphosphate, in conjunction with x-ray therapy. *Brit. J. Cancer 2:* 351-359, 1948.

Myelokentric and Lymphokentric Acids

MILLER, F. R., HERBUT, P. A., and JONES, H. W. The treatment of lymphoblastic leukemia with crude myelokentric acid. *Blood 2:* 15-39, 1947.

MILLER, F. R., WEARN, J. T., and HEINLE, R. W. Proliferation of myeloid and lymphoid cells induced by extracts of urine from leucemic patients. *Proc. Soc. Exper. Biol. & Med. 41:* 479-480, 1939.

NOSTRUMS

Council on Pharmacy and Chemistry, American Medical Association. Cancer and the need for facts. *J.A.M.A. 139:* 93-98, 1949.

CHAPTER 30

Applied Exfoliative Cytology

S. Charles Kasdon

The major purpose of this chapter is the clarification of three important aspects of exfoliative cytology, the knowledge of which is essential to proper utilization and interpretation of this adjunct to the field of diagnostic medicine. The first, a short historical background and statement of the present-day value of exfoliative cytology and its limitations, will of necessity be restricted to broad principles. The second, a description of the criteria used for identification of exfoliated cells and the technic for proper management of tissue fluids by those obtaining the specimens, is important since adequate specimens are essential for cytologic interpretation. Third, an attempt will be made to clarify the vocabulary which is used in reporting the results of cytologic studies.

This chapter is not intended to serve as a text for those desirous of becoming expert cytologists. Rather it is offered as a concentrated source of information for medical students, research workers, and physicians who use exfoliative cytology in research and diagnostic medicine.

The epithelium lining the genital tract in the female has a tendency to desquamate its superficial layers which then form "pools" of exfoliated cells. This characteristic is common to all epithelium-lined organs and means that surface cells are slowly cast off and pass down the tract towards the point of exit from the body. Thus, the vaginal secretion is rich in superficial exfoliated cells from the tubes, uterus, cervix, and vagina; the sputum contains cells from alveoli, bronchioles, bronchi, trachea, and oral cavity, etc. The decreased mutual adhesiveness described by Coman (1944) for squamous cell carcinoma cells makes for a greater desquamation and concentration of malignant cells in the exfoliated pool than one would expect if the sloughing process had a simple linear relationship to the surface area involved. Oxorn (1948) has called it a "kind of natural curettage going on without interruption, and always providing fresh and easily obtainable material for study."

HISTORY, VALIDITY, AND LIMITATIONS OF CYTOLOGY

Attempts at diagnosis by cytologic means are more than a century old according to Fremont-Smith, Graham, and Meigs (1948) who mentioned Pouchet's use of unstained preparations of vaginal fluid in 1847. It was seventy years later that Stockard and Papanicolaou (1917) used the vaginal smear successfully for the study of estrus cycles in the guinea pig. Finally, Papanicolaou (1928, 1933) suggested the use of cytologic material obtained by the smear method for the diagnosis of genital cancer. The monograph published in 1943 by Papanicolaou and Traut fully described the criteria essential for interpretation of exfoliated cell smears, and corroborative reports (Meigs *et al.* 1943, Batres Gonzales 1944, Ayre 1944) soon followed. It must be borne in mind that the pathologic examination of the biopsy tissue specimen still remains the final method of establishing the diagnosis of malignancy. Any technic suggested for alternative or conjunctive use with biopsy must be biologically sound, statistically dependable, simple in execution, reproducible, and have some definite advantages over the biopsy. The method of exfoliative cytology appears to fulfill these basic requirements.

The biologic validity of exfoliative cytology is attested to by the use of vaginal smears in physiology for identification of the estrus state, and the reflection of ovarian activity in clinical endocrine disorders such as hyperestrinism, menopause, and ovulation. The fact that it is at all possible to establish consistently dependable criteria for the identification of clearly malignant characteristics and to find that these criteria are essentially the same irrespective of the site of origin or the type of malignancy adds to the basic soundness of cytology.

The value of the cytologic method of study as an adjunct to the standard biopsy procedures has been clearly demonstrated by Graham, Sturgis, and McGraw (1948) in the study of 181 cases of proved epidermoid carcinoma of the cervix. The surgical biopsy was correctly positive in 90 per cent; the original vaginal smear in 91 per cent; the two methods combined were 99 per cent accurate. Only those cases with primary epidermoid carcinoma of the cervix were considered.

The reasons for the failure of the biopsy methods were considered to be three: (1) The majority of errors occurred because the surgeon did not choose the proper area to biopsy. Some early cancers are grossly undetectable and even with Schiller's iodine test and colposcopic examination, the proper area for biopsy is not easily ascertainable. (2) There are occasional errors in pathologic interpretation of the biopsy specimens submitted for examination. (3) In some cases insufficient tissue was secured for examination.

In the same 181 cases of epidermoid carcinoma there were 17 or 9.4 per cent in which the first vaginal smear obtained was falsely reported negative. These negative smears were later carefully reviewed and 8 showed cancer cells which had been missed on the first reading.

The reasons offered for diagnostic failure of the vaginal smear again are three: (1) There is an occasional tumor of the cervix which will not desquamate cells into the vagina and these cases of necessity will result in false negative reports. (2) Cancer cells may actually be present on the slide but they may be missed because of inexperience, carelessness, or by chance. (3) Typically malignant appearing cells may be misinterpreted as being benign on a casual reading. When the two methods of diagnosis were combined it was evident that there was only 1.7 per cent error in the initial diagnosis, and this emphasizes the complementary nature of the two technics for diagnosis. The vaginal smear technic has an additional advantage in that it provides material for examination originating in areas beyond the cervix and vagina and not readily accessible for simple biopsy procedures.

The false positive reports in the literature vary with the source of the material, but in any case have been found to range from zero to 9 per cent, (Jones *et al*, 1945, Meigs *et al*, 1945, Ayre 1946, Kernodle *et al*, 1948, Parrett *et al*, 1948, Peters and Madden 1950, Rakoff 1948, Wiles *et al*, 1948, Kano 1949, Papanicolaou 1949, Reicher *et al*, 1950, Graham *et al*, 1950, and Botsford 1950). A good discussion of the statistical aspects of exfoliative cytology has been presented by Gates and Warren (1947). The steadily growing volume of reports on the efficacy and dependability of this diagnostic method increasingly establishes its reliability.

According to Oxorn (1948) the *disadvantages* of the cytologic method are the following: (1) Specialized training is required in order to make an accurate interpretation. (2) The test does not show the grade of malignancy, although it may give some hint as to prognosis. (3) It does not supply information as to the mitotic activity of the malignant cell or its relationship to the adjoining tissue. (4) The type and origin of the malignancy are not always clear.

On the other hand the *advantages* of the exfoliative cytologic technic are the following: (1) the test is a simple and painless office procedure. (2) It is relatively rapid and specimens can be taken, stained, and reported in the same day. (3) It is inexpensive. (4) It can be repeated as often as necessary without harm to the patient, and thus it is of great value in the follow-up of patients who, for instance, have had radiation treatment. (5) No hospitalization or specialized technic is required. (6) It permits diagnosis in relatively early stages even before the appearance of clinical symptoms. It also reveals the presence of carcinoma *in situ*. (7) The characteristic modifications of nucleus and cytoplasm in the cancer cells are more apparent in the smear where the cells appear isolated than in tissue sections. (8) It is of great value in the screening of large numbers of patients. (9) It is reliable in the hands of experienced workers. (10) It does not conflict in any way with established methods of pathologic diagnosis, such as biopsy and curettage, on the contrary, it is a valuable complementary procedure to these technics. (11) At the time of the menopause, cytologic tests have a significant role to play, giving immediate indication whether irregular bleeding may be benign and when it is dangerous.

Differences in the technic of obtaining smears partly account for the discrepancies found in statistics published to date (Foote *et al.* 1948). Other important factors are strictness of criteria, experience in cytologic diagnosis, and careful screening and technic throughout the preparation of the specimens. In addition, the attitude of the cytologist—the personal factor—is of some interest. The cytologist emotionally fearful of missing a single cancer in those specimens submitted for interpretation, will tend to have more false positive reports than another with statistical accuracy uppermost in mind. These subjective factors may eventually be eliminated by such improvements of technique as the microfluorometric scanner proposed by Mellors and Silver (1951).

Still another aspect of interest is the type of population being evaluated.

Papanicolaou, and Gates and Warren have shown that the asymptomatic women in a cancer screening test will show many fewer false positives and/or negatives as well as a smaller incidence of cancer than a group with symptoms or signs suspicious of malignancy.

PRECLINICAL CANCER

The discovery of cancer cells in exfoliated tissue debris before symptoms appear i.e. in *preclinical cancer* or when symptoms are present but biopsy methods have failed to reveal the cause, is one of the most important aspects of cytology. It is obvious that in women presenting symptoms compatible with genital cancer, but where the cervix appears normal on palpation and inspection, the choice of site for biopsy examination is haphazard and difficult. In such cases the pool of exfoliated cells used for cytologic study is representative of all neighboring surface areas.

Evaluation of the comparative effectiveness of exfoliative cytologic smears and biopsy procedures for early or noninvasive cervical cancer was made by Nieburgs and Pund (1950). All class III smears, that is, suspicious smears, were classified as positive by these authors. A total of 10,000 women were investigated, in most instances by one examination although in others repeated endocervical smears were taken. Of these 3.3 per cent were found to allow a positive cytologic diagnosis of cancer. In this group, 234 or 2.3 per cent were further investigated with the result that 180 or 1.8 per cent of 10,000 women had positive biopsies while 49 or 0.5 per cent showed false positive cytologic results. As far as it is known, there were only 5 or 0.05 per cent false negative results, consisting of 2 cases of endometrial cancer, 2 cases of preinvasive squamous carcinoma of the cervix, and 1 case of invasive squamous carcinoma of the cervix. A total of 60 of the 185 positive cases were preinvasive cancer and 7 were so-called "borderline" cancer which emphasizes the essential nature of this technic for the early diagnosis of cancer of the cervix and/or uterus.

The latter point is illustrated by a study done by Graham and McGraw (1950) dealing with an analysis of the 70 false positive vaginal smears encountered in their laboratory since 1943. Review of these slides revealed that in 62 the false positive report had been rendered because of cells previously thought to be carcinoma but later recognized as histiocytes, basal cells, or endocervical cells. In the other 8 cases the smears still meet the criteria for diagnosis of malignant growth as used in their laboratory. Of the 8 smears which are still thought to be positive even though unconfirmed, 5 are considered consistent with fairly well differentiated adenocarcinoma. It appears that the smear diagnosis of adenocarcinoma might have certain limitations in this respect. The incidence of errors in smears which are reported positive and consistent with squamous carcinoma is extremely low. Eight uteri have become available for study in patients who had received reports considered "false positive." Positive smears were not confirmed by pelvic examination, cervical biopsy, or curettage and none of the uteri showed any recognizable gross malignant tumor when they were opened after surgical removal. Four of the uteri eventually proved to harbor a squamous carcinoma *in situ* of the cervix. Smears for these patients had been reported positive and consistent with squamous carcinoma. Four of the uteri failed to reveal any lesion which could be diagnosed as carcinoma. Smears from three of these had been considered positive and consistent with adenocarcinoma.

Fremont-Smith and Graham reported in 1948 that of 200 smears taken from women without particular gynecologic complaints (21 had some minor gynecologic trouble), 5 were found to have positive smears for cancer and of these 3 revealed carcinoma in situ of the cervix. This agrees closely with the expected incidence of cancer in the cervix (approximating 2 per cent of the female population). It further emphasizes the value of cytologic examination of the vaginal smear in screening procedures for women over 35 years of age.

Gates, McMillan, and Middleton (1949) have reported that in the majority of instances malignant epithelial cells that have not yet invaded the stroma of the cervix may be detected readily by examination of vaginal fluid. It is probably easier, they say, to recognize malignant cells exfoliated from early tumors than those from advanced growths, since superficial necrosis is apt to occur when the tumor is well developed, thus obscuring the malignant characteristics of the cells.

Cancer "in situ" or noninvasive intraepithelial cancer of the cervix uteri has been shown to occur at an average age of 36 years (Pund *et al.* 1946) fully ten years earlier than the average time of occurrence of invasive cancer of the cervix. From reports of the incidence for carcinoma in situ of the cervix one must assume that it approximates that of invasive cervical cancer. There is therefore a probable period of ten years between the appearance of the noninvasive in situ cancer and the more dangerous invasive form. It is in this period that exfoliative cytology offers an advantage over routine biopsy procedures in the diagnosis of cancer.

Cytology is useful in the occasional diagnostic problem in which direct visualization of the lesion for biopsy is impossible because of its inaccessibility. This is particularly true in the case of pulmonary lesions beyond reach of bronchoscopy, in cancer of the stomach, intrapleural and intraperitoneal lesions, and when drainage from the nipple occurs in cancer involving the mammary duct system.

TECHNIC

VAGINAL AND CERVICAL SMEARS

Preparation of Smear

The secretion is aspirated from the posterior fornix by a glass pipette with a capillary opening to which a rubber bulb is attached. The secretion is immediately blown on a marked new clean glass slide and spread evenly with the tip or flat surface of the pipette. A paper clip is attached to the marked end of the slide to keep the specimen from rubbing off the slide. The slide is immersed immediately in the fixative, a mixture of half ether and half 95 per cent ethyl alcohol. The slide can be removed from the fixative in one or more hours and allowed to dry in air before mailing, or can be sent to the laboratory in the fixative solution. It may remain in the fixative for several days without deterioration. Cervical smears obtained with a wooden applicator from the surface of the lesion are spread on the slide in a similar manner and immersed directly into the fixative. It is essential to obtain the smears before any vaginal examination or manipulation.

Additional technics have appeared for obtaining vaginal or cervical smears. The cervical spatula or scraper has been developed by Ayre (1947). The use of a gelatin sponge for scraping cells from the surface of a lesion has been evolved by Gladstone (1948). Still another direct contact technic has been presented by Hyams *et al.* (1950). Myller (1950) has suggested the use of a metal cervical scraper.

INTERPRETATION

Familiarity with normal exfoliative cytology is essential before a clear concept of discrete aberrations pathognomonic of malignancy can be developed.

Although many staining technics have been suggested and applied to exfoliated cell smears, including hematoxylin and eosin (Richardson *et al.* 1949), Wright's (Shen *et al.* 1950), silver-osmic acid (Arcilla 1950), and fluorescent dyes (Friedman, 1950), the descriptions in this text refer exclusively to specimens stained with Papanicolaou's trichrome method (1943). This technic has the advantages of good nuclear-cytoplasmic detail and delicate variation in colors, which make identification by the cytologist more accurate.

The color of the cytoplasm is variable and is dependent upon hydration, penetration of mucus and blood serum into the cell, *p*H of the fluid in which the cells are found, as well as the degree of maturity of the cells and the presence of eleidin. Dependence upon the color of cytoplasm alone for information is hazardous, but together with specific cytoplasmic changes, it can be very helpful.

The cyclic changes which occur in the genital tract increase the complexity of the interpretation of the smears for the diagnosis of malignancy. This factor of physiologic change which is not present in material from the respiratory tract, gastrointestinal tract, or urinary tract makes it necessary to deal more extensively with the normal exfoliative cytology of vaginal fluid.

The vaginal fluid obtained for cytologic examination consists essentially of superficial exfoliated cells from the vagina, exocervix, endocervix, and endometrium mixed with mucus, leukocytes, histiocytes, bacteria and, occasionally, erythrocytes. Accordingly, the normal vaginal smear will show basal cells, precornified cells, cornified cells, endocervical cells, endometrial cells, and nonepithelial cells.

The significant characteristics of the *basal cells* are dependent upon their maturity. The squamous epithelium of the female genital tract is separated histologically into three layers; germinal, transitional (basal), and superficial (precornified and cornified) zones. The germinal layer is of little interest to the cytologist, since its cells are rarely seen in exfoliated cell pools. They may be more common in tissue scrapings. The basal cells are separated for practical purposes into inner and outer basals. The outer basals are larger in size than the inner basals. The cytoplasm is strongly basophilic and in the inner basal the rim of cytoplasm is approximately equal in diameter to that of the nucleus (ratio 1:1). The cells are generally round or oval and appear as separate, easily definable units. The nucleus of the outer basal cell is about the same size as that of the inner basal, but the rim of cytoplasm is about twice as wide in radius (ratio 3:1) (Fig. 136). The cytoplasm becomes less dense (lighter blue). The basal cell nuclei are generally centrally placed and have a round or oval shape. This cell offers little diagnostic difficulty except when degeneration or unusual activity is present in the transitional layers. Regularity in size and shape of the nucleus is a helpful differential sign. The presence of vaginal trichomonas infestation may tend to make hyperchromatism more apparent in the basal cells and lead to more difficult diagnostic problems. The presence of the trichomonas organisms should be a warning of the presence of aberrant benign basal cells. In these instances the cytoplasm frequently shows vacuolization and degeneration.

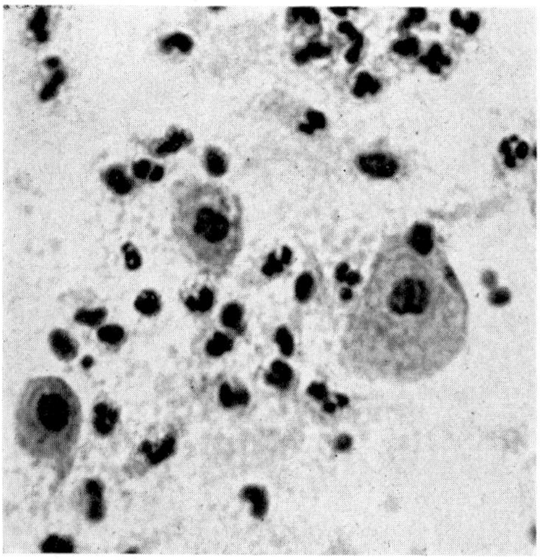

FIG. 136. Basal cells from vaginal and cervical squamous epithelium. Polymorphonuclear leukocytes are frequently present in vaginal smears. The basal cells predominate in low-estrogen states (postmenopause, ovarian failure, etc.).

Precornified Cells. The cells which make up the superficial layers of the squamous epithelium are the precornified and the cornified cells (Fig. 137). They predominate in most vaginal smears. As squamous cells degenerate (mature) the cytoplasm becomes larger in area, more pale and less dense, and the nucleus becomes smaller in size and increasingly pyknotic. The precornified cells are larger cells than the outer basals and polygonal. Usually they have a basophilic cytoplasm and a vesicular (transparent) nucleus which is smaller than that of the basal cell. It is often placed near the center of the cell. Some of the flattened cells are folded along the edges and many have irregular outlines. The diameter of the nucleus is approximately one-third to one-quarter the radius of the cytoplasmic rim (ratio 10:1).

The presence of large numbers of bacteria tends to cause disintegration of the cytoplasm. One must not depend upon cytoplasmic color for identification of normal cells, since local conditions make the acidophilic or basophilic nature of the cytoplasm variable. As stated by Graham *et al.*, (1950), a vesicular nucleus in a superficial cell indicates the precornified stage irrespective of the staining reaction of the cytoplasm. Although such an attitude may be arbitrary, it provides a reliable standard for interpretation and can be used as a criterion for cornification with staining technics other than the Papanicolaou method.

Cornified Cells. The cornified cell is flat, folded, or polygonal in shape and usually takes an acidophilic stain. The nucleus is pyknotic with an even, well-defined border and is usually placed near the center of the cell. The diameter of the

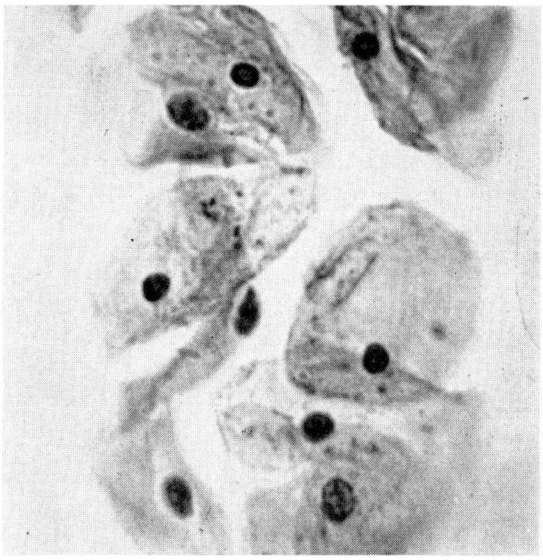

FIG. 137. Precornified and cornified cells from vaginal and cervical squamous epithelium. Cornified cells predominate in high-estrogen states.

nucleus is one-sixth or one-seventh the radius of the cytoplasmic rim (ratio 20:1). The red-orange color of the cell is to some extent due to the presence of eleidin, a substance peculiar to cornified cells. The relative number of cornified cells in the smear has been correlated with cyclic phenomena of the menstrual cycle. The superficial cornified cells are apt to wrinkle or fold which enhances their irregular cytoplasmic outline. Small basophilic or eosinophilic granules may be seen in the cytoplasm. It is noteworthy that degeneration in squamous cells is marked by nuclear pyknosis and disintegration wheras degeneration of columnar cells is most marked in the cytoplasm which disappears early.

The use of "cornification counts" to evaluate estrogen activity from vaginal smears has been extensively reviewed by de Allende and Orias (1947). Daily counts of the cells with plotting of the proportion of each squamous cell type results in characteristic curves. Ovulatory and nonovulatory cycles can be identified in this way. The method used is fundamentally the same as that applied in differential blood counts. Only epithelial cells are counted. The cornification curve so plotted (de Allende *et al.* 1943) appears closely related to the estrogenic level of the organism. A minimum of 400 cells in at least 7 fields is considered satisfactory for dependable counts. A close correlation has been reported between the types of cells found and urinary estrogen excretion (Rubenstein *et al.* 1941).

Complete keratinization occurs infrequently in humans. The keratinized cell has lost its nucleus and its site may be marked by a lighter transparent shadow. The cytoplasm takes a deep orange color.

Endocervical Cells. The site of the junction of squamous and columnar epithelium in the cervix, the *endocervix* is the origin of a large number of cervical malignancies. Histologically the change is abrupt from the multilayered squamous cells of the outer cervix to the single layer of columnar cells. These columnar endocervical cells with nuclei near the basement membrane, occasionally ciliated when well preserved, are seen irregularly in specimens obtained by means of the Papanicolaou pipette. Their presence is more notable in smears obtained by scraping, rubbing, or aspiration of the cervix. Because of their relative infrequency and also since they show normally great variability they are often mistakenly considered presumptive of malignancy.

As has been mentioned earlier, the cytoplasm of columnar cells degenerates more rapidly than the nucleus. This results in the presence of naked nuclei—nuclei without cytoplasmic borders—in the smear. This increases the difficulty of differentiating these cells from malignant cells. In general, the largest number of false positive cancer diagnoses is caused by degenerating endocervical cells.

The nuclei are usually quite granular and "active" in appearance, containing clumps of chromatin of varying size. The nucleus is usually round or oval, has a smooth membrane, and shows wide variation in size, varying up to ten times normal size even in benign endocervical cells. When such marked variation in nuclear size is seen, it can be differentiated from that in malignant nuclei by the lack of variation in the chromatin content of the nuclei. The nuclear pattern tends to be evenly granular and normally contains less than three clumps of chromatin. The lack of variation from the oval or round shape is of further assistance in identifying such nuclei as benign. The nuclei tend to clump and may overlap one another. The nucleus, which takes a purple stain, may be at one pole of the well-preserved cell in the typical columnar arrangement.

The cytoplasm, when present, varies greatly in amount depending on the state of preservation. The cell border is usually indistinct and the cytoplasmic color varies from pale blue to pink-orange. The cytoplasm is finely granular or coarsely vacuolated. Fine tails of the degenerating cytoplasm may be seen attached to one portion of the nucleus.

Distinct vacuolization may occur near the eccentric nucleus and is suggestive of the secretory nature of the columnar cells. The size of the endocervical cell is midway between the leukocyte and the inner basal cell of the squamous epithelium, but is variable and at its largest approaches that of superficial squamous cells.

Endometrial Cells. Endometrial cells are frequently seen in vaginal smears, and predominate during the menstrual phase of the cycle. Degeneration of cytoplasm is usually advanced and the nuclei are often found in tight groups. The size of the darkly pigmented round endometrial cell varies from one to three times that of the leukocyte and the separate identification of each cell might be difficult at times. However, since endometrial cells generally are seen in tight irregular groups, their specific nature is clarified. There is a sharp nuclear border and the chromatin content is arranged in fairly regular clumps. The cytoplasm, when present, is usually little more than a pink to green rim around the nucleus. The nuclei are blue-purple and tend to overlap one another. Leukocytes and histiocytes are common within clumps of endometrial cells.

The distinction between endometrial and endocervical cells rests on the smaller and relatively constant size of the endometrial cell but is subject to factors of personal interpretation.

The endometrial cell can be distinguished from small undifferentiated malignant cells by the smooth, evenly distributed chromatin clumps of the endometrial nucleus and by its regularity in size and shape. Endometrial cells which desquamate from endometrial hyperplastic tissue, however, tend to demonstrate greater variability in the nuclear size and chromatin content of the cells.

Nonepithelial Cells. Typical *polymorphonuclear leukocytes* are common in most vaginal smears and frequently are unrelated to the presence of inflammatory conditions. Hyperestrinism may be accompanied by a scarcity of leukocytes.

Other elements of blood are found in many smears and appear in three separate forms. (1) as fresh *erythrocytes* taking a pink-yellow stain, (2) as *fibrin*, appearing as long strands of amorphous orange material, (3) as *blood pigment* in the form of orange or light green granules or in the form of ferns and other geometric patterns.

Mucus appears in many smears as blue-stained amorphous strands. It can easily be distinguished from blood fibrin, which takes an orange stain.

Histiocytes may be the source of appreciable difficulty in interpretation. The large *phagocytic histiocyte* has typical vacuoles containing ingested debris and is fairly easy to identify. Its size approaches that of large basal cells. The small histiocytes are more numerous and about the size of the endocervical cell with which they may easily be confused. The multinucleated giant cell or foreign-body giant cell represents many typical histiocyte nuclei in one large cell with vacuolization and containing phagocytized particles. The cytoplasm of the histiocyte is foamy, made up of many fine vacuoles. It takes a light blue-green stain. The cell border is clear in the well-preserved cells and less distinct in the degenerating cells.

The nuclei of the histiocytes are round, oval, or bean-shaped, usually eccentrically placed within the cytoplasm and showing discrete nuclear membranes surrounding several clumps of chromatin. There is a fair degree of constancy in the pattern of these chromatin clumps. Mitotic figures, when present in the vaginal smear, are usually found in histiocytes. The symmetrical nature of the mitotic figure in histiocytes differentiates it from malignant mitoses which are bizarre.

Criteria of Malignancy

In the cytologic morphology of malignancy there is no single pathognomonic sign for cancer but rather an accumulation of many alterations from the normal which taken together imply malignancy. Most of these changes concern the cell nuclei. As all desquamated cells are degenerating or dead, mitoses are rarely seen in cells originating from a neoplastic lesion. Even in the presence of numerous mitotic figures visible in histologic preparations of a tumor the cytologic material derived from the very same tumor may show but few mitotic figures.

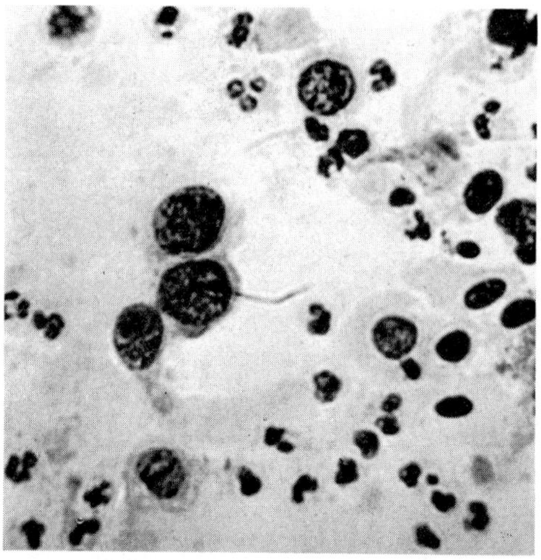

Fig. 138. A group of undifferentiated cancer nuclei showing paucity of cytoplasm, gross hyperchromatic clumps and mounds, and variation in size of nucleus.

Other characteristics of malignancy, such as variation in cell size, shape, and density, become more apparent on cytologic smears than in histologic preparations. This may be due to the fact that desquamating cells are degenerating and therefore more subject to these variations and they are not confined by adjoining tissues.

For purposes of description malignant cells may be considered as either differentiated or undifferentiated depending on the degree of distinction of their cell borders and the amount of cytoplasm present.

Undifferentiated Malignant Cells. The undifferentiated cancer cells are found in all sloughed or scraped material from cancer tissue independent of the degree of differentiation of the tumor of origin. They have the following general characteristics (Figs. 138, 139):

1. *Little or no cytoplasm.* The nuclei generally appear as "naked" nuclei. The coloration of the cytoplasm is of little diagnostic significance.

2. *No cell borders.* When cytoplasm is present in any degree, it has indistinct borders which tend to blend with the background.

3. *Increase in nuclear-cytoplasmic ratio.* The increase in size of the nucleus is grossly out of proportion to the amount of cytoplasm present. It has been stated at times that very large malignant nuclei are frequently associated with highly malignant tumors.

4. *Sharp nuclear border.* The enlarged, variably shaped malignant nucleus has a darkly pigmented nuclear membrane. A deposition of fine chromatin particles is frequently noted as its cause.

5. *Variation in nuclear size and shape.* Although variation in size and shape of the malignant nucleus is usually grossly apparent, this alteration should be viewed with caution if it appears alone.

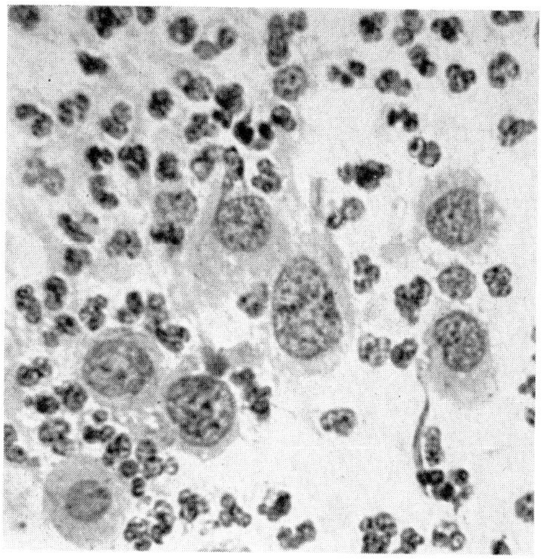

FIG. 139. A group of undifferentiated cancer nuclei showing paucity of cytoplasm, poor cytoplasmic cell membrane, chromatin clumps in the nucleus, and gross variation in size.

6. *Enlargement of the nucleolus.* The nucleolus, when identifiable, takes an acidophilic (red) stain in contrast to the purple-black coloration of the large chromatin particles. It has a distinct nucleolar border or membrane and when present in its enlarged malignant form is helpful as a sign of malignancy. It is, however, absent in most malignant cells.

7. *Hyperchromatism and chromatin pattern.* The hyperchromatic nucleus is the most significant and most dependable single aspect of interest in the diagnosis of cancer. All malignant nuclei show hyperchromatism, due to clumping of chromatin particles in bizarre irregular patterns. Frequently the clumps are concentrated near the nuclear membrane. Irregular and uneven distribution of chromatin with a relative decrease in hyperchromatism may also be considered as suspicious. It is the irregular pattern of chromatin clumps which differentiates benign actively

proliferating cells from malignant cells. In the benign cell the chromatin clumps are quite evenly dispersed.

The diagnosis of malignancy is usually made from several cells in a smear which may be seen spread in flat groups (squamous carcinoma) or in clumped groups (adenocarcinoma). A moderate number of malignant multinucleated giant cells are seen in cancer smears, and in these as many as ten or more nuclei with characteristics as described above may be found.

Differentiated Malignant Cells. The characteristic which distinguishes the differentiated malignant cell is the presence of cytoplasm with fairly clear cell borders. This difference is often sufficient to identify specific types such as squamous

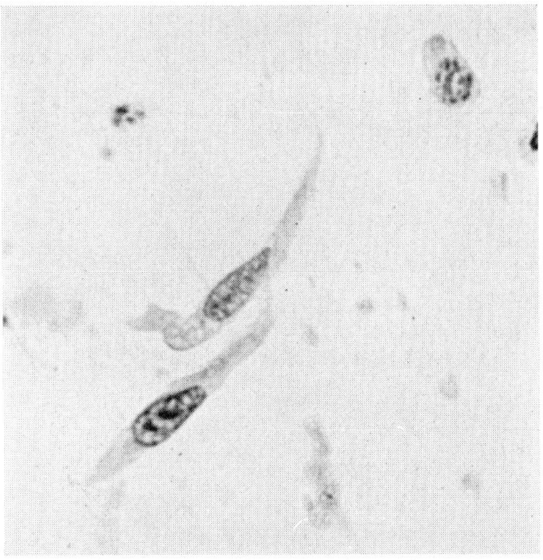

FIG. 140. Differentiated cancer cells, tadpole type, found in epidermoid carcinoma. Note large clumps of chromatin in nucleus and taillike streamers of cytoplasm.

carcinoma or adenocarcinoma as the tissue of origin. A mixture of differentiated squamous cancer cells and adenocarcinoma cells in a single smear suggests adenoacanthoma.

1. *Tadpole cells.* These cells are found in the exfoliated material from epidermoid (squamous) carcinoma (Fig. 140). Cytoplasm is present in fair quantity and is distributed as a long tail. The nucleus has all the characteristics of the undifferentiated malignant nucleus enumerated above. There are frequently several nuclei in one tadpole cell, as many as ten having been seen in a single cell. The cytoplasm varies in color from pink to blue.

2. *Fiber cells.* These cells are found only in material from epidermoid cancer (Fig. 141). The cytoplasm present is distributed as long fibers frequently extending over more than one high power field. The nuclei are elongated and usually so hyperchromatic that they may appear pyknotic. There is great variation in dimensions of the nuclei. They usually are found in groups of strandlike cells. Several

nuclei may be found in each cell. The cytoplasm is usually yellow-orange, but occasionally takes a blue stain.

3. *"Superficial dyskariosis" cells.* This cell type is of great importance, since it is frequently found in specimens from early invasive cancer or carcinoma *in situ.* It had earlier been called "Birkhead's disease" by Papanicolaou (1949), and the "third type differentiated cell" by Graham. These cells are most often erroneously called benign since their appearance is close to that of the normal cell. The nucleus of this cell is enlarged out of proportion to the amount of cytoplasm present and has an irregularly dispersed hyperchromatic network. The nucleus frequently has a wrinkled appearance. More often than not the cytoplasm is orange, but basophilic

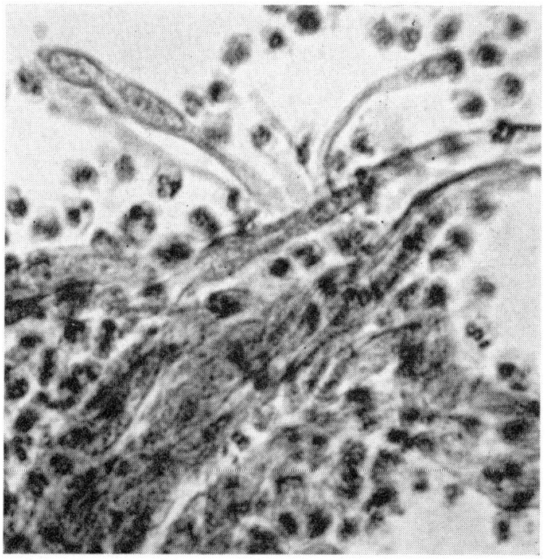

FIG. 141. Differentiated cancer cells, fiber type, found in epidermoid carcinoma. Note clumps of fiber-shaped cells and hyperchromatin-containing nuclei, compressed longitudinally.

cytoplasm may be found. The cytoplasm usually reveals a clear round cell border. Pund and Auerbach (1946) considered this cell fairly typical of preinvasive carcinoma of the cervix. The main distinguishing feature was the unusually large size and the greater amount of cytoplasm. Contrary to the above description there may be nuclei with distinct borders and a particular type of granularity unlike that found in invasive carcinoma. In addition, there is usually a striking predominance of cornified normal cells in the vaginal smear. Although the patient may be in the secretory phase of the cycle or of the postmenopausal age, this difference in morphologic appearance of cells from preinvasive cancer appears only in smears and is not found in biopsy material. The evident cause for this difference is the fact that individual cells and their particular characteristics stand out so much more clearly in cytologic exfoliative preparations than they do in the closely packed, densely filled tissue sections available for histologic study.

4. *Adenocarcinoma cells.* The diagnosis of malignancy from the exfoliated cells of this neoplasm is more difficult since normally the endocervical columnar epithelium has hyperchromatic nuclei; the cells are smaller in size, and naked nuclei without cytoplasm are frequently present. In malignant smears these cells have a thin rim of cytoplasm surrounding the typical though small malignant nucleus. The nucleus appears too large for the cytoplasm present. Vacuolization is quite frequent.

Effect of Irradiation on the Cytologic Smear

The effect of irradiation on the vaginal cells in cervical malignancy was first described by Graham (1947). Although the primary usefulness of exfoliative cytology lies in the initial diagnosis of malignancy, it has its applications in the field of post-treatment care and choice of therapy. Clear-cut and varied changes produced in the vaginal cytologic smear by irradiation require some explanation for their satisfactory interpretation. The alterations which occur in the "irradiated" vaginal smear are such as to make the diagnosis of persistent or recurrent malignancy more difficult and complex.

The basal cells are the first to show the effects of irradiation and the cytoplasmic stain, which is usually blue, becomes yellow-brown. The presence of grossly aberrant forms is particularly notable. The cells appear elongated and often have tails of cytoplasm, similar to those seen in the atrophic smear. Pyknosis and karyorrhexis are common findings in these smears. About two weeks after the radiation has been applied the most striking effect on the smear is noted. The cells become inflated three to four times the normal size with the cytoplasm often showing fibrils. The cytoplasmic-nuclear ratio is not disturbed in contrast to the disturbed nuclear-cytoplasmic ratio in the malignant cell. Fine granulation in the nucleus is common, giving it a smooth yet granular appearance. The size of the basal cells often approximates that of the moderately large precornified cells. However, two factors make it appear to be basal in origin. In the first place the cytoplasm lacks the clear transparency of the precornified cells. Second, the nucleus is much too large and vesicular for the precornified cells. Abnormal vacuolization of the cytoplasm is also common. Multinucleated basal cells may occur in the postradiation smears. They may contain up to seven nuclei. These multinucleated cells can be differentiated from the multinucleated malignant cells by the smooth, benign appearance of the nucleus and the lack of hyperchromatism (cf. Fig. 142).

Radiation changes of the superficial, cornified, and precornified cells occur later in the course following radiation therapy. Increase in cell size up to six times normal is common here too. Once more the cytoplasm and nucleus increase similarly in size, so that the nuclear-cytoplasmic ratio is not disturbed. The occasionally pyknotic nucleus of the precornified cells shows degenerative changes with dark and wrinkled chromatin material and less structural detail. The nuclei may be irregular and the surface may appear folded and wrinkled. A clear perinuclear space may frequently be present. The change in the cytoplasm of these cells is similar to that found in the basal cells. The appearance of polymorphonuclear leukocytes within the precornified cells is moderately frequent and occurs during the third week after irradiation. Leukocytes are common in postradiation smears and often clump upon the cells, almost obscuring them completely. This may occur early in the treatment but actual inclusion of leukocytes is usually seen later in the course after therapy.

In the case of cervical malignancy showing response to roentgen-ray or radium emanations, the changes show a peak at the end of the therapy, at which time almost all the benign cells show the effect of irradiation. As a rule, most of the effects in the vaginal smear resulting from irradiation have disappeared by three to four months after the treatment, but in some instances typical late postradiation changes have been seen in smears as long as ten to twelve years after therapy. The

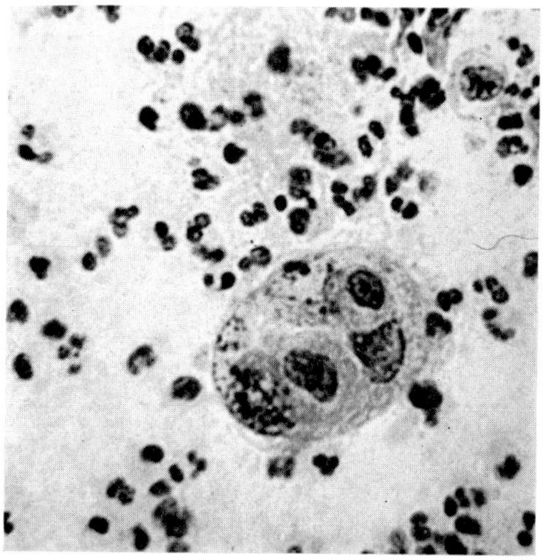

FIG. 142. Multinucleated giant cancer cell. Note hyperchromatic content, gross variation in shape and size of nuclei.

changes produced by radiation in the malignant cells of squamous carcinoma are similar to those seen in the cells described above. The nuclei increase greatly in size and their characteristics appear accentuated because of their large size. Differentiated cells tend to show fewer changes.

Although the vaginal smear can be of great value in identifying early recurrences after treatment of cancer in the cervix and uterus, it is often difficult to distinguish without cytologic examination between radiation reaction in normal tissue and a recurrence of malignant growth. The stenosis which occurs in the genital tract following adequate irradiation renders difficult biopsy procedures as well as manual and clinical examinations. Here the identification of malignant cells is of immense value for adequate cancer control. Many cases of recurrent genital tract malignancy have been identified by cytology weeks or months before their clinical manifestations are found.

One of the problems that the gynecologist of today faces in the control of cervical malignancy is the choice between the surgical approach (radical hysterectomy and pelvic lymphadenectomy) and the application of radiation (roentgen-rays or radium). Certainly those patients whose tumors are not sensitive to irradiation should be subjected to surgical procedures. The technic of cytologic diagnosis, which pays particular attention to the aberrations in the smear from roentgen-ray and radium, may prove of great assistance in identifying those patients whose tumors may be radiosensitive. It has been suggested (Graham 1947), for instance, that by the end of one month following irradiation, it is possible to identify the number of sensitive tumors as opposed to radioinsensitive tumors. This can be done by frequent counts on the vaginal smear following irradiation. The number of benign vaginal cells showing irradiation effect should rise in the period of thirty days to a good percentage of the total present (75 to 100 per cent). At the same time the number of malignant cells in the smear should decrease from the first untreated state to a number approaching zero at the end of one month. With the smear showing a great irradiation effect on the benign cells and a marked decrease in the number of malignant cells, one should clearly expect a good five-year result and Graham (1947) has reported a two-year study in such a group in which the number of recurrences or deaths from the malignant tumor were minimal.

Similarly, in those patients who show little or no decrease in the malignant cells or a small percentage of benign cells with irradiation changes after a period of one month has elapsed, one might expect radioresistance. In this group was found a larger number of recurrences and/or deaths due to the malignancy. This technic has been applied to the identification of those patients who should be offered surgical procedures for the treatment of cancer of the cervix (Sarkisian 1950).

URINE AND PROSTATIC SECRETION

Preparation of Smear

An entire fresh, morning urine specimen is centrifuged at 1500 RPM for twenty minutes, in several tubes if necessary. Smears of the collected sediment are placed, by means of a wire loop, evenly and thinly on three glass slides, previously prepared with a drop of a mixture of egg albumen 75 per cent and glycerine 25 per cent. The slides are then properly marked and clipped with a paper clip and immersed immediately in the standard ether-alcohol fixative. If there is no centrifuge available, the addition of 10 cc. of 40 per cent formalin helps to preserve the cells. Prostatic fluid should be smeared evenly on the slide prepared with albumen-glycerin and immersed immediately into the fixative. It may be air-dried after one hour of fixation and mailed to the laboratory. Centrifuged specimens can be sent to the laboratory with supernatant fluid poured off and absolute alcohol added to cover the sediment. Care should be taken in massaging only that portion of the prostate which is suspicious to palpation since the addition of cells from other parts of the prostate may serve to confuse the picture. Unless the tumor extends into the seminal vesicles, this area should not be massaged. It is usually more desirable to deposit prostatic fluid directly upon the slide which has been prepared with a drop or two of egg albumen spread more or less evenly upon it and placed directly into the fixative. As the drops of secretion appear at the external urethral meatus, one drop is collected on each of three glass slides. A second clean glass slide may then be drawn evenly over the eggalbumen–coated slide in order to make a spread similar to that used in the study of blood smears. The fresh specimen is so much more easily surveyed than the degenerating specimen that speed of handling is quite essential in the management of urine and prostatic secretions.

Interpretation of Smear

The reliability of the diagnosis of cancer in the urinary tract by means of cytologic examination of smears from the urinary sediment or the prostatic secretions varies from investigator to investigator and the figures for falsely positive diagnosis range from as low as 1 per cent (Herbut and Lubin 1947) to as high as 7.36 per cent (Papanicolaou 1947). The figures for falsely negative findings range from 3.45 per cent (Papanicolaou 1947) to 18.2 per cent (Herbut and Lubin 1947). Other pertinent papers in this field are those by Chute and Williams (1949), Schmidlapp and Marshall (1948 and 1950), Herbut (1949), and Alpers, McDonald, and Thompson (1949). The evidence suggests that smears from the urinary tract provide a reliable diagnostic tool, although it must be emphasized that, as is true for cytology in any site, the final positive diagnosis of cancer that will determine therapy must be confirmed by biopsy.

Papanicolaou has reported the appearance of a characteristic cell in urine sediments during pregnancy (1948) which he calls the "navicular type cell" corresponding to those described in the vaginal smear of pregnancy. He feels that the presence of this "navicular" cell in the urinary sediment is consistent with the diagnosis of pregnancy and in a group of 38 pregnant women these cytologic changes were found in all. The earliest specimen was obtained in a 14-weeks gestation and the latest at 7 months.

Normal Cytology. The normal cytology of urinary sediments reflects the fact that the lower urinary tract as well as the ureter and kidney pelvis are lined by transitional cells. These are the same large flat pavement cells that are so frequently encountered in the conventional urinary sediment examination. The shape of individual cells varies markedly, from small ones similar to the inner basal cells to elongated forms almost approaching columnar epithelium. The nuclei of the transitional cells vary considerably in shape from round smooth granular ones to those having large irregular shapes and irregular depositions of chromatin granules. Variation in size may be a frequent source of difficulty in diagnosis. Multinucleated cells are not infrequent. The normal cells do, however, show the usual nuclear-cytoplasmic ratio. Frequently mineral and organic crystals may be present in urine sediments.

Prostatic secretions are made up of two types of cells, epithelial and inflammatory. The epithelial cells have been described as of three types: urethral, prostatic, and seminal vesicle cells. The urethral cells, described above, are the large flat pavement cells that are polyhedral and have sharp cellular borders. The cytoplasm is hazy and its staining properties are variable. The nuclei are vesicular but may contain irregular clumps of chromatin granules.

Multinucleated cells of the pavement variety are most commonly found in material obtained on ureteral catheterization. The normal prostatic cells appear singly or in small groups of not more than 3 or 4 cells, and are quite small, measuring not more than one or two times the size of the polymorphonuclear leukocytes. The single cells are usually cuboidal, oblong, or somewhat irregularly shaped but their margins are clearly defined. The cytoplasm takes a blue to green stain. When these cells show degeneration the cytoplasm may become two to four times the normal size and reveal many small foamy vacuoles.

The nucleus of the prostatic cell occupies about one-half of the cell volume and as a rule is of purplish color. Its borders are moderately sharply defined and the chromatin may form fine clumps evenly distributed throughout the nucleoplasm. The nuclei are usually free from nucleoli.

Secretions of the hypertrophied prostate usually reveal enlarged polyhedral cells. Cells from the seminal vesicles are usually found singly and are two to four times the size of the prostatic cells. They are round and have clearly defined cytoplasmic borders, and round, deeply staining eccentric nuclei which contain a minimal amount of chromatin. The cytoplasm contains some small highly pigmented granules. Spermatozoa are frequently seen in close apposition to these cells.

Many leukocytes may be present in the smears which contain malignant cells. These are mostly polymorphonuclear leukocytes. Occasionally small histiocytes are found as well. Elements of the blood may also be present in the form of preserved cells, fibrin, or pigment.

Because of the lack of uniformity in the polygonal flat pavement cells of the urinary tract, the number of false-positive diagnoses in urine smears is reported to be consistently higher than in any other kind of fluid. The fact that the normal cells show little conformity in shape and size of the nucleus as well as less uniformity in the chromatin structure makes for a large number of errors.

Malignant Cytology. The malignant cytology of urine sediments and prostatic fluid is characterized by the predominance of the undifferentiated type of neoplastic cells. These resemble the undifferentiated malignant cells seen in vaginal smears with the difference that nucleoli are relatively infrequent in malignant cells desquamating from cancers of the urinary tract. Single neoplastic cells may be seen but often clusters of cancer cells may facilitate the diagnosis. Care has to be taken not to confuse the multinucleated giant cells so frequently seen in normal urine specimens with neoplastic multinucleated cells. The differential diagnosis rests in the last analysis with the typical appearance of the malignant nucleus.

SPUTUM AND BRONCHIAL SECRETIONS

Preparation of Smear

An early morning sputum specimen is collected in a glass receptacle containing 70 per cent alcohol. The sputum is examined for blood-flecked areas and these areas of the specimen are spread, as early as possible after collection, thinly and evenly on three new, clean glass slides properly marked for identification with a paper clip at the marked ends. A wooden swab stick is used to spread the material. The slide is immediately immersed in a fixative of half ether and half 95 per cent ethyl alcohol. If no suspicious areas are seen in the sputum specimen an attempt is made to secure representative thick and thin portions of the sample for the smears. Bronchial aspiration material should be managed in the same way. If it is possible, the bronchial secretion may be delivered in the aspiration chamber to the laboratory within thirty minutes of the time of collection for processing.

Interpretation of Smear

Most of the reports on respiratory tract cytology suggest that the examination of sputum is far from being a substitute for such time-honored and time-proven methods as bronchoscopy with biopsy. However, when cytologic sputum examination, a simpler procedure, is added to examination of the secretion obtained at bronchoscopic aspiration, the results compare favorably with the incidence of positive diagnoses obtainable through the bronchoscopic biopsy methods. When the two methods are combined, one might expect the rate of correct positive diagnoses to approach 80 per cent of the cases with pulmonary malignancy (Dudgeon and Wrigley 1935, Wandall 1944, Papanicolaou 1946, Herbut and Clerf 1946, Woolner and McDonald 1947, 1949, McKay *et al.* 1948, Diggs 1948, Farber, *et al.* 1950.)

There has been some controversy as to whether sputum or bronchial aspirations yield the more reliable diagnosis of respiratory carcinoma. The evidence seems to indicate that the study of either or both is most helpful as an ancillary diagnostic method.

The normal cytology of sputum reflects the cellular structure of the lining of the various portions of the respiratory tract. Cells from the stratified squamous epithelium of the mouth resemble the superficial cells found in vaginal smears. In bronchial material they are naturally less abundant or altogether absent. They do not offer differential diagnostic difficulties except for the so called "deep cell" described by Graham *et al* (1950) which may occasionally be confused with malignant cells. The columnar cells which line the bronchial tree resemble the endocervical cells of the vaginal smears and, like these, are subject to rapid degeneration. If this is allowed to happen, and particularly when such cells occur in groups, they may be mistaken for neoplastic cells.

Leukocytes, plasma cells, and lymphocytes are commonly present in sputa. Fibrin strands, blood pigments and red cells must arouse suspicion when seen.

Histiocytes containing carbon pigment or brownish red blood pigment may frequently be seen and are good evidence that the sputum containing them is an adequately representative sample containing aliquots originating in the deep portions of the respiratory tract.

The cytology of malignancy in the respiratory tract is much the same as in the genital tract. The final decision as to the malignant nature of the cells rests again on the nuclear morphology. Occasionally cells from squamous cell carcinomas of the lung have peculiar shades of dark orange which should call attention to such cells but in itself is not conclusive evidence of malignancy. The oat cell carcinoma of the lung may reveal itself by the typical appearance of such cells on smears.

GASTRIC JUICE

Preparation of Smear

Either gastric aspiration fluid or gastric saline washings are centrifuged immediately after collection at 1500 RPM for twenty minutes and smears of the sediment are spread evenly on three clean new glass slides. The slides are then placed immediately in the ether-alcohol fixative, a paper clip being applied to protect the smear. Proper marking of the slides is essential. It is important to handle this material rapidly in order to avoid cell deterioration. The use of atropine or histamine adds little to the value of the smear. More satisfactory smears will be obtained if the following measures are carried out:

1. Use #14 Levine tube with additional holes staggered to a point 14 inches from the tip.
2. Permit the drinking of 100 cc. of water to facilitate swallowing of the tube.
3. Following the withdrawal of the fasting specimen for centrifugation, 150 cc. normal saline is injected into the tube. The tube is then clamped off and the patient is allowed to move about for ten minutes.
4. The patient should not receive food or water for twelve hours before aspiration.

Various technics for improvement of the collection of gastric aspirates for the diagnosis of cancer have been suggested by Tomenius (1949), Papanicolaou and Cooper (1947), Hollander, Hess, and Sober (1947), Panico, Papanicolaou, and Cooper (1950), Ulfelder, Graham, and Meigs (1948), Richardson, Queen, and Bishop (1949), and Botsford and Tucker (1950), amongst others. This method has been applied to the diagnosis of malignant lesions of the esophagus and of the stomach by Anderson, McDonald, and Olsen (1949).

The cytologic technic has been applied by Lemon and Byrnes (1949) to the diagnosis of cancer of the biliary tract and the pancreas through the study of duodenal aspiration fluid. In 38 control patients with nonmalignant disease no false positive observations were made. In 16 cases of cancer of the biliary tract or pancreas proved pathologically, the disease in 11 was suspected or diagnosed from the cytology of the duodenal aspiration fluid.

Due to the presence of the digestive juices and because of the peculiar anatomical situation characteristic of the gastrointestinal tract, the reliability of the cytologic method for the diagnosis of gastrointestinal cancer must be expected to be less than in other sites.

Indeed, the correct positive diagnoses of cancer of the stomach obtained in competent hands have ranged from 40 to 60 per cent (Graham *et al.* 1948, Pollard *et al.* 1949). A negative smear from gastric contents is therefore of little significance, but in view of the relatively low incidence of falsely positive findings, a suspicious or positive report calls for serious consideration and intensive study of the patient's gastrointestinal tract by all available clinical diagnostic methods.

Normal cytology. The normal cytology of the gastric contents reveals squamous cells from the linings of the mouth and the esophagus and columnar cells from the gastric lining. These cells may vary greatly in their appearance depending on their state of preservation. The smear may also show epithelial cells from the respiratory tract which differ somewhat from those of gastric origin. Histiocytes containing carbon particles may be seen and probably originate from the lungs. Leukocytes of all types partly also originating in the respiratory tract and partly from the gastrointestinal wall may be abundant. Elements of the blood should arouse suspicions of ulcers or malignant changes. Fat cells and muscle fibres from undigested food may be found and indicate, if present in large quantities, that the specimen may not be suitable for cytological evaluation.

Malignant Cytology. The malignant cells found in smears of gastric secretions are almost always of the undifferentiated type, differing but little from this type of cell found in the vaginal fluid in the presence of cancer.

Carcinoma cells are usually accompanied by leukocytes, mucus, bacteria, and elements of blood.

PLEURAL AND ASCITIC FLUIDS

Preparation of Smear

The entire specimen is placed in centrifuge tubes as soon as possible after collection and spun down at 1500 RPM for twenty minutes. The sediment is then spread by means of a wire loop on three clean new slides previously prepared with albumen-glycerine. The slides, properly marked, are immersed immediately in the ether-alcohol fixative and handled as above. If it is not possible to centrifuge the specimen immediately, the addition of 10 cc. of 40 per cent formalin to the specimen, or the addition of an approximately equal amount of 95 per cent alcohol will help to preserve the cells. This latter preparation is not as satisfactory as rapid centrifugation, but the entire specimen can then be centrifuged in the laboratory.

Shen and Homburger (1950) have added an interesting refinement to the technic and management of serous fluids. They added effusion fluid to homologous or absorbed human serum in order to suspend the tumor cells, which were then stained with a modified Wright technic. Identification of malignant cells in such a preparation was reported to be simpler than that in the Papanicolaou smear and in a small series of cases was shown to improve the positive diagnostic potentialities. Application of the cytologic method to diagnosis of malignant lesions in other fluid such as that emanating from the breast (Kaufman *et al.* 1950) as well as washings from the maxillary sinus (Fitz-Hugh *et al.* 1950) have been reported.

COLONIC WASHINGS

Preparation of Smear

The cytologic examination of colonic washings is carried out according to the following technic: The patient is given a strong cathartic the night before and an enema the next morning. Two to three hours after the enema saline washings are obtained from the lower bowel and about 100 cc. mixed immediately with equal parts of alcohol (95 per cent ethyl, isopropyl, or methyl). This material is then spun down at 1500—2000 RPM for twenty minutes and the supernatant decanted.

The sediment is then spread upon clean marked slides previously prepared with egg albumen.

The reliability of the diagnosis of cancer from the cytologic study of various exudates and transudates depends upon the anatomical location of the tumor causing the exudate and consequently must be expected to vary greatly from case to case. The problem has been reviewed by Phillips and McDonald (1948) and by Saphir (1949) and forms the subject of a substantial body of old and modern literature.

The malignant cells found in exudates differ in no way from those seen elsewhere. One should not be misled by the varying size of the mesothelial cells found in transudates and exudates of nonmalignant nature.

Depending on the nature of the exudate varying amounts of fibrin, bacteria, leukocytes and red cells will be present.

INTERPRETATION OF REPORTS ON CYTOLOGIC SMEARS

There are two methods of reporting cytologic smears which have been described in the literature and are in general use. The simplest form is that of calling a smear either "positive for malignancy," "negative for malignancy," or "suspicious" and this has widespread application. A more elaborate classification of smears has been evolved by Papanicolaou. His classification is as follows:

Class I, no tumor cells are found and only the normal physiologic variation is seen.

Class II, no tumor cells are found but there is evidence of abnormal benign conditions manifested by many leukocytes, red blood cells, atrophic and atypical cells, trichomonas, histiocytes, or hyper- or hypoestrinism.

Class III, questionable cells are found which may or may not be malignant. Repeated smears should be obtained.

Class IV, a few unmistakable malignant cells are found on the slide.

Class V, many cancer cells are found and the diagnosis is unequivocal.

VAGINAL SMEARS IN PHYSIOLOGIC STATES

The criteria for measuring estrin effect are useful clinically but are relatively inaccurate for quantitative estimation. They have been presented in the monograph by De Allende and Orias (1950). A smear which shows little or no estrin effect is almost entirely made up of basal cell-layer cells. A smear with 25 per cent basal cells and 75 per cent precornified cells can be considered to represent very slight estrin effect. Slight estrin effect shows almost all precornified cells in the smear and for moderate estrin effect, the majority of the cells are precornified (75 per cent) with a few cornified cells (approaching 25 per cent). Marked estrin effect is manifested by a change to almost complete cornification in the smear (greater than 75 per cent) with some precornified cells being present. Completely keratinized cells bearing large amounts of eleidin may also be present.

A smear made up predominantly of basal cells is characteristic of premenarche girls and of postmenopausal women. It is usually interpreted as showing atrophy or inactivity of the female genital tract. When the ovaries produce little or no estrin the squamous epithelial layers of the vagina and cervix are inordinately low, and as a result the vaginal secretion contains mainly basal cells. A smear, therefore, which reveals predominantly basal cells can be assumed to represent a hypoestrin state. However, it must be recalled that the presence of cells of cornified epithelium or precornified epithelium may well be found long after the advent of the menopause. Fully 40 per cent of women with smears taken after the menopause will exhibit cornified and precornified cells in relative abundance.

Endometrial cells found in the vaginal smear are usually associated with the menstrual flow or the first day or two after its cessation. The smear at this time usually contains many degenerated superficial cells or red blood cells and fibrin, and moderately numerous clumps of endometrial cell nuclei. It must be recognized that the presence of blood in the vaginal smear is considered an abnormal factor except at the time of the menstrual flow. This point serves to emphasize the necessity for an adequate history accompanying the cytologic smears. It is similarly essential to know whether the patient is postmenopausal since the presence of endometrial cells or blood at this time is clearly abnormal. Occasionally a smear will be declared falsely suspicious if the background for the patient's symptoms is not known to the examiner.

When the superficial squamous cells of the vagina in postmenopausal women tend to show a high proportion of cornification and when endometrial cells are also found in the specimen, the factor of estrogen activity in relation to endometrial malignancy must be considered. These patients in most instances must be reported as *suspicious* in the postmenopausal period even though the material in their smears may reveal no evidence of malignant cells. In any case, such reports should be labeled "repeat smear."

It cannot be overemphasized that the administration of estrogens to the patient in the menopausal state or in hypoactivity of the ovary would also result in hyperplastic changes of the endometrium and cornification in the squamous cells of the vagina. These changes will be reflected by greater variability in the size of the endometrial cell as well as by a strong tendency towards cornification in the vaginal smear. It is very important that information of such therapy should be available to the cytologist at the time of interpretation of the material. Smears can be more intelligently reviewed and diagnoses will be more accurate.

Polymorphonuclear leukocytes are common in most vaginal smears except in those indicating a high estrogen level. Such smears may be reported as demonstrating "leukopenia" of the smear. It is difficult if not impossible to correlate the number of leukocytes present with vaginal or cervical infection since many leukocytes are present in the genital tract in the absence of infectious or inflammatory processes. The leukocyte may be considered as the reference standard for cell size in the vaginal smear since variation in the size of the leukocyte is uncommon.

PREGNANCY

During gestation the cyclic variation in the ovarian activity is suppressed and the epithelium of the accessory organs becomes hypertrophic. The vaginal smears from day to day assume a more uniform pattern which at first resembles that of the early premenstrual state. Large bacillary organisms of the Döderlein type are common and the acidophilic cells gradually decrease in number until they become scanty. The nuclei generally show increase in size and there are many so-called "navicular" cells of Papanicolaou. Generally, the predominant cell in the slide obtained in pregnancy is precornified or cornified. A moderate number of outer basal cells may be present. Leukocytes are usually found in large numbers while red blood cells are only present in pathologic states of pregnancy. Mucus is generally not secreted in abundance. Tight clumping and dense conglomerations of cells are usual. The normal variability of the vaginal contents renders the diagnosis of pregnancy by vaginal smear uncertain.

Occasionally, an increase in the amount of mucus and in the number of leukocytes and cornified cells with the presence of erythrocytes in the vaginal smear of a pregnant woman may indicate a tendency for abortion. In the postpartum period the trend is for greater cornification of cells in the smears, and an increase in the number of leukocytes and in the amount of mucus. Red cells are found in varying numbers depending on the type of lochia present. Cells of the outer basal type become more numerous. Most of them are round or oval and some may have aberrant elongated forms or reveal a transition form close to that of the early precornified cell. Histiocytes are usually numerous in the postpartum fluid and show great variation in size. Some grow so large that they resemble cells of the cornified or precornified state. They usually contain phagocytized degenerated particles. The vaginal smear may be of some use as well in the identification of fetal skin remnants where the amniotic sac has ruptured. These cells usually resemble those of totally cornified cells, with which they may be confused. They have been described by Bourgeois (1942). Embryonic lanugo hair may also be found in the fluid from the ruptured amniotic sac (Bonime 1949).

Functional Amenorrhea

In functional amenorrhea the vaginal smears show changes comparable to those found after the menopause. Most of the cells are basal cells. Leukocytes are usually scarce. Patients with hyperestrinism and endometrial hyperplasia show a scarcity of leukocytes. The predominance of cornified cells with eosinophilic staining is common to hypersecretion of the estrogenic hormones. Red cells are frequently found since abnormal bleeding is a frequent concommitant of hyperestrinism. Groups of endometrial cells may occasionally be seen and in these the endometrial hyperplastic cell with the relatively large nucleus is found. These cells are occasionally confused with malignant degeneration in the endometrial cavity.

Presence of trichomonas infestation in the vaginal tract is usually accompanied by an excess of atypical eosinophilic cells of the cornified type. Trichomonas organisms can be found occasionally in vaginal smears where hanging drop preparations are negative for motile organisms.

REFERENCES

GENERAL

Papanicolaou, G. N., and Traut, H. F. *Diagnosis of Uterine Cancer by the Vaginal Smear.* New York, The Commonwealth Fund, 1943.

Gates, O., and Warren, S. *A Handbook for the Diagnosis of Cancer of the Uterus by the Use of Vaginal Smears.* Cambridge, Harvard University Press, 1947.

Papanicolaou, G. N., Traut, H. F., and Marchetti, A. A. *The Epithelia of Woman's Reproductive Organs.* New York, The Commonwealth Fund, 1948.

Staff of Vincent Memorial Laboratory. *The Cytologic Diagnosis of Cancer.* Philadelphia, W. B. Saunders Co., 1950.

Farber, S. M., Rosenthal, M., Alston, E. F., Benioff, M. A., and McGrath, A. K., Jr. *Cytologic Diagnosis of Lung Cancer.* Springfield, Charles C Thomas, 1950.

De Allende, I. L. C., and Orias, O. *Cytology of the Human Vagina.* New York, Paul B. Hoeber, Inc., 1950.

SPECIFIC

Albers, D. D., McDonald, J. R., and Thompson, G. J. Carcinoma cells in prostatic secretions. *J.A.M.A. 139:* 299-303, 1949.

Andersen, H. A., McDonald, J. R., and Olsen, A. M. Cytologic diagnosis of malignant lesions of the esophagus and cardia of the stomach. *Minnesota Med. 32:* 1181-1185, 1949.

Arcilla, Angelina, A. Clinical evaluation of the silver stain for vaginal smears in the diagnosis of uterine cancer. *Philippine J. Surg. 5:* 3-26, 1950.

Ayre, J. E. A simple office test for uterine cancer diagnosis. *Canad. M. A. J. 51:* 17-22, 1944.

Ayre, J. E. Importance of cytologic test in early diagnosis of cancer of the uterus. *Southern M. J. 39:* 847-852, 1946.

Ayre, J. E. Selective cytology smear for diagnosis of cancer. *Am. J. Obstet. & Gynec. 53:* 609-617, 1947.

Ayre, J. E., and Dakin, E. Cervical cytology test in cancer diagnosis: Glycerin technic for mailing. *Canad. M. A. J. 54:* 489-491, 1946.

Batres Gonzales, O. Diagnostico precoz del cancer uterino por la citologia de la secrecion vaginal. *Juventud. Med., Guatemala 1:* 419-433, 1944.

Bonime, R. G. Application of the vaginal smear to the diagnosis of pregnancy. *Am. J. Obstet. & Gynec. 58:* 524-531, 1949.

Botsford, T. W., and Tucker, M. R. Application of cytologic smear methods to cancer diagnosis in a general hospital. *J.A.M.A. 142:* 975-979, 1950.

Bourgeois, G. A. The identification of fetal squamas and the diagnosis of ruptured membranes by vaginal smear. *Am. J. Obstet. & Gynec. 44:* 80-87, 1942.

Cahan, W. G., and Farr, H. W. Tracheal aspiration: An additional method for the early diagnosis of carcinoma of the lung. *Cancer 3:* 475-480, 1950.

Chute, R., and Williams, D. W. Experiences with stained smears of cells exfoliated in the urine in the diagnosis of cancer in the genito-urinary tract: A preliminary report. *J. Urol. 59:* 604-613, 1948.

Coman, D. R. Decreased mutual adhesiveness, a property of cells from squamous cell carcinoma. *J. Cancer Research 4:* 625-629, 1944.

De Allende, I. L. C. *La Citologia Vaginal Humana en Condiciones Normales y Patologicas: Su Importancia para el Diagnostico y Contraeor Terapeutico en Ginecologia. El Ateneo*, Florida 340, Buenos Aires, 1947.

De Allende, I. L. C., Shorr, E., and Hartman, C. G. A comparative study of the vaginal smear cycle of the Rhesus monkey and the human. *Contributions to Embryol., Carnegie Institution of Wash., D. C., 31:* 1-26, 1943.

Diggs, L. W. Use of Wright's Stain in diagnosis of malignant cells in bronchial aspirations. *Am. J. Clin. Path. 18:* 293-302, 1948.

Dudgeon, L. S., and Wrigley, C. H. On demonstration of particles of malignant growth in sputum by means of wet-film method. *J. Laryng. & Otol. 50:* 752-764, 1935.

Fishman, W. H., Homburger, F., and Kasdon, S. C. Beta-glucuronidase alterations in human cervical and breast cancer. *Cancer Research 11:* 248, 1951.

Fitz-Hugh, G. S., Moon, C. N., Jr., and Lupton, C. H., Jr. Cytological smear technique in the diagnosis of carcinoma of the maxillary sinus. *Laryngoscope 60:* 376-387, 1950.

Foote, F. W., and Li, K. Smear diagnosis of in situ carcinoma of the cervix. *Am. J. Obstet. & Gynec. 56:* 335-339, 1948.

Fremont-Smith, M., and Graham, R. M. The vaginal smear. *J.A.M.A. 137:* 921-922, 1948.

Fremont-Smith, M., Graham, Ruth M., and Meigs, J. V. Early diagnosis of cancer by study of exfoliated cells. *J.A.M.A. 138:* 469-474, 1948.

Friedman, H. P., Jr. The use of ultraviolet light and fluorescent dyes in the detection of uterine cancer by vaginal smear. *Am. J. Obstet. & Gynec. 59:* 852-859, 1950.

Gates, O., MacMillan, J. C., and Middleton, M. The vaginal smear as a means of investigating early carcinoma of the cervix. *Cancer 2:* 838-844, 1949.

Gladstone, S. A. Sponge biopsy in cancer diagnosis. *Am. J. Med. 5:* 849-852, 1948.

Graham, Ruth M. The effect of radiation on vaginal cells in cervical carcinoma. *Surg., Gynec. & Obstet. 84:* 153-165, 1947.

Graham, Ruth M., and McGraw, J. Investigation of "false positive" vaginal smears. *Surg., Gynec. & Obstet. 90:* 221-230, 1950.

Graham, Ruth M., Sturgis, S. H., and McGraw, J. A comparison of the accuracy in diagnosis of the vaginal smear and the biopsy in carcinoma of the cervix. *Am. J. Obstet. & Gynec. 55:* 303-307, 1948.

Graham, Ruth M., Ulfelder, H., and Green, T. H. The cytologic method as an aid in the diagnosis of gastric cancer. *Surg., Gynec. & Obstet. 86:* 257-259, 1948.

Herbut, P. A. Cytologic diagnosis of carcinoma of the prostate. *Am. J. Clin. Path. 19:* 315-319, 1949.

Herbut, P. A., and Clerf, L. H. Bronchogenic carcinoma: Diagnosis by cytologic study of bronchoscopically removed secretion. *J.A.M.A. 130:* 1006-1012, 1946.

Herbut, P. A., and Lubin, E. N. Cancer cells in prostatic secretions. *J. Urol. 57:* 542-551, 1947.

Hollander, F., Hess, M., and Soper, H. A. New technique for studying the cytology of gastric aspirate in man. *J. Nat. Cancer Inst. 7:* 365-366, 1947.

Hyams, M. N., Hyams, R. G., and Wainess, E. E. Direct contact vaginal cytology smear technique. *Am. J. Obstet. & Gynec. 59:* 445-447, 1950.

Jones, C. A., Neustaedter, T., and MacKenzie, L. L. Value of vaginal smears in diagnosis of early malignancy. *Am. J. Obstet. & Gynec. 49:* 159-168, 1945.

Kano, I. Papanicolaou method of cancer diagnosis: An evaluation. *Minnesota Med. 32:* 54, 1949.

Kaufman, W., and Fiege, H. R., Jr. Cytologic diagnosis of malignant disease in a general office practice. *Surg., Gynec. & Obstet. 90:* 451-454, 1950.

Kernodle, J. R., Cuyler, M. K., and Thomas, W. L. Diagnosis of genital malignancy by vaginal smears. *Am. J. Obstet. & Gynec. 56:* 1083-1089, 1948.

Lemon, H. M., and Byrnes, W. W. Cancer of the biliary tract and pancreas: Diagnosis from cytology of duodenal aspirations. *J.A.M.A. 141:* 254-257, 1949.

McKay, D. G., Ware, P. F., Atwood, D. A., and Harken, D. E. The diagnosis of bronchogenic carcinoma by smears of bronchoscopic aspirations. *Cancer 1:* 208-222, 1948.

Meigs, J. V., Graham, Ruth M., Fremont-Smith, M., Janzen, L. T., and Nelson, G. B. Value of vaginal smear in diagnosis of uterine cancer: Report of 1015 cases. *Surg., Gynec. & Obstet. 81:* 337-345, 1945.

Meigs, J. V., Graham, Ruth M., Fremont-Smith, M., Kapnick, I., and Rawson, R. W. The value of the vaginal smear in diagnosis of uterine cancer. *Surg., Gynec. & Obstet. 77:* 449-461, 1943.

Mellors, R. C., and Silver, R. A microfluorimetric scanner for the differential detection of cells: Application to exfoliative cytology. *Science 114:* 356-360, 1951.

Myller, E. A cervical "scraper." *New York State J. Med. 50:* 304, 1950.

Nieburgs, H. E., and Pund, E. R. Detection of cancer of the cervix uteri. *J.A.M.A. 142:* 221-226, 1950.

Oxorn, H. Cervical cytology: Key to diagnosis of early uterine cancer. *Surg., Gynec. & Obstet. 87:* 197-205, 1948.

Panico, F. P., Papanicolaou, G. N., and Cooper, W. A. Abrasive balloon for exfoliation of gastric cancer cells. *J.A.M.A. 143:* 1308-1311, 1950.

Papanicolaou, G. N. New cancer diagnosis. *Proc. Race Betterment Conf.*, pp. 528-534, 1928.

Papanicolaou, G. N. The sexual cycle in the human female as revealed by vaginal smears. *Am. J. Anat. 52:* (supplement), 519-637, 1933.

Papanicolaou, G. N. Diagnostic value of exfoliated cells. *J.A.M.A. 131:* 372-378, 1946.

Papanicolaou, G. N. Cytology of urine sediment in neoplasms of urinary tract. *J. Urol. 57:* 375-379, 1947.

Papanicolaou, G. N. Diagnosis of pregnancy by cytologic criteria in catheterized urine. *Proc. Soc. Exper. Biol. & Med. 67:* 247-249, 1948.

Papanicolaou, G. N. Cytologic diagnosis of uterine cancer by examination of vaginal and uterine secretions. *Am. J. Clin. Path. 19:* 301-308, 1949.

Papanicolaou, G. N., and Cooper, W. A. The cytology of the gastric fluid in the diagnosis of carcinoma of the stomach. *J. Nat. Cancer Inst. 7:* 357-360, 1947.

Papanicolaou, G. N., and Cromwell, H. A. Diagnosis of cancer of lung by cytologic method. *Dis. of Chest 15:* 412-422, 1949.

Parrett, V., Small, C., and Winn, L. Vaginal cytologic survey in gynecologic cancer. *Am. J. Obstet. & Gynec. 56:* 360-365, 1948.

Peters, H., and Madden, W. L. The cervical smear in office practice. *J.A.M.A. 142:* 624-626, 1950.

Phillips, S. K., and McDonald, J. R. Evaluation of various examinations performed on serous fluids. *Am. J. Med. Sc. 216:* 121-129, 1948.

POLLARD, H. M., BRYANT, H. C., BLOCK, M., and HALL, W. C. Diagnosis of gastric neoplasms by cytologic examination of gastric secretions. *J.A.M.A. 139:* 71-74, 1949.

POUCHET, F. A. *Théorie positive de l'ovulation spontanée et de la fecondation des mammifères et de l'espèce humaine, basée sur l'observation de toute la série animale.* Paris, Balliere, 1847.

PUND, E. R., and AUERBACH, S. H. Preinvasive carcinoma of the cervix uteri. *J.A.M.A. 131:* 960-963, 1946.

RAKOFF, A. E. The endocrine factors in pelvic tumors with a discussion of the Papanicolaou smear method for diagnosis. *Radiology 50:* 190-201, 1948.

REICHER, N. B., MASSEY, B. W., and BECHTOLD, E. A clinical evaluation of 3500 vaginal cytologic studies. *Am. J. Obstet. & Gynec. 59:* 860-866, 1950.

RICHARDSON, H. L., QUEEN, F. B., and BISHOP, F. H. Cytohistologic diagnosis of material aspirated from stomach. *Am. J. Clin. Path. 19:* 328-340, 1949.

RUBENSTEIN, B. B., and DUNCAN, D. R. L. A technique for assay of estrogen by evaluation of human vaginal smears and comparison with urinary estrogen assay on the mouse uterus. *Endocrinology 28:* 911-914, 1941.

SAPHIR, O. Cytologic diagnosis of cancer from pleural and peritoneal fluids. *Am. J. Clin. Path. 19:* 309-314, 1949.

SARKISIAN, S. S. Early detection of carcinoma of cervix uteri. *U. S. Armed Forces M. J. 1:* 1021-1025, 1950.

SCHMIDLAPP, C. J. II, and MARSHALL, V. F. The detection of cancer cells in the urine: A clinical appraisal of the Papanicolaou method. *J. Urol. 59:* 599-603, 1948.

SCHMIDLAPP, C. J. II, and MARSHALL, V. F. The diagnostic value of urinary sediment: A review based on the Papanicolaou method. *New York State J. Med. 50:* 56-58, 1950.

SHEN, S. C., and HOMBURGER, F. Studies on effusions: II. A simple technique for the discovery of cancer cells in neoplastic exudates. *Cancer 3:* 36-42, 1950.

STOCKARD, C. R., and PAPANICOLAOU, G. N. The existence of typical oestrus cycle in guinea-pig, with a study of its histological and physiological changes. *Am. J. Anat. 22:* 225-283, 1917.

TOMENIUS, J. H. The cytologic examination of the gastric juice and mucus. *Am. J. Digest. Dis. 16:* 425-450, 1949.

ULFELDER, H., GRAHAM, RUTH M., and MEIGS, J. V. Further studies on the cytologic method in the problem of gastric cancer. *Ann. Surg. 128:* 422-424, 1948.

WANDALL, H. H. A study of neoplastic cells in sputum as a contribution to the diagnosis of primary lung cancer. *Acta Chir., Scandinav. 91:* 1-143, 1944.

WILES, J. B., and HELLWIG, C. A. Evaluation of Papanicolaou's method of cancer diagnosis. *Am. J. Clin. Path. 18:* 283-292, 1948.

WOOLNER, L. B., and MCDONALD, J. R. Diagnosis of carcinoma of the lung: The value of cytologic study of sputum and bronchial secretions. *J.A.M.A. 139:* 497-502, 1947.

WOOLNER, L. B., and MCDONALD, J. R. Cytologic diagnosis of bronchogenic carcinoma. *Am. J. Clin. Path. 19:* 765-769, 1949.

CHAPTER 31

Applied Radiation Therapy

L. Henry Garland

Knowledge on applied radiation therapy in the treatment of cancer has increased greatly in the last decade as a result of the more extensive use of radiation for cure as well as for palliation. Radiation may be administered by means of roentgen-rays, radium rays, rays from radioactive isotopes, and other forms of electromagnetic and particulate energy. To treat cancerous diseases efficiently with radiation the physician must understand the nature of the radiations employed, the most effective safe means of their application to the area of disease, and the precise type and extent of the disease under treatment. Technical equipment and elaborate housing are not sufficient; one must know the physical properties of the beams emanating from that equipment and the natural history of the disease. The first requires a reasonable knowledge of radiation physics, and the latter a sound clinical knowledge of cancer.

Two main types of curative attack on malignant neoplasms exist at present: surgical and radiologic. There are some neoplasms which can be cured only by surgery, some which can be cured only by radiation, and others in which combined methods are required. There are cases in which although either method may be used, one is clinically superior to the other. Even when dealing with the same type of malignancy, the physician may require, at different stages of the disease, to vary the treatment from surgery to radiation or vice versa. The ensuing chapter is a summary of facts known at present on applied radiation in cancer therapy. It must be as terse as would be a chapter of equal length on applied surgery in this field.

It is estimated that radiation therapy in some form is used in the care of about 60 per cent of patients with cancer.[32] There are about 225 new cases of cancer per 100,000 population per annum in this country.[26] Approximately one-half of these cases are recognized while *cure* is still possible; in the other half *palliation* is all that is possible at the present time. Radiation is useful for cure in the following specific types of cancer: cancer of the skin, lip, oral cavity, larynx, cervix, and corpus uteri. It is useful for palliation in the large group of cases of primarily inaccessible cancer (brain, bronchus, kidney, bladder, etc.), in the lymphoblastomas and in selected cases of inoperable, recurrent, or metastatic cancer. The principal weapon in clinical radiation work is roentgen therapy; radium therapy is a necessary adjunct. Radioactive isotopes are of value in a very limited group of malignant processes; however, radiocobalt may augment available radium supplies in the near future.

GENERAL PRINCIPLES

Radiotherapy is essentially a destructive weapon. It may be used in an attempt to destroy all the cells in a given area, or to destroy selectively only those cells which are apparently more sensitive than their fellows. Such radiotherapy is *radical* treatment in an attempt to cure. When the status of the tumor or its host is such as to render attempt at cure impractical or unwise, the physician must attempt merely to *palliate* the lesion as far as possible, in order to control its associated symptoms—pain, bleeding or discharge, etc.

For clinical purposes, most cases of cancer can be divided into two broad groups: the clinically accessible group and the clinically inaccessible group.[26, 71, 91] The accessible group includes cancers of the skin, lip and oral cavity, breast, cervix, and rectum. These constitute some 50 per cent of all cases of cancer seen in general medical practice in the United States at the present time. The inaccessible group includes especially the cancers of the intestinal tract (notably the stomach and colon), cancer of the lung, prostate, bladder, central nervous system, and so forth. Most of the accessible group of cancers can be detected by simple physical examination and are readily confirmed by biopsy, but many lesions of the inaccessible group require special examinations of various kinds for their detection.

STAGE AND GRADE OF LESION

Once the presence of a malignant tumor has been established, it is essential that the physician attempt to decide its apparent extent or clinical "stage." It is usually worthwhile to attempt to classify tumors into four stages: Stage I refers to a small, localized tumor, while Stage IV refers to a tumor with distant metastases; the other two stages include lesions in between these extremes, the specific details varying with the different tumor types and sites. This staging may be made on a clinical or pathologic basis, the former being the more generally employed; when based on histopathologic information, this fact should always be stated. Besides anatomic *extent*, some tumors may be divided into histologic subtypes or grades. A very well-differentiated or orderly growth is labeled Grade I; an undifferentiated or highly anaplastic growth, Grade IV; intervening subtypes are labeled Grades II and III. *Grading* is often useful for prognosis in certain tumors, but is not as important as clinical *staging* in planning and executing treatment of most cases.

For apparently localized and accessible tumors (Stage I or II), radical treatment is usually indicated in an attempt to cure, the treatment being surgical or radiologic depending on the type of lesion, the tissue in which it arises, and the specialist available. Such radical therapy for cure must be pursued with equal skill and ruthlessness, whether it be surgical or radiologic. On the other hand, for advanced lesions, palliation may be the kindest treatment possible and must be pursued just as thoroughly and patiently as would be the treatment of any other incurable disorder. For a small number of tumors, a combination of preoperative irradiation and surgery is indicated; for a relatively larger number the irradiation should be postoperative.

ADVANTAGES OF RADIATION THERAPY

Since surgery is the method that has long established itself, one may reasonably ask why and when is radiation therapy preferable? We believe that irradiation is preferable in the treatment of suitable lesions for the following reasons:

1. Better cosmetic results (e.g., in cancer of the skin of the face, especially about the eyes);
2. Improved functional results (e.g., in cancer of the lip, tongue, larynx);
3. Greater clinical benefit (e.g., in cancer of the cervix uteri, in Hodgkin's disease, lymphosarcoma, medullablastoma);
4. Less physical stress on patients in poor general condition (cancer of fundus in a hypertensive);
5. Less economic strain (hospitalization is usually unnecessary);
6. Reduced psychic trauma (in persons with chirurgophobia, etc.).

METHODS

ROENTGEN THERAPY

Clinical roentgen therapy is performed with beams ranging as a rule from 50 Kv. to 500 Kv.; a few installations provide beams of still higher voltage and slightly greater penetrability. The statement of voltage is a relatively inaccurate one, except in the case of constant potential apparatus, and it is customary to indicate the quality of the beam by describing its half value layer. In practice, low-voltage beams (50 to 140 Kv.) are filtered to provide half-value layers of from 1 mm. aluminum to 0.25 mm. copper. Such beams are used for the more superficial types of malignancies. Higher-voltage beams ranging from 180 to 500 Kv., and filtered by varying amounts of copper or tin, are used to provide ionization of deep-seated lesions. With suitable designs of tubes, insulation and delimiting cones, roentgen-ray beams may be applied to internal body cavities as well as to external sites. Of the two features, high flexibility and high voltage, many clinical therapists prefer high flexibility, since the advantages of supervoltage (500–2000 Kv.) are distinctive only under exceptional circumstances.[12, 45, 72] Theoretically, the decreased skin effect with supervoltage should permit the application of greater amounts of radiation in certain lesions, but with most deep-seated tumors it is not skin tolerance which is the limiting factor, but lung or bowel tolerance. By suitable application of ordinary voltage units (200–300 Kv.), all the radiation that the deeper mucous membranes will tolerate can be administered without permanent skin damage.

RADIUM THERAPY

For clinical purposes, radium can be applied in a manner very similar to roentgen therapy (external teleradium units; surface applicators and intracavitary sources).

In addition, it can also be applied interstitially by suitable needles or small containers, either permanent or removable. Permanent interstitial sources are sometimes termed "seeds," are commonly made of gold or other heavy metal, and contain radon gas. In recent years, radioactive cobalt has been used in a manner similar to radium and with apparently comparable results. For most cases, radium is used with such filtration that only the gamma rays are of importance. There is no significant difference in the biologic effect of gamma rays and hard roentgen-rays. In few fields is clinical experience as necessary as in radium therapy, inasmuch as the common tendency is to place the radium source too close to the lesion under treatment; the fall-off in energy at a short distance from the source is so great that close application usually results in the outermost portion of a tumor not receiving adequate irradiation.

TYPES OF RADIATION

The clinical radiotherapist has, in theory, a wide choice of ionizing beams at his disposal:

Conventional roentgen rays (50–500 Kv.)
Supervoltage roentgen rays (1000–2000 Kv.)
Radium rays (gamma rays of about 2 million volt energy)
Neutron rays
Betatron or synchrotron beams (to provide either electron beams or megavoltage roentgen-rays)
Radioactive isotopes (P^{32} for beta particles, I^{131} for beta and gamma rays, Co^{60} for gamma rays, and several other activated chemicals)

However, in practice, the vast majority of cancers susceptible to palliation or cure by ionization are being treated effectively by conventional roentgen rays and radium. These forms of energy will therefore be the ones most frequently referred to in this outline.

METHODS OF APPLICATION

Quality of Beam

The method of application is the fundamental part of radiation therapy. The plan of treatment must be worked out in advance *for each case*. The selection of the quality of the beam to be used will depend on the specific location and extent of the tumor at hand. A superficial tumor (about 2 cm. in depth and diameter) may be cured with a beam of low half-value layer, produced by a 100 Kv. roentgen-ray unit, using aluminum filtration, while a deep-seated tumor (at about 10 cm. depth) must be treated with a harder beam, for example 200 Kv. roentgen-rays filtered to produce a half-value layer equivalent to 1 mm. or more of copper. An infiltrating tumor in the cervix uteri should be treated by a combination of external, high-voltage x-ray beams and internal (intracavitary) radium applicators.

Record of Treatment

The radiation therapist must select his factors of filter, field size and target-skin distance to give the optimum distribution of ionizing energy throughout the entire area of the tumor.* The rate of delivery of the ionization, the number of treatments and the spacing of those treatments are all factors of extreme importance and should be planned in advance and recorded in detail. The total dose is expressed in roentgens (r), delivered in a unit of time to a measured area. In other words, if one wishes to describe a dose of radiation, one must indicate the number of roentgens delivered, the duration of therapy hours or days and the size of the field or area treated. For example, the expression "3000 r" means very little; "3000 r in five days to an area 5 cm. in diameter" signifies much (to the patient as well as to the radiotherapist); "3000 r in three months to an area 5 cm. in diameter," if evenly spread over that time, constitutes a relatively small dose, not sufficient to cure an average skin cancer.

Tumor Dose

It is desirable that the *tumor dose* be estimated and recorded. The tumor dose is described in roentgens even though the physical unit refers only to air ionization. However, until such time as a tissue unit is agreed upon, we must continue in everyday clinical work to use the former term. Theoretically and practically, roentgen-ray roentgens (delivered by conventional apparatus) and gamma-ray roentgens (from radium applicators) are not identical.[49] Some therapists believe it is important not to "add" the estimated tumor dose from each of these sources of energy when describing a given dose in the case of combined roentgen-ray and radium treatment; other therapists believe it is permissible to do so. The tumor dose is calculated to a certain point in the tumor, usually the midpoint (midtumor dose), or to the two points of extreme difference (maximum and minimum tumor dose).

Shielding

When applying ionizing beams to tumors, it is desirable that the noninvolved areas be shielded as carefully and thoroughly as possible. This requires considerable time and care at each session. Many therapists now use special beam-centering devices, together with radiographic and fluoroscopic checks on the fields treated. Few nontherapists realize the time and diligence required in precise centering of the radiant beam at each treatment visit, and the need for constant and exquisite vigilance on the part of the radiologist to avoid erroneous aiming or positioning. By adequate shielding, the total volume dose, and thereby the constitutional effects of irradiation, may be kept to a minimum. This dose may be recorded in megagram roentgens.[71]

In recent years there has been a recrudescence of interest in *rotation* therapy and also in so-called *grid* therapy. Clinical results of treatment of cancer of the esophagus with rotation therapy have been published, and are not superior to those obtainable with multiple, carefully aimed separate fields. No five-year clinical data are available on any large series of cases treated with so-called grid therapy, and therefore this method will not be considered futher at this time.

* In this connection, readers are urged to peruse a long-forgotten classic by Failla, G. and Quimby, E. H.[22]

TISSUE EFFECTS OF RADIATION

In the care and attempted cure of cancer by irradiation, different degrees of tissue effect must be produced. These vary from "suppressive," through "selective," to "destructive" changes. The fundamental effects of therapeutic doses of radiation are destructive or at least injurious. Mitosis decreases or ceases entirely. Glucksmann[32] regards the process in some cases as being one of increasing differentiation of cells, but Andersen[3] believes that he cannot confirm such differentiation despite observations on almost 700 malignant tumors in both human beings and experimental animals. In Andersen's opinion, all of the changes in irradiated tumors represent nonspecific cellular degeneration. It is of interest to note that the changes seen in cells injured by radiation are not specific or unique; different injurious agents, chemical, mechanical, and otherwise, may result in the same gross and microscopic picture of damage.

One of the problems in evaluating cellular damage is that in clinical work it must be done largely on a morphologic basis; the chemical changes which follow irradiation and which ultimately result in the death of a cell are not usually demonstrable by ordinary clinical microscopic studies; morphologically some of the cells which are believed to be permanently damaged may show very little change for several months. Erroneous conclusions can therefore be made on the basis of biopsy examination in the early weeks following irradiation. Rutishauser[87] has emphasized the wide variations between the clinical effect of radiation and the morphologic changes.

It is important to note that radiation is never stimulating: Cells are damaged by irradiation. However, if mitosis decreases but is not abolished in a treated area, it will show a compensatory increase after the cells have recovered from their initial injury. Studies of sections taken at this time may show apparent increase in activity, and this in the past has been erroneously interpreted as evidence of stimulation.

Radiosensitivity

Some cells are more readily injured or destroyed than others. Such cells are often termed "radiosensitive." Unfortunately, cells that are highly radiosensitive are often part of a tumor which is highly incurable. The degree of radiosensitivity cannot be predicted for many tumors. It requires a therapeutic trial of irradiation. Comparatively radioresistant tumors (resistant in the sense of requiring very large doses to destroy microscopic evidence of cancer) are often radiocurable. Nevertheless, the radiosensitivity of tumors does tend to follow the sensitivity of the tissue from which it develops. Tumors arising from lymphoid tissue are the most sensitive to irradiation; those from nerve or bone tissue the most resistant. However, there are exceptions in practice; for example, one of the nerve tissue tumors, the medulloblastoma, is relatively sensitive. The tumor bed is also a factor in sensitivity. Tumors arising in highly vascular beds are often more radiosensitive (or at least radiocurable) than those arising in areas of poor circulation.

With regard to the so-called "selective effect" of irradiation, it is believed that differences in the rate of recovery of cells contribute to the apparent differential action of radiation on tumor and normal tissues when protracted irradiation is used. If the normal cells recover more rapidly from each daily dose than the tumor cells, then a total dose may be delivered which is destructive of the tumor cells without being permanently injurious to the normal cells.

The latter, with a faster rate of recovery, survive. It is probable that by judicious protraction of irradiation some tumors at present regarded as radioresistant and relatively incurable may be brought within the curable range. Of all the factors at the disposal of the clinical radiologist, that of protraction of treatment is probably the least exploited to date.

BIOLOGIC EFFECT OF PROTRACTION

Protraction of the dose is essential in the cure of some cancers by external irradiation; for example, cancer of the larynx. It obviously requires an increase of the total dose administered. How great should that increase be?

For certain qualities of radiation, and for certain types of tissue effect, various authors have attempted to compute the dose in *x* days biologically equivalent to that given in a single day. If 500 r are required to produce an erythema in a single sitting, 750 r (375×2) will be required in two sittings on successive days (Quimby). Table 78 shows Quimby's calculated dosage increase requirements for erythema production.

TABLE 78. FRACTIONATION REQUIRED TO PRODUCE AN "ERYTHEMA REACTION"

Dose × Days	*Total dose* (r)	*Increase* (%)
500 r × 1	500	—
375 r × 2	750	50
267 r × 3	800	60
212 r × 4	850	70
180 r × 5	900	80
150 r × 7	1050	110
100 r × 12	1200	140
50 r × 27	1300	170

In a study of a group of irradiated skin and lip cancers (280 cases; 97 squamous, and 183 basal cell type), receiving roentgen irradiation with the below-mentioned factors, Strandquist[93] calculated the cumulative dose which produced various types of reaction—the number of cases with apparent cure, the failures (recurrence within one year), and the complications (cutaneous injury). With large doses, the cures were frequent but the danger of injury greater; with small doses cures were fewer but the risk of injury less; but within a certain range of dosage, there were for each tumor and tumor site optimal doses, following which the recurrence and injury were minimal. He believes that for his type of material these "safe" curative doses were of the following order: about 2250 r in one day, 4200 r in six days, or 6000 r in 30 days.

Strandquist's technical factors were as follows: 100–175 Kv. with half-value layer

0.1–1.7 mm. Cu. The field size in the majority of cases was 5–30 sq. cm. (median size 16.2 sq. cm.), the distance 25–50 cm., and the intensity 30–200 r per minute. Some cases were given massive single doses of 1000–2700 r; others divided doses over a period of two to thirty days, the total dose varying from 2000 to 6000 r. When fractionated technic was used, doses of 400–700 r daily were not uncommon (Fig. 143).

The fractionation factors at which he arrived were relatively close to those of Quimby. For example, for the first nine days they were respectively 126, 147, 160, 170, 179, 187, 193, 199 and 204.

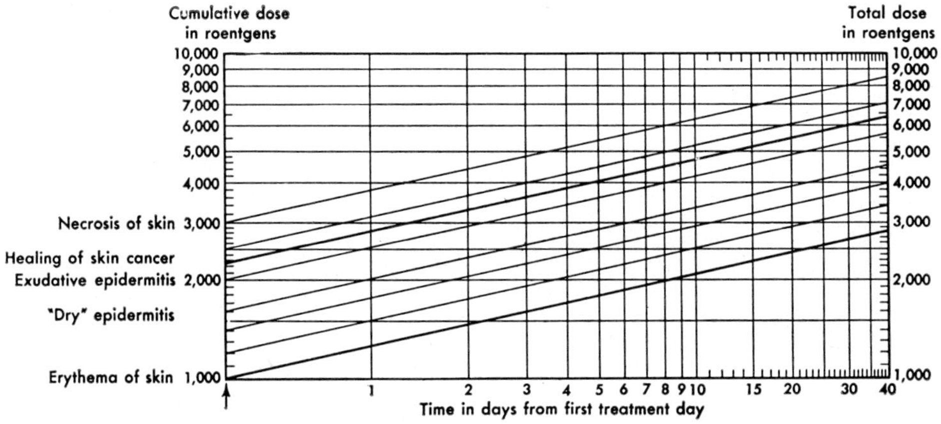

FIG. 143. Fractionation diagram for skin cancer (from Strandquist[93]).

Ellis[21] has published tables giving further fractionation factors according to the size of field, etc. Cohen[15] has attempted complete "biological effect" dose nomograms for various lesions and regions.*

REACTION TO RADIATION

After a short, intensive course of radiation there is a latent period of from one to two weeks during which there is little reaction, beyond an early transitory erythema. After this latent period, a marked erythema develops, followed by a moist inflammatory reaction (epidermitis) involving the superficial layers of the dermis. A fibrous exudate develops, the underlying tissue being raw, tender, and easily induced to bleed. This reaction recedes during the ensuing seven to fourteen

* It is of historic interest to note that it was Regaud who established in 1922 the experimental evidence dealing with the efficiency of protraction. He found it easier to sterilize permanently the testicle of the ram by a moderate dose fractionated and administered at equal intervals, than by a very large dose administered at a single sitting. Regaud[81] thought that protraction beyond twelve days was not efficient, and might produce "radio-immunization of the tumor." Coutard[17] in 1929 reported the feasibility of protraction to several weeks in the treatment of epidermoid carcinomas of the pharynx and larynx. As Regato[1] observed, while protraction of the treatment does increase the margin of safety, it also increases the necessity for strict clinical control of patients. Baclesse[4] has recently extended protraction to four months! For certain inoperable tumors his palliation has been very good.

days and the surface of the area gradually re-epithelizes (from the edge towards the center, or both from the edges and from multiple islands in the area of reaction). Weeping and crusting may be marked in some cases. In hair-bearing areas there will be epilation, new hair growth usually starting after an interval of weeks or months, depending upon the total dose delivered. The reaction of the mucous membranes of the treated area is essentially similar to that of the skin, but develops earlier. The fibrous exudate in the oropharyngeal area may form a tough, adherent membrane in some cases, but this sheds and a relatively normal mucosa reappears. After some months, or years, variable degrees of telangiectasis and atrophy appear in the radiated zone, the degree of such change varying with the biologic dose and the individual patient.

Undesirable Reactions. Those include several degrees of destruction of cells in and about the tumor area with necrosis and ulceration. By efficient planning of the dose, this type of reaction can be obviated or reduced to a minimum. However, if the irradiation has been incorrectly administered or given to an area previously irradiated, then undesirable sequelae are apt to develop, sometimes months or years after the treatment. The blood vessels in the excessively irradiated areas are permanently damaged and the tissues show effects secondary to this damage, plus such infection as may develop (necrosis, fibrosis, ulceration, etc.). Finally, after the passage of years, neoplastic metaplasia of some of the damaged cells may occur and the paradox of radiation-induced carcinoma arises.

TABLE 79. REACTIONS AND COMPLICATIONS (POTENTIAL OR ACTUAL) TO RADIOLOGIC OR SURGICAL TREATMENT OF DEEP-SEATED CANCER

Radical irradiation	*Radical surgery*
Shock (rare)	Shock (rare)
Nausea and vomiting	Nausea and vomiting
Pain (erythema, etc.)	Pain (incision, etc.)
Anemia	Anemia (temporary)
Leukopenia	Infection (peritoneal, etc.)
Pneumonitis (thoracic fields)	Pneumonia (rare)
Necrosis (early)	Pulmonary embolism
Telangiectasis and atrophy	Scar and keloid formation
Tissue necrosis (late)	Adhesions

By judicious planning and administration of treatment, by correct clinical care during and after treatment, and by painstaking follow-up, these reactions and late effects can be kept to a minimum. Just as radical surgical treatment has its side-effects and complications, so has curative radiotherapy: in proportion to the hazards of the disease under treatment, these effects are usually acceptable in the best interests of the patient (Table 79).

RADIATION PHYSICS

It has been stressed that the clinical radiotherapist must know the character and physical properties of the ionizing beams he proposes to use, as well as the probable location and extent of the tumor he is attempting to cure. However, it is not suggested that extremely detailed measurements and calculations are essential in regular clinical (as opposed to teaching) work.

One of the outstanding radiologic physicists, Professor Rolf Sievert of Stockholm, makes these pertinent observations in an article published in 1950[90]:

> In Sweden preparations were made for collaboration in radiology between clinicians and physicists, during the years of 1919-1920, which became of more permanent character at the end of 1920 at Radiumhemmet in Stockholm.
>
> As is so often the case, when representatives of the so-called exact sciences turn their attention to medical or biologic questions, there was much optimism concerning the possibilities of giving substantial support to the development of medical radiology within a short time. For example, at Radiumhemmet detailed calculations and radiation measurements were started with the intention of improving results of radium application. After about two years' work, however, we found that the experienced radiotherapist, with the support of the results he saw in his daily work while using various combinations of preparations, had already arrived in a surprising number of cases at methods which gave most expedient distribution of radiation, in practice, while physical measurements and calculations had not nearly the great practical importance that had been hoped. It may be worth while to mention, therefore, that even today physicists sometimes concentrate too much on problems in which medical experience has already arrived empirically at satisfactory solutions.

SELECTION OF CASES

To demonstrate current radiologic opinion concerning a basic approach to the planning of cancer treatment, tumors have been grouped according to whether or not radiation appears to be the primary therapeutic method of choice (Tables 80 to 83). In reading these tables, it must be realized that in individual cases circumstances may require departure from the general plan.[26, 27] However, the arrange-

TABLE 80. SURGICAL THERAPY USUALLY TREATMENT OF CHOICE

ACCESSIBLE SITES

1. Breast (Stage I)
2. Metastatic cervical nodes
3. Corpus uteri (operable)
4. Salivary glands
5. Thyroid

INACCESSIBLE SITES (TUMOR OPERABLE)

1. Brain and spinal cord
2. Esophagus and stomach
3. Small intestine
4. Colon and rectum
5. Kidney
6. Bladder
7. Prostate
8. Lung, etc.

TABLE 81. RADIATION THERAPY USEFUL ADJUNCT TO SURGERY

1. Breast (Stage II, postoperative)
2. Thyroid, postoperative
3. Uterus, corpus, preoperative
4. Ovary, postoperative
5. Testis, postoperative
6. Bladder
7. Kidney (bulky adenocarcinoma and Wilm's tumor)
8. Miscellaneous tumors, including postoperative recurrence, incomplete removal, etc. (e.g., breast, brain, skin)

TABLE 82. RADIATION THERAPY USUALLY TREATMENT OF CHOICE

ACCESSIBLE SITES

1. Skin
2. Lip and mouth, including tongue
3. Breast (Stage III)
4. Cervix uteri
5. Anal and urethral orifices

INACCESSIBLE SITES

1. Embryonal tumors (kidneys, testis, ovary)
2. Endotheliomas (Ewing's tumor, etc.)
3. Medulloblastoma
4. Cancer of the larynx and nasopharynx (selected cases)
5. Cancer inoperable (e.g. lung, esophagus)
6. Cancer metastatic (especially in bone, skin, etc.)
7. Lymphoblastoma (Hodgkin's disease and lymphosarcoma) and leukemia

TABLE 83. RADIATION THERAPY RARELY OR NEVER INDICATED

1. Osteogenic sarcoma
2. Miscellaneous "adult" sarcomas
3. Cancer of the intestines
4. Cancer of the gallbladder
5. Cancer of the liver
6. Cancer of the pancreas
7. Advanced cancer with cachexia
8. Acute leukemia
9. Melanoma (primary, operable)

ment of the types of cancer into the four groups permits an orderly approach to the individual patient presenting himself or herself for treatment.

General Plan of Treatment

Having decided that the patient has a lesion which is amenable to radiation therapy, the next decision to be made is "will the treatment be given in an attempt to cure or in an attempt to palliate?" After making this decision, the radiologist must decide on the tumor dose he intends to give and the time during which it will be given. He is then in a position to prepare the patient physically and psychologically for the therapeutic procedure.

These preparations are just as important in radiation therapy as in surgery, and require just as much effort on the part of the attending physician and his colleagues. Apprehension, anemia, and infection all require care. For curable cases, a clear program can and should be outlined to the patient and family; in this manner, all-important cooperation will usually be secured.

In curative treatment, the tumor dose may range from 2000 to 6000 r in from one to thirty days. The field or fields required to deliver that dose will vary with the size and extent of the lesion, its depth, and the general condition of the patient.

For example, a Stage I cancer of the lip (less than 3 cm. diameter) will usually be curable with a tumor dose of 3000 r. However, late telangiectasis or atrophy of the treated area will not develop if instead of a single dose reasonable protraction is used. The optimum degree of protraction is not yet known; in general, 400–500 r daily for ten days will give as much chance of cure as 3000 r in a single dose, and will result in a better cosmetic result. The larger and deeper the lesion, the greater the degree of protraction required. *Doses as low as 200 r daily for twenty to thirty days may be needed for safe cure of extensive lesions.*

When radiation therapy is designed for palliation, or for long-term control of lesions in the lymphoblastoma and leukemia group, dosage and dose rates must vary widely with the individual case. Space does not permit detailed consideration of these factors.

Reasons for Failure

Reasons for failure of radiotherapy include the following: *On the part of the patient*: (1) Advanced tumor (Stage III or IV), especially in patients in poor physical condition; (2) tumor in a patient who fails to complete his planned course of treatment (irresponsible person, or person developing complications such as severe coronary lesion); and (3) radioresistant tumor. *On the part of the radiotherapist*: (1) inadequate total dose; (2) inadequate treatment field; (3) poor correlation of dose and protraction; and, occasionally, (4) excessive dose.

STANDARDS OF RECORDING RESULTS

The results of radiotherapy of cancer are measured in terms of cure and palliation. Strictly speaking, the term "arrest" or "survival" without evidence of disease, is preferable to the term "cure" since late recurrences may develop in certain cancers long after apparent radiologic (or surgical) cure. This is particularly true of sites such as the breast. However, for other sites (e.g. skin, lip, cervix, sigmoid colon, etc.) ten- and twenty-year arrests are numerous and the term "cure" is perhaps permissible after the five year period, at least as a generalization.

Arrests (or "cures") are determined after the lapse of agreed periods of time (e.g. five or ten years following treatment). Palliation is determined after the lapse of months or a few years. By careful follow-up and records, radiologists and surgeons throughout the world have accumulated more factual scientific data on the results of treatment of cancer than are available in connection with any other single entity in medicine. This point is not nearly as well appreciated as it should be. True, some results are published in incomplete form or with considerable bias towards a given method or technic. Nevertheless, thousands of cases are being carefully followed and valuable survival data accumulated.

In reading reports of therapeutic results, one must always note the time element (whether five years, ten years or merely preliminary), and the precise type of results claimed, e.g. whether the cases are *survivals* (with or without disease), or *arrests* (apparent cures). If figures or percentages are given, the reader should note whether these apply to all cases seen (*absolute* results), all cases treated (*relative* results), all cases traced (incomplete, relative results).

TABLE 84. FIVE-YEAR "CURABILITY" OF CANCER OF RECTUM COMPUTED BY VARIOUS METHODS

Basis of calculation	*Five-year survivals* (%)	*Five-year "cures"* (%)
All patients included	12.8	*7.9*
Only proved cases	16.5	11.2
All proved determinate cases	16.9	11.5
All cases of resection	25.3	15.6
All cases of resection except those with remote metastases	26.6	17.3
All resection cases surviving operation	32.0	20.8
All resection cases surviving operation except those with remote metastases	*35.4*	23.0

From Ottenheimer.[69]

The widely different "results" obtainable for a representative lesion are illustrated by Ottenheimer.[69] In a careful analysis of cases of cancer of the *rectum* occurring in Connecticut (1935–1945), he showed that by choosing the appropriate figure, five-year results could be quoted at any level from the approximately correct (absolute arrest) figure of 8 per cent to the optimistically high (relative survival) figure of 35 per cent (Table 84).

It would be desirable if all authors gave *absolute* survival or arrest figures, in addition to such other data as they record. Some workers advise the use of crude survival rates corrected for age; given reasonably reliable correction factors, these corrected rates would undoubtedly be the best reflection of a given therapeutic method.

RESULTS IN ACCESSIBLE SITES

SKIN

The various forms of cancer of the skin constitute the most frequent and readily curable cancers seen in clinical practice. Histologic examination is desirable to distinguish between the squamous and basal cell varieties, and to rule out the nonmalignant lesions which clinically resemble cancer. Squamous cell skin cancers may metastasize to nodes, and therefore the follow-up examinations in this variety must be painstaking. Since the cosmetic and functional results of correctly used radiation are in general superior to those obtainable by other known methods of

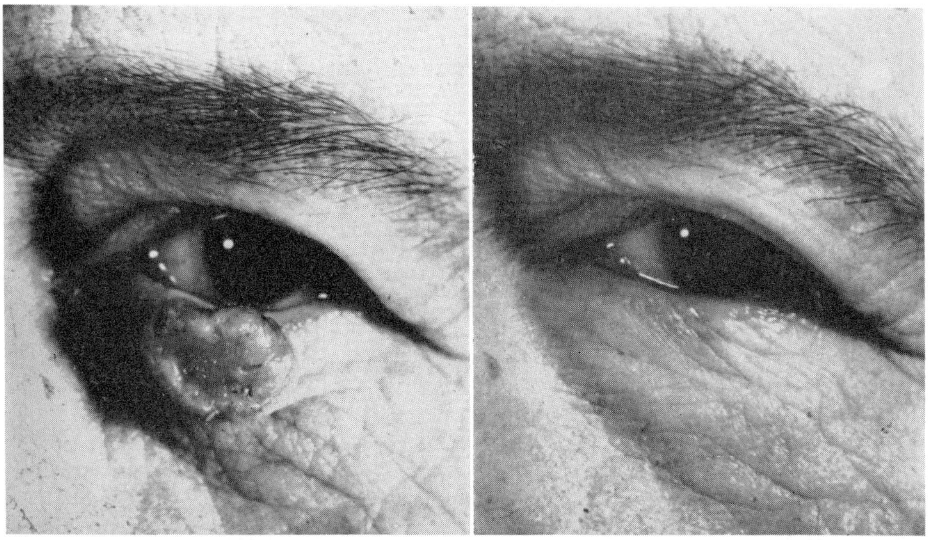

FIG. 144. Basal cell cancer of skin, cured by radiotherapy. Male, age 60, with biopsy-proven basal cell cancer of left lower eyelid. Given ten x-ray treatments, 600 r each, half value layer 1 mm. Al during period of two weeks; lead shield inserted behind lid for each treatment. Total dose 6000 r air. Photo on left made before treatment, on right made five years after treatment. Clinically cured twelve years to date. Functional result excellent; no ectropion. Radiotherapy is the method of choice for curing cancers of this type, in this location. (Reproduced by courtesy of the *American Journal of Roentgenology*.)

treatment (surgery, electrodessication, cauterization, chemosurgery,[65] and so forth), irradiation is the most generally advised treatment today (Fig. 144). Some very small lesions can be cured by the simple excision required for biopsy. Others are so advanced when first seen that there is extensive secondary infection with bone invasion; for this type, radical excision is probably the best hope for cure. Between these two extremes lie the majority of cases in whom irradiation is considered to be the method of choice.

The general principles of curative radiation therapy for skin cancer are:

1. The treatment must be carefully planned in advance; the first chance at cure is the optimum and may be the only one.

2. The amount of irradiation delivered must be sufficient to destroy or permanently alter all of the tumor cells, and this lethal dose must be delivered to the deepest cells of the tumor.

3. A sufficiently wide margin must be used to include the nonpalpable but presumably existing microscopic extension. This margin should in general be wider for basal than for squamous cell lesions.

4. The adjacent, and especially the subjacent normal tissues should be spared as much as possible, by judicious choice of quality of beam and distance.

5. Carcinomas arising in those regions of the body which tolerate heavy radiation poorly should be treated primarily by surgery (dorsum of the hand, sole of the foot, large lesions involving the ear, and large lesions involving skin of elderly patients in pressure sites such as back of scalp, buttocks, etc.)

6. If there is clinical evidence of regional lymph node involvement, surgical removal of operable nodes is indicated (after control of the primary). If the involvement is extensive and the nodes appear to be inoperable (fixed, extensive bilateral involvement, etc), irradiation will provide temporary control in a fair number of cases and permanent arrest in a few. Prophylactic lymph node dissection is not recommended in connection with skin lesions.

The five-year absolute cure rate in early lesions (Stage I and II) is about 90 per cent. For late (Stage III and IV) lesions it is approximately 40 per cent.

Paterson[72] reports 74 per cent five-year cures of 599 early (Stage I or II) squamous cell cancers treated by low-voltage roentgen-ray therapy; age-corrected, this equalled 94 per cent in his material. Other workers[46, 80] report similar results, ranging from 67 to 85 per cent arrests of all cases.

Recurrences. Central recurrences and large marginal recurrences should be treated by surgery. Small marginal recurrences can be successfully retreated by irradiation in selected cases.

Complications. Late radiation necrosis of the skin may develop in about 1 per cent of cases. It will be more common after intensive interstitial radium therapy than after protracted roentgen therapy. Small ulcers, if kept clean and treated by simple ointments, will heal gradually; large ulcers (over 3 cm. diameter) which do not heal promptly should be treated by excision and plastic repair of the defect.

Malignant Melanoma

True malignant melanoma usually requires very large doses of irradiation to cure, and many are extremely radioresistant. For this reason, it is believed that wide and deep surgical excision is the primary treatment of choice. If surgery is contraindicated (by concurrent disease, age, etc.), radiation should be employed. A small percentage of melanomas of the skin are quite radiosensitive. The method of choice is protracted roentgen therapy, giving a minimum tumor dose of approximately 6000 r in less than four weeks. Operable metastatic nodes should be treated surgically; inoperable nodes may be treated by external roentgen therapy to skin tolerance. One group secured 69 per cent five-year arrests in 42 roentgen-treated cases of malignant melanoma, but this is exceptional.

CANCER OF THE LIP

The common variety is squamous cell cancer. The staging recommended is as follows:

Stage I: Lesion less than 3 cm. diameter
Stage II: Lesion 3 to 5 cm. diameter
Stage III: Lesion over 5 cm. diameter
Stage IV: Lesion with extension to bone or with metastasis

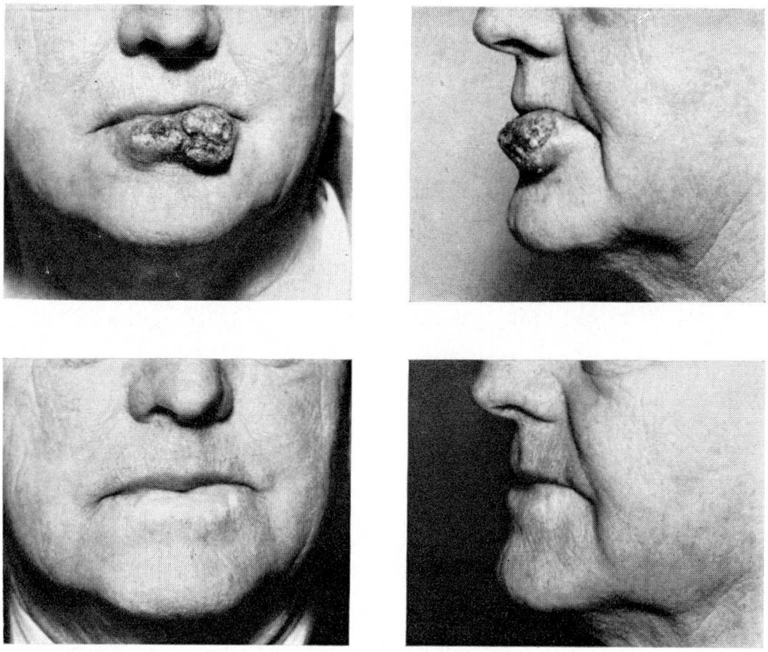

FIG. 145. Squamous cell cancer of lip, cured by radiotherapy. Male, age 73, with tumor measuring 3×2.5×4 cm. involving lower lip. Biopsy diagnosis: squamous cell carcinoma. Given 200 r daily to a field 4×6 cm., with a lead shield behind the lower lip; total dose 4000 r air in twenty-two days; half value layer of beam 1 mm. Cu. Minimum tumor dose approximately 4500 r in three weeks. Upper pair of photographs taken before treatment and lower pair five years after treatment. Clinically cured ten years to date. Radiotherapy is regarded as the treatment of choice for cancer of the lip of the type shown. (Reproduced by courtesy of the *American Journal of Roentgenology.*)

We believe that the best method of treatment of cancer of the lip is fractionated roentgen therapy (Figs. 145, 146). Daily doses of 200 to 500 r, calculated to the depth of the tumor, up to a total dose of from 4000 to 6000 r, in one to four weeks, appear to give the best long-term cures.

Results. The relative five-year arrest rate for all cases treated is about 65 per cent. Ebenius[20] reported 80 per cent five-year arrests in 541 cases in which the carcinoma was confined to the lip, and 25.5 per cent five-year arrests in 208

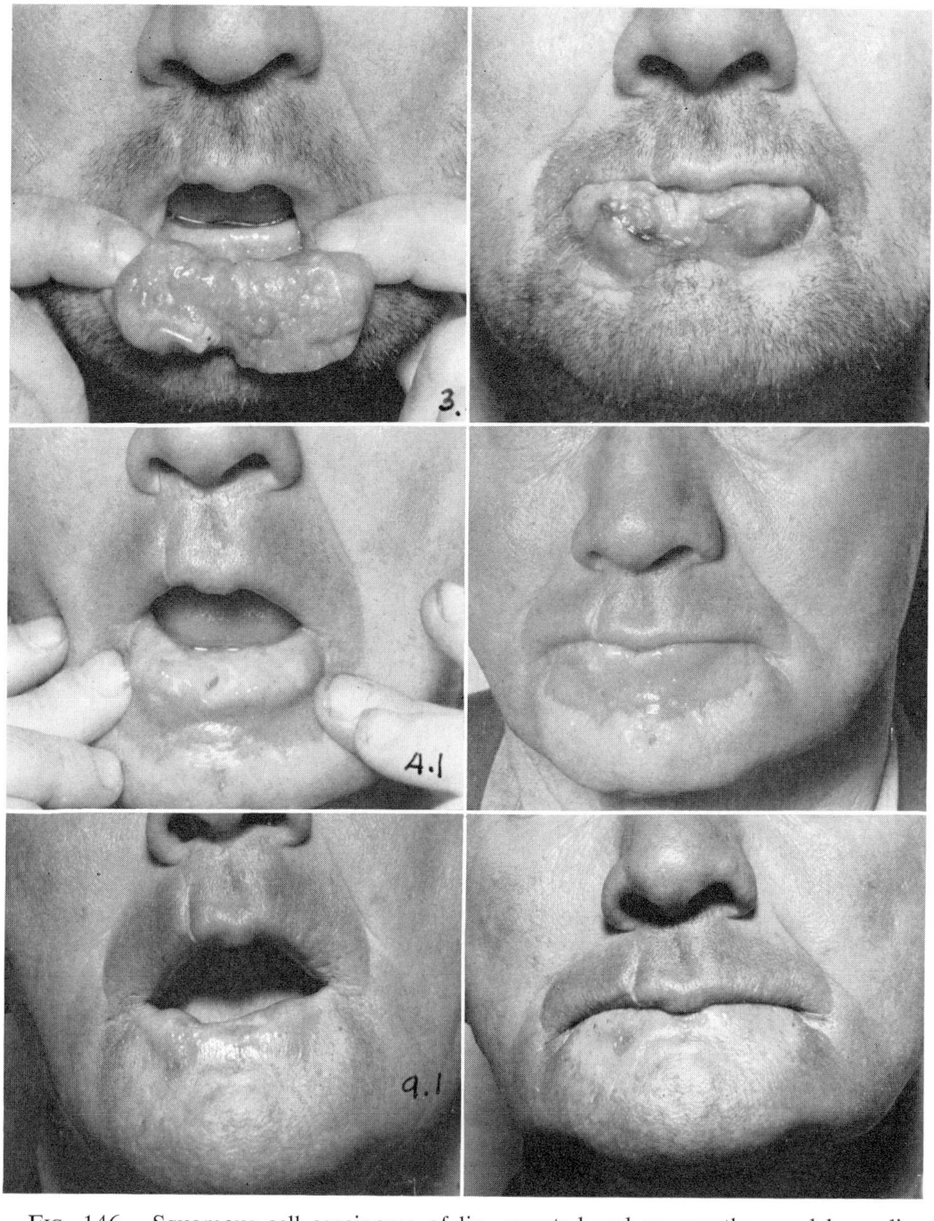

FIG. 146. Squamous cell carcinoma of lip, arrested and apparently cured by radiotherapy. Male, age 56, with large squamous cell carcinoma of lower lip, measuring about 6×3 cm.; no palpable nodes. Lesion given a tumor dose of 6000 r in three and a half weeks, using half value layer 1 mm. Cu, and a field ranging from 7×6 cm. down to 7×3 cm. Clinically well two years later, but further followup prevented by patient leaving country. No adenopathy developed in the two years following treatment, but extensive lesions of this type require painstaking followup in order to detect and promptly treat such adenopathy as may develop. The above series of photographs were made with the mouth open and closed, immediately before treatment (*top*), one week after the termination of treatment (*middle*), and six months after treatment (*bottom*).

cases with metastases to the regional nodes (the latter treated surgically). Paterson reported very similar figures in 1945; his most recent group of 244 cases gave a relative five-year arrest rate of 63 per cent; when corrected for age this equalled 80 per cent.

Recurrence. The recurrence rate is approximately 7 per cent; as in the case of the skin, small marginal recurrences can be re-irradiated with success in some cases, but large marginal recurrences and most central recurrences should be excised.

Radiation Necrosis. This develops in from 1 to 8 per cent of cases, the percentage increasing with the use of interstitial radium therapy. By judicious treatment[31] it can be kept under 1 per cent.

Lymph Node Involvement. The percentage of patients reported with enlarged neoplastic lymph nodes on admission varies from 8 to 30 per cent. The incidence of metastic nodes developing after radical treatment of the primary lesion is from 2 to 8 per cent. Radical surgery gives about 30 per cent relative arrests; radiotherapy 5 per cent, except in the hands of C. L. Martin, who is able to control 27 per cent of cases (combined roentgen and radium therapy).[59]

CANCER OF THE ORAL CAVITY

This includes cancers of the tongue, floor of the mouth, palate, cheek, alveolar ridges, and fauces.

Cancer of the Tongue

Lesions are staged roughly as for lip cancer. Those in the anterior two-thirds are relatively accessible to radiotherapy or surgery; those in the posterior third only to radiotherapy. Cancer in the anterior two-thirds is controllable by skilful irradiation in about 30 per cent of cases if the lymph nodes are not involved; but in only about 15 per cent if the nodes are involved. Lesions in the posterior one-third of the tongue are seldom cured in our experience. The over-all salvage rate for tongue lesions ranges from 12 to 25 per cent absolute five-year cures (see Table 85).

Table 85. CANCER OF THE TONGUE: FIVE-YEAR RESULTS OF IRRADIATION

			Five-year arrests		
Author	*No. of cases*	*No. of five-year arrests*	Based on "determinate cases" (%)	Based on all cases (absolute) (%)	Based on treated cases (relative) (%)
Berven[8]	302	75	31	25	28
Baud[6]	1056	174	—	12	—
Cade[14]	365	99	31	27	—
H. Martin[60]	233	59	30	25	—
Richards[84]	274	69	33	25	—
Windeyer[104]	279	49	21	17	—
Wood[106]	182	47	—	—	26
Paterson[72]	429	117	—	—	27

Most cases require a combination of external roentgen irradiation, followed by carefully given intraoral roentgen or radium irradiation to produce a minimum tumor dose of 6000 r in four weeks' time. The incidence of metastatic nodes in carcinoma of the tongue is so high that some authors advise a routine neck dissection. We believe it is preferable to observe the patient carefully, except in the case of highly anaplastic primary tumors. In the latter, prophylactic neck dissection is probably advisable. Jacobson, quoted in,[31] reported 51 per cent control of 103 primary cases of cancer of the tongue treated with irradiation, and 15 per cent control of 130 cases with metastasis. Paterson's[73] figures are 42 per cent and 10 per cent respectively.

The most detailed recent report from the Curie Foundation in Paris, where treatment consisted mainly of radium needle insertion in the primary and routine block dissections of the nodes, gave for anterior two-third lesions (638 cases) relative arrests of 21 per cent at five years, and for posterior third lesions (331 cases) arrests of 10 per cent.[6] These posterior third lesions were treated mainly with roentgen therapy. Windeyer[104] and Wood[106] obtained respectively 10 per cent and 18 per cent relative five-year arrests in such lesions. Since the latter used radium beam therapy in her work, with a tumor dose of about 6000 r in the primary and lymph node areas, her results suggest that for this particular type of tumor, external teleradium therapy does have something to offer over and above conventional roentgen therapy. It must be noted that all of the above figures are relative, and that the number of cases seen but not accepted for intensive irradiation is not given.

We must agree with Pohle[75] that, in general, the over-all results in the treatment of cancer of the tongue are poor; in our personal experience they do not exceed 20 per cent relative five-year arrests. Taylor[95] and Puestow[80] had similar findings.

Oral Cavity

In the case of carcinoma of the floor of the mouth, the cheek and the alveolar ridges, judicious combinations of external and intraoral roentgen therapy, radium therapy and surgery or electrodessication permit salvage of a reasonable percentage of cases. As usual, small lesions (up to 2 cm. diameter) without lymph nodes are highly curable by any of several methods; advanced, infected lesions in elderly patients, with bilateral node metastases, are rarely curable. In general the five-year relative arrests range from about 60 per cent of the Stage I lesions down to about 5 per cent of the Stage IV lesions. The over-all results (relative five-year arrests) are about 40 per cent.

Cancer of the Fauces

This group includes lesions of the tonsil and tonsillar pillars. External and peroral roentgen therapy, radium therapy and combinations of the two methods permit five-year arrests of approximately 60 per cent in the Stage I lesions, with decreasing results in Stage IV (less than 5 per cent). The over-all results vary in different clinics; Paterson[72] and Holmes[47] each estimate 15 per cent relative five-year arrests; Pohle

50 per cent. The writer's own experience agrees with the former. However, it must be noted that in these lesions the degree of palliation is high.

The difficulty in curing some of the faucial lesions is that even an apparently early lesion, may already have extended towards the base of the tongue when first seen. This extension is often impossible to detect early by clinical examination, and may manifest itself only some months or years after apparent cure of the primary tumor. Re-treatment under these circumstances is not productive of satisfactory results. A certain number of tonsillar neoplasms are of the lympho-epithelioma type. While more radiosensitive than ordinary squamous cell carcinoma, these are more apt to recur following treatment and require just as vigorous dosage as the squamous cell lesion.

CANCER OF THE BREAST

The incidence of cancer of the breast is approximately 60 per 100,000 females per annum. In the average physician's practice in this country, perhaps 60 per cent of the cases will appear operable when first seen, and about 40 per cent inoperable (that is, with clinical or other evidence of spread beyond the breast and axillary area).

Staging. The initial classification is a clinical one, based on Steinthal's original description; many writers modify this by the findings at surgery. Stage I is essentially a movable tumor confined to the breast; Stage II a movable tumor with palpable, mobile axillary nodes; Stage III a tumor with evidence of spread beyond the axilla, or with extensive skin involvement (see Haagensen,[37] Paterson,[71] Portmann *et al.*[77] for details and further modification). It is reported that about 30 per cent of cases of clinical Stage I have microscopic evidence of carcinoma in the axillary nodes at time of surgery; and that about 30 per cent of cases of clinical Stage II have no microscopic evidence of cancer in the enlarged nodes palpated prior to operation. Staging is therefore always crude at best.

The standard method of treatment in most institutions in the United States at the present time is:

For microscopically verified Stage I: radical surgery. *For microscopic Stage II*: radical surgery and postoperative irradiation of the chest wall and regional lymph nodes. *For clinical Stage III*: radiation therapy alone, usually by external roentgen therapy to the primary lesion and adjacent nodes, employing a minimum tumor dose of about 4000 r in four weeks.

The treatment of metastatic lesions in skin and bone is primarily by irradiation; steroid hormone therapy is a good alternative method in cases with very extensive involvement or who cannot be moved to a competent radiotherapist. Most cerebral metastases are also very radiosensitive and should be treated. Radiotherapy gives poor results in pulmonary, hepatic, and visceral metastases, although occasional palliation of pleuropulmonary lesions is obtained.

It is extremely difficult to evaluate any particular form of therapy in cancer of the breast. Inadvertent or intentional selection of cases prior to treatment is commonplace. In connection with postoperative treatment in Stage II, it is common practice for the surgeon to recommend no postoperative irradiation when he believes that he has removed all of the tumor; however, when he is in doubt he tends to recommend treatment. The first group of such cases would include a much higher proportion of favorable material than the second; yet comparisons are often made between two such groups in order to attempt evaluation of postoperative irradiation.

Stenstrom and Baggenstoss[92] collected a series of microscopically verified Stage II cases treated by surgery alone and by a combination of surgery and postoperative irradiation. The relative five-year survivals with surgery alone in 1037 cases was 25.2 per cent; with surgery plus postoperative irradiation this figure in 2358 cases was 30.4 per cent. The difference represents a relative improvement of 20 per cent with postoperative irradiation in apparently comparable groups of cases.

Nohrman,[68] in his comprehensive monograph based on 1042 cases of breast cancer (all of them traced!), quotes some 34 authors favoring postoperative irradiation and 6 others noting no significant improvement with it. When one observes what can be done with irradiation in some Stage III cases, one cannot question the possibility that it may be of great benefit in a certain proportion of Stage II lesions. This should apply especially to those cases with evidence of lymph node perforation. In Berven's material, some 15 per cent of 842 cases (Stages I and II) had palpable or microscopic evidence of lymph node perforation at time of surgery. As a consequence of this finding the Swedish school recommends *pre*operative as well as *post*-operative irradiation in most cases of breast cancer, believing that it has shown statistically a significant improvement in such cases over those treated by surgery alone. They believe that the preoperative irradiation helps to devitalize or destroy the cells in a certain proportion of those cases which have such perforation.

TABLE 86. RESULTS OF RADICAL SURGERY IN CANCER OF THE BREAST

Author	*No. of cases*	*Five-year survivals* (%)
Taylor[94]	7974	31
Hutchinson[48]	7000	28
Portmann[78]	10,000	28
Hansson[40]	4268	29

Some surgeons (including Wangensteen[101]) advise extremely radical operation, even for Stage II cases. They divide the clavicle, remove the first rib, excise the supraclavicular nodes, remove most of the internal mammary vessels and the available upper mediastinal nodes, especially those at the level of the second intercostal space. There is not a sufficiently significant amount of five-year data on this radical procedure to permit its evaluation at this time.

In order to assess the place of radiotherapy in cancer of the breast, one must first study the results of surgery. Table 86 shows the collected surgical results on some 30,000 cases of cancer of the breast, and reveals the fact that the average five year survival figure is about 30 per cent. Note that this figure applies to *operated* cases or chiefly Stage I and II lesions.

In order to evaluate the influence of radiation therapy in combination with surgery, Table 87 should be studied. Note that it deals only with Stage II lesions.

In recent years some workers have recommended the combination of simple mastectomy and full postoperative irradiation as being superior to the radical operation, with or without postoperative irradiation; the most distinguished proponent of this school is McWhirter of Edinburgh. After observing his work and that of the Swedish school, and studying the results reported by leading American surgeons in 1950, it is the writer's impression that McWhirter's plan has much to offer. The following list summarizes what appear to be advantages of his program.

TABLE 87. COMPARISON OF SURGICAL AND COMBINED TREATMENT

Author	*Surgery only* (%)	*Surgery and post-operative x-ray* (%)
Taylor[96]	33	—
Haagensen[38]	37	—
Bell[7]	40	24
Harrington (cited, [68])	—	39
Stenstrom (cited, [68])	—	41
Nohrman[68]	—	41
Adair (cited, [68])	—	44
Maisin (cited, [68])	35	50
Engelstad (cited, [68])	—	52

Cases are Stage II. Results are relative five-year arrests.

1. Decreased chance of cancer dissemination as a result of prolonged handling of tissues involved in axillary dissection.
2. Reduced operative morbidity and mortality (less than one hour under general anesthesia, as opposed to about five hours in the Haagensen radical operation).
3. Almost complete absence of postoperative arm edema (as opposed to 5 to 15 per cent after radical operation).
4. Earlier return of patient to occupation or housework than after radical operation.
5. Radiation procedure more feasible and less time consuming than the Swedish technique of *pre-* and postoperative irradiation.
6. Better absolute five-year results than by the radical procedure alone, with the single exception of Haagensen's data. *Absolute* five-year clinical cures: Haagensen 38 per cent; McWhirter 35 per cent; Taylor 32 per cent; Bell 32 per cent (Table 88).

It is McWhirter's opinion that in cancer of the breast, the *absolute* five-year survival figure is more significant than any other. He bases his figures on all cases *admitted*; most authors base theirs on all cases treated. We have dealt with his data on both bases, and analyzed the results of four of the leading proponents of radical surgery in similar fashion. The best published results are those of Haagensen;[37] next are those of McWhirter[57] and Nohrman;[68] then those of the

Massachusetts General Hospital[95] and the University of California Hospital Groups (Bell[7]). Haagensen's material consists of a relatively selected group all operated on in one institution; McWhirter's cases are relatively unselected, from surgeons in different hospitals in Scotland.

TABLE 88. CANCER OF THE BREAST; FIVE-YEAR RESULTS

Author and period	*Cases admitted*	*Cases accepted for treatment*	*Operable (%)*	*Type of treatment*	*Absolute*		*Relative*	
					Survivals	Arrests	Survivals	Arrests
Haagensen 1935–42	668	631	74	Radical surg. with or without x-ray	47.2	38.6	58.2	48.7
Taylor 1936–40	?	637	62	Principally radical surg.	?	32.0	?	52.0
Bell 1932–43	819	736	58	Radical surg. with or without x-ray	?	32.0	?	43.0
Berven 1936–41	1055	950	80	Radical surg. and x-ray	41.0	35.0	51.0	43.0
McWhirter 1941–42	480	408	76	Simple mastectomy and x-ray	41.0	35.0	45.0	41.0

If one considers the operable cases only (Stages I and II), McWhirter's experience is as follows: by *radical* operation and postoperative irradiation (1935-40, all cases), *50 per cent* absolute five-year survivals; by *simple* operation and postoperative irradiation (1941-1945, 162 cases), *62 per cent* absolute five-year survivals.

During this latter period, the absolute five-year survival rate for all cases treated, Stages I to III, reached the excellent figure of 44 per cent; these cases included many advanced lesions.

The reader is again reminded of the importance of noting the nature of the "five-year results" published by different authors. Most are relative results(based only on patients treated); a few are absolute (based on all cases seen). Some are clinical cure results (arrests) and others are survivals (that is, persons surviving five years with or without clinical evidence of tumor). Table 80 shows the percentage of *relative* five-year arrests in *operable* cases (radical surgery).

The striking regressions obtainable with palliative irradiation are illustrated in a paper on 131 advanced cases by Levi.[55] In 33 per cent of these cases, "good results" were achieved.

Treves *et al.*[99] report good palliative results with orchiectomy in a small group of breast cancers occurring in males.

The estimated survival in *untreated* cases of cancer of the breast, calculated from the onset of first symptoms, has been reported by Greenwood,[35] Daland,[19] Wade,[100] and others. The average of these authors' figures shows 13 per cent of five-year survivals in untreated cases. However, since less than 0.5 per cent of 200

Stage III cases observed *and treated* by Nohrman survived five years, it is apparent that Greenwood *et al.*'s material must have included a fairly large number of Stages I and II lesions. Nevertheless, the figure of 13 per cent five-year survival of untreated cases must be borne in mind in evaluating any worker's results.

TABLE 89. CANCER OF THE BREAST; RELATIVE FIVE-YEAR ARRESTS IN OPERABLE CASES

	Stage		
Author	I	II	III
Haagensen	72	37	0
G. Taylor	75	33	0
Pack and Livingston	70	22	0
Bell	70	40	?

In summary, operable cases of clinical Stages I and II cancer of the breast should be treated by radical surgery. If there is microscopic evidence of axillary or other node involvement, full postoperative roentgen therapy should be added. Clinical Stage III cases, and cases in earlier stages inoperable on account of associated conditions should be treated by irradiation alone. If other workers confirm the excellent results obtained by McWhirter with simple mastectomy and full postoperative irradiation, this program may well become the one of choice.

Palliation. The treatment of Stage III lesions, and of patients with recurrent or metastatic breast cancer, includes roentgen therapy as well as other measures. Ovarian radiation is frequently of benefit in metastatic cases. The value of roentgen castration in Stage III with metastases was best shown by Thayssen, at the Radium Center in Copenhagen.[97] He treated 99 women between the ages of 26 and 59, and compared the results with a control group of 100 cases of similar average age. The former were treated by surgery and local radiation to the metastases, plus roentgen castration; the latter merely by surgical and local radiation treatment. The survival times were significantly increased in the castrated group (Table 90).

TABLE 90. CANCER OF THE BREAST; RESULTS OF CASTRATION

Survival Times	*Castrated group* (%, 99 cases)	*Non-castrated* (%, 100 cases)
2 years+	40	11
5 years+	20	0

The comparative results of roentgen and steroid hormone therapy were determined by Garland *et al.*[30] in a group of cases of breast cancer metastatic to bone. Their results are summarized as follows: About 70 per cent of patients with painful bone metastases are relieved of pain by roentgen therapy; 25 per cent show re-

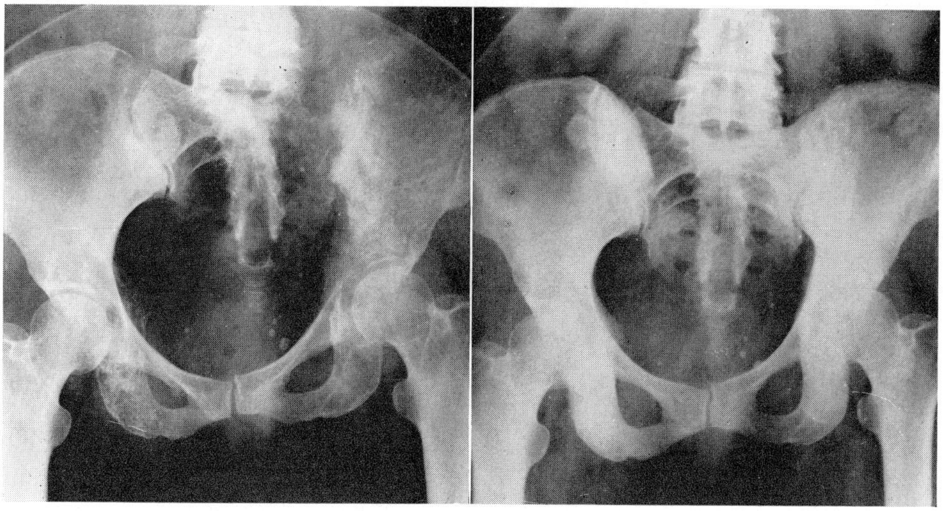

FIG. 147. Palliation of bone metastasis from breast cancer, using radiotherapy. Female, age 52, with excruciating backache and left sciatic pain, developing one year after radical mastectomy for carcinoma of the breast. Patient given a "tumor" dose of approximately 900 r in six days, using large fields (35 cm. diameter) and half value layer 1 mm. Cu. Prompt and complete relief of symptoms. Survived two years and died with liver metastases. The illustration on the left was made before, and that on the right, following radiotherapy. The recalcification of the destroyed areas in the sacrum and innominate bones is clearly visible. Pain relief is obtained with correctly administered radiotherapy in about 80 per cent of bone lesions metastatic from breast cancer; recalcification occurs in about one-third of these cases.

calcification of their lesions; a few cases live five years but the average survival is only one year. About 40 to 70 per cent of patients with painful bone metastases get pain relief from steroid hormone therapy (40 per cent with estrogens, 70 per cent with androgens); 10 to 20 per cent show recalcification; a few cases live several years but most survive only nine months (Fig. 147). The complications of hormone therapy are more frequent and more serious than those of radiotherapy (Table 91).

TABLE 91. SUMMARY OF COMPARATIVE EFFECTS OF ROENTGEN AND STEROID HORMONE THERAPY IN TREATMENT OF OSSEOUS METASTASES

Treatment	*Subjective improvement (pain relief)* (%)	*Objective improvement (x-ray recalcif.)* (%)	*Clinically troublesome side effects* (%)	*Lesions apparently made worse* (%)
Irradiation	70	26	5	0
Androgens	75	16	25	0.7
Estrogens	38	18	15	2.5

CANCER OF THE UTERUS

CANCER OF THE CERVIX

A generally accepted classification of cancer of the cervix is that of the League of Nations, Stage I being a lesion confined to the cervix itself; Stage II a lesion extending to adjacent structures but not invading the pelvic wall or floor; Stage III a cancer involving the pelvic wall or floor; and Stage IV a growth invading the bladder, rectum, or distant structures. The type of clinical material appears to vary greatly in different institutions. In the reports from 18 centers published in the *Fourth Annual Review of Cancer of the Cervix* (League of Nations Series) the following variations are noted in the proportion of cases in each stage:

Stage I: Between 1 and 24 per cent of cases
Stage II: Between 10 and 44 per cent of cases
Stage III: Between 31 and 54 per cent of cases
Stage IV: Between 4 and 45 per cent of cases

These variations are due to differences in clinical material, in the personal estimates of staging and other factors. Because of these tremendous variations, total five-year results obtained at one clinic may not be comparable to those at another.

Physicians in the Scandinavian radiotherapy centers are responsible for the treatment of *all* cases of cervical cancer in that geographic area; the following is the most recently reported distribution[43] of the four stages in Scandinavia: I 15 per cent, II 35 per cent, III 35 per cent, IV 15 per cent.

In recent years cases of so-called preinvasive carcinoma of the cervix are being diagnosed not infrequently, thanks in part to the use of cytologic smear technics and in part to the greater use of conventional biopsies. True carcinoma *in situ* may be the forerunner of clinically stageable cancer, but such cases should still be kept distinct from Stage I when results are being tabulated. They are often considered as Stage O.

The best results in the treatment of cancer of the cervix are obtained with intracavitary radium therapy combined, in most cases, with external roentgen irradiation.[13] One important unsettled question at the present time is whether it is better to give the external roentgen therapy before or after the radium therapy; a small number of workers use both methods simultaneously. In favor of giving the external radiation first is the fact that it decreases the amount of pelvic inflammation, decreases the size of bulky tumors, and thereby increases the efficiency of subsequent intracavitary radium therapy. In favor of radium therapy first is the fact that the vaginal vault is often not contracted (as sometimes follows roentgen therapy), that the patient is not fatigued by the long course of external irradiation and can better tolerate local intense radiotherapy, and finally, that external roentgen therapy does not add significantly to the results obtainable in early lesions. No standard technic is applicable to all cases; a general policy should be formulated and each case treated individually according to the anatomic extent of the tumor and the associated pathologic and other conditions. The great importance of avoiding excessive irradiation is nowhere more evident than in the treatment of cervical cancer; this point has been elucidated by British radiotherapists with commendable candor.

The aim in radiation is to deliver a dose of approximately 6000 roentgens into all the involved tissue in the pelvis during a period of from four to six weeks. In order to deliver this dose, it is necessary to apply many times 6000 roentgens to the tissues in the immediate vicinity of the cervical canal; fortunately, this high local dosage is well tolerated by cervical tissues.

TABLE 92. RELATIVE FIVE-YEAR RESULTS, CANCER OF CERVIX, RADIATION THERAPY

	Relative cures									
	All cases		*I**		*II**		*III**		*IV**	
	No.	(%)	No.	%	No.	%	No.	%	No.	%
Holt Radium Institute Manchester	1709	28.1	85	64.7	694	40.2	508	23.7	422	6.4
Institute du Cancer Paris	1512	31.8	72	67.4	228	48.7	881	33.3	331	6.6
Institut du Radium Paris	2199	37.1	298	63.4	942	42.8	739	27.6	220	9.1
Marie Curie Hospital London	1514	37.1	118	77.1	420	56.4	769	28.2	207	7.7
Memorial Hospital New York	1037	28.6	200	53	339	33.1	454	17.4	44	0
Radium Centre Copenhagen	468	44.4	49	67.3	224	51.8	142	35.9	53	15.1
Radiumhemmet Stockholm	2392	34.9	212	63.9	1168	46.5	733	22.1	279	8.2

* League of Nations classification.

The results of radiotherapy of cancer of the cervix in various centers are rather similar, despite differing technics and varying emphasis on external and intracavitary irradiation (Table 92). The experiences in Paris, Copenhagen, Manchester and in the United States confirm the fact that the combination of roentgen and radium therapy improves the results in Stages III and IV. The most recent report of the League of Nations shows relative five-year arrest rates (for all stages combined) ranging from 27 to 44 per cent. For the early or Stage I cases, the figures range from 53 to 77 per cent, and for Stage II from 33 to 56 per cent.

Cancer of the cervical stump is curable by irradiation in a reasonable proportion of cases. Pomeroy[76] secured 29 per cent five-years cures in 55 stump cases; Costolow[16] and 31 per cent in 165 such cases.

COMPLICATIONS OF RADIATION THERAPY FOR CANCER OF THE CERVIX

The normal reactions are variable degrees of epidermitis, vaginitis, proctitis, cystitis, and radiation sickness. If a lethal disease such as cancer of the cervix is to be cured these reactions must be accepted, as well as a small proportion of late complications (about 5 per cent). These include late ulcerations of the rectal or small bowel mucosa; fibrosis of rectum, bladder, or ureters; and occasionally fistulae. Such complications are scarcely more frequent than those resulting from a radical Wertheim operation, in which Meigs has reported an incidence of 10 per cent ureteral necrosis, and an even higher percentage of other pelvic disturbances. Late radiation osteitis is occasionally seen after external roentgen therapy, the patient developing either small zones of decalcification in or spontaneous fractures of femoral necks, pubic rami, etc. Most of these heal spontaneously; some are discovered incidental to roentgen examination of the pelvis for other conditions many years after treatment of the cervix.

The early and late reactions to improperly given irradiation are indeed serious. When radium has not been correctly placed in the cervix or vaginal vault, when packing is not adequate to maintain it in place, when treatment is incorrectly spaced or when excessive external irradiation is applied, a host of serious complications may be expected. We believe that if radium and high-voltage roentgen therapy equipment were available only to those who had received adequate training and experience, the number of disappointing results from irradiation would be greatly reduced. There is no field which has brought radium therapy into lower repute than that of amateur treatment of cancer of the cervix by the physician or surgeon who sees only one or two cases a year and who rents his radium from some hospital or radium company. Radium treatment is very easy to apply—incorrectly; it is not difficult to administer correctly if one knows and understands the physics of irradiation, the dangers incident to its application, and the method of preliminary dose calculation. A history of previous pelvic inflammatory diseases is a contraindication to intra-uterine radium application. The only mortality which this writer has seen from radium therapy has been in a patient in whom a latent or quiescent pelvic infection had been reactivated by rather vigorous dilatation of the cervix and intrauterine application of radium.

Recurrences. In a carefully studied group of 105 cases of patients with Stage I cancer of the cervix seen at the Curie Foundation up to 1941 and treated with radium alone, Baud[5] obtained 70 per cent five-year arrests. Eighteen patients had recurrences prior to the five-year period. Six patients had recurrences after the five-year period. The reasons for these recurrences is unknown, but presumably involved radioresistance of the tumors. The histopathology, clinical extent, dosage, and other factors in both groups were comparable. When detected early enough, some of the recurrences were cured by a Wertheim operation. It is important that this should not be undertaken until sufficient time has elapsed after the initial radium treatment to permit healing of the tissues (about three months).[5]

Palliation. Many patients with advanced cervical cancer may be made more comfortable by simple irradiation. Baclesse[4] treated 78 Stage III and IV cases with roentgen therapy alone, and secured 14 five-year clinical arrests. Four of 7 cases with involvement of the entire vagina were controlled.

CANCER OF THE CORPUS UTERI

The classification, clinical or histologic, of corpus uteri malignancies is not completely satisfactory. All grades of neoplasia occur: adenoma malignum, frank adenocarcinoma, carcinosarcoma, and chorioepithelioma. The cure rates in the former are good; in the latter very poor. The treatment of this condition may be by radiotherapy alone, by combined radiation therapy and surgery, or by surgery alone. Results are reported from large groups of cases treated by these three methods, all tending to the same general figures of 50–60 per cent relative five-year survivals. In view of the extensive handling of the uterus necessary at the time of operation, it is not unreasonable to give preoperative irradiation, preferably by a combination of intracavitary radium plus external roentgen therapy. This will take from one to four weeks; after an interval, radical removal of the uterus can be done. On the other hand, if the tumor is apparently small, immediate surgery may be the best method of treatment. If at time of surgery there is evidence of extension into the broad ligaments or nodes, then a full course of postoperative irradiation to the pelvis is indicated. The contraindications of irradiation are similar to those in cancer of the cervix. The dosage and incidence of complications are lower.

The desirability of giving the preoperative irradiation in the form of external roentgen therapy alone is suggested by recent figures from the University of Michigan (Lampe and Miller). By such a technic, these authors secured 88.6 per cent of five-year survivors in 70 patients with endometrial carcinoma.

From Manchester[72] the most recent report on 254 cases of cancer of the corpus uteri treated by radium alone shows 36 per cent relative five-year arrests; of 143 technically operable cases, 50 per cent were cured. Paterson has come to the conclusion that radiotherapy cures cancer of the uterus at least as often as does surgery. He uses radium insertion alone, a simple arrangement of intrauterine and vaginal applicators, inserted for two applications of 48 hours each, to deliver a dose of approximately 8000 r at a point 2 cm. from the central line of the tube.

Heyman[44] reports a relative five-year cure rate of 65 per cent with radium therapy alone, or radium plus postirradiation operation in cases of failure: during the same period the cure rate by hysterectomy did not exceed 55 per cent.

Trapp and Hardie,[98] using Heyman's radium technic, secured 67 per cent three-year arrests of 46 patients, most of whom were clinically inoperable.

Cancer of the Vulva and Vagina. Cancer of the vulva is usually squamous cell in type and often develops on a pre-existing leukoplakia. Inguinal adenopathy develops early. For small lesions (up to 3 cm. diameter), without adenopathy, local radical irradiation or surgery will cure a significant proportion of cases. It is important that the tumor dose be calculated to the depth of the lesion, and reach between 4000 and 6000 r in one to four weeks. For larger lesions and for all those with adenopathy, radical removal or electrodessication, with postoperative irradiation, is regarded by many as the method of choice. For extensive inoperable lesions, palliative roentgen irradiation, cross-firing the entire vulvar region, is indicated. The five-year relative results for all cases range from 21 per cent to 38 per cent.

Carcinoma of the vagina is usually of the squamous cell type; if adenocarcinoma is found, an endometrial implant should be suspected. Sarcoma is seen in children. If the lesion is definitely not uterine in origin, and is apparently localized to the vagina, intracavitary radium therapy is a satisfactory method of treatment; involved nodes should be excised. The five-year relative arrests are not good: about 15 per cent for carcinoma and 0 per cent for sarcoma.

CANCER OF THE RECTUM

Most rectal malignancies are of the squamous cell type or adenocarcinomas; a few are sarcomas (lymphosarcoma, reticulum cell sarcoma, etc.). The best treatment for carcinoma is radical surgery. The relative five-year results in this group range from 11 to 54 per cent; adequate data are not available on the sarcomatous lesions.

Pack and McNeer are enthusiastic about combined preoperative roentgen therapy and surgery in tumors of borderline operability (see their chapter in Pohle[75]).

The place of radiation therapy in *inoperable* cancer of the rectum is not clearly defined. With external roentgen therapy and, occasionally, supplementary intracavitary or interstitial radium, a small group is salvaged (8 per cent five-year arrests in 40 cases).[103] The occasional value of radiation is exemplified by the two patients with large inoperable cancers of the rectum reported by Brindley and White[9]; these were treated only by colostomy followed by vigorous local radiation therapy. They are both well and apparently free of disease, eight and nine years respectively after treatment. These results are mentioned *not* to encourage radiation therapy of operable lesions, but to remind readers of its usefulness in inoperable ones.

RESULTS IN INACCESSIBLE SITES

RESPIRATORY TRACT

NASOPHARYNX

The staging of these tumors is not satisfactory. Some of them manifest themselves by metastatic nodes before the primary lesion is detectable. Many develop nodes during or after treatment, even though the primary tumor is small or arrested. Some invade the base of the skull or metastasize to the lungs relatively early. Most of the lesions are squamous cell carcinomas; when these arise in lymphoid tissue they are termed lymphoepitheliomas or even transitional cell carcinomas. Some of the lesions are adenocarcinomas, lymphosarcomas, endotheliomas, and mixed tumors. The principal treatment is radiologic, owing to anatomic problems involved in attempted radical removal. By judicious external roentgen irradiation alone in the anaplastic tumors, and by a combination of external irradiation plus intracavitary radium applications in the more differentiated ones, a satisfactory degree of palliation and a small number of five-year survivals are obtained. External roentgen irradiation of involved nodes is probably the best method of treatment except in the occasional case of operable nodes appearing after control of a well differentiated primary lesion. The importance of using adequately large fields for administering external x-ray beams cannot be overstressed.

Graham and Meyer[34] had 19 per cent relative five-year arrests in a small group treated by roentgen therapy.

LARYNX

The classification and staging of cancer of the larynx which we recommend is as follows:

Intrinsic: Tumor arising from true cord or laryngeal ventricle.

Stage I. Single cord, without fixation.

Stage II. Both cords, or one cord with partial fixation.

Stage III. One or both cords, with cartilage invasion or metastases.

Extrinsic: Tumor from upper surface of false cord, epiglottis, aryepiglottic fold, arytenoid, laryngeal surface or pyriform sinus, postcricoid area and subglottic area.

Stage I. Less than 1 cm. in diameter.

Stage II. From 1 to 3 cm., but without cartilage invasion.

Stage III. Over 3 cm., or with cartilage invasion, or metastases.

The clinical importance of this classification is shown by Table 93.

TABLE 93. DIFFERENCES BETWEEN INTRINSIC AND EXTRINSIC CANCER OF THE LARYNX

	Intrinsic	*Extrinsic*
Common location	Ventral ⅔ of true cord	Aryepiglottic area
Chief symptoms	Hoarseness	Dyspnea or dysphagia
Histopathology (commonly)	Well-differentiated squamous cell	Poorly differentiated squamous cell
Course	Slow: metastases rare	Rapid: metastases common

About 96 per cent of cases are squamous cell cancers; the remainder are various types of malignancy. The optimum method of treatment depends on the stage of the disease. Surgical and radiologic methods of treatment are more keenly competitive in early larynx cancer than in almost any other malignant growth. Intrinsic Stage I lesions may be treated equally well by surgery or irradiation, with an 80 per cent or greater chance of cure. The voice after laryngofissure and cordectomy is not quite as good as after irradiation, and for this reason we believe irradiation to be the method of choice. Stage II and III, intrinsic or extrinsic, should be treated with radiation, except when: (1) diffuse infection or chondritis is present prior to treatment; (2) discrete hard cervical nodes are present and the biopsy has disclosed a well-differentiated tumor; or (3) when there is moderate subglottic extension. When any of these three conditions exist, laryngectomy with neck dissection will usually offer a better chance of cure than roentgen therapy.

Edema of the larynx and necrosis of cartilage may be kept to a minimum or avoided entirely by judicious maintenance of dose level and by keeping the maximum dose below 4000 r to each side of the neck in six weeks' time, using fields of reasonable size. Chondronecrosis has been greatly exaggerated in the literature as a complication of radiotherapy for laryngeal cancer. We have seen as many patients with uncomfortable or hazardous complications following radical surgery as we have seen following radical irradiation.

It is commonly argued by proponents of surgery that "if you remove a tumor there is no chance of its recurring, and therefore surgical removal is best." This would be tenable were it not for the fact that there is only a 60 per cent salvage rate with laryngectomy (all stages considered); in the other 40 per cent all of the tumor cells were not removed by surgery. Therefore, surgical "removal" alone does not always prevent recurrence.

TABLE 94. CANCER OF THE LARYNX; RESULTS WITH ROENTGEN THERAPY

	Cases	*Per cent*
5-Year (Jackson, Blady *et al.* [49])	69	64
5-Year (Harris *et al.* [42])	67	55*
10-Year (Harris *et al.* [42])	33	51

* Intrinsic 73 per cent, extrinsic 40 per cent.

In the writer's experience with a group of 125 cases of laryngeal cancer treated by irradiation, the five-year cure rate in the small number of cases confined to a true cord was 100 per cent; for cases of moderate extent, either extrinsic or intrinsic, the salvage rate dropped to 70 per cent, and for Stage III cases to 16 per cent. The over-all arrest rate was 29 per cent. This is similar to Lenz's figure (30 of 110 cases).[54]

Coutard[17] has taught us the importance of examining the larynx during treatment; this aids in gauging the extent and severity of the biologic reaction and in adjusting the dose to the conditions at hand.

TABLE 95. CANCER OF THE LARYNX: COMPARISON OF RADIATION AND SURGERY

	Treatment	*Cases*	*Percentage*	
"Early Cases"	Laryngofissure	102	88	J.
	Roentgen therapy	23	86	H.
"More Advanced"	Laryngofissure	31	65	
	Roentgen therapy	69	64	J.

J: Jackson, Blady[49] *et al.*; H: Harris *et al.*[42]

Recurrences or failures to control small intrinsic lesions with irradiation can be corrected by radical laryngectomy. On the other hand, surgical failures can rarely be rescued by radiation, although useful palliation may often be achieved.[23]

Blady and coworkers[49] report five-year relative arrests of intrinsic lesions of 59 per cent and of extrinsic lesions 25 per cent (with tumor doses of from 3600 to 4600 r in four weeks). The roentgen therapy results of Harris[42] are unusually good (Table 94).

Comparison of the surgical and radiological results (relative five-year arrests) obtained by these workers and their colleagues is most instructive (Table 95).

LUNG

Most primary malignant pulmonary tumors arise as bronchial carcinomas. A small number originates in the parenchyma, or in the mediastinum (invading the lungs). Squamous cell carcinomas predominate; adenocarcinomas, malignant adenomas, and many other subtypes are found. The principal hope of cure of early bronchiogenic carcinoma is radical pneumonectomy; however, only a minority of cases will have the tumor sufficiently localized at time of exploration to warrant radical surgery. For the nonresectable group, cough, hemoptysis, or pain may be controlled in a reasonable number of cases by judicious external roentgen therapy.[25] By precise centering (with fluoroscopic and radiographic checks) one may deliver suppressive doses of irradiation to the more sensitive tumors and secure palliation for periods up to two years; in exceptional cases five-year arrests will be obtained. Intrabronchial application of radium or heavy irradiation of the hilum at the time of thoracotomy are no longer recommended.

The current results of surgery are of interest: Graham[33] reports that from January, 1945, through September, 1948, he had 434 proven cases of bronchiogenic carcinoma. Of these, 58 per cent were considered worthy of exploration, but in only 23 per cent could pneumonectomy be performed. The mortality of operation was 7 per cent. Of 53 pneumonectomies which he performed prior to 1942, 28 per cent were living and well after five or more years (15 cases). If a similar figure applied to the 101 cases above-mentioned, then 28 per cent might be arrested; this equals *6.4 per cent* absolute arrest of the entire 434 cases and *11 per cent* relative arrest of the 251 cases operated on. Only 3 squamous cell cancers were arrested.

Paterson[72] reported a 5 per cent five-year arrest rate in 66 cases treated with radiation up to 1940, and a similar percentage in 74 cases subsequently irradiated.

Palliation. Shorbon[89] reported fair results in a group treated with roentgen therapy alone. In the untreated patients, the average duration of life after appearance of symptoms was six and a quarter months; in the treated patients fifteen and a half months. Our own experience is similar (Figs. 148, 149).

Metastatic pulmonary tumors are of miscellaneous type; those secondary to embryonal tumors of the testis, ovary, etc., to Ewing's tumor, and to neuroblastomata may be radiosensitive and well worth treating. Others, metastatic from such lesions as osteogenic sarcoma, are rarely radiosensitive and treatment is usually not recommended. As usual, the only sure test is the actual trial of irradiation. A midlung or midtumor dose of 1000–2000 r delivered in two or three weeks should be attempted. With such irradiation there have been occasional reports of five- and ten-year arrests of metastatic seminoma, metastatic thyroid carcinoma, etc.

GASTROINTESTINAL TRACT

Salivary Gland Tumors

Parotid tumors are of various types, mostly benign. The malignant parotid tumors include various types of mixed tumors, squamous cell carcinomas, and other neoplasms. Some are difficult to classify and are termed "semi-malignant." The optimum treatment is radical removal. Many surgeons, notably in Sweden and

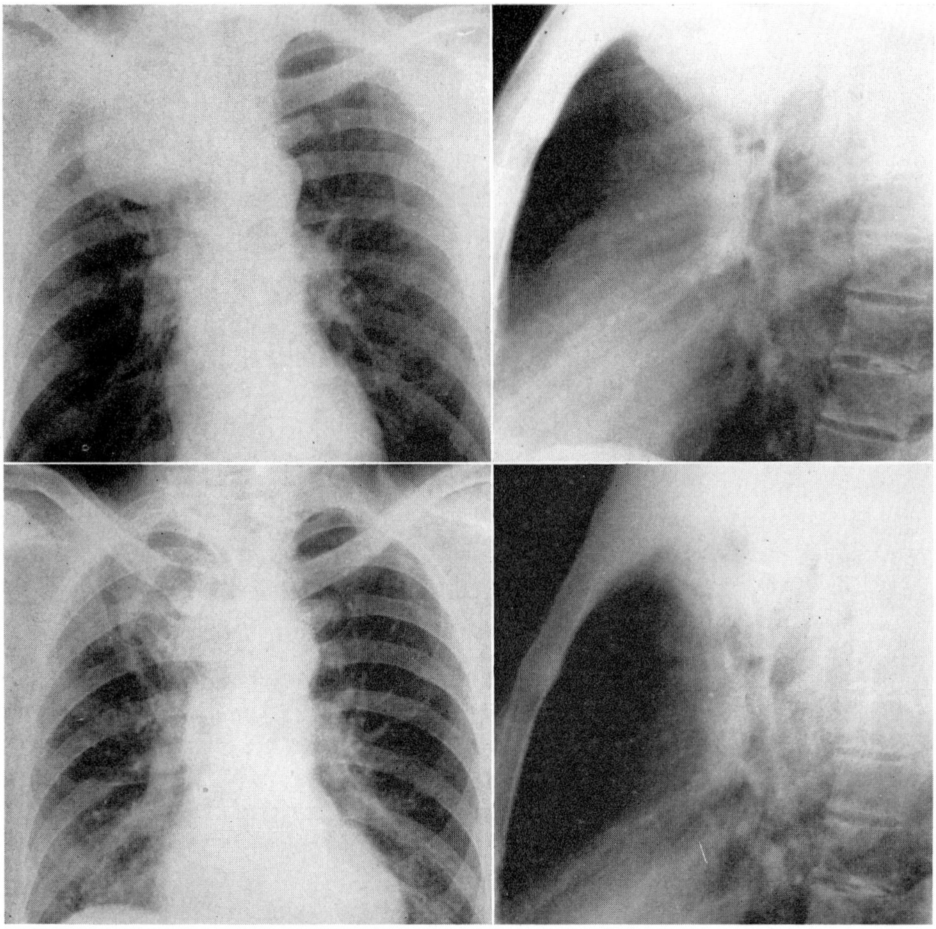

FIG. 148. Palliation of pulmonary cancer with radiotherapy. Male, age 55, with cough, hemoptysis, and slight chest pain. Microscopic examination of tissue from right upper lobe bronchus showed adenocarcinoma. Patient regarded as inoperable (he also refused surgical exploration); given a tumor dose of 3000 r in three weeks, using large fields (18 cm. diameter) and half value layer 2 mm. Cu. Upper pair of films made before, and lower pair two months following radiotherapy. Clinical symptoms much improved for about one year; patient developed signs of cerebral metastases and died within two years.

Britain, advise full preoperative irradiation followed by surgery, and frequently, postoperative therapy. Local application of radium into the operative site may be feasible, but the problem of safe adequate dosage is considerable. Radiation therapy alone is indicated in inoperable tumors, and in the small group of operable but highly radiosensitive tumors. Roentgen therapy plus surgery usually gives about 30 per cent five-year arrests in definite malignancies. Paterson[72] reports the remarkable figure of 67 per cent five-year arrests in 114 parotid cancers treated by surgery plus irradiation, or irradiation alone.

Esophagus

Carcinoma of the esophagus is usually squamous cell or epidermoid in type. It seldom comes to attention early. The possibility of cure by excision is therefore small; nevertheless, radical surgical removal probably offers a better chance of comfortable survival than radical irradiation. Radical irradiation is performed by various methods, including multiple small external fields and rotation therapy (in which the patient is revolved slowly on a chair while exposed to a slender beam of radiation, aimed at the esophageal lesion with continuous fluoroscopic control). A tumor dose of 5000–6000 r in four to eight weeks can be given by either

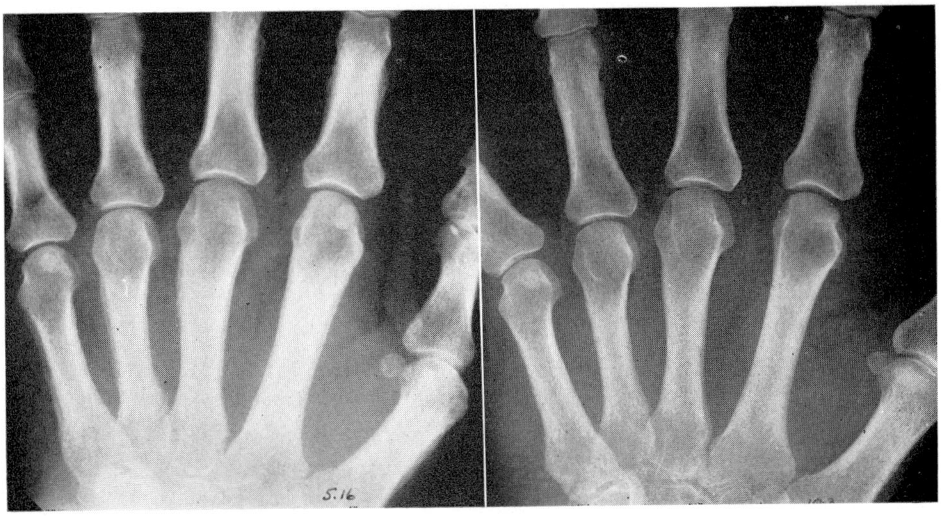

FIG. 149. Recession of pulmonary osteoarthropathy after thoracic radiotherapy. Left hand of patient shown in Fig. 148 before, and five months after, radiotherapy of lungs, showing complete recession of his associated hypertrophic pulmonary osteoarthropathy. Note the marked periosteal thickening along the shafts of the metacarpals and phalanges in the left hand figure, and the disappearance of that thickening in the right. The concomitant improvement in the soft tissue changes was also marked.

method, in suitable cases. This will destroy many of the tumors, but unfortunately after a year or two it is not uncommon to find metastases developing at a site distant from the primary lesion (usually in the mediastinum).

Nielsen in Copenhagen has had the greatest experience with rotation therapy, and has achieved a five-year salvage rate of only 3 per cent. (The cure rate with surgery is even smaller!) Paterson[72] secured a five-year survival rate of 4 per cent in a group of 51 cases treated with radical roentgen irradiation. However, one of the two cases developed late hemorrhagic bronchitis, possibly from radiation effect on the lungs; the other died of metastases to the liver and thoracic spine after the five-year period had ended. In a subsequent series of 142 cases, none survived five years.

The palliative results of roentgen therapy are frequently satisfactory in lesions involving the upper third of the esophagus, but only occasionally so in those involving the lower third.

Stomach

Malignant tumors of the stomach are the most frequently seen of all visceral neoplasms, and are probably next in frequency to cancers of the skin and breast, all ages and sexes combined. Adenocarcinoma is the most frequent type; about 1.5 per cent of gastric tumors are sarcomas (one-half of them lymphosarcomas).

Radical surgery is the procedure of choice. Relative five-year arrests as high as 33 per cent have been reported; absolute arrests are probably less than 5 per cent. Pack reported 5 per cent of 303 gastrectomized cases alive at three years: other authors record from 4 to 15 per cent relative five-year survivals.

Radiotherapy by external roentgen and radium rays, intragastric roentgen cones, radium tubes, and balloons, interstitial needles, and so forth have been tried with little success. However, about 20 per cent of a group reported by Pack and McNeer (quoted in [75]) received "worthwhile palliation" (one-fourth of them to a remarkable degree). These were presumably highly anaplastic lesions. Lymphosarcoma and gastric Hodgkin's disease may receive long-term palliation (we have seen a few controlled for as long as 10 years); Taylor had 13 cases of lymphosarcoma well five or more years (5 with radiotherapy, 8 with combined treatment).

Colon

Adenocarcinomas are the common growth, usually well differentiated. The primary method of cure is surgical. Inoperable, anaplastic tumors of the distal bowel, which are bleeding heavily or causing much pain or discharge, and lymphosarcomas may be palliated by tumor doses of 2000–4000 r delivered in four to six weeks.[103] As previously reported, there are occasional long survivals with this method. Relative five-year cures (surgery) range from 17 to 29 per cent.

Pancreas

The possibility of alleviating carcinoma of the pancreas with radiation is remote; some of the more anaplastic tumors, including the malignant lymphomata may be temporarily palliated. The primary choice in therapy is surgery.

GENITOURINARY TRACT

Kidneys

Most malignant tumors of the kidney are adenocarcinomas (so-called hypernephromas or clear-ceîl carcinomas). The primary treatment is surgical. In inoperable cases roentgen irradiation to tolerance may achieve occasional arrest. Results of surgery are reported as between 8 and 25 per cent relative five-year arrests.

Embryonal carcinomas of the kidney (Wilms' tumor) occur especially in children. If pulmonary metastases are not present, surgical removal should be attempted. If the tumor is bulky, preoperative irradiation will usually diminish it sufficiently to make surgical removal possible or easier. If the surgeon believes that he has not succeeded in removing the entire tumor at operation, postoperative irradiation should be given to tolerance. Romer and Sather[85] reported 6.4 per cent five-year survivals in 828 collected cases. Paterson[72] recorded 2 out of 8 cases as arrested. Survivors may show growth disturbances in irradiated bone.

Renal pelvic carcinomas (or epidermoid, papillary, or squamous cell) constitute a minority of renal neoplasms and should be treated surgically.

BLADDER

Small or moderately advanced carcinomas of the bladder should be treated by surgical removal of as much of the tumor as possible, followed by careful interstitial radium treatment. Bulky tumors should be treated by a combination of external roentgen therapy followed, if necessary, by removal of residual tumor. Various

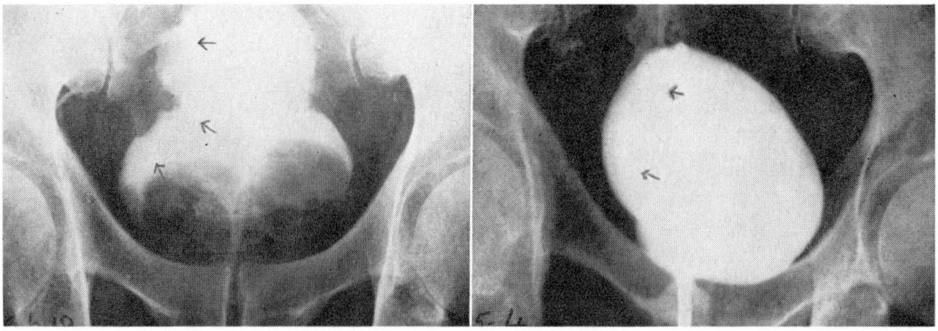

FIG. 150. Temporary control of cancer of bladder with roentgentherapy. Male, age 72, with hematuria. Extensive nodular tumor in right side of bladder. Biopsy showed moderately well differentiated carcinoma. Tumor dose 3200 r in four weeks, using half-value layer 1 mm. Cu. Bleeding arrested. Follow-up roentgenogram made seven months later, showing smooth bladder outline; cystoscopic examination showed no evidence of tumor. After two years, the tumor recurred and ultimately proved fatal. External roentgen therapy is *not* the method of choice for curable bladder cancer; however, for some incurable cases it will greatly diminish symptoms and increase comfortable survival.

special technics, such as direct insertion of contact roentgen-ray therapy tubes into the bladder at time of operation, insertion of special balloon catheters with radium in the center, and use of radio-active solutions in balloon catheters, etc., have been tried, but are not of proven value. By the judicious use of multiple external fields about the bladder, tumor doses of as much as 4500 r can be delivered in a period of four to six weeks. With anaplastic lesions, five-year arrests will be obtained in a modest number of cases. Wirth *et al.*, quoted in[6, 11, 12,] had 10 five-year survivals in 68 patients treated with supervoltage roentgen therapy.

By a combination of cystotomy plus intravesical radon, Paterson[72] secured 50 per cent five-year arrests of 34 early cases (the over-all, early and late five-year results being about 20 per cent). Others report from 17 to 37 per cent relative arrests. Late recurrences are common (Fig. 150). Perhaps the higher figures came from medical centers in which the pathologist diagnosed all papillomas as grade I carcinomas.

Prostate

The preferred treatment is hormonal or surgical. If such is not feasible, and the patient has severe pain, bleeding, or other such symptoms, external roentgen irradiation should be used. For the treatment of bony metastases, doses of from 600 to 1200 r into the involved bone in a period of two to four weeks will usually alleviate the pain. Relative five-year survivals with hormonal and surgical therapy are reported in the 13 to 23 per cent range.

Testis

Malignant tumors of the testis are teratomatous; frequently one type of tissue predominates. The use of a multiplicity of terms has confused classification. About 75 per cent of these tumors are embryonal carcinomas or seminomas; the remainder are miscellaneous types of carcinoma, adult teratoma and rare interstitial cell tumors and choriocarcinoma.[66]

Following removal of the primary lesion and histologic study, a full course of irradiation is given to the abdominal nodes in the case of embryonal carcinomas or seminomas (1500–2500 r in three to five weeks). The miscellaneous carcinomas may warrant radical node dissection; the adult teratomas orchidectomy alone. The teratomas are merely observed. When pulmonary metastases are present, these should be treated. No matter how large the metastases, irradiation is indicated, since occasional long survivals are obtained.

With adequate surgery and irradiation, Moore[66] reported relative five-year arrests as follows: seminoma 65 per cent, embryonal carcinoma 25 per cent; about 95 per cent of the small group of adult teratomas survived after surgical treatment. Paterson[72] reported 53 per cent five-year arrests in an unselected group of 87 seminomas. Kelly and Stentstrom[51] had five-year arrests in 100 testicular tumors (37 seminomas, 29 carcinomas, 34 unclassified) as follows: seminomas 56 per cent, carcinomas 3 per cent; unclassified 29 per cent. Since there were known metastases before treatment in two-thirds of the cases, these results are good and largely creditable to irradiation.

Ovary

The classification of ovarian carcinomas is notoriously difficult. The basic method of treatment is surgical; postoperative irradiation is indicated when removal is incomplete or not feasible. Both ovaries should always be removed if possible. In the author's own experience, in only 12 per cent of patients treated by a combination of surgery and postoperative irradiation was ovarian carcinoma arrested for five years. However, about half of the treated cases showed worthwhile palliation, surviving on an average two years. Complete hysterectomy and bilateral oophorectomy had not been performed in all of our cases and therefore optimum conditions had not been established. From comparable series of cases published in the literature, one gets the impression that postoperative irradiation increases the five-year salvage rate to a significant degree, even up to 50 per cent in some series. A "tumor" dose of from 1500 to 2500 r in twenty to thirty days to the abdominal cavity is desirable as the initial postoperative course in the average case in which radiation is indicated. Over a period of some years this course may be repeated once or twice for the control of ascites, recurrent masses, etc.

The results of surgical treatment published in the literature vary from 5 to 20 per cent (relative five-year survivals), and of surgery plus postoperative irradiation from 15 to 46 per cent. Paterson[72] reports 26 per cent five-year arrests in 125 cases treated by surgery and irradiation. It is probable that some of the higher figures were obtained in groups which included "histologically malignant" but "clinically benign" lesions.[29]

BRAIN TUMORS

The malignant brain tumors include certain varieties of gliomas, meningiomas, acoustic neuromas, and rarer primary growths; the metastatic growths; and the invasive (usually nasopharyngeal) lesions. Many histologically benign but clinically serious growths also occur, notably the craniopharyngiomas, dermoids, and hemangiomas. The treatment of brain tumors, with the exception of medulloblastoma and pituitary adenoma, is primarily surgical. The radiosensitivity of the gliomas appears to follow the general pattern—the well-differentiated ones being less sensitive to radiation than the undifferentiated. However, there is much divergence of opinion on this point. Postoperative irradiation of certain inoperable gliomas, notably glioblastoma multiforme and polar spongioblastoma, has been recommended by Naffziger[67] and other neurosurgeons, but the degree of palliation is hard to assess.

McWhirter[58] and Paterson[72] report some radiosensitive hemangioblastomas, ependynomas, and pinealomas. Pierce and Bouchard[74] report these results with postoperative roentgen irradiation (tumor doses up to "7500 r" in six and one half weeks!): glioblastoma multiforme: 8 per cent survivals of 30 months or more; astrocytoma: 24 per cent survivals of six years or more. Since most writers regard 6000 r in four to six weeks as the upper safe limit of brain tissue tolerance, these heavy doses must be viewed with reservation.

Medulloblastomas should usually be treated by roentgen irradiation to the posterior half of the calvarium and the entire spinal cord: the skull is cross-fired through two large lateral fields; the spinal cord through two or three long dorsal fields. The attempt is made to deliver a tissue dose of about 3000 r in four to six weeks. The five-year salvage rate is less than 10 per cent.

Cerebral metastases from carcinomas of the breast and some other sites are frequently worth irradiating; the tissue dose aimed at is usually in the range of 1000 to 2000 r; the treatment is palliative but occasionally remarkably beneficial.

SPINAL CORD TUMORS

These may be primary or metastatic, and of diverse type: many are histologically benign but locally as destructive as a malignant growth. Following microscopic verification, local irradiation may be indicated in addition to attempted radical surgical removal. However, for lymphoblastoma, metastatic mammary carcinoma and some primary inoperable tumors of the vertebral column, a judicious combination of biopsy or decompressive laminectomy and radiation is indicated.

Pituitary Tumors

Most pituitary tumors are benign adenomas and, strictly speaking, constitute problems of the endocrine system. However, they are commonly considered with other intracranial lesions and often dealt with successfully by irradiation. They include acidophilic adenomas (gigantism or acromegaly; occasional visual and other neurologic disturbances; frequent headaches); basophilic adenomas (Cushing's syndrome); and chromophobe adenomas (hypopituitarism, visual disturbances, and headaches). Chromophobe tumors are by far the most common. In the presence of a clear-cut clinical picture, and in the absence of rapidly developing loss of vision, careful roentgen irradiation is indicated in most of these lesions, certainly in the first two types. Complete relief of symptoms for periods of decades is usually obtained by judicious irradiation (2000–3000 r tumor in three to six weeks); basophilic lesions apparently require only one-half this amount. Many patients with chromophobe adenomas require observation only. However, since some of these lesions do grow and compress the remaining functioning gland it is often advisable to irradiate them. Five-year survival figures are of little import, because of the protracted clinical course.

Retinoblastoma

Unilateral retinoblastoma should be treated by enucleation. If bilateral (as is frequent), an attempt may be made to salvage the less-involved eye by vigorous irradiation of the retina. If possible, from 3500 to 4500 r is delivered into the retinal area with the minimal amount of the beam striking the lens. Martin and Reese[61] have reported on the results obtainable by intense roentgen therapy in a few cases; 6 out of 8 survived five years, only 2 with vision. The doses which they recommend are such that severe late damage to skin, bone and intervening tissues must be anticipated in some of the survivors.

Carcinoma of the conjunctiva may be treated by excision or by very careful external roentgen irradiation. With suitable immobilization of the eye and aiming of the roentgen beam it is possible to deliver such irradiation to small growths without damage to a major portion of the lens.

OSSEOUS SYSTEM AND ADJACENT STRUCTURES

Primary malignant bone tumors include, for practical purposes, Ewing's sarcoma, reticulum cell sarcoma, multiple myeloma, and osteogenic sarcoma. All are difficult to cure by any means. If diagnosed early, radical amputation may result in a few arrests. In the case of Ewing's sarcoma (malignant endothelioma) and reticulum cell sarcoma, some authors believe that irradiation offers more than surgery. This writer is not convinced. However, it must be admitted that the ultimate results of either method are so poor that there is probably little to choose between the two methods as far as saving life is concerned; comfortable survival may be greater after judicious irradiation than after amputation. It is probably the reverse after injudicious radiotherapy. Bony and pulmonary metastases from these two tumors are not uncommon and may be palliated successfully for variable periods of years.

Myeloma, in the majority of cases, is multicentric in origin. Therefore, radical resection of a single involved bone is usually futile. Once the diagnosis has been established by biopsy, heavy irradiation of the solitary lesion (4000 r in four weeks) is probably the best method of treatment.[24] In the case of multiple myeloma, irradiation of selected sites with a gentle dose (perhaps 2500 r in a period of from two to four weeks) may result in prolonged improvement.

Metastatic Tumors

Bone metastases secondary to carcinoma of the breast, kidney, thyroid and lung are relatively common. Tissue doses of from 500 to 1000 r in from two to fourteen days will usually give as much pain relief as heavier irradiation and will not delay the development of favorable recalcification.

Soft Tissue Sarcomas

Sarcomas of the soft tissues adjacent to bone, malignant synoviomas, and similar lesions are poorly radiosensitive and rarely aided by irradiation. The main hope is surgical. Inoperable cases may be palliated.

HEMOPOIETIC AND ALLIED SYSTEMS

Malignant dyscrasias of these systems include the leukemias, the lymphosarcomas, and Hodgkin's disease. Some of the leukemias are fairly clear-cut, acute or chronic entities; some are subacute and some blend with, or evolve from, the lymphomata in irregular fashion. Other cases change their character either spontaneously or under treatment, so that what appears to be a lymphosarcoma one week may appear to be an aleukemia or acute leukemia another.

Leukemia

Only the common myelogenous and lymphatic types will be considered here. The acute leukemias are not amenable to radiation therapy and it is not recommended. For details on the acute leukemias, aleukemic leukemia, and leukemia developing as a terminal phase of lymphoblastoma, the reader is referred to any of the numerous texts on this subject. Since the treatment of monocytic leukemia is essentially the same as that for myelogenous, this subtype also will not be discussed.

Chronic and Subacute Leukemia. Chronic lymphatic or myelogenous leukemia, with symptoms or with the finding of an excessively high white count, should be treated. There is a multiplicity of cytotoxic weapons now available to the internist and radiologist, with a corresponding multiplicity of ideas and confusion as to their indications.[39] The weapon with which the greatest amount of clinical experience has been developed, and the one which can be most carefully measured and controlled, is irradiation by external roentgen beams. Irradiation by internally administered radioactive isotopes is an alternative weapon, provided one has the elaborate facilities for measuring the amounts given and retained. Certain of the nitrogen mustards have been tried extensively, but Rhoads[83] and many others have come to the conclusion that "these are really not more useful than is x-ray"; Griffin *et al.*[36] have pointed out that the nitrogen mustards are carcinogenic in experimental animals and that their clinical usage "should be viewed with some concern as a consequence." Many reports on nitrogen mustard therapy suggest that it should be used early in the disease to produce remissions; actually, these are the stages which respond best to judicious roentgen therapy; the use of severe myelotoxic drugs is not warranted at such stages.

In chronic myelogenous leukemia, it is best to start with small doses of roentgen irradiation to the spleen, using adequately large fields (20×20 cm.) and doses of from 25 to 100 r, measured in air. Dosage will vary with the total white cell and platelet counts, the symptoms and the general physical condition. Treatments are continued two or three times a week in doses of up to 600 r in air, depending upon the patient's response. The white cells after an initial rise will sometimes fall following roentgen irradiation and must not be driven down precipitously, nor should the platelets be allowed to fall below 100,000. Repeated blood counts must therefore be made during the course of treatment and for some months thereafter. In chronic lymphatic leukemia, similar small courses of irradiation are given to the more troublesome lymph node masses, or to the spleen, but usually not to more than two areas in one day. When and if local response is no longer obtained, total body radiation in doses of 10–25 r will usually produce satisfactory remission. Careful explanation to the patient of the need for frequent examination, even in the absence of symptoms, and judicious use of blood transfusions will result in a significant number of five-year survivals. It is believed that radiation increases the over-all survival rate little, but it does increase greatly the comfort and efficiency of the patient during his remaining years. Krebs[53] reported the average duration of life after onset of symptoms in 44 cases of irradiated chronic myelogenous leukemia to be 41 months.

Lymphoblastoma

The lymphoblastomas include Hodgkin's disease, lymphosarcoma, and the less common giant follicular lymphosarcoma and reticulum cell sarcoma. The clinical manifestations of these diseases are as protean as the histologic appearances. The primary focus may appear in any site. Radiation therapy is the method of choice, usually by external roentgen irradiation. The dose and area treated must vary according to the signs and symptoms present. In one case the abdomen alone may need treatment; in another, the peripheral lymph node areas; in a third, the mediastinum; in a fourth, the skin. While the tumor sometimes manifests itself in a single site for some years, the probability of multicentric origin is so great that attempts at radical eradication of an apparent primary lesion are usually futile. Nevertheless, there are a few lymphosarcomas and reticulum cell sarcomas in which radical excision or irradiation of a "solitary" lesion has apparently produced long arrest. In the irradiation control of many cases it is important that skin tolerance be aided by using technical factors to deliver the maximum amount of irradiation to the involved tissues with the minimum skin effect (heavy filtration, long distance, and suitably large fields). The initial doses should usually be small (50–100 r); the platelets should be counted periodically, and occasional roentgen examination of the thorax made. Not only do silent yet extensive lymphomatous masses develop in the thorax, but in long-standing cases complicating pulmonary tuberculosis is not a rare eventuality. Five-year survival rates from 11 to 20 per cent in Hodgkin's disease and from 14 to 26 per cent in the lymphosarcomas are reported. The average survival in all treated cases is believed to be about thirty months. Some authors believe that improved survival rates in Hodgkin's disease were obtained by improved technics of irradiation.

TABLE 96. RESULTS OF RADIATION THERAPY IN LEUKEMIA AND LYMPHOBLASTOMA

	Five-year survivals (%)			
Type	Craver[18]	Puestow[80]	Hamann[39]	Paterson[71]
Leuk., chronic, myelogenous	5	6	14	2
Leuk., chronic, lymphatic	16	10	23	0
Hodgkin's disease	20	11	21	22
Lymphosarcoma	26	14	9	30

Nitrogen mustard therapy is indicated in cases of generalized lymphoblastoma which are advanced and no longer responsive to irradiation. The remissions obtained are short (1 to 27 weeks in Roswit's series,[86] the average being 7 weeks), but the degree of palliation is often marked (see also Chapter 29).

MISCELLANEOUS SITES

CERVICAL LYMPH NODE METASTASES

These commonly arise from malignant tumors of the lip, tongue, oral cavity, and nasopharynx; any malignant process in the head and neck, and some in the breasts, lungs and abdominal viscera may give rise to such nodes.

If the primary lesion is controlled or controllable, and the nodes are operable, radical surgery is the treatment of choice; if not, radiation, radical or palliative (depending upon the circumstances), is indicated.[20]

In the case of operable nodes secondary to squamous cell cancer of the lip or oral cavity, operation is advisable after control of the primary lesion (usually about six weeks after irradiation when that treatment has been employed). A suprahyoid dissection is often adequate for lip lesions; bilateral radical neck dissection is needed for most other types of operable node metastases. When a small group of nodes is involved, and operation is refused by the patient or contraindicated for other reasons, radical irradiation should be employed. An attempt should be made to deliver 4000–6000 r into the nodes in four weeks or less. For superficial nodes, less than 5 cm. diameter, this may be done by external roentgen therapy alone; for deep or bilateral nodes, roentgen therapy plus interstitial radium treatment or teleradium therapy is advisable.

The results of neck dissection are rather variable. Brown and McDowell[10] collected data on 410 cases secondary to lesions in lip, tongue, and oral cavity: relative five-year survivals were 25 per cent, absolute about 15 per cent. These included the cases reported by Duffy, in which he had relative five-year survivals of 20 per cent.

Roentgen and radium therapy results range from 9 per cent (Paterson[72]) to 27 per cent (C. Martin[59]): these are relative five-year arrests. Palliation is frequently satisfactory with roentgen therapy alone (the patient succumbing to distant spread, with the cervical area controlled).

Thyroid

Malignant tumors include malignant adenoma, papillary carcinoma, adenocarcinoma and undifferentiated carcinoma, plus several uncommon lesions (carcinosarcoma, lymphosarcoma and other sarcomatous tumors). The degree of malignancy varies widely, and even metastasizing tumors may occasionally be associated with long survival. The treatment of choice for all operable lesions is radical surgery; for inoperable tumors and for tumors very anaplastic histologically, showing blood vessel invasion or evidence of incomplete removal, a full course of roentgen radiation is indicated. Late skin fibrosis and telangiectasis may be expected, but this is regarded as a minor penalty for a potentially life-saving procedure.

To evaluate the place of irradiation, Portmann[79] made careful studies on two groups with comparable types and stages of malignancy: five-year survivals in those treated by surgery alone were 14 per cent, and in those treated by combined surgery and irradiation 29 per cent. In a series of 200 consecutive cases of thyroid cancer treated by surgery or combined methods, the five-year survival rate was 20 per cent. Papillary carcinomas and "nonadenomatous" adenocarcinomas had a good prognosis, malignant adenomas a poor one.

Hare[41] reported results of combined treatment in 231 cases: approximately 44 per cent survived five or more years. Paterson[72] treated 63 cases, largely by combined methods, with 25 per cent five-year survivals.

Thyroid irradiation by external means (roentgen rays) is regarded as invaluable in selected cases of thyroid malignancy, both primary and metastatic. Irradiation by internal means (radioactive iodine, I^{131}) is an alternative method in a very small percentage of cases.[45] Therapeutic amounts of radioactive iodine are spontaneously taken up by only about 6 per cent of thyroid cancers; a small additional number may be converted into iodine acceptors by certain hormones or drugs. This latter procedure entails a risk of tumor acceleration scarcely justifiable if roentgen therapeutic aid is available. For advanced cases, with generalized metastases, radioiodine will greatly help a small number, especially since the metastases often take up the radioactive iodine in contradistinction to the primary tumor.

Thymus

Malignant thymic tumors include carcinoma, sarcoma, and subtypes (lymphoepithelioma, lymphosarcoma, etc.) They may be difficult to distinguish from leukemic masses, malignant lymphomata, malignant dermoid tumors, and other anterior mediastinal lesions. The optimum treatment for malignant thymoma appears to be wide surgical removal; if this is not feasible, or if the surgical specimen indicates that all of the tumor has not been resected, irradiation of the mediastinum should be given to the tolerance point (3000–4000 r tumor in four weeks). In all patients (including infants) the white blood count or platelet count must *not* be reduced precipitously. Palliative results are good; permanent arrest is apparently exceptional.

Adrenal

Malignant tumors of the adrenal are of diverse types. The carcinomas are not generally regarded as radiosensitive: the diagnostic procedure involved in their recognition often entails radical surgery. The malignant tumors of the medulla (and of adjacent sympathetic anlage) include the neuroblastomas or sympatheticoblastomas. These tumors occur especially in infants, are radiosensitive but are generally so widespread when discovered that cure is impossible. Moderate dosage to the primary site and metastases may produce fairly long remissions.

SUMMARY

The place of radiotherapy in the cure and palliation of malignant disease has been summarized. In the successful treatment of many lesions the skilled radiotherapist is as essential for cure as is the skilled surgeon. However, just as the knife alone does not cure cancer, so x-rays and radium alone do not cure malignant disease; it is the physician trained in the use of the knife or ionizing beam who may be able to do so.

The indications for surgery and radiology in present-day clinical practice are reasonably well defined. By early consultation and joint planning of treatment these indications can be realized in the best interest of the patient.

The results summarized in this chapter show that *arrests* are obtainable with competent radiotherapy in from 35–95 per cent of patients with cancer of accessible sites. In the group termed inaccessible, the arrest rate is much lower and the procedure of choice is frequently surgery alone, or surgery and postoperative radiotherapy. For inoperable or selected cases in this group, radiotherapy is of proven benefit for palliation.

The actual figures published here have been drawn from several sources, all regarded as reliable. However, it must be noted that many are from outstanding radiologists and surgeons, and reflect a degree of skill and experience not everywhere available. There is reason to believe that in average hands, that is, in the average clinic or hospital where a large number of cancers are *not* seen, the results (especially for the more difficult procedures) do not often attain the levels described. This difference in attainment applies to every field of endeavor, surgical, radiologic, and otherwise, and is an argument in favor of reasonable centralization of cancer therapy—not necessarily in "cancer hospitals" but at least in the hands of physicians (in or out of institutions) whose experience, enthusiasm and facilities for such work are maintained at high levels.

Radiotherapy in some form is useful in the treatment of about 60 per cent of patients with cancer. It is "curative" in perhaps half of these and palliative in the remainder.* The quotation marks around the word "curative" arise from the fact that in some tumors, notably those of the breast and bladder, late recurrences tend to adulterate five-year arrest results; however, in others, notably cancer of the skin, lip, cervix, and larynx, a majority of five-year arrests are maintained at ten-year reviews, allowing for factors such as age and intercurrent disease. These long-term results illustrate the permanent control of malignant disease obtainable by radiotherapy in certain sites.

REFERENCES

1. Ackerman, L. V., and del Regato, J. A. *Cancer.* Mosby Co., St. Louis, 1947.
2. Adair, F. E. Cancer therapeutic results, Memorial Hospital. Cancer is Curable. *Symposium, Am. Coll. Surgeons,* Chicago, 1950, pp. 16-20.
3. Andersen, S. R. Differentiation and irradiation. *Acta Radiol. 33:* 57-69, 1950.
4. Baclesse, F. Advanced cervico-uterine cancer. *Am. J. Roent. 63*: 252-254, 1950.
5. Baud, J. Carcinoma of the cervix (stage I) treated intracavitarily with radium alone. *J.A.M.A. 138:* 1138-1142, 1948.
6. Baud, J. End results of radiotherapy of cancer of the tongue. *Am. J. Roent. 63:* 701-711, 1950.
7. Bell, H. G. Cancer of the breast. *Am. Surg. 130:* 310-317, 1949.
8. Bervin, E. End results of treatment of cancer of the tongue. *Am. J. Roent. 63:* 712-715, 1950.
9. Brindley, G. V., and White, R. R. Report of five-year survivals in cancer of large intestine. Cancer is Curable. *Symposium, Am. Coll. Surgeons,* 1950, pp. 27-28.
10. Brown, J. B. and McDowell, F. Metastatic carcinoma of the neck. *Ann. Surg., 119:* 543-555, 1944.
11. Buschke, F. and Cantril, S. T. Roentgen therapy of bladder carcinoma, *Surg., Gyn., & Obst., 82:* 29-35, 1946.
12. Buschke, F., Cantil, S. T., and Parker, H. M. *Supervoltage Roentgen Therapy.* Thomas, Springfield, 1950.
13. Cantil, S. T. *Radiation Therapy in the Management of Cancer of the Uterine Cervix.* Thomas, Springfield, 1950.
14. Cade, S. Treatment of cancer of the tongue. *Am. J. Roent., 63:* 716-718, 1950.
15. Cohen, L. Clinical radiation dosage. *Brit. J. Radiol., 22:* 160-164, 706-713, 1949; *ibid. 23:* 25-27, 1950.
16. Costolow, W. E. Cancer of the cervical stump. *Radiology, 52:* 41-45, 1948.
17. Coutard, H. Die Roentgenbehandlung der epithelialen Krebse. *Strahlentherapie, 33:* 249-252, 1929.
18. Craver, L. Quoted by Adair, Ref. 2. See also *J.A.M.A., 136:* 244-249, 1948.
19. Daland, E. M. Untreated cancer of the breast. *Surg., Gyn. & Obst., 44:* 264-270, 1947.

* Actual data on five-year radiotherapy results from Paterson's[72] clinic are as follows: 33 per cent absolute survivals of 9872 registered cases with malignant disease; 39 per cent relative survivals of 8538 treated cases. Early lesions (Stages I and II) gave 62 per cent control; advanced lesions (Stages III and IV) gave 16 per cent. These do not include 1740 cases of basal cell carcinoma, in which about 99 per cent arrest was obtained.

20. EBENIUS, B. Cancer of the lip. *Acta Radiol. Suppl. 48:* 1943.
21. ELLIS, F. Tolerance dose with 200 KV rays. *Brit. J. Radiol., 15:* 348-350, 1942.
22. FAILLA, G. and QUIMBY, E. H. Economics of dosimetry in radiotherapy. *Am. J. Roent. 10:* 944-967, 1923.
23. GARLAND, L. H. Radiation therapy of laryngeal carcinoma. *West. J. Surg., 55:* 352-353, 1947.
24. GARLAND, L. H. and KENNEDY, B. R. Roentgen treatment of multiple myeloma. *Radiology, 50:* 297-317, 1948.
25. GARLAND, L. H. Radiation therapy of bronchogenic carcinoma. *Med. Staff Conferences, Univ. California 1:* 19-22, 1948.
26. GARLAND, L. H. The roles of surgery and radiology in the treatment of cancer. *Am. J. Roent. 62:* 858-870, 1949.
27. GARLAND, L. H. Radiological end results in the control of cancer. *J. Kansas M. Soc., 51:* 63a-70a, 1950.
28. GARLAND, L. H. The treatment of metastatic cervical nodes; discussion. *Radiology, 55:* 70, 1950.
29. GARLAND, L. H. and SISSON, M. A. Cancer of the ovary: Results of treatment in 79 cases. *J. Faculty Radiologists, 3:* 66-75, 1951.
30. GARLAND, L. H., BAKER, M., PICARD, W. H., JR., and SISSON, M. A. Roentgen and steroid hormone therapy in mammary cancer metastatic to bone. *J.A.M.A., 144:* 997-1004, 1950.
31. GARLAND, L. H. and SISSON, M. A. Results of irradiation in cancer of the lip, tongue and ear. *California Med., 73:* 312-318, 1950.
32. GLUCKSMANN, A. Preliminary observation on quantitative examination of human biopsy material. *Brit. J. Radiol., 14:* 187-198, 1941.
33. GRAHAM, E. Bronchogenic carcinoma. Cancer Is Curable. *Symposium, Am. Coll. Surgeons*, Chicago, 1950, pp. 25-27.
34. GRAHAM, H. and MEYER, N. Carcinoma of the nasopharynx. *Radiology, 50:* 83-91, 1948.
35. GREENWOOD, M. Natural duration of cancer. H.M.S.O., London, 1926.
36. GRIFFIN, A. C., BRANDT, E. L., and TATUM, E. L. Nitrogen mustards as cancer-inducing agents. *J.A.M.A. 144:* 571, 1950.
37. HAAGENSEN, C. D. Carcinoma of the breast. *J.A.M.A. 138:* 196-292, 1948.
38. HAAGENSEN, C. D. The treatment and results in cancer of the breast at the Presbyterian Hospital, New York. *Am. J. Roent. 62:* 328-334, 1949.
39. HAMANN, A. External irradiation with roentgen rays and radium in treatment of human leukemias, lymphomas, and allied disorders of hemopoietic system. *Radiology 50:* 378-385, 1948.
40. HANSSON, C. J. Resultatet vid prae—och postoperative behandling av cancer mammae vid Radiumhemmet. *Nord. Med. 8:* 2739-2745, 1940.
41. HARE, H. F. Cancer of thyroid. *Surg. Clin. North America 27:* 561-568, 1947.
42. HARRIS, W. Roentgen therapy for carcinoma of the larynx. *Radiology 51:* 708, 1948.
43. HEYMAN, J. International agreement on stage grouping in cancer of the cervix. *Acta obst. et gyn. Scandinav. 28:* 175-185, 1949.
44. HEYMAN, J. Cancer of the corpus. *Brit. J. Radiol. 20:* 85-91, 1947.
45. HODGES, F. J., LAMPE, I., and HOLT, J. F. Radiology for Medical Students. Yearbook Pub., Chicago, 1947.

46. Hodges, F. J. Recorded cancer results. Cancer Is Curable. *Symposium, Am. Coll. Surgeons*, Chicago, 1950, pp. 14-16.
47. Holmes, D. W., and Schultz, M. D. *Therapeutic Radiology*. Lea & Febiger, Philadelphia, 1950.
48. Hutchinson, R. G. The value of radiation therapy in cancer of the breast. *Surg., Gyn. & Obst. 62:* 653-663, 1936.
49. Jackson, C. L., Blady, J. V., Norris, C. M., and Maloney, W. H. Cancer of the larynx: Five year end results in series of patients treated between 1930-1942. *J.A.M.A. 138:* 1080-1083, 1948.
50. Karnofsky, D. A. Chemotherapy of neoplastic disease. *New England J. Med. 239:* 226-305, 1948.
51. Kelly, G. N., and Stentstrom, K. W. Testicular tumors. *Radiology 48:* 1-7, 1947.
52. Kinsell, L. W., Rogers, H., Baker, C., and Jenkins, B. J. Monocytic leukemia treated with ACTH. *J.A.M.A. 144:* 617-618, 1950.
53. Krebs, C., and Bichel, J. Roentgen treatment of chronic myelogenous leucosis. *Acta Radiol. 28:* 697-704, 1947.
54. Lenz, N. Roentgen therapy in cancer of the larynx. *J.A.M.A. 134:* 117-122, 1947.
55. Levi, L. M. Cancer of the breast. *Am. J. Surg. 68:* 355-357, 1950.
56. Low-Beer, B. V. A. *The Clinical Use of Radioactive Isotopes.* Thomas, Springfield, 1950.
57. McWhirter, R. Treatment of cancer of the breast by simple mastectomy and roentgentherapy. *Arch. Surg. 59:* 830-842, 1949.
58. McWhirter, R. Cerebral tumors. *Proc. Roy. Soc. Med. 39:* 673-680, 1946.
59. Martin, C. L. Treatment of cervical lymph node metastases with radiation alone. *Radiology 55:* 62-71, 1950.
60. Martin, H. Tongue cancer. Abstract, printed program, 30th Ann. Meet. Am. Radium Soc., 1948.
61. Martin, H., and Reese, A. B. Treatment of bilateral retinoblastoma (retinal glioma) surgically and by irradiation. *Arch. Ophthal. 33:* 429-439, 1945, *et ante.*
62. Merner, T. B., and Stentstrom, K. W. Roentgentherapy in Hodgkin's disease. *Staff Bull. Univ. Minnesota 17:* 262-277, 1947.
63. Meredith, W. J. *Radium Dosage.* Williams & Wilkins, Baltimore, 1947.
64. Modlin, J. J. Five-year results, Ellis Fischel State Cancer Hospital. Cancer Is Curable. *Symposium, Am. Coll. Surgeons,* Chicago, 1950, pp. 38-41.
65. Mohs, F. E. Chemosurgery in cutaneous malignancy. *California Med. 71:* 173-177, 1949.
66. Moore, R. A. Tumors of the testis. *J. Kansas M. Soc. 51:* 70a-75a, 1950.
67. Naffziger, H. C., and Boldrey, E. D. Cancer of the nervous system. *J.A.M.A. 136:* 96-105, 1948.
68. Nohrman, B. Cancer of the breast. *Acta Radiol. Suppl. 77*, 1948.
69. Ottenheimer, E. J. Experiences in the Curability of Cancer in Connecticut. Cancer Is Curable. *Symposium, Am. Coll. Surgeons,* Chicago, 1950, pp. 34-37.
70. Pack, G., and Livingston, C. N. *Treatment of Cancer and Allied Diseases.* Hoeber, New York, 1940.
71. Paterson, R. *Treatment of Malignant Disease by Radium and X-Ray.* Williams & Wilkins Co., Baltimore, 1948.
72. Paterson, R., Tod, M., and Russell, M. *Results of Radiotherapy in Malignant Diseases* (3rd statistical report). Livingstone, Edinburgh, 1950.

73. PATERSON, R. Treatment of cancer of the tongue. *Proc. Roy. Soc. Med. 40:* 412-415, 1947.
74. PIERCE, C. B., and BOUCHARD, J. Radiation therapy in brain tumors. *Radiology 55:* 337-344, 1950.
75. POHLE, E. A. *Clinical Radiation Therapy.* Lea & Febiger, Philadelphia, 1950.
76. POMEROY, L. Cancer of the cervix. *Am. J. Roent. 60:* 387-388, 1948.
77. PORTMANN, U. V. Cancer of the breast: Classification. *J.A.M.A. 144:* 513-516, 1950.
78. PORTMANN, U. V. Surgery and x-ray in cancer of the breast. *Radiology 10:* 377-387, 1928.
79. PORTMANN, U. V., in Pack and Livingston, Ref. 70.
80. PUESTOW, C. B. Cancer cures in a V.A. Hospital. Cancer Is Curable. *Symposium, Am. Coll. Surgeons*, Chicago, 1950, pp. 42-46.
81. REGAUD, C. Influence de la durée d'irradiation, etc. *Compt. rend. Soc. de biol. 86:* 787-790, 1922.
82. REINHARD, E. H. Chemotherapy of malignant neoplastic diseases. *J.A.M.A. 142:* 383-390, 1950.
83. RHOADS, C. P. Trends in cancer research. Tech. Bull. 10-66, Vet. Adm., Washington, D. C., Aug., 1950.
84. RICHARDS, G. Tongue cancer. Abstract, printed program, 30th Ann. Meet. Am. Radium Soc., 1948.
85. ROMER, R. J., and SATHER, T. O. Wilms's tumor. *Stanford M. Bull. 8:* 162-166, 1950.
86. ROSWIT, B., and KAPLAN, G. Nitrogen mustard in malignant disease. *Am. J. Roent. 61:* 626-636, 1949.
87. RUTISHAUSER, E. Carcinoma mammae. *Schweiz. Ztschr. f. Path. u. Bakt. 10:* 102-112, 1947.
88. SCARBOROUGH, J. E. Cancer cures in a university hospital (Atlanta). Cancer Is Curable. *Symposium, Am. Coll. Surgeons*, Chicago, 1950, p. 24.
89. SHORBON, L. N. Bronchial carcinoma. *Brit. J. Radiol. 20:* 443-449, 1947.
90. SIEVERT, R. N. Medical radiophysics in Sweden 1920 to 1950. *Acta Radiol. 33:* 191-252, 1950.
91. SMITHERS, D. W. *X-ray Treatment of Accessible Cancer.* Williams & Wilkins, Baltimore, 1946.
92. STENSTROM, K. W., and BAGGENSTOSS, O. J. Surgery and radiation for cancer of the breast. *Acta Radiol. 28:* 623-632, 1947.
93. STRANDQUIST, M. Studien über die kumulative Wirkung der Roentgenstrahlen bei Fraktionierung. *Acta Radiol. Suppl.* 55-56, 1944.
94. TAYLOR, G. W. Cancer of the breast. *Internat. Abs. Surg. 55:* 1, 1932.
95. TAYLOR, G. W. Cures of cancer at the Massachusetts General Hospital. Cancer Is Curable. *Symposium. Am. Coll. Surgeons,* Chicago, 1950, pp. 21-23.
96. TAYLOR, G. W. Treatment and results in cancer of the breast. *Am. J. Roent. 62:* 341-344, 1949.
97. THAYSSEN, V. E. Influence of castration by Roentgen on carcinoma of the breast. *Acta Radiol. 29:* 189-204, 1948.
98. TRAPP, E., and HARDIE, M. Cancer of the corpus. *Canad. M. A. J. 58:* 115-118, 1948.
99. TREVES, N., ABELS, J. C., WOODARD, H. Q., and FARROW, J. H. Effect of Orchiectomy on primary and metastatic carcinoma of the breast. *Surg., Gyn. & Obst. 79:* 589-605, 1944.

100. WADE, P. Untreated cancer of the breast. *Brit. J. Radiol. 19:* 272-280, 1946.
101. WANGENSTEEN, O. Discussion of Bell, H. G., see Ref. 7.
102. WETHERELL, F. S. Variables in attainment of five-year cancer cures. Cancer Is Curable. *Symposium, Am. Coll. Surgeons*, Chicago, 1950, pp. 9-13.
103. WILLIAMS, I. G. Carcinoma of rectum: high voltage roentgen radiation results. *Brit. J. Surg. 36:* 376-381, 1949.
104. WINDEYER, B. W. End results and treatment of cancer of the tongue. *Am. J. Roent. 63:* 719-726, 1950.
105. WINDEYER, B. W. Present position of radiotherapy in medical practice. *J.A.M.A. 140:* 665-669, 1949.
106. WOOD, C. A. P. The technique and results of treatment of cancer of the tongue with 10 gram radium beam unit. *Am. J. Roent. 63:* 727-738, 1950.

CHAPTER 32

Applied Radiation in Diagnosis (Isotopes)

Bertram Selverstone

The fact that important metabolic differences exist between malignant and normal tissues forms the basis for the infant technology of cancer detection by means of radioactive isotopes. Application of isotopic tracer technics to studies of the fate of various metabolites in normal and malignant tissues has resulted in a rapid increase in our knowledge of these differences. The present narrow field of usefulness for isotopes in the diagnosis of cancer cannot fail to expand with the growth of our understanding of the metabolism of neoplastic tissue.

Before the advent of tracer technics, methods for investigation of the metabolic fate of a compound were largely unphysiologic. It was necessary to administer a large excess of the substance in the hope that, by means of analytic chemistry, variations in uptake might be detected in neoplastic as compared with normal tissues. Such experiments did not necessarily reflect differences which would have been produced by the administration of physiologic amounts of the material. Then, too, it was not possible to distinguish the fate of the newly administered molecular species from that of similar molecules already in the tissue. "Tagging" of compounds by the substitution of detectable chemical substances provided an early approach to the problem, a successful one in the hands of Knoop, for example, who was able to use phenylated fatty acids in order to demonstrate beta-oxidation. Such methods are, however, unphysiological, and their usefulness must depend upon the fortuitous presence of a biochemical "blind spot" in the system under consideration.

Fortunately, there exist or can be produced detectably different *isotopes* of the various chemical elements. The chemical properties of each element depend upon the configuration of its outermost shell of orbital electrons. The various isotopes of a single element have identical outer shells and chemical properties. Compounds incorporating various isotopes of the same element must, therefore, undergo virtually identical metabolic changes in the body. Isotopes of the same element do differ, however, in the masses and configurations of their nuclei. The nuclei of some isotopes are stable; they can be distinguished from other isotopes of the same element and their abundance can be determined by means of mass spectrometry or by careful measurements of their density. The nuclei of many isotopes are unstable; these can be detected with much greater ease, since they can be distinguished from chemically identical species by their radioactive emission.

It is clear, then, that metabolic pathways can be traced by the utilization of a detectable isotope of the atomic species to be studied, either as an element or, more commonly, after its incorporation into an appropriate chemical compound. Hevesy,[23] in 1923, first employed a radioactive isotope as a metabolic tracer. The existence of a naturally occurring radioactive isotope of lead made it possible for him to study the absorption and distribution of lead in plants. Tracer studies of important biologic significance were reported by Schoenheimer and Rittenberg[57] in 1935 employing the stable isotope of hydrogen, H^2, which had been discovered by Urey in 1932. In 1934 Joliot and Curie[25] announced the discovery of artificially induced radioactivity. Since that time, an increasing variety of radioactive isotopes of biologically important substances has been made available, both from the cyclotron and now, in increasing variety and abundance, from the nuclear reactor, or "atomic pile." Hevesy,[24] Lawrence and Hamilton,[31] Kamen,[27] and Siri[67] have provided useful introductions to the extensive literature dealing with the application of tracer technics to biologic and medical problems. This discussion will be restricted to the use of radioactive substances in the diagnosis of cancer.

RADIOACTIVE PHOSPHORUS

EXPERIMENTAL BASIS

An increased uptake of radioactive phosphorus, P^{32}, in animal tumors was demonstrated by Jones, Chaikoff, and Lawrence[26] and by Lawrence, Erf, and Tuttle.[30] Kenney, Marinelli, and Woodard[28] administered radioactive phosphate ion to patients with carcinoma of the breast and other malignant tumors. They measured the uptake of P^{32} in carcinoma, normal breast, metastases, lymph nodes, fat, and other tissues. Higher activities were demonstrated in the carcinoma than in normal breast tissue, with high activities also in lymph nodes, both normal and diseased. Activity in muscle was comparable to that in the tumor. It is noteworthy that the lowest activity was found in fat. Schulman, Falkenheim, and Gray[58] showed that the rate of turnover of phosphorus by gastric carcinoma is 45 per cent higher than the rate in normal gastric mucosa, although the total phosphorus content of the two do not differ. Selverstone and Solomon[61] administered buffered radioactive phosphate solution intravenously to patients with brain tumors. The radioactivity of the tumor was found to be from 5 to 112 times that of adjacent normal white matter. Although the total phosphorus content of brain tumors is consistently less than that of normal brain, the rate of uptake of P^{32} in tumors is much higher than in brain. The phospholipid and, to a lesser extent, the acid-soluble fractions of brain tumors are chiefly responsible for these differences, although the nucleoprotein fraction does show significant differences.[60] Changus, Chaikoff, and Ruben[6] demonstrated that the turnover of P^{32} in the lipid fraction of normal brain is lower than that in other organs. It appears that the strikingly greater uptake of P^{32} in brain tumors than in normal brain results, in large part, from the low uptake of P^{32} in normal cerebral tissue.

PROPERTIES OF P^{32}

Radioactive phosphorus, P^{32}, has a half-life of 14.3 days, a period sufficiently long to permit reasonable convenience in obtaining and storing it, yet short enough to minimize the exposure of the patient to its ionizing radiation. When administered as buffered sodium phosphate solution, it has virtually no chemical toxicity. Its radiation consists purely of negative beta particles with a maximum energy of 1.69 million electron volts. Such an energy level has been shown to permit a maximum penetration in the tissues (assuming a density of 1.0) of approximately 7 mm.[16] This characteristic of its radiation has the advantage of permitting considerable precision of localization, but obviously makes it unsatisfactory for the localization of lesions farther than 7 mm. from the nearest point to which a Geiger-Mueller counter or other detector can be brought.

The energetic beta particles of P^{32} are ideally suited for detection by means of the Geiger-Mueller counter. The shape and size of the sensitive volume of the counter will depend upon its specific application. The beta particles of P^{32} are also readily detectable by means of the radioautographic technic.

DIAGNOSIS OF CARCINOMA OF THE BREAST

Following the observation of Marinelli and Goldschmidt[40] that malignant cutaneous lesions might be demonstrated by means of increased uptake of P^{32}, Low-Beer and his associates[34, 35, 36, 41] at the University of California undertook to determine whether malignant breast tumors and their lymph-node metastases, lying within 7 mm. of the surface, could be localized by similar means. They sought also to discover whether benign lesions could be distinguished from carcinomas by this method. After intravenous administration of from 300 to 500 microcuries of P^{32}, surface measurements were made at intervals of from two to 48 hours, using glass-window Geiger-Mueller counters of diameter from 1.5 to 2.5 cm. Counts were made over the palpable breast tumor, over a comparable area of the opposite normal breast, and over various other portions of the body. Assays of tumor, breast tissues, skin, fat, and muscle were made after operation.

In 16 of 17 patients with benign breast lesions, no increase in counting rate was obtained. In 14 patients with cellular carcinomas, an increased activity of 25 per cent or more was found. In 3 patients with mucoid carcinoma, 2 with deeply placed lesions, and 1 with a very small lesion, significant increases in activity were not demonstrated. Excellent demonstrations of postoperative recurrence, or of lymph node metastases could be obtained in 15 cases. Inflamed or ulcerated lesions, whether benign or malignant, showed marked increases in radioactivity. Two patients whose metastatic skin nodules were assayed before and after hormone therapy showed decreased readings after such therapy. Similar observations were noted in patients whose metastatic lesions had been irradiated.

Although measurements were frequently suggestive as early as six hours after administration of P^{32}, more reliable observations could be made after twenty-four to forty-eight hours. Low-Beer emphasizes the importance of selecting truly comparable control areas in terms of blood supply, proximity to large vessels, closeness to bone, etc.

Detection of carcinoma of the breast by means of P^{32} is an accomplished fact, but it must be considered as a confirmatory rather than a diagnostic test. Falsely positive indications will be obtained in inflammatory lesions; from the clinical point of view these errors are not nearly so serious as the falsely negative counts obtained from small, localized malignant lesions. Deep cancers also may not be detected. A negative P^{32} study of a patient with a suspected lesion of the breast should never delay excision biopsy, with preparation for radical mastectomy.

LOCALIZATION OF BRAIN TUMORS

In the attack upon a subcortical cerebral tumor, precise localization is a major problem. Neurologic examination and careful study of ventriculograms permit, with rare exceptions, the planning of a craniotomy directly overlying the neoplasm. The appearance of the exposed cortex, however, may frequently give no adequate clue as to the exact situation or extent of the underlying lesion. Soundings taken with a ventricular cannula are so frequently unsatisfactory, unless a cyst is encountered, that a more precise method has long been sought. Even when a definite tumor has been found, its gross appearance and consistency are frequently much like those of normal cerebral tissue, so that it may fade almost indistinguishably into the surrounding brain. Seeking a method for the location and demarcation of brain tumors, Selverstone and Solomon[61] found a much higher uptake of P^{32} in cerebral tumors than in brain tissue. In 1948, using a miniature Geiger-Mueller counter designed and constructed by Robinson,[54, 55] they successfully located brain tumors at operation. Selverstone, Solomon, and Sweet[62] subsequently reported 14 such cases; additional reports now include 114 cases.[59, 64, 65]

The patient is given an intravenous injection of 1–2 mc. of buffered radioactive phosphate ion from twelve to twenty-four hours before operation. No other preparation is necessary. The standard methods for approximate brain tumor localization are employed where appropriate, often including either ventriculography or arteriography. When the condition of the patient does not permit such special studies, a large craniotomy is planned on the basis of clinical localization, with the comforting assurance that the precise location and extent of the lesion can be determined at operation by means of the probe counter.

After exposure of the cortex, a "control area" is chosen, usually in the periphery of the exposed field, in a region considered least likely to be the site of the tumor. The probing Geiger-Mueller counter, 2 mm. in diameter, is then introduced into the brain. By means of a preamplifier and scaling circuit or, even more simply, using a battery-operated portable count-rate meter as shown in Fig. 151, readings are made at 1 cm. increments of depth. Each reading requires only twelve to twenty-four seconds with the scaler, or half that time with the count-rate meter. The counter is then employed in suspected regions in a similar manner until a sharp increase in counting rate indicates that the neoplasm has been reached. After the tumor has been located in this manner, the counter is cleansed with hydrogen peroxide in order to prevent possible spread of malignant cells, and successive approaches are made from the peripheral normal brain toward the tumor in order to demarcate its boundaries.

A preliminary delineation on the surface of the brain of a large fatal glioblastoma multiforme is shown (Fig. 152), together with the actual extent of the tumor at postmortem examination. The correlation of counting rates at operation with the gross extent of the tumor is clear. It is not implied that, microscopically, a number of tumor cells may not extend out for long distances in relatively normal brain.

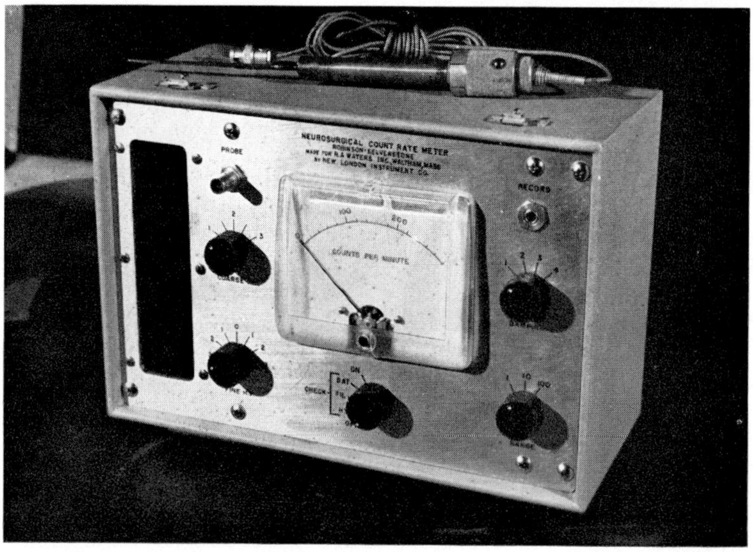

FIG. 151. Neurosurgical count-rate meter used in the operating room for localization and demarcation of brain tumors. The probing counter, 2 mm. in diameter, is also shown.

The method does, however, make it possible for the surgeon to obtain a valid biopsy from active tumor tissue, to decide in advance whether the size and location of a neoplasm make it inoperable, or to plan a radical lobectomy, if indicated.

RADIOACTIVE IODINE

EXPERIMENTAL BASIS

The normal thyroid concentrates iodine several thousandfold, an observation which was made by Marine[38] long before the advent of radioactive tracer technics. A test dose of radioactive iodine is rapidly concentrated by the thyroid; its arrival can be simply and strikingly demonstrated by means of an externally placed Geiger-Mueller counter.[17, 20] The applicability of *in vivo* tracer technics to quantitative studies of thyroid function in clinical hyperthyroidism was early recognized.[19, 21] Since synthesis and release of its hormone parallel uptake by the thyroid of iodine

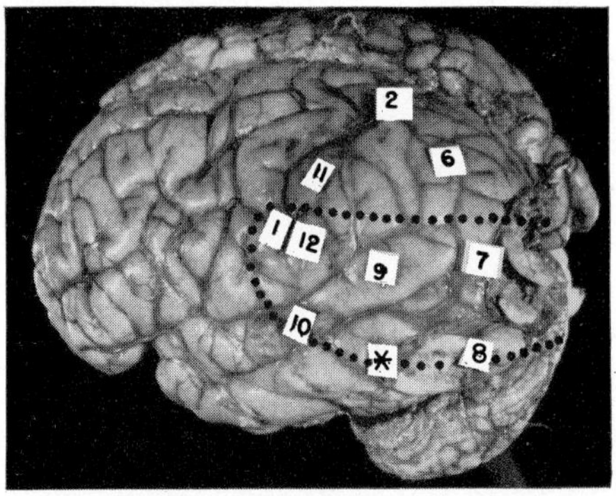

••••••Indicate actual extent of deep tumor

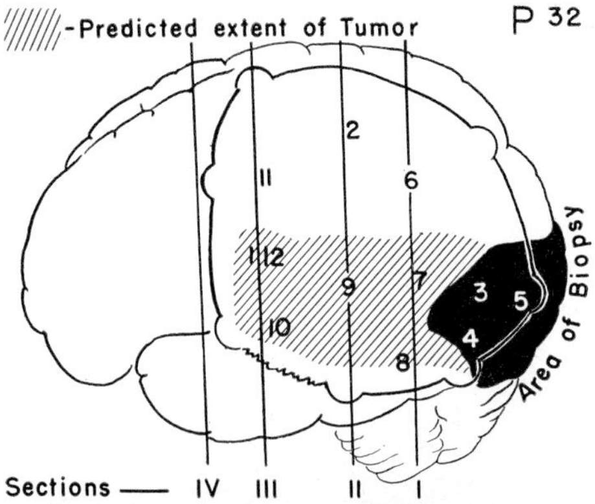

Sections —— IV III II I

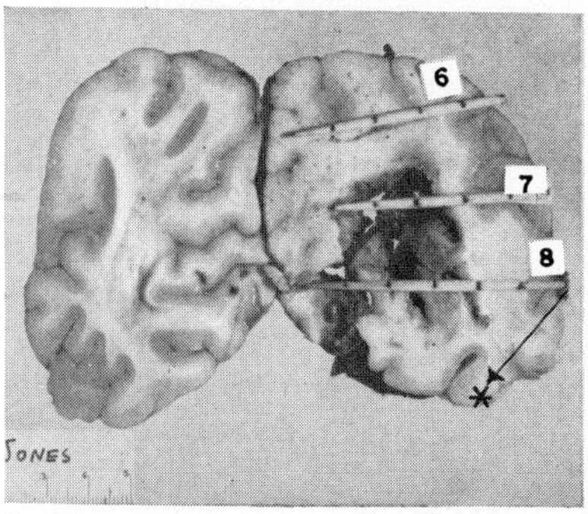

Section-I ——Depth——

Geiger C/M Site	5.5 cm.	4 cm.	3 cm.	2 cm.	*
6		370		275	
7		2370		6362	
8	11320			8187	665

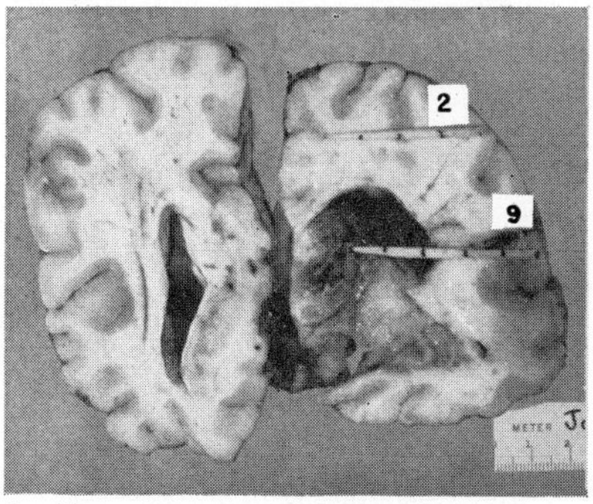

Section - II ——Depth——

Geiger C/M Site	4 cm.	3 cm.	2 cm.	1 cm.
2	330		571	
9	13385		1390	

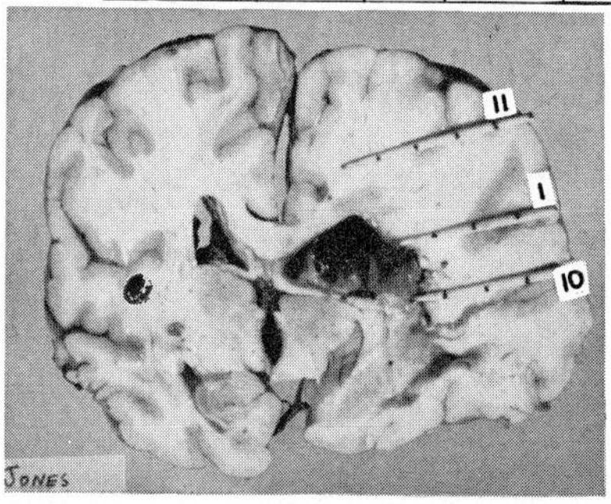

Section-III ——Depth——

Geiger C/M Site	4 cm.	3 cm.	2 cm	1 cm
11	460		340	
1-12	4845	2485		
10		12,585	2675	

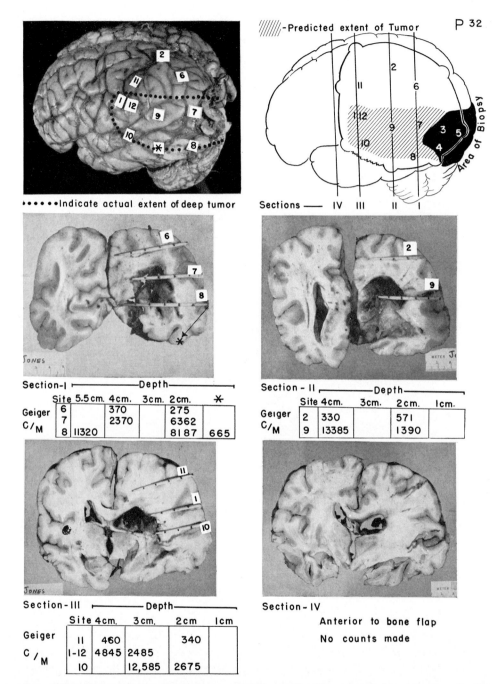

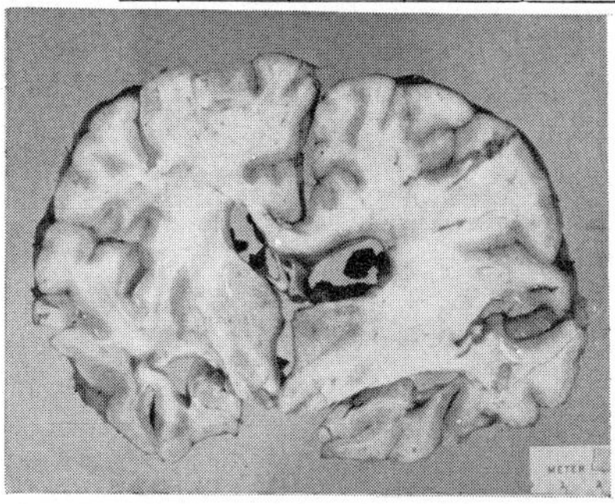

Section - IV

Anterior to bone flap
No counts made

FIG. 152. Deep-seated glioblastoma multiforme.[65] (By permission of the J. B. Lippincott Company.)

from the blood stream, simple external measurements of radioactivity afford a useful index of thyroid function.

Benign tumors of the thyroid exhibit capacities for concentration of radioactive iodine which have been shown by Cope, Rawson, McArthur, Dobyns, and their collaborators to be correlated closely with their histologic structure.[7, 11, 52] Non-functioning adenomas, and especially those which are least differentiated, concentrate iodine either not at all, or much less than does the normal thyroid. Dobyns and Lennon[11] showed that adenomas with uniform cellular hyperplasia may concentrate iodine to a remarkable degree, while those which show variation in cell heights may be completely lacking in this property.

It is not surprising that there is much variation in the degree to which carcinomas of the thyroid concentrate radioactive iodine. Hamilton, Soley, and Eichorn,[18] in the first reported study of thyroid carcinoma by these technics, found no concentration of radioiodine in their two cancers. Keston, Ball, Frantz, and Palmer[13, 29] first succeeded in demonstrating selective concentration of radioactive iodine in carcinoma of the thyroid. Marinelli and his collaborators found that iodine uptake was closely correlated with an orderly arrangement of cells and the presence of colloid in the carcinoma.[39] Malignant adenomas and mixed tumors show a marked uptake of radioiodine, in contrast to papillary carcinomas and poorly differentiated lesions.[14] Rawson and Trunnell[53] report that the iodine-concentrating capacity of certain metastatic carcinomas of the thyroid can be significantly increased by total removal or destruction of the normal thyroid, by the administration of thyroid stimulating hormone, or by prolonged treatment with thiouracil. Should methods such as these for altering isotopic uptake prove to be more generally applicable, they may be of fundamental importance both in the diagnosis and in the treatment of cancer by means of radioactive isotopes.

PROPERTIES OF I^{131}

Iodine^{131}, which has a half-life of 8 days, is a much more convenient substance for clinical use than the 25-minute I^{128} or the 12.6-hour I^{130} of the early investigators. When administered as sodium iodide solution, either by mouth or intravenously, it has virtually no chemical toxicity. I^{131} emits both beta particles and gamma rays of several energy levels, the maximum of each type having an energy of about 0.6 million electron volts. The beta particles are readily detectable by means of end-window Geiger-Mueller counters but are of no value for external localization. For precise histologic localization of the isotope, these beta particles have an energy well suited to radioautographic methods. For external localization, the gamma rays of I^{131} may be measured by means of the Geiger-Mueller counter, although special types employing cathodes of platinum, bismuth, lead, or copper are desirable in order to obtain reasonably high gamma counting efficiency. Better results are obtained when gamma radiation is measured by means of the scintillation counter.

DIAGNOSIS OF CARCINOMA OF THE THYROID

Although many carcinomas of the thyroid show a significant uptake of I^{131}, the normal gland takes up the isotope in even higher concentration. While certain benign adenomas do show an uptake of I^{131} higher than that of the normal thyroid, no such avidity has been demonstrated in malignant tumors. It is possible that, with the development of increasingly precise methods of gamma-ray scanning,[5] a *negative* image of an area of *decreased* function may be correlated with the site of a carcinoma. A nonfunctioning benign tumor would, however, produce a similar pattern. At the present time, a primary carcinoma of the thyroid cannot be diagnosed or localized by means of I^{131}.

Functioning metastases from thyroid carcinoma may be readily detected by means of I^{131}.[33] Either a Geiger-Mueller or a scintillation counter may be used. It should be provided with a suitable lead shield 2–3 cm. in thickness in order to provide directional collimation of the gamma rays from the lesion. Methods employed in many hospitals for the study of total I^{131} uptake in thyroid disease are not generally suitable for precise localization of a metastasis. Counts may be made from eight to twenty-four hours after administration of a "tracer dose" (100–150 μc.) of I^{131} by mouth. A striking increase in counting rate should immediately be apparent when a functioning metastasis is brought within the solid angle viewed by the lead "telescope."

A similar technic may be employed during the immediate postoperative period, in order to verify the completeness of a radical thyroidectomy for carcinoma. I^{131} may also be used in order to distinguish local recurrences of *functioning* carcinoma from inflammatory lymphadenopathy.

RADIOACTIVE POTASSIUM

EXPERIMENTAL BASIS

Radioactive potassium has been widely used in studies of body electrolytes and of adrenal physiology. Its predominantly intracellular localization suggests, however, that it may be a substance of increasing usefulness in cancer diagnosis. As the major intracellular cation, potassium offers an obvious analogy to phosphate, the principal anion. Selverstone, Sweet, and Ireton[63] administered ionic K^{42} to 45 patients with brain tumors. Samples of tumor tissue taken during the first six hours after injection, in 8 patients with glioblastoma multiforme, showed that the isotope had been concentrated from 20 to 97.9 times as compared with the cerebral white matter. After eighteen hours, the ratio between tumor and white matter had fallen to values between 3.9 and 9.6. Results with other types of cerebral tumors were similar; in one case of metastatic carcinoma the concentration ratio of the isotope reached 168:1. Astrocytomas, however, did not usually yield such useful ratios as did other tumors.

PROPERTIES OF K^{42}

The isotope of potassium which is at present widely available from the nuclear reactor is K^{42}. Its half-life of 12.44 hours makes it inconvenient for routine clinical use, but it can be obtained in sufficiently high specific activity to permit its use for about 72 hours after shipment. Because of its high specific activity, the chemical toxicity of reasonable doses of ionic K^{42} has not been a problem; electrocardiographic tracings during a one-minute injection have shown no abnormalities. K^{42} emits beta particles of high energy, 2.04 and 3.58 million electron volts. Its gamma ray of 1.51 million electron volts is unusually energetic, requiring cumbersome lead shielding both for shipment and for directional collimation. The beta particles are readily detectable by ordinary Geiger-Mueller counters, as are the gamma rays. For high counting efficiency, the scintillation counter is especially suited to gamma counting of K^{42}, and it is the gamma ray which must be used for external localization of all but the most superficial tumors.

If K^{43} should become widely available, its increased half-life of 22.4 hours and less energetic gamma radiation of 0.4 million electron volts may increase the clinical usefulness of radioactive potassium. Since K^{43} must be obtained from the cyclotron, where it is produced by the bombardment of argon by deuterons,[49] it is not as readily obtainable as K^{42}.

DETECTION OF BRAIN TUMORS

Localization of brain tumors at operation with K^{42} can be undertaken by means of the probing 2-mm. Geiger-Mueller counter of Robinson. Inasmuch as the beta particles of K^{42} possess an energy more than twice those of P^{32}, it is theoretically possible to obtain some increased counting at distances as great as 1.8 cm. from the tumor, through normal brain. The gamma rays of K^{42} fortunately do not constitute a major problem, since the 2-mm. counter is relatively inefficient for this type of radiation. Selverstone and White[65] reported 35 correct and 1 false negative localization study, using this method, which is essentially similar to the probe-counting technic employing P^{32}. Useful counting ratios are obtained more rapidly with K^{42} than with P^{32}, within as little as ten to fifteen minutes in some cases, a property which may be of advantage in an emergency. The greater range of the more energetic beta particles of K^{42} saves time in locating a small tumor, but makes for less accurate demarcation of the lesion after it has been found.

Detection of cerebral tumors through the intact skull and scalp is possible with K^{42} because of its gamma ray. It poses problems, however, which are not encountered when a probe counter is introduced directly into a neoplasm. While the uptake of K^{42} is ordinarily much higher in the tumor than in the brain, its uptake in the scalp and muscles is intermediate between these levels. The operation of the inverse square law exaggerates scalp and muscle counts and minimizes the contribution of a deep tumor to the observed total counting rate. For example, let us consider a small counter which is placed in line with a point source *S*, representing scalp radioactivity, and an equivalent point source *T*, representing radioactivity within a brain tumor. If the counter lies 0.5 cm. from *S* and 5 cm. from *T*, the contribution from *T* to the total counting rate will be only 1/100 that from *S*. Scalp counts would thus far overshadow those from the tumor. If the counter is now removed 10 cm. farther from *S*, to a point 10.5 cm. from *S* and 15 cm. from *T*, counts recorded from *T* will be approximately one half as numerous as those from *S*, and observed scalp activity will no longer completely overshadow the contribution of the tumor to the total counting rate.

Using the technic of Selverstone, Sweet, and Ireton,[63] the patient receives an intravenous dose of approximately 1 mc. of a solution of $K^{42}Cl$. Within twenty to thirty minutes, counting is begun with a heavily shielded scintillation counter at various standard sites over the calvarium, keeping the "telescope" always perpendicular either to the coronal or to the sagittal plane of the head. Symmetrical regions on the two sides are counted consecutively, going back and forth as often as necessary, in order to minimize the standard deviation of the counting rate.

When the counter was separated from the scalp only by the thin shield used to eliminate superficial beta emission, increases in counting rate caused by the tumor were usually in the range of 15 per cent to 25 per cent with a maximum of 65.4 per cent in one case. Eight of 10 supratentorial tumors were so localized and 7 of 8 negative studies were proved correct by pneumography or by operation. No indication of the presence of a tumor was obtained in 5 subtentorial neoplasms, where the thick suboccipital muscle mass was interposed. The results of Susen, Small, and F. D. Moore,[71] reported at the same meeting, were in essential agreement with these, although they found some evidence also of late localization of K^{42} in certain tumors.

When the sensitive volume of the counter is withdrawn 10 cm. from the scalp, increases have been found in net counting rate of from 49 per cent to 547 per cent in 15 cases. Nevertheless, 3 supratentorial tumors, 2 of which were meningiomas of 6 and 8 gm. respectively, were not localized. This new method was still ineffective for subtentorial tumors. In 10 cases where no tumor was subsequently found, no falsely positive indications were obtained.

Although radioactive potassium offers promise as a substance which may be useful for external localization of brain tumors, it must still be considered to be of confirmatory value only. A negative study does not rule out a brain tumor nor does a positive study provide sufficient confidence to justify a craniotomy without the more reliable indications obtained from ventriculography or angiography.

DETECTION OF CARCINOMA OF THE BREAST

Since diagnosis of carcinoma of the breast by means of the P^{32} method of Low-Beer and his associates[35] is limited to lesions within 7 mm. of the surface, the gamma radiation of K^{42} has been used. Baker, Nathanson, and Selverstone[2] have given K^{42} intravenously in doses from 300 to 500 μc. to 60 patients, in an attempt to differentiate between benign and malignant lesions of the breast. Adipose tissue, which constitutes a large proportion of the bulk of most female breasts, has a low uptake of K^{42}. When the shielded counter is directed from a lateral position, attempting to remove the mass of the thorax from the solid angle viewed by the "telescope," striking increases in counting rate are frequently observed when a carcinoma is present. Thirty of 33 malignant tumors were correctly predicted. Two of the falsely negative studies occurred in patients with small intraductal Grade I adenocarcinomas, one of which was found on only a single slide of the frozen sections. The third incorrect study was made in a patient with Paget's disease of the nipple. In 27 patients with benign lesions, 2 of which were inflammatory, no falsely positive indications were obtained.

Here again, this method for the detection of a carcinoma by means of a radioactive isotope must be considered to be of confirmatory value only. A negative isotope study should not influence the clinical management of a patient with a lesion of the breast.

RADIOACTIVE DYES

EXPERIMENTAL BASIS

The notion that a foreign dyestuff might be found which would localize in malignant tissues is an attractive one. A number of investigators, studying malignant tumors in animals, have demonstrated such localization, using trypan blue,[37] acid azo-dyes,[22] and fluorescein.[66] Localization of dyes in tumors apparently occurs in the stroma, a function either of abnormally permeable blood vessels, of associated reticuloendothelial elements, or both.[77] In an attempt at clinical application of such observations, Moore[44] gave fluorescein intravenously to patients with carcinoma of the stomach, attempting to demonstrate differential fluorescence of the neoplasm at operation. Using ultraviolet illumination, he observed differences between carcinoma and surrounding tissues, but results were not sufficiently reliable or consistent to be clinically useful.

Friedemann[15] points out that the cerebral capillaries are impermeable to negatively charged dyes. This property, one of the manifestations of the so-called "blood-brain barrier," is not necessarily shared by tumors of the brain. Sorsby, Wright, and Elkeles[68] attempted to stain cerebral tumors in vivo, using a 10 per cent solution of kiton green. The dye passed through the capillary walls of granulomatous lesions and of traumatized brain, but did not stain gliomas. Using fluorescein, G. E. Moore[44] succeeded in producing differential staining of cerebral tumors, including gliomas, and with Peyton, French, and Walker,[51] applied the method as a clinical tool in neurosurgery. Patients receive 1.0 gm. of sodium fluorescein immediately before craniotomy. At operation, superficial tumors are seen to fluoresce when the cortex is examined under ultraviolet light. Biopsies from deep tumors have this property also, and can be examined with a Woods' lamp in the operating room.

F. D. Moore and Tobin[42, 73] synthesized di-azo dyes, tagged with radioactive bromine, Br^{82}. By means of in vivo counting, they demonstrated the concentration of such radioactive dyes in areas of inflammation and, with Aub[43] studied their distribution in tumor-bearing mice. G. E. Moore[45] synthesized radioactive diiodofluorescein and, in 1948, reported its use in 12 cases for localization of brain tumors.

LOCALIZATION OF BRAIN TUMORS

G. E. Moore with Peyton, French, and their collaborators in Minneapolis have reported excellent results with diiodofluorescein for preoperative, external localization of cerebral tumors.[46, 47, 48] One millicurie of the radioactive dye is injected intravenously and, one half to four hours later, symmetrical areas of the head are measured for radioactivity by means of a shielded Geiger-Mueller or scintillation counter. Moore emphasizes that the test does not differentiate between tumors and other lesions, such as localized encephalitis, which may disrupt the blood-brain barrier. Decreased counting rates over subdural hematomas led occasionally to false localization of a tumor in the opposite hemisphere. In general, however, most brain tumors, and especially the more malignant lesions, concentrated the dye sufficiently to permit satisfactory localization studies. In a recent series of 33 consecutive patients, Moore and his collaborators report 28 accurate diagnoses, 2 errors, and 3 patients still under observation.

Ashkenazy, Davis, Martin, and their group in Chicago emphasize the importance of determining "normal" values for the concentration of the radiodye.[1, 9] In a series of normal controls, they determined the range of external counting rates in 32 standard locations on the skull, at various time intervals after injection. After injecting 1.0–1.2 mc. of Tabern's purified, highly stable preparation of I^{131}, the counting tube is placed in a standard position over the left temporal muscle and kept there for fifteen to forty minutes until the counts reach a plateau. Symmetrical areas of the skull are consecutively counted for three-minute periods until all 32 positions have been assayed. Symmetrical areas are said to differ, in normal individuals, by less than 40 counts per minute, with differences from 40 to 90 c.p.m. in slowly growing lesions to as high as 200 c.p.m. in anaplastic or highly vascular lesions. The count rate over a vascular or neoplastic lesion is said to exceed by 100–600 c.p.m. the rate to be expected at the comparable site in a normal individual. The Chicago group report the accurate diagnosis of 52 of 60 gliomas, together with a large number of miscellaneous lesions, some of which were localized by an increased and others by a decreased counting rate. Only 17 "proven inaccuracies" were encountered in 340 studies, including both positive and presumed negative cases. Ashkenazy has recently had much experience with the use of human serum albumen tagged with radioactive I^{131}. He has obtained results essentially similar to those which he has reported with radioactive diiodofluorescein but has found it possible, with labeled albumen, to make repeated determinations over a twenty-four-hour period.

Belcher and Evans[3] designed a highly efficient scintillation counter for detection of brain tumors by means of radioactive diiodofluorescein. Their theoretical computations[4] indicated that a tenfold concentration of the dye in tumor would permit the detection of a 14 ml. tumor at a depth of 5 cm. or a 36 ml. tumor at a depth of 8 cm., in the center of the brain. DeWinter,[10] working with Belcher and Evans, attempted to localize 20 verified brain tumors. Only one of the 20 tumors investigated was definitely picked up by means of radioactive diiodofluorescein. In the remaining 19 cases, including gliomas of several types, meningiomas, and an acoustic neurinoma, it was impossible to detect any asymmetry that could be related to a concentrating lesion at a definite position. Svien and his collaborators at the Mayo Clinic[72] have also been disappointed with the use of radioactive diiodofluorescein and radioactive iodinated human serum albumen. In their recent series they have been able to obtain satisfactory localization of lesions in only 26 per cent of cases.

Schlesinger[56] has attempted to outline specific causes of failure of the diiodofluorescein method. Eliminating all cases in which "there was the slightest suspicion of hemisphere to hemisphere differences in dye uptake," 14 cases remained in 100 patients with space-occupying lesions. Errors fell into 3 groups: tumors which did not have a rich blood supply, cysts, and vascular anomalies.

The place of radiodyes in the diagnosis of brain tumors has not yet been determined. Their usefulness in the hands of certain investigators makes it clear that there is sufficient promise to justify development of improved technics, both chemical and physical, in this field. The radiodye methods may perhaps be likened to electroencephalography, a useful confirmatory test for supratentorial brain tumor. Clinical examination and radiographic contrast methods are still the mainstays of brain tumor diagnosis.

INSTRUMENTATION

The physical armamentarium for diagnosis of cancer by means of radioactive isotopes has begun to surpass the biochemical and metabolic information necessary for its application. Wrenn, Good, and Handler[76] have described a most ingenious method for the localization of brain tumors, employing substances which emit positrons. Since positrons are rapidly annihilated, with the simultaneous emergence of two oppositely directed gamma rays, counting of these quanta in coincidence should provide a truly directional counting system, with the directional characteristic inherent in the radiation itself. The problem remaining is the discovery of an isotope which, like P^{32} or K^{42}, will concentrate in the brain tumor, but which is an emitter of positrons. A dye, sulfonated copper phthalocyanine, synthesized with Cu^{64}, a positron emitter, has been studied by Wrenn, Good, and Handler. In our hands, this dye has failed to concentrate usefully in human cerebral tumors.

Copeland and Benjamin[8] suggest a pinhole camera which might be used to form an image of a biologic gamma ray source. Such a device may be made reasonably sensitive by the interposition of a phosphor before the photographic film. There remains, however, the problem of concentrating a gamma emitter in a neoplasm in sufficiently high differential concentration to provide a useful image.

Radioautography has become a tool of considerable precision in the hands of Steinberg and Solomon,[70] LeBlond,[32] Pelc,[50] Evans,[12] and others. Dobyns and Lennon[11] and Steinberg and Selverstone[69] have used the method in diagnosis in an attempt to add quantitative physiologic data to the morphologic criteria ordinarily employed in the characterization of a neoplasm.

AVAILABILITY

The Isotopes Division of the United States Atomic Energy Commission has encouraged and fostered the use of radioactive substances in the diagnosis of cancer. Protection of the patient is afforded by the Subcommittee on Human Applications, who provide a panel of experienced investigators to consider the safety and fruitfulness of proposed projects. An excellent catalog[75] of available isotopes is published, and standard requirements have now been set for the qualification of investigators[74] to receive radioactive isotopes from the Commission.

REFERENCES

1. Ashkenazy, M., Davis, L., and Martin, J. An evaluation of the technic and results of the radioactive di-iodo-fluorescein test for the localization of intracranial lesions. *J. Neurosurg. 8:* 300-314, 1951.
2. Baker, W. H., Nathanson, I. T., and Selverstone, B. Unpublished data.
3. Belcher, E. H., and Evans, H. D. A directional scintillization counter for clinical measurements. *J. Sc. Instr. 28:* 71-75, 1951.
4. Belcher, E. H., and Evans, H. D. The localisation of cerebral tumours with radioactive derivatives of fluorescein. *Brit. J. Radiol. 24:* 272-279, 1951.
5. Cassen, B., Curtis, L., and Reed, C., and Libby, R. Instrumentation for I^{131} use in medical studies. *Nucleonics 9:* 46-50, 1951.
6. Changus, G. W., Chaikoff, I. L., and Ruben, S. Radioactive phosphorus as an indicator of phospholipid metabolism: phospholipid metabolism of the brain. *J. Biol. Chem. 126:* 493-500, 1938.
7. Cope, O., Rawson, R. W., and McArthur, J. W. Hyperfunctioning single adenoma of thyroid. *Surg., Gynec. & Obst. 84:* 415-426, 1947.
8. Copeland, D. E., and Benjamin, E. W. Pinhole camera for gamma-ray sources. *Nucleonics 5:* 44-49, 1949.
9. Davis, L., Martin, J., Ashkenazy, M., LeRoy, G. V., and Fields, T. Radioactive diiodofluorescein in diagnosis and localization of central nervous system tumors. *J.A.M.A. 144:* 1424-1432, 1950.
10. DeWinter, J. G. Some preliminary clinical observations on the use of radioactive isotopes for the localisation of brain tumors. *Brit. J. Radiol. 24:* 280-284, May, 1951.
11. Dobyns, B. M., and Lennon, B. Study of histopathology and physiologic function of thyroid tumors, using radioactive iodine and radioautography. *J. Clin. Endocrinol. 8:* 732-748, 1948.
12. Evans, T. C. Selection of radioautographic techniques for problems in biology. *Nucleonics 2:* 52-58, 1948.
13. Frantz, V. K., Ball, R. P., Keston, A. S., and Palmer, W. W. Thyroid carcinoma with metastases, studied with radioactive iodine. *Ann Surg. 119:* 668-689, 1944.
14. Frantz, V. K., Quimby, E. H., and Evans, T. C. Radioactive iodine studies of functional thyroid carcinoma. *Radiology 51:* 532-551, 1948.
15. Friedemann, U. Blood-brain barrier. *Phys. Rev. 22:* 125-145, 1942.
16. Glendenin, L. E. Determination of the energy of beta particles and photons by absorption. *Nucleonics 2:* 12-32, 1948.
17. Hamilton, J. G., and Soley, M. H. Studies in iodine metabolism by use of new radioactive isotope of iodine. *Am. J. Physiol. 127:* 557-572, Oct. 1939.
18. Hamilton, J. G., Soley, M. H., and Eichorn, K. B. Deposition of radioactive iodine in thyroid tissue. *Univ. Cal. Pubs. Pharmacol. 1:* 339-367, (Berkeley) 1940.
19. Hertz, S., and Roberts, A. Radioactive iodine as indicator in thyroid physiology; use of radioactive iodine in differential diagnosis of two types of Graves' disease. *J. Clin. Investigation 21:* 31-32, 1942.
20. Hertz, S., Roberts, A., and Evans, R. D. Radioactive iodine as an indicator in the study of thyroid physiology. *Proc. Soc. Exper. Biol. & Med. 38:* 510-513, 1938.

21. HERTZ, S., ROBERTS, A., and SALTER, W. T. Radioactive iodine as an indicator in thyroid physiology: metabolism of iodine in Graves' disease. *J. Clin. Investigation 21:* 25-29, Jan. 1942.
22. HESS, M. Localization of acid azodyes in tumors. *J. Path. & Bact. 51:* 309-311, 1940.
23. HEVESY, G. Absorption and translocation of lead by plants: A contribution to the application of the method of radioactive indicators in the investigation of the change of substance of plants. *Biochem. J. 17:* 439-445, 1923.
24. HEVESY, G. *Radioactive Indicators.* New York, Interscience, 1948.
25. JOLIOT, F., and CURIE, I. Artificial production of a new kind of radio-element. *Nature 133:* 201-202, 1934.
26. JONES, H. B., CHAIKOFF, I. L., and LAWRENCE, J. H. Radioactive phosphorus as an indicator of phospholipid metabolism; phospholipid turnover of fraternal tumors. *J. Biol. Chem. 133:* 319-327, 1940.
27. KAMEN, M. D. *Radioactive Tracers in Biology* (ed. 2). New York, Acad. Press, 1951.
28. KENNEY, J. M., MARINELLI, L. D., and WOODARD, H. Q. Tracer studies with radioactive phosphorus in malignant neoplastic disease. *Radiology 37:* 683-687, 1941.
29. KESTON, A. S., BALL, R. P., FRANTZ, V. K., and PALMER, W. W. Storage of radioactive iodine in a metastasis from thyroid carcinoma. *Science 95:* 362-363, 1942.
30. LAWRENCE, J. H., ERF, L. A., and TUTTLE, L. A. Intracellular irradiation. *J. Applied Physiol. 12:* 333-334, 1941.
31. LAWRENCE, J. H., and HAMILTON, J. G. *Advances in Biological and Medical Physics.* New York, Acad. Press, 1948, Vol. I.
32. LEBLOND, C. P., FORTMAN, M. B., PUPPEL, I. D., and CURTIS, G. M. Radioiodine autography in studies of human goitrous thyroid glands. *Arch. Path. 41:* 510-515, 1946.
33. LEITER, L., SEIDLIN, S. M., MARINELLI, L. D., and BAUMANN, E. J. Adenocarcinoma of thyroid with hyperthyroidism and functional metastases; studies with thiouracil and radio-iodine. *J. Clin. Endocrinol. 6:* 247-261, 1946.
34. LOW-BEER, B. V. A. Surface measurements of radioactive phosphorus in breast tumors as possible diagnostic method. *Science 104:* 399, Oct. 25, 1946.
35. LOW-BEER, B. V. A. *The Clinical Use of Radioactive Tracers.* Springfield, Ill., Charles C Thomas, 1950.
36. LOW-BEER, B. V. A., BELL, H. G., MCCORKLE, H. J., and STONE, R. S. Measurement of radioactive phosphorus in breast tumors in situ: Possible diagnostic procedure: Preliminary report. *Radiology 47:* 492-493, Nov. 1946.
37. LUDFORD, R. J. Vital staining of normal and malignant cells: Staining of malignant tumors with trypan blue. *Proc. Roy. Soc., London 104:* 493-502, 1929.
38. MARINE, D. Quantitative studies on the in vivo absorption of iodine by dogs' thyroid glands. *J. Biol. Chem. 22:* 547-550, 1915.
39. MARINELLI, L. D., FOOTE, F. W., HILL, R. F., and HOCKER, A. F. Retention of radioactive iodine in thyroid carcinomas: Histopathologic and radio-autographic studies. *Am. J. Roentgenol. 58:* 17-32, 1947.
40. MARINELLI, L. D., and GOLDSCHMIDT, B. Concentration of P^{32} in some superficial tissues of living patients. *Radiology 39:* 454-463, Oct. 1942.

41. McCorkle, H. J., Low-Beer, B. V. A., Bell, H. G., and Stone, R. S. Clinical and laboratory studies on uptake of radioactive phosphorus by lesions of breast. *Surgery 24:* 409-415, 1948.
42. Moore, F. D., and Tobin, L. H. Studies with radioactive diazo dyes: I. The localization of radioactive di-brom trypan blue in inflammatory lesions. *J. Clin. Investigation 21:* 471-481, 1942.
43. Moore, F. D., Tobin, L. H., and Aub, J. C. Studies with radioactive diazo dyes: III. The distribution of radioactive dyes in tumor-bearing mice. *J. Clin. Investigation 22:* 161-168, 1943.
44. Moore, G. E. Fluorescein as an agent in the differentiation of normal and malignant tissue. *Science 106:* 130-131, 1947.
45. Moore, G. E. Use of radioactive diiodofluorescein in the diagnosis and localization of brain tumors. *Science 107:* 569-571, 1948.
46. Moore, G. E., Caudill, C. M., Marvin, J. T., Aust, J. B., Chou, S. N., and Smith, G. A. Clinical and experimental studies of intracranial tumors with fluorescein dyes. *Am. J. Roentgenol. 66:* 1-8, 1951.
47. Moore, G. E., Kohl, D. A., Marvin, J. F., Wang, J. C., and Caudill, C. M. Biophysical studies of methods utilizing fluorescein and its derivatives to diagnose brain tumors. *Radiology 55:* 344-357, Sept. 1950.
48. Moore, G. E., Peyton, W. T., Hunter, S. W., and French, L. The clinical use of sodium fluorescein and radioactive diiodofluorescein in the localization of tumors of the central nervous system. *Minnesota Med. 31:* 1073-1076, 1948.
49. Overstreet, R., Jacobson, L., and Stout, P. R. An evidence for a new isotope of potassium. *Phys. Rev. 75:* 231-233, 1949.
50. Pelc, S. R. Autoradiograph technique. *Nature* (London) *160:* 749-750, 1947.
51. Peyton, W. T., French, L. A., and Walker, W. W. The clinical use of fluorescein in neurosurgery. *J. Neurosurg. 5:* 392-398, 1948.
52. Rawson, R. W., McArthur, J. W., Dobyns, B. M., Fluharty, R. G., and Cope, O. Functional activity of thyroid tumors, benign and malignant, as gauged by their collection of radioactive iodine. *West. J. Surg. 56:* 82-95, 1948.
53. Rawson, R. W., and Trunnell, J. B. In Hahn, P. F.: *A Manual of Artificial Radioisotope Therapy.* New York, Acad. Press, 1951, pp. 103-138.
54. Robinson, C. V. A study of small ether-argon Geiger-Müller counters. *Rev. Scient. Instr. 19:* 911-914, 1948.
55. Robinson, C. V. Small probing Geiger-Müller counters. *Rev. Scient. Instr. 21:* 82-84, 1950.
56. Schlesinger, E. B. "Experiences with the Moore Technique of Localization of Cerebral Tumors with Radioactive Substances." In *Surgical Forum.* Philadelphia, Saunders, 1951, pp. 368-370.
57. Schoenheimer, R., and Rittenberg, D. Deuterium as an indicator in the study of intermediary metabolism. *J. Biol. Chem. 111:* 163-168, 1935.
58. Schulman, J., Jr., Falkenheim, M., and Gray, S. J. The phosphorus turnover of carcinoma of the human stomach as measured with radioactive phosphorus. *J. Clin. Investigation 28:* 66-72, 1949.
59. Selverstone, B. Les isotopes dans la localisation des tumeurs cérébrales. *Presse méd. 59:* 1093-1094, 1951.
60. Selverstone, B., and Moulton, M. Unpublished data.
61. Selverstone, B., and Solomon, A. K. Radioactive isotopes in the study of intracranial tumors: Preliminary report of methods and results. *Tr. Am. Neurol. A.* pp. 115-119, 1948.

62. SELVERSTONE, B., SOLOMON, A. K., and SWEET, W. H. Location of brain tumors by means of radioactive phosphorus. *J.A.M.A. 140:* 277-278, May 21, 1949.
63. SELVERSTONE, B., SWEET, W. H., and IRETON, R. J. "Radioactive potassium, a new isotope for brain tumor localization." In *Surgical Forum.* Philadelphia, Saunders, 1951, pp. 371-375.
64. SELVERSTONE, B., SWEET, W. H., and ROBINSON, C. V. The clinical use of radioactive phosphorus in the surgery of brain tumors. *Ann. Surg. 130:* 643-651, 1949.
65. SELVERSTONE, B., and WHITE, J. C. Evaluation of the radioactive mapping technique in the surgery of brain tumors. *Ann. Surg. 134:* 387-396, 1951.
66. SHAPIRO, D. M., and LANDING, B. M. Significance of distribution of fluorescein in sarcoma 180 in mice. *Science 108:* 304-306, 1948.
67. SIRI, W. E. *Isotopic Tracers and Nuclear Radiations.* New York, McGraw-Hill, 1949.
68. SORSBY, A., WRIGHT, A. D., and ELKELES, A. Vital staining in brain surgery. A preliminary note. *Proc. Roy. Soc. Med. 36:* 137-140, 1943.
69. STEINBERG, D., and SELVERSTONE, B. Radioautography of cerebral tumors. *Proc. Soc. Exp. Biol. Med. 74:* 304-308, 1950.
70. STEINBERG, D., and SOLOMON, A. K. The detection of Ca^{45}, I^{131}, P^{32} and Zn^{65} by photographic film. *Rev. Scient. Instr. 20:* 655-659, 1949.
71. SUSEN, A. F., SMALL, W. T., and MOORE, F. D. "Experiences with the Moore technique of localization of cerebral tumors with radioactive substances." In *Surgical Forum.* Philadelphia, Saunders, 1951, pp. 362-367.
72. SVIEN, H. J. Personal communication.
73. TOBIN, L. H., and MOORE, F. D. Studies with radioactive di-azo dyes. II. The synthesis and properties of radioactive di-brom trypan blue and radioactive di-brom Evans blue. *J. Clin. Investigation 22:* 155-159, 1943.
74. United States Atomic Energy Commission. Isotope availability and allocation procedures. *Isotopics 2:* 1-4, July, 1952.
75. United States Atomic Energy Commission. *Isotopes.* Catalog and Price List. July, 1952.
76. WRENN, F. R., JR., GOOD, M. L., and HANDLER, P. The use of positron-emitting radioisotopes for the localization of brain tumors. *Science 113:* 525-527, May 4, 1951.
77. ZAHL, P. A., and WATERS, L. L. Localization of colloidal dyes in animal tissues. *Proc. Soc. Exper. Biol. & Med. 48:* 304-310, 1941.

Index

As used in the index, "cancer" applies only to cancer in man; the term "experimental cancer" includes all varieties of induced and transplantable tumors in animals. Numbers in bold face type refer to figures in the text.